PHOTOCHEMISTRY

Jack G. Calvert

Professor of Chemistry
The Ohio State University

James N. Pitts, Jr.

Professor of Chemistry
University of California, Riverside

John Wiley & Sons, Inc.

New York   London   Sydney

1966

To the man who taught us: F. E. B.
and our wives who tolerated us: D. A. C. and N. A. P.

Preface

Two decades have passed since the appearance of the most recent English language books on photochemistry by R. K. Rollefson and M. Burton (1939), W. A. Noyes, Jr., and P. A. Leighton (1941), and E. J. Bowen (1946). During this period the primary literature of photochemistry has progressed at a phenomenal rate.

In recent years the growth of photochemistry has been stimulated anew by the keen interests of not only the physical chemists but also the physical-organic, organic, and inorganic chemists, molecular spectroscopists, kineticists, and photobiologists. In spite of the rapid growth of photochemical knowledge, the efforts to keep current the secondary literature of photochemistry have been minimal. The recent Wiley-Interscience series on *Advances in Photochemistry* serves well to summarize the present status of selected areas of research in photochemistry. However, there are many facets of the theory and experimental methods of photochemistry, especially important for the beginning student and researcher, which cannot be adequately covered in these reviews. Furthermore the interrelationships of spectroscopy, molecular structure, and primary photochemical processes may not be readily apparent in the isolated reviews of restricted areas of interest. We have written this book in an attempt to satisfy these pressing needs for a current textbook and reference book on all major aspects of photochemistry.

The presentation of those sections dealing with course material is aimed at the level of the advanced undergraduate and first-year graduate student and the professional, academic, or industrial chemist with no previous experience in photochemistry. However, the sections of chapters devoted to reviews of current knowledge of primary photochemical processes in molecules (Chapters 2, 3, 4, and 5) and experimental methods in photochemistry (Chapter 7) should be of value to most veteran researchers in the areas of photochemistry as well as the person with limited experience in the field.

Sections selected from the first six chapters form the backbone of quarter-year or semester courses in photochemistry which we have given at our universities over the past fifteen years. The material is arranged in a fashion which provides first a review of the fundamental theory and relations of optics, spectroscopy, kinetics, etc.; the discussion of the primary photophysical and photochemical processes which follows is then based on these fundamentals when possible. Because of the large scope of the material covered and the need for some degree of brevity, the discussion of photochemical systems in the first five chapters is restricted largely to those aspects which bear on the nature of the primary processes. However, the intermolecular reactions of excited molecules and major synthetic and mechanistic aspects of "organic photochemistry" are summarized in Chapter 5, particularly in Secs. 5-2, 5-9, and 5-10.

In Chapter 1 the brief review of the properties of light through the consideration of the formulas and terminology is designed to serve both as a convenient résumé of value in understanding the laws of interaction of light with matter and, when used in conjunction with the experimental details of Chapter 7, as an aid in the construction of simple optical systems and equipment for photochemical use. In Chapter 2 the reactions of the electronically excited atoms, conceptually the simplest of the photochemical systems, are studied. In Chapter 3 the photochemistry of simple molecules and in Chapters 4 and 5 the photochemistry of more complex molecules are covered. In each of these presentations a brief review of the elements of the spectroscopy of the particular system is given first: the photochemistry of the systems, including photophysical and photochemical processes, is then considered with reference to this background. In all cases the accent in the first five chapters is on the nature of the primary processes and their relation to molecular structure and spectra. The references to the original literature are extensive but not exhaustive: reference is given only to the original classic studies and to the pertinent current literature from which the data discussed were taken and in which other earlier work is reviewed.

The various techniques which may be applied to the determination of the photochemical reaction mechanisms are discussed and evaluated in Chapter 6. These considerations are designed to help the beginning researcher in photochemistry to interpret original data obtained in photochemical experiments. In the quarter-year and semester courses in photochemistry, we have found the material of Chapter 6 to be a convenient termination point for the course. Thus the material of the previous five chapters is brought into focus as the student is faced with the evaluation of experimental data in the attempt to elucidate a reaction mechanism. The problems at the end of Chapter 6, as well as those following Chapters 1, 2, 3, and 5, have proved to be a useful stimulant of further thought and study of the subject in our classes.

In Chapter 7 we have given in some detail a description of the current experimental methods of photochemistry: the types of light sources, the methods of isolation of monochromatic radiation, the design of photochemical systems, the measurement of light intensities, the determination of quantum yields, etc. We feel that many aspects of this chapter will be of value not only to the scientist initiating his first studies of photochemistry but to the experienced researcher as well. For example, our material on solution filters for isolation of mercury arc lines represents the efforts of many people over a period of several years: many of the observations given are of great importance in the proper use of the filters, but to our knowledge they have never been published elsewhere.

Some extensive and important areas of photochemistry, such as photosynthesis and the photographic process, are given little attention here. Modern treatises on these subjects exist, and some degree of brevity of the text had to be maintained.

We are very grateful to our many friends and associates who helped in the preparation and the review of the manuscript. Professors Francis E. Blacet and George S. Hammond and Dr. E. J. Bowen, F.R.S., gave us invaluable help through their constructive criticism of the early manuscript; Professors W. A. Noyes, Jr., and P. A. Leighton and the late Dr. E. W. R. Steacie encouraged us and taught us much about the subject. We are appreciative of the editorial help and comments concerning certain sections of the book given by Professors Steve Filseth, Harry E. Gunning, Garnett R. McMillan, and Albert Padwa, and Drs. Edward Baum, Jack Foote, LaVerne Hess, Wayne Morganroth, Gwillym Owen, James Sharp, Sandra S. Thomas, Edwin F. Ullman, John Vernon, J. K. S. Wan, Frank Wilkinson, and Ahmed M. Zahra.

Special spectral and filter studies published in this book were made by Mrs. Veronique McMillan, Miss Judith Banks, and Mr. Richard Massengale. The care and extra effort of those who assisted in the preparation and typing of the manuscript are acknowledged with thanks: Mrs. Collette Armstrong, Mrs. Doris Calvert, Miss Diana Cockcroft, Mrs. Dorothy Cook, Miss Judith Ferrazzi, Mr. C. J. W. Gutch, Mrs. Mildred Jacobs, Mrs. Frances Lewis, Miss Jean McConnell, Mrs. Olive Peters, Mrs. Trudy Reiser, Mrs. Jane Scully, Mr. Romulas Simonaitis, Mrs. Elizabeth Sutter, and Miss Donna Winkle.

One of us (J. N. P.) acknowledges gratefully a Guggenheim Fellowship spent in working on this manuscript at Oxford University. The stimulation and encouragement of members of the Physical Chemistry Laboratory and of Merton and University Colleges, Oxford, are most appreciated.

We hope that our many friends and colleagues who have borne with us so patiently during the hectic years of preparation of this book will be pleased with it.

Jack G. Calvert
James N. Pitts, Jr.

Contents

Appendix

1

Light and the Laws of Photochemistry

The study of photochemistry deals with a unique type of chemical reaction. It is concerned with the "bimolecular" interaction of a light quantum and a molecule and the subsequent chemical and physical changes which result from this interaction. Light is always one of the reactants in a photochemical system, so it is important that we begin our study with a brief review of the interesting and unusual properties of light. A knowledge of these properties is a prerequisite to our consideration of the laws of interaction of light with matter and the nature of the photochemical changes which follow molecular excitation by light absorption.

Furthermore the elementary considerations, formulae, and terminology of light reviewed in this chapter, although normally encountered in one's first physics course, also serve as a convenient résumé; these formulae and definitions, used in conjunction with the experimental details of Chapter 7, should be of practical value in the design and construction of simple optical systems for photochemical use.

1-1 LIGHT AND ENERGY

The heating effect which can be obtained from light becomes evident when a lens is used to concentrate the radiation from the sun. Paper placed at the focus of the lens is heated rapidly to the kindling temperature. Since we speak of energy as heat or anything transformable into heat, we must conclude that light is a form of energy, sometimes referred to as radiant energy.

1-2 THE VELOCITY OF LIGHT

The seventeenth-century astronomer Roemer made the first successful, although approximate, determination of the tremendous velocity of light. Essentially he measured the time required for light from one of Jupiter's moons to travel across the orbit of the Earth. Since then, many accurate determinations have been made by several methods: measurement of the transit time for light (including short-wavelength radio waves) over accurately measured terrestrial distances, the use of the resonant cavity,[1] calculations based on accurate molecular constants from infrared spectroscopy,[2] and others. The recent data from many different sources suggest that the velocity of light in a vacuum, symbolized by c, is 2.9979×10^{10} cm/sec.

It is a fundamental hypothesis of Einstein's restricted theory of relativity,[3] now quite generally accepted, that the velocity of light is independent of the motion of its source. The Doppler effect observed with moving sources of light, as with the stars, represents a change of frequency and not of velocity. The velocity does vary, however, with the nature of the medium through which the light travels. The velocity c' in a nonconducting medium of dielectric constant ϵ and magnetic permeability μ is

$$c' = \frac{c}{\sqrt{\epsilon\mu}} \tag{1-1}$$

Here ϵ and μ are the familiar proportionality constants in the equations describing the force of attraction F between electric charges Q_1 and Q_2 separated by a distance r ($F = Q_1 Q_2/\epsilon r^2$) and the force between two magnetic poles m_1 and m_2 ($F = m_1 m_2/\mu r^2$); ϵ and μ respectively reflect the magnitude of the insulating character of the medium to the electric and magnetic interactions.

In a dispersing medium, that is, one in which the velocity varies with wavelength, a distinction has to be made between *phase velocity*, which is the velocity of idealized infinite trains of monochromatic waves, and *group velocity*, which is the speed with which energy is transferred by the light beam.[16] Most direct measurements of light velocity give the second quantity.

1-3   THE WAVE PROPERTIES OF LIGHT

It has been shown experimentally that in a vacuum the velocity of light is exactly the same (within a small experimental error) as that of electromagnetic radiation of any wavelength. (For other than a vacuum the velocity of light or electromagnetic radiation is a function of the wavelength.) The equality of these velocities leads one to the conclusion that light is a form of electromagnetic radiation like radio waves and thus can be considered to be wave-like in character. However, no one model is completely satisfactory in the description of all the properties of light. Certain of its properties are most conveniently explained in terms of the wave theory of electromagnetic radiation, but others, for example the photoelectric effect, necessitate the particle theory of light. In terms of our present knowledge we are led to the inescapable conclusion that there is a duality in the properties of light.

Maxwell presented his classic electromagnetic field theory in the year 1862.[4] In the years that followed, this theory was used to explain the principal properties which were then recognized for electromagnetic fields and waves. Today it is still convenient to consider light to be electromagnetic radiation and to use a picture based on this theory to describe reflection, refraction, diffraction, interference, and polarization of light.

Electromagnetic radiation is described in terms of a transverse plane wave involving associated electric and magnetic fields. It is supposed that the electric vector $\mathbf{E}$ and magnetic vector $\mathbf{H}$ which describe the respective field strengths are aligned in planes at right angles to one another, with both planes perpendicular to the direction of propagation of the wave. A convenient model for the variation of the field strengths as a function of time t and distance x along the axis of propagation is given in Cartesian coordinates by the sinusoidal functions 1-2 and 1-3:

$$\mathbf{E}_y = A \sin 2\pi\left(\frac{x}{\lambda} - \nu t\right) \tag{1-2}$$

$$\mathbf{H}_z = \sqrt{\frac{\epsilon}{\mu}}\, A \sin 2\pi\left(\frac{x}{\lambda} - \nu t\right) \tag{1-3}$$

In these equations $\mathbf{E}_y$ is the electric field strength vector lying in the xy-plane and increasing along the y-axis (see Fig. 1-1), $\mathbf{H}_z$ is the magnetic field strength vector lying in the xz-plane and increasing along the z-axis, A is the amplitude of the electric vector (the *intensity* of the wave is proportional to A^2), ϵ is the dielectric constant, and μ is the magnetic permeability of the medium through which the wave is transported. In a vacuum $\epsilon = \mu = 1$, and they are approximately unity in air. The wavelength of the wave, the distance between adjacent maxima in the vectors measured at any instant along the direction of wave propagation (the x-axis) is λ, while ν is the frequency or number of complete cycles of vector position change per second. The quantities λ and ν are related by $c/\nu = \lambda$, where c is the velocity of the radiation. The frequency ν is independent of the medium through which the radiation passes, while λ and c are dependent on ϵ and μ of the medium (Eq. 1-1). A graphical representation of Eqs. 1-2 and 1-3 is given in Fig. 1-1 for $t = 0$. This figure shows the spatial arrangement of the electric and magnetic vectors at a given instant as a function of the distance x along the direction of travel of the wave.

A mechanical model such as this is admittedly incomplete and naive; however, it is mathematically successful in accounting for many observations concerning light, and the theory can be used with success in the explanation of a variety of practical phenomena associated with optics, as seen in the following sections.

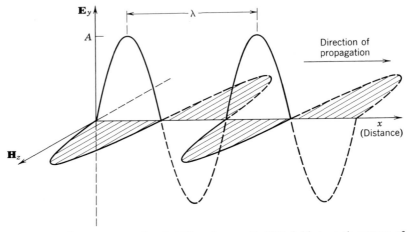

Fig. 1-1 The instantaneous electric ($\mathbf{E}_y$) and magnetic ($\mathbf{H}_z$) field strength vectors of a light wave as a function of position along the axis of propagation (x).

1-3A Reflection and Refraction of Light

When a beam of light encounters an interface between two transparent media in which its velocity is different (ϵ, μ different), two phenomena are observed. A portion of the beam is reflected (Fig. 1-2), while that portion of the beam transmitted suffers an abrupt change in direction at the interface and is said to be *refracted*. The electromagnetic wave theory predicts, and it is experimentally verifiable, that the angle of incidence of the beam i is equal to the angle of reflection i', while the angle of refraction r is related to i by

$$\frac{\sin i}{\sin r} = \frac{c_1}{c_2} = \mathbf{n}_{21} \qquad (1\text{-}4)$$

where c_1 and c_2 are the *phase* velocities of the light in phases 1 and 2, respectively, and $\mathbf{n}_{21}$ is defined as the refractive index of phase 2 with respect to 1.* Direct measurements of velocities in different media do

---

* It is common practice to speak of the "refractive index" of a liquid or solid without mention of phase 1 when air or a vacuum is this reference phase. The wavelength of light used in the determination should always be stated, since the velocity of the light and hence the refractive index are functions of this variable.

not give exactly the same ratio n_{21}, since they represent *group* velocities. For highly dispersive media the differences may amount to several per cent.

The quantity n is usually calculated from Eq. 1-4, using experimental values of i and r. Since c varies with wavelength in any medium other than free space, the refraction angles vary with wavelength. Advantage is taken of this difference in a prism monochromator to separate light of many

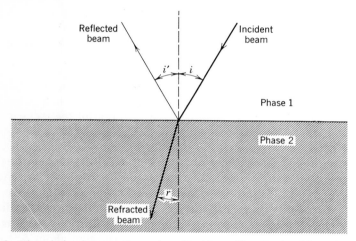

Fig. 1-2   The relation between the angles of incidence (i), reflection (i'), and refraction (r) at a phase boundary.

wavelengths into *monochromatic light*, that is, light which contains essentially one wavelength or a small band of wavelengths. The long-wavelength (low-frequency) radiation is refracted less than the short-wavelength (high-frequency) radiation, so that red light with $\lambda = 0.00007$ cm is refracted less than violet light with $\lambda = 0.00004$ cm. This effect is illustrated in Fig. 1-3, which shows the elements of a prism monochromator. It is also made very clear when one compares the focal length of a quartz lens at 2537 A with its much longer focal length at 7000 A. The great difference is of practical concern in the design of optical systems in photochemistry.

From the electromagnetic wave theory Fresnel derived a useful and experimentally verified expression relating the reflection at an interface and the refractive index. The ratio of the intensity I_r of the beam of light reflected at an interface of phase 1 and 2 to the intensity of the perpendicularly incident beam of unpolarized light I_0 is as follows:

$$\frac{I_r}{I_0} = \left(\frac{n_{21} - 1}{n_{21} + 1}\right)^2 \tag{1-5}$$

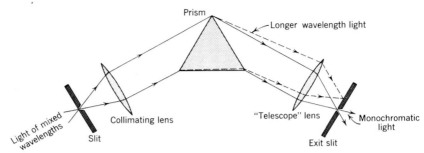

Fig. 1-3   The elements of a prism monochromator; note that there is less refraction of the longer wavelengths of light.

Light which is not perpendicularly incident is much more strongly reflected (see Fig. 7-38). For a light beam which passes from a phase 2 to a phase 1 where n_{21} is greater than 1, total reflection of the incident beam occurs for angles of incidence greater than the critical angle α, where $\sin \alpha = 1/n_{21}$.

Corrections for reflections at windows in quantitative photochemical studies are often made by using Eq. 1-5. In the calculations, the refractive indices for the particular wavelength of light employed must be used. Such corrections are often an appreciable fraction of the incident radiation. For example, a total of about 10% of the near-ultraviolet light incident perpendicularly on a quartz window in air is reflected, about 5% at the air-quartz interface and about 5% at the quartz-air interface. As the velocities of light in media 1 and 2 become more nearly equal and **n** approaches unity, the fraction of the incident radiation reflected at the interface between 1 and 2 becomes less. Thus in practice lenses are often coated with a material (such as cryolite) with a refractive index intermediate to that of air and the lens material to decrease the loss of light by reflection in an optical system.

1-3B   Diffraction and Interference of Light

If one inserts an opaque object between a point source and a screen, one will observe alternate bands of light *within the geometrical shadow* of the object. This phenomenon is known as *diffraction*. In its simplest form it can be explained in terms of Huyghens' principle, which states that each point on a wave front of light acts as if it were a center of disturbance sending out a secondary wavelet which spreads out in all directions.*

---

* More sophisticated theory shows that the amplitude of the secondary wavelet is a maximum in the direction of the light beam and zero in the opposite direction.

From the photochemist's point of view the most important application is in terms of monochromators utilizing diffraction gratings to disperse the light, and it is in these terms that we shall discuss the subject.

A diffraction grating consists of a large number (many thousands per centimeter) of evenly spaced, parallel, opaque lines ruled on a transparent or a reflecting plate. The diagram in Fig. 1-4 shows a portion of a *transmission* diffraction grating G in which the spacing between lines is a cm. Light from a single point source S (shown as four parallel rays) travels to the grating G. The majority of the light incident on the transparent spaces passes straight through to A. However, in accordance with Huyghens' principle, the wave fronts developed at the openings act to send out little wavelets away from the source and at various angles, θ, to the direction of the incident beam. A lens gathers the light (without introducing a phase change) for observation at B. When θ is such that a given beam travels a distance d equal to some multiple of one-half a wavelength (e.g., $d = n\lambda/2$, $n = 1, 2, 3$, etc.), then the waves reaching the observer combine so that the resultant vectors vanish, and a dark line is seen. For values of θ where $d = n\lambda$, $n = 1, 2, 3$, etc., reinforcement of the waves will occur, and a bright line will be observed at B. The line is termed first order, second order, third order, etc., for $n = 1, 2, 3$, etc., respectively. It is seen from Fig. 1-4 that $d = a \sin \theta$, where a is the distance between the centers of adjacent spaces. The wavelength λ of the light can be found by determining θ for $n = 1, 2, 3$, etc., and utilizing Eq. 1-6:

$$\lambda = \frac{a \sin \theta}{n} \tag{1-6}$$

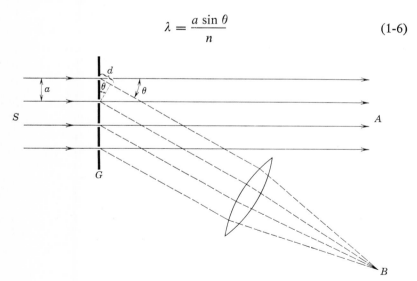

Fig. 1-4   Diffraction through a plane grating.

Since the position of reinforcement of diffraction lines varies with λ, a diffraction grating can be used as a means of separating light of mixed wavelengths, and this is the principle employed in monochromators with diffraction gratings (see Chapter 7 for examples). Note that the angle through which the light is diffracted is greater the larger λ is; this is the opposite trend to that observed for refraction through a prism and leads to highly efficient dispersion of long-wavelength visible and infrared light.

1-3C   Polarization of Light

Wave theory suggests that *unpolarized light* is made up of a great number of electromagnetic waves. Each individual wave has its electric and magnetic vectors undulating in fixed planes, but the planes of the various waves are randomly oriented with respect to one another. This is the type of light which we encounter most often. Ordinary incandescent bodies and all unoriented emitting systems give unpolarized light.

Plane polarized light is presumed to consist of many waves, all of which have their electric vectors oriented in a given direction in space. This type of light is useful in determining the orientation of molecular species, the rotation of the vectors of light by optically active molecules, and other interesting effects. Plane polarized light may be made by reflection from plane surfaces or transmission by doubly refracting crystals.[16] Light reflected from transparent plane surfaces is highly polarized with the electric vector of the light waves parallel to the reflecting surface.

In experimental work with partially plane polarized light it is convenient to consider the degree of polarization, P:

$$P = \frac{I' - I''}{I' + I''} \tag{1-7}$$

where I' and I'' are the maximum and minimum intensities of light observed through a Nicol prism or other analyzer which is gradually rotated $360°$ around its axis. Light reflected from a highly polished, transparent surface is not completely polarized, and the degree of polarization differs with each material and angle of incidence. Presumably materials with refractive index $n = 1.46$ provide the maximum degree of polarization possible, but for each reflecting surface there is some angle of incidence for which P is a maximum; this angle is called the polarizing angle, θ_p. It has been found that the incident and refracted beams are at right angles to one another when P is a maximum. Accepting this, it follows from Eq. 1-4 that $n = \tan \theta_p$.

Certain double-refracting crystalline materials, such as calcite, resolve unpolarized light by transmission into ordinary and extraordinary rays which are plane polarized, the plane of polarization of one at right angles to that of the other. It is possible to separate one ray from the other by reflection using calcite crystals of special shape, an example being the Nicol prism. A recent type of commercial polarizer consists of stretched films of polyvinyl alcohol with iodine molecules aligned along the oriented polymer molecules. Such a film is dichroic. It strongly absorbs visible light when the electric vector lies along the length of the iodine molecules and shows negligible absorption when the vector lies across them. Unpolarized light (within the range of the iodine absorption band, which practically covers the visible region) is therefore converted into plane polarized light by passage through the film.

Elliptically polarized light may be described in terms of the wave theory as a light wave compounded from two plane waves of equal wavelength and frequency. They have identical directions of propagation, but their electric vectors are perpendicular to one another and out of phase. The name is derived from the fact that the resultant electric vector of the wave sweeps out an ellipse as viewed along the line of propagation. For simplification, it is usual to consider only the electric field vector in the description of polarized light. It is the interaction of this vector with various systems which is of the greatest consequence to the photochemist. Of course the magnetic field vector always reflects the variations in position and size of the electric vector, but its direction in space is rotated 90° about the axis of propagation. The equation of an elliptically polarized light wave can be derived by simple vector addition of the components. Equations 1-8 and 1-9 describe the length of the component electric vectors as a function of distance x along the direction of propagation at a fixed time.

$$\mathbf{E}_y = A \sin 2\pi \frac{x}{\lambda} \tag{1-8}$$

$$\mathbf{E}_z = B \sin 2\pi \left(\frac{x}{\lambda} + \tau \right) \tag{1-9}$$

The quantity τ is not zero and represents the fraction of a cycle by which wave 1-9 leads wave 1-8. Vector addition of $\mathbf{E}_y$ and $\mathbf{E}_z$ leads to the length of the resultant electric vector $\mathbf{E}_r$:

$$\mathbf{E}_r^2 = A^2 \sin^2 2\pi \frac{x}{\lambda} + B^2 \sin^2 2\pi \left(\frac{x}{\lambda} + \tau \right) \tag{1-10}$$

$\mathbf{E}_r$ is always directed away from the axis of propagation and is perpendicular to it. The angle θ between the resultant electric vector and the xz-plane is given in 1-11 as a function of the distance x along the wave axis:

$$\cot \theta = \frac{B}{A}\left[\cos 2\pi\tau + \left(\cot 2\pi\frac{x}{\lambda}\right)(\sin 2\pi\tau)\right] \tag{1-11}$$

Circularly polarized light is a special case of elliptical polarization where $A = B$ and $\tau = \frac{1}{4}$ cycle in Eqs. 1-10 and 1-11. These equations then

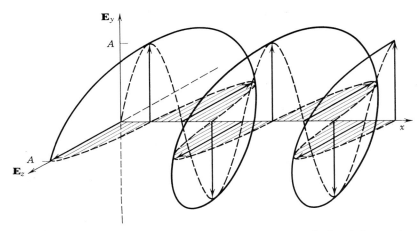

Fig. 1-5 The solid curve represents the instantaneous magnitude of the resultant electric vector in circularly polarized light as a function of distance along the axis of propagation.

reduce to 1-12 and 1-13, which define the length and position in space for the resultant electric vector:

$$\mathbf{E}_r = A \tag{1-12}$$

$$\theta = 2\pi\frac{x}{\lambda} \tag{1-13}$$

Viewed along the direction of travel of the wave, the resultant electric vector sweeps out a circle. Its properties can be described in terms of a simple model; it may be compounded from two plane waves whose electric vectors are perpendicular to one another and equal in amplitude but out of phase by one-quarter of a cycle. In Fig. 1-5 the equations are plotted for the electric vectors which may be compounded to yield a circularly polarized wave, and the resultant electric vector is shown for several positions along the wave. The trace of the path of the head of the resultant electric vector of circularly polarized light is seen to be a helix; for elliptically or circularly polarized light the path will simulate either a right- or left-handed screw. It will appear to rotate counterclockwise or clockwise when viewed along the axis of propagation of the wave, depending on the phase relations of the component waves.

Some of the interactions of circularly or elliptically polarized light with matter are very interesting. For example, the right-handed (or left-handed) form is absorbed with different efficiencies by the *dextro* and *levo* forms of a given optically active compound (the *Cotton effect*). If decomposition of the compound follows light absorption, as is often the case, then preferential decomposition of one of the enantiomorphs occurs, and a partial resolution of a racemic mixture can be effected by the irradiation. In consideration of asymmetric photochemical synthesis by preferential degradation of one of the enantiomorphs through the use of circularly polarized light, the size of the anisotropy factor determines the success of the method; this factor is defined as $(\epsilon_l - \epsilon_r)/\epsilon_0$, where ϵ_l, ϵ_r, and ϵ_0 represent molar extinction coefficients at a given wavelength for left-handed circularly polarized, right-handed circularly polarized, and unpolarized light, respectively.

Circularly and elliptically polarized light can be produced by the use of a transparent plate of a uniaxial crystal cut so that the optic axis lies in the plane of the plate. Plane polarized light is passed at normal incidence through this plate with its electric vector at 45° to the optic axis.[16] The refractive index of the plate is different for light with an electric vector along or across the optic axis. Mathematical resolution of the vector of the incident light in these two directions gives two beams having equal intensity but traveling at different speeds, so that on emergence from the crystal plate their two vectors are in general no longer in phase and cannot recombine to the original plane polarized light. With a retardation of $\lambda/4$, circularly polarized light is formed; with $\lambda/2$, plane polarized light with the vector turned through 90° appears; with a full wave retardation the original vector direction is restored. Intermediate retardations give elliptical polarization represented by shapes lying between a circle and a straight line.

1-4 THE PARTICLE PROPERTIES OF LIGHT

The importance and usefulness of the wave theory of light cannot be minimized, but there are many important experimental results involving light which this theory cannot explain. These concern primarily the absorption and emission of light and the effects which absorbed light produces.

1-4A   Black-Body Radiation

It may seem remarkable that a theory as important to the development of science as the quantum theory had its origin in experiments dealing with "black-body radiation." A perfectly black body is one which absorbs completely all radiation incident upon it. According to Kirchhoff's law, a perfect absorber is also a perfect emitter. A mathematical statement of the law is

$$\frac{\mathscr{E}_1}{a_1} = \frac{\mathscr{E}_2}{a_2} = \frac{\mathscr{E}_i}{a_i} \tag{1-14}$$

Here $\mathscr{E}_1, \mathscr{E}_2, \ldots, \mathscr{E}_i$ are the total emissive powers of bodies $1, 2, \ldots, i$, respectively, given as total radiant energy emitted per unit time per unit area at any given temperature; and $a_1, a_2, \ldots, a_i$ are the absorptivities of these bodies measured as the fraction of radiant energy incident on the surface which is absorbed. It is seen from 1-14 that a surface which is black not only absorbs light strongly but must emit strongly as well. Highly reflecting surfaces, on the other hand, are poor radiators of energy. A theoretically nearly perfect black-body radiator (or absorber) would be made from a large hollow sphere of matter which is perfectly black (perfectly absorbing to invisible as well as visible radiation) on its inner surface. Radiation is taken from (or enters) the sphere through a small hole in its wall. The practical construction of black-body radiators is described by Coblentz;[5a] more recently improved models have appeared.[5b,c]

Many detailed studies have been made of the wavelength and energy distributions of black-body radiators at various temperatures. Some typical energy-wavelength data of Lummer and Pringsheim[6] are shown in Fig. 1-6 for several temperatures.

Many attempts were made to describe mathematically from the electromagnetic wave theory the energy distribution of black-body radiators. Wien suggested

$$\mathscr{E}_\lambda = \frac{a_1 e^{-a_2/\lambda T}}{\lambda^5} \tag{1-15}$$

The product $\mathscr{E}_\lambda \, d\lambda$ is the emissive power of the radiator at wavelengths in the range λ to $\lambda + d\lambda$ at the temperature $T°\text{K}$; a_1 and a_2 are constants. Equation 1-15 describes the observed variation well for the short-wavelength region but fails completely at long wavelengths. On the suggestion of Rayleigh, Jeans derived Eq. 1-16 using wave theory:

$$\mathscr{E}_\lambda = \frac{aT}{\lambda^4} \tag{1-16}$$

Equation 1-16 is accurate for long wavelengths but fails completely in describing data at short wavelengths.

In 1901 Planck[7] proposed a radically new concept of the origin of black-body radiation. He postulated that the energy of the electric oscillators in the atoms in the walls of the black body from which the radiation originated could not vary continuously but could take only certain discrete

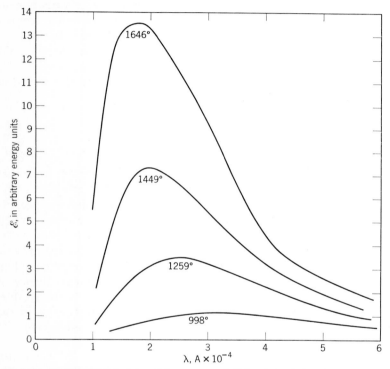

Fig. 1-6 Some selected data of Lummer and Pringsheim,[6] showing the wavelength distribution of the energy emitted by a black-body radiator at several temperatures, °K.

values. This theory led to the concept of a unit of energy E, called the quantum of radiation, emitted as the oscillator jumped between energy levels. This energy is proportional to the frequency of the radiation, that is,

$$E = h\nu = \frac{hc}{\lambda} \tag{1-17}$$

where h is a proportionality constant, now called Planck's constant, equal to 6.6256×10^{-27} erg-sec/quantum. E presumably represents the difference between the final and initial energy states in the oscillator. In terms of this picture Planck derived Eq. 1-18:

$$\mathscr{E}_\lambda = \frac{8\pi hc}{\lambda^5} \frac{1}{e^{hc/\lambda kT} - 1} \tag{1-18}$$

where **k** is Boltzmann's constant, 1.38054×10^{-16} erg/deg-quantum, and the other symbols have their usual significance. Planck's result was successful in the quantitative description of the energy distribution of black-body radiators over the entire range which has been tested, temperatures from 300 to 1700°K and wavelengths from 5000 to 520,000 A. It is interesting to note that Eq. 1-18 reduces to 1-15 at short wavelengths and to 1-16 at long wavelengths. The success of the quantum hypothesis of Planck in the treatment of black-body radiation renewed the interest of scientists in the particle theory of light.

1-4B   The Photoelectric Effect

Hertz found that light of sufficiently short wavelength incident on a metal surface causes the instantaneous emission of electrons from that surface. This phenomenon is called the photoelectric effect. Careful experimentation showed that the number of electrons emitted was proportional to the intensity, but that the kinetic energy of the electrons emitted was proportional to the frequency and independent of the intensity of the incident radiation. Classical electromagnetic wave theory failed completely to account for the observed phenomenon. In 1905 Einstein[8] proposed an explanation of the effect in terms of the then-new quantum theory of Planck. He suggested that a quantum of light of energy $h\nu$ is absorbed by the metal and used to eject the electron. Thus the kinetic energy of the electron $m_e v^2/2$ was related to the absorbed energy by the expression

$$\frac{m_e v^2}{2} = h\nu - \omega_0 \tag{1-19}$$

where ω_0 is the minimum energy necessary to remove an electron from the metal (work function). Millikan[9] tested Eq. 1-19 extensively, using many different metals and frequencies of radiation. He found that a plot of the kinetic energy of the photoelectrons versus the frequency was a straight line for each metal and that the slopes of the lines were identical as required by Eq. 1-19. Furthermore, the absolute value of the slopes was equal within the experimental error to the constant h of the Planck theory for black-body radiation. The intercepts ω_0 were different for each metal, but the values were shown to agree well with the work function of the metals derived independently from thermionic emission. Again the quantum or particle theory of light was successful when the wave theory had failed.

1-4C   The Compton Effect

When a monochromatic beam of X-rays encounters a scattering medium, the scattered rays are found to consist of new longer-wavelength radiation as well as that which was incident. Using monochromatic radiation, Compton[10] carefully determined the wavelengths scattered from carbon. In explaining his results he found it necessary to assume that the radiation behaved as a particle or quantum with energy $h\nu$ and momentum $h\nu/c$. The quantum is presumed to lose energy on collision with an electron in the scattering material, and this is reflected in a decrease in ν and an increase in λ ($\lambda = c/\nu$). Conserving the energy and momentum of the quantum and of the electron, Compton derived the relation

$$\lambda - \lambda_0 = 0.0242(1 - \cos\theta) \tag{1-20}$$

where λ is the wavelength (in angstrom units) of the radiation which is scattered at an angle θ with respect to the direction of the incident beam of wavelength λ_0. The validity of the relation has been established by many detailed studies. Radiation was thus demonstrated to possess particle character which follows the laws applicable to the collisions between particles of matter.

1-4D   Photochemical Reactions and the Quantum Theory of Radiation

Although the fact is often overlooked today, good evidence for the particle or quantum nature of light is to be found in the study of the chemical changes induced by light. In photochemistry the quantum theory is assumed, and a quantity called the over-all quantum yield Φ is determined for a given photochemical product. Φ of product B resulting from the photodecomposition of A, $A + h\nu \rightarrow B$, is defined as

$$\Phi_B = \frac{\text{Molecules of } B \text{ formed per unit volume per unit time}}{\text{Quanta of light absorbed by } A \text{ per unit volume per unit time}} \tag{1-21}$$

The quantity which appears in the numerator of 1-21 is found by conventional chemical analysis. The value of the denominator is calculated from the measured total energy of the absorbed light of wavelength λ and the assumption that each quantum has energy equal to $h\nu$ or hc/λ. The size of Φ varies greatly with the different reaction systems (e.g., from 0.000 to 10^6), and, as we shall see in detail in subsequent chapters, crucial information concerning the photochemical reaction mechanism is derived from determinations of quantum yields.

In terms of the quantum theory it is highly significant that for certain systems Φ is accurately equal to unity. For example, acetone undergoes photodecomposition to form carbon monoxide as one of the products, and at temperatures above $125°$ and pressures below about 100 mm, Φ_{CO} from acetone $= 1.0$. That this number is not fortuitous is evident from the fact that over wide ranges Φ_{CO} is independent of the wavelength of the absorbed light (3130 A to the far ultraviolet), the concentration of acetone (over a wide range), and the temperature.[11] The value of unity suggests that essentially every molecule of acetone which absorbs light under these conditions undergoes decomposition to form a molecule of CO; hence by implication the light must be quantized. All other chemical and physical evidence available supports this conclusion, and confidence in the quantum theory of light is gained.

1-5   WAVE PROPERTIES OF MATTER

From the examples given it should be clear that light has truly a dual nature, and in photochemistry it is at times convenient to consider it wave-like, at times particle-like. This duality is also true for matter. Thus certain wave properties of matter have been predicted and demonstrated experimentally. The key relationship is that of de Broglie,[12] who proposed on purely theoretical grounds in 1924 that certain wavelengths could be associated with moving particles. The wavelength λ is described as

$$\lambda = \frac{h}{mv} \tag{1-22}$$

where m is mass, v the velocity of the particle, and h Planck's constant. Equation 1-22 has been verified through the use of high-energy electrons,[13] helium atoms,[14] and neutron beams.[15] Diffraction was observed, and from the interference pattern, λ was calculated and shown to agree with that predicted by the de Broglie relation.

1-6   A WORKING PICTURE OF THE NATURE OF LIGHT

The idea of oscillating electric and magnetic vectors provides a convenient model for the consideration of many of the phenomena related to light. However, one cannot think of light as traveling in a wave train of infinite length that extends from the emitter to the receiver. The radiation must travel through space in discrete units called quanta or photons with energies equal to $h\nu$ or hc/λ. The intimate tie between the wave and quantum theories is reflected in the fact that the actual particle or quantum of light has an energy which is calculated by using a wavelength derived from an experiment in which the wave character of light is assumed.

A number of quantities useful in photochemistry can be derived from the considerations of the previous sections. For example, the energy in ergs of a single quantum of electromagnetic radiation is calculated from Eq. 1-17, $E = hc/\lambda$, in which h is 6.6256×10^{-27} erg-sec/quantum and $c = 2.9979 \times 10^{10}$ cm/sec. A chemist, however, usually thinks in terms of kilocalories of energy and moles of material. Thus the relationship

$$E \text{ (kcal/einstein)} = 2.8591 \times 10^5/\lambda \text{ (in angstrom units)} \qquad (1\text{-}23)$$

in which an *einstein* refers to a mole of quanta, is often utilized. Table 1-1

TABLE 1-1   Relation of Energy Units[a]

$$
\begin{array}{rl}
1 \text{ erg/molecule} & \equiv 1.4394 \times 10^{16} \text{ cal/mole} \\
& \equiv 6.2418 \times 10^{11} \text{ ev} \\
& \equiv 5.0345 \times 10^{15} \text{ cm}^{-1} \\
1 \text{ cal/mole} & \equiv 6.9473 \times 10^{-17} \text{ erg/molecule} \\
& \equiv 4.3364 \times 10^{-5} \text{ ev} \\
& \equiv 0.34976 \text{ cm}^{-1} \\
1 \text{ electron volt (ev)} & \equiv 23{,}060 \text{ cal/mole} \\
& \equiv 1.6021 \times 10^{-12} \text{ erg/molecule} \\
& \equiv 8065.7 \text{ cm}^{-1} \\
1 \text{ cm}^{-1} & \equiv 2.8591 \text{ cal/mole} \\
& \equiv 1.9862 \times 10^{-16} \text{ erg/molecule} \\
& \equiv 1.2398 \times 10^{-4} \text{ ev}
\end{array}
$$

[a] Relations refer to the thermochemical calorie.

relates the units commonly used to express the energy of electromagnetic radiation.

Table 1-2 summarizes the wavelengths, common names, and energies associated with many kinds of electromagnetic radiation. The absorption of a quantum of microwave radiation may produce a change in the orientation of the nuclear spin vector in an atom in a magnetic field or increase the internal rotation of some group of atoms in a molecule. A quantum of long-wavelength infrared radiation (far infrared) commonly increases the frequency of end-over-end tumbling of the absorbing molecule, while absorption of short-wavelength infrared radiation (near infrared) by a molecule is accompanied by an increased amplitude of some characteristic vibration of the atoms in the molecule. Since most chemical bonds are of the order of magnitude of 40 or more kcal/mole, it can be readily understood why photochemistry deals primarily with light of wavelengths less

TABLE 1-2 The Wavelength, Frequency, and Energy of Typical Electromagnetic Radiation

Approximate Description	Typical Wavelength, A	Frequency, cycles/sec	Wave Number, cm^{-1}	Energy, kcal/einstein	
Radio wave	1.00×10^{13} (1000 m)	3.00×10^{5} (300 kc)	1.00×10^{-5}	0.000000286	
Short-wave radio wave	1.00×10^{11} (10 m)	3.00×10^{7} (30 Mc)	1.00×10^{-3}	0.00000286	
Microwave	1.00×10^{8} (1 cm)	3.00×10^{10}	1.00	0.00286	
Far infrared	1.00×10^{5} (10 μ)	3.00×10^{13}	1.00×10^{3}	2.86	
Near infrared	1.00×10^{4} (1 μ)	3.00×10^{14}	1.00×10^{4}	28.6	
Visible light					
Red	7.00×10^{3} (700 mμ)	4.28×10^{14}	1.43×10^{4}	40.8	
Orange	6.20×10^{3}	4.84×10^{14}	1.61×10^{4}	46.1	
Yellow	5.80×10^{3}	5.17×10^{14}	1.72×10^{4}	49.3	
Green	5.30×10^{3}	5.66×10^{14}	1.89×10^{4}	53.9	Photochemistry region
Blue	4.70×10^{3}	6.38×10^{14}	2.13×10^{4}	60.8	
Violet	4.20×10^{3}	7.14×10^{14}	2.38×10^{4}	68.1	
Near ultraviolet	3.00×10^{3}	1.00×10^{15}	3.33×10^{4}	95.3	
Far ultraviolet	2.00×10^{3}	1.50×10^{15}	5.00×10^{4}	142.9	
Schumann ultraviolet	1.50×10^{3}	2.00×10^{15}	6.67×10^{4}	190.6	
Long X-ray	3.00×10^{2}	1.00×10^{16}	3.33×10^{5}	953.0	Radiation chemistry region
Short X-ray	1.00	3.00×10^{18}	1.00×10^{8}	285,910	
Gamma ray	1.00×10^{-2}	3.00×10^{20}	1.00×10^{10}	28,591,000	

than 7000 A, for it is only the quanta of these wavelengths which are sufficiently energetic to rupture bonds and produce chemical changes in molecules which absorb them.*

In describing light it is customary to state its wavelength or wave number ω ($\omega = 1/\lambda$, where λ is in centimeters), rather than its frequency, since the wavelength is the only quantity which can actually be measured. Frequency must be calculated, using $\nu = c/\lambda$. The units used for wavelength vary with the region of radiation considered and the backgrounds of the researchers. Common units are summarized in Table 1-3. The units of

TABLE 1-3 Wavelength and Frequency Units Commonly Used in the Description of Light

Name	Symbol	Definition	Region of Common Usage
Angstrom unit	A (or Å)	$1 \text{ A} = 1 \times 10^{-10} \text{ m} = 1 \times 10^{-8} \text{ cm}$	Visible, ultraviolet, X-ray, gamma ray
Millimicron	$m\mu$	$1 \text{ m}\mu = 1 \times 10^{-9} \text{ m} = 1 \times 10^{-7} \text{ cm}$ $= 10 \text{ A}$	Ultraviolet and visible
Micron	μ	$1 \mu = 1 \times 10^{-6} \text{ m} = 1 \times 10^{-4} \text{ cm}$	Infrared
Wave number	ω	$\omega = 1/\lambda \text{ cm}^{-1}$ (number of waves/ cm of wave train)	Infrared, visible, and ultraviolet

λ most common to photochemical work are the angstrom unit A and the millimicron $m\mu$; however, the spectroscopist and photochemist often use the wave number ω. Plots using ω instead of λ have certain marked advantages. If a spectrum shows vibrational structure, the magnitude of a vibrational quantum appears as a simple difference. Band areas on a wave-number plot can be tl.eoretically related to the mean radiational lifetime of the excited molecule. Lastly, if fluorescence and absorption spectra are plotted together, good approximations to mirror-image relationships are often found on ω, but not on λ, plots (see Chapter 4 and Figs. 4-6 and 4-7).

1-7 THE LAWS OF PHOTOCHEMISTRY

The first law of photochemistry, formulated in the works of Grotthus (1817) and Draper (1843) more than a century ago, states: *Only the light which is absorbed by a molecule can be effective in producing photochemical change in the molecule.* The law and its consequences are such truisms today that they are commonly taken for granted by photochemists.

---

* This of course assumes that absorption is a one-quantum process. In special cases of relatively long lifetimes and very high, laser-like intensities, biphotonic processes might give photochemical reactions with near-infrared radiation.

Obviously, there must be some overlap between the wavelengths of light entering the reaction cell and those absorbed by the desired compound or sensitizer if a photochemical reaction is to occur. However, it is worth re-emphasizing that for definitive, quantitative studies the law must be applied seriously to *all* aspects of a given photochemical system. Thus one should know, in addition to the absorption spectrum of the compound being photolyzed, the emission spectrum of the light source, and the absorption spectra of the filter (or its equivalent, the bandwidth of the light from the monochromator), the reaction cell windows, the solvent, and the possible photolysis products.

The second law of photochemistry was deduced by Stark (1908–12) and Einstein (1912–13) and in its original form stated: Each molecule taking part in a chemical reaction caused by light absorbs one quantum of the radiation which causes the reaction. Subsequently Stark and Bodenstein (1913) each pointed out that the law should apply only to the primary process, since secondary thermal chain reactions could follow the primary process, leading to over-all quantum yields greater than unity (e.g., $\Phi_{HCl} = 10^5$–10^6 in gas-phase photochlorinations). The second law as restated is: *The absorption of light by a molecule is a one-quantum process, so that the sum of the primary process quantum yields φ must be unity;* that is, $\Sigma\varphi_i = 1.00$, where φ_i is the quantum yield of the ith primary process, which may include dissociation, isomerization, fluorescence, phosphorescence, radiationless transitions, and all other reaction paths which lead to the destruction or deactivation of the excited molecule.

The validity of the one-quantum-absorbed-per-molecule aspect of the second law depends upon a relatively short lifetime for the electronically excited molecule and a relatively modest level of light intensity such as is found in the conventional photochemical systems illuminated continuously with steady monochromatic radiation (10^{13}–10^{15} quanta absorbed/cc-sec). In these cases there is a very low concentration of electronically excited molecules, and absorption of a second quantum of light by an excited molecule is highly improbable. However, in recent years, biphotonic excitation has been observed in several systems. The flash photolysis systems provide a classic example. A high-intensity flash of light ($\sim 10^{18}$–10^{20} quanta/cc-millisec or μsec of flash duration) generates a relatively high concentration of electronically excited molecules or other transients. A second short flash of light, which is practically continuous in nature, is passed through the system a short time after the initial flash; the absorption of a second quantum of light by some of the excited species may occur, and a characteristic absorption spectrum of the transient can be observed. (See the discussion in Secs. 6-4A and 7-1F.) Similar considerations apply to laser experiments in which exceedingly high intensities of monochromatic light are available and biphotonic processes have been claimed. Of course, neither of these examples is a violation of the Stark-Einstein law; they are an expected consequence of very high light intensities and, in the case of triplet-triplet absorption, the relatively long lifetime of the excited state.

1-8 THE BEER-LAMBERT ABSORPTION LAW

The absorption of a monochromatic beam of light by a homogeneous absorbing system is described well by the familiar combined Beer-Lambert law. One form of the law, commonly employed in photochemical studies, is

$$\frac{I}{I_0} = 10^{-\epsilon cl} \tag{1-24}$$

where I_0 represents the light energy (or number of quanta) of strictly monochromatic light incident per unit of time at the front of a column of a single absorbing species of concentration c, moles/liter; I is the energy per unit time transmitted through the column of material, l cm in length; and ϵ (liters/mole-cm), the molar extinction coefficient,* is a constant for a given pure absorbing species at a given wavelength and is a measure of the probability that the quantum-molecule interaction will lead to absorption of the quantum.

Relation 1-24 is derived readily by assuming that the probability of light absorption is simply proportional to the number of bimolecular encounters between light quanta and absorbing molecules.[17] For the relation to hold rigorously, interactions between the molecules must be unimportant at all concentrations. Apparent deviations from the Beer-Lambert law can arise from molecular associations (simple deviations from the perfect gas laws, dimerization equilibria, etc.) or from effects which are more subtle in origin. For example, when systems having a very narrow line or banded structure are irradiated with a relatively broader-bandwidth "monochromatic" analyzer beam, the necessary condition for the derivation of

---

* ϵ is also called the molar absorptivity, the molar absorbancy index, and the absorption coefficient, and is symbolized by a, a_M, etc. There is no general agreement on the terminology employed, although there have been frequent pleas for uniformity of usage. Note that many concentration units and measures of path length may be used with the Beer-Lambert law, so that the units of the constant ϵ must be given if the data are to be of value to others. Furthermore the use of e, the base of the natural logarithms, is often made in formulating the absorption law, $I/I_0 = e^{-\alpha cl}$, where α, which is equal to 2.303 ϵ, is also designated by a variety of names, including absorption coefficient. In this text the symbol ϵ will always refer to the constant in the decadic form, as in Eq. 1-24, with units of liters per mole-centimeter; where other forms of the Beer-Lambert law are employed, units will be given.

1-24, that is, constant ϵ over the entire band of the analyzer beam, cannot hold. Furthermore, for the very narrow-line absorption, the bandwidth and ϵ change with temperature and pressure (see Sec. 2-7B) so that Eq. 1-24 cannot apply. In highly fluorescent systems, a false measure of the transmitted beam intensity may be received by the detector and lead to an apparent failure of 1-24. However, for most gaseous systems of reasonable molecular complexity and for nearly all non-associated molecules in solution, the use of relation 1-24 is a convenient and accurate procedure for treating light absorption data. Nevertheless, if in doubt, one should always run an experimental test of the law for the particular system under study.

When more than one absorbing compound is present in a homogeneous mixture, the Beer-Lambert law assumes the form

$$\frac{I}{I_0} = 10^{-(\epsilon_1 c_1 + \epsilon_2 c_2 + \cdots)l} \tag{1-25}$$

where ϵ_1 and c_1 refer to the usual parameters for compound 1, ϵ_2 and c_2 are those for compound 2, etc., at a particular wavelength.

1-9 COMPARISON OF THE REACTIONS OF LIGHT-EXCITED AND THERMALLY EXCITED MOLECULES

There are several unique features of photochemical reactions, not usually encountered in thermal systems, which should be noted from our discussions in this chapter. Thermal reactions commonly involve molecules in their ground electronic states whose vibrational, rotational, and translation energies are in the upper range of the distribution described by the Maxwell-Boltzmann law; reaction can occur, with a certain probability, between any of the molecules which have energies above some minimum amount necessary for the reaction. Monoenergetic thermal reactants have only been realized in special systems through the use of molecular beams, and in these cases only a few extremely simple reactions have been studied. However, in photochemical systems it is possible to control closely and relatively simply the degree of excitation of the reactant molecules through the use of monochromatic radiation of any desired wavelength or energy, provided the molecules are capable of absorbing it. This follows from the facts that for the usual experimental conditions employed in photochemical work a given molecule will absorb only one quantum of light, and the energy of the quantum is determined solely by the wavelength of the radiation employed; that is, $E = hc/\lambda$.

The reactions of an electronically excited molecule may occur from an entirely different array of potential energy surfaces from those encountered in thermal systems. Hence the products of a photochemical reaction may differ drastically from those found in a pyrolysis or other thermal process carried out at a temperature "equivalent" to the energy introduced by absorption of the photon. A given molecular and electronic configuration of an electronically excited molecule may never be reached thermally because in the latter case a variety of other reaction paths of much lower energy is available, and these paths will be utilized before the molecule can reach the desired state. An important consequence of this fact is that unique, thermodynamically highly unstable, structurally strained compounds may be *normal* photolysis products formed in good synthetic yields but completely inaccessible to "dark" chemistry.

One further difference between the reactions of thermally excited and photochemically excited molecules is worth noting. The usual pyrolytic decomposition of a complex molecule often forms a large spectrum of free-radical and molecular fragments, each with a Boltzmann distribution of energies. There is a high reactivity of the free-radical transients as a result of the high temperatures used in the pyrolysis, so that they are very short lived and occur at such low concentrations that studies of their reactions are most difficult. On the other hand, in theory specific bond cleavage and other forms of chemical change can be effected photochemically with the reactant molecule at any desired initial temperature; photodecomposition of a molecule may occur even when it is frozen into a solid state at liquid-nitrogen or liquid-helium temperature. Thus photochemical techniques are ideally suited to the generation of free radicals and the study of their reactions.

PROBLEMS

1. Calculate the fraction of 5000 A light (perpendicularly incident) reflected from (a) a single air-glass interface and (b) air-cryolite-glass layer; $n_{glass-air} = 1.60$, $n_{cryolite-air} = 1.35$.

2. A cell is constructed with planar Pyrex windows as indicated in Fig. 1-7. Calculate the fraction of a parallel beam of light (perpendicularly incident at *A*)

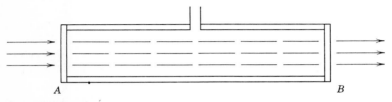

A   *B*

Fig. 1-7   Light incident on the front window of the photolysis cell (*A*) is transmitted in part to *B*; see Problem 2.

which is transmitted through the cell to B when the cell is (a) completely evacuated, (b) filled with water, and (c) filled with 2-nitroso-2-methylbutane at 50.0-mm pressure at 25° (ϵ = 10.0 liters/mole-cm at 6500 A). 6500 A light is used; assume that no absorption of light occurs in Pyrex or water and that there are no imperfections in the glass. At 6500 A $n_{Pyrex\text{-}air}$ = 1.472, $n_{H_2O\text{-}air}$ = 1.331. (In your calculations consider the amount of light reflected at each interface, rereflected to B, etc.)

3. Demonstrate mathematically, through the use of Eqs. 1-2 and 1-3, the phenomena of interference and reinforcement of light waves.

4. Derive Eqs. 1-10, 1-11, 1-12, and 1-13, which describe the size and position of the electric vector of elliptically and circularly polarized light waves. Give the equations for both right- and left-handed screw-like paths traced by the vector head.

5. Calculate the de Broglie wavelength (in angstrom units) for (a) an electron beam having a velocity of $c/5$, (b) a neutron beam when the velocity of the neutrons is $c/100$, and (c) a beam of bowling balls which weigh 16 lb each and have velocities of 20 miles/hr. (The mass m of a body with velocity v is related to its rest mass, m_0, by $m = m_0/\sqrt{1 - (v^2/c^2)}$.)

6. X, Y, and Z of Fig. 1-8 are containers of equal size. Surfaces labeled S are coated with bright silver, and surfaces labeled C are coated with lampblack. All

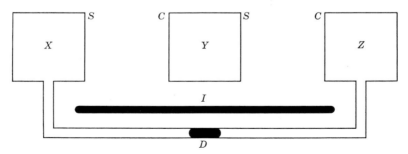

Fig. 1-8   Experimental arrangement described in Problem 6.

the other surfaces of the containers are identical. D is a liquid drop which isolates X from Z but is free to move. Containers X and Z are sealed and contain air. The distance between X and Y is equal to that between Y and Z. A heat-insulating shield I separates Y from D. When the system is in thermal equilibrium boiling water is placed in Y. Describe the movement of the drop D; explain.

7. Calculate the energy per quantum of radiation of wavelength 3130 A (a) in ergs/quantum and (b) in kilocalories/einstein.

8. Calculate the maximum kinetic energy (in ergs) of an electron which is ejected from tungsten by a quantum of radiant energy of wavelength 2537 A, The work function of an electron in tungsten is 4.52 ev.

9. A quantum of radiation of wavelength 0.020 A is scattered by a free electron which is essentially at rest. The scattered quantum has a direction 60° from its incident line of travel. Find (a) the wavelength of scattered radiation and (b) the kinetic energy of the electron after impact.

10. Using Planck's equation 1-18, show that the wavelength λ_m at which $\mathscr{E}_\lambda$ has its maximum for the temperature T is given by:

$$\lambda_m = \frac{ch}{4.965\ kT}$$

11. The compound 2-nitroso-2-chloro-1,4-diphenylbutane (I) when irradiated in methanol solution undergoes decomposition to form HCl and an unsaturated nitroso derivative. At 6500 A, $\Phi_{HCl} = 0.80$; $\epsilon = 12.33$ liter/mole-cm in methanol solution. A photolysis cell of 10 cm length and 50 cc volume is filled with a 0.1 M solution of compound I in methanol. It is irradiated with a parallel beam of circularly polarized light of 6500 A wavelength. Under the conditions of the experiment 4.5×10^{15} quanta/sec enter the solution at the front of the cell. The specific rotation of the pure compound in its optically active forms is 2.63° at 20°C and 5300 A. The anisotropy factor for the isomers at 6500 A is 0.04.

(a) The solution described above is irradiated for a period of 48 hr. Calculate the expected optical rotation of the solution after irradiation when it is measured in a 1 dm polarimeter tube at 5300 A and 20°C.

(b) To what extent (%) should the decomposition be allowed to proceed to give the maximum obtainable rotation of the remaining solution? (One approach to this problem has been given by Kuhn and Knopf.[18])

(c) What will be the magnitude of the rotation at the maximum?

(d) If the anisotropy factor for the optical isomers was 0.08 at 6500 A, what would be the rotation of the solution at its maximum?

REFERENCES TO CHAPTER 1

1. (a) K. Bol and W. W. Hanson, *Phys. Rev.*, **80**, 298 (1950); (b) L. Essen, *Nature*, **165**, 582 (1950).
2. (a) E. K. Plyler, L. R. Blaine, and W. S. Conner, *J. Opt. Soc. Am.*, **45**, 102 (1955); (b) C. A. Aslakson, *Nature*, **164**, 711 (1949); (c) E. Bergstrand, *Nature*, **165**, 405 (1950).
3. A. Einstein, *Ann. Physik*, **17**, 891 (1905).
4. For an excellent discussion of the electromagnetic wave theory and references to the earlier literature see F. K. Richtmyer and E. H. Kennard, *Introduction to Modern Physics*, McGraw-Hill Book Co., New York, 1947, Chapter 2.
5. (a) W. W. Coblentz, *Natl. Bur. Standards (U.S.) Bull.*, **10**, 1 (1914); (b) F. Anacker and R. Mannkopff, *Z. Physik*, **155**, 1 (1959); (c) G. F. Sitnik, *Astron. Zhur.*, **37**, 1076 (1960); *Soviet Astron.*, **4**, 1013 (1961).
6. O. Lummer and E. Pringsheim, *D. Phys. Ges. Verhandlungen*, **2**, 163 (1900).
7. M. Planck, *Ann. Physik*, **4**, 553 (1901).

8. A. Einstein, *Ann. Physik*, **17,** 132 (1905).

9. R. A. Millikan, *Phys. Rev.*, **7,** 355 (1916).

10. A. H. Compton, *Phys. Rev.*, **21,** 715 (1923); *ibid.*, **22,** 409 (1923).

11. (a) D. S. Herr and W. A. Noyes, Jr., *J. Am. Chem. Soc.*, **62,** 2052 (1940); (b) E. I. Akeroyd and R. G. W. Norrish, *J. Chem. Soc.*, **1936,** 890; (c) H. S. Taylor and C. Rosenblum, *J. Chem. Phys.*, **6,** 119 (1938); (d) J. A. Leermakers, *J. Am. Chem. Soc.*, **56,** 1899 (1934); C. A. Winkler, *Trans. Faraday Soc.*, **31,** 761 (1935).

12. L. de Broglie, *Phil. Mag.*, **47,** 446 (1924).

13. C. Davisson and L. H. Germer, *Phys. Rev.*, **30,** 705 (1927).

14. I. Estermann, R. Frisch, and O. Stern, *Z. Physik*, **73,** 348 (1931).

15. D. P. Mitchell and P. N. Powers, *Phys. Rev.*, **50,** 486 (1936).

16. R. W. Wood, *Physical Optics*, 3rd Edition, Macmillan Co., New York, 1934, p. 21.

17. F. H. Lohman, *J. Chem. Educ.*, **32,** 155 (1955).

18. W. Kuhn and E. Knopf, *Z. Physik. Chem.*, **B7,** 292 (1930).

2

The Interaction of Light with Atoms; Atom-Photosensitized Reactions

Conceptually the simplest of the photochemical systems are those involving absorption of light by atoms and the subsequent chemical reactions induced by these atoms. Many of the principles which have been applied in recent years to the more complex molecular systems were first clearly enunciated in atomic systems. For example, the idea of triplet-triplet energy transfer, so useful in "molecular photochemistry" today, is certainly nothing new in principle to the area of photochemistry; it originated in the early work on excited-atom sensitized systems. The inherent simplicity of these systems makes it attractive to study the laws of absorption and the reactions of excited atoms as an important introduction to the field of molecular photochemistry.

A basic understanding of spectroscopy is of general interest, since much of our fundamental knowledge of the quantum theory and the structure of atoms and molecules has been derived from studies of emission and absorption spectra. Experimental and theoretical spectroscopy play particularly significant roles in photochemistry. For example, the proper choice of a light source for a photochemical reaction depends upon the absorption spectrum of the molecule being studied and the availability of arcs or sparks with sufficiently intense atomic or molecular emission spectra in the desired absorption region. Furthermore, the methods of theoretical spectroscopy have had some success in explaining certain photochemical reactions, particularly in recent years.

In the first section of this chapter a brief review of atomic spectroscopy is given as an aid to the proper interpretation of photochemical experiments. For further study of atomic spectroscopy the reader is referred to the excellent treatises on the subject.[1-5] In the latter part of the chapter the development and present status of knowledge in atom-sensitized reactions is discussed and reviewed. In most of the discussions we shall use the mercury atom as our model system, since the great majority of studies of atom-photosensitized reactions have involved this system.

27

2-1   ATOMIC SPECTRA AND ATOMIC STRUCTURE; EVIDENCE FOR DISCRETE ENERGY STATES

The essential feature of the absorption and emission of radiation by atoms or molecules is that these processes are quantized; that is, transitions occur between discrete, well-defined energy levels. The first strong experimental evidence for this concept arose out of the research of Balmer on the emission spectrum of the hydrogen atom in the visible and near-ultraviolet regions.[1] This spectrum is shown in Fig. 2-1.

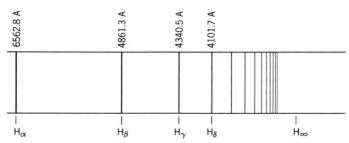

Fig. 2-1   The Balmer series in the emission spectrum of atomic hydrogen; the theoretical convergence limit is H_∞. From Herzberg,[1] p. 5.

Before Balmer's paper in 1885 it was well known that atoms of hydrogen and many other elements when sufficiently excited by thermal or electrical energy gave off intense light which could be separated into a group of bright lines by passage through a suitable dispersing system. Although numerous investigators attempted to apply the equations of acoustics and searched for some sort of harmonic relations that would account in a regular fashion for the distribution of these lines throughout the spectrum, it remained for Balmer to describe precisely the location and distribution of nine of these hydrogen emission lines by means of the simple formula

$$\lambda = \frac{n_1^{\,2}}{n_1^{\,2} - 4}\, G$$

where n_1 is an integer equal to 3, 4, 5, . . . , G is a constant, 3645.6, and λ is the wavelength in angstrom units. This expression is more often written as

$$\omega = R\left(\frac{1}{2^2} - \frac{1}{n_1^{\,2}}\right) \tag{2-1}$$

where ω, in cm^{-1}, is the frequency in wave numbers, and R is another constant. Substitution of $n_1 = 3$ into Balmer's expression gives a predicted line at 6562.08 A, whereas Ångström found experimentally that the strong H_α line fell at 6562.10 A.

The excellent agreement stimulated intense studies of more complex line spectra, culminating in the general equation of Rydberg, Eq. 2-2. This equation accounted for many observed series in line spectra, particularly those of hydrogen and the alkali and alkaline earth metals.

$$\frac{1}{\lambda} = \omega = \frac{R}{(n_2 + \mu_2)^2} - \frac{R}{(n_1 + \mu_1)^2} \qquad (2\text{-}2)$$

In this equation n_1 and n_2 are integers, and μ_1 and μ_2 are small constants. The Rydberg constant R is particularly significant since it holds for a large number of series of spectral lines from many atoms. The two quantities on the right-hand side of Eq. 2-2 are called *terms*, and any line in a series can be represented as the difference between two such terms. If n_2 is constant and n_1 has allowed integral values greater than n_2, a series of lines is generated as the difference between a *fixed term* and a *running term*. When μ_1 and μ_2 are set equal to zero, the general equation reduces to

$$\omega = R\left(\frac{1}{n_2^{\,2}} - \frac{1}{n_1^{\,2}}\right) \qquad (2\text{-}3)$$

from which one can calculate the several series of line spectra of the hydrogen atom. Thus, if n_2 is fixed at 1 and n_1 is allowed to vary subject to the restriction that it must be an integer greater than n_2, the Lyman series in the far ultraviolet is generated. The Balmer, Paschen, Brackett, and Pfund series correspond to values of n_2 of 2, 3, 4, and 5, respectively.

During his studies on sodium and potassium Rydberg discovered that the line spectra for these elements actually contain several series of lines, including a set of sharply defined doublets, the *sharp* series, and a second set of rather blurred doublets, the *diffuse* series. Other series include the *principal* series, which generally contains the bright and persistent resonance line of a spectrum (e.g., the sodium D line), and the *fundamental* series. Each of these series is adequately described by Eq. 2-2 if one assigns n_2 and μ_1 and μ_2 constant values, and allows n_1 to vary in the usual manner.[2] In later practice the symbols μ_1 and μ_2 were replaced by S, P, D, or F, depending on the appearance of the lines in a given series. Subsequently these symbols became far more general in meaning and are presently used to designate quantum states (e.g., s, p, d, and f) and atomic term symbols [e.g., $Hg6(^1S_0)$].

As an extension to his theory, Rydberg proposed that, if the first term on the right-hand side of Eq. 2-2 were allowed to vary in a manner similar to the second term, many new intercombination lines, or series, would be generated. These were soon discovered by Ritz, who then proposed the

Ritz combination principle stating that the frequency in wave numbers of *any* spectral line is the difference between two terms T_1 and T_2, that is,

$$\omega = T_1 - T_2 \qquad (2\text{-}4)$$

2-2 THE BOHR THEORY

The fact that thousands of emission and absorption lines in the spectra of atoms could be expressed empirically as the difference between two terms was historically of great theoretical interest. However, all initial attempts to employ the Rutherford model of the atom and to deduce expressions of this type from the laws of classical mechanics failed. The crux of the difficulty was the fact that classical electrodynamic theory predicted that an electron revolving about a positive nucleus in a coulombic field of force would be accelerated toward the nucleus and in the process would radiate energy as light of continuously increasing frequency. This was completely contrary to experiment. Bohr in 1913 resolved the problem by devising a radically new theory based upon the following highly original postulates.

As an electron revolves about the nucleus of an atom under a coulombic field of force, its path is restricted to certain discrete orbits, not to the infinite number predicted by classical mechanics.

The allowed orbits are characterized by the fact that the angular momentum of the electron, $m_e vr$, must be an integral multiple, n, of $h/2\pi$.

$$m_e vr = \frac{nh}{2\pi} = n\hbar \qquad (2\text{-}5)$$

where $n = 1, 2, 3, \ldots$, and m_e is the mass of the electron, v its velocity, and r the radius of its circular orbit.

No radiation is emitted when an electron is revolving in a given orbit. Light is emitted or absorbed only in a quantum process that involves the transition of the electron from one quantum state to another of different energy.

The frequency of a line in a spectrum, v, is given by the difference between the energies of the two quantum states. It can be expressed by the equation

$$E_{n_1} - E_{n_2} = hv \qquad (2\text{-}6)$$

where E_{n_1} is the energy of the initial excited state, and E_{n_2} that of the lower state.

The striking feature of the Bohr theory was the fact that, with these postulates and the assumption that coulomb's law of force and Newton's laws of motion were valid at atomic dimensions, Eq. 2-7, which is equivalent to the empirical equation of Balmer, could be derived theoretically for a Rutherford model of the hydrogen atom, or for a hydrogen-like atom such as He^+, of atomic number Z.

$$\omega = \frac{1}{hc}(E_1 - E_2) = \frac{2\pi^2 m_e e^4}{ch^3} Z^2 \left(\frac{1}{n_2^2} - \frac{1}{n_1^2}\right) \tag{2-7}$$

In this expression n_2 is the principal quantum number of the final (lower) state, and n_1 is that of the initial (upper) state. By combining the quantities to the left of the parenthesis into one constant R, and setting $n_2 = 2$, we see that the form of Eq. 2-7 is identical with that of Balmer's empirical expression, Eq. 2-1. As a quantitative check, substitution of the appropriate constants into the factor $(2\pi^2 m_e e^4/ch^3)$ gives 109,737 cm^{-1}, which is in good agreement with the experimental value for the Rydberg constant for hydrogen, 109,677.581 cm^{-1}.

2-2A Grotrian Energy-Level Diagrams

A useful way to describe the Bohr energy levels of atoms and the spectral lines arising from transitions between these levels is in terms of a *Grotrian energy-level diagram*. In Fig. 2-2, the energy levels (neglecting fine structure) for the hydrogen atom are graphically represented. The ordinate is an energy scale on which each horizontal line represents the energy level corresponding to a particular value of the principal quantum number n in the expression $R_H(1 - 1/n^2)$. Spectral lines result from transitions between these levels in accordance with the Bohr frequency condition. The units of energy are wave numbers, plotted on the right, and electron volts, plotted on the left. The wavelengths of lines in the Lyman and Balmer series also are given.

In considering Fig. 2-2 in some detail we see that at $n = \infty$ complete separation of the electron occurs (ionization). Beyond the wave number corresponding to this point the spectrum loses all line structure and becomes a continuum. If we substitute ∞ for n_2 and 1 for n_1 in Eq. 2-7, we obtain 13.595 ev as a calculated value for the ionization potential of the hydrogen atom. From their research with electron impact techniques, Franck and Hertz obtained an experimental value of 13.54 volts, in agreement with the Bohr theory. Actually, experimental determinations of convergence limits in the spectra of different elements have given the most accurate information on the ionization potentials of the elements.

A transition from one energy level to another is represented by a line connecting the two levels. The vertical length of the line is directly proportional to the wave number or energy of the spectral line, while in

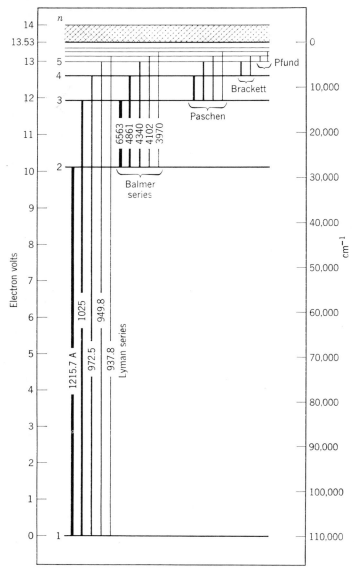

Fig. 2-2   Grotrian energy-level diagram for atomic hydrogen; the widths of the vertical lines are roughly proportional to the transition probabilities; the ionization potential is 13.53 ev.   From Herzberg,[1] p. 24.

this diagram (Fig. 2-2) the thickness is roughly proportional to the probability of the transition between the two levels, that is, the intensity of the spectral line.

Hydrogen atoms in the ground state, $n = 1$, can be raised to excited states in which $n > 1$ by several means, including collision with electrons of sufficiently high energy, the electron impact method. Another important mode of excitation is by absorption of radiation of suitable wavelength. Thus we see from Fig. 2-2 that if 972.5 A radiation is absorbed by hydrogen atoms in the ground state these atoms will be raised from the $n = 1$ level to the excited state $n = 4$. The excited hydrogen atoms may then emit quanta of 972.5 A radiation and drop back to the ground state. This process is not instantaneous; excited atoms have mean lives of 10^{-8} to 10^{-9} sec or longer, depending on factors which will be discussed later.

In addition to this direct return to the $n = 1$ level the electron may drop first from the $n = 4$ to the $n = 2$ level, from which it subsequently returns to the ground state. These transitions are accompanied by the emission of 4861.3 A radiation, the H_β line of the Balmer series, and the 1215.7 A line of the Lyman series. An alternative sequence for the electron in the $n = 4$ level could be $n = 4 \rightarrow n = 3 \rightarrow n = 2 \rightarrow n = 1$ in which the 18751.1, 6562.8, and 1215.7 A lines are emitted.

This process in which the atom is excited by absorption of light and then emits radiation and returns to a lower energy level is known as atomic fluorescence. The longest wavelength capable of exciting fluorescence, in the case of the hydrogen atom the 1215.7 A line, is called a *resonance line*, and the emitted radiation of the same wavelength as the absorbed light is *resonance radiation* or *resonance fluorescence*.

2-2B   Refinements to the Bohr Theory

The initial success of the Bohr theory for the hydrogen atom led to its extension to other systems, including hydrogen-like ions such as He^+. In the more refined treatment, one recognizes that the nucleus has a finite mass and assumes that the electron and the nucleus revolve around a common center of gravity. The mass of the electron m_e is now replaced by the reduced mass μ, defined by

$$\mu = \frac{m_e M}{m_e + M} \tag{2-8}$$

where M is the mass of the nucleus. If one further assumes quantization of the angular momentum of the entire system of electron and nucleus, the more general form of Eq. 2-7 becomes, for hydrogen and hydrogen-like ions,

$$\omega = \frac{2\pi^2\mu e^4}{ch^3} Z^2\left(\frac{1}{n_2^{\,2}} - \frac{1}{n_1^{\,2}}\right) \tag{2-9}$$

where Z represents the charge on the hydrogen-like ion. Thus, theory predicts that the Rydberg constant should be dependent on the mass of the nucleus, becoming less so as the atomic number Z increases. This prediction has been well confirmed by experiment. For example, it follows from Eq. 2-9 that the spectrum of He^+ should contain a series of lines with wave numbers ω given by

$$\omega = 4R\left(\frac{1}{n_2^{\,2}} - \frac{1}{n_1^{\,2}}\right)$$

where R is the Rydberg constant for the hydrogen atom. Such lines do occur for He^+, and in fact the analogous series has been observed for hydrogen-like atoms as heavy as O^{7+}.

Equation 2-9 indicates that the emission spectra of two atoms of the same atomic numbers Z, but with nuclei of different masses (i.e., isotopes), should be very similar except that a slight displacement of the lines would exist because of the difference in the reduced masses, μ. In 1932 Urey, Brickwedde, and Murphy[6] utilized this isotope shift to prove the existence of deuterium.

Sommerfeld extended the Bohr theory to include the case of elliptical orbits for the electron, and later applied relativistic mechanics to its motion. This treatment leads to a more complex expression for the energies of various electron orbits in the hydrogen atom and predicts that for a given principal quantum number there are actually many terms with energies very close together. Thus, this refinement of theory predicts groups of lines differing only slightly in wavelength—the *fine structure* of a spectrum—instead of the individual lines originally proposed. By the use of spectrographs with high resolving power this fine structure was observed in the hydrogen spectrum, although the agreement of observed lines with theory was not very satisfactory. In view of this fine structure it is necessary to consider the energy-level diagram, Fig. 2-2, as a simplified version that gives only the gross aspects of the energies of the electronic states in the hydrogen atom.

In summary, the Bohr theory, with Sommerfeld's generalization, was successful in explaining the major aspects of the line spectrum of hydrogen atoms and hydrogen-like ions. The theory led to a value for the radius of the hydrogen atom and predicted an isotopic shift due to differences in mass that was utilized in the discovery of deuterium. Despite these achievements, there were severe limitations to the original quantum theory of spectra. It broke down when the spectrum of a two-electron atom such as helium was considered. Furthermore, although accurate predictions of the frequencies of spectral lines of hydrogen were possible, the theory did not provide a means for the calculation of their intensities. It remained for the development of modern wave mechanics to provide satisfactory solutions to these problems.

2-3 WAVE-MECHANICAL VIEW OF ENERGY STATES IN ATOMS

Wave mechanics departs radically from the rather comfortable realm of the Bohr theory in which a "physical picture" of the atom and its quantum states is employed, and substitutes instead a highly mathematical theory. A detailed consideration of this theory is out of place here. However, it is worthwhile to consider briefly the contributions of wave mechanics to our present knowledge of the electronic structure and spectra of atoms, in particular the hydrogen atom.

2-3A The Schrödinger Wave Equation

The wave equation for the hydrogen atom as formulated by Schrödinger (1926) from the de Broglie relationship (Eq. 1-22) and the classical equation of harmonic wave motion is

$$\frac{\partial^2 \psi}{\partial x^2} + \frac{\partial^2 \psi}{\partial y^2} + \frac{\partial^2 \psi}{\partial z^2} + \frac{8\pi^2 \mu}{h^2} \left(E + \frac{e^2}{r} \right) \psi = 0 \qquad (2\text{-}10)$$

where ψ is the amplitude of the atomic wave function, μ is the reduced mass (Eq. 2-8), E is the total energy of the system, and e^2/r is the coulombic energy between an electron and a proton. If the function ψ is subjected to the restrictions that it be continuous, single valued, and finite, and that it vanish at infinity, the equation can be solved, but only for certain values of the total energy E called *eigenvalues*.[7,8,9,10] These *eigenvalues* are the possible energy levels corresponding to the allowed states of the atom, the *eigenstates*, and are given explicitly by

$$E = - \frac{2\pi^2 \mu e^4 Z^2}{h^2 n^2} \qquad (2\text{-}11)$$

where n must be a positive integer.

This expression is identical with the expression for the energy of a Bohr orbital for hydrogen and thus leads to the same theoretical value for the Rydberg constant. The quantity n is equivalent to the Bohr principal quantum number, but in contrast to the original Bohr-Sommerfeld quantum theory n in the Schrödinger treatment is not introduced by an arbitrary assumption. Instead, the concept of quantization of energy levels in terms of the integer n arises as a natural result of the solution of the equation for wave motion, the integers representing the number of nodes in the wave structure.

A useful picture of the physical significance of ψ was given by Born, who suggested that it can be related to the probability that the electron will be found at some specified position with respect to the nucleus. Thus $\psi^2\, d\tau$ is considered to be the probability that the electron will occupy a given volume element $d\tau$ in the atom.*

When ψ^2 is viewed as a probability distribution function, the position of the electron cannot be considered as localized to a definite orbit of the Bohr type. This would, in fact, violate the Heisenberg uncertainty principle, which tells us that it is not possible to determine simultaneously the position and momentum of the electron to any desired degree of accuracy. Instead, when the electron is in one of the stationary states with a total energy given by Eq. 2-11, we can think of it as being smeared over space in a continuous charged cloud. We may also consider it as a point charge rapidly moving within its space so that the density of the smeared cloud corresponds to the probability of finding the electron at any chosen point. Questions as to what the electron really is or what kind of motion it really executes are meaningless because the uncertainty principle tells us that electrons cannot be sharply pictured like macroscopic objects. Care must be taken to avoid taking any physical picture of an electron's behavior too literally; on the other hand, the mathematical description of its behavior provides close agreement with experimental observations.

2-3B   Quantum Numbers

Three parameters arise naturally from the solution of the Schrödinger wave equation for the hydrogen atom. These quantities, and a fourth that results from Dirac's relativistic mechanics, are called *quantum numbers*. They play highly significant roles in our understanding of the electronic transitions responsible for the line spectra of atoms, and furnish a logical explanation for the periodic behavior of the elements.

The quantity n in Eq. 2-11 is the most important parameter in determining the energy levels in the hydrogen atom and is called the *principal quantum number*. Just as in the Bohr theory, n is a positive integer that is

---

* For the more general case one should write $|\psi|^2\, d\tau$ or $\psi\psi^*\, d\tau$, where ψ^* is the complex conjugate of ψ, instead of $\psi^2\, d\tau$. However, for all real values of ψ, $\psi^2\, d\tau$ is correct, and we shall use this more convenient form.

a measure of the position of the electron in relation to the nucleus. Thus the orbitals with $n = 1, 2, 3, \ldots$ correspond to the familiar K, L, M, $\ldots$ shells within the atom.

The other two quantum numbers arising from the solution of Eq. 2-10 deal with the angular momentum possessed by the electron. According to wave mechanics, the orbital angular momentum is a vector quantity that is quantized and equal to $[l(l + 1)]^{1/2} h/2\pi$, where l, the *azimuthal quantum number*, can have values of $0, 1, 2, \ldots, (n - 1)$.

Each of the principal orbitals, or shells in the Bohr terminology, except that for which $n = 1$ (and therefore $l = 0$)—i.e., the K shell—contains subshells with energies dependent upon l. When l = zero, the total orbital angular momentum is zero, so that the orbital is spherically symmetrical, whereas when $l \neq 0$ the orbital is asymmetric and the atom has a net orbital angular momentum. This produces a significant change in the total energy of the atom.

In Sec. 2-1 it was noted that, long before the Bohr theory was proposed, certain lines in the spectra of alkali atoms were empirically designated as *sharp, principal, diffuse,* and *fundamental.* In a somewhat confusing blend of empiricism and theory the symbols s, p, d, and f are now used to designate the states $l = 0$, $l = 1$, $l = 2$, and $l = 3$, respectively. Thus the ground state of the valence electron in sodium has $n = 3$ and $l = 0$, and it is called a $3s$ electron. If this electron is excited to the state in which $n = 3$ and $l = 1$, it becomes a $3p$ electron.

Associated with the orbital angular momentum of the electron is a magnetic moment μ_l, given by the expression

$$\mu_l = [l(l + 1)]^{1/2} \frac{eh}{4\pi m_e c} \tag{2-12}$$

where m_e and e are the mass and the charge of the electron. The quantity $(eh/4\pi m_e c)$ is a common unit of magnetic moment defined as a Bohr magneton. It is symbolized as μ_B and is equal to 0.9273×10^{-20} erg/gauss. Now if the radiation source, the excited atom, is placed in a strong magnetic field, the interaction of this field with the magnetic moment of the electron will cause the orbital angular momentum vector $\sqrt{l(l + 1)}\,h/2\pi$ to precess about the direction of the external field. However, as a fundamental quantum condition, only those orientations of $\sqrt{l(l + 1)}\,h/2\pi$ are allowed for which the component in the direction of the applied field is $m_l h/2\pi$, where m_l is the *magnetic quantum number*. The allowed magnetic moments in the direction of the field are

$$\mu = m_l \frac{eh}{4\pi m_e c} = m_l \mu_B \tag{2-13}$$

The magnetic quantum number is restricted to the values $m_l = l, (l - 1)$, $(l - 2), \ldots, 0, \ldots, -l$.

Although the magnetic quantum number is an added postulate to the Bohr theory, it is a natural result of the solution of the Schrödinger wave equation. From this standpoint, m_l is the factor that determines the orientation of an orbital, or orbital wave function ψ, with respect to some particular axis, which might be within the atom (e.g., the direction of the vector $\sqrt{l(l + 1)}h/2\pi$), or might be external in the form of the direction of a magnetic field. In terms of a mechanical model values of m_l equal but opposite in sign correspond to orbitals which have the same shape, but in

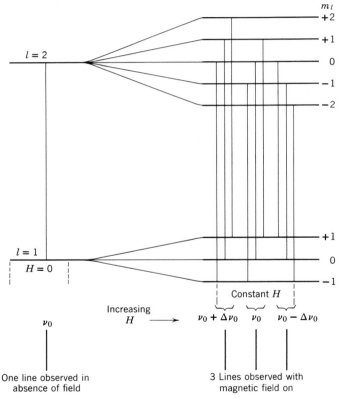

Fig. 2-3   Energy diagram showing orbital and magnetic quantum numbers and the splitting of each of the energy levels $l = 1$ and $l = 2$ into $2l + 1$ sublevels (normal Zeeman effect) as a strong magnetic field of strength H is applied in the direction of the z-axis. A single emission line is seen when $H = 0$, and three lines are seen when the magnetic field is applied. Transitions obey the selection rule $\Delta m_l = 0, \pm 1$ and have frequencies ν_0, $\nu_0 + \Delta\nu_0$, and $\nu_0 - \Delta\nu_0$.

which the electron moves in opposite directions, namely, clockwise and counterclockwise, with respect to the given axis.

In the absence of an external magnetic field, orbitals with the same value of n and l but different values of m_l have equal energies. These states are said to be *degenerate*. An electron in the 2p level can have three states of equal energy corresponding to $m_l = 1$, 0, or -1, so that the 2p state is triply degenerate. It follows that the d orbitals are fivefold degenerate, while the s orbitals are non-degenerate.

The degeneracy of a group of orbitals can be removed by placing the emitting atom in a strong magnetic field of strength **H** (measured in oersteds). The interaction of the external magnetic field with the orbital magnetic moment of the electron will, in the case of a singlet line, split the 2p level into three independent levels differing in energy by ΔE, where

$$\Delta E = m_l \mathbf{H} \mu_\mathrm{B} \text{ Bohr magnetons} \tag{2-14}$$

This treatment neglects electron "spin" (see the following paragraphs). When this effect is included, one obtains

$$\Delta E = m_j \mathbf{H} g \mu_\mathrm{B} \tag{2-15}$$

in which m_j is a quantity analogous to m_l except that it represents the projection of the *total* angular momentum vector of the electron on the axis of the magnetic field. The quantity g is the "Landé g factor" that gives the splitting of the energy levels, and describes the "anomalous" Zeeman effect.[1]

Figure 2-3 illustrates diagrammatically the relationship between the magnetic quantum number m_l and the azimuthal quantum number l and shows the splitting of the energy levels $l = 1$ and $l = 2$ in a singlet line when an external magnetic field is applied. Figure 2-4 is an example of the *Zeeman effect*, for rhodium.[2]

An intense electric field can interact with the internal field forces between the nucleus and its orbital electrons to produce line splitting. This *Stark effect* is much more difficult to demonstrate than the Zeeman effect because high electric field intensities of the order of 10^5 volts/cm are required to affect significantly the very strong internal field between the electrons and the nucleus (about 10^{10} volts/cm for a hydrogen atom in the ground state).

We have seen that the quantum numbers n, l, and m_l arise naturally as parameters in the solution of the Schrödinger equation. However, experiment shows that an additional factor must be introduced to explain the fine structure of atomic spectra. Spectrographs of high resolution showed that the emission lines of the alkali elements consist of two closely spaced lines (doublets) rather than single lines as predicted by theory.

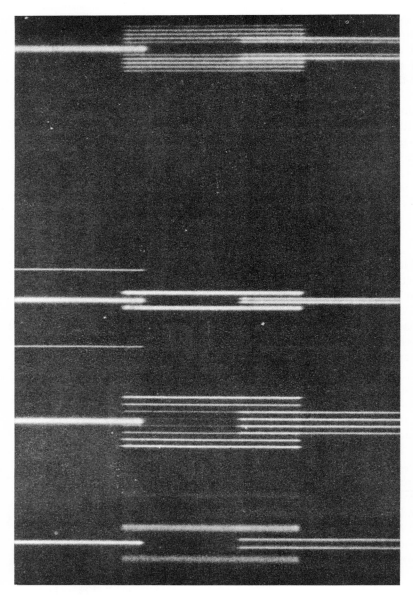

Fig. 2-4   Zeeman effect in rhodium, showing the normal near-ultraviolet emission spectrum (top) in the absence of a magnetic field and in the presence of a field of 90,500 oersteds. The middle spectrum shows the perpendicularly polarized, and the bottom the parallel polarized, Zeeman effect.   From Harrison, Lord, and Loofbourow;[2]   originally from Molnar and Hitchcock.[179]

Pauli (1925) and Goudsmit and Uhlenbeck (1925) proposed that an electron moving in its orbit rotates simultaneously about its own axis. They further postulated that the spin contribution to the total angular momentum of the system was quantized with the allowed values of $s(h/2\pi)$, where s, the spin quantum number, would equal $\pm\frac{1}{2}$; presumably the spin of the electron could be in one of two directions and would have associated with it a magnetic moment, $\mu_s = 2s(eh/4\pi m_e c) = 2s\mu_B$ magnetons. Later wave-mechanical theory gave the spin angular momentum vector as $[s(s + 1)]^{1/2}h/2\pi$, and the corresponding spin magnetic moment is $2[s(s + 1)]^{1/2}\mu_B = \sqrt{3}$ Bohr magnetons.

It is interesting that the concept of a spin quantum number s, as well as n, l, and m_l, is a natural result of Dirac's relativistic wave mechanics. The fact that the four quantum numbers are no longer arbitrary postulates as in the Bohr theory but instead are derived quantities is a great achievement of modern wave mechanics.

2-3C   Electron Orbitals for Hydrogen-like Atoms

The wave equation can be transformed into polar coordinates and the wave function factored into the product of three functions:

$$\psi(r, \theta, \phi) = R(r)\Theta(\theta)\Phi(\phi) \tag{2-16}$$

Here R is a function only of the distance r of the electron from the nucleus, Θ depends only on the angle θ, and Φ depends only on the angle ϕ (see the polar coordinate system in Fig. 2-5). The solution of the wave

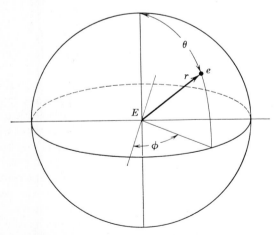

Fig. 2-5   Polar coordinates as used in the discussion of the Schrödinger equation for the hydrogen atom; the vertical axis corresponds to the usual z-axis.

equation in this form is only possible for certain discrete energy states which are characterized by the quantum numbers n, l, and m_l. The wave function, which is a solution of these equations, for the lowest energy state $(n = 1, l = 0, m_l = 0)$ is given by the following relation ($a_0 = 0.529$ A, the radius of the classical Bohr orbit):

$$\psi_{1s} = \frac{1}{\sqrt{\pi}} \left(\frac{Z}{a_0}\right)^{3/2} e^{-Zr/a_0} \tag{2-17}$$

The wave functions for the lowest-lying excited states are as follows:

$(n = 2, l = 0, m_l = 0)$

$$\psi_{2s} = \frac{1}{4\sqrt{2\pi}} \left(\frac{Z}{a_0}\right)^{3/2} \left(2 - \frac{Zr}{a_0}\right) e^{-Zr/2a_0} \tag{2-18}$$

$(n = 2, l = 1, m_l = 1)$

$$\psi_{2p_x} = \frac{1}{4\sqrt{2\pi}} \left(\frac{Z}{a_0}\right)^{3/2} \frac{Zr}{a_0} e^{-Zr/2a_0} \sin\theta \cos\phi \tag{2-19}$$

$(n = 2, l = 1, m_l = -1)$

$$\psi_{2p_y} = \frac{1}{4\sqrt{2\pi}} \left(\frac{Z}{a_0}\right)^{3/2} \frac{Zr}{a_0} e^{-Zr/2a_0} \sin\theta \sin\phi \tag{2-20}$$

$(n = 2, l = 1, m_l = 0)$

$$\psi_{2p_z} = \frac{1}{4\sqrt{2\pi}} \left(\frac{Z}{a_0}\right)^{3/2} \frac{Zr}{a_0} e^{-Zr/2a_0} \cos\theta \tag{2-21}$$

Other functions in increasing complexity describe the higher energy states.*

One characteristic of all $l = 0$ states, or s states, evident in the examples given is the absence of any angular dependence in the wave function; the "electron cloud" about the atom is completely symmetrical about the origin or nucleus, and there are n maxima in the ψ_{ns}^2 function which reflect the most probable regions for finding the electron. The magnitude of the ψ^2 functions for $l = 1$ states has a strong angular dependence on θ and ϕ as well as r. When the square of the angular dependent portion of the functions is plotted in polar coordinates, so that the radial parameter is proportional to the density of electronic charge in the given direction of space (that is, proportional to the probability of finding the electron if

---

* For further examples see W. Kauzmann,[8] p. 220.

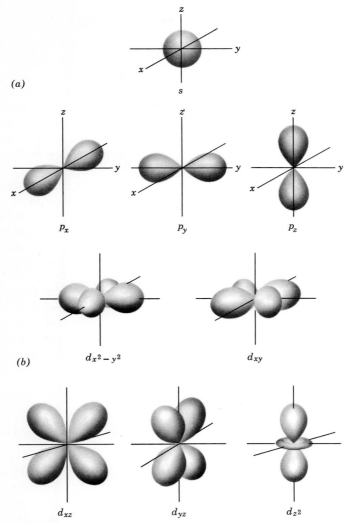

Fig. 2-6   Atomic orbital models for the s, p, and d states of the hydrogen atom.

one goes out from the origin in that direction within a small solid angle), the familiar s-, p-, and d-orbital pictures result; see Fig. 2-6.

The radial dependent wave function R always exhibits $(n - l)$ positions of maxima as one progresses out from the nucleus. It is interesting to note that the maximum in the ψ_{1s}^2 function occurs at $r = 0.529$ A, exactly the radius of the classical first Bohr orbit.

2-4   THE ELECTRONIC STRUCTURE OF ATOMS

The simple picture of the available orbital systems for the electrons in the hydrogen atom has been extrapolated to the multielectron case by the application of approximate methods. The same quantum numbers which define the energy states of the hydrogen atom can be employed to gain a rational basis for the electronic arrangements of the complex atoms.

In this section we shall discuss the manner in which electrons are distributed among the various electronic energy levels of atoms, a subject bearing directly on the fundamental processes of absorption and emission of radiation.

We have seen that an electron in an atom can be described by the four quantum numbers n, l, m_l, and s. Electrons with the same value of the principal quantum number n are said to occupy the same *shell*, and electrons with the same n and l are in the same *subshell* (often called subgroup or sublevel). A shell is classified as K, L, M, ..., etc., when $n = 1, 2, 3, ...$, etc. Subshells are designated by s, p, d, or f corresponding to azimuthal quantum numbers of $l = 0, 1, 2,$ or 3. Thus in the shorthand of the spectroscopist an electron with $n = 3$ and $l = 1$ is in the $3p$ state (or is a $3p$ electron), the convention being to write the value of n as a prefix to that of l. The number of electrons in a given subshell is written as a superscript to l, so that the symbol $3p^2$ specifies that a second electron has been added to the $3p$ subshell in the atom. For example, the electronic ground state of sodium is written as $1s^2$, $2s^2$, $2p^6$, $3s^1$.

2-4A   The Pauli Exclusion Principle

The maximum number of electrons in a subshell is determined by the restrictions on the quantum numbers,

$$n = 1, 2, 3, ..., \infty$$
$$l = 0, 1, 2, ..., n - 1$$
$$m_l = +l, ..., 0, -l$$
$$s = \pm \tfrac{1}{2}$$

and the Pauli exclusion principle. This states that no two electrons in an atom can have the same values of the four quantum numbers. Thus, in an orbital, an electronic state with given values of n, l, and m_l can accommodate two electrons with the same values of n, l, and m_l, but their spins must be opposite.

With the aid of these rules we can now consider a mechanism for building up the periodic table. Hydrogen has one electron, and in the ground state the electron will occupy the vacant orbital of *minimum* energy, in this case the 1s orbital. If the charge on the nucleus goes to +2 and a second electron is added to the system to give helium, the second electron can also fall into the 1s orbital, but its spin must be antiparallel to the first electron; that is, if $s = +\frac{1}{2}$ for the first electron, then $s = -\frac{1}{2}$ for the second. This follows because both electrons have the same values of n, l, and m_l, and parallel spins would violate the Pauli exclusion principle, since all four quantum numbers would be the same.

When Z is increased to 3, giving the lithium nucleus, two and only two electrons can occupy the 1s orbital, so that the third electron must fall into the next vacant orbital with minimum energy—the 2s orbital. Thus the electronic structure of lithium is $1s^2$, $2s^1$.

The four electrons of beryllium complete the 1s and 2s orbitals so that the next electron must go into either the 2p or the 3s sublevel, depending on which has the lower energy. Figure 2-7 shows the relative stability of

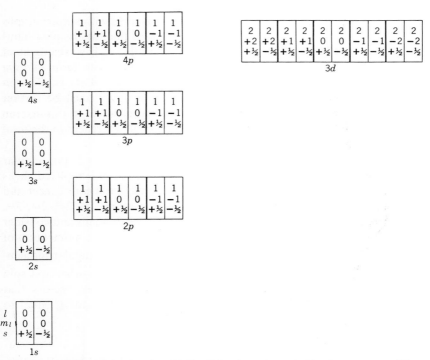

Fig. 2-7   Stability of the atomic orbitals of the elements up to krypton; energy of the orbitals increases toward the top of the figure. Note that the 2p orbital is more stable than the 3s orbital. Electrons fill these orbitals following the Pauli principle and in the order providing a maximum multiplicity for a given element.

the atomic orbitals of the elements up to krypton, and it can be seen that a $2p$ orbital is more stable than a $3s$ orbital. Hence the electronic structure of boron is $1s^2, 2s^2, 2p^1$.

The next question concerns the capacity of the $2p$ level. In this level $l = 1$, $m_l = +1, 0$, or -1, and $s = +\frac{1}{2}$ or $-\frac{1}{2}$ (Fig. 2-7), so that there can be a maximum of six electrons in this sublevel (neon, $1s^2, 2s^2, 2p^6$) without violating the Pauli exclusion principle. By similar reasoning we see that the capacities of the d and f levels are ten and fourteen electrons, respectively.

Table A-7 in the Appendix contains the electronic structures of the elements, as well as the term symbols for their normal ground states, a subject to be discussed in Sec. 2-6.

2-5 THE MULTIPLET STRUCTURE OF LINE SPECTRA AND THE ENERGY STATES OF SUBSHELLS

When line spectra of the alkali metals are examined with spectrographs of high resolving power, one observes that each of the lines is split. Thus the well-known sodium D line is actually a doublet with wavelengths at 5889.96 A and 5895.93 A. This *fine structure* arises from *term splitting* for either the upper term or the lower term, or both. That is, electron energy levels characterized by given values of n and l must be further split up into terms differing only slightly in total energy. In this section we shall see that this subdivision is a result of small differences in the total angular momentum of the atoms.

We must first consider how to deal with the orbital and spin angular momenta of electrons in closed shells. The electrons in completed shells are paired so that, as a good approximation, their momenta cancel and can be neglected. Thus, in the case of a sodium atom, $1s^2, 2s^2, 2p^6, 3s^1$, one can neglect the contribution from the $1s$, $2s$, and $2p$ shells and consider only the effect of the $3s$ electron. The total orbital angular momentum of the atom, $\mathbf{l}$, is then equal to $\sqrt{l(l + 1)}h/2\pi$, and the spin angular momentum, $\mathbf{s}$, equals $\sqrt{s(s + 1)}h/2\pi$, where l and s are the azimuthal and spin quantum numbers of the $3s$ electron. These momenta are vectors that interact (*couple*) to give the *total* angular momentum vector $\mathbf{j}$, equal to $\sqrt{j(j + 1)}h/2\pi$ from wave mechanics. Thus,

$$\mathbf{j} = \mathbf{l} + \mathbf{s}$$

Since l and s are directly proportional to angular momenta, we can also write

$$j = l + s$$

Now, for a given value of l, we know that s can be $+\frac{1}{2}$ or $-\frac{1}{2}$, so that two values of j result, and these correspond to the "split" energy level within the atom. Thus doublet line structure is a direct manifestation of electron spin.

In an atom with several optical (unpaired) electrons the situation is more complex because of the strong interelectron coupling between spin and angular momenta. However, for the lighter elements one can obtain the correct number and types of terms by treating this interaction in the following way. Electrons in the closed shells are ignored, but each optical electron is assigned a value of l that corresponds to infinitely small coupling. Then the net orbital angular momentum of the electrons, **L**, is given by

$$\mathbf{L} = \frac{[L(L+1)]^{\frac{1}{2}}h}{2\pi} \cong \frac{Lh}{2\pi}$$

where $L = \Sigma l_i$. Similarly, the total *spin* angular momentum **S** is given by

$$\mathbf{S} = \frac{[S(S+1)]^{\frac{1}{2}}h}{2\pi} \cong \frac{Sh}{2\pi}$$

where $S = \Sigma s_i$. (l_i and s_i are vector quantities, and L and S are *vector* sums.)

Finally, the total angular momentum of the atom **J** is the vector sum of $\mathbf{L} + \mathbf{S}$. Thus,

$$\mathbf{J} = \frac{[J(J+1)]^{\frac{1}{2}}h}{2\pi} \cong \frac{Jh}{2\pi}$$

where $\mathbf{J} = \mathbf{L} + \mathbf{S}$ and $J = L + S$.

This type of coupling is called Russell-Saunders coupling. An example is shown in Fig. 2-8 for a two-electron atom in which $L = 1$ and $S = 1$

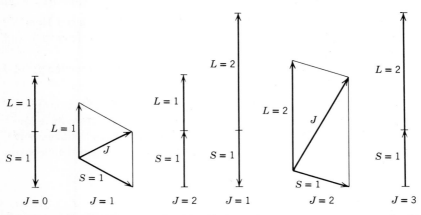

Fig. 2-8 Russell-Saunders coupling of orbital angular momentum vector L and spin angular momentum vector S to give the total angular momentum vector, J.

and also for $L = 2$ and $S = 1$. It is obvious that many closely spaced energy levels arise from the different ways of coupling L and S, and this leads to the multiplet structure of the spectral lines.

In the heavier elements a different type of coupling called j-j coupling predominates. In this case the orbital and spin angular momenta couple for each individual optical electron to form a resultant j. The individual j's are less strongly coupled with each other to form the resultant J. There is no definite L and S for this type of coupling; however, J remains well defined. We shall consider only the L-S (Russell-Saunders) coupling in the subsequent discussion.

2-6 TERM SYMBOLS AND THE GROUND STATE OF ATOMS

As we have just seen, the energy of a given electronic state, or term, is determined by the values of n, L, S, and J of the atom. These quantities are commonly combined into a term symbol of the form

$$n(^{2S+1}L_J); \quad \text{e.g., } Hg6(^1S_0)$$

in which $n =$ the principal quantum number of the electron undergoing the transition (we assume that only one electron is excited). Often n is obvious and is left out of the term symbol.

$L = \Sigma m_l$. When $\Sigma m_l = 0, 1, 2, 3, 4, 5, 6, \ldots$, the states are S, P, D, F, G, H, I, $\ldots$.

$S = \Sigma s_i$, and $2S + 1 =$ the multiplicity of the state.

$J = L \pm S$ for Russell-Saunders (L-S) coupling (L-S coupling is a good approximation for the lighter elements). The quantity J specifies the *total* electronic angular momentum of the atom, **J**, since $\mathbf{J} = [J(J+1)]^{1/2}h/2\pi$.

Thus the term symbol of the ground state of the mercury atom $Hg6(^1S_0)$ indicates that this state is a singlet (there are no unpaired electrons), and the atom has no net angular momentum.

The following rules are helpful in deriving term symbols for the ground states of atoms:

1. Electrons enter unfilled orbitals, thus giving maximum multiplicity. Triplet states in which the electron spins are parallel therefore have lower energies than their corresponding singlet states (Hund's rule). For example, atomic carbon has the electronic structure $1s^2$, $2s^2$, $2p^2$, and the electrons are distributed in their orbitals as

$$\underset{1s^2}{\downarrow\uparrow} \quad \underset{2s^2}{\downarrow\uparrow} \quad \underset{2p^1}{\uparrow} \quad \underset{2p^1}{\uparrow} \quad \underset{2p^0}{}$$

so that its ground state is a *triplet* $[2(\frac{1}{2} + \frac{1}{2}) + 1] = 3$. The arrows indicate relative electron spin direction.

2. When the atom has two or more *equivalent electrons* (electrons each having the same values of n and l), the lowest-lying or ground state will be the one with values of m_l that will make Σm_l a maximum, subject to the condition that no two electrons have the same m_l. In carbon there are two equivalent p electrons and three possible values of m_l: $+1$, 0, and -1. One chooses $+1$ and 0 so that $\Sigma m_l = +1$, the maximum, and the atom is in a P state.

3. For shells half or less completed, $J = |L - S|$ has the lowest energy. For shells more than half completed, $J = |L + S|$ has the lowest energy. In the case of carbon, $L = 1$, $S = 1$, and the p shell is less than half completed. Therefore $J = 1 - 1 = 0$, and the overall term symbol is $C2(^3P_0)$ or simply $C(^3P_0)$ (carbon triplet P zero state).

The following additional examples may be helpful:

a. N $1s^2, 2s^2, 2p^3$

$$\underset{1s^2}{\downarrow\uparrow} \quad \underset{2s^2}{\downarrow\uparrow} \quad \underset{2p^1}{\uparrow} \quad \underset{2p^1}{\uparrow} \quad \underset{2p^1}{\uparrow}$$

$$m_l = +1 \quad m_l = 0 \quad m_l = -1$$

$$\Sigma m_l = 0, \text{ so } L = 0 \text{ and } J = |L - S| = |0 - \tfrac{3}{2}| = \tfrac{3}{2}$$

$$\therefore \text{N}(^4S_{3/2}) \text{ is the ground state.}$$

b. F $1s^2, 2s^2, 2p^5$

$$\underset{1s^2}{\downarrow\uparrow} \quad \underset{2s^2}{\downarrow\uparrow} \quad \underset{2p^2}{\uparrow\downarrow} \quad \underset{2p^2}{\uparrow\downarrow} \quad \underset{2p^1}{\uparrow}$$

$$S = \tfrac{1}{2} \text{ and } (2S + 1) = 2$$

$$\Sigma m_l = +1, \text{ so a } P \text{ state.}$$

$$J = |L + S| = 1 + \tfrac{1}{2} = \tfrac{3}{2}$$

$$\therefore \text{F}(^2P_{3/2})$$

c. Mn $1s^2, 2s^2, 2p^6, 3s^2, 3p^6, 4s^2, 3d^5$

Consider only the d orbitals (the rest are filled and can be ignored).

$$\underset{3d \text{ orbitals}}{\uparrow \quad \uparrow \quad \uparrow \quad \uparrow \quad \uparrow}$$

$$S = \tfrac{5}{2}, \text{ and } 2S + 1 = 6$$

$$\Sigma m_l = +2, +1, 0, -1, -2 = 0, \text{ so an } S \text{ state.}$$

$$J = |L - S| = |0 - \tfrac{5}{2}| = \tfrac{5}{2}$$

$$\therefore \text{Mn}(^6S_{5/2})$$

2-7 NATURE OF THE ABSORPTION SPECTRUM OF ATOMS

We shall now consider factors influencing the absorption of radiation by atoms. Mercury is an excellent example because of its theoretical and practical importance in photochemistry, and we shall focus our attention on it. However, we should note that many of the considerations of atomic absorption spectra have important analogs in molecular electronic spectroscopy, so that the material in this section has wider utility than might be apparent initially. Several references of general utility dealing with absorption by atoms are 1-5, 11, 12, and 13.

Key features of any absorption spectrum are the frequencies, intensities, and shapes of the absorption lines. In principle these quantities can be calculated exactly for atomic and molecular electronic transitions; in practice this becomes impossible when the system becomes much more complex than the hydrogen atom or molecule, and one resorts to a variety of approximations. Details of these are beyond the scope of this book. We shall simply note that the solution of the Schrödinger equation for the hydrogen atom leads to a set of eigenvalues which constitute a set of discrete states, the energies of which depend primarily on the principal quantum number n and have the order shown on the Grotrian energy diagram, Fig. 2-2. The excitation energy required to raise an atom from a lower to an upper state determines the location of the absorption lines in the spectrum. Thus the Lyman series for atomic hydrogen starts at 1216 A and extends further into the vacuum ultraviolet; the second series (Balmer) starts at 3970 A and runs through the visible region.

2-7A Intensities of Transitions;
Theory of Light Absorption by Atoms

In order for an atom (or molecule) to absorb electromagnetic radiation and jump from a stable ground state of energy E_1 to an electronically excited state of energy E_2, two criteria must be satisfied. First the frequency of the quantum must equal $(E_2 - E_1)/h$. If the frequency of the electromagnetic radiation does not correspond exactly to the energy difference between stationary states, an electron may still be set into forced oscillations by interaction with the electric vector of the quantum, but the duration of the interaction is about 10^{-14} sec. This results in phenomena such as Rayleigh scattering and reduction of light velocity. (See Sec. 3-2A.)

The second requirement for absorption to occur is that there must be a specific interaction of the electric vector of the light quantum which induces the transition of the electron from its ground-state orbital to its new orbital in the excited state. The "inducement" proceeds according to theory through the development of an oscillating electric dipole within the atom in the direction of the electric vector of the light quantum. This is pictured in a qualitative fashion in Fig. 2-9. A hydrogen atom in the spherically symmetric $1s$ state absorbs a quantum of 1216 A Lyman radiation, plane polarized with its electric vector in the plane of the drawing. In the absorption process the electron is set into oscillation by the electric vector of the light quantum; since the energy per quantum of the radiation corresponds exactly to that necessary to promote the $1s \rightarrow 2p$

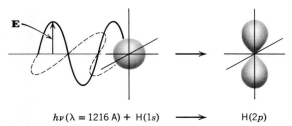

$$h\nu\ (\lambda = 1216\ \text{A}) + \text{H}(1s) \quad\longrightarrow\quad \text{H}(2p)$$

Fig. 2-9   Orbital representation of a hydrogen atom absorbing 1216 A Lyman radiation causing the $1s \rightarrow 2p$ transition; E represents the electric vector of the light wave which induces the $1s$ electron to the $2p_z$ orbital; polarization of the original electric vector is reflected in the orientation of the p orbital formed. Modified from Bowen,[14] p. 78.

transition and the selection rules are not violated (see the following section), an excited $2p$ state is formed. Note that the axis of the p orbital formed is in the same direction as that of the electric vector of the light quantum which induced the transition. After about 10^{-7} to 10^{-8} sec (barring gross perturbations) the excited atom re-emits a 1216 A quantum; the polarization of the electric vector will be in the direction of the p-orbital axis at the time of emission.

The quantitative wave-mechanical picture of light absorption suggests that the probability of a light quantum-atom interaction causing a change in state of an atom from the initial state m with the total wave function Ψ_m to the final state n with the wave function Ψ_n is proportional to the dipole strength D, defined as

$$D = \left(\int \Psi_m \mathbf{M} \Psi_n\, d\tau \right)^2 = \mathbf{m}^2 \qquad (2\text{-}22)$$

Here **m**, the value of the integral, is called the *transition moment integral*; **M** is the *dipole moment operator* or dipole moment vector and is defined thus:

$$\mathbf{M} = \sum_{i=1}^{n} er_i \qquad (2\text{-}23)$$

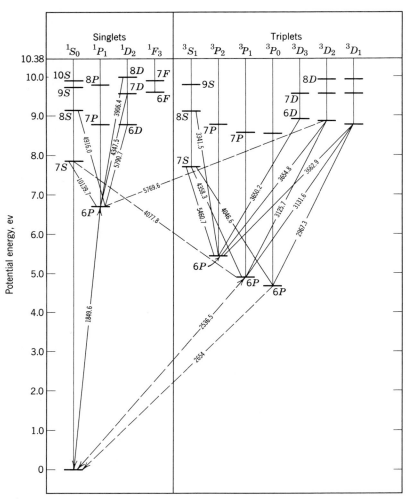

Fig. 2-10   Grotrian energy-level diagram for mercury, showing origin of the lines most important in photochemistry (many others are omitted for clarity). The "forbidden" triplet-singlet transitions are dashed. Actually they are strong because the selection rule $\Delta S = 0$ breaks down for heavy atoms. Only two transitions are possible in absorption at ordinary temperature, the allowed one at 1849 A and the "forbidden" one at 2537 A. The "forbidden" 2654 line appears only in emission from the metastable $6(^3P_0)$ state. No absorption is possible because in addition to the rule $\Delta S = 0$ the more rigid rule, $J = 0 \leftrightarrow J = 0$, would be violated (see text). Adapted from Rollefson and Burton,[41] p. 15.

where e is the charge on the electron, and r_i is the distance of the ith electron from the nucleus. The summation extends over all electrons. The integral **m** gives a measure of the charge displacement which occurs during passage from the lower state to the excited state. If only the position (or wave function) of one electron is altered significantly as the transition occurs (this is the common case), then all electrons which are unchanged contribute nothing to the integral **m**; the integration will give the average distance r of these electrons from the nucleus, and this must be zero for any single orbital, since these are always symmetrical about the nucleus. Then the evaluation of D can be carried out approximately by using the appropriate wave functions for the particular states of the single electron undergoing change. Actually promotion of a single electron will also alter the distribution of the other electrons to some extent so that the results of this treatment can only be approximate.

2-7A-1   Selection Rules

In the detailed analysis of the procedure outlined, one finds that transitions are probable only between states characterized by wave functions of a particular class; that is, an electron in an s-type atomic orbital can be promoted to a p-type atomic orbital (D is not zero), but the promotion of an s-type to an s-type, a p-type to a p-type, etc., has zero probability ($D = 0$). These results are conveniently summarized in the form of selection rules which are commonly formulated in terms of the quantum numbers that describe the electronic states involved:

$\Delta n = 0, 1, 2, \ldots$ (no restriction)

$\Delta l = \Delta L = \pm 1$ (for one optical electron)

$\Delta L = 0, \pm 1$ (for several optical electrons)

$\Delta J = 0, \pm 1$ (except that the transition $J = 0 \rightarrow J = 0$ is forbidden)

$\Delta S = 0$

These rules, particularly $\Delta S = 0$, assume Russell-Saunders coupling, which is strictly valid for only the lightest elements. However, the clear distinction between singlet and triplet states which is possible for the lighter elements breaks down for the heavier ones, and the existence of *intercombination lines* may be explained in quantum-mechanical terms by saying that the singlet states have a partly triplet character and the triplet states a dash of singlet character. Such an intercombination line is the photochemically very useful 2537 A resonance radiation (Fig. 2-10), arising from the triplet $\rightarrow$ singlet transition $Hg6(^3P_1) \rightarrow Hg6(^1S_0)$, which is forbidden by the rule prohibiting a change in multiplicity, $\Delta S = 0$.

Theory shows that there is a relationship between the probability for light absorption by an atom which passes from state m to a state n on interaction with a light quantum with the appropriate energy, and the probability for light emission by an atom in passing from state n to m. The probability per second that an atom in energy state m will absorb a quantum and pass to a high-energy state n is given by $B_{mn}I$, where I is the intensity (quanta/cc-sec) of radiation of the appropriate frequency such that $\nu = (E_n - E_m)/h$, and B_{mn} is related to the Einstein transition probability for absorption.* The probability for spontaneous decay of the excited molecules in state n to state m through the emission of light, symbolized by A_{nm}, the Einstein transition probability for spontaneous emission, is related to B_{mn} thus:

$$\frac{A_{nm}}{B_{mn}} = \frac{2h\nu^3 g_m}{c^2 g_n} \qquad (2\text{-}24)$$

where g_m and g_n are the statistical weights of the m and n states, respectively.

Since we observe that $Hg(^3P_1)$ atoms have a significant probability for emission of 2537 A radiation, we know from 2-24 that the reverse of this transition also must occur with a high probability. Indeed the extinction coefficient for 2537 A radiation is so large that it provides the basis for sensitive mercury-vapor detectors.

Only one other transition from the ground state is observed for mercury (Fig. 2-10); this is the *allowed* resonance transition $Hg6(^1S_0) \rightarrow Hg6(^1P_1)$ at 1849 A. This transition obeys the selection rules and has an exceedingly high probability. Thus the low vapor pressure of mercury even at dry ice temperature is sufficient to absorb almost all of the 1849 A radiation in a few centimeters of path length. Emission must also be allowed from this state, and indeed the lifetime of the $^1P_1$ state is much shorter than the $^3P_1$, 1.3×10^{-9} versus 1.1×10^{-7} sec.

In practice, absorption of the 1849 A line by water vapor, oxygen, normal quartz, etc., generally reduces its intensity to a fraction of that at 2537 A. Nevertheless one should keep in mind that the line is sufficiently bright and is absorbed so strongly that under certain conditions (thin windows, short path length, etc.) it may actually be a contaminating line when "pure" 2537 A radiation is assumed.

Since mercury has two $6s$ optical electrons, its ground state is $^1S_0$. In accordance with rules 1 and 3 concerning relative energy levels (Sec. 2-6) we see from the Grotrian diagram, Fig. 2-10, that the excited states $6(^3P_0)$, $6(^3P_1)$, and $6(^3P_2)$ increase in energy progressively (4.64, 4.86, and 5.43 ev) and that the $7(^3S_1)$ term is lower than the excited singlet $7(^1S_1)$.

---

* The original Einstein B coefficient was defined in terms of radiation density rather than intensity and is equal to $B_{mn}(c/4\pi)$.

It is clear that the selection rules $\Delta L = \pm 1$ and $\Delta J = 0, \pm 1$ are rigorously obeyed for all transitions, but, as mentioned earlier, the rule $\Delta S = 0$ is violated and several intercombination lines are observed (the dashed lines in Fig. 2-10).

An interesting situation occurs when an atom falls into an excited state from which all radiative transitions to lower levels are forbidden. There are several ways by which an atom can escape from such a *metastable state* into another state from which such transitions to lower levels can occur. It may (a) absorb radiation and go to a higher state, (b) be deactivated by collision, or (c), if neither (a) nor (b) occurs, finally undergo the "forbidden" radiative transition. The photochemically useful 2654 A line of mercury results from the doubly forbidden transition $6(^3P_0) \rightarrow 6(^1S_0)$ (see Fig. 2-10). Thus it violates not only the $\Delta S = 0$ rule but also the far more stringent requirement that the transition $J = 0 \rightarrow J = 0$ is not allowed. As a consequence 2654 A radiation is not absorbed by mercury atoms, and it is not a resonance line. However, atoms in the $6(^3P_1)$ state can be collisionally deactivated to the $6(^3P_0)$ state, and if no reverse activation step occurs the atom will stay in this *metastable* state until it finally emits the "forbidden" 2654 A radiation and returns to the ground state. Considerations of the relative populations, reactivities, and lifetimes of these $6(^3P_1)$ and $6(^3P_0)$ states are important when considering physical and chemical quenching processes in mercury-photosensitized reactions and will be treated in more detail in Sec. 2-9. Mrozowski[57] gives an admirable treatment of selection rules, forbidden lines, and metastable states of atoms, including $Hg(^3P_0)$, and should be consulted for details.

2-7A-2 Temperature

The effect of the population of the energy levels upon atomic absorption spectra is vividly illustrated in the case of mercury vapor. At *room temperature* the absorption spectrum consists solely of the two resonance lines at 2537 and 1849 A. Other lines are not observed because there are not enough atoms in the excited states to absorb detectable amounts of radiation. For example, consider the relative populations of mercury atoms in the $6(^1S_0)$ ground state (state 1) and the lowest excited state $6(^3P_0)$ (state 2) at 4.64 ev, in thermal equilibrium at $T°$K. The ratio of the number of atoms in state 2 to that in state 1, N_2/N_1, is given by the Boltzmann expression:

$$\frac{N_2}{N_1} = \frac{g_2}{g_1} e^{-(E_2 - E_1)/kT} \tag{2-25}$$

If the energy difference is expressed in ergs, then $\mathbf{k}$ (Boltzmann's constant) is 1.381×10^{-16} erg/molecule/deg, and g_1 and g_2, the statistical weights of states 1 and 2, are given by $g = (2J + 1)$. If we insert the appropriate values into Eq. 2-25, we find that $N_2/N_1 \sim 3.4 \times 10^{-79}$ at $300°K$!

In certain electric discharges, thermal equilibrium is not maintained, and the Boltzmann factor becomes approximately unity (this is equivalent to assuming a high temperature for the gas). The relative populations of states 2 and 1 then reduce to

$$\frac{N_2}{N_1} = \frac{g_2}{g_1}$$

the ratio of the statistical weights.

Thus the manner in which the intensity of a spectral line varies with temperature is determined by the temperature dependence of the population of the state from which the transition originates. If thermal equilibrium exists, it is evident from Eq. 2-25 that the population of the upper states increases exponentially with temperature. This results in greater intensities of those lines, arising from the higher energy terms.

2-7B   Absorption Coefficients and the Shape of Absorption Lines

Several factors can lead to the broadening of an atomic spectral "line."[5,11,12,15,16] It is important to note, however, that although a line

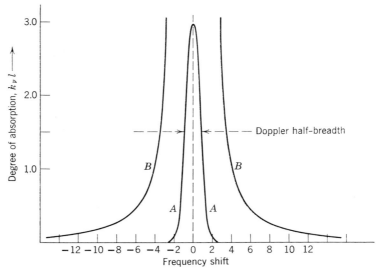

Fig. 2-11   Variation of the quantity $k_\nu l$ (degree of absorption) with frequency for weak absorption (narrow, Doppler-type line *A-A*) and strong absorption (*B-B*). The frequency shift is given by the function $2(\nu - \nu_0)(\sqrt{2})/\Delta\nu_D$. ν_0 is the center of the Doppler line in sec^{-1} where the function is zero and $k_\nu = k_0$. From Mitchell and Zemansky,[12] p. 105.

may be broadened by the various factors which we will consider, theory suggests that (barring serious perturbations) the integral, $\int_{\omega_1}^{\omega_2} \epsilon \, d\omega$, is a constant and is characteristic of the particular atom and the transition involved; see Eq. 3-41. The integration extends over the entire band which corresponds to the particular transition. That is, ϵ must decrease at all wave numbers if the range of ω over which the band extends (ω_1 to ω_2) increases; conversely, ϵ is greater the sharper the band. The magnitude of "line" broadening is usually expressed in terms of the *half-intensity* width or *half breadth* of absorption. These are the widths of the line at the intensity one-half of the maximum intensity of emission or absorption and are symbolized by $\Delta \nu$ (sec^{-1}) or $\Delta \lambda$ (A) (Fig. 2-11). Line broadening has important practical applications and implications in both absorption and emission phenomena in photochemistry and will be discussed in the following sections.

2-7B-1 Natural Line Width

According to the Heisenberg principle, there is an inherent uncertainty ΔE in the energy of an electronic state, and the time Δt that it exists in that state, given by the expression

$$\Delta E \, \Delta t = \frac{h}{2\pi} \tag{2-26}$$

Replacing Δt by τ_0, the mean radiative lifetime of the excited state, and substituting $h \, \Delta \nu$ for ΔE, we find that the *natural width* of a spectral line is given by

$$\Delta \nu_N = \frac{1}{2\pi \tau_0} \tag{2-27}$$

or in terms of wavelength

$$-\Delta \lambda_N = \frac{\lambda^2}{2\pi c \tau_0} \tag{2-28}$$

The natural broadening (or natural damping) $\Delta \nu_N$ or $\Delta \lambda_N$ is an inherent property of the atom, increasing as the radiative lifetime decreases and independent of external effects. Values of $\Delta \nu_N$ and $\Delta \lambda_N$ and natural lifetimes are given in Table 2-1 for the important resonance lines of mercury, sodium, and cadmium. Note that the natural breadth of the 2537 A line of mercury is only 3×10^{-6} A.

2-7B-2 Doppler Broadening

The shift in frequency of radiation, $\Delta \nu'$, emitted by an atom moving with velocity v at an angle θ between the direction of motion and line of

TABLE 2-1 Wavelengths, Lifetimes, Natural Broadening, and Doppler Broadening for Resonance Lines of Mercury, Sodium, and Cadmium[a]

Atom	Transition	λ, A	τ_0, sec	Natural Width		Doppler Width		$\dfrac{\Delta\nu_N}{\Delta\nu_D}$
				$\Delta\nu_N$, sec^{-1}	$\Delta\lambda_N$, A	$\Delta\nu_D$, sec^{-1}	$\Delta\lambda_D$, A	
Hg	$6(^1S_0)-6(^3P_1)$	2537	1.1×10^{-7}	1.4×10^6	3.1×10^{-6}	1.0×10^9 (20°C)	0.0021	0.0014
Na	$3(^2S_{1/2})-3(^2P_{1/2})$	5896	1.6×10^{-8}	1.0×10^7	1.2×10^{-4}	1.6×10^9 (160°C)	0.019	0.0063
Cd	$5(^1S_0)-5(^1P_1)$	2288	2.0×10^{-9}	0.8×10^8	1.4×10^{-4}	1.9×10^9 (200°C)	0.033	0.042

[a] Adapted from Mitchell and Zemansky,[12] p. 101.

sight of the observer is given by the expression

$$\Delta \nu' = \nu_0 \frac{v \cos \theta}{c} \tag{2-29}$$

where ν_0, the central frequency, is the frequency of radiation (sec^{-1}) when the velocity $v = 0$ and c is the velocity of light.[5] If one assumes that the emitting atoms follow a Maxwellian distribution of velocities, the Doppler broadening of an emission or absorption line, $\Delta \nu_D$, is given by

$$\Delta \nu_D = 1.67 \frac{\nu_0}{c} \sqrt{\frac{2RT}{M}} \tag{2-30}$$

or, since $d\nu/\nu = -d\lambda/\lambda$,

$$-\Delta \lambda_D = 1.67 \frac{\lambda_0}{c} \sqrt{\frac{2RT}{M}} \tag{2-31}$$

where $\Delta \nu_D$ refers to the half-intensity width, R is the gas constant, 8.314×10^7 ergs/°K-mole, and M is the gram-atomic weight of the atom (grams/mole). Thus Doppler broadening increases as the square root of the temperature and is inversely proportional to the square root of the mass of the atom. Note that by observing at right angles to an "atomic beam," where there is no motion along the line of sight, the term $\cos \theta$ in Eq. 2-29 becomes zero, and Doppler broadening can be eliminated for spectral work on fine structure. For Hg 2537 A radiation, Doppler broadening $\Delta \lambda_D$ is 0.002 A (20°C) compared to 0.03 A (200°C) for the Cd 2288 A resonance line (see Table 2-1).

The absorption coefficient of a gas, k_ν, displaying only Doppler broadening (natural broadening is neglected) is given by

$$k_\nu = k_0 \exp \left\{ -[2(\nu - \nu_0)\sqrt{\ln 2}/\Delta \nu_D]^2 \right\} \tag{2-32}$$

where k_0 is the maximum absorption coefficient at the central frequency ν_0. In this system the absorption coefficient k_ν is defined by the expression[12]

$$I = I_0 e^{-k_\nu l} \tag{2-33}$$

When the thickness of the absorbing layer l is in centimeters, the units of k_ν are cm^{-1}.* Curve AA in Fig. 2-11 is an example of "pure" Doppler broadening of an absorption line.

The ratios of natural broadening to Doppler broadening in resonance absorption are 0.0014 (20°C), 0.0063 (160°C), and 0.042 (200°C) for mercury, sodium, and cadmium, respectively (Table 2-1). Thus, in many cases natural broadening can be neglected. However, Mitchell and

---

* When k_ν is compared with the molar extinction coefficient ϵ, which is in units of liters/mole-cm, we see that $k_\nu = 2.303\epsilon c$, where c is in moles/liter (Eq. 1-24).

Zemansky[12] point out an interesting effect of the degree of absorption on the relative importance of the two types of broadening. In cases of weak absorption at low pressures and short path lengths ($p = 10^{-7}$ to 10^{-4} mm, $l = 0.1$ to 3 cm), where the product $k_0 l$ [that is, $\ln(I_0/I)$] is about 3, the *edges* of the line may be neglected and the entire line treated as a pure Doppler line (Fig. 2-11). However, at strong absorptions ($p = 10^{-4}$ to 10^{-2} mm), where $k_0 l$ is in the region of 3000, the center of the line is completely absorbed and absorption *in the edges becomes important*. Furthermore, it can be shown that the extent of absorption in the edges is determined *entirely by the natural line width*, $\Delta\nu_N$.[12]

The effects of weak and strong absorption on line shape are shown in Fig. 2-11. Curve AA for weak absorption is a pure Doppler shape, while BB shows the pronounced absorption in the edges characteristic of a large value of the quantity $k_\nu l$. Actually the term "strong" absorption could be somewhat misleading because one might have a low extinction coefficient for a substance but a long path length and high concentration, so that the product $k_\nu l$ is large and absorption in the edges becomes important.

2-7B-3   Pressure Broadening

An elastic collision of one atom with another atom about to emit or absorb radiation may produce a sudden change in the phase and amplitude of the radiation.[5] This phenomenon, referred to as collision damping or collision broadening, manifests itself as *Lorentz broadening*, in which molecules of a foreign gas collide with the emitting or absorbing atom, and *Holzmark broadening*, caused by collisions between the atoms of the absorbing or emitting gas.* Experimentally, as the foreign gas pressure is increased in a system containing atoms absorbing resonance radiation one observes:

1. The absorption line broadens.
2. The frequency of the absorption maximum is shifted toward the red.
3. The profile of the absorption line becomes asymmetric.

The first of these phenomena can be explained by the simple, classical theory of Lorentz, but the second two require quantum-mechanical treatment.[12] We shall not consider the theory but shall note that for visible light and room temperature and pressure Lorentz broadening is of the same order of magnitude as Doppler broadening.[5]

An example of these effects is shown in Fig. 2-12 in which the absorption profile of the Hg 2537 resonance line is shown with 10 atm and 50 atm

---

* Actually some authors treat these two cases as being essentially identical.[12]

pressure of nitrogen as the inert gas.[17] Note both the asymmetry (red shift) and broadening of the line. The dotted lines are drawn to illustrate the deviation from a symmetrical curve. More recently several studies have been made on the perturbation of the 2537 A line by high pressures of

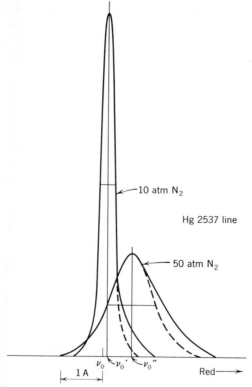

Fig. 2-12 Absorption by mercury atoms of 2537 A resonance line at 10 atm and 50 atm pressure of nitrogen. Note the Lorentz broadening, the displacement of the maximum to the red from ν_0, and the asymmetry of the lines. From White,[5] p. 432, modified to show absorption by equal numbers of atoms; original data from Füchtbauer *et al.*[17]

helium,[18,19] and the possibility of weakly bound molecules of mercury-inert gas has been treated theoretically to explain certain satellite bands that appear with argon and krypton.[20]

2-7B-4   Stark Effect

In the typical electric discharge of a mercury arc, ions as well as excited atoms are present. When an ion collides with an atom about to emit radiation, the strong local electric field of the ion leads to a splitting of the emitted line in a manner analogous to the Stark effect. The actual splitting may be too small to observe directly, but the overall effect is a symmetrical broadening of the observed line comparable in magnitude to the Doppler effect or pressure broadening. Stark-splitting is also caused by interatomic field effects from atoms or molecules possessing quadruple moments, and, in a sense, the phenomenon of collisional broadening of absorption and emission spectra might be classed as a "second-order" Stark effect. Actually, in most gas-phase systems where

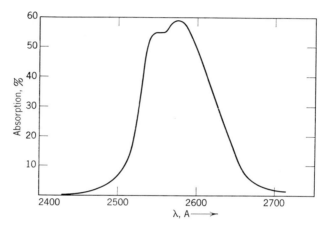

Fig. 2-13 Absorption spectrum of mercury in liquid decane. From Phibbs and Darwent.[21]

absorption by atoms is involved, the Stark effect is negligible. It is, however, an important source of line broadening in most arcs, sparks, and discharges at high temperatures.

In atomic absorption spectra in condensed phases all of the above effects act to produce a huge broadening of a "line." This is illustrated in Fig. 2-13, which shows the absorption spectrum of mercury dissolved in decane.[21] What was once a narrow "line" of natural bandwidth 3 × 10⁻⁶ A has broadened to about 100 A in width.

2-7C Emission and Self-Absorption of Resonance Radiation

The emission of resonance radiation is subject to the same types of line-broadening phenomena as absorption, but because of the more extreme conditions found in most arcs, sparks, discharges, etc., the effects are more pronounced and more difficult to treat by theory.

In addition to broadening, the effects of *self-absorption* and *imprison-ment of radiation* can drastically alter the shape of an emission line. An atom which has a high probability of emitting a resonance line also has a high probability of absorbing one. Hence, except in low-pressure dis-charges resonance lines may appear as two lines with a dark band sepa-rating them. This phenomenon is due to self-absorption in the center of the broadened line and is shown schematically in Fig. 2-14.[15] It is also

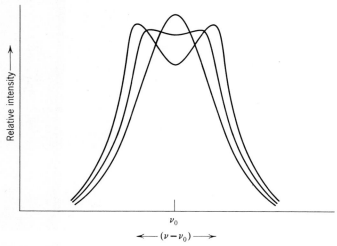

Fig. 2-14   Change in the spectral profile of an emission line as the amount of self-absorption is increased.   From Gunning and Strausz.[15]

demonstrated dramatically in Fig. 2-15, where high-resolution emission spectra of mercury in the region of 2537 A are shown for a mercury-argon resonance lamp, a medium-pressure arc (about 1 atm), and a high-pressure arc.[20]   With the resonance lamp operating at room temperature and relatively low pressures only the sharp resonance line at 2537 A is observed.

The medium-pressure arc operates hot at about 1 atm, and its resonance line appears split into two components, both pressure broadened, with a dark band between.   This is due to self-absorption by mercury atoms in the relatively cool sheath surrounding the central arc plasma.   Since they are much cooler than the emitting atoms, there is less line broadening and the absorption band appears quite sharp.   Radiation at 2537 A from a medium-pressure arc is referred to as a reversed "line."

The high-pressure arc shows extreme asymmetrical pressure broadening of both the resonance absorption and the emission.   The 2535.3 *non-resonance* line is absent with the resonance lamp, is sharp with the medium-pressure arc, and appears as an intense broad, asymmetric line with the high-pressure arc.* As a practical point in selecting sources for photo-chemical reactions one should note that the extreme broadening of the 2537 line and the high degree of self-absorption drastically reduce the intensity of high-pressure mercury arcs below about 2900 A (see Fig. 7-1).

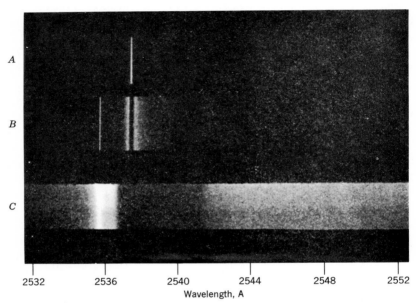

Fig. 2-15 The emission spectrum of mercury from three types of sources of 2537 A, photographed in the fourth-order region, using a 21-ft grating with a slit at 0.15 mm. *A* is the spectrum from a mercury-argon resonance lamp (2.5 min exposure), showing a sharp, unreversed resonance line at 2537 A and no other line. Plate *B* is from a medium-pressure arc (20 min exposure), showing broadened 2537 A line with complete reversal in the middle and the appearance of a sharp, non-resonance 2535 A line. *C* is a high-pressure arc (60 min exposure) showing extensive broadening, asymmetry, self-absorption of the 2537 A resonance line, and the effect of pressure broadening on the 2535 A line. From Noyes and Leighton,[11] p. 38.

The effect of simultaneous Doppler and collision broadening and of hyperfine structure (Sec. 2-7D) on the imprisonment of resonance radiation has been treated theoretically by Walsh,[23] who extended the method developed by Holstein.[24] Calculations are in good agreement with the experimental data,[25] which indicate that imprisonment lifetimes of 2537 A

---

* Strictly speaking, comparisons are not completely valid because of the different exposure times: 2.5 min, 20 min, and 1 hr, respectively.

radiation range from 5×10^{-6} sec at 3×10^{14} atoms Hg/cc to 1×10^{-4} sec at 1.0×10^{16} atoms Hg/cc. These can be compared to a natural radiative lifetime of 1.1×10^{-7} sec for the $Hg(^3P_1)$ state.

Tako[16] also has achieved a good agreement of theory with experiment for imprisonment lifetimes for cadmium as well as mercury resonance radiation, using a simple theoretical "model" in which the emitting atoms decrease linearly from a maximum at the center to zero at the wall. He also discusses in detail factors affecting line shape.[16]

2-7D   The Hyperfine Spectrum of Mercury

The photochemical implications of the preceeding sections are evident when one considers the technique of monoisotopic mercury photosensitization first demonstrated by Mrozowski (1932)[26] followed by Zuber (1935),[27] McDonald and Gunning (1952),[28] and Zelikoff et al. (1953).[29,30] Subsequently, the utility of this technique as a photochemical means of isotope separation and of determining the primary act in mercury-sensitized reactions has been well demonstrated. The latter aspect is a subject of a detailed review by Gunning and Strausz,[15] so we shall simply point out the general aspects of the technique and illustrate its utility with several examples (see Secs. 2-15G and 6-5).

Natural mercury, ^{N}Hg, has seven stable isotopes, five of even mass number and two of odd. The five even mass isotopes have zero nuclear spin and hence show only one hyperfine line.* The isotopes ^{199}Hg and ^{201}Hg have nuclear spins of $\frac{1}{2}$ and $\frac{3}{2}$ and therefore they have two and three hyperfine lines, respectively. The relative intensities in the hyperfine structure (hfs) of the 2537 resonance line of ^{N}Hg are shown in Fig. 2-16; actually the lines are broadened by effects discussed in Sec. 2-7B. In practice ^{196}Hg is too weak to use, and the other nine lines fall into five resolvable "lines" separated by approximately 0.01–0.015 A.

The monoisotopic sensitization technique utilizes a resonance lamp powered by a microwave discharge and containing only a single, pure mercury isotope as the emitter, e.g., ^{202}Hg. Radiation from this source enters the reaction cell containing normal mercury, ^{N}Hg, and a substrate and is selectively absorbed only by the ^{202}Hg component of the mercury.

---

* The resultant angular momentum of the whole atom (including nuclear spin) is described by the quantum number $F = J + I, J + I - 1, \ldots, |J - I|$, where I is the nuclear spin; this gives $2J + 1$ states for atoms with $J < I$ and $2I + 1$ states for $J > I$. In the case considered, $Hg(^1S_0)$ and $Hg(^3P_1)$ are of $J = 0$ and $J = 1$, respectively; since $I = \frac{1}{2}$ for the ^{199}Hg isotope, $J < I$, and there are $2I + 1 = 2$ hyperfine lines due to nuclear spin splitting. $I = \frac{3}{2}$ for the ^{201}Hg isotope, $J > I$, and there are $2J + 1 = 3$ hyperfine lines.

The excited ²⁰²Hg atom then initiates photosensitized reactions of the substrate which are followed by subsequently analyzing products and reactants for their isotopic distribution. Photochemical results are given in Sec. 2-15; here we shall consider briefly the hfs of the Hg 2537 line and the spectroscopic problems inherent in this type of study.

It is essential in the monoisotopic photosensitization technique that the edges of the emission band of the emitting pure isotope do not overlap

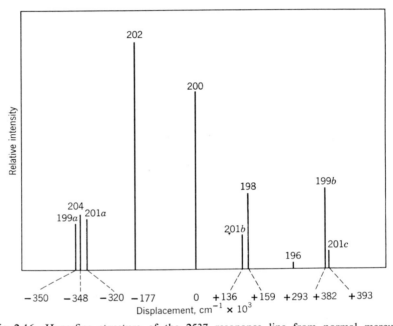

Fig. 2-16 Hyperfine structure of the 2537 resonance line from normal mercury. Intensities are relative. This is idealized, showing sharp lines; in practice these are modified by various types of broadening (Sec. 2-7B). From Gunning and Strausz.[15] Even mass isotopes show a single peak; odd mass isotopes show a multiplet structure (labeled *a, b, . . .*).

the absorption wings of the adjacent hyperfine lines of the other isotopes in natural mercury; otherwise these would also be excited and isotopic selectivity would diminish. Line broadening is thus minimized by using a well-cooled, low-pressure electrodeless discharge at the lowest power consistent with steady operation.[15] Figure 2-17 shows the calculated spectral profile of the ²⁰²Hg line from such a lamp. Emission was assumed to be pure Doppler altered by self-absorption. The validity of the calculation has been checked experimentally;[28,29] the irradiation of natural mercury vapor in certain H_2O- and O_2-containing mixtures with the hyperfine line emission from a ^{202}Hg resonance lamp has led to a mercuric oxide product which was 90% or more enriched in ^{202}Hg.

The splitting of the three levels in the hfs of ^{201}Hg, $F = \frac{1}{2}, \frac{3}{2}$, and $\frac{5}{2}$, has been determined accurately by optically pumping with light from a ^{198}Hg lamp a sample of ^{201}Hg vapor contained in a resonance cell in the

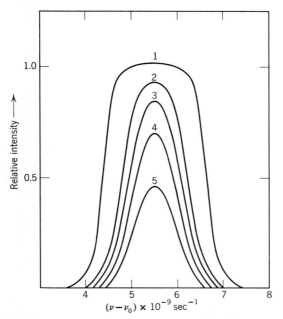

Fig. 2-17 Calculated spectral profile of an emission line (1) from a monoisotopic source, ^{202}Hg isotope in natural mercury for several concentrations (^{202}N$l \times 10^{-12} =$ 4.5, 3.13, 2.0, and 1.0 atoms/cm^2, respectively, where ^{202}N is the number of atoms of this isotope/cubic centimeter and l is the path length in centimeters). From Gunning and Strausz;[15] original source Osborne, McDonald, and Gunning.[22]

cavity of an NMR unit.[33,34] The single line from the ^{198}Hg source coincides exactly with the $F = \frac{3}{2}$ state of the ^{201}Hg isotope. Thus, upon irradiating the cell with ^{198}Hg light and simultaneously scanning the magnetic field, one observes resonances at 7551.613 ± 0.013 mc/sec and 13,986.557 ± 0.008 mc/sec. These correspond to the transitions $F(\frac{1}{2} \leftrightarrow \frac{3}{2})$ and $F(\frac{3}{2} \leftrightarrow \frac{5}{2})$. Several means of detecting the ^{201}Hg($^3P_1$) resonances have been used,[33,34] including the ingenious optical method of Kohler[34] with which these accurate hfs splittings were obtained. An atomic-beam magnetic resonance technique[35] of electron bombardment to produce a beam of narrowly collimated metastable Hg($^3P_0$) atoms has been used to measure the hfs of the metastable $^3P_2$ level of ^{199}Hg and ^{201}Hg.

2-8 PRIMARY PROCESSES IN ATOM-SENSITIZED REACTIONS

The interdisciplinary nature of spectroscopy and photochemistry is well illustrated by the definition of *primary photochemical processes* given by Noyes, Porter, and Jolley:[36] "The primary photochemical process comprises the series of events beginning with the absorption of a photon by a molecule, and ending either with the disappearance of that molecule or with its conversion to a state such that its reactivity is statistically no greater than that of similar molecules in thermal equilibrium with their surroundings."

Usually a variety of paths exists for the degradation of electronic energy of excitation involved in the primary photochemical process. Some of these, such as intramolecular rearrangements or valence isomerization, produce new products directly from the excited molecule. Others form free radicals or excited molecules which can initiate *secondary* thermal *processes* leading to chemical change. Generally there also will be included in the over-all process radiative and non-radiative *photophysical* processes which do not lead to over-all chemical change, but provide alternative paths for the degradation of electronic excitation energy. These include fluorescence and intersystem crossing (see Secs. 4-6 and 4-8B). These photophysical acts are of great interest to both spectroscopists and photochemists for, as Noyes *et al.*, point out, "The complete elucidation of a primary photochemical process must include an understanding of all that transpires, whether or not a chemical reaction occurs."[36]

In Chapters 3, 4, and 5 we shall consider the primary photochemical processes of diatomic and polyatomic molecules; here, after our discussion of atomic spectroscopy, we shall deal with the simplest system, at least conceptually: excited atoms and primary processes in atom-sensitized photochemical reactions. Characteristics of secondary photochemical reactions, direct and sensitized, are considered in Chapter 6.

Far more work has been carried out on primary processes of excited mercury atoms than all other types of atoms combined. Thus we shall use mercury atoms as our model system, but, when appropriate, shall extend our discussions to other metal atoms and the rare gases. With but a few exceptions the discussion will be restricted to ordinary temperatures and to the vapor phase, since little has been published for other conditions.

Recent reviews of mercury-photosensitized reactions include those of Cvetanovic (1964)[37] and Gunning and Strausz (1963).[15] Important earlier references, particularly on gas-phase metal-sensitized reactions of hydrocarbons, include the comprehensive review and critical discussion in Steacie's monograph (1954);[38] also see Ref. 39 and Laidler's (1942)[40] stimulating series of papers dealing with the theoretical aspects of these systems. Physical quenching processes are considered in the monographs of Pringsheim (1949)[13] and Mitchell and Zemansky (1934).[12] Excellent general treatments include those of Bowen (1946),[14] Noyes and Leighton (1941),[11] and Rollefson and Burton (1939).[41]

The primary processes of excited mercury atoms are outlined in Table 2-2; the energies of the lower excited states and transitions between them of particular interest for mercury-sensitized reactions are given in the simplified Grotrian energy diagram, Fig. 2-18 (Fig. 2-10 is the more complete diagram).

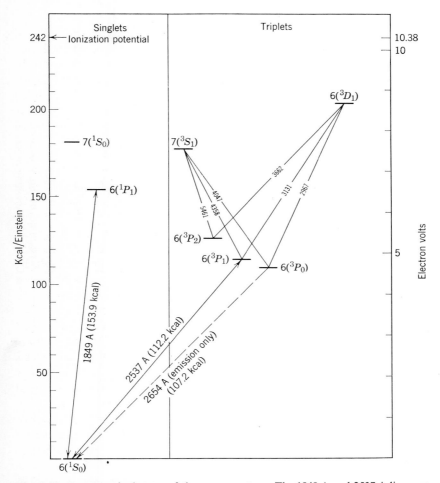

Fig. 2-18   Lower excited states of the mercury atom. The 1849 A and 2537 A lines are resonance radiation and appear in absorption from and emission to the ground state, while the 2654 line appears only in emission (Sec. 2-7).

TABLE 2-2 Primary Processes of Excited Mercury Atoms

$Hg(^1S_0) + hv\ (2537\ \text{Å}) \rightarrow Hg(^3P_1)$ ⟶ $Hg(^1S_0) + hv\ (2537\ \text{Å})$	Resonance phosphorescence	(2-34)
$\xrightarrow{M} Hg(^1S_0) + M^*$	Deactivation to ground state	(2-35)
$\xrightarrow{N_2} Hg(^3P_0) + N_2^*$	Deactivation to metastable state	(2-36)
$\xrightarrow{Na3(^2P)} Hg(^1S_0) + Na9(^2S) \searrow \begin{array}{l} Na3(^2P) + hv'' \\ \rightarrow \text{Products} \end{array}$	Sensitized fluorescence	(2-37)
$\xrightarrow{RH} Hg(^1S_0) + RH^*$	Chemical quenching via an excited molecule	(2-38)
$\xrightarrow{RH} Hg(^1S_0) + R + H$	Chemical quenching, one-step dissociation	(2-39)
or		
$\rightarrow HgH + R \rightarrow Hg(^1S_0) + H + R$	Chemical quenching, dissociation via intermediate	(2-39a)
$Hg(^3P_0)$ (metastable state) ⟶ $Hg(^1S_0) + hv'\ (2654\ \text{Å})$	Phosphorescence	(2-40)
$\xrightarrow{M} Hg(^1S_0) + M^*$	Deactivation to ground state	(2-41)
$\xrightarrow{N_2} Hg(^3P_1) + N_2$	Reactivation	(2-42)
$\xrightarrow{+hv''} Hg7(^3S_1)$	Triplet-triplet absorption	(2-43)
$\xrightarrow{RH} Hg(^1S_0) + RH^* \rightarrow \text{Products}$	Chemical quenching	(2-44)
$\xrightarrow{RH} Hg(^1S_0) + R + H$	Chemical quenching	(2-45)
$\xrightarrow{Hg,M} (Hg_2)^* \rightarrow 2Hg(^1S_0) + hv'''$	Excited dimer formation	(2-46)
$Hg(^1S_0) + hv''''\ (1849\ \text{Å}) \rightarrow Hg(^1P_1)$ ⟶ $Hg(^1S_0) + hv''''\ (1849\ \text{Å})$	Resonance fluorescence	(2-47)
$\rightarrow$ Physical quenching processes		(2-48)
$\rightarrow$ Chemical quenching processes		(2-49)

The modes of decay by which a $Hg(^3P_1)$ atom can lose its electronic excitation energy fall into five broad categories; the first three are photophysical primary processes, the last two, photochemical.

1. A radiative transition to the ground state, resonance phosphorescence, process 2-34.

2. Physical quenching to the lower metastable excited state, with no chemical reaction ($\Delta E = 112.2 - 107.2 = 5$ kcal), process 2-36.

3. Physical quenching to the ground state with complete transfer of electronic energy to the quencher M; M* decays by non-radiative physical processes, process 2-35. Alternatively the quencher is an atom, e.g., $Na3(^2P)$, which is raised to a higher excited state by triplet transfer, $Na9(^2S)$, and then undergoes a radiative decay, (sensitized fluorescence), process 2-37.

4. Chemical quenching in which the $Hg(^3P_1)$ atom returns to the ground state, and the quencher by triplet-triplet transfer gains 112.2 kcal of electronic energy. This excited molecule subsequently reacts to form chemically new products, process 2-38.

5. Chemical quenching via one-step dissociation of the quenching molecule, process 2-39 or 2-39a.

Mercury atoms in their metastable $^3P_0$ state have relatively long lifetimes because radiative decay to the ground state is forbidden by the selection rules, $\Delta S = 0$, and $J = 0 \leftrightarrow J = 0$ (Sec. 2-7A-1). Thus, in addition to emitting 2654 A phosphorescence, process 2-40, and being quenched physically, process 2-41 or 2-46, or chemically, process 2-44 or 2-45, they may undergo two excitation processes. These are collisional reactivation to the $^3P_1$ level, process 2-42, and, when illuminated with light of the appropriate wavelength, triplet-triplet absorption to reach a higher electronic state [e.g., the $7(^3S_1)$ state by absorbing 4047 A light, Eq. 2-43].

2-9 PHYSICAL QUENCHING OF MERCURY ATOMS IN THE $^3P_1$ STATE

We shall now deal in some detail with the deactivation of electronically excited mercury atoms in the $^3P_1$ state by paths that are solely physical; no overall chemical change occurs in the system.

2-9A The Non-perturbed System; Resonance Phosphorescence

The relative probabilities of the several primary processes of the $Hg(^3P_1)$ state depend greatly upon the environment of the excited atoms. In a system containing only mercury vapor at low pressures, process 2-34, *resonance phosphorescence*, is virtually the sole mode of decay of $Hg(^3P_1)$ atoms. The rate of emission of 2537 A follows a first-order rate law for which $k = 9.1 \times 10^6$ sec^{-1}; this corresponds to a lifetime ($\tau = 1/k$) of 1.1×10^{-7} sec for an isolated Hg($^3P_1$) atom,[12] about one hundred times longer than that for the isolated Hg($^1P_1$) atom which emits the normal resonance fluorescence, Hg($^1P_1$) → Hg($^1S_0$) + $h\nu$ (1849 A) with $\tau = 1.3 \times 10^{-9}$ sec. The relatively long life of the Hg($^3P_1$) state reflects the "forbidden" nature of the triplet → singlet intersystem crossing.

We should point out here that a variety of terms exists in the literature for 2537 A emission from mercury. Among others it has been called fluorescence, resonance fluorescence[12] (most common), "slow" fluorescence,[13] and resonance phosphorescence. We prefer *resonance phosphorescence* because the 2537 A "line" arises from a *radiative transition between states of different multiplicity*.[42] This is in accord with the mechanistic definition of phosphorescence advanced by G. N. Lewis and universally accepted today to describe the "forbidden" triplet-singlet emission from polyatomic organic molecules. *Fluorescence* is defined as a *radiative transition between states of like multiplicity* so that 1849 A radiation from the transition Hg($^1P_1$) → Hg($^1S_0$) + $h\nu$ is resonance fluorescence. Finally, 2654 A radiation from the ($^3P_0$) state is simply *phosphorescence*; the modifier resonance is dropped because direct absorption to the Hg($^3P_0$) state does not occur.

We shall follow this mechanistic terminology throughout this book because we prefer it to that based on the lifetimes of excited states, and because pedagogically it presents a consistent terminology applicable throughout photochemistry. Actually in many cases (e.g., the 2537 A Hg line) confusion in terminology is avoided by simply using the term *emission* (i.e., 2537 A emission).

The quantum yield of phosphorescence φ_p ($= I_p/I_a$) is equal to unity in the unperturbed system. When the system is altered by increasing the pressure or adding a foreign gas, processes 2-35 through 2-39 may occur, depending on the nature of the additive. These processes, of course, reduce the quantum yield of resonance phosphorescence (i.e., *quench* the phosphorescence). We shall now outline the several types of physical quenching.

2-9B   Quenching of Hg6($^3P_1$) Atoms to the Ground State

The three general types of primary processes encountered in quenching experiments with Hg($^3P_1$) atoms are

$$\text{Hg}(^1S_0) + h\nu \text{ (2537 A)} \longrightarrow \text{Hg}(^3P_1) \tag{I}$$

$$\text{Hg}(^3P_1) \longrightarrow \text{Hg}(^1S_0) + h\nu \text{ (2537 A)} \tag{1}$$

$$\text{Hg}(^3P_1) + \text{A} \longrightarrow \begin{cases} \text{Hg}(^1S_0) + \text{A}' & \tag{2} \\ \text{Hg}(^3P_0) + \text{A}'' & \tag{3} \end{cases}$$

where A is the quenching gas, and reactions 2 and 3 include all non-radiative quenching reactions resulting in deactivation of the $^3P_1$ atoms to the $^1S_0$ and $^3P_0$ states, respectively. The efficiencies of these quenching reactions are generally reported in one of two ways; these methods are equivalent but one uses the terminology of chemists, the other that of physicists. Thus one may use the bimolecular quenching rate constant k_Q (liters/mole/sec) to express the *quenching efficiency* of the reaction. The other method is to put k_Q equal to the normal frequency of bimolecular collisions as given by kinetic theory and then to refer to the inefficiency, or superefficiency, of the reaction by using an effective collisional cross section σ_Q^2 which will be smaller, or larger, than the "normal" gas kinetic collision cross section σ^2. The latter, more "physical" approach has generally been employed when the rate of quenching is followed by measuring the changes in intensity of 2537 A resonance phosphorescence when quenching gases are added. The two quantities k_Q and σ_Q^2 are related by Eq. 2-50 (discussed in more detail in Sec. 6-7C, which deals with the kinetics of quenching of fluorescence and phosphorescence, the Stern-Volmer mechanism, etc.):

$$k_Q = \sigma_Q^2 \left[8\pi RT \left(\frac{M_{Hg} + M_A}{M_{Hg} M_A} \right) \right]^{1/2} \tag{2-50}$$

Unfortunately there is a great deal of uncertainty in the *absolute* values of quenching cross sections. This arises primarily because of the difficulty in treating quantitatively the effect of "imprisonment" of 2537 A resonance radiation (radiation diffusion) in mercury-photosensitized reactions (see Sec. 2-7C), although there are other difficult experimental problems as well.[12,37] Three methods of theoretically treating radiation diffusion have been employed; each leads to a significantly different absolute value for cross sections.

Cvetanovic[37] reviews the confused situation, considers two of the theoretical methods, and clarifies the situation by specifying cross sections as being determined by "Procedure I" or "Procedure II." The former refers to values from Zemansky's (1930)[43] original paper. These were subsequently recalculated by using Sampson's[44] (1932) theory of radiation diffusion and published in Mitchell and Zemansky's (1934)[12] monograph. The latter values fall under "Procedure II." The quenching cross sections for nitrogen σ_Q^2 by the two procedures are 0.19 and 0.27 A^2, respectively. From independent experiments and by the use of Procedure II in his calculations Sampson obtained σ_Q^2 for $N_2 = 0.33$ A^2. Generally the values calculated by Procedure II are a factor of about 1.43 larger than those by Procedure I reported in the original Zemansky paper[43] (Table 2-3). Unfortunately, in the extensive literature on cross sections often it is not

TABLE 2-3 Quenching Cross Sections σ_Q^2 and Quenching Efficiencies k_Q for Mercury Atoms in the $^3P_1$ and $^3P_0$ States[a]

Compound	Hg($^3P_1$), Physical Determinations			Hg($^3P_1$), Chemical Data			Hg($^3P_0$)[b]	
	σ_Q^2, A²	Preferred Values		σ_Q^2, A²		k_Q[c]	σ_Q^2, A²	k_Q[c]
	Proc. I	σ_Q^2, A² Proc. II	k_Q[c] Proc. II	Proc. I	Proc. II	Proc. II		
Inorganic Compounds								
H₂	6.01[d]	8.60	29.0				0.08	0.3
D₂	8.41[e]	11.9	28.5				0.2	0.2
O₂	13.9[d]	19.9	18.0				Very small	Very small
N₂	0.192[d]	0.274	0.26				0.006	0.007
H₂O	1.00[f]	1.43	1.67					
D₂O	0.46[e]	0.66	0.74					
NO	24.7[f]	35.3	32.9	23[g]	33	31	0.6	0.5
N₂O				12.6[h]	18.0	14.3	1.5	1.0
NH₃	2.94[d], 2.99[e]	4.20	5.04					
ND₃	1.09[e]	1.56	1.74					
CO	4.07[d]	5.82	5.59				0.08	0.07
CO₂	2.48[d]	3.54	2.80				0.0035	0.003
H₂S	23[j]	33	29					
CS₂	35[k]	50	32					
Saturated Hydrocarbons								
CH₄	0.059[f]	0.085	0.11	0.10[h]	0.14	0.13	0.05	0.05
C₂H₆	0.421[f], 0.11[i]	0.16	0.15	1.2[i]	1.7	1.3		
C₃H₈	1.60[f], 1.3[i], 1.6[j]	2.3	1.8					
CH₃CD₂CH₃				0.17[l]	0.24	0.19		

	A	B	C	D	E	F	G	H	I
CD$_3$CH$_2$CD$_3$	4.06[f], 3.0[i], 5.1[j]	4.0	5.7	4.0	1.0[l]	1.4	1.1	0.8	0.7
CD$_3$CD$_2$CD$_3$	4.9[i]	4.9	7.0	5.0	0·09[l]	0.13	0.10		
n-C$_4$H$_{10}$					3.6[h,l]	5.1	3.6		
iso-C$_4$H$_{10}$					4.8[l]	6.9	4.9		
(CH$_3$)$_3$CD					0.44[l]	0.63	0.44		
n-C$_5$H$_{12}$	8.6[i], 10.3[j]	9.4	13.4	8.8					
iso-C$_5$H$_{12}$	12[i]	12	17	11					
neo-C$_5$H$_{12}$	1.5[i]	1.5	2.1	1.4					
n-C$_6$H$_{14}$	16[i]	16	23	14					
2-Me-pentane	20[i]	20	29	18					
3-Me-pentane	23[i]	23	33	20					
2,2-DiMe-butane	5.7[f]	5.7	8.2	5.0					
2,3-DiMe-butane	15[i]	15	21	13					
2,2,3-TriMe-butane	19.7[f]	19.7	28	16					
n-C$_7$H$_{16}$	24.0[f], 29[i]	26	37	22					
Cyclopropane	1.1[j]	1.1	1.6	1.3	0.29[l]	0.41	0.31		
Cyclo-C$_3$D$_6$									
Cyclobutane	4.4[j]	4.4	6.3	4.5					
Cyclopentane	13[j]	13	19	13					
Cyclohexane	14[j]	14	20	12					
Unsaturated Hydrocarbons									
C$_2$H$_4$	26[k]	26	37	36	22[h]	31	30		
C$_3$H$_6$	32[k]	32	46	37	29.8[l]	42.6	34.4		
CD$_2$:CDCD$_3$	39[k]	39	56	40	28.7[l]	41.0	31.3		
C$_4$H$_8$-2	37[k]	37	53	38	39[g]	56	40		
iso-C$_4$H$_8$	43[k]	43	61	40					
n-C$_5$H$_{10}$-1	45[k]	45	64	40					
n-C$_6$H$_{12}$-1	50[k]	50	71	44					
n-C$_6$H$_{12}$-2									

TABLE 2-3 (Continued)

Compound	Hg($^3P_1$) Physical Determinations				Hg($^3P_1$), Chemical Data				Hg($^3P_0$)[b]	
	σ_Q^2, A²	Preferred Values			σ_Q^2, A²		k_Q^c		σ_Q^2, A²	k_Q^c
	Proc. I	σ_Q^2, A²		k_Q^c	Proc. I	Proc. II	Proc. I	Proc. II		
		Proc. I	Proc. II	Proc. II						
(CH₃)₂C=C(CH₃)₂	43[k]	43	61	38						
n-C₇H₁₄-1	45.8[f]	45.8	66	39						
n-C₇H₁₄-3	55.9[f]	55.9	80	47						
1,3-Butadiene	36[k]	36	51	37						
1,4-Pentadiene	39[k]	39	56	37						
1,5-Hexadiene	44[k]	44	63	39						
C₂H₂	23[k]	23	33	33						
C₂H₅C≡CH	33[k]	33	47	34						
CH₃C≡CCH₃	35[k]	35	50	36						
C₆H₆	41.9[f]	41.9	60	38						
Halogen-Containing Compounds										
CF₄	Very small	Very small								
CHF₃	0.005[j]	0.005	0.007	0.005						
CCl₄	46[j]	46	66	34						
CHCl₃	42[j]	42	60	33						
CH₂Cl₂	31[j]	31	44	27						
CH₃Cl	24[j]	24	34	25						
CH₃Br	28[j]	28	40	24						
CH₃I	41[j]	41	59	31						
C₂F₄	7.9[k]	7.9	11.3	6.6						
C₂HCl₃	52[k]	52	74	40						

Nitrogen-Containing Compounds							
CH_3CN	35[k]	35	50	41			
CH_3NH_2	33.5[j]	33.5	48	44			
$(CH_3)_2NH$	36[j]	36	51	40			
$(CH_3)_3N$	32[j]	32	46	32			
$(CH_3)_2N_2$	29[j]	29	41	30			
Oxygen-Containing Compounds							
CH_3OH	8[j]	8	11	10			
$(CH_3)_2O$	7[j]	7	10	8			
$(CH_3)_2CO$	32[k]	32	46	34	37[h]	53	39
CH_3CHO					29[h]	41	32
Ethylene oxide	2.7[k]	2.7	3.9	3.1	2.7[h]	3.9	3.1
trans-β-Butene oxide					19[h]	27	18
Miscellaneous Organic Compounds							
C_2H_5SH	29[j]	29	41	28			
$(CH_3)_2S$	34.5[j]	34.5	49.3	34			
$(CH_3)_2Hg$	46[j]	46	66	30			

[a] Taken directly from the table of Cvetanovic.[37]

[b] From data of Callear and Norrish.[55] (See Sec. 2-9C.)

[c] At 25°C; units of liters/mole/sec $\times 10^{-10}$.

[d] Zemansky.[43]

[e] M. G. Evans, *J. Chem. Phys.*, **2**, 445 (1934).

[f] J. R. Bates, *J. Am. Chem. Soc.*, **52**, 3825 (1930); **54**, 569 (1932).

[g] Cundall and Palmer.[102]

[h] Cvetanovic[78]; Cvetanovic and Doyle.[141]

[i] Darwent.[46a]

[j] Darwent and Phibbs.[46b]

[k] Darwent, Phibbs, and Hurtubise.[46c]

[l] Y. Rousseau and H. E. Gunning, *Can. J. Chem.*, **41**, 465 (1963). (Determinations made by the nitrous oxide technique (Ref. 47).)

made clear which procedure was the basis for the calculations, and a confusing situation has resulted.

In 1953 Matland[45] reported a technique of illuminating pure mercury vapor, carefully purified N_2-Hg mixtures, and measuring the decay time of imprisoned radiation when the irradiation ceased. Using Holstein's theory of imprisoned radiation,[23,24,25] he calculates an absolute value of σ_Q^2 for N_2 at 325°C significantly less than the values of Sampson and Zemansky (Procedure II).

Clearly a large uncertainty exists in these absolute values, and it is difficult to judge which approach is correct, although Procedure II seems favored somewhat.[37] When quoting σ_Q^2 values we shall simply try to indicate whether they were based on Procedure I or II (see Table 2-3 for a list of σ_Q^2 assembled by Cvetanovic[37]).

Happily there seems to be a reasonably good agreement on *relative* values for quenching cross sections obtained in various laboratories. For example, the studies of Darwent *et al.*[46] show that self-consistent values of cross sections can be assigned to fragments of hydrocarbons (e.g., CH_2, CH, and CH_3) that when added up give a calculated σ_Q^2 in good agreement with the experimental value for the molecule.

Furthermore, Cvetanovic (1955)[47] has developed a chemical method of obtaining relative cross sections that is highly useful. It is based on competitive rates of mercury-photosensitized reactions between the quencher A and added N_2O The latter decomposes cleanly into $N_2 + O$, and by measuring Φ_{N_2} for a series of runs with different ratios of $[A]/[N_2O]$, accurate values for the ratio σ_Q^2 for A/σ_Q^2 for N_2O can be obtained.[37] Clearly, if an accurate absolute value for a cross section could be determined, then the relative values from a number of laboratories could be normalized to that result.*

The deactivation of a mercury atom in the $^3P_1$ state directly to the ground state $^1S_0$ by a *collision of the second kind*† with an argon atom is an example of *total physical quenching*. In an atom-atom interaction of this kind the 112 kcal excitation energy appears as kinetic energy of the recoiling mercury

---

* In this regard, Yarwood, Strausz, and Gunning recently reported an accurate experimental method for determining absolute quenching cross sections.[165c] They cite results for a wide range of compounds and compare their values with those in the literature. For example, σ_Q^2 for *n*-butane is 4.9 A² by their physical method, compared to 3.6 A² by the chemical method (Table 2-3).

† Noyes and Leighton define collisions of the first and second kinds in the following way: "Collisions in which translational energy is transformed into energy of excitation (i.e., electronic, vibrational, and rotational) are termed *inelastic collisions of the first kind*. Collisions in which energy of excitation is converted either into other energy of excitation or into kinetic energy may be called *inelastic collisions of the second kind*." Ref. 11, p. 212.

and argon atoms. Since the direct conversion of large amounts of electronic energy into kinetic energy is a highly inefficient process, $\sigma_Q{}^2$ for argon is very small.

Jablonski (1931)[48] has explained this quenching by a rare gas in terms of Fig. 2-19. Curve I represents the potential energy of the system $Hg(^3P_1) + Ar$ as a function of interatomic distance r. Curve II is that of the ground-state atom $Hg(^1S_0) + Ar$. At a very small value of r, r_x, the two curves intersect. If a collision between an excited mercury atom and a

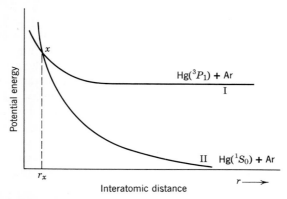

Fig. 2-19   Quenching of an excited mercury atom by collisions of the second kind with an argon atom in its ground state. The atoms approach along the potential energy curve I, and at point x there is a small but finite chance to cross over to curve II and to separate with the 112 kcal/mole electronic energy of the electronically excited mercury now distributed as kinetic energy of the two recoiling atoms.

ground-state argon atom is sufficiently "energetic" that they approach within the distance r_x, a rearrangement of the electronic energy levels of the excited mercury atom to those of the ground state would permit the system to cross over to curve II. The perturbing influence of the rare gas atom in close proximity to the $Hg(^3P_1)$ atom facilitates this electronic rearrangement so that *both* atoms wind up in their ground states, but separate, with 112 kcal of additional kinetic energy distributed between them. This theory suggests that the quenching efficiency of argon should increase with temperature (increased frequency of "energetic" collisions in which $r = r_x$), and indeed $\sigma_Q{}^2$ for argon increases by a factor of almost 4 at 750°C.[49]

Total quenching by molecules is generally much more efficient because the electronic excitation energy of the mercury atom may be removed by the quenching molecule as some combination of electronic, vibrational, rotational, and kinetic energy. Since usually it is difficult, if not impossible, to distinguish the relative contributions of physical and chemical processes to total quenching, we will defer consideration of total quenching by molecules to Sec. 2-11.

2-9C   Quenching to a Metastable State

The $^3P_0$ state is the lowest excited level of atomic mercury. It lies only 5 kcal below the $^3P_1$ state (Fig. 2-18), and in certain systems excited $Hg(^3P_1)$ atoms can be deactivated to this level instead of directly to the ground state (*partial* quenching). An atom in the $^3P_0$ state will remain in this state until it (1) gains back 5 kcal of energy by a collision of the first kind and returns to the $^3P_1$ state, from which it can emit 2537 A radiation, (2) transfers its electronic energy to a quenching molecule, or (3) finally emits 2654 A radiation (phosphoresces). The radiative transition is doubly forbidden (Sec. 2-7A-1), and at room temperature only about one collision in approximately 5000 has energy enough for reactivation to the $^3P_1$ level to occur. Thus the $^3P_0$ state has a relatively long lifetime and might be expected to play a significant role in mercury-sensitized reactions. In fact, the relative importance of partial versus total quenching and the relative reactivities of the $^3P_0$ and $^3P_1$ states with quenching molecules have been a matter of interest, speculation, and experimentation for at least three decades.

Until recently little in the way of definitive, unequivocal answers to these questions was available. It was well known that nitrogen could deactivate $^3P_1$ atoms to the $^3P_0$ level*; the question was whether other molecules, particularly the hydrocarbons, whose mercury-photosensitized reactions were being extensively studied, could do the same.

In a definitive set of flash photolysis experiments (Sec. 6-4) with mercury vapor and various added gases Callear and Norrish (1962)[55] followed directly the buildup and decay of mercury atoms in the $^3P_0$ state. After the flash of mercury vapor with 750 mm of added nitrogen, absorption lines were observed at 4047, 2967, 2535, and 2378 A, the latter three corresponding to the transitions $6(^3P_0) \rightarrow 6(^3D_1)$, $6(^3P_0) \rightarrow 7(^3D_1)$ and $6(^3P_0) \rightarrow 8(^3D_1)$. They made the important observation that, although metastable $6(^3P_0)$ atoms are formed when quenching the $^3P_1$ state by N_2, H_2O, and

---

* For example, addition of small amounts of N_2 quenched 2537 A emission, and concurrently lines at 4047 and 2967 A (among others) appeared in the absorption spectrum.[50,51,52,53] They correspond to the transitions

$$Hg6(^3P_0) + h\nu(4047 \text{ A}) \rightarrow Hg7(^3S_1)$$
$$Hg6(^3P_0) + h\nu(2967 \text{ A}) \rightarrow Hg6(^3D_1)$$

The 5461 A fluorescence emitted by the $Hg7(^3S_1)$ state has been used to monitor the concentration of $^3P_0$ atoms.[54]

CO, these atoms were *not* produced in quenching by H_2, C_2H_4, C_2H_6, O_2, NO, and N_2O.

Callear and Norrish point out that their values of rate constants and reaction cross sections are at best reliable to a factor of 2. Nevertheless they seem sufficiently definitive for the following conclusions:

1. Quenching to the metastable state, $^3P_1 + A \rightarrow {}^3P_0 + A$, is important only in a few systems, N_2, H_2O, and CO. Partial quenching is *not important* with H_2, C_2H_6, C_2H_4, CO_2, O_2, NO, and N_2O.

2. Metastable $Hg(^3P_0)$ atoms have a significantly lower reactivity than $Hg(^3P_1)$ atoms.

TABLE 2-4 Cross Sections for the Total Quenching of $^3P_0$ and $^3P_1$ Mercury Atoms to the $^1S_0$ State, and Rate Constants for the Quenching of the $^3P_0$ State to the Ground State[a]

Quenching Gas	k_Q,[b] l/mole/sec $\times 10^{-10}$	σ_Q^2 Hg($^3P_0$),[b] A^2	σ_Q^2 Hg($^3P_1$),[c] A^2 Proc. I	Proc. II
Hg	8.2	22	. . .	. . .
CO	0.07	0.08	4.07	5.82
N_2	Very small	Very small	0.19	0.27
O_2	0.2	0.2	13.9	19.9
H_2	0.3	0.08	6	8.6
C_2H_6	0.05	0.05	0.11	0.16
NO	0.5	0.6	24.7	35.3
C_2H_4	0.7	0.8	25	37
N_2O	1.0	1.5	12.6	18.0
H_2O	0.007	0.006	1.0	1.43
CO_2	0.003	0.0035	2.48	3.54

[a] See Sec. 2-9B and Ref. 37. Table taken from Ref. 37.
[b] For the quenching of $Hg(^3P_0)$ to $Hg(^1S_0)$. Data of Callear and Norrish.[55]
[c] From Table 2-3. Original references there.

The order of reactivity of the $^3P_0$ atoms in the quenching process $Hg(^3P_0) + A \rightarrow Hg(^1S_0) + A^*$ is

$$N_2O > C_2H_4 > NO > H_2 > O_2 > C_2H_6 > H_2O > CO_2 > N_2$$

This is evident from the data in Table 2-4, where their rate constants, k_Q, and cross sections for quenching, σ_Q^2, for the reaction

$$Hg(^3P_0) + A \rightarrow Hg(^1S_0) + A^*$$

are compared with literature values of quenching cross sections for the competing process

$$Hg(^3P_1) + A \rightarrow Hg(^1S_0) + A^*$$

As a result of this work of Callear and Norrish, we shall assume in our subsequent discussion that the role of $Hg(^3P_0)$ atoms in mercury-photo-sensitized reactions is minor for most compounds, including hydrocarbons. This assumption may not be strictly true in all cases, but it seems the best that can be done at present.

Two aspects of quenching of excited mercury atoms that have been debated for some years are the mechanisms of deactivation of $^3P_1$ mercury atoms by N_2 as compared to CO and the importance of the excited molecule $(Hg_2)^*$ in $Hg-N_2$ mixtures irradiated at 2537 A. We shall consider these briefly.

The relative cross sections for quenching of 2537 A phosphorescence by CO and N_2 are 4.07 and 0.19 A^2, a striking difference for two gases that often behave in a similar manner. In the older literature it was assumed that both compounds quenched $^3P_1$ atoms to the metastable $^3P_0$ state. The factor of 20 difference in $\sigma_Q{}^2$ was explained in terms of a "resonance" between the 5 kcal difference in energy between the $^3P_1$ and $^3P_0$ states of mercury, and the energy of the quantum required to raise the CO molecule to its first excited vibrational level. Presumably the resonance facilitated the deactivation of the $^3P_1$ to the $^3P_0$ state by CO, whereas N_2 did not have the appropriate vibrational spacing, and hence quenching was inefficient. A rather detailed theory was developed along this line and quite generally accepted.

However, experiments of Scheer and Fine (1962)[56] indicate that the efficiencies of N_2 and CO for partial quenching to the $^3P_0$ state are about *equal*! Thus about 95 % of the time CO must quench $^3P_1$ atoms directly to the ground state, and the basis for the "resonance" theory no longer exists. It is proposed instead that the high *total* quenching efficiency of CO is due to the formation of an intermediate mercury carbonyl compound which is unstable and dissociates into $Hg(^1S_0)$ atoms and highly vibrationally excited CO molecules.

This idea of the formation of an unstable intermediate that acts to facilitate energy transfer from an excited mercury atom to the quenching atom or molecule is consistent with the observation that quenching efficiency seems more dependent on the chemical nature of the primary quenching act than on whether or not the overall process is physical or chemical quenching. For example, excited sodium atoms in the ^2P state have 48.5 kcal of electronic energy, far too little for *overall chemical* quenching by hydrocarbons. However, the relative cross sections for physical quenching of excited ^2P sodium by olefins versus paraffins are the same as for chemical quenching of $Hg(^3P_1)$ atoms, large $\sigma_Q{}^2$ for olefins, small $\sigma_Q{}^2$ for paraffins. In this case overall physical quenching by olefins might proceed through a short-lived chemical intermediate (perhaps a charge transfer complex involving the π electrons of the olefin). This could facilitate transfer and conversion of the electronic energy of the sodium atom into vibrational and rotational energy of the olefin.

Another type of short-lived chemical intermediate, $(Hg_2)^*$, has been believed to be the source of the emission band centered at about 4850 A that occurs concurrently with resonance phosphorescence when gaseous mixtures of mercury and nitrogen are illuminated with 2537 radiation.[†] The proposed mechanism is

$$Hg(^1S_0) + h\nu \ (2537 \ A) \rightarrow Hg(^3P_1) \xrightarrow[N_2]{} Hg(^3P_0)$$

$$Hg(^3P_0) + Hg(^1S_0) + (N_2) \rightarrow (Hg_2)^* + (N_2) \tag{1}$$

$$(Hg_2)^* \rightarrow 2Hg(^1S_0) + h\nu' \ (4850 \ A \ band) \tag{2}$$

Nitrogen serves two purposes: it quenches $^3P_1$ atoms to the metastable $^3P_0$ state and acts as a "third body" to stabilize the excited molecule $(Hg_2)^*$.[50,51]

Mrozowski[57] has proposed that the $(Hg_2)^*$ molecule is in the $^3O_u^-$ state, Fig. 2-20, from which radiative return to the ground state is forbidden. However, under certain circumstances, such as very small values of r or collision with another atom or molecule, the excited state is perturbed sufficiently (perhaps it passes over to a $^3\Sigma_u^+$ state[57]) that emission of radiation occurs and the molecule dissociates into two normal mercury atoms.

Although the details, experimental and theoretical, of the mechanism of emission are not resolved and Mrozowski's theory has been questioned,[58,59] the reaction of $Hg(^1S_0)$ and $Hg(^3P_0)$ atoms to form $(Hg_2)^*$ seems quite well established. Additional evidence is the very large cross section of mercury for quenching excited atoms in the $^3P_0$ state, σ_Q^2 for mercury $= 22 \ A^2$, reported by Callear and Norrish.[55] This could be rationalized in terms of the species $(Hg_2)^*$ being an intermediate in the primary quenching process.[‡]

Finally it is interesting that a process quite analogous to $(Hg_2)^*$ formation has been proposed to explain long-lived emission from irradiated aromatic hydrocarbons. Presumably the radiation is emitted by an excited bimolecular species (sometimes called an "excimer") formed on

---

[†] A second band at 3350 A was reported by a number of earlier workers[57,58,59] but was not found in the more recent work of Kimball and LeRoy.[51,53] Furthermore they found no 4850 A emission until a trace of N_2 was added.

[‡] Kimball and LeRoy, however, do not include deactivation of $Hg(^3P_0)$ atoms by $^1S_0$ atoms as an important step in their mechanism for the kinetics of reactions in N_2-Hg mixtures irradiated at 2537 A.[53]

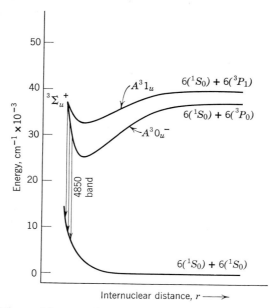

Fig. 2-20 Proposed lower excited states of the unstable molecule $(Hg_2)^*$ formed by collision between $Hg(^3P_0)$ and $Hg(^1S_0)$ atoms. Radiative transitions from the $A^3O_u^-$ state to the ground state are forbidden, but perturbations occurring at small values of r permit emission of the 4850 A band. Adapted from Mrozowski.[57]

collision between an electronically excited molecule and a similar one in the ground state (see Sec. 4-9A).

2-9D   Sensitized Fluorescence

Franck predicted in 1922 that a transfer of electronic energy could occur between excited atoms and atoms of a different species in their ground states.[60] He further stated that the efficiency of the transfer should increase for various systems as the difference in electronic energy levels of the excited donor atom D* approached the difference in energy levels of the non-excited atom A (i.e., approached resonance).

This prediction was soon verified by Cario and Franck, who irradiated mixtures of mercury and thallium vapors with the Hg 2537 A line, to which the thallium was transparent. They observed *sensitized fluorescence* from the excited states of thallium which lie near or below the 4.86 ev of $^3P_1$ mercury.[61]

The effect of resonance between energy levels of the excited donor and the ground-state acceptor on the efficiency of energy transfer (as measured by the yield of sensitized fluorescence) was demonstrated by Beutler and Josephy[62] in 1927. They studied the photosensitized fluorescence of sodium by excited mercury (Eq. 2-37) and found that the $Na9(^2S) \rightarrow 3(^2P)$ transition (actually a doublet, 4423 and 4420 A) was strong, whereas the $Na4(^2D) \rightarrow 3(^2P)$ lines (5688.2 and 5682.7 A) were very weak. This is the opposite of their behavior in normal emission processes. It results from the almost exact resonance of $9(^2S)$ sodium with $^3P_1$ mercury (4.88 versus 4.86 ev, respectively) and the lack of resonance between the $Na4(^2D)$ and $Hg(^3P_1)$ states (4.26 versus 4.86 ev, respectively), leaving 0.6 ev to appear as kinetic energy in this transfer process. When nitrogen was added to the mixture of metal vapors, the $Na7(^2S) \rightarrow 3(^2P)$ line (4750 A) substantially increased in relative intensity. This is reasonable, since the added nitrogen builds up the population of mercury atoms in the $^3P_0$ state, which at 4.64 ev is only 0.07 ev from the $Na7(^2S)$ state (4.71 ev), and this 0.07 ev can be obtained by utilizing the kinetic energy of the colliding $Hg(^3P_0)$ and $Na3(^2P)$ atoms.

The effective cross sections of the quenching of $Hg(^3P_1)$ atoms by sodium have been calculated from the measured intensities of the lines in the sensitized emission.[63] The theory subsequently was extended to sensitized fluorescence in mercury-thallium mixtures and the effect of added argon and helium studied.[64] Mercury $(^3P_1)$-sensitized fluorescence also has been observed with vapors of the other alkali metals and silver, cadmium, zinc, lead, tin, and indium.[13]

2-10 PHYSICAL PRIMARY PROCESSES OF OTHER ATOMS

In Table 2-5 are summarized the resonance lines and the corresponding lifetimes, when available, of several metals of utility as sources for direct or photosensitized photolyses. Also included are the noble gases and, for comparison's sake, calcium and sodium.

Next to mercury, cadmium has been most widely used in photosensitization studies, and considerable work also has been done on its fluorescence quenching. Since the processes of physical quenching are similar to those in mercury, we shall not consider them here. We should note, however, the factor of about 10^{-3} in the lifetime of the resonance phosphorescence of the $Cd5(^3P_1)$ state, compared to the resonance fluorescence from the $Cd5(^1P_1)$ state (2×10^{-6} versus 2×10^{-9} sec). This is in keeping with the selection rule $\Delta S = 0$. The shorter lifetime of the $Hg(^3P_1)$ state (1×10^{-7} versus 2×10^{-6} sec for cadmium) agrees with the theory that this rule breaks down for heavy atoms.

With cadmium the $5(^3P_0)$ state lies only 1.6 kcal below the emitting $5(^3P_1)$ level (versus 5.1 kcal for mercury). Thus, although quenching to

TABLE 2-5   Wavelengths of Resonance Lines and Energies and Lifetimes of Excited States for Atoms of Importance in Sensitized Reactions

	Metal				
	Hg	Cd	Zn	Ca	Na
Principal quantum number, n:	6	5	4	4	3
Singlet $\rightarrow$ Singlet					
$n(^1P_1) \rightarrow n(^1S_0) + h\nu$	1849	2288	2139	4227	
Energy, kcal/einstein:	154.6	125.0	133.7	67.6	
Radiative lifetime, sec:	1.3×10^{-9}	$1\text{--}2 \times 10^{-9}$	$<10^{-7}$	3.5×10^{-9}	
Triplet $\rightarrow$ Singlet					
$n(^3P_1) \rightarrow n(^1S_0) + h\nu$	2537	3261	3076	6537	
Energy, kcal/einstein:	112.7	87.7	92.9	43.7	
Radiative lifetime, sec:	1.1×10^{-7}	2×10^{-6}			
Doublet $\rightarrow$ Doublet					
$n(^2P_{3/2}) \rightarrow n(^2S_{1/2}) + h\nu$					5890
$n(^2P_{1/2}) \rightarrow n(^2S_{1/2}) + h\nu$					5896
Energy, kcal/einstein:					48.5
Radiative lifetime, sec:					1.6×10^{-8}

	Rare Gases				
	He	Ne	Ar	Kr	Xe	Rn
Wavelength[a]	584.7	743.7	1066.7	1235.8	1469.6	1786.1
Energy, kcal/einstein:	489.2	384.4	268.0	231.4	194.5	160.1
Wavelength		735.9	1048.2	1164.9	1295.6	1149
Energy, kcal/einstein:		388.5	272.8	245.4	220.7	248.8

The heats of formation of the metal hydrides from the gaseous atoms (kcal/mole) are:[38] NaH, 51.6; HgH, 8.5; CdH, 15.5; ZnH, 23.1.
[a] Emission from helium involves the electronic change $He(2p1s) \rightarrow He(1s^2) + h\nu$, and $np^5(n + 1)s \rightarrow np^6 + h\nu$ for the other rare gases. The splitting to $^2P_{3/2}$ and $^2P_{1/2}$ excited states results from j-j coupling in the case of these elements.

this lower state occurs, the reverse process of reactivation through collisions of the first kind is almost equally probable. The steady-state concentration of $Cd5(^3P_0)$ atoms is thus much lower than that for mercury, and absorption lines originating from this level have not been observed.

2-11   CHEMICAL QUENCHING; MERCURY-PHOTO-SENSITIZED DISSOCIATION OF HYDROGEN

Certain elements have excited states with resonance levels of sufficient energy that collision with many types of molecules leads to primary *photochemical* processes. Those that also have vapor pressures of about 10^{-3} mm or more at temperatures where the molecule is stable, and are capable of being excited in a low-pressure discharge to give an intense resonance line or lines, may be effective sensitizers for inducing decomposition of a wide variety of molecules which are transparent to the incident resonance radiation itself. Several of these are tabulated in Table 2-5.

The contrast between *direct* and *photosensitized* processes is shown below for methane, which is transparent at 2537 A but absorbs below 1440 A.

Direct photolysis

$$CH_4 + h\nu \, (\lambda < 1440 \text{ A}) \rightarrow CH_2 + H_2$$

Mercury-photosensitized reaction

$$Hg(^1S_0) + h\nu \, (2537 \text{ A}) \rightarrow Hg(^3P_1)$$

$$Hg(^3P_1) + CH_4 \rightarrow Hg(^1S_0) + CH_3 + H$$

The products of a direct photolysis may differ greatly from those of a photosensitized process, as seen above. Thus, if one wishes to study *direct photolyses* with the light source being a metal atom resonance line, one must be extremely careful to avoid the slightest trace of contamination of the reaction system by the metal itself (see Sec. 7-1A).

Other atoms whose resonance radiation is photochemically useful include cadmium and, to a lesser extent, zinc and sodium. The noble gases, argon, xenon, and krypton, have resonance lines which fall in the vacuum ultraviolet and are highly useful for direct and sensitized photolyses (Table 2-5 and Sec. 2-17).

The first evidence for chemical quenching of photoexcited metal atoms was that of Cario and Franck[65] in 1922. They illuminated a gaseous mixture of hydrogen and mercury with 2537 A resonance radiation and detected "active hydrogen" capable of reducing metallic oxides. The formation of hydrogen atoms was subsequently verified by thermal conductivity measurements.

The results of Cario and Franck are explained by the processes

$$Hg(^1S_0) + h\nu \, (2537 \text{ A}) \rightarrow Hg(^3P_1)$$

$$Hg(^3P_1) + H_2 \rightarrow Hg(^1S_0) + 2H(^2S_{1/2})$$

The total cross sections for quenching are σ_Q^2 for $H_2 = 8.6$ A^2 and σ_Q^2 for $D_2 = 11.9$ A^2, compared to $\sigma_Q^2 = 0.27$ A^2 for N_2. Thus virtually every collision of a hydrogen molecule with a mercury atom in the $^3P_1$ state quenches fluorescence, since the gas-kinetic *collision* cross section is about 10 A².

These cross sections include both physical and chemical processes, and their relative efficiencies are in doubt. Thus, in 1948 Thomas and Gwinn[66] determined the rate of production of hydrogen atoms by Hg($^3P_1$) atoms and suggested that the sensitized dissociation of H_2 is several times *less* probable than overall *physical* quenching of Hg($^3P_1$) (to the $^3P_0$ or $^1S_0$ state or both). Their results, however, cannot be said to be conclusive until the role of possible secondary hydrogen-atom-removing reactions has been more clearly defined (see Sec. 2-13). Furthermore, if H_2 physically quenches the $^3P_1$ atoms directly to the ground state, it cannot occur simply by transfer of electronic energy to form an excited molecule of H_2, as the lowest-lying electronic state of hydrogen is an unstable triplet ($^3\Sigma_u^+$) which would dissociate immediately if formed (see Fig. 3-20). Possibly the mercury hydride HgH is an intermediate (Sec. 2-13-A), but again the overall quenching would be chemical in nature.

Reactions of hydrogen atoms generated by the mercury-sensitized dissociation of H_2 or by the reaction of Hg($^3P_1$) atoms with *n*-butane[67] have been widely studied (see Refs. 38 and 68). For example, hydrogen atoms add rapidly to olefins to produce alkyl radicals whose subsequent reactions can thus be followed. This interesting field is beyond the scope of this book; however, it has been reviewed by Cvetanovic.[68]

2-12   THE SPIN CONSERVATION RULE; ALLOWED ELECTRONIC ENERGY TRANSFER PROCESSES

An important and widely useful generalization when considering possible primary processes in metal-photosensitized reactions is the Wigner *spin conservation rule.*

This states that in the transfer of electronic energy between an excited atom or molecule and a molecule in its ground or excited states the overall spin angular momentum of the system should not change.

We have found it helpful to consider the possible allowed spin states in the following rather naive manner: electrons are represented as arrows, and $\uparrow$ is spin $+\frac{1}{2}$, $\downarrow$ is spin $-\frac{1}{2}$. The Wigner rule says that we may combine these in any fashion we choose (ignoring chemistry for the moment) as long as the overall spin stays unchanged, that is, as long as we do not invert spin. Thus for the singlet-singlet, triplet-singlet, and triplet-triplet transfer we have the following possibilities (an asterisk represents the electronically excited molecule):

Multiplicities of Reactants	Multiplicities of Products

Singlet-Singlet

$(↑↓)^* + (↑↓)$ ⟶

→ (↑↓) + (↑↓)*   (singlet + singlet*)
→ ↑↓↑ + ↑   (doublet + doublet)
→ ↑↓ + ↑ + ↓   (singlet + doublet + doublet)

Triplet-Singlet

$(↑↑)^* + (↓↑)$ ⟶
  A   B

→ ↑↓ + (↑↑)*   (singlet + triplet*)
   A   B
→ ↑↑↓ + ↑   (doublet + doublet)
→ ↑↑ + ↓ + ↑   (triplet + doublet + doublet)
→ ↑ + ↑ + ↓↑   (doublet + doublet + singlet)
→ (↑↑↓↑)*   (triplet*)

Triplet-Triplet

$(↑↑)^* + (↑↑)^*$ ⟶

→ ↑↑ + ↑ + ↑   (triplet + doublet + doublet)
→ ↑↑↑ + ↑   (quartet + doublet)
→ (↑↑↑↑)*   (quintet*)

$(↑↑)^* + (↓↓)^*$ ⟶

→ ↑↑↓ + ↓   (doublet + doublet)
→ ↑↓ + ↑↓   (singlet + singlet)

Some of the possibilities may not represent chemical reality; however, some rather unexpected excited states have been suggested recently, and conservation of spin has been cited as a basis for their being "allowed." For example, triplet-triplet quenching to produce a quintet state has been proposed from spectroscopic evidence (Sec. 4-9A).

It is important to note that conservation of spin implies different reactivities in photophysical and photochemical energy transfer processes for electronically excited atoms and molecules in their singlet and triplet states. Thus the Wigner spin rule is widely applied to photophysical spectroscopic processes (for examples predicting allowed electronic states of triplet-triplet annihilation processes, Sec. 4-9A) and to a variety of photochemical primary processes. For example, transfer of electronic energy from a donor molecule in its triplet state to an acceptor molecule in its singlet state in many cases leads to completely different (and often unique) products from those obtained by direct irradiation of the acceptor molecule (Sec. 4-10B-4).

In view of the current interest in energy transfer processes it is interesting to note that the concept of invoking the spin conservation rule in these elementary reactions was proposed by Laidler[40] in 1947 to rationalize the experimental results to date on the metal-photosensitized reactions of hydrocarbons. His approach was successful then and appears equally successful today in providing a general means of predicting whether primary processes in photosensitized reactions go through excited molecules in their singlet or triplet states or whether direct dissociation of the quenching molecule occurs.

Because of the widespread use of the spin conservation rule in a variety of energy transfer processes it is helpful to illustrate Laidler's approach with the specific example of gas-phase mercury-photosensitized reactions of hydrocarbons, utilizing some data on $Hg6(^1P_1)$ reactions that became available in 1964.

The allowed spin states of the products of a primary reaction between a mercury atom in its excited $6(^1P_1)$ state (1849 A) and a hydrocarbon in its ground singlet state $^1\Sigma$ are shown below. The symbols for the excited molecular states $(^1\Sigma)^*$ and $(^3\Sigma)^*$ simply specify that they are electronically excited singlet and triplet species; $(^1\Sigma)^v$ refers to a molecule in a vibrationally excited ground state. No other spectroscopic properties are implied.*

Singlet-Singlet

$$Hg(^1P_1)(154.6 \text{ kcal}) + RH(^1\Sigma)$$

$$\longrightarrow Hg(^1S_0) + RH(^1\Sigma)^* \qquad (1)$$
$$\longrightarrow Hg(^1S_0) + RH(^1\Sigma)^v \qquad (2)$$
$$\longrightarrow Hg(^1S_0) + R(^2\Sigma) + H(^2S) \quad (3)$$
$$\longrightarrow [HgH(^2\Sigma)] + R(^2\Sigma) \qquad (4)$$

For $^3P_1$ mercury they are as follows:

Triplet-Singlet

$$Hg(^3P_1)(112.7 \text{ kcal}) + RH(^1\Sigma)$$

$$\longrightarrow Hg(^1S_0) + RH(^3\Sigma)^* \qquad (5)$$
$$\longrightarrow Hg(^1S_0) + R(^2\Sigma) + H(^2S) \quad (6)$$
$$\longrightarrow [HgH(^2\Sigma)] + R(^2\Sigma) \qquad (7)$$

Several important predictions can be made by comparing the allowed energy transfer processes of $Hg6(^1P_1)$ atoms (1849 A) and $Hg6(^3P_1)$ atoms (2537 A).

1. The reaction with hydrocarbons of excited mercury atoms in their singlet state $^1P_1$ will be different from that of mercury atoms in their triplet state $^3P_1$.

2. The formation of either electronically excited $RH(^1\Sigma)^*$ or highly vibrationally excited (but ground-state) $RH(^1\Sigma)^v$ molecules, or of both, is

---

* In Chapter 4 we use the symbols S_1 and T_1 for the first excited singlet and triplet states, but here the symbol S_0 may be confused with the term symbol for the mercury atom.

possible in mercury-photosensitized reactions at 1849 A but not at 2537 A because the processes are not spin allowed.

$$Hg(^3P_1) + RH(^1\Sigma) \nearrow Hg(^1S_0) + RH(^1\Sigma)^* \qquad (8)$$
$$\searrow Hg(^1S_0) + RH(^1\Sigma)^v \qquad (9)$$

3. The relative possibility of primary processes by excited molecule formation versus direct dissociation of RH will depend upon the energy levels of the singlet and triplet states of the olefins and paraffins.

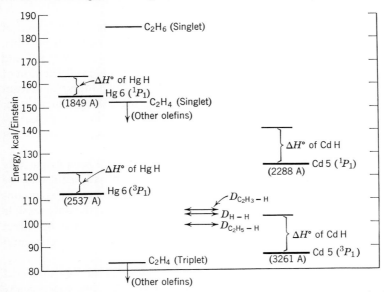

Fig. 2-21   Energies of resonance levels of mercury and cadmium compared with the first excited singlet states of ethane and ethylene, the lowest triplet of ethylene, and the C-H bond strengths in these two hydrocarbons.

Figure 2-21 shows the energies of the $^1P_1$ and $^3P_1$ states of mercury and cadmium and indicates approximately the energy regions of the singlet and triplet states of olefins and paraffins. The C-H bond strengths in ethane and ethylene and the heats of formation of the hydrides HgH and CdH are indicated, since this energy is available for bond dissociation with excited cadmium atoms, and *may* be with mercury (see Sec. 2-13A).

The alkanes have singlet states significantly greater than 154.6 kcal; hence reaction 1 is ruled out on energetic grounds, and since process 5 is eliminated by the spin conservation rule the only processes to consider at 1849 A are direct formation of a highly vibrationally excited ground state, process 2, or a direct dissociation, processes 3 and 4. Direct transfer of a large amount of electronic energy from an atom to produce a vibrationally excited molecule is highly improbable; hence quenching by process 2 would be expected to be very small and direct dissociation by 3 or 4 the most probable process in mercury photosensitization of paraffins at 1849 A.

These conclusions are in line with experimental results by Holroyd and Pierce[69] on the mercury-photosensitized decomposition of propane, isobutane, and n-pentane at 1849 A. They propose that quenching of $Hg(^1P_1)$ atoms by paraffins is "by direct interaction with, and cleavage of, carbon-hydrogen bonds."

Olefins, however, have singlet states which lie just below the $^1P_1$ level of mercury (154.6 kcal) so that singlet-singlet transfer is energetically possible. Preliminary results for the mercury-sensitized reactions of ethylene[72] and propylene[71] at 1849 A suggest that the primary act is indeed formation of an excited molecule. Pertel[70] and Heller and Gordon[71] found significant differences in product distribution at 1849 A versus 2537 A, but whether this discrepancy was due to different spin states of the excited molecules (singlet versus triplet) or to the 42 kcal energy difference, or both, is not known.

Reactions sensitized by $Hg(^3P_1)$ atoms at 2537 A have been extensively studied; although numerous controversies exist, the broad features fit the Laidler proposal. Thus, with processes 8 and 9 eliminated by spin considerations and process 5 ruled out on energetic grounds, the only feasible chemical quenching of alkanes would appear to take place by direct dissociation, process 6, or by the hydride, 7. The mass of experimental data on alkanes supports this view (Sec. 2-13A-1).

Olefins have their lowest singlets well above the $^3P_1$ state, but their first triplets lie below so that process 5, triplet transfer, is feasible energetically and obeys the Wigner rule. The experimental results to date support such an excited molecule mechanism (Sec. 2-13B).

Although the results presently available support Laidler's suggestion of conservation of spin, other explanations may be possible[37] (though not as attractive). Detailed studies at 1849 A and other investigations using singlet and triplet cadmium and zinc atoms as sensitizers for the decomposition of a variety of substrates, would be most valuable to test further the generality of the hypothesis.

2-13 PRIMARY PROCESSES IN MERCURY-PHOTOSENSITIZED REACTIONS

We have considered the general aspects of quenching cross sections (data tabulated in Table 2-3) and the utility of the spin conservation rule in predicting allowed types of electronic energy transfer processes. Now we shall present experimental results from gas-phase studies on several classes of organic and inorganic compounds which seem to offer interesting, significant, and reliable insight into the nature and efficiencies of primary processes in mercury-photosensitized reactions. We shall also consider briefly the current theoretical and mechanistic concepts advanced to explain these results. No attempt has been made to present a complete literature survey or review (see Refs. 15, 37, and 38), and many excellent studies have been omitted because of space limitations. This consideration also has precluded discussion of secondary reactions of reactive species generated by atom-photosensitization techniques (see Ref. 38 for a comprehensive review to 1954, and Ref. 68 for a review to 1963 and discussion of the addition of atoms to olefins).

Finally, in the light of the important findings of Callear and Norrish[55] (Sec. 2-9C) we shall not consider possible chemical reactions initiated by $^3P_0$ mercury atoms.

2-13A Alkanes

The major products of the $Hg(^3P_1)$ sensitized reactions of alkanes, RH, at room temperature are typical of those expected from secondary reactions of alkyl radicals and hydrogen atoms, that is, hydrogen, the radical recombination products R_2, and olefins formed from disproportionation reactions of the alkyl radicals. In each case the products are consistent with the primary quenching act being a direct C-H bond scission.

Mercury hydride, HgH, has been suggested as an unstable intermediate in the quenching of alkanes, and this seems reasonable. However, there is no direct evidence for its formation.[72] Cadmium hydride is a required intermediate in the $Cd(^3P_1)$ sensitized reactions of alkanes because the 15.5 kcal heat of formation of CdH must be added to the 87.3 kcal of the 3261 A quantum to achieve enough energy to break a C-H bond in the paraffins. Emission of the CdH resonance line has been observed in cadmium sensitized reactions at 3261A,[73] but in corresponding circumstances emission from HgH has not been detected.[72]

Low primary quantum yields were first reported for $Hg(^3P_1)$ sensitized reactions with the alkanes. Subsequently it was realized that hydrogen atoms formed in the primary act add rapidly to the olefins formed in the secondary disproportionation reactions and that the low quantum yields were due to this "self-scavenging."[67,74-77] For example, at very low conversions ($<0.01\%$) and pressures of n-butane > 200 mm Φ_{H_2} levels off at a value greater than 0.9 (curve I, Fig. 2-22) and probably is unity at infinitely small conversions.[67,77] Curve II, Fig. 2-22, shows the reduced Φ_{H_2}

due to self-scavenging at "normal" conversions.[78] The rapid rise of Φ_{H_2} to a constant value at high pressures is good evidence that the primary act is a direct dissociation and does not go through a short-lived excited molecule (RH).*

Quenching cross sections and reaction products of the sensitized decompositions of the alkanes follow reasonable patterns in terms of the structures of the molecules and the radicals produced in the primary act. Thus in

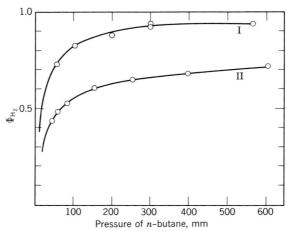

Fig. 2-22 Quantum yields of hydrogen versus pressure of *n*-butane in the Hg($^3P_1$) sensitized reaction of *n*-butane. Curve II is for "normal conversions," and I for very low conversions, illustrating the self-scavenging of hydrogen atoms formed in the primary act by butene produced in the secondary disproportionation reaction of the butyl radicals. Φ_{H_2} is based on Φ_{N_2} from N_2O being unity. From Cvetanovic.[37]

1950 Darwent[46a] showed that the quenching cross sections of the paraffinic hydrocarbons can be reasonably well estimated by assigning collisional diameters to CH_3, CH_2, and CH groups and considering the overall quenching diameter of a paraffin to be the sum of the various increments. The much greater quenching efficiency of a tertiary CH group, in comparison to a secondary or primary bond, is seen from the σ_Q^2 of n-C_5H_{12}, iso-C_5H_{12}, and neo-C_5H_{12}: 13.4, 17, and 2.1 A^2, respectively (Procedure II, Table 2-3).

In contrast to the other alkanes the Hg($^3P_1$) sensitized reactions of methane seem particularly complex,[79] while neopentane has been reported to be remarkably unreactive.[80,81] However, recent work at low percentage conversions[181] contradicts this and suggests that the reactivity of neopentane is "normal" relative to other branched alkanes.

Mercury-sensitized reactions of the alkanes have been carried out at elevated temperatures; the results seem predictable on the basis of the thermal stability and reactivity of the radicals produced in the primary act. Thus, although the quantum yield of ethane reacted doubles in going from 100 to 475°C, the reaction products are similar, presumably because of the stability of the ethyl radical.[82] However, Bywater and Steacie (1951)[83] found that in sensitized reactions of butane and isobutane the decomposition products of the normal and isobutyl radicals appeared above 260°.

2-13A-1   Structure and Reactivity in Primary Processes of Alkanes

Since the early 1940's the effect of molecular structure on the primary processes of mercury-sensitized reactions of hydrocarbons has been intensively studied, particularly by Steacie and his associates. In the past decade the site of attack of $Hg(^3P_1)$ atoms in paraffins has become clarified by several types of experiments, including the use of isotopically labeled compounds and the direct mass spectrometric detection of products of the primary photochemical act.

The latter technique, developed by Lossing and coworkers,[84] involves carrying out mercury-photosensitized reactions at low pressures of the reactant (in the micron range; millimeter pressures of helium added as a carrier gas) in a fast-flow reactor, one section of which contains the "leak" into the ionization chamber of a mass spectrometer. Under appropriate conditions it is possible to determine the rates of production of free radicals as well as stable molecules produced in mercury-sensitized reactions and to establish the relative efficiencies of competing primary processes. Results using this technique for a variety of compounds are cited in detail later in this chapter. The utility of the method is illustrated in Palmer and Lossing's[85] studies of the efficiencies of the two major primary processes of isobutane,[37]

$$(CH_3)_3CH + Hg(^3P_1) \rightarrow (CH_3)_3C + H + Hg(^1S_0) \qquad (1)$$
$$\rightarrow (CH_3)_2CHCH_2 + H + Hg(^1S_0) \qquad (2)$$

The t-butyl and isobutyl radicals are formed in primary processes 1 and 2. In order to better clarify the rates of 1 and 2, $(CD_3)_2Hg$ was added to the system to provide a source of CD_3 radicals (a "clean" mercury photosensitized process of dimethyl mercury). In the reaction chamber these "trapped" the t-butyl and isobutyl radicals, forming stable compounds with definitely different mass spectrometric cracking patterns. The ratio of tertiary to secondary C-H bond scission, k_1/k_2, was found to be about 7. It is interesting that when a deuterium atom was substituted in the tertiary position a dramatic isotope effect occurred; the ratio k_1/k_2 for $(CH_3)_3CD$ actually inverted and became $1/2$.

A second, chemical approach to determine the site of attack of $Hg(^3P_1)$ atoms has been employed by Gunning and coworkers.[15] Paraffins are labeled with deuterium at appropriate sites on the molecule, and the mercury-photosensitized reactions are run with a small amount of nitric oxide or nitric oxide-olefin mixtures as free-radical traps (Sec. 6-6). Table 2-6 shows the relative primary yields of n-propyl and isopropyl radicals from propane and several deuterium-labeled propanes.[86] Also given for

TABLE 2-6 Relative Rates of Decomposition and Percentage of n-Propyl Radicals Initially Formed in the Reaction of $Hg6(^3P_1)$ Atoms with Propane and Several Deuterated Propanes[a]

Molecule	n-Propyl Radicals, mole %		Relative Rate of Decomposition[c]
	Chemical Inhibition[b]	Mass Spectrometric Detection[c]	
$CH_3CH_2CH_3$	42	45	1
$CH_3CD_2CH_3$	77	87	0.8
$CD_3CH_2CD_3$	26	13	0.55
$CD_3CD_2CD_3$	49	53	0.5

[a] Taken from Gunning and Strausz.[15]

[b] Woodall and Gunning.[86]

[c] Avrahami and Kebarle.[87]

comparison are the results of Avrahami and Kebarle,[87] including the relative rates of the primary processes for the several propanes. They used a fast-flow reactor and mass spectrometric detection apparatus similar to that of Lossing. Considering the difference in experimental methods, the agreement is excellent. Note the large increase in the primary yield of n-propyl radicals when the methylene carbon is deuterated.

Another useful approach to the determination of the nature and yields of free radicals formed in the primary step of photosensitized reactions is to add ethylene-^{14}C to trap the initial radicals. This generates the $^{14}C_2H_5$ radical scavenger from which labeled hydrocarbon products are formed and the type and primary yield of radical deduced. Thus, for example, in $Hg(^3P_1)$ sensitized reactions at 2537 A, Holroyd et al.[69,88] find the relative rates of removal of tertiary, secondary, and primary hydrogen atoms from alkanes to be in the ratio 350:65:1. This may be compared to 12:3:1 when $Hg(^1P_1)$ atoms are the sensitizer at 1849 A. Furthermore, whereas with $^3P_1$ atoms at 2537 A the initial yields of t-butyl and isobutyl radicals from isobutane were found to be about 97% and 3%, respectively, at 1849 A they were 58% and 42%. No C-C bonds were broken at 1849 A. It seems reasonable to assume that the decrease in discrimination between the excited singlet and the excited triplet mercury atom is probably due to the much larger exothermicity involved. However, possible differences in the chemistry of the intimate interaction of singlet versus triplet mercury atoms with the R-H bond in alkanes may exist.

The intimate mechanistic path by which the dissociation of the C-H bond is effected is wide open to speculation. Certainly, the formation of mercury hydride, HgH, is an attractive hypothesis in view of its certainty as an intermediate in the analogous reactions of the similar excited atom cadmium, but as yet HgH has never been identified as a primary product. One would feel that overlap of the p orbital of the excited mercury atom with the s orbital of the hydrogen atom might provide a transitory type of bond through which energy could be transferred and the hydrogen atom "abstracted" by the triplet mercury.

While the relative rates and yields of the primary radicals formed in mercury-sensitized reactions are now becoming well established, little is known about the intimate aspects of the actual act of energy transfer from the excited mercury atom to the alkane. Gunning and Strausz[15] have presented a detailed mechanistic picture of this transfer process in a series of paraffins, based in part upon the electrophilic character of triplet mercury as compared to oxygen and sulfur atoms (O > S > Hg). The first step is pictured as a selective partial bond formation between the excited $Hg(^3P_1)$ atom and a primary, secondary, or tertiary hydrogen atom to form an excited complex. This is followed by cyclization to form a transient five-membered ring (the optimum size for alkanes, according to their theory); the ring then selectively reopens, and the complex dissociates into hydrogen atoms (or HgH) and the corresponding free radicals. The sequence is illustrated for propane.

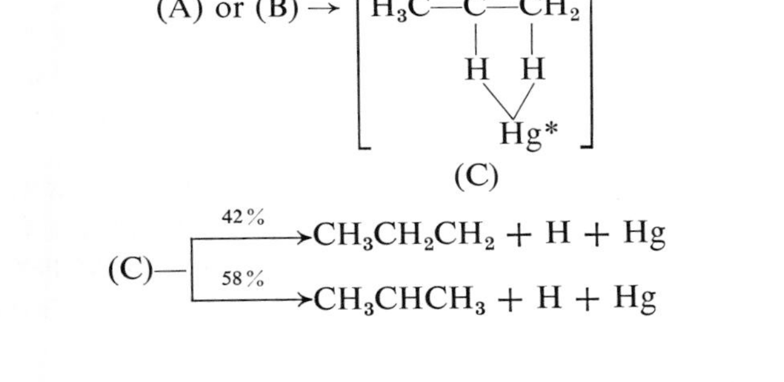

$$Hg(^3P_1) + C_3H_8 \rightarrow \underset{\overset{|}{H}}{CH_3CH_2\overset{H}{C}} \cdots Hg^* + \underset{\underset{\geq 87\%}{H\cdots Hg^*}}{\overset{|}{CH_3CHCH_3}}$$

$$\qquad\qquad\qquad\qquad (A) \qquad\qquad\qquad (B)$$

$$(A) \text{ or } (B) \rightarrow \left[\begin{array}{c} H \\ | \\ H_3C-C-CH_2 \\ |\quad | \\ H\ \ H \\ \diagdown\diagup \\ Hg^* \end{array} \right]$$

$$(C)$$

$$(C)-\begin{array}{l} \xrightarrow{42\%} CH_3CH_2CH_2 + H + Hg \\ \xrightarrow{58\%} CH_3CHCH_3 + H + Hg \end{array}$$

This is an interesting and provocative theory which recently has been applied to a variety of types of molecules.[15] However, the evidence to date does not offer a unique choice between alternative mechanisms.

2-13B   Olefins

In sharp contrast to the alkanes, quenching cross sections of olefins are large (e.g., $\sigma_Q{}^2 = 46$ and 2.3 A^2 for propylene and propane, respectively), and the rates of their $Hg(^3P_1)$ photosensitized reactions *decrease* as the pressure is raised. Thus in 1941 LeRoy and Steacie[89] proposed that for ethylene (and it is now generally agreed for olefins[90] in general) the primary act is triplet energy transfer to produce a relatively long-lived, vibrationally excited triplet state of the olefin (Sec. 2-12). The specific fate of the excited triplet RĊHĊHR depends on the structure of the olefin and the pressure, as we shall see in the following discussion.[15,37,38,46c]

2-13B-1   Ethylene

The major products of the $Hg(^3P_1)$ sensitized decomposition of ethylene are hydrogen and acetylene. Their quantum yields are about 0.4 each[91] and are temperature independent; these values decrease as the pressure of C_2H_4 is increased or inert gas, CO_2, is added.[92]

These facts suggest an excited molecule mechanism (versus direct dissociation of the paraffins), and excellent direct evidence for this was obtained by Cvetanovic and Callear (1955)[93] who ran the $Hg(^3P_1)$ sensitized reaction of an equimolar mixture of C_2H_4 and C_2D_4 and found virtually no HD or mixed acetylenes. Actually some dissociation of the excited molecule into vinyl + H also occurs,[91] but it is less than 3% of the total reaction.[92]

An important spectroscopic and mechanistic concept, the possibility of two excited states participating in olefin-$Hg(^3P_1)$ reactions, was originally invoked to explain the kinetic behavior of hydrogen production from ethylene.[37,95] An important feature of the mechanism is the deactivation step, and Darwent (1951)[96] originally proposed that it was either termolecular or occurred at the wall.

$$C_2H_4{}^* + 2C_2H_4 \longrightarrow 3C_2H_4 \tag{a}$$

$$C_2H_4{}^* \xrightarrow{\text{wall}} C_2H_4 \tag{b}$$

Subsequently Callear and Robb (1954)[97] developed an ingenious thermal method of investigating fast gas-phase reactions and used this technique together with studies of the dependence of rate on light intensity to establish the quantum yield as about 1 and to eliminate the wall reaction. They suggested that the apparent three-body deactivating collision probably occurred in two successive collisions.

An alternative explanation which gave an even better kinetic fit between experimental and theoretical rate expressions and which did not involve a ternary deactivation step was offered by Callear and Cvetanovic (1956).[95] They assumed that two electronically and vibrationally excited states of approximately equal lifetimes were involved in the overall reaction; both were subject to collisional deactivation, but only one decomposed.

$$C_2H_4 + Hg(^3P_1) \rightarrow C_2H_4^* + Hg(^1S_0) \tag{1}$$

$$C_2H_4^* \rightarrow C_2H_4^{**} \tag{2}$$

$$C_2H_4^* + C_2H_4 \rightarrow 2C_2H_4 \tag{3}$$

$$C_2H_4^{**} \rightarrow C_2H_2 + H_2 \tag{4}$$

$$C_2H_4^{**} + C_2H_4 \rightarrow 2C_2H_4 \tag{5}$$

Treatment of the rate expression derived from this mechanism led to calculated lifetimes of about 4×10^{-9} sec for the excited states $C_2H_4^*$ and $C_2H_4^{**}$.

Strong supporting evidence came from the mercury-sensitized reactions of *cis*-ethylene-d_2. Not only were D_2, HD, and H_2 (in the ratio $1:6:2$) and the corresponding acetylenes formed, but also there was extensive isomerization to the *trans* isomer and the unsymmetrical isomer, $H_2C:CD_2$. These results are well accommodated by the two-excited-states proposal if it is assumed that the primary quenching step (1) is triplet energy transfer from an $Hg(^3P_1)$ to produce a vibrationally excited triplet state $(C_2H_4^*)$ and that the only fate of this species is deactivation to the ground state (*cis* or *trans*) (3) or isomerization to $C_2H_4^{**}$, possibly vibrationally excited triplet ethylidine (2). This could then dissociate by the molecular process to give H_2, HD, or D_2, plus the corresponding acetylenes (4), or rearrange to *unsym*-$H_2C:CD_2$ or the *sym* form (*cis* or *trans*) and be deactivated (5).

Rabinowitch et al.[98] investigated the $Hg(^3P_1)$ reaction with *trans*-ethylene-d_2 and found as major products *cis*-$C_2H_2D_2$, *unsym*-$H_2C:CD_2$ and isotopically mixed acetylenes and hydrogens. Their proposed mechanism involves two excited states and is basically that of Callear and Cvetanovic.

2-13B-2   Propylene and 1-Butene

Dissociation of C-C bonds becomes an important process in the mercury-sensitized reactions of the higher olefins (it does not occur at all with alkanes, even at 1849 A). While at least 90% of excited propylene molecules split into allyl + H,[84] perhaps 10% go to vinyl plus methyl radicals.[99] No molecular elimination of hydrogen occurs in the primary act.

The relatively weak β-C-C bond in 1-butene facilitates dissociation into allyl and methyl radicals,[84] and at moderate pressures (15-200 mm) it is about 1.3–1.6 times as probable as a primary C—H split.[100] α-Bond cleavage also takes place with butene-1 and the pentenes, but, as Majer, Mile, and Robb[101] demonstrate, it is a minor process.

Although isomerization of 1-butene to 2-butene occurs,[101] it is a minor process;[100,102] a reaction of major importance is isomerization to methyl cyclopropane.[100] This is one of the major products of the reaction and has interesting mechanistic implications. For example, the other thirty-three products of the reaction (most of them very minor) have maximum quantum yields at the lowest pressure studied (15 mm). In striking contrast Cvetanovic and Doyle[100] found that $\Phi_{\Delta-CH_3}$, which approached zero at low pressures, rose to a maximum of 0.066 at 65 mm and then dropped off to 0.042 at 230 mm. This kinetic behavior is good evidence for two excited states being involved, as originally suggested for ethylene, and the following mechanism, which gives a good kinetic fit, is proposed:

$$1\text{-}C_4H_8(S_0) + Hg(^3P_1) \rightarrow C_4H_8(T_1^v) + Hg(^1S_0) \tag{1}$$

$$C_4H_8(T_1^v) \rightarrow \text{Products} \tag{2}$$

$$\searrow$$

$$(C_4H_8)^* \tag{3}$$

$$C_4H_8(T_1^v) + M \rightarrow 1\text{-}C_4H_8 + M \tag{4}$$

$$(C_4H_8)^* \rightarrow \text{Products} \tag{5}$$

$$(C_4H_8)^* + M \rightarrow \Delta\text{-}CH_3 + M \tag{6}$$

The initial energy transfer process presumably forms the vibrationally excited triplet state of 1-butene, $C_4H_8(T_1^v)$, which can then dissociate or rearrange into a second excited state, $(C_4H_8)^*$, which is possibly the vibrationally excited triplet state of methyl cyclopropane. Large deuterium isotope effects are observed and cited as evidence for a hydrogen atom rather than a CH_3 radical shift in this rearrangement.[100]

2-13B-3   2-Butene

Cis-*trans* isomerization is the major primary process in the reaction of $Hg(^3P_1)$ atoms with either the *cis* or the *trans* 2-butene. Thus on prolonged irradiation of the *cis* isomer a 1:1 mixture of *trans* and *cis* results,[100,102] and at pressures above 30 mm $\varphi_{c-t} = \varphi_{t-c} = 0.5$. This reaction, as

Cundall[102,103] has suggested, shows promise as an actinometer in mercury-photosensitized reactions. Presumably it also occurs through an intermediate vibrationally excited triplet state. The photoisomerization can also be carried out with benzene and SO_2 as sensitizers.[102,*]

Mass spectrometric detection of the primary products formed in sensitized reactions in a fast-flow reactor shows that at low pressures both hydrogen atom and CH_3 radical cleavage occurs with *cis*-butene-2, but isomerization to the *trans* form is the major process.[104] Under similar reaction conditions the primary act of dissociation of isobutene is formation of β-methallyl radical and a hydrogen atom.[84]

2-13B-4 Other Photosensitized Reactions of the Olefins

Preliminary reports of the mercury-sensitized reactions of ethylene[70] and propylene[71] at 1849 A have appeared recently. In both cases the distribution of products differs from that obtained at 2537 A, and it is suggested that the primary act is formation of an excited molecule, presumably a singlet. Pertel[70] notes that the direct photolysis of C_2H_4 at 1849 A gives different products from the $Hg(^1P_1)$ sensitized reaction.

Five primary reactions of excited propylene at 1849 A are proposed by Heller and Gordon[71] to explain their products.

$$C_3H_6 + Hg(^1P_1) \rightarrow C_3H_6{}^* + Hg(^1S_0)$$

$$C_3H_6{}^* \rightarrow H + C_3H_5 \tag{1}$$

$$\rightarrow CH_3 + C_2H_3 \tag{2}$$

$$\rightarrow \text{cyclo-}C_3H_6 \tag{3}$$

$$\rightarrow CH_4 + C_2H_2 \tag{4}$$

$$\rightarrow H_2 + C_3H_4 \tag{5}$$

The extent of these primary reactions apparently varies with wavelength (2537 versus 1849 A) and with substitution of C_3D_6 for C_3H_6. Reactions 3-5 are very minor, and reaction 5 cannot be detected at 2537 A. At this time there is not enough information to decide whether the different product distributions at 1849 A for C_2H_4 and C_3H_6 relative to 2537 A are due to different reactivities of the excited states (singlet versus triplet) or to the 42 kcal/einstein difference in energy.

The products from the $Cd5(^1P_1)$ sensitized reaction differ significantly from those with $Hg(^3P_1)$ run under similar conditions,† and Arai and

---

* See Refs. 103 and 180 for excellent discussions of direct and sensitized *cis-trans* photoisomerizations by Cundall and Hammond *et al.*
† See the review to 1954 of Steacie.[38]

Shida[105] suggest that a different mechanism is involved, probably a direct dissociation:

$$Cd5(^1P_1) + C_2H_4 \rightarrow Cd5(^1S_0) + C_2H_3 + H$$
$$or \quad \rightarrow CdH + C_2H_3$$
$$\searrow$$
$$Cd + H$$

This seems reasonable, since formation of an excited triplet of C_2H_4 would violate the Wigner spin rule, and the first excited singlet of C_2H_4 lies well above the 125 kcal available from the $Cd5(^1P_1)$ line.

Very little quantitative work on sensitized reactions at elevated temperatures has been carried out since LeRoy and Steacie[91] showed in 1942 that the quantum yield of the ethylene reaction increases by a factor of 5-10 in going from 25° to 300°. Recently Arai and Shida[105] investigated the mercury $^3P_1$ and cadmium $^1P_1$ sensitized reactions of ethylene at 350°C. The major products with $Hg(^3P_1)$ atoms are the same as at 25°, and indeed the kinetics of the reaction fit quite well the Cvetanovic mechanism.[95]

2-13C   Cycloalkanes

With the exception of cyclopropane the cycloalkanes seem quite "clean" in their reactions. For example, in the $Hg(^3P_1)$-cyclopentane reaction at 24°, 107 mm pressure, and low percentage conversions Gunning *et al.*[106,107b] found that the reaction is solely free radical in nature; the only products are hydrogen, bicyclopentyl, and cyclopentene* with quantum yields of 0.8, 0.4, and 0.4, respectively. They were explained by a simple mechanism with the primary act being a direct C—H split. Similar mechanisms seem to apply to cyclobutane[108] and cyclohexane.[107a]

In studies of $Hg(^3P_1)$-cyclohexane mixtures over the range 60–400°C, Arai, Sato, and Shida (1960)[110] found that below 200° the major products are hydrogen, bicyclohexyl, and cyclohexene, in accord with Gunning *et al.*[107] Above 300° the ring ruptures, and products include propylene, methane, ethylene, ethane, butadiene, propane, and butene, presumably arising from decomposition of the cyclohexyl radical formed in the primary act. The quenching cross section of cyclohexane was estimated to be 1.9 A².

The cyclopropane-$Hg(^3P_1)$ reaction is particularly interesting in that cyclopropane itself is not polymerized by free radicals, yet a low-molecular-weight polymer has been reported as the major product of the

---

* It is interesting that the major product of the reaction of $Hg(^3P_1)$ atoms with cyclopentene is vinyl cyclopropane with a quantum yield of 0.24.[109]

photosensitized reaction;[111,112] many of its structural features were reported by Ivin (1956).[112] Subsequently, however, it was reported that with highly purified cyclopropane a solid polymer was produced.[113]

Recently Setser, Rabinowitch, and Spittler[114a] in a definitive experiment showed that significant *trans-cis* isomerization occurred at 25° and 65° with no change in the isotopic distribution when *trans*-cyclopropane-d_2 reacted with $Hg(^3P_1)$ atoms. Furthermore, added oxygen had no effect on the isomerization.[114b] They suggest that the polymerization aspect of the overall reaction went through a direct C—H split in a competing primary process and that subsequent reactions of the cyclopropyl radical and hydrogen atoms led to the polymer. Cvetanovic[37] suggests that by analogy with the olefins, where two excited states appear to be involved, the sole primary act with cyclopropane may be quenching to an excited triplet cyclopropane, a biradical. The latter could then recyclize, initiate polymerization, or dissociate into allyl + H atoms; in this way all kinetic and structural requirements seem to be met.[37]

2-13D   Other Hydrocarbons

The direct and mercury-photosensitized photolysis of cyclooctatetraene has been studied in detail by Yamazaki and Shida,[115,116] who find the major products to be acetylene, benzene, an orange liquid (possibly the bicyclo form of C_8H_8), a polymer, and a trace of styrene. The pressure dependence of the quantum yield ($\Phi_{C_8H_8} = 0.17$ and 0.10 at 2.5 and 5.0 mm Hg, respectively) suggests that in both the direct and the sensitized reaction an excited state, presumably a triplet, is involved. (It should be the triplet in the sensitized case to conserve spin.)

Benzene, just as in the direct photolysis, is stable toward decomposition in a mercury-sensitized reaction at 2537 A.[117,118] At 400°C, however, the major product, biphenyl, is formed with a quantum yield of about 0.1.[118] It appears that the primary act is excited molecule formation.

Toluene also is stable at ordinary temperatures ($\Phi_{H_2} = 5 \times 10^{-4}$ at 150°C), but at 400° appreciable reaction occurs, and Φ_{H_2} is about 0.1. Products include hydrogen, methane, and ethane; their pressure dependence, as in the case of benzene, also suggests that an excited molecule is formed in the primary act with an $Hg(^3P_1)$ atom.[119]

The main products from the mercury-photosensitized reaction of tetrafluoroethylene at 30° are hexafluorocyclopropane and polytetrafluoroethylene.[120] In contrast to the behavior of C_2H_4 (Sec. 2-13B-1) the quantum yields *increase* with pressure in the range 10–300 mm, suggesting that a relatively long-lived excited molecule is not involved. Atkinson proposes a primary split into CF_2 followed by addition to C_2F_4 to give the cyclopropyl compound or to initiate polymerization.

Some interesting results of $Hg(^3P_1)$ atom reactions with several acetylenes and diolefins are summarized below. When known, the primary acts and major products are given.

1,2-Butadiene[121]

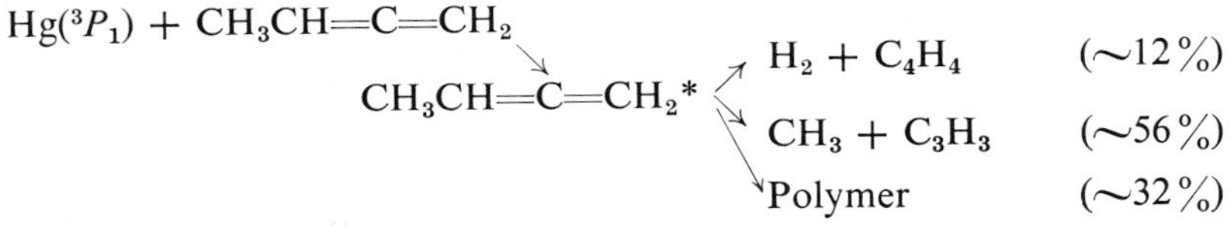

$$Hg(^3P_1) + CH_3CH{=}C{=}CH_2$$

$$CH_3CH{=}C{=}CH_2{}^*$$

$$\nearrow H_2 + C_4H_4 \qquad (\sim 12\%)$$
$$\searrow CH_3 + C_3H_3 \qquad (\sim 56\%)$$
$$\searrow Polymer \qquad (\sim 32\%)$$

1,3-Butadiene[121]

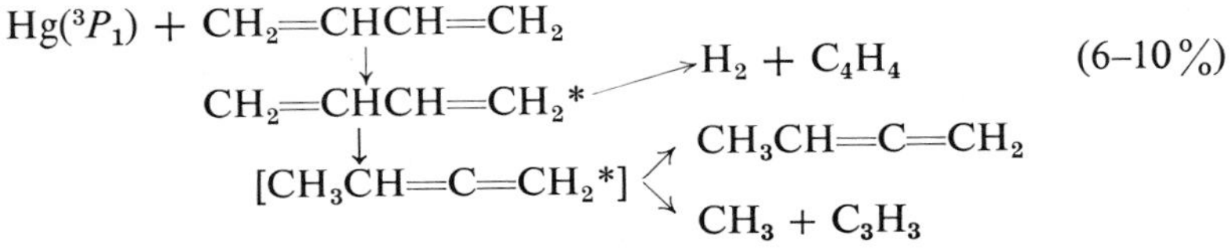

$$Hg(^3P_1) + CH_2{=}CHCH{=}CH_2$$
$$\downarrow$$
$$CH_2{=}CHCH{=}CH_2{}^*$$
$$\downarrow$$
$$[CH_3\dot{C}H{=}C{=}CH_2{}^*]$$

$$\rightarrow H_2 + C_4H_4 \qquad (6{-}10\%)$$
$$\nearrow CH_3CH{=}C{=}CH_2$$
$$\searrow CH_3 + C_3H_3$$

Acetylene[122–125]

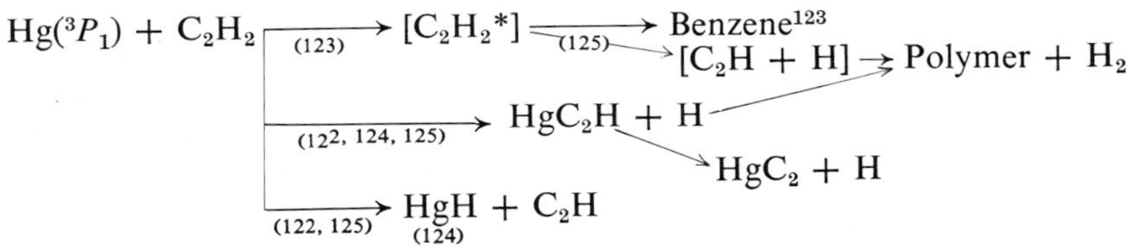

$$Hg(^3P_1) + C_2H_2$$

$$\xrightarrow[(123)]{} [C_2H_2{}^*] \xrightarrow[(125)]{} Benzene^{123}$$
$$\searrow [C_2H + H] \rightarrow Polymer + H_2$$
$$\xrightarrow[(122,\ 124,\ 125)]{} HgC_2H + H$$
$$\searrow HgC_2 + H$$
$$\xrightarrow[(122,\ 125)]{} HgH + C_2H$$
$$(124)$$

Methyl acetylene[125]

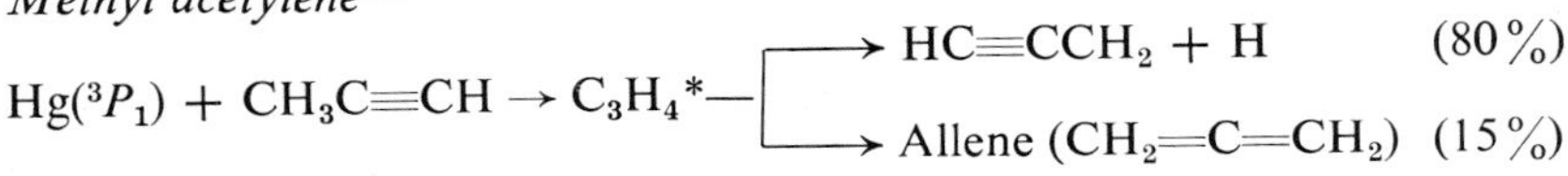

$$Hg(^3P_1) + CH_3C{\equiv}CH \rightarrow C_3H_4{}^*$$

$$\rightarrow HC{\equiv}CCH_2 + H \qquad (80\%)$$
$$\rightarrow Allene\ (CH_2{=}C{=}CH_2)\ (15\%)$$

1-Butyne[125]

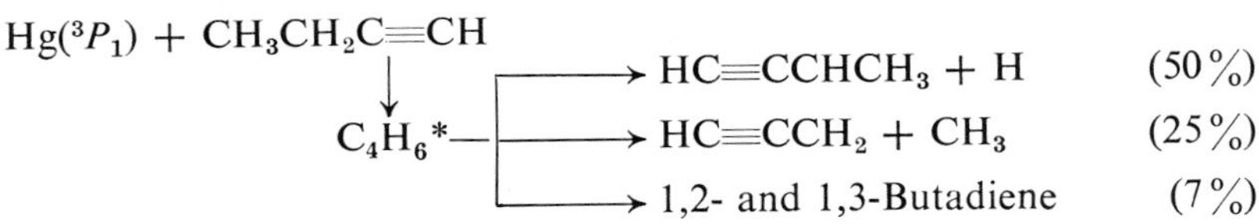

$$Hg(^3P_1) + CH_3CH_2C{\equiv}CH$$
$$\downarrow$$
$$C_4H_6{}^*$$

$$\rightarrow HC{\equiv}CCHCH_3 + H \qquad (50\%)$$
$$\rightarrow HC{\equiv}CCH_2 + CH_3 \qquad (25\%)$$
$$\rightarrow 1{,}2{-}\ and\ 1{,}3{-}Butadiene \qquad (7\%)$$

The quantum yield of acetylene disappearance is much less than that of either methyl acetylene or 1-butyne.[125]

Mercury-sensitized reactions of paraffins have been run on a relatively large scale to investigate the process as a possible commercial means of producing branched alkanes or olefins of higher molecular weight. Generally the reactions are run in a flow system in the range from room temperature to 400°C. Some typical results are these: 98% *n*-butane $\xrightarrow{\text{Hg}(^3P_1)}$ "liquid hydrocarbon" at an energy consumption rate of 3.15 kw/lb;[126] propane and isobutane in a 3.4:1 mole ratio $\xrightarrow[135°C]{\text{Hg}(^3P_1)}$ 36.5% 2,2,3-trimethyl butane, 18.0% 2,2,3,3-tetramethyl butane, and 16.5% 2,3-dimethyl butane;[127] *n*-butane gave a maximum yield of olefins in the C_6-C_{12} (average C_8) range under the following conditions: 2400 watt Hg pool source, intensity at cell 0.1 watt/cm², 315°C, and exposure time 3 sec.[128]

Mercury-photosensitized oxidations are important, in part because of their relationship to the mechanism of combustion. However, space limitations prevent their discussion here; the excellent monograph of Minkoff and Tipper[129] treats the subject in some detail and provides original literature references. The papers of Nalbandyan *et al.*,[130] on mercury-sensitized oxidations of the simple alkanes are an example of a significant long-term study in this area.

2-14 ORGANIC OXYGEN-CONTAINING COMPOUNDS

The quantitative aspects of this broad area have not been extensively studied. We have selected several interesting systems to discuss, with no effort to be comprehensive in our coverage.

2-14A Aliphatic Alcohols

Two processes have been proposed for the primary act between $Hg(^3P_1)$ atoms and the simple alcohols:

$$CH_3OH + Hg(^3P_1) \rightarrow CH_2OH + H + Hg(^1S_0) \qquad (1)$$

$$\rightarrow CH_3O + H + Hg(^1S_0) \qquad (2)$$

Two quite different and independent sets of experiments show that process 2 is the major if not the exclusive one. Thus, Pottie, Harrison, and Lossing[131] photolyzed at low pressures a mixture of CD_3OH and $(CD_3)_2Hg$, the latter being used as a source of CD_3 radicals to trap CD_2OH or CD_3O radicals formed by process 1 or 2. The product was CD_3OCD_3, confirming the dominance of primary process 2.

Concurrently Knight and Gunning[132] carried out a series of quantitative experiments with the simple alcohols over a range of normal pressures and under a variety of conditions, including intermittent illumination with short flashes of light. The latter approach was designed to reduce the average concentration of radicals and to minimize the recombination reaction

$H + R \rightarrow RH$, where $R = H$, CH_3O, or CH_2OH, thus increasing H_2 formation. Presumably a limiting value of Φ_{H_2} would be approached at low pressures and would equal φ, the primary quantum yield of the process. Nitric oxide in trace amounts was also used in some cases to trap radicals formed in the primary act. The results are excellent evidence for process 2 being the major primary act. Initial quantum yields of hydrogen for the sensitized decomposition of methanol, ethanol, and isopropanol are 0.89, 0.96, and 1.0, respectively, while the overall quantum yields of H_2 after irradiation are 0.46, 0.53, and 0.72. The 50% larger value of Φ_{H_2} from isopropanol is reasonable because of the significantly weaker bond strength of the secondary hydrogen atom, thus facilitating abstraction by hydrogen atoms produced in the primary process. Other products are consistent with this mechanism when effects due to secondary reactions of $Hg(^3P_1)$ atoms with the products are considered.

2-14B   Aldehydes, Ketones, and Acids

In the first application of the mass spectrometric technique for the detection of free radicals from $Hg(^3P_1)$ sensitized processes, Lossing et al.[133,134] showed that the major primary process of acetone was a C—C split into $CH_3 + CH_3CO$ radicals, the same as in direct photolysis. The sensitized reaction was used by Moseley and Robb[135] to generate CH_3 radicals (at elevated temperatures, $CH_3CO \rightarrow CH_3 + CO$) for their interesting technique of direct determination of rate constants of radical recombinations.

Under the conditions similar to those with acetone, Lossing[134] found that acetaldehyde dissociated with at least 95% efficiency into CH_3 (and presumably CHO) radicals, reaction 1. This is comparable to its behavior in direct photolysis at 3130 A. However, in direct photolysis, iodine-scavenging techniques suggested that at 2537 A about 50% of the reaction went by the intramolecular process 2.

$$CH_3 + CHO \qquad (1)$$
$$CH_3CHO + h\nu \text{ (direct)} \nearrow \qquad $$
$$\searrow CH_4 + CO \qquad (2)$$

A possible explanation for the absence of process 2 in the sensitized reaction is that process 1 arises from an excited triplet state reached by intersystem crossing whereas 2 involves direct decomposition from the excited singlet state; this is not available by triplet energy transfer from $Hg(^3P_1)$ atoms to acetaldehyde.

The primary processes of several other aldehydes and ketones as established by the mass spectrometric technique are given below. References to the original work are in parentheses.

$$\text{Hg}(^3P_1) + \text{HCHO} \quad \underset{(136a)}{} \quad \begin{array}{l} \xrightarrow{40\%} \text{H}_2 + \text{CO} \\[1em] \xrightarrow{60\%} \text{HCO} + \text{H} \end{array}$$

$$\text{Hg}(^3P_1) + \underset{(136b)}{\text{CH}_3\overset{\text{O}}{\overset{\|}{\text{C}}}\overset{\text{O}}{\overset{\|}{\text{C}}}\text{CH}_3} \xrightarrow{100\%} 2\text{CH}_3\text{CO}$$

The products from the biacetyl-Hg* system are CO, CH_3COCH_3, CH_2CO, C_2H_6, and CH_4. At high light intensities $\text{Hg}(^3S_1)$ atoms formed by stepwise excitation react with biacetyl to form B**, which reacts with another B**, 2B** → B + products.

$$\text{Hg}(^3P_1) + \underset{(136b)}{\text{CH}_3\overset{\text{O}}{\overset{\|}{\text{C}}}\text{CH}_2\overset{\text{O}}{\overset{\|}{\text{C}}}\text{CH}_3} \rightarrow$$
$$\{\text{CH}_3,\ \text{CH}_3\text{CO},\ \text{CH}_2\text{COCH}_3,\ \text{CH}_2\text{CO},\ \text{CH}_3\text{COCH}_3\}$$

$$\text{Hg}(^3P_1) + \underset{(136b)}{\text{CH}_3\overset{\text{O}}{\overset{\|}{\text{C}}}\text{CH}_2\text{CH}_2\overset{\text{O}}{\overset{\|}{\text{C}}}\text{CH}_3} \rightarrow \text{CH}_3\text{CO} + \text{C}_2\text{H}_4\text{COCH}_3$$
$$\searrow \text{CH}_3\overset{\cdot}{\text{C}}\text{H}\overset{\text{O}}{\overset{\|}{\text{C}}}\text{CH}_3$$

$$\text{Hg}(^3P_1) + \underset{(136c)}{\text{H}_2\text{C}=\text{CHCHO}} \quad \begin{array}{l} \xrightarrow{\text{major}} \text{H}_2\text{C}=\text{CH}_2 + \text{CO} \\[0.8em] \xrightarrow{\text{minor}} \text{H}_2\text{C}=\text{CH} + \text{CHO} \\[0.8em] \xrightarrow{\text{minor}} \text{H}_2\text{C}=\text{CHCO} + \text{H} \end{array}$$

$$\text{Hg}(^3P_1) + \underset{(136c)}{\text{CH}_3\text{CH}=\text{CHCHO}} \quad \begin{array}{l} \xrightarrow{\text{major}} \text{CH}_3\text{CH}=\text{CH}_2 + \text{CO} \\[0.8em] \xrightarrow{\text{minor}} \text{CH}_3\text{CH}=\text{CH} + \text{CHO} \\[0.8em] \xrightarrow{\text{minor}} \text{CH}_3\text{CH}=\text{CHCO} + \text{H} \end{array}$$

$$\text{Hg}(^3P_1) + \underset{(136c)}{\left\langle\!\!\bigcirc\!\!\right\rangle\!-\!\overset{\text{O}}{\overset{\|}{\text{C}}}\text{H}} \quad \begin{array}{l} \xrightarrow{\text{major}} \text{Polymer} \\[0.8em] \xrightarrow{\text{minor}} \text{C}_6\text{H}_6 + \text{CO} \\[0.8em] \xrightarrow{\text{minor}} \text{C}_6\text{H}_5 + \text{CHO} \end{array}$$

$$\text{Hg}(^3P_1) + \underset{\substack{(137) \\ (A)}}{\left\langle\!\!\bigcirc\!\!\right\rangle\!-\!\text{OCH}_3} \xrightarrow[\substack{\text{primary} \\ \text{dissociation}}]{\text{Exclusive}} \left\langle\!\!\bigcirc\!\!\right\rangle\!-\!\text{O} + \text{CH}_3$$

In the latter reaction polymer also was formed, possibly by A* → polymer. A yield of 0.6–0.7 was obtained for the formation of methyl radicals per molecule of A decomposed. An interesting process was noted; addition of CD_3 to the ring followed by hydrogen transfer to the oxygen atom may occur.

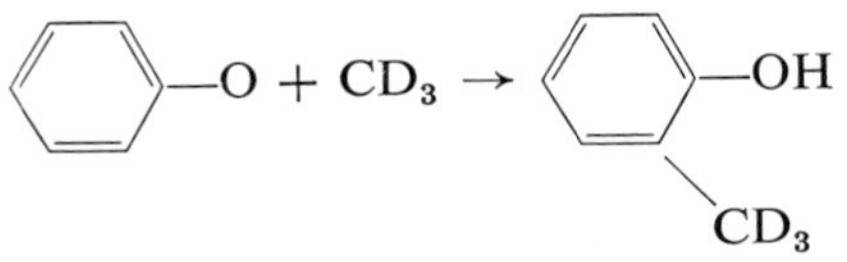

A fascinating example of the possibilities of employing sensitized reactions with more complex molecules is afforded by Srinivasan's[138] study of norcamphor (I) at 80°. Some runs were carried out on a "preparative" scale, that is, 1–5 grams in a 2-liter flask. The structures of the

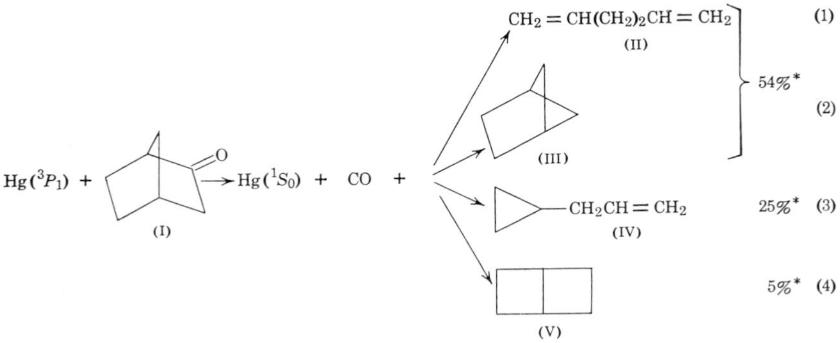

products of the reaction are shown above; (II) = 1,5-hexadiene; (III) = bicyclo[2.1.1]hexane (8–10%);† (IV) = allyl cyclopropane (7–8%);† (V) = bicyclo[2.2.0]hexane (1–2%).† Processes 1 and 2 are the important modes of direct photolysis of norcamphor.[138] These are also important in the sensitized reaction, but the interesting processes 3 and 4 also occur. In fact, Srinivasan points out that, despite its low yield, reaction 4 was at that time (1961) the most convenient synthetic route to bicyclo[2.2.0]-hexane.

The process producing allyl cyclopropane was shown to proceed through an excited intermediate by using deuterium-labeled norcamphor in sensitized reactions 3a and 3b, and demonstrating that two allyl cyclopropane-d_2's were formed in about equal amounts.[138b]

---

* Indicates the percentage of the carbon monoxide yield.
† Indicates the preparative yield, not the quantum yield.

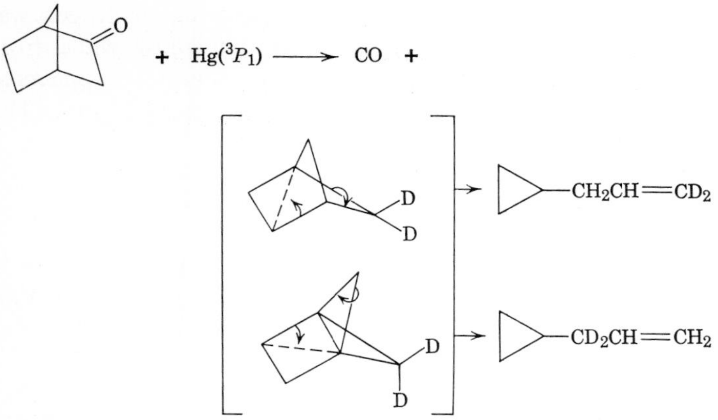

Formic acid is an interesting case; the results obtained by Kebarle and Lossing (1959), using the mass spectrometer for detection of products,[139] were in excellent agreement with those of Bates and Taylor (1927)[140] carried out in a conventional system some thirty years earlier. Only two intramolecular processes occurred, in the ratio of about $R_1/R_2 = 3/1$.

$$\mathrm{HCOOH + Hg(^3P_1)} \Big\langle \begin{array}{l} \nearrow\ \mathrm{CO + H_2O + Hg(^1S_0)} \qquad\qquad (1) \\ \searrow\ \mathrm{CO_2 + H_2 + Hg(^1S_0)} \qquad\qquad (2) \end{array}$$

In considering the status of mercury-sensitized reactions of carbonyl compounds Cvetanovic[37] reaches the conclusion that the primary act is triplet-triplet energy transfer to form an excited molecule, probably a vibrationally excited triplet. In this sense the carbonyl compounds are analogous to the olefins.

2-14C Ethers

Only a limited amount of work has been carried out on the mercury-sensitized reactions of the ethers and epoxides. As an example of the complexity of the system Cvetanovic and Doyle[141] found as products from butylene oxide (*trans*-2,3-epoxybutane), isobutanal, C_2H_6, CO, C_2H_4, C_3H_8, CH_3CHO, C_2H_5CHO, $CH_3COC_2H_5$, CH_4, and H_2. Its quenching cross section is 19 A^2 relative to 3.6 A^2 for *n*-butane.

Many reaction products are produced in the ethylene oxide-$Hg(^3P_1)$ reaction;[142,143] they include CO, H_2, C_2H_6, CH_2CO, C_2H_4, and various aldehydes.[143] However, the overall decomposition is similar to that obtained from direct photolysis and pyrolysis. The quantum yield of hydrogen is 0.22. By the photosensitized reaction of a 1:1 mixture of

C_2D_4O-C_2H_4O it was shown that a small fraction of the hydrogen was formed in an intramolecular primary process, but most came from hydrogen atom attack on the substrate. The major primary act appears to be excited molecule formation followed by dissociation into CH_3 and CHO radicals.

2-15   INORGANIC COMPOUNDS

Quenching cross sections for several inorganic compounds are given in Table 2-3. Here we shall consider briefly several cases in which quantitative studies have been reported.

2-15A   Nitrous Oxide

One of the most useful examples of mercury-photosensitized reactions is that of N_2O, first followed with manometric techniques by Manning and Noyes (1932).[144] Products were N_2 and HgO, and they proposed either (a) or (b) as the primary process but favored (a):

$$Hg(^3P_1) + N_2O \rightarrow N_2(^1\Sigma) + O(^3P) + Hg(^1S_0) \qquad \text{(a)}$$
$$\rightarrow NO(^2\Pi) + N(^4S) + Hg(^1S_0) \qquad \text{(b)}$$

In 1955 Cvetanovic[47] reinvestigated the reaction and at small conversions found the products to be almost exclusively nitrogen and oxygen in the ratio $2:1$ with $\Phi_{N_2} = 0.8$; thus the primary act must be (a).

Reaction (a) has been widely used as a "clean" source of triplet oxygen atoms for kinetic and mechanistic studies of oxygen atom reactions (see Ref. 68) and also as a means of chemically determining relative rate constants (see Table 2-3 and Ref. 37).

Hoffman and Bernstein[145] have reported interesting kinetic studies of the reaction of $Hg(^3P_1)$ atoms with isotopically labeled N_2O. They find that the relative rates of quenching are $^{14}N^{14}N^{18}O \simeq {}^{14}N^{14}N^{16}O > {}^{14}N^{15}N^{16}O > {}^{15}N^{14}N^{16}O$. Theoretical treatment of the results, however, is complex.

2-15B   Nitric Oxide

The reaction of $^3P_1$ mercury atoms with NO was first investigated by Noyes (1931),[146] who determined that the rate was first order in both intensity and nitric oxide pressure (0.003–0.13 mm range) and suggested on the basis of his kinetic data that the primary act was formation of a long-lived vibrationally excited molecule. Since then the system has been studied by several investigators with conflicting results (see Refs. 32 and

147). Strausz and Gunning[147] carried out a detailed study, under static conditions, over the pressure range 1–286 mm. Major products were N_2 and N_2O (previously unreported) and higher oxides of nitrogen, with $\Phi_{N_2+N_2O} = 1.9 \times 10^{-3}$. The ratio Φ_{N_2O}/Φ_{N_2} varied from 0.050 at 10 mm NO to 0.50 at 120 mm, but at $p > 4$ mm the sum $\Phi_{N_2} + \Phi_{N_2O} =$ constant. An excellent kinetic fit of the data is obtained if the primary act is assumed to be triplet quenching to form electronically excited NO* (presumably in the $^4\Pi$ state[148]). This species either may be deactivated by collision with another NO molecule or may form the excited dimer $(NO)_2$*. This in turn either dissociates giving N_2 and O_2 (consumed in the reaction) or reacts with NO to give $N_2O + NO_2$.

$$\text{NO* + NO} \longrightarrow \begin{cases} \longrightarrow 2\text{NO} \\ \longrightarrow (\text{NO})_2\text{*} \end{cases} \longrightarrow \begin{cases} \longrightarrow N_2 + O_2 \\ \xrightarrow{+\text{NO}} N_2O + NO_2 \end{cases}$$

2-15C   Oxygen

The formation of ozone and HgO by the reaction of $Hg(^3P_1)$ atoms and oxygen was first reported by Dickinson and Sherrill (1926).[149] Volman[150] has reported values as large as 60 molecules of O_3 formed per atom of mercury passing through the reaction zone when a flow system is used. In a static system Callear, Patrick, and Robb[151] report $\Phi_{O_3} = 0.14$ at oxygen pressures below 200 mm. They propose that O_3 attacks mercury in a dark reaction.

Although it is agreed that the products are O_3 and HgO, there is a spirited controversy over the nature of the primary act of energy transfer from excited mercury to the oxygen molecule. The following primary processes should be considered:

$$Hg(^3P_1) + O_2(^3\Sigma_g^-) \longrightarrow \begin{cases} \longrightarrow Hg(^1S_0) + 2O(^3P); \quad \Delta H = 5.5 \text{ kcal} \quad (1) \\ \longrightarrow HgO(g) + O(^3P); \quad \Delta H = -87 + \lambda \quad (2) \\ \longrightarrow Hg(^1S_0) + O_2\text{*} \quad (3) \\ \longrightarrow (Hg\cdot O_2)\text{*} \quad (4) \end{cases}$$

The first three are discussed in the following terms by Volman in his review article:[152]

Reaction 1 is sufficiently endothermic that only one collision in 10^4 may be effective. Thus, since the quantum yield of O_3 lies in the range 0.03[153] to 0.14[151] and chains are not involved, reaction 1 must be unimportant.

While process 2 is exothermic, the extent depending on the value of the heat of sublimation λ (estimated < 23 kcal[152]), solid HgO is formed and mercury removed from the reaction zone. Since at least 60 atoms of O_3 are formed per mercury atom entering the reaction zone of the flow reactor, if process 2 is to be significant mercury must be regenerated by reaction with O_2, and the following reaction has been suggested:

$$HgO(g) + O_2 \rightarrow Hg + O_3; \quad \Delta H = 68 - \lambda \qquad (5)$$

However, if the heat of sublimation λ is 23 kcal or less, as seems likely, reaction 5 will be highly endothermic, and thus 2 seems an unlikely primary process. Furthermore, Volman cites the fact that Pertel and Gunning (1959)[154] reported no isotopic enrichment in ^{202}HgO when the radiation source was a ^{202}Hg monoisotopic resonance lamp. This seems to be strong evidence against primary process 2, but, as we shall see, in later work a large enrichment of the HgO was found in this system.

Finally, the effects of foreign gases were studied in the sensitized reaction at 2537 A and the direct photolysis at 1849 A.[150,153] The relative O_3 yields drop in the order 1.0, 0.6, 0.6, and 0.4 for He, Ar, Ne, and CO_2, and Volman suggests that the added gases deactivate the excited oxygen formed in primary process 3 before it can undergo the proposed secondary ozone-generating reactions,

$$O_2{}^* + O_2 \rightarrow O_3 + O$$
$$O_2{}^* + M \rightarrow O_2 + M^*$$
$$O + O_2 + M \rightarrow O_3 + M$$
$$O_3 + Hg \rightarrow HgO + O_2$$

Since the HgO is formed in a secondary process, no isotopic enrichment in ^{202}HgO would be expected. Thus, Volman[152] concludes that 3 is the major primary process, as do Callear, Patrick, and Robb,[151] and notes that several possible states of the excited molecule have been proposed.[155,156]

Recently, however, Gunning and Strausz[15] reported that, with $^{202}Hg(^3P_1)$ sensitization of oxygen-butadiene mixtures, mercuric oxides containing 88–95% ^{202}Hg were recovered; they point out this "would militate against the significance of any isotopic exchange reactions, at least in the HgO process." This significant result was not available to Volman at the time of his review article, in fact, the opposite result had been reported and accepted. It opens up the possibility of process 4, formation of the excited "complex" $(Hg \cdot O_2)^*$, being a likely primary process, as it could lead to isotopic enrichment of the ultimate product HgO.

The idea of forming an unstable excited species $HgO_2{}^*$ in the primary process was originally proposed by Chen[157] in 1957 and subsequently advanced also by Desnoyer et al.[31] Presumably the "complex" dissociates in a quenching reaction to form O_3 and HgO.

Clearly the situation is unresolved, but it would seem that the sequence

$$Hg(^3P_1) + O_2 \rightarrow (Hg \cdot O_2)^*$$
$$(Hg \cdot O_2)^* + M \rightarrow Hg + O_2 + M$$
$$(Hg \cdot O_2)^* + O_2 \rightarrow HgO + O_3$$

might be consistent with both the inert-gas kinetic results of Volman and the isotopic enrichment studies of Gunning et al.

2-15D   Water

The quantum yield of the reaction of $Hg(^3P_1)$ atoms with water vapor is low, increasing from 0.02 at 45° to 0.04 at 580°C,[158] with the reaction products being H_2, O_2, and HgO. No H_2O_2 has been reported as found in the sensitized reaction in flow systems,[159] in contrast to the direct photolysis, where it is produced in flow systems but not static systems. However, in view of the analytical problems and the low overall efficiency of the reaction small amounts of H_2O_2 might be formed but not detected.[152]

The $Hg(^3P_1)$-H_2O reaction has been widely studied by the monoisotopic sensitization technique,[30] and up to 85% enrichment of ^{202}Hg in the HgO has been reported (see Refs. 15, 37, and 153 for reviews and discussion). However, there is no general agreement on the major primary process, although formation of the excited complex $(Hg \cdot H_2O)^*$ in the initial act has been suggested.[31] Presumably it could be deactivated or could dissociate by several paths to give the observed products and still retain isotopic specificity in the HgO.

2-15E   Carbon Dioxide

The mercury-sensitized reaction of CO_2 at 2537 A is particularly interesting because despite its low quantum yield ($\Phi_{CO} < 0.01$) the rate depends on the *square* of the light intensity; this is quite unique in atom-sensitized reactions. On the basis of this observation and their kinetic studies under a variety of conditions Strausz and Gunning[160] suggest the following mechanism, the key step of which is the bimolecular reaction of electronically excited triplet CO_2^* with a mercury atom in its $^3P_1$ or $^3P_0$ state:

$$Hg(^1S_0) + h\nu \ (2537 \ A) \rightarrow Hg(^3P_1) \tag{1}$$
$$Hg(^3P_1) + CO_2 \rightarrow CO_2^* + Hg(^1S_0) \tag{2}$$
$$CO_2^* + CO_2 \rightarrow 2CO_2 \tag{3}$$
$$CO_2^* + Hg(^3P_1) \rightarrow CO + O + Hg(^1S_0) \tag{4}$$
$$O + Hg \rightarrow HgO \ (s) \tag{5}$$

There was no significant isotopic enrichment of the HgO formed in the reaction; hence the possible primary process

$$CO_2 + Hg(^3P_1) \rightarrow CO + HgO$$

was ruled out. The C-O bond-dissociation energy in CO_2 is 126.7 kcal, so that CO_2^* must possess at least 14.5 kcal energy (126.7 − 112.2) for reaction 4 to occur.

An interesting effect was noted when mixtures of CO_2 and Hg plus added nitrogen were illuminated at 2537 A and simultaneously irradiated with 4047 A light. The rate of CO production increased by as much as a factor of 1.58 when 7.4 mm of N_2 was added to 3.74 mm CO_2.[160] This might be attributed to the sequence

$$Hg6(^1S_0) + h\nu \; (2537 \; A) \rightarrow Hg6(^3P_1)$$

$$Hg6(^3P_1) + N_2 \qquad\qquad \rightarrow Hg6(^3P_0) + N_2'$$

$$Hg6(^3P_0) + h\nu \; (4047 \; A) \rightarrow Hg7(^3S_1)$$

after which the $Hg7(^3S_1)$ atom (or an excited decay product) could dissociate CO_2 or CO_2^*. The latter is speculative, but the effect is real and is being investigated further.[160]

We should note that Mori[161] found that the $Hg(^1P_1)$ sensitized reaction of CO_2 at 1849 A also was an inefficient process although there is no energy deficiency here.

2-15F   Ammonia

The mercury-sensitized decomposition of ammonia has been widely studied. In a static system the products are hydrogen and nitrogen, but with a fast-flow system McDonald and Gunning[162] found hydrazine as a major product. The quantum yield of consumption of ammonia increased from 0.09 at 650 mm to close to unity as $p \rightarrow 0$, while the preparative yield of hydrazine (molecules N_2H_4/molecules NH_3 decomposed) went from zero in the static system to 95% at fast flow rates. There seems little doubt that the primary act is

$$Hg(^3P_1) + NH_3 \rightarrow NH_2 + H + Hg(^1S_0)$$

or $$\qquad\qquad\qquad \rightarrow NH_2 + HgH$$

This is followed by a series of secondary reactions of NH_2 radicals and hydrogen atoms.

2-15G   Monoisotopic Sensitization

The technique of monoisotopic sensitization has led to useful information concerning the primary act in mercury sensitization of a variety of compounds, including HCl and various alkyl chlorides[163] (see Sec. 6-5). These systems will not be reviewed here, as they have been well covered by Gunning and Strausz[15] and Cvetanovic.[37] We should note, however, that in mercuric oxide-forming reactions (e.g., $^{202}Hg(^3P_1) + H_2O$, N_2O, etc.) a primary act in which ^{202}HgO is formed directly is very inefficient. However, with HCl and the n-alkyl chlorides, calomel (HgCl) is formed in a one-step primary act with a quantum yield of about 0.3. Other substituted alkyl chlorides (e.g., fluorine substituted) have primary yields less than or equal to 0.3, depending on the structure.[15]

2-15H   Inorganic Hydrocarbon Analogs

The silicon hydrides are analogous to the paraffin hydrocarbons, but with the important difference, in terms of mercury-photosensitized reactions, that the analogs of the olefins do not exist. Hence in some respects the system $Hg(^3P_1)$ + silanes is simpler; in others it is more complex (for example, a polymer forms readily with monosilane). Recently studies of the reaction of $Hg(^3P_1)$ atoms with monosilane[164,165] and the methyl silanes[165] have been reported; quenching cross sections are included.[165c]

Products from $SiH_4 + Hg(^3P_1)$ include hydrogen, disilane, and trisilane with quantum yields of about 1.8, 0.6, and 0.06, respectively, plus polymeric silicon hydride. Primary processes have not been established conclusively, as yet. However, the direct split into $SiH_3 + H$ is favored. Niki and Mains[164] state that the reaction $H + SiH_4$ appears very rapid and suggest that monosilane may find use as a hydrogen atom scavenger.

In a parallel study Rousseau and Mains[166] report that at 25° the reaction of $Hg(^3P_1)$ atoms with monogermane gives hydrogen, digermane, trigermane, tetragermane, and a polymer. Hydrogen and Ge_2H_6 are the main products at low conversion ($\Phi_{H_2} \sim 1.0$). The proposed mechanism, based in part on mixed photolysis of GeH_4 and GeD_4, includes the primary act

$$GeH_4 + Hg(^3P_1) \rightarrow GeH_3 + H + Hg(^1S_0)$$

This is analogous to the one suggested for monosilane.

Studies by Gunning and co-workers of the $Hg(^3P_1)$ reactions with a series of substituted methyl silanes[165] show that the primary act is exclusively Si-H bond scission or, if no Si-H bonds are present, C-H bond cleavage. The quenching efficiency of the Si-H bond is 10–500 times that of a C-H bond, but the order of effectiveness is in the same sequence as with the C-H bonds: tertiary > secondary > primary > H_3Si-H. All the substrates yielded hydrogen and the dimer of the radical formed in the primary act, and at higher conversions $Hg(^3P_1)$ attack on the dimer became significant. It is interesting that temperature up to 420°C had no effect on the quantum yield values of the trimethyl silane reaction, but the efficiency of the primary C-H split relative to the Si-H split increased. There was no temperature effect on the $(CH_3)_2SiH_2$ system up to 240°C.

Mercury-photosensitized processes in the system diborane-$Hg(^3P_1)$ were reported by Hirata and Gunning.[167] The products are hydrogen and tetraborane with initial yields of 0.50 and 0.25, respectively; long irradiation led to extensive decomposition and formation of solid products.

To summarize, it appears that the silicon, germanium, and boron analogs of the paraffins undergo the analogous primary reaction with $Hg(^3P_1)$ atoms, splitting off of a hydrogen atom with the generation of a radical. However, the major fate of these is dimerization; polymerization occurs, but apparently not disproportionation.

2-16   SENSITIZED REACTIONS IN CONDENSED MEDIA

To date, experimental problems have limited the quantitative study of mercury-sensitized reactions in solution, and only a few investigations have been reported. The first quantitative study was on the system mercury-decane. Mercury is relatively soluble in decane; however, its 2537 Å resonance absorption spectrum is no longer a line. It is a wide band because of extreme pressure broadening; Stark effect splitting divides the maximum into two peaks (see Fig. 2-13).

Phibbs and Darwent (1950)[168] studied the sensitized reaction to see whether energy transfer from $Hg(^3P_1)$ atoms to the solvent could lead to chemical quenching and give products similar to the gas phase. They found hydrogen and eicosanes ($C_{20}H_{42}$) as products, with Φ_{H_2} rising from 0.1 at 0°C to 0.45 at 134°C. In the gas phase at 120° the same products were formed but $\Phi_{H_2} = 0.51$. No decenes were found, but in view of subsequent mercury-photosensitized studies of the alkanes in the vapor and liquid it seems that self-scavenging of hydrogen atoms occurred and reduced the olefin yield to a value not detectable by techniques available in 1950. However, clearly the mercury-sensitized reaction did occur in solution, and the primary process appeared to be the same as in the vapor:

$$Hg(^3P_1) + C_{10}H_{22} \rightarrow Hg(^1S_0) + C_{10}H_{21} + H$$

or
$$\rightarrow C_{10}H_{21} + HgH$$

A detailed study with a variety of alkanes has been reported by Kuntz and Mains[169] (see this for reference to earlier work). In parallel to their photochemistry study they investigated methods of determining the solubility of mercury in hydrocarbons.[170] The optical density at 2560 A proved to be a reliable measure of the solubility, and the molecular extinction coefficient in n-hexane was found to be $\epsilon = 7.35 \times 10^3$ liters/mole/cm. Hildebrand's equation for solubility of regular solutions could also be used to estimate the solubilities in various solvents. Products of the $Hg(^3P_1)$ reaction in solution include hydrogen, parent olefin, and parent dimer; no C-C bond scission was observed. Quantum yields of hydrogen production were approximately unity, indicating complete chemical quenching of the $Hg(^3P_1)$ atoms. In hydrocarbons with only secondary and primary hydrogen atoms the quantum yield of olefin was about 0.4; the presence of tertiary hydrogen atoms increases the quantum yield of olefin.

The mechanism is apparently similar to that in the vapor phase, that is, C-H bond scission in the primary act. However, some kinetic evidence has been obtained for the formation of a mercury complex in a primary process, and it is suggested that a small fraction (1/2000) of the primary acts go through formation of HgH, which is presumably partially stabilized in solution.

The complications resulting from trace contaminants which combine with mercury in solution are clearly set forth. With the low solubility of mercury in these solutions any mercury-removing impurities drastically alter the fraction of light absorbed, and this is reflected in the value of Φ.

Recently the photosensitized decomposition of hydrocarbons and alcohols in the solid phase has been reported by Voevodskii et al.[171]

2-17 SENSITIZATION BY THE RARE GASES

While it is clearly possible to sensitize reactions by the excited rare gases, their resonance lines fall into the vacuum ultraviolet (see Table 2-5 for wavelengths and energies), and the experimental techniques are more difficult. Thus to date there are few quantitative data in this area, although several interesting qualitative studies have been reported. (Reference 172 gives a recent review of vacuum ultraviolet photochemistry by McNesby and Okabe.)

Xenon and krypton have pairs of resonance lines at 1469.6 and 1295.6 A and 1235.8 and 1164.9 A, respectively. Actually each of these lines is a doublet with splitting about 0.1 ev in each case. Radiative transitions to the ground state from each of these lower states is forbidden. As with the $Hg(^3P_1)$-$Hg(^3P_0)$ states, the lower level is metastable and will become populated by collisional deactivation of the emitting resonance state.

However, the reverse process, collisional reactivation from the metastable to the allowed state, is more favorable than with mercury because the energy difference is only 0.1 ev versus 0.22 ev (Sec. 2-9C). Probably at room temperature there will be a significant population of the long-lived metastable states of krypton and xenon which could participate, along with atoms in the allowed resonance state, in sensitized reactions. However, the relative reactivities of rare gas atoms in the two states are not known, and one cannot assume *a priori* that because of their nearly equal energies they will be the same, since we saw in Sec. 2-9C that metastable $Hg(^3P_0)$ atoms are much less reactive than those in the $^3P_1$ state. It may be that in addition to spin conservation other "optical" selection rules (e.g., $J = 0 \leftrightarrow J = 0$) play a role in the efficiency of atom-molecule electronic energy transfer.

Among the first and most interesting of the rare-gas-sensitized processes cited to date is the krypton-photosensitized dissociation of nitrogen reported by Groth,[173,174] the pioneer of vacuum ultraviolet photochemistry. When molecular hydrogen is present, products include ammonia and hydrazine. Subsequently he found that the mercury-sensitized reactions of a gaseous mixture of C_2H_6, NH_3, and H_2O yielded small amounts of glycine, alanine, and sarcosine as well as higher amino acids and polymers. Similar products were found with NH_3, CH_4, and H_2O mixtures photolyzed directly at high pressures with 1470 and 1295 A resonance radiation and at 1235 and 1165 A at low pressures. In view of the possibility of an original reducing atmosphere on the primitive earth the possible role of such reactions furnishes interesting speculation.[175]

An example of xenon photosensitization is the formation of a solid product and fluorine from irradiation of CF_4-Xe mixtures with the Xe 1470 resonance line. No reaction was observed by Dacey and Hodgins[176] with mercury sensitization at 1849 (155 kcal) and 2537 A (113 kcal). It was also observed that hydrogen atoms produced from $Hg6(^3P_1)$ or $6(^1P_1)$ states did not react with CF_4.

The rare-gas-sensitized ionization of several oxygenated compounds and of NO has been detected by the ion current measurements of Tanaka and McNesby.[177,178]

Recently the Lyman resonance line was used by Tanaka and McNesby[177] to excite hydrogen atoms to their ^2P state:

$$H(^2S) + h\nu \ (1215 \ A) \rightarrow H(^2P)$$

The excited hydrogen atoms apparently react with nitrogen to form ammonia and with oxygen to give an interesting chemi-ionization process.[178]

$$H(^2P) + O_2 \rightarrow HO_2^+ + e^-$$

PROBLEMS

1. (a) Using the empirical Rydberg equation, calculate λ in angstrom units for the first two lines of the Lyman, Balmer, and Paschen series.

(b) To what region of the electromagnetic spectrum do the various lines belong (visible, infrared, etc.)?

(c) Compare your values calculated in (a) with the experimental values.

2. Calculate from the Rydberg equation the minimum energy (in ergs/atom and electron volts) necessary to remove completely the electron from a $^2S_{1/2}$ hydrogen atom (ionization potential).

3. (a) Derive the equation

$$\frac{1}{\lambda} = \frac{2\pi^2 \mu e^4}{ch^3} \left(\frac{1}{n_2{}^2} - \frac{1}{n_1{}^2} \right)$$

from the postulates of Bohr and the Bohr atom model (μ is the reduced mass of the proton-electron pair).

(b) Evaluate the constant term in this relation, using current values for m_e, m_H, e, c, and h, and compare this with the empirical Rydberg constant.

4. The electron configuration of titanium is $1s^2 2s^2 2p^6 3s^2 3p^6 3d^2 4s^2$. From this and the rules governing quantum states of electrons, show that the term symbol for the ground state of the titanium atom is ($^3F_2$).

5. Calculate the ratio of the numbers of atoms in the $3(^2S_{1/2})$ and $3(^2P_{3/2})$ states of sodium at (a) 27°C, (b) 5000°C, (c) 50,000°C. [The transition $3(^2P_{3/2}) \rightarrow 3(^2S_{1/2})$ is accompanied by the emission of a quantum of radiation of wavelength 5890.0 A.] Indicate by term symbols a few of the probable transitions expected on *absorption* of light at the proper wavelength by sodium atoms in the vapor state at (d) 27°C and (e) 50,000°C.

6. The natural half-intensity width of the 5000 A radiation absorbed by a given atom is 0.0005 A. Calculate the mean lifetime of the excited state formed.

7. A tube contains $^2S_{1/2}$ sodium atoms at 1000°C and at 1 mm pressure. Calculate the half-intensity band width of the radiation near 5890.0 A absorbed to form $3(^2P_{3/2})$ sodium atoms. (Neglect collision broadening here.)

8. Resonance emission is observable in pure mercury vapor at low pressures and temperatures when excited with 2537 A radiation, but it is almost completely absent in mercury vapor containing a large excess of C_3H_8 gas. Explain briefly what factors cause this.

9. What is the feasibility of effecting a photochemical enrichment of the ^{235}U isotope present in uranium which has this natural distribution of isotopes: ^{235}U, 0.71%; ^{238}U, 99.29%? Give your reasoning. If you consider such enrichment feasible, describe the experimental conditions under which you would choose to attempt it.

10. Show that the most probable distance from the nucleus at which the electron can be found in a hydrogen atom in its $1s$ orbital is at the first Bohr radius; note that $R^2\, dr = \int_0^{2\pi}\int_0^{\pi} \psi^2 r^2\, dr\, \sin\theta\, d\theta\, d\phi = 4\pi\psi^2 r^2\, dr.$

11. Which of the following atomic transitions will occur on exposure of the atom to the appropriate frequency of light? Show the reasoning which you use in arriving at your answer.

(a) $H1s(^2S_{1/2}) + h\nu \to H2s(^2S_{1/2})$
(b) $H1s(^2S_{1/2}) + h\nu \to H2p(^2P_{3/2})$
(c) $H1s(^2S_{1/2}) + h\nu \to H4p(^2P_{1/2})$
(d) $H1s(^2S_{1/2}) + h\nu \to H3d(^2D_{3/2})$
(e) $K4s(^2S_{1/2}) + h\nu \to K5p(^2P_{3/2})$
(f) $Ca4s^2(^1S_0) + h\nu \to Ca4s5p(^3P_1)$
(g) $Ca4s^2(^1S_0) + h\nu \to Ca4s4p(^1P_1)$

12. Predict the major physical and chemical results of the irradiation of the following mercury-vapor-containing mixtures with 2537 A resonance radiation from a low-pressure mercury arc. The other elements and compounds are transparent at 2537 A. Reference to the thermal data (Appendix) and spectral data for these or analogous compounds (Chapter 5) may be useful in formulating your answers.

(a) Hg, Cd vapor at 100°, low pressure.
(b) Hg, n-C_5H_{12} vapor at 25°, 10 mm.
(c) Hg, n-C_5H_{12} vapor at 400°, 10 mm.

(d) Hg, ⬡ vapor at 25°, 10 mm.

(e) Hg, C_2F_6 vapor at 100°, 10 mm.
(f) Hg, CH_3OCH_3 vapor at 25°, 10 mm.

REFERENCES TO CHAPTER 2

1. G. Herzberg, *Atomic Spectra and Atomic Structure*, 2nd Edition, Dover Publications, New York, 1944.
2. G. R. Harrison, R. C. Lord, and J. R. Loofbourow, *Practical Spectroscopy*, Prentice-Hall, Englewood Cliffs, N.J., 1948.
3. R. A. Sawyer, *Experimental Spectroscopy*, 2nd Edition, Prentice-Hall, Englewood Cliffs, N.J., 1951; 3rd Edition, Dover, New York, 1963.
4. F. K. Richtmeyer and E. H. Kennard, *Introduction to Modern Physics*, 4th Edition, McGraw-Hill Book Co., New York, 1947.
5. H. E. White, *Introduction to Atomic Spectra*, McGraw-Hill Book Co., New York, 1934.
6. H. C. Urey, F. C. Brickwedde, and G. M. Murphy, *Phys. Rev.*, **39**, 164, 864 (1932).
7. H. Eyring, J. Walter, and G. E. Kimball, *Quantum Chemistry*, John Wiley & Sons, New York, 1944.
8. W. Kauzmann, *Quantum Chemistry*, Academic Press, New York, 1957.

9. K. S. Pitzer, *Quantum Chemistry*, Prentice-Hall, Englewood Cliffs, N.J., 1953.
10. L. Pauling and E. B. Wilson, Jr., *Introduction to Quantum Mechanics*, McGraw-Hill Book Co., New York, 1935.
11. W. A. Noyes, Jr. and P. A. Leighton, *The Photochemistry of Gases*, Reinhold Publishing Corp., New York, 1941.
12. A. C. G. Mitchell and M. W. Zemansky, *Resonance Radiation and Excited Atoms*, Cambridge University Press, 1934, Reprinted 1961.
13. P. Pringsheim, *Fluorescence and Phosphorescence*, Interscience Publishers, New York, 1949.
14. E. J. Bowen, *Chemical Aspects of Light*, 2nd Edition, Oxford University Press, Oxford, 1946.
15. H. E. Gunning and O. P. Strausz, "Mercury Photosensitization," *Advances in Photochemistry*, Vol. 1, ed. by W. A. Noyes, Jr., G. S. Hammond, and J. N. Pitts, Jr., Interscience Publishers, a division of John Wiley & Sons, New York, 1963, p. 209.
16. T. Tako, *J. Phys. Soc. Japan*, **16**, 2016 (1961).
17. C. Füchtbauer, G. Joos, and O. Dinkelacker, *Ann. Physik*, **71**, 204 (1923).
18. J. Robin, *Compt. Rend.*, **238**, 1491 (1954).
19. A. Michels and H. de Kluiver, *Physica*, **22**, 919 (1956).
20. A. Michels, H. de Kluiver, and C. A. ten Seldam, *Physica*, **25**, 1321 (1959).
21. M. K. Phibbs and B. de B. Darwent, *J. Chem. Phys.*, **18**, 679 (1950).
22. K. R. Osborn, C. C. McDonald, and H. E. Gunning, *J. Chem. Phys.*, **26**, 124 (1957).
23. P. J. Walsh, *Phys. Rev.*, **116**, 511 (1959).
24. T. Holstein, *Phys. Rev.*, **83**, 1159 (1951); *ibid.*, **72**, 1212 (1947).
25. D. Alpert, A. O. McCoubrey, and T. Holstein, *Phys. Rev.*, **76**, 1257 (1949).
26. S. Mrozowski, *Z. Physik*, **78**, 826 (1932).
27. K. Zuber, *Helv. Phys. Acta*, **8**, 488 (1935); *ibid.*, **9**, 285 (1936); *Nature*, **136**, 796 (1935).
28. C. C. McDonald and H. E. Gunning, *J. Chem. Phys.*, **20**, 1817 (1952).
29. M. Zelikoff, L. M. Aschenbrand, and P. H. Wyckoff, *J. Chem. Phys.*, **21**, 376 (1953).
30. B. H. Billings, W. J. Hitchcock, and M. Zelikoff, *J. Chem. Phys.*, **21**, 1762 (1953).
31. M. Desnoyer, G. Nief, and E. Roth, *J. Chim. Phys.*, **60**, 209 (1963).
32. T. Dingle and H. E. Gunning, unpublished data.
33. B. Cagnac, *J. Phys. Radium*, **19**, 863 (1958).
34. R. H. Kohler, *Phys. Rev.*, **121**, 1104 (1961).
35. M. N. McDermott and W. L. Lichten, *Phys. Rev.*, **119**, 134 (1960).
36. W. A. Noyes, Jr., G. B. Porter, and J. E. Jolley, *Chem. Rev.*, **56**, 49 (1956).
37. R. J. Cvetanovic, "Mercury Photosensitized Reactions," *Progress in Reaction Kinetics*, Vol. 2, ed. by G. Porter, The Macmillan Co., New York, 1964, p. 39.
38. E. W. R. Steacie, *Atomic and Free Radical Reactions*, 2nd Edition, Vols. 1 and 2, Reinhold Publishing Corp., New York, 1954.
39. E. W. R. Steacie, *Can. J. Research*, **B26**, 609 (1948).
40. (a) K. J. Laidler, *J. Chem. Phys.*, **10**, 43 (1942); (b) *ibid.*, **10**, 34 (1942); (c) *ibid.*, **15**, 712 (1947).
41. G. K. Rollefson and M. Burton, *Photochemistry*, Prentice-Hall, Englewood Cliffs. N.J., 1939.
42. J. N. Pitts, Jr., F. Wilkinson, and G. S. Hammond, *Advances in Photochemistry*, Vol. 1, ed. by W. A. Noyes, Jr., G. S. Hammond, and J. N. Pitts, Jr., Interscience Publishers, a division of John Wiley & Sons, New York, 1963, p. 16.
43. M. W. Zemansky, *Phys. Rev.*, **36**, 919 (1930).

44. E. W. Sampson, *Phys. Rev.*, **40**, 940 (1932).
45. C. G. Matland, *Phys. Rev.*, **92**, 637 (1953).
46. (a) B. de B. Darwent, *J. Chem. Phys.*, **18**, 1532 (1950); (b) B. de B. Darwent and M. K. Phibbs, *J. Chem. Phys.*, **22**, 110 (1954); (c) B. de B. Darwent, M. K. Phibbs, and F. G. Hurtubise, *J. Chem. Phys.*, **22**, 859 (1954).
47. R. J. Cvetanovic, *J. Chem. Phys.*, **23**, 1203 (1955).
48. A. Jablonski, *Z. Physik*, **70**, 723 (1931).
49. O. Oldenberg, *Z. Physik*, **49**, 609 (1928); *ibid.*, **50**, 580 (1928).
50. J. A. Berbert and K. C. Clark, *Phys. Rev.*, **100**, 506 (1955).
51. G. H. Kimbell, Ph.D. Thesis, University of Toronto, 1961.
52. R. W. Wood and E. Gaviola, *Phil. Mag.*, **6**, 271 (1928).
53. G. H. Kimbell and D. J. LeRoy, *Can. J. Chem.*, **38**, 1714 (1960).
54. T. Asada, R. Ladenburg, and W. Tietze, *Z. Physik*, **29**, 549 (1928).
55. A. B. Callear and R. G. W. Norrish, *Proc. Roy. Soc. (London)*, **A266**, 299 (1962).
56. M. D. Scheer and J. Fine, *J. Chem. Phys.*, **36**, 1264 (1962).
57. S. Mrozowski, *Revs. Modern Phys.*, **16**, 153 (1944).
58. T. Holstein, D. Alpert, and A. O. McCoubrey, *Phys. Rev.*, **76**, 1259 (1949).
59. A. O. McCoubrey, *Phys. Rev.*, **84**, 1073 (1951).
60. J. Franck, *Z. Physik.* **9**, 259 (1922).
61. G. Cario and J. Franck, *Z. Physik*, **17**, 202 (1923).
62. H. Beutler and B. Josephy, *Naturwiss.*, **15**, 540 (1927); *Z. Physik*, **53**, 747 (1929).
63. S. Frish and E. Kraulinga, *Doklady Akad. Nauk S.S.S.R.*, **101**, 837 (1955).
64. R. A. Anderson and R. H. McFarland, *Phys. Rev.*, **119**, 693 (1960).
65. G. Cario and J. Franck, *Z. Physik*, **11**, 161 (1922).
66. L. B. Thomas and W. D. Gwinn, *J. Am. Chem. Soc.*, **70**, 2643 (1948).
67. K. R. Jennings and R. J. Cvetanovic, *J. Chem. Phys.*, **35**, 1233 (1961).
68. R. J. Cvetanovic, "Addition of Atoms to Olefins," *Advances in Photochemistry*, Vol. I, ed. by W. A. Noyes, Jr., G. S. Hammond, and J. N. Pitts, Jr., Interscience Publishers, a division of John Wiley & Sons, New York, 1963, p. 115.
69. R. A. Holroyd and T. E. Pierce, *J. Phys. Chem.*, **68**, 1392 (1964).
70. R. Pertel, *Abstracts Sixth Informal Photochemistry Conference*, University of California, Davis, June, 1964.
71. C. A. Heller and A. S. Gordon, *Abstracts Sixth Informal Photochemistry Conference*, University of California, Davis, June, 1964.
72. C. R. Masson and E. W. R. Steacie, *J. Chem. Phys.*, **18**, 210 (1950).
73. E. W. R. Steacie and D. J. LeRoy, *J. Chem. Phys.*, **12**, 34 (1944).
74. R. A. Back, *Trans. Faraday Soc.*, **54**, 512 (1958).
75. R. A. Back, *Can. J. Chem.*, **37**, 1834 (1959).
76. R. J. Cvetanovic, Paper presented to the Royal Society of Canada, Annual Meeting, Edmonton, 1958; *Proc. and Trans. Roy. Soc. Can.*, **52** (Abstract).
77. R. J. Cvetanovic, W. E. Falconer, and K. R. Jennings, *J. Chem. Phys.*, **35**, 1225 (1961).
78. R. J. Cvetanovic, *J. Chem. Phys.*, **23**, 1208 (1955).
79. R. A. Back and D. van der Auwera, *Can. J. Chem.*, **40**, 2339 (1962).
80. B. de B. Darwent and E. W. R. Steacie, *Can. J. Research*, **27B**, 181 (1949).
81. B. de B. Darwent and E. W. R. Steacie, *J. Am. Chem. Soc.*, **70**, 2285 (1948).
82. E. W. R. Steacie and R. L. Cunningham, *J. Chem. Phys.*, **8**, 800 (1940).
83. S. Bywater and E. W. R. Steacie, *J. Chem. Phys.*, **19**, 172 (1951).
84. F. P. Lossing, D. G. H. Marsden, and J. B. Farmer, *Can. J. Chem.*, **34**, 701 (1956).
85. T. F. Palmer and F. P. Lossing, *Can. J. Chem.*, **41**, 2412 (1963).

86. G. N. C. Woodall and H. E. Gunning, *Bull. Soc. Chim. Belges*, **71**, 725 (1962); Y. Rousseau, G. N. C. Woodall, and H. E. Gunning, *J. Chem. Phys.*, **37**, 2722 (1962).
87. M. Avrahami and P. Kebarle, *Can. J. Chem.*, **41**, 335, 347 (1963).
88. R. A. Holroyd and G. W. Klein, *J. Phys. Chem.*, **67**, 2273 (1963).
89. D. J. LeRoy and E. W. R. Steacie, *J. Chem. Phys.*, **9**, 829 (1941).
90. R. J. Cvetanovic, H. E. Gunning, and E. W. R. Steacie, *J. Chem. Phys.*, **31**, 573 (1959).
91. D. J. LeRoy and E. W. R. Steacie, *J. Chem. Phys.*, **10**, 676 (1942).
92. D. Line and D. J. LeRoy, *J. Chem. Phys.*, **13**, 307 (1945).
93. R. J. Cvetanovic and A. B. Callear, *J. Chem. Phys.*, **23**, 1182 (1955).
94. P. Kebarle, *J. Phys. Chem.*, **67**, 716 (1963).
95. A. B. Callear and R. J. Cvetanovic, *J. Chem. Phys.*, **24**, 873 (1956).
96. B. de B. Darwent, *J. Chem. Phys.*, **19**, 258 (1951).
97. A. B. Callear and J. C. Robb, *Discussions Faraday Soc.*, **17**, 21 (1954).
98. D. W. Setser, B. S. Rabinowitch, and D. W. Placzek, *J. Am. Chem. Soc.*, **85**, 862 (1963).
99. M. Avrahami and P. Kebarle, *J. Phys. Chem.*, **67**, 354 (1963).
100. R. J. Cvetanovic and L. C. Doyle, *J. Chem. Phys.*, **37**, 543 (1962).
101. J. R. Majer, B. Mile, and J. C. Robb, *Trans. Faraday Soc.*, **57**, 1342, 1692 (1961).
102. R. B. Cundall and T. F. Palmer, *Trans. Faraday Soc.*, **56**, 1211 (1960).
103. R. B. Cundall, *Progress in Reaction Kinetics*, Vol. II, ed. by G. Porter, Macmillan Co., New York, 1964, p. 167.
104. P. Kebarle and M. Avrahami, *J. Chem. Phys.*, **38**, 700 (1963).
105. S. Arai and S. Shida, *J. Chem. Phys.*, **38**, 694 (1963).
106. R. L. Stock and H. E. Gunning, *Can. J. Chem.*, **38**, 2295 (1960).
107. (a) P. W. Beck, D. V. Kniebes, and H. E. Gunning, *J. Chem. Phys.*, **22**, 678 (1954); (b) *J. Chem. Phys.*, **22**, 672 (1954).
108. D. L. Kantro and H. E. Gunning, *J. Chem. Phys.*, **21**, 1797 (1953).
109. W. A. Gibbons, W. F. Allen, and H. E. Gunning, *Can. J. Chem.*, **40**, 568 (1962).
110. S. Arai, S. Sato, and S. Shida, *Nippon Kagaku Zassi*, **81**, 1790 (1960).
111. H. E. Gunning and E. W. R. Steacie, *J. Chem. Phys.*, **17**, 351 (1949).
112. K. J. Ivin, *J. Chem. Soc.*, 2241 (1956).
113. H. W. Ford, P. J. Kozak, and H. E. Gunning, 137th Meeting American Chemical Society, April, 1960; *Abstract*, p. 35R.
114. (a) D. W. Setser, B. S. Rabinowitch, and E. G. Spittler, *J. Chem. Phys.*, **35**, 1840 (1961); (b) D. W. Setser, D. W. Placzek, R. J. Cvetanovic, and B. S. Rabinowitch, *Can. J. Chem.*, **40**, 2179 (1962).
115. H. Yamazaki and S. Shida, *J. Chem. Phys.*, **24**, 1278 (1956); *J. Chem. Soc. Japan*, **77**, 500 (1956).
116. H. Yamazaki, *Bull. Chem. Soc. Japan*, **31**, 677 (1958); H. Yamazaki and S. Shida, *J. Chem. Phys.*, **28**, 737 (1958).
117. G. S. Forbes and J. E. Cline, *J. Am. Chem. Soc.*, **63**, 1713 (1941).
118. E. J. Y. Scott and E. W. R. Steacie, *Can. J. Chem.*, **29**, 233 (1951).
119. A. H. Sehon and B. deB. Darwent, *J. Chem. Phys.*, **23**, 822 (1955).
120. B. Atkinson, *J. Chem. Soc.*, **1952**, 2684; *Nature*, **163**, 291 (1949).
121. J. Collin and F. P. Lossing, *Can. J. Chem.*, **35**, 778 (1957).
122. D. J. LeRoy and E. W. R. Steacie, *J. Chem. Phys.*, **12**, 117 (1944).
123. S. Shida, Z. Kuri, and T. Furvoya, *J. Chem. Phys.*, **28**, 131 (1958).
124. A. G. Sherwood and H. E. Gunning, *Can. J. Chem.*, **38**, 466 (1960).
125. P. Kebarle, *J. Chem. Phys.*, **39**, 2218 (1963).

126. H. E. Cier, U.S. Patent 2,762,768, Sept. 11, 1956; *C.A.*, **51**, 3300c.

127. H. E. Cier, U.S. Patent 2,640,023, May 26, 1953; *C.A.*, **47**, 8359f.

128. H. G. Schotze and H. E. Cier, U.S. Patent 2,655,474, Oct. 13, 1953; *C.A.*, **48**, 10046g.

129. G. J. Minkoff and C. F. H. Tipper, *Chemistry of Combustion Reactions*, Butterworths Scientific Publications, London, 1962.

130. A. A. Mantashyan and A. B. Nalbandyan, *Izvest. Akad. Nauk Armyan. S.S.R. Khim Nauk*, **15**, 3 (1962).

131. R. F. Pottie, A. G. Harrison, and F. P. Lossing, *Can. J. Chem.*, **39**, 102 (1961).

132. A. R. Knight and H. E. Gunning, *Can. J. Chem.*, **39**, 1231 (1961); *ibid.*, **39**, 2251 (1961); *ibid.*, **39**, 2246 (1961); *ibid.*, **40**, 1134 (1962).

133. J. B. Farmer, F. P. Lossing, D. G. H. Marsden, and E. W. R. Steacie, *J. Chem. Phys.*, **23**, 1169 (1955).

134. F. P. Lossing, *Can. J. Chem.*, **35**, 305 (1957).

135. F. Moseley and J. C. Robb, *Proc. Roy. Soc. (London)*, **A243**, 119 (1957).

136. (a) A. G. Harrison and F. P. Lossing, *Can. J. Chem.*, **38**, 544 (1960); (b) *ibid.*, **37**, 1478 (1959); (c) *ibid.*, **37**, 1696 (1959).

137. J. B. Homer, I. P. Fisher, and F. P. Lossing, *Abstracts Sixth Informal Photochemistry Conference*, University of California, Davis, June, 1964.

138. (a) R. Srinivasan, *Advances in Photochemistry*, Vol. I., ed. by W. A. Noyes, Jr., G. S. Hammond, and J. N. Pitts, Jr., Interscience Publishers, a division of John Wiley & Sons, New York, 1963, p. 105; (b) R. Srinivasan, *J. Am. Chem. Soc.*, **83**, 4923 (1961).

139. P. Kebarle and F. P. Lossing, *Can. J. Chem.*, **37**, 389 (1959).

140. J. R. Bates and H. S. Taylor, *J. Am. Chem. Soc.*, **49**, 2438 (1927).

141. R. J. Cvetanovic and L. C. Doyle, *Can. J. Chem.*, **35**, 605 (1957).

142. M. K. Phibbs, B. deB. Darwent, and E. W. R. Steacie, *J. Chem. Phys.*, **16**, 39 (1948).

143. R. J. Cvetanovic, *Can. J. Chem.*, **33**, 1684 (1955).

144. W. M. Manning and W. A. Noyes, Jr., *J. Am. Chem. Soc.*, **54**, 3907 (1932).

145. M. Z. Hoffman and R. B. Bernstein, *J. Chem. Phys.*, **33**, 526 (1960).

146. W. A. Noyes, Jr., *J. Am. Chem. Soc.*, **53**, 514 (1931).

147. O. P. Strausz and H. E. Gunning, *Can. J. Chem.*, **39**, 2549 (1961).

148. R. J. Fallon, J. T. Vanderslice, and E. A. Mason, *J. Phys. Chem.*, **63**, 2082 (1959).

149. R. G. Dickinson and M. S. Sherrill, *Proc. Natl. Acad. Sci. U.S.*, **12**, 175 (1926).

150. D. H. Volman, *J. Am. Chem. Soc.*, **76**, 6034 (1954).

151. A. B. Callear, C. R. Patrick, and J. C. Robb, *Trans. Faraday Soc.*, **55**, 280 (1959).

152. D. H. Volman, *Advances in Photochemistry*, Vol. I, ed. by W. A. Noyes, Jr., G. S. Hammond, and J. N. Pitts, Jr., Interscience Publishers, a division of John Wiley & Sons, New York, 1963, p. 52.

153. D. H. Volman, *J. Chem. Phys.*, **24**, 122 (1956).

154. R. Pertel and H. E. Gunning, *Can. J. Chem.*, **37**, 35 (1959).

155. D. H. Volman, E. K. Gill, and K. E. Laidler, *J. Chem. Phys.*, **30**, 589 (1959).

156. R. J. Fallon, J. T. Vanderslice, and E. A. Mason, *J. Phys. Chem.*, **64**, 505 (1960).

157. S. Chen, *Hua Hsueh Hsueh Pao*, **23**, 188 (1957).

158. H. W. Melville, *Proc. Roy. Soc. (London)*, **A157**, 621 (1936).

159. H. Basseches, "The Mercury Photosensitized Decomposition of Water Vapor," Ph.D. Dissertation, The Ohio State University, 1951.

160. O. P. Strausz and H. E. Gunning, *Can. J. Chem.*, **39**, 2244 (1961).

161. Y. Mori, *Bull. Chem. Soc. Japan*, **34**, 1128 (1961).

162. C. C. McDonald and H. E. Gunning, *J. Chem. Phys.*, **23**, 532 (1955).

163. (a) J. K. S. Wan, O. P. Strausz, W. F. Allen, and H. E. Gunning, *Can. J. Chem.*, **42**, 2056 (1964); (b) *ibid.*, **43**, 318 (1965); (c) M. G. Bellas, J. K. S. Wan, W. F. Allen, O. P. Strausz, and H. E. Gunning, *J. Phys. Chem.*, **68**, 2170 (1964).
164. H. Niki and G. J. Mains, *J. Phys. Chem.*, **68**, 304 (1964).
165. (a) O. P. Strausz, M. A. Nay, and H. E. Gunning, *Abstracts Sixth Informal Photochemistry Conference*, University of California, Davis, June, 1964; (b) M. A. Nay, G. N. C. Woodall, O. P. Strausz, and H. E. Gunning, *J. Am. Chem. Soc.*, **87**, 179 (1965); (c) A. J. Yarwood, O. P. Strausz, and H. E. Gunning, *J. Chem. Phys.*, **41**, 1705 (1964).
166. Y. Rousseau and G. Mains, *Abstracts Sixth Informal Photochemistry Conference*, University of California, Davis, June, 1964.
167. T. Hirata and H. E. Gunning, *J. Chem. Phys.*, **27**, 477 (1957).
168. M. K. Phibbs and B. deB. Darwent, *J. Chem. Phys.*, **18**, 679 (1950).
169. R. R. Kuntz and G. J. Mains, *J. Am. Chem. Soc.*, **85**, 2219 (1963).
170. R. R. Kuntz and G. J. Mains, *J. Phys. Chem.*, **68**, 408 (1964).
171. N. N. Bubnov, N. M. Bazhin, and V. V. Voevodskii, *Kinetika i Kataliz*, **5**, 357 (1964).
172. J. R. McNesby and H. Okabe, *Advances in Photochemistry*, Vol. III, ed. by W. A. Noyes, Jr., G. S. Hammond, and J. N. Pitts, Jr., Interscience Publishers, a division of John Wiley & Sons, New York, 1964, p. 157.
173. W. Groth, *Z. physik. Chem.*, NF **1**, 300 (1954).
174. W. Groth, *Z. Elektrochem.*, **58**, 752 (1954).
175. W. Groth, "Photochemistry of the Liquid and Solid State," Symposium, Dedham, Mass., 1957, p. 21.
176. J. R. Dacey and J. W. Hodgins, *Can. J. Research*, **28B**, 90, 173 (1950).
177. I. Tanaka and J. R. McNesby, *J. Chem. Phys.*, **36**, 3170 (1962).
178. I. Tanaka, unpublished results.
179. J. P. Molnar and W. J. Hitchcock, *J. Opt. Soc. Am.*, **30**, 523 (1940).
180. G. S. Hammond, J. Saltiel, A. A. Lamola, N. J. Turro, J. S. Bradshaw, D. O. Cowan, R. C. Counsell, V. Vogt, and C. Dalton, *J. Am. Chem. Soc.*, **86**, 3197 (1964).
181. R. J. Norstrom, O. P. Strausz, and H. E. Gunning, *Can. J. Chem.*, **42**, 2140 (1964).

3

The Interaction of Light with Simple Molecules; The Photochemistry of the Simple Molecules

In the first sections of this chapter we consider briefly, and largely in an elementary fashion, some of the aspects of the spectroscopy of the simple diatomic molecules; these will be of direct interest to us in interpreting the photochemistry of simple molecules, covered in the later sections of the chapter.

3-1 THE ABSORPTION AND THE EMISSION OF RADIATION BY SIMPLE MOLECULES

In discussing the absorption of radiation by atoms we dealt with the energies and moments associated with the rapid motion of light electrons about heavy positive nuclei. With molecular spectra we must consider, in addition to the intramolecular motion of the electrons, energies associated with the rotation of the molecule as a whole and with the periodic vibrations of the atoms constituting the molecule. Like the electronic energy levels of atoms, molecular electronic, vibrational, and rotational energy levels are quantized and each set can be represented by expressions involving integers, the *molecular electronic, vibrational,* and *rotational* quantum numbers.

Electronic absorption falls generally in the region from about 7500 A in the red end of the visible spectrum down to 1100–1200 A in the far ultraviolet or Schumann region. This range corresponds to spacings between electronic energy levels of the order of 38 kcal/einstein ($\sim$13,000 cm^{-1} or 1.7 ev) in the red down to around 250 kcal/einstein ($\sim$80,000 cm^{-1} or 11 ev) in the far ultraviolet. Vibrational levels lie about 1–10 kcal/mole apart ($\sim$350–3500 cm^{-1} or 0.04–0.4 ev), and absorption is in the infrared from about 3 to 30 microns. Energy levels for pure rotation are usually close together (except for very light molecules such as hydrogen) with spacings about 0.1 kcal ($\sim$35 cm^{-1} or 0.004 ev), and pure rotational spectra lie in the far infrared beyond 30 microns.

Figure 3-1 illustrates schematically the distribution of energy levels in a typical diatomic molecule and shows some allowed transitions between them.

In the following sections we shall summarize briefly, from the viewpoint of the photochemist, the equations which describe molecular, rotational,

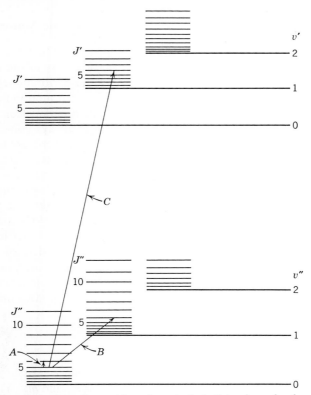

Fig. 3-1   Energy levels and transitions in a typical diatomic molecule; the energy changes shown are as follows: *A*, pure rotational (far infrared); *B*, vibrational-rotational (near infrared); *C*, electronic transition (visible-ultraviolet).

vibrational, and electronic energy levels, the selection rules for transitions between these levels, and the interpretation of observed molecular absorption spectra in terms of these factors and the physical state of the molecule. Our considerations will be simplified by the fact that as a reasonable first approximation one can deal independently with these three types of energy possessed by molecules, so that we can write $E_{\text{total}} = E_r + E_v + E_e$. This is feasible because of the great differences in frequency of the rotational, vibrational, and electronic motion. Characteristic frequencies are of the order of 10^{10}, 10^{12}, and 10^{15} sec^{-1}, respectively. Thus during an electronic transition which occurs in about 10^{-15} to 10^{-16} sec the vibrating nuclei are so slightly displaced that they can be considered stationary and only the electronic transition need be considered. This fact is the basis of the highly important Franck-Condon principle.

3-1A   Energy Levels and Infrared Spectra of Diatomic Molecules

In order for a molecule to absorb radiant energy the increase in energy must be accompanied by a change in the electric center of the molecule. Thus in absorption of infrared radiation only those vibrational and rotational modes are active in which the intramolecular motion produces a change in the dipole moment. As a result, all homonuclear diatomic molecules, in which the center of positive charge always coincides with the center of negative charge and the dipole moment is zero, are inactive in the infrared. However, in contrast to O_2, Cl_2, H_2, etc., heteronuclear diatomic molecules such as HCl, CO, and NO possess permanent dipole moments, and they have pure rotational and vibrational-rotational spectra in the infrared with the intensity of absorption related to the strength of the dipoles. The energies involved in these infrared transitions are far too small (<10 kcal/mole) to break normal bonds, and their chief interest to the photochemist is in the structural information to be derived from the spectra. Thus they will be treated briefly. Electronic transitions, on the other hand, involve energies of the order of 40 kcal/mole or more, and some understanding of molecular electronic spectra is of great importance photochemically.

3-1A-1   Pure Rotational Spectra

Let us consider a heteronuclear diatomic molecule and assume a fixed interatomic distance, r, between the atoms of mass m_1 and m_2. The energy of rotation of this dumbbell type of rigid rotor, E_r, is given by

$$E_r = \tfrac{1}{2}I\omega^2 \tag{3-1}$$

where $I = \mu r^2$ (μ being the reduced mass), and $\omega =$ the angular velocity (recall that ω is the symbol for wave numbers). From classical mechanics the angular momentum, P, equals $I\omega$, so that $E_r = P^2/2I$. If we now quantize the angular momentum of the molecule in a manner analogous to the Bohr postulate for an electron and say that P must be an integral multiple, m, of $h/2\pi$, we obtain the quantum-mechanical result,

$$E_r = \frac{h^2}{8\pi^2 I} m^2 \tag{3-2}$$

where $m = 0, 1, 2. \ldots$ A similar, but more quantitative result, Eq. 3-3, is obtained from wave mechanics by setting the potential energy $V = 0$ in the Schrödinger equation and solving for E_r the allowed energy levels:

$$E_r = \frac{h^2}{8\pi^2 I} (J)(J + 1) \tag{3-3}$$

Thus the energy levels of a rigid rotor are quantized with J, the rotational quantum number, being an integer with the values $0, 1, 2, \ldots$.

Equation 3-3 gives E_r in ergs if h and I are given in cgs units. To convert to wave numbers we recall that $E = hc\omega$ and symbolize the energy of the rotational *term* as F in cm^{-1} so that

$$F = \frac{h}{8\pi^2 cI} (J)(J + 1) \text{ cm}^{-1} \tag{3-4}$$

For a given molecule the quantity $h/8\pi^2 cI$ is a constant, the *spectral constant B*, and Eq. 3-4 reduces to

$$F = B(J)(J + 1) \text{ cm}^{-1} \tag{3-5}$$

Substituting the values for the natural constants, we obtain $B = (27.98 \times 10^{-40}/I)$ cm^{-1}, when I is in gram-centimeters squared.

Equation 3-5 gives the allowed rotational energy levels for a rigid rotator.

The application of quantum mechanics to the light absorption and emission processes resulting in rotational energy changes demands that only those changes can occur for which the selection rule $\Delta J = \pm 1$ is obeyed. For this case, the wave number of the absorption line ω arising from the transitions $J \rightarrow J + 1$ and $J \rightarrow J - 1$ becomes

$$(F_{J+1} - F_J) = \omega_1 = 2B(J + 1) \text{ cm}^{-1}; \quad \Delta J = +1 \tag{3-6a}$$

$$(F_J - F_{J-1}) = \omega_2 = 2B(J) \text{ cm}^{-1}; \quad \Delta J = -1 \tag{3-6b}$$

In each case $\omega = 2B \times$ (rotational quantum number of the upper rotational state).

Theoretically, then the pure rotational spectrum of a gaseous diatomic molecule should consist of lines with frequencies $2B$, $4B$, $6B$, etc., and equal spacings $\Delta\omega$ of $2B$. Hydrogen chloride exhibits such a spectrum in the 40–80 micron region. It is shown in Fig. 3-2, and actual values are given in Table 3-1. The spacings are approximately equal, although there is a significant decrease as J increases. The increased centrifugal force results in a lengthening of the bond distance r and thus an increase in the moment of inertia I. This is accounted for in precise work by adding additional correctional terms to Eq. 3-5, giving

$$F = B(J)(J + 1) - D(J)^2(J + 1)^2 + \cdots \tag{3-7}$$

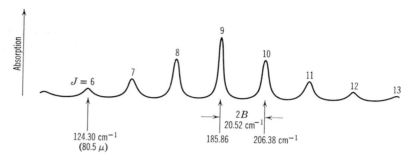

Fig. 3-2 Pure rotational spectrum of HCl(g) in the far infrared (40–80 μ). Rotational quantum numbers of the final state are given. From Herzberg,[1] p. 57.

A value of r can be calculated from these values of $\Delta\omega$, utilizing relations 3-4 and 3-6. Thus a spacing of 20.6 cm^{-1} gives $r_{HCl} = 1.30$ A.

Until the development of radar and microwave spectroscopy in World War II the study of pure rotational spectra was limited by extreme

TABLE 3-1 Pure Rotational Spectrum of HCl Vapor in the Far Infrared[a]

Final State, J	ω, cm^{-1}	$\Delta\omega$, cm^{-1}
6	124.30	
		20.73
7	145.03	
		20.48
8	165.51	
		20.35
9	185.86	
		20.52
10	206.38	
		20.12
11	226.50	

[a] Taken from Czerny.[2]

experimental difficulties; today microwave techniques are widely utilized in the 3 mm to 20 cm wavelength range, where the rotational bands lie. These methods provide a resolving power of the order of 10^5 times better than optical gratings and a resulting accuracy of about seven significant figures. With the excellent resolving power, accurate bond distances can be determined. However, mathematical analysis of spectra becomes a limiting factor as the molecular geometry becomes more complex. Thus molecules having different moments of inertia along each axis, such as water, have exceedingly complex spectra, and no simple general expression has been derived for their rotational energies.

3-1A-2 Vibrational-Rotational Spectra

The classical concept of a harmonic oscillator provides us with a simple yet highly useful means of treating the fundamental vibrational frequency of a diatomic molecule, ν_e. Assuming that the atoms resist displacement from their equilibrium positions with a force F proportional to their displacement x (i.e., Hooke's law is followed, $F = -kx$) and applying the laws of classical mechanics, one can obtain the expression for the fundamental frequency ν_e of the diatomic vibrator:

$$\nu_e = \frac{1}{2\pi} \sqrt{\frac{k}{\mu}} \ \text{sec}^{-1} \tag{3-8}$$

where μ is the reduced mass, and k is the bond force constant (constant in Hooke's law). As such, k is a measure of the "stiffness" or strength of the chemical bond between the atoms. A large force constant and/or a small reduced mass lead to high vibrational frequencies.

A simple but highly useful equation for vibrational energy levels of a diatomic molecule can be derived by inserting for the potential energy U in the Schrödinger equation the Hooke's law value, $U = \frac{1}{2}k(r - r_e)^2$. This gives

$$\frac{\partial^2 \psi}{\partial x^2} + \frac{8\pi^2 \mu}{h^2} [E - \frac{1}{2}k(r - r_e)^2]\psi = 0 \tag{3-9}$$

Equation 3-9 can be solved quite readily[3] with the result that vibrational energies are quantized and only certain eigenvalues E_v are permissible:

$$E_v = h\nu_e(v + \tfrac{1}{2}) \tag{3-10}$$

The quantity v is the *vibrational quantum number* and can have only the integral values $0, 1, 2, \ldots$, etc. When given in units of wave numbers the energy levels are usually represented by the *term symbol* G, so that

$$\text{G} = \frac{E_v}{hc} = \omega_e(v + \tfrac{1}{2}) \ \text{cm}^{-1} \tag{3-11}$$

According to this simple picture, a plot of the potential energy of the ground state of a diatomic molecule as a function of interatomic distance, Fig. 3-3, would give a simple quadratic parabola with the vibrational energy levels as a series of equally spaced lines (in contrast to rotational energies which go up as the square of J), and with one-half unit of vibrational energy, the zero point energy. The molecule retains this zero point energy even at absolute zero where for all molecules $v = 0$; for hydrogen this amounts to 6.2 kcal/mole. The quantum-mechanical treatment of the light absorption and emission processes related to vibrational change suggests the selection rule, $\Delta v = \pm 1$. The vibrational absorption spectrum would thus be expected to be a single band corresponding to the energy of a quantum required to raise the molecule from one vibrational level to the next. Since, as we will see shortly, most molecules at room

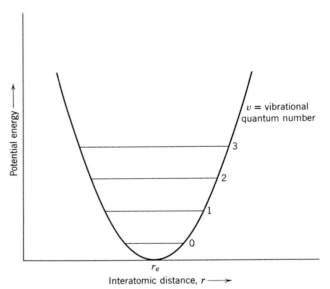

Fig. 3-3   Potential energy as a function of interatomic distance r, for a hypothetical diatomic molecule obeying Hooke's law; vibrational energy levels are equally spaced lines corresponding to the various quantum numbers, v.

temperature are in their ground state, $v = 0$, the most probable transition would be $v'' = 0 \rightarrow v' = 1$; double and single primes specify lower and upper states, respectively.

Hydrogen chloride has a strong absorption band centered at 3.46 μ (2885.9 cm^{-1}) that is attributed to this transition, but the actual spectrum, as shown in Fig. 3-4, is more complex. The complexity arises from transitions between rotational energy levels $J \rightarrow J + 1$ and $J \rightarrow J - 1$, occurring simultaneously with the vibrational transition $v'' = 0 \rightarrow v' = 1$. Thus relation 3-12 is an appropriate expression for a given vibrational energy level since it includes both the vibrational and rotational energy,

$$E_v + E_r = (v + \tfrac{1}{2})hv_e + \frac{h^2}{8\pi^2 I} J(J + 1) \text{ ergs} \qquad (3\text{-}12)$$

Thus ΔE for a transition in the infrared is

$$\Delta E = \Delta E_v + \Delta E_r = h\nu_e \pm \frac{Jh^2}{8\pi^2 I}, \quad J = 1, 2, 3, \ldots \quad (3\text{-}13)$$

The quantum-mechanical treatment of the light absorption and emission processes for the diatomic vibrator-rotator requires that the selection rules $\Delta v = \pm 1$ and $\Delta J = \pm 1$ apply. Transitions in which $\Delta J = +1$ give rise to the so-called R branch, while $\Delta J = -1$ yields the P branch.

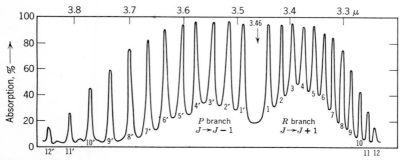

Fig. 3-4   Infrared absorption spectrum of fundamental vibrational band of $HCl(g)$; the "parallel band" is centered at 3.46 μ, and the Q branch is absent. From Herzberg,[1] p. 57; originally from Imes.[5]

Figure 3-5 is a diagram of such "allowed" transitions and the resulting theoretical spectrum for HCl.

The separation of the individual absorption lines, corresponding to $2B$ and $\Delta J = \pm 1$, is approximately 20 cm^{-1} for HCl, in conformity with the value found in the pure rotational spectrum (Table 3-1). As might be expected from Eq. 3-13, one can obtain values of the bond force constant k, the moment of inertia I, and the internuclear distance r from such a spectrum.

As shown in Figs. 3-4 and 3-5 the Q branch, corresponding to $\Delta J = 0$, is absent in HCl. This is rationalized in terms of a quantum-mechanical selection rule which forbids this transition. In certain vibrations of linear polyatomic molecules (e.g., CO_2) the dipole moment vibrates perpendicularly to the molecular axis; for these the rotational selection rules $\Delta J = 0, \pm 1$ apply, and one finds a Q branch as well as a P and an R branch. When $\Delta J = 0$ there is no change in rotational energy, so all members of a Q branch have the same frequency corresponding to the center of the band. Carbon dioxide, as shown in Fig. 3-6a, has such a band, called the perpendicular band in contrast to the HCl parallel band, with the Q branch at 15 μ. Figure 3-6b, showing the 6.7 μ band of water

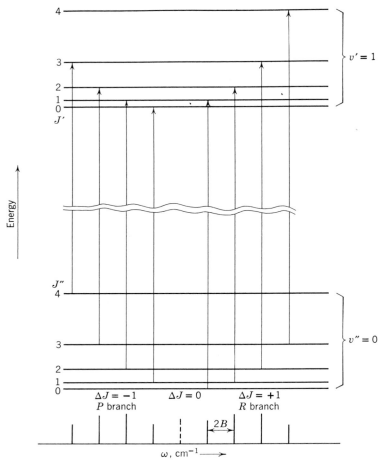

Fig. 3-5 The calculated 3.46 μ vibration-rotation band for HCl vapor, allowed transitions shown. After Herzberg,[1] p. 112.

vapor, is included as a classic example of the spectral maze arising from infrared absorption by a non-linear molecule that in many respects might be classified as a "simple" non-linear triatomic molecule.

Although the assumption that a diatomic molecule acts as a harmonic oscillator following the ordinary quadratic potential function $V = \frac{1}{2}k(r - r_e)^2$ is satisfactory at small values of $(r - r_e)$, it breaks down completely at large displacements. Thus the simple Hooke's law function gives a symmetrical parabolic potential energy curve at all values of $(r - r_e)$ which is contrary to the observed asymmetric form shown in Fig. 3-7 for the actual H_2 molecule, and is incompatible with the molecular

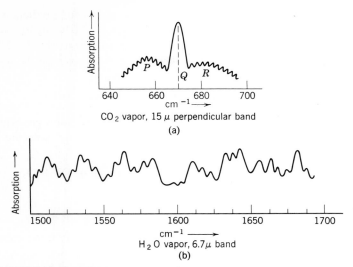

Fig. 3-6 Infrared absorption spectra: (a) CO_2 vapor, 15 μ perpendicular band;
(b) $H_2O(g)$, 6.7 μ band. From Harrison, Lord, and Loofbourow,[221] p. 282.

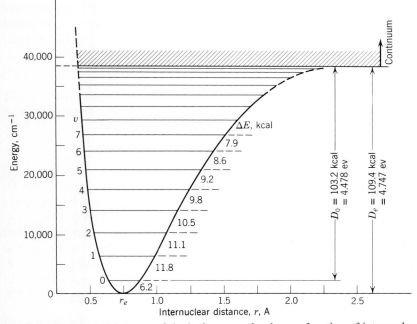

Fig. 3-7 The potential energy of the hydrogen molecule as a function of internuclear
distance, and the position of its vibrational energy levels. Adapted from Moore,[41] p. 250.

dissociation process. Furthermore the simple treatment predicts a series of equally spaced energy levels, whereas they actually begin to converge at large values of v until they blend into a continuum at the dissociation limit (see Fig. 3-7). The latter difficulty can be circumvented by adding a cubic term to the simple quadratic function, giving

$$V = \tfrac{1}{2}k(r - r_e)^2 - k'(r - r_e)^3 \qquad (3\text{-}14)$$

where $k \gg k'$. If Eq. 3-14 is substituted into the Schrödinger equation, it turns out that the allowed energy states of the vibrating molecule E_v are given by

$$E_v = hv_e(v + \tfrac{1}{2}) - hv_e\mathrm{x}_e(v + \tfrac{1}{2})^2 + hv_e\mathrm{y}_e(v + \tfrac{1}{2})^3 + \cdots \qquad (3\text{-}15)$$

or in units of wave numbers

$$G = \omega_e(v + \tfrac{1}{2}) - \omega_e\mathrm{x}_e(v + \tfrac{1}{2})^2 + \omega_e\mathrm{y}_e(v + \tfrac{1}{2})^3 + \cdots \qquad (3\text{-}16)$$

where x_e and y_e are anharmonicity constants. Now, as v increases, the spacing between energy levels decreases, and transitions where $\Delta v = 2, 3$, etc., are permitted, thus explaining observed overtones "or harmonics" in infrared spectra. Furthermore, the shape of the potential function is more realistic than that of the quadratic.

At moderate displacements Eq. 3-14 fails to predict the experimental values, and a more complex empirical expression such as 3-17, proposed by Morse,[4] is required to fit experimental curves such as the one for hydrogen shown in Fig. 3-7.

$$V_{(r-r_e)} = D_e[1 - e^{-\beta(r-r_e)}]^2 \qquad (3\text{-}17)$$

(Here $D_e =$ spectroscopic dissociation energy* in centimeters^{-1}.) By inserting the potential function 3-17 into the Schrödinger equation and solving for allowed energy states Morse determined that

$$\beta = \frac{2\pi^2 c \mu_A}{D_e h} \; \omega_e = 1.218 \times 10^7 \omega_e \sqrt{\frac{\mu_A}{D_e}}$$

where $\mu_A =$ reduced mass in atomic mass units. In the case of the H_2 molecule the Morse function fits well from $r = 0.4$ to $r = 1.6$ A but gives values for V which are progressively too low as r gets larger.

A qualitative meaning of these potential energy curves can be obtained by reference to the simplified drawing in Fig. 3-8. The curve represents potential energy V of the vibrator as a function of internuclear distance r. The horizontal lines show E_v, the total of kinetic plus potential energy of the vibrator in the vibrational level characterized by $v = 0, 1, 2, 3$, and 4.

---

* The thermal heat of dissociation D_0 is less than D_e by the zero point energy, 6.2 kcal for H_2.

As the molecule vibrates, E_v is partitioned between potential energy and kinetic energy; the potential energy is given by the ordinate of the curve at the particular r_e, while the kinetic energy is equal to the value of E_v, represented by the horizontal line for the pertinent vibrational state, minus the potential energy at the particular r_e of concern. Consider that the molecule is in the $v = 4$ vibrational level and originally in the compressed

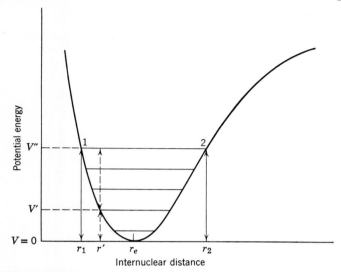

Fig. 3-8   The potential energy of a hypothetical diatomic molecule as a function of internuclear distance.

state with the nuclei spaced at a distance r_1. Then all the energy is stored as potential energy, so that V = maximum and the kinetic energy of the vibrator is zero. Now as the molecule is allowed to vibrate between r_1 and r_2 the potential energy fluctuates from V'' at both extremes to zero at $r = r_e$. At an intermediate distance r', an amount of potential energy $V'' - V'$ is converted into kinetic energy, leaving V' still as potential energy.

Following this classical oscillator approach, one would predict that the extremes in the amplitude of the vibrational motion should be reached at the two turning points 1 and 2 in Fig. 3-8, and that the oscillator should spend most of the time at these two points. Actually wave mechanics predicts regions of large probability in the region of the turning points, but displaced significantly toward the center. This is shown in Fig. 3-9, where the vibrational probability density distribution $\psi_v\psi_v^*$ is plotted versus internuclear distance for a harmonic oscillator. Instead of simply the classic two positions of maximum probability (A-A', B-B', C-C', D-D')

we see from Fig. 3-9 there are $v + 1$ maxima. At large values of the vibrational quantum number v (e.g., $v = 10$ is shown) the two major maxima lie close to the classic turning points and the other maxima are small. Thus the wave-mechanical picture blends into the classical form. The classical oscillator in the 0th vibrational level shows one maximum, at $r = r_e$, implying that transitions from the ground state $v = 0$ to excited

levels will usually occur when the nuclei are within a certain small range of values near a distance r_e apart, at the center of the potential energy curve. This is in qualitative agreement with the classical model of the diatomic vibrator which shows no vibration of the nuclei in the lowest vibrational state; transitions are pictured as originating with the nuclei precisely at r_e for the classical oscillator in its lowest level.

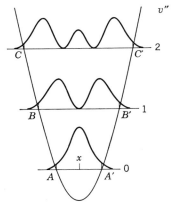

Fig. 3-9 The probability density distribution $\psi\psi^*$ of a harmonic oscillator. From Herzberg,[1] p. 77.

3-1A-3 Effect of Temperature on the Population of Vibrational and Rotational Energy Levels

Although we have discussed the several allowed vibrational and rotational energy levels of a diatomic molecule, we have not considered the probability of a molecule being in any given level. This probability is strongly dependent on the spacing between levels and the temperature, as shown by Eq. 3-18, the Boltzmann expression for the ratio of the number of molecules n_1 in the upper state to the number n_0 in the lower energy state:

$$\frac{n_1}{n_0} = e^{-(E_1-E_0)/RT} = e^{-\Delta Ghc/kT} \tag{3-18}$$

The quantity $E_1 - E_0$ represents the energy difference (ergs/molecule, cal/mole, etc.) between the two levels, and R is the gas constant in the same energy units. ΔG is the energy difference in cm^{-1} and k is the Boltzmann constant. Table 3-2 gives some typical examples of the ratios of the

TABLE 3-2   Ratio of the Number of Molecules in the First Vibration Level to That in the 0th Level for 300 and 1000°K[a]

Gas	G, cm^{-1}	$e^{-\Delta Ghc/kT}$	
		For 300°K	For 1000°K
H_2	4160.2	2.16×10^{-9}	2.51×10^{-3}
HCl	2885.9	9.77×10^{-7}	1.57×10^{-2}
N_2	2330.7	1.40×10^{-5}	3.50×10^{-2}
CO	2143.2	3.43×10^{-5}	4.58×10^{-2}
O_2	1556.4	5.74×10^{-4}	1.07×10^{-1}
S_2	721.6	3.14×10^{-2}	3.54×10^{-1}
Cl_2	556.9	6.92×10^{-2}	4.49×10^{-1}
I_2	213.2	3.60×10^{-1}	7.36×10^{-1}

[a] Taken from Herzberg,[1] p. 123.

numbers of molecules in the first vibrational level to the numbers in the ground vibrational state at 300 and 1000°K. At room temperature this fraction is small (except for I_2), so that most of these diatomic molecules are in their 0th vibrational level and absorption of infrared radiation produces the transition $v'' = 0 \rightarrow v' = 1$; of course this occurs only in those molecules with a permanent dipole: HCl, CO, etc. Iodine alone with its closely spaced energy levels has an appreciable fraction, 27%, of its molecules above the ground vibrational state. It is interesting that even at 1000°K the vast majority of molecules of H_2, HCl, N_2, and CO are still in their ground vibrational state.

The population of a given rotational level N_J can be expressed as

$$N_J \propto (2J + 1)e^{-E_r/kT} \tag{3-19}$$

where E_r is given by Eq. 3-3. A plot of $N_J/N_{J=0}$ versus J for HCl at 300°K is shown in Fig. 3-10. It is evident that most of the molecules

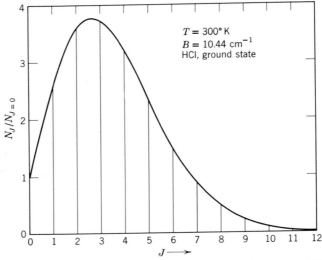

Fig. 3-10 The relative population of the rotational levels in the HCl molecule $(N_J/N_{J=0})$ as a function of rotational quantum number. From Herzberg,[1] p. 124.

possess several quanta of rotational energy at room temperature and a significant number exist with $J = 8$ or 9.

3-1B Electronic Band Spectra

Molecular electronic spectra are generally complex even for diatomic molecules. Thus the relatively simple emission spectrum of the PN molecule shown in Fig. 3-11 has what at first glance appears to be a bewildering number of lines. This complexity is understandable when we consider that in a group of molecules undergoing a given electronic transition there is *no selection rule* regarding v; see below; hence many vibrational transitions may occur. Superimposed upon this vibrational coarse structure, and discernible with a spectrograph of high resolving power, is a *fine structure* arising from simultaneous transitions between the many rotational energy levels. When we now add the possibility of several electronic transitions occurring simultaneously, it is no wonder that successful mathematical analysis of complex band spectra requires a large measure of spectroscopic intuition as well as analytical ability on the part of the investigator.

Space limitations preclude a detailed discussion of band spectra, but in view of their great importance in photochemistry it is hoped that the reader will consult treatises on the subject such as the comprehensive work by Herzberg.[1]

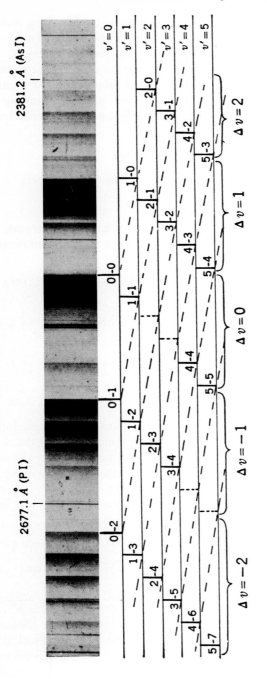

Fig. 3-11   The emission band spectrum of the PN molecule; the lower portion of the figure shows the vibrational and rotational assignments of the various lines.   From Herzberg,[1] p. 33; originally from Curry, Herzberg, and Herzberg.[42]

The electrical forces acting on the electrons and nuclei in a molecule are of the same order of magnitude, yet the very much smaller mass of the electron permits one to consider the nuclei as fixed during the 10^{-15} sec required for an electronic transition. Thus we can consider the electronic states of the molecule to be independent of the vibrational and rotational states. As a further, though somewhat less valid, approximation we shall consider the latter states also to be independent and shall write for the total energy of the molecule E (in ergs)

$$E = E_e + E_v + E_r \text{ ergs}$$

or using different symbols for energy expressed in wave numbers,

$$W = T + G + F \text{ cm}^{-1}$$

If we specify the upper state by a single prime and the lower state by a double prime, as we shall throughout the text, we can write for an electronic transition

$$\Delta E = (E' - E'') = (E_e' - E_e'') + (E_v' - E_v'') + (E_r' - E_r'') \text{ ergs} \tag{3-20a}$$

In units of *wave numbers* the frequency of an observed line in a band spectrum in cm^{-1}, ω, becomes

$$\omega = (T' - T'') + (G' - G'') + (F' - F'') \text{ cm}^{-1} \tag{3-20b}$$

3-1B-1   Vibrational Structure

We shall simplify our analysis of the formation of band structure by first assuming that there is no change in rotational energy during the change in electronic state (i.e., $F' = F''$) so that we may consider only the vibrational or *coarse structure* of the spectrum. We shall further assume that the energy of a vibrational level G, in cm^{-1}, is given by Eq. 3-16. We insert this value into Eq. 3-20b and find that the frequency of any line in the coarse structure of a molecular band spectrum is given by

$$\omega = (T' - T'') + [\omega_e'(v' + \tfrac{1}{2}) - \omega_e' x_e'(v' + \tfrac{1}{2})^2 + \omega_e' y_e'(v' + \tfrac{1}{2})^3]$$
$$- [\omega_e''(v'' + \tfrac{1}{2}) - \omega_e'' x_e''(v'' + \tfrac{1}{2})^2 + \omega_e'' y_e''(v'' + \tfrac{1}{2})^3] \text{ cm}^{-1} \tag{3-21}$$

Band *progressions* arise when the vibrational quantum number of either the upper state v' (a v' progression) or the lower state v'' (a v'' progression) is held *constant* and the other is allowed to vary. *Sequences* result from electronic transitions in which the *change* in vibrational quantum numbers, $v' - v'' = \Delta v$, is held *constant*. Thus for a given electronic transition the changes $v' = 2 \rightarrow v'' = 0$, $v' = 3 \rightarrow v'' = 1$, $v' = 4 \rightarrow v'' = 2$, etc., would lead to a *sequence* of emission lines with $\Delta v = 2$. If the spacings of the vibrational levels in the excited state are similar to those in the ground state, the lines in a given sequence will fall close together.

Formation of band *progressions* and *sequences* in emission spectra may perhaps be best understood by referring to energy-level diagrams, Figs. 3-12 and 3-13, which are essentially self-explanatory. Figure 3-11,

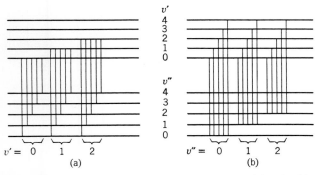

Fig. 3-12   Energy-level diagrams representing progressions of bands, (a) v' progressions; (b) v'' progressions. From Herzberg,[1] p. 153.

showing the coarse structure in the emission band spectrum of the PN molecule, provides a remarkably good actual illustration of such band progressions and sequences in a diatomic molecule.

Absorption band spectra are usually simpler than emission spectra, since at ordinary temperatures virtually all the molecules are in their ground vibrational level, $v'' = 0$, and only the $v'' = 0$ bands occur. In the case of a heavy molecule such as iodine an appreciable fraction of the molecules are in the $v'' = 1$ state (cf. Table 3-2), so a second $v'' = 1$ band is present. Figure 3-14 illustrates schematically the formation of the banded spectrum of iodine and the continuum and can be compared with an actual spectrogram for iodine vapor shown in Fig. 3-15.

3-1B-2   Rotational Fine Structure

If we now examine Eq. 3-20b and remove the restriction that $F' = F''$, it is obvious that *fine structure* due to changes in rotational energy will be added to the coarse vibrational structure of a band system. The wavelengths of the possible lines are given by

$$\omega = \omega_e + F'(J') - F''(J'')$$

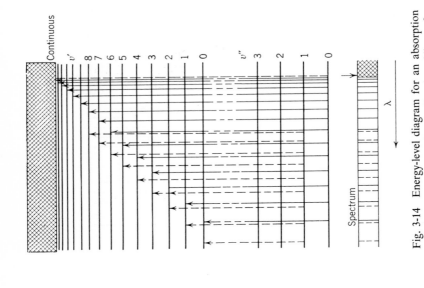

Fig. 3-14   Energy-level diagram for an absorption band system similar to that for I_2; dotted lines refer to transitions from $v'' = 1$ level, appreciably populated for a heavy weakly bound molecule such as I_2. Adapted from Herzberg,[1] p. 156.

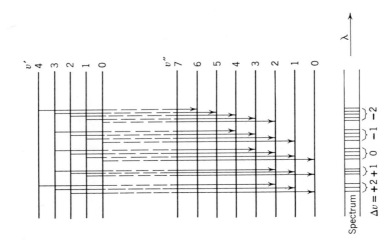

Fig. 3-13   Energy-level diagram representing the sequences in the band system of PN; see Fig. 3-11. From Herzberg,[1] p. 159.

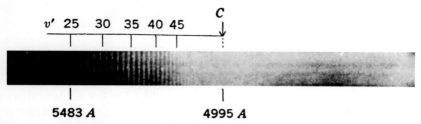

Fig. 3-15   Absorption spectrum of I_2 vapor; C denotes the position of the convergence limit of the bands (emission is shown in black; absorption in white). From Herzberg,[1] p. 38.

where $F'(J')$ and $F''(J'')$ are the *rotational terms* of the upper and lower states, respectively (cf. Eq. 3-5). If there is a difference in the electronic angular moments Ω of the upper and lower electronic states of the molecule, quantum-mechanical theory suggests that the selection rule for changes in rotational quantum number ΔJ is

$$\Delta J = J' - J'' = 0, \pm 1$$

and three branches designated P, Q, and R, corresponding to $\Delta J = -1, 0$, and $+1$, respectively, are superimposed upon a given vibrational line. If, however, $\Omega = 0$ for both the upper and lower states, a $^1\Sigma \to {}^1\Sigma$

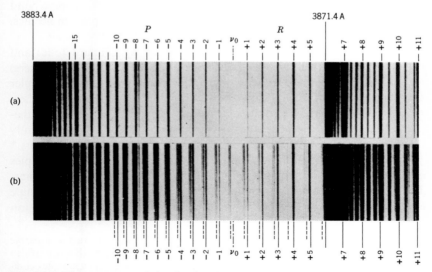

Fig. 3-16   Fine structure of the CN band 3883 A (0-0 band) (a) at low and (b) at intermediate temperatures. From Herzberg,[1] p. 44.

transition, the selection rule becomes

$$\Delta J = J' - J'' = \pm 1$$

and the Q branch vanishes. Figure 3-16 shows the rotational fine structure of the 0-0 band at 3883 A of the CN molecule at low temperatures. This band consists of a P and an R branch, the Q branch being absent, since $\Delta \Omega = 0$ for the electronic transition and the band $\Delta J = 0$ is not permitted. The numbers over the P branch are values of J'', and those over the R branch are J'. For more details on vibrational and rotational structure a treatise on spectroscopy should be consulted. Intensities of lines in band spectra will be considered in Secs. 3-1C and 3-1D.

3-1B-3   Molecular Orbital Picture of the Electronic Structure of Diatomic Molecules

Although we discussed the vibrational and rotational bands associated with a particular electronic transition, we left unanswered two questions of primary importance to photochemists: (1) What are the number and spacing of electronic energy levels in a given molecule? (2) What are the factors determining the stability of the molecule in its several electronic states? Now we shall consider qualitatively the means by which the method of molecular orbitals (MO) is employed to solve these problems for the simplest cases of homonuclear diatomic molecules. For a mathematical treatment of MO theory, consideration of the alternative valence-bond theory, and an extension of MO theory to more complex molecules, advanced works on the subject should be consulted.[1,6,7,8,9]

The method of molecular orbitals (introduced by Lennard-Jones and expanded by Mulliken, Herzberg, Longuet-Higgins, Coulson, and others) is discussed here because it seems conceptually and pedagogically simpler than valence-bond theory (Heitler, Slater, London, and Pauling). Furthermore, the MO method permits approximations which make the mathematics much less involved than in valence-bond theory. Consequently more complex molecules can be treated theoretically to yield useful results. *

The electron configuration of molecules is derived by using principles analogous to those we employed to explain electronic structure in atoms. Thus one first obtains the allowed electronic states (MO's) for a single electron in a field of two nuclei, that is, for the hydrogen molecule ion

---

* Linnett has proposed that the Lewis-Langmuir octet should be treated as a *double quartet* of electrons rather than as four pairs. This interesting approach has provided a simple and satisfactory explanation of the stability of both simple and complex compounds, the existence of which cannot otherwise be understood so readily (e.g., NO).[180,209]

$H_2{}^+$. Then as a first approximation one *assumes* that the number and distribution of these MO's are *not affected* by the addition of other electrons to the system (i.e., no electron-electron interaction). The electronic structure of a polyelectron molecule is next obtained by feeding the electrons into the available MO's, starting with the MO of lowest energy and adding electrons to levels in accordance with the Pauli exclusion principle. This *aufbau* or "building up" principle is the same one we used in Sec. 2-4A when we first obtained the allowed energy states of the hydrogen atom and then, by feeding electrons into these atomic orbitals in accord with the Pauli principle, derived the electron configuration of the rest of the elements.

Exact solution of the Schrödinger equation for an electron in the field of two nuclei of varying internuclear distance r is difficult even for the simplest case of $H_2{}^+$, and virtually impossible for polyelectron molecules larger than H_2. However, by considering the two extremes encountered in diatomic molecules, $r \rightarrow 0$ and $r \rightarrow \infty$, approximate solutions can be obtained that give the permitted electronic energy levels in the *united atom* (i.e., the case where $r = 0$) and in the separated atoms ($r \rightarrow \infty$). The distribution of MO's in actual molecules falls between these two extremes.

3-1B-3a   The United Atom Approach to MO's. The first method of generating MO's for the one-electron system $H_2{}^+$ is to visualize bringing together the hydrogen atom H_A and the ion $H_B{}^+$ until at $r = 0$ the nuclei coalesce, forming a united atom of nuclear charge $+2$ and mass 2, with one orbital electron. If repulsion between the nuclei is neglected, this corresponds to the He^+ ion. The Schrödinger equation can be solved exactly for this case of a spherically symmetrical field, yielding the molecular wave functions Ψ_i of the permitted MO's as well as the four quantum numbers n, l, m_l, and s which together specify completely the energies of these orbitals. In this united atom, assuming a field of central symmetry and no relativity effect, n and l have the same significance as in a free hydrogen atom. Thus, as is shown in column A of the correlation diagram, Fig. 3-22 (see p. 162), states with the same value of n but different values of l have the same energy, that is, are degenerate.

When we include the relativity effect in solving the Schrödinger equation for this field of central symmetry, the degeneracy in l is removed and the levels split, as shown in column B of Fig. 3-22. Now if we imagine the united atom to be split into its constituents, atom H_A and ion $H_B{}^+$, but with r kept very small and constant, we in effect generate a strong Stark type of electric field (Sec. 2-7B-4) that is cylindrically symmetric about the internuclear axis. Under these more realistic conditions (actually a good approximation for $H_2{}^+$, H_2, and He_2 in which r is small) n and l lose their quantitative validity but still retain the same meaning as in the spherical field. More significantly, the degeneracy of the quantum number m_l (which in a free atom is the vector measure of the electron orbital angular momentum in the direction of an external field, magnetic = Zeeman, electric = Stark) is removed and further splitting of energy levels occurs, as shown by the MO's in column C, Fig. 3-22. (Note, however, that the order of increasing energy of MO's of H_2^+ does not correspond to the order shown in column C, which applies to diatomic molecules in the first row of the periodic table.) The atomic quantum number m_l is now replaced by the molecular quantum number λ, which retains its validity at *all* values of the internuclear distance r. The absolute magnitude of λ determines the vector component of orbital angular momentum along the internuclear axis. From an equivalent but chemically more descriptive viewpoint, λ determines the shape of an MO in space, as we shall see in the following discussion.

Just as with the quantum numbers of free atoms, n is any integer, $l = +n - 1, n - 2, \ldots, 0$, and $s = \pm\frac{1}{2}$, and the molecular quantum number $\lambda = +l, l - 1, \ldots, 0, -l + 1, -l$ (only the absolute values are usually significant). Values of λ of 0, 1, 2, ... correspond to σ, π, and δ orbitals, analogous to s, p, and d atomic orbitals (AO's). A molecular orbital of a molecule with a small internuclear distance such as H_2^+ or H_2 is specified, in united atom terminology, by writing $nl\lambda$. Thus MO's of H_2^+ are $1s\sigma$, $2s\sigma$, $2p\sigma$, $2p\pi$, $3s\sigma$, ...

Absolute values of the electronic states of the hydrogen molecule and other hydrides calculated by this united atom approach are in reasonably good agreement with the experimental results. This is not unexpected, since r is small in these cases and the united atom model is a reasonable approximation. Quantitative agreement between theory and experiment can be obtained for H_2 if we modify our model to include the contribution of each electron to the electrostatic field in which the other electron travels (i.e., if we now assume electron-electron interaction).

For molecules such as Li_2 and larger the quantitative aspects of the united atom picture break down. The internuclear distance r is too large, and the K-shell electrons in the lithium atoms which do not contribute to molecular bonding enter into the electron distribution of the united atom and give a distorted picture. However, the concept is useful in constructing "correlation diagrams" such as Fig. 3-22 (p. 162).

3-1B-3b   Separated Atoms and LCAO Approximation to Molecular Orbitals. We now go to the other extreme and consider the distribution of MO's at large internuclear distances, that is, the separated atom approach. Under these conditions an electron moves in an orbit which extends into the neighborhood of both nuclei but spends a significant amount of time in the force field of *each* nucleus, where its wave function is essentially that of an electron in the free atom. Thus, following the original idea of Lennard-Jones,[10] we assume, as a first approximation,

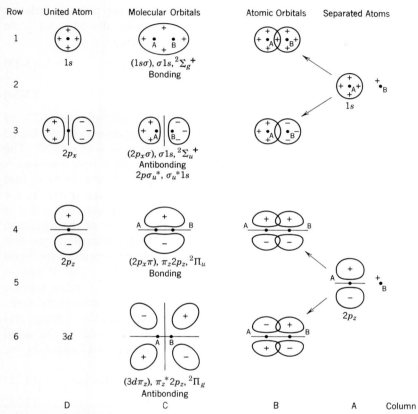

| Row | United Atom | Molecular Orbitals | Atomic Orbitals | Separated Atoms |

Fig. 3-17   Molecular orbitals of H_2^+ and their correlation with atomic orbitals in the separated and united atoms. Adapted from West,[43] p. 59.

that the molecular wave function of a molecule may be made up by a linear combination of the known atomic wave functions of the separated atoms (LCAO approximation).

For example, consider forming the hydrogen molecule ion $H_AH_B^+$ from the free hydrogen atom H_A and the proton H_B^+. Initially the electron is in a pure, spherically symmetric coulombic field of the proton H_A^+, and its AO is $\psi(A:1s)$, as shown in column A, Fig. 3-17. As the proton H_B^+ approaches atom H_A, interaction occurs and a one-electron bond is formed.

The electron now spends an equivalent time with each nucleus, so a $1s$ orbital, $\psi(B:1s)$ is assigned to $H_B{}^+$ (column B, Fig. 3-17). Now, combining the two $1s$ AO's by the LCAO approximation, we have

$$\Psi = \psi(A:1s) + \gamma\psi(B:1s) \tag{3-22}$$

The quantity γ may be considered a measure of the polarity (relative electronegativity) of the orbital. With a homopolar diatomic molecule $\gamma = \pm1$, and Eq. 3-22 becomes, for the $H_2{}^+$ molecule,

$$\Psi_g = \psi(A:1s) + \psi(B:1s); \quad \sigma_g 1s \tag{3-23}$$

and

$$\Psi_u = \psi(A:1s) - \psi(B:1s); \quad \sigma_u{}^*1s \tag{3-24}$$

It is highly significant that with the LCAO approximation two MO's are formed. One of these, Ψ_g (the $\sigma_g 1s$ level; nomenclature to be explained later), the *sum* of the two AO wave functions, is a *bonding* orbital. The other MO, Ψ_u, is the *difference* between two AO wave functions and is *antibonding*, with an energy higher than either AO. The shapes of Ψ_g and Ψ_u are shown in Column C, Fig. 3-17. The subscripts g and u refer to the German *gerade* (even) and *ungerade* (odd). A wave function is g if it is symmetric with respect to inversion through the center of the molecule, that is, no change in sign of the function occurs with inversion; one that is antisymmetric is designated u. For heteronuclear molecules there is no symmetry about the center, and this suffix is discarded. The $+$ and $-$ symbols in these diagrams designate the sign of Ψ in the various regions.

Just as with an AO, the molecular wave function Ψ determines the shape of the electron cloud, $|\Psi|^2$ is a measure of the charge density in space, and $|\Psi|^2 d\tau$ is the probability that the electron will be found in the small volume element $d\tau$. Thus, squaring both sides of Eqs. 3-23 and 3-24, we obtain

$$\Psi_g{}^2 = \psi^2(A:1s) + \psi^2(B:1s) + 2\psi(A:1s)\,\psi(B:1s) \tag{3-25}$$

$$\Psi_u{}^2 = \psi^2(A:1s) + \psi^2(B:1s) - 2\psi(A:1s)\,\psi(B:1s) \tag{3-26}$$

In the first case the distribution of electronic charge in the molecule is that of a $1s$ electron residing alternately in the neighborhood of the protons $H_A{}^+$ and $H_B{}^+$, *plus* the contribution $2[\psi(A:1s)\,\psi(B:1s)]$ of the transition structure corresponding to the electron being in the field of both nuclei. This increase in charge density between the nuclei acts as an attractive force between them, thus the term *bonding orbital* for Ψ_g. In the second case, $\Psi_u{}^2$, the contribution $2[\psi(A:1s)\,\psi(B:1s)]$ is subtracted, and the electron cloud is diminished accordingly. Hence Ψ_u is *antibonding*. The profound difference in the character of these two types of MO's is evident from the drawings of Ψ_g and Ψ_u in column C, Fig. 3-17. For Ψ_u

the nodal plane perpendicular to the internuclear axis A-B represents a plane of zero electronic charge, so that Ψ_u might be expected to be less binding and of a higher energy than Ψ_g, which has no such plane.

An excited hydrogen atom in a P state may mathematically be regarded as having three "dumbbell"-shaped $2p$ AO's, p_x, p_y, and p_z, each mutually perpendicular (cf. Fig. 2-6). In the H_2^+ molecule these wave functions of the proton and hydrogen atom can be combined to give two distinctly different types of orbitals, one with $\lambda = 0$ and one with $\lambda = \pm 1$. The latter type is doubly degenerate, corresponding to the electron (or electron current) moving "clockwise" or "counterclockwise" in the molecule. The most stable combination of AO's is that of two p_x orbitals, since there is maximum overlap along the internuclear axis A-B (the x-axis). The wave functions of the two MO's are

$$\Psi_g = \psi(A:2p_x) + \psi(B:2p_x); \quad \sigma_g 2p \tag{3-27}$$

$$\Psi_u = \psi(A:2p_x) - \psi(B:2p_x); \quad \sigma_u{}^*2p \tag{3-28}$$

Both Ψ_g and Ψ_u are symmetric about the internuclear axis; hence the angular momentum is zero, and we have excited sigma states ($\sigma_g 2p$ and $\sigma_u{}^*2p$) in which the MO's are similar to the $\sigma_g 1s$ and $\sigma_u{}^*1s$ states shown in rows 1 and 3 of column C, Fig. 3-17.

Combination of wave functions for two p_z AO's by the LCAO method gives a bonding and an antibonding MO distinctly different from the sigma types. Thus, as two p_z orbitals are brought together with the wave functions additive (Fig. 3-17, row 4), one can visualize the electron clouds coalescing to give two sausage-shaped streamers of charge density, one above and one below the nodal plane passing through the internuclear axis. There is now no symmetry about the line of centers, and since the molecule has one unit of angular momentum, $\lambda = 1$, we have a pi state, $\pi 2p_z$.

Subtracting the two p_z wave functions gives the antibonding MO, π^*2p_z, which has a nodal plane perpendicular to the internuclear axis and is thus a repulsive state of high energy. Combination of two p_y AO's also gives two molecular pi states, $\pi_y 2p$ and $\pi_y{}^*2p$, which correspond to $\pi_z 2p$ and $\pi_z{}^*2p$ except that the MO's are rotated $90°$ about the axis.

The energies of the MO's derived from the LCAO approximation for separated atoms are defined by the quantum numbers n, l, s, and the molecular quantum number λ. Only λ retains its validity as a measure of the vector component of electronic angular momentum along the internuclear axis for all values of internuclear distance r. At both small and large internuclear distances n and l are directly related to the corresponding atomic quantum numbers. At intermediate separations the relationship is obscure, and for actual molecules Mulliken[11] replaces n and l with the arbitrary symbols $z\sigma$, $y\sigma$, $x\sigma$, $w\pi$, etc., with the $z\sigma$ MO having the lowest energy. For pedagogical reasons, however, we shall usually use the somewhat more descriptive systems of united atom nomenclature for the states of H_2^+ and H_2, and the excited states of He_2, all of which at equilibrium have relatively small values of r, and separated atom terminology for diatomic molecules in the first row of the periodic table. The relationship between the two systems is shown on the correlation diagram (Fig. 3-22), where the lines connect the terms at $r = 0$ (united atom) with the equivalent terms at $r = \infty$.

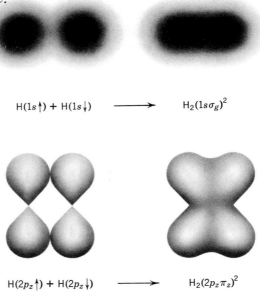

$$H(1s\uparrow) + H(1s\downarrow) \longrightarrow H_2(1s\sigma_g)^2$$

$$H(2p_z\uparrow) + H(2p_z\downarrow) \longrightarrow H_2(2p_z\pi_z)^2$$

Fig. 3-18   Electron density clouds showing formation of the molecular orbitals $(1s\sigma_g)^2$ and $(2p_z\pi_z)^2$ states of the H_2 molecule.

In expressing the term symbol of a given MO by the separated atom approach the following considerations apply:

1. Symmetry about the internuclear axis is expressed by the quantum number λ. Symmetric orbitals have zero net angular momentum about the internuclear axis so that $\lambda = 0$, and they are σ orbitals. π orbitals ($\lambda = 1$) have a nodal plane parallel to and intersecting the internuclear axis (Fig. 3-18) and have one unit of angular momentum.

2. An antibonding MO is designated by an asterisk over the symbol for λ; bonding orbitals lack the asterisk. The suffix g (*gerade*) indicates that the wave function is symmetric with respect to inversion through its center, u (*ungerade*) specifies an antisymmetric function.

3. The AO's of the separated atoms out of which, by the LCAO method, the wave function of the MO is approximated must be specified. Thus we state the value of λ, either σ, π, or δ, followed by n and the azimuthal quantum number l for the separated atoms. For example, the ground states of the H_2^+ and H_2 molecules have zero net angular momentum so $\lambda = 0$, and they are symbolized as $\sigma_g 1s$ and $\sigma_g 1s^2$ (corresponding to $1s\sigma_g$ and $(1s\sigma_g)^2$ united atom states.)

3-1B-3c Molecular Quantum Numbers.

The electronic states of a diatomic molecule are classified in terms of several molecular quantum numbers in a manner analogous to atomic electronic states. The first of these, Λ, is the component of the total electronic orbital angular momentum L along the internuclear axis. Λ can be determined precisely from an analysis of the band spectrum of a molecule (see Herzberg[1]), whereas L cannot because it is susceptible to perturbing effects (collisions, internal fields, etc.) and it is not included in a molecular term symbol. Values of Λ of 0, 1, 2, 3 are classified as Σ, Π, Δ, and Φ states.

From the viewpoint of wave mechanics, Λ arises from the solution of the wave equation that describes the shape of the molecular electron cloud. Thus $\Lambda = 0$, a Σ state, describes a cloud with rotational symmetry about the internuclear axis. This is the plum-shaped cloud shown for the bonding $1s\sigma_g$ state (or $\sigma_g 1s$, using separated atom terminology); see Fig. 3-18. It also applies to the $2p_x\sigma_u^*$ (or $\sigma_u^* 1s$) state. This has a nodal plane perpendicular to the internuclear axis and is a repulsive state, yet the MO is still symmetrical about that axis; hence $\Lambda = 0$, and again we have a Σ state. The state $\Lambda = 1$, a Π state, has one unit of angular momentum and has the typical shape of the π-electron cloud shown in Fig. 3-18.

The molecular quantum number S is the sum of the vectors of the individual electron spin momenta in units of $h/2\pi$, analogous to atoms. Thus S, which also can be determined *experimentally*, is integral, including zero, for even numbers of electrons, and half-integral for odd. When only positive values and zero are taken for S, the multiplicity of a molecular state is $2S + 1$ just as with atoms. Thus the ground state, $1s\sigma_g$, for the H_2^+ molecule is $^2\Sigma$, the multiplicity being written as a superscript preceding Λ.

The relationship of the total electron spin angular momentum with the internal molecular electric field is described by the quantity Σ. It is the vector component of S in the direction of the internuclear axis. Σ can equal $+S$, $(S-1)$, ..., $(-S+1)$, $-S$. Note the difference between Σ describing spin and Σ referring to $\Lambda = 0$. In contrast to Λ, Σ can be positive, negative, or zero.

In molecules containing atoms of low atomic weight the total electronic angular momentum along the internuclear axis is defined by the quantum number Ω, the vector sum of Λ and Σ, that is,

$$\Omega = |\Lambda + \Sigma|$$

Thus, Ω is analogous to J in atoms where $J = L + S$ for Russell-Saunders coupling.

In addition to these molecular quantum numbers certain other properties of the MO must be specified to define completely its energy. Thus, if the wave function changes sign when the coordinates of all the electrons are replaced by their negative values (this operation is called *reflection* at the center of symmetry), the state is *ungerade, u*. If Ψ is unaffected, the state is *gerade, g*. These symbols are added as subscripts to Λ.

The two states—even, g, and odd, u—occur in homonuclear diatomic molecules because of the molecular parity principle. Qualitatively, we can see that it is impossible to distinguish the case when atom 1 is in state A and atom 2 is in state B from the reverse case, atom 1 in state B and atom 2 in state A. In heteronuclear diatomic molecules, however, such distinction is possible and the symbols g and u lose their significance and are dropped.

The symbols $+$ and $-$, written as superscripts to Λ, refer to two types of sigma states, Σ^+ and Σ^-. If the wave function is unaltered by reflection about a plane through the two nuclei, the state is *positive*, $+$; if it changes sign, the state is *negative*, $-$.

3-1B-3d Electronic States of the H_2^+ Molecule. We have seen that wave functions for molecular electronic states can be approximated by the united atom approach of the LCAO method. We now raise a highly important question: given these approximate wave functions, how does one calculate the energies of the corresponding eigenstates (molecular orbitals)? A detailed discussion is beyond the scope of this book, but the following brief treatment indicates one useful approach.

In classical mechanics the total energy E of a system, in which the potential energy U is *independent* of time, is the sum of U plus T, the kinetic energy. The sum $T + U$ is called the Hamiltonian, and *classically* one writes $H = E$ as the concise form of the law of conservation of energy. However, in the transition to wave mechanics the Hamiltonian, H assumes the form of an operator that acts in a specified manner on the wave function to change it to another function. Thus, the *time-independent* wave equation in its simplest form is

$$H\psi = E\psi \qquad (3\text{-}29)$$

That is, the Hamiltonian H operating on the wave function ψ equals a new function which is the product of the energy value of the eigenstate and the ψ function. If one multiplies both sides of Eq. 3-29 by ψ and integrates over all the coordinates involved, one obtains the very important formula

$$E = \frac{\int \psi H \psi \, d\tau}{\int \psi^2 \, d\tau} \tag{3-30a}$$

or, if ψ is complex,

$$E = \frac{\int \psi^* H \psi \, d\tau}{\int \psi \psi^* \, d\tau} \tag{3-30b}$$

The denominators of 3-30a and 3-30b are normalization factors, with $d\tau$ representing the volume element in the coordinates involved; they equal unity if normalized wave functions are used.

If the Hamiltonian and wave function ψ are known, then the energy of the corresponding state can be calculated and expressed as a function of internuclear separation r (similar to Fig. 3-19). If a minimum in energy is observed, formation of a stable molecule is indicated. Usually, however, ψ is not known, and the highly useful *variation method* is employed. In this procedure one makes educated guesses of possible wave functions, substitutes them into Eq. 3-30, and, knowing the Hamiltonian operator,

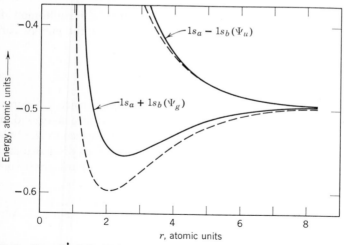

Fig 3-19 Energy of the H_2^+ molecular ion as a function of separation r, calculated by the variation method (solid lines) and exact solutions (dotted lines); 1 atomic unit = 27.2 ev on energy scale; on the r scale, 1 atomic unit = 0.529 A, the Bohr radius. From Kauzmann,[8] p. 381.

calculates corresponding energy values E which approximate the true energy E for the state in question (usually a ground state). The variation principle then specifies that all the approximate energies obtained must be greater than the true energy, and the best approximation to the wave function is the ψ that gives the lowest value of E (i.e., the value closest to the true E).

Kauzmann[8] illustrates this approach with the H_2^+ ion molecule, although this case is special in that the wave equation can, with some difficulty, be solved exactly. (This is not true, however, for H_2 and more "complex" molecules, for which this variation method is required.) Thus, for H_2^+ the Hamiltonian in atomic units is

$$H = \tfrac{1}{2}\nabla^2 - \frac{1}{r_a} - \frac{1}{r_b} + \frac{1}{R} \qquad (3\text{-}31)$$

where ∇^2 is the Laplacian,* r_a is the distance of the electron from proton a, r_b is the distance of the electron from proton b, and R is the distance between the two protons. The Born-Oppenheimer assumption is made that the nuclei of the molecule are stationary; hence their kinetic energy is neglected and $(1/R)$ is a constant.

Kauzmann tested two trial wave functions. In case 1 the assumption was made that the electron in H_2^+ is restricted to one proton, a, in a $1s$ atomic orbital, so that

$$\psi_1 = 1s_a = \pi^{-\frac{1}{2}} e^{-r_a} \qquad (3\text{-}32)$$

Substituting ψ_1 into Eq. 3-30, operating on it with the Hamiltonian, Eq. 3-31, and performing the integrations, he obtains for the energy corresponding to the wave function ψ_1

$$E_1 = -\frac{1}{2} + \left(1 + \frac{1}{R}\right)e^{-2R} \qquad (3\text{-}33)$$

This function ψ_1 does not lead to a stable molecule, since E_1 increases monotonically to infinity as R approaches zero. Hence a second trial function is selected. This time the trial function ψ_2 is formed by the LCAO method from the *sum* of *two* $1s$ atomic wave functions as discussed earlier and is identical with Ψ_g shown in Eq. 3-23. The resultant approximate ground-state energy is

$$E_2 = -\frac{1}{2} + \frac{1}{R} + \frac{(R+1)e^{-2R} - R(R+1)e^{-R} - 1}{R[(1 + R + \tfrac{1}{3}R^2)e^{-R} + 1]} \qquad (3\text{-}34)$$

---

* The symbol ∇^2 (read as "del squared") is an operator defined by the relation

$$\nabla^2 \equiv \left(\frac{\partial^2}{\partial x^2} + \frac{\partial^2}{\partial y^2} + \frac{\partial^2}{\partial z^2}\right)$$

The function E_2 is plotted in Fig. 3-19 and compared with the true energy function E_g obtained from an exact solution of the Schrödinger equation. A substantial minimum is observed in E_2, indicating that a stable bond is formed, and the values of 1.76 ev for D_e and 1.32 A for r at the potential energy minimum are in reasonable agreement (*good* considering the simplicity of the LCAO approximations) with the accurate values of 2.78 ev and 1.23 A.

An approximate potential energy curve for the first excited state of the H_2^+ molecule can be obtained by taking the wave function corresponding to the *difference* in the two atomic 1s wave functions and proceeding as outlined above. This yields the solid curve, $1s_a$-$1s_b$, shown in Fig. 3-19, which is in remarkably good agreement with the dotted curve representing the exact solution for this state. In contrast to the ground $1s\sigma_g$ state, this $1s\sigma_u^*$ state has no minimum and is thus repulsive at all separations r. Subtraction of two identical 1s wave functions (Eq. 3-24) leaves a region of zero electron density midway between the two protons; hence no stable bond can be formed. Similar considerations apply to calculation of potential energy curves for higher electronic energy states of the H_2^+ molecule ion.[8]

3-1B-3e Electronic States of the Hydrogen Molecule.

Addition of a second electron to the H_2^+ molecule introduces a repulsive electronic term in the Hamiltonian that prohibits direct solution of the Schrödinger equation. Thus, for hydrogen and more complex molecules recourse must be made to approximate solutions. One useful approach is analogous to the procedure described in Chapter 2, where the electronic structure of atoms was built up by using atomic wave functions that were the products of hydrogen-like AO's. Similarly, for the hydrogen molecule, as a first approximation one drops the term expressing the mutual repulsion between two electrons so that the Schrödinger equation becomes separable in the coordinates of the two electrons. This gives two equations equivalent to that for the hydrogen molecule ion. On this basis the wave functions for H_2 and more "complex" diatomic molecules can be taken as the *products* of suitable orbitals of H_2^+. Thus, if the LCAO approximation is employed the wave function for hydrogen in the ground state becomes

$$\Psi_{H_2} = \Psi_g \cdot \Psi_g' = [\psi(A:1s) + \psi(B:1s)][\psi(A:1s)' + \psi(B:1s)'] \quad (3\text{-}35)$$

Substituting this function into Eq. 3-30 and solving gives an energy versus nuclear separation curve for the ground state of H_2 similar to Fig. 3-19 for H_2^+, with a minimum indicating that a stable molecule is formed. The calculated values for $D_e = 2.68$ ev and $r_e = 0.85$ A obtained by Coulson[12] differ considerably from the actual values of 4.75 ev and 0.74 A. (See Fig. 3-7.) But, considering the approximations involved, the agreement is sufficiently good to warrant confidence in the application of the MO method and the *aufbau* principle to the determination of molecular electronic configuration for hydrogen and other homonuclear diatomic molecules, as shown in the next section.

In two-electron systems of homonuclear diatomic molecules such as H_2, two σ electrons can only combine to give Σ states. If they are both in

TABLE 3-3   Characteristics of Potential Energy Curves of Hydrogen[a]

Electronic Configuration	Energy of Minimum,[b] cm^{-1}		R_{min}, A		Nuclear Vibration Frequency, cm^{-1}	
	Singlet	Triplet	Singlet	Triplet	Singlet	Triplet
$(1s\sigma_g)^2 \, ^1\Sigma_g^+$	124429	...	0.7417	...	4395	...
$1s\sigma_g 2p\sigma_u^* \, ^{1,3}\Sigma_u^+$	32739	~68000[c]	1.2927	Unstable	1357	Unstable
$1s\sigma_g 2p\pi_u \, ^{1,3}\Pi_u$	24386	28685	1.0331	1.038	2443	2465
$1s\sigma_g 2s\sigma_g \, ^{1,3}\Sigma_g^+$	24366	28491	1.012	0.9887	2589	2665
$1s\sigma_g 3d\sigma_g \, ^{1,3}\Sigma_g^+$	11636	11652	1.085	1.83?	~2400	2266
$1s\sigma_g 3d\pi_g^* \, ^{1,3}\Pi_g$	11364	11421	1.060		2265	2268
$1s\sigma_g 3d\delta_g \, ^{1,3}\Delta_g$	11025	11231	1.077		2220	2265
$1s\sigma_g 3p\sigma_u^* \, ^{1,3}\Sigma_u^+$		16652		1.107		2196
$1s\sigma_g 3p\pi_u \, ^{1,3}\Pi_u$	10541	11659	1.034	1.05	2325	2372
$1s\sigma_g 3s\sigma_g \, ^{1,3}\Sigma_g^+$	10540	11659	1.065	1.0496	2538	2395
$(2p\sigma_u^*)^2 \, ^1\Sigma_g^+$	20949	...	2.32	...	1000	...
$1s\sigma_g(H_2^+) \, ^2\Sigma_g^+$	0		1.06_0		2297	

[a] Taken directly from Kauzmann,[8] p. 396.

[b] Below the minimum of H_2^+.

[c] Energy at internuclear distance of 1.29 A; this state does not have a minimum in its potential energy curve.

the lowest orbital, the electron configuration is $(1s\sigma_g)^2$ (united atom terminology is used for H_2^+, H_2, and He_2), and from the Pauli principle their spins must be opposite. Thus $S = 0$, the ground state of hydrogen is singlet, $^1\Sigma_g^+$, and hydrogen would be predicted to be diamagnetic, which it is.

Application of MO theory to H_2 as outlined above for H_2^+ gives a theoretical distribution of excited energy levels of hydrogen in reasonable agreement with the observed low-lying states given in Table 3-3. (Compare also Figs. 154 and 160 of Herzberg,[1] and see Kauzmann,[8] pp. 391–398.) From the electron configurations shown in this table it is evident that transition to any of the first nine excited states involves excitation of only one of the electrons; the other remains in the $1s\sigma_g$ MO, and the electron configuration of the first excited state of the hydrogen molecule becomes $(1s\sigma_g)(2p\sigma_u{}^*)$. Since the electrons occupy different orbitals, a singlet $(1s\sigma_g)(2p\sigma_u{}^*)$, $^1\Sigma_u^+$, and a triplet $(1s\sigma_g)(2p\sigma_u{}^*)$, $^3\Sigma_u^+$, exist. If Hund's

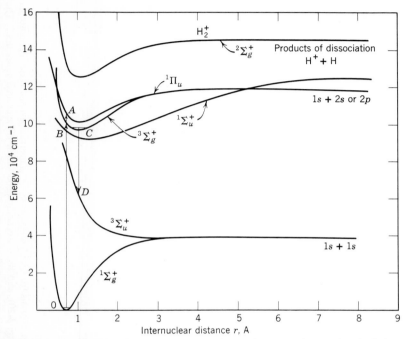

Fig. 3-20 Potential energy curves for several electronic states of H_2 and H_2^+ of photochemical interest; transitions $B \leftarrow O$ and $A \leftarrow O$ correspond to important absorption bands at 1109 and 1002 A, respectively. The transition $C \rightarrow D$ results in the continuum which is of great value as an ultraviolet source for absorption spectroscopy. Adapted from Bowen,[7] p. 89, and Kauzmann,[8] p. 397.

rule applies to molecules as well as to atoms (Sec. 2-6), the triplet should lie at a lower energy. The data in Table 3-3 reveal that it does by some 100 kcal/mole at $r = 1.29$ A (cf. also Fig. 3-20). It is necessary to specify internuclear distance because no minimum exists in the potential energy curve of the $^3\Sigma_u^+$ state (Fig. 3-20); the excited molecule is unstable, and dissociation into two $1s$ hydrogen atoms occurs at all values of r. This is not surprising since the repulsive force of the $2p\sigma_u{}^*$ antibonding MO exceeds the attractive power of the $1s\sigma_g$ bonding orbital, and an unstable molecule would be expected. However, other more subtle factors also

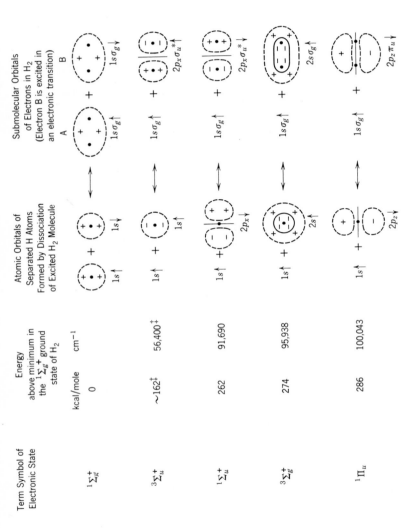

Fig. 3-21   The submolecular orbitals for four photochemically important excited states of molecular H_2 involving the $1s\sigma_g$ orbital (Fig. 3-20), and the dissociation products of these excited molecules.‡ The $^3\Sigma_u^+$ state does not have a minimum in its potential energy curve; this value equals the energy at an internuclear distance of 1.29 Å.

influence the overall bond strength. Thus, the potential energy curve for the $^1\Sigma_u^+$ state, also shown in Fig. 3-20, has a minimum, and a "stable" excited molecule exists in this state (see Kauzmann,[8] pp. 396–398 and footnote on p. 392).

The second excited MO for H_2^+ is $2p\pi_u$, and the corresponding molecular orbital for excited hydrogen is $(1s\sigma_g)(2p\pi_u)$. (Note that this order differs from the MO's for He_2 and other diatomic molecules shown in the correlation diagram, Fig. 3-22, in which the $2s\sigma_g$ MO is more stable than the $2p\pi_u$ orbital.) This again leads to singlet, $^1\Pi_u$, and triplet, $^3\Pi_u$, states with the latter having the lower energy of the two. Actually, stabilization due to triplet formation occurs to such an extent that the $^3\Sigma_g^+$ state involving excitation to the third excited MO, $2s\sigma_g$, has a lower energy than the $^1\Pi_u$ state. Thus, the order of increasing energy of states for hydrogen is $^1\Sigma_g^+$, $^3\Sigma_u^+$, $^1\Sigma_u^+$, $^3\Pi_u$, $^3\Sigma_g^+$, $^1\Pi_u$, . . . (see Table 3-3).

Although Table 3-3 lists ten excited states for the hydrogen molecule, application of molecular selection rules (see Sec. 3-1C-3) restricts the number that are of prime interest in photochemistry to the four whose potential energy curves are shown in Fig. 3-20. Thus, at ordinary temperatures electronic absorption bands can arise solely from the ground state $^1\Sigma_g^+$. Furthermore, the selection rules, $\Delta\Omega = 0$, ± 1, $g \leftrightarrow u$ but $g \not\leftrightarrow g$, and $\Delta S = 0$, restrict probable transitions to just the $^1\Sigma_u^+$ and $^1\Pi_u$ levels, so that in molecular absorption only the 1109 A and 1002 A lines, respectively, are observed.

The transition $^3\Sigma_g^+ \rightarrow {}^3\Sigma_u^+$ results in a highly useful continuum ranging from the Schumann region in the far ultraviolet to about 3500 A in the near ultraviolet. As we have seen (Fig. 3-20), the lower state is repulsive at all values of r; hence transitions to it from the higher $^3\Sigma_g^+$ level result directly in the liberation of light and the formation of two $1s$ hydrogen atoms. These carry off the electronic excitation energy as non-quantized kinetic energy, so that an intense continuum, often used as a light source, is generated.

Kauzmann[8] gives the potential energy curves for all ten excited states of hydrogen and points out that, in all but the $(2p\sigma_u{}^*)^2$, $^1\Sigma_g^+$, the $(1s\sigma_g)$ $(2p\sigma_u{}^*)$, $^1\Sigma_u^+$, and the $^3\Sigma_u^+$ states, the minima in their potential curves fall near 1.05 A, very close to r_e for the hydrogen molecule ion (see Table 3-3). Furthermore, as seen in Fig. 3-20, the shapes of the curves near the equilibrium distance r_e are very similar to the shape for H_2^+. This implies that most of the bonding in these excited states is due to each sharing one electron in the $1s\sigma$ submolecular orbital, which is strongly bonding. In Fig. 3-21 submolecular orbitals for these four excited states and atomic orbitals for the dissociation products of these states are shown schematically.

3-1B-3f   Electronic Structures of Diatomic Molecules in the First Period.
In determining the electronic structure of multielectron atoms we used the
aufbau or "building up" principle of adding electrons to hydrogen-like
AO's in the order of increasing energy and in accord with the Pauli
exclusion principle.   Similarly we can feed electrons into the MO's
determined for the H_2^+ molecule ion and, by neglecting electron-electron
interaction, obtain an approximation of the electronic structure of more
complex molecules.

The relative distribution of MO's for H_2^+-like homonuclear diatomic
molecules at a large *fixed value* of r, determined by Mulliken[11] from a study
of molecular structure, is

$$\sigma 1s < \sigma^* 1s < \sigma 2s < \sigma^* 2s < \sigma 2p$$

$$< (\pi_y 2p = \pi_z 2p) < (\pi_y^* 2p = \pi_z^* 2p) \quad (3\text{-}36)$$

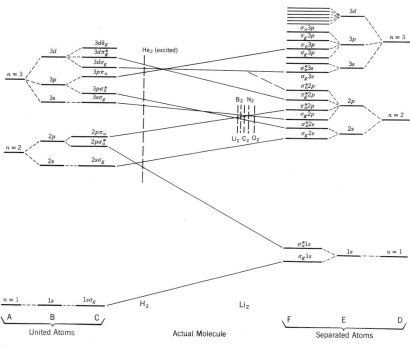

Fig 3-22   Correlation diagram showing approximate relative energies of MO's of
homonuclear diatomic molecules as derived from the united atom and separated atom
methods; correlation between the two types of MO's is shown by lines connecting
states of the same λ value and same symmetry (non-crossing rule applies). Adapted
from Herzberg,[1] p. 329.

Actually the order of increasing energy of these MO's depends upon the internuclear distance r. Thus in the correlation diagram, Fig. 3-22, the states for large values of r (the separated atom discussed in Sec. 3-1B-3b) are shown in column F. The order of increasing energy of these states is that shown in relation 3-36. The states into which they are transformed when $r \rightarrow 0$ and a united atom is formed are shown in column C. Vertical lines indicate the approximate positions of several homonuclear diatomic molecules in the first period. In preparing the diagram the *non-crossing* rule is applied. This specifies that lines joining two levels which have the same symmetry properties cannot cross as r is varied. Thus a σ_g line must not cross another σ_g line, but it may cross a σ_u line.

At best, the locations of the vertical lines indicating actual molecules with intermediate values of r are only approximate, since the scale for r is non-linear. It is rapidly compressed at the larger values, and the lines should be curved rather than straight. Furthermore Fig. 3-22 is not suitable for use with H_2 and H_2^+, and another correlation diagram (Kauzmann,[8] p. 228) is required for these small molecules. However, the accuracy is sufficient in the figure to warrant its use in describing the energy levels of homonuclear diatomic molecules in the first row of the periodic table.

In addition to considering relative energy levels in these molecules, we can also use MO theory to predict approximate bond dissociation energies and bond lengths. Thus Herzberg[1] defines the quantity *bond order as*

$$\tfrac{1}{2} \times [(\text{no. of bonding electrons}) - (\text{no. of non-bonding electrons})]$$

Bond orders of 1 and 2 would be roughly equivalent to the "single bond" and "double bond," respectively, in the chemist's terminology.

With these concepts and the correlation diagram (Fig. 3-22) we are in a position to derive the ground-state electronic configuration for molecules from He_2^+ through Ne_2. The results, including H_2^+ and H_2, which were covered previously, are summarized in Table 3-4. For consistency, all molecular orbitals will be classified by means of the separated atom terminology, although the united atom nomenclature is preferable for He_2^+.

1. He_2^+. This molecule is formed by combining a helium atom with two $1s$ electrons and a helium ion having only one electron in its $1s$ orbital. Since only two electrons with opposite spins can occupy the lowest $\sigma_g 1s$ MO, the third electron must go into the next higher energy level, the anti-bonding $\sigma_u^* 1s$ orbital. The electron configuration becomes $(\sigma_g 1s)^2(\sigma_u^* 1s)$.

$$He(1s)^2 + He^+(1s) \rightarrow He_2^+(\sigma 1s)^2(\sigma^* 1s); \quad (^2\Sigma_u)$$

The bond order is $\tfrac{1}{2}(2 - 1) = \tfrac{1}{2}$; hence the He_2^+ molecule should have about one half of a chemical bond and be somewhat stable. It has been

TABLE 3-4 Summary of Properties of Ground States of Some Simple Diatomic Molecules[a]

Molecule	Electronic Configuration	State	N_b = No. of Bonding Electrons	N_a = No. of Antibonding Electrons	$\frac{1}{2}(N_b - N_a)$ = No. of Bonds	Dissociation Energy, ev	Bond Length, A	Force Constant, dyne cm^{-1} × 10^5
H_2^+	$(\sigma_g 1s)$	$^2\Sigma_g^+$	1	0	$\frac{1}{2}$	2.648	1.06	1.56
H_2	$(\sigma_g 1s)^2$	$^1\Sigma_g^+$	2	0	1	4.476	0.74	5.60
He_2^+	$(\sigma_g 1s)^2(\sigma_u{}^*1s)$	$^2\Sigma_u^+$	2	1	$\frac{1}{2}$	(3.1)	1.08	3.13
He_2	$(\sigma_g 1s)^2(\sigma_u{}^*1s)^2(= KK)$	$^1\Sigma_g^+$	2	2	0	0	...	...
Li_2	$KK(\sigma_g 2s)^2$	$^1\Sigma_g^+$	2	2	0	1.03	2.67	0.25
Be_2	$KK(\sigma_g 2s)^2(\sigma_u{}^*2s)^2$	$^1\Sigma_g^+$	2	2	0	...	...	...
B_2	$KK(\sigma_g 2s)^2(\sigma_u{}^*2s)^2(\pi_u 2p)^2$	$^3\Sigma_g^-$	4	2	1	(3.0)	1.59	3.60
C_2	$KK(\sigma_g 2s)^2(\sigma_u{}^*2s)^2(\pi_u 2p)^3(\sigma_g 2p)$	$^3\Pi_u$	6	2	2	(5.9)	1.31	9.55
N_2^+	$KK(\sigma_g 2s)^2(\sigma_u{}^*2s)^2(\pi_u 2p)^4(\sigma_g 2p)$	$^2\Sigma_g^+$	7	2	$2\frac{1}{2}$	8.73	1.12	20.1
N_2	$KK(\sigma_g 2s)^2(\sigma_u{}^*2s)^2(\pi_u 2p)^4(\sigma_g 2p)^2$	$^1\Sigma_g^+$	8	2	3	9.756	1.09	23.1
O_2^+	$KK(\sigma_g 2s)^2(\sigma_u{}^*2s)^2(\pi_u 2p)^4(\sigma_g 2p)^2(\pi_g{}^*2p)$	$^2\Pi_g$	8	3	$2\frac{1}{2}$	6.48	1.12	16.6
O_2	$KK(\sigma_g 2s)^2(\sigma_u{}^*2s)^2(\pi_u 2p)^4(\sigma_g 2p)^2(\pi_g{}^*2p)^2$	$^3\Sigma_g^-$	8	4	2	5.080	1.21	11.8
F_2	$KK(\sigma_g 2s)^2(\sigma_u{}^*2s)^2(\pi_u 2p)^4(\sigma_g 2p)^2(\pi_g{}^*2p)^4$	$^1\Sigma_g^+$	8	6	1	(1.6)	1.44	4.45
Ne_2	$KK(\sigma_g 2s)^2(\sigma_u{}^*2s)^2(\pi_u 2p)^4(\sigma_g 2p)^2(\pi_g{}^*2p)^4(\sigma_u{}^*2p)^2$	$^1\Sigma_g^+$	8	8	0	0	...	...

[a] Adapted from Herzberg,[1] p. 343; from Kauzmann,[8] p. 706.

observed spectroscopically and its bond dissociation energy estimated at about 60 kcal/mole.

2. He_2. The electron configuration is

$$2He(1s)^2 \rightarrow He_2(\sigma 1s)^2(\sigma^*1s)^2; \quad (^1\Sigma_g^+)$$

Since an antibonding orbital is generally more relaxing than a bonding orbital is binding, He_2 would be expected to be unstable (zero bond order), and indeed it does not exist in the ground state. However, when one of the σ^*1s electrons is raised, by electronic excitation, to a higher energy bonding orbital, there is a net surplus of bonding electrons and a stable molecule exists. A number of such excited He_2 molecules have been formed in gas discharges, and their spectroscopic constants evaluated. The first two stable states of excited He_2 involve the transition of an electron from the σ_u^*1s MO to the $\sigma_g 2s$ MO so that the configuration of the molecule is $(\sigma_g 1s)^2(\sigma_u^*1s)(\sigma_g 2s)$. The states are $^1\Sigma_u^+$ and $^3\Sigma_u^+$, the triplet being the lowest in accord with Hund's rule. The singlet state is important in that transitions from this level to the unstable ground state of He_2, that is, the $^1\Sigma_u^+ \rightarrow {}^1\Sigma_g^+$ transition, result in a very intense continuous emission spectrum in the far-ultraviolet region, 600–1000 A. This spectrum was first observed in helium discharges by Hopfield[13] and studied more extensively by Tanaka.[14]

Other stable states of He_2 can be predicted from the order for helium orbitals shown in the correlation diagram, Fig. 3-22. (Spectroscopic constants can be obtained from Kauzmann,[8] Table 11-3, p. 399.)

3. Li_2. Since only the valence electrons need be considered in forming the bond, one writes

$$2Li(1s^2 2s) \rightarrow Li_2[KK(\sigma 2s)^2; \quad (^1\Sigma_g^+)$$

where KK specifies that both K shells are fully occupied. The bond strength in Li_2 is low, 23.7 kcal/mole, and the bond length large, $r = 2.672$ A, compared to 103 kcal/mole and 0.742 A for H_2. The diffuse nature of the $2s$ AO's of the lithium atoms results in a reduction of the electron density along the internuclear axis of the Li_2 molecule, and thus the bond is weakened.

4. Be_2, B_2, and C_2. In the case of Be_2 the electron configuration is $KK(\sigma_g 2s)^2(\sigma_u^*2s)^2$, $^1\Sigma_g^+$. The bond order is zero, and no stable Be_2 molecule has been observed. Boron can form a diatomic molecule having several possible ground-state configurations, since it lies close to the crossing point of the $\sigma_g 2p$ and $\pi_u 2p$ correlation lines (Fig. 3-22). In either case there are four bonding and two antibonding electrons; therefore the bond order is 1 and a stable molecule is expected. This is observed, and B_2 has a D_e of about 69 kcal/mole and r_e of 1.59 A.

The molecule C_2 has been shown to be $^3\Pi_u$ in the ground state, suggesting that its configuration is $KK(\sigma_g 2s)^2(\sigma_u *2s)^2(\pi_u 2p)^3(\sigma_g 2p)$. Apparently the additional stability afforded the triplet state results in the fourth $\pi_u 2p$ electron being promoted to the $\sigma_g 2p$ level. The important Swan bands found in emission and absorption spectra of discharges from carbon arcs, flames, tails of comets, etc., result from the transition $^3\Pi_g \rightarrow {}^3\Pi_u$.

5. N_2. The formation of nitrogen may be represented as

$$2N(1s^2 2s^2 2p^3) \rightarrow N_2[KK(\sigma 2s)^2(\sigma *2s)^2(\sigma 2p)^2(\pi 2p)^4]; \quad (^1\Sigma_g^+)$$

The bonding power of the $(\sigma 2s)^2$ orbital is essentially cancelled by the antibonding of the $(\sigma_g *2s)^2$ orbital. Thus there are six bonding electrons, and the order is 3. N_2 is known to be very stable ($D_e = 9.756$ ev = 225 kcal/mole), and it has a triple bond between the nitrogen atoms. One is a σ bond; the others are the degenerate π_y and π_z bonds, with electron clouds in alternating positions parallel to the internuclear axis and 90° apart.

6. O_2. The oxygen molecule is interesting, since the electron pair theory of valence failed to explain satisfactorily the fact that the ground state of O_2 is a triplet ($^3\Sigma$) and the molecule is strongly paramagnetic. These facts are explained naturally by application of MO theory. Thus we write

$$2O(1s^2 2s^2 2p^4) \rightarrow$$
$$O_2[KK(\sigma 2s)^2(\sigma *2s)^2(\sigma 2p)^2(\pi_y 2p)^2(\pi_z 2p)^2(\pi_y *2p)(\pi_z *2p)]; \quad (^3\Sigma_g^-)$$

The orbitals are filled in the usual manner up to the $\pi *2p$ level, which is degenerate since it contains $\pi_y *2p$ and $\pi_z *2p$ MO's, each of which will hold two electrons with antiparallel spins. Only two electrons are left, and to achieve maximum stability (Hund's rule) one goes into the $\pi_y *2p$ MO and the other, with parallel spin, into the $\pi_z *2p$ MO. Thus the ground state of oxygen should have two unpaired electrons and be a paramagnetic triplet state. This is in complete accord with experimental facts and represents one of the earliest successes of MO theory.

It is interesting to consider how MO theory treats the relative stability of O_2 versus O_2^+ and N_2 versus N_2^+ molecules. If one electron is removed from the O_2 molecule, it will presumably be the one of highest energy, either $\pi_y *2p$ or $\pi_z *2p$. Since this is antibonding, the O_2^+ molecule will now have eight bonding and three antibonding electrons and a bond order of $(8 - 3)/2 = 2\frac{1}{2}$. Thus D_{O-O} in O_2^+ should be *greater* than D_{O-O} in O_2, as indeed it is (6.48 ev, versus 5.08 ev of Table 3-4). In the case of $N_2 \rightarrow N_2^+$ a $\pi_y 2p$ bonding electron is removed, and the bond order of N_2^+ becomes $(7 - 2)/2 = 2\frac{1}{2}$, so that D_{N-N} in N_2^+ should be *less* than D_{N-N} in N_2. This is confirmed by the experimental facts (8.73 ev versus 9.76 ev for N_2).

3-1B-3g Heteronuclear Diatomic Molecules. The principles followed in building up homonuclear molecules can be extended to heteropolar binding where the two nuclei differ. Thus bonding occurs only between AO's having nearly equal energies and the same symmetry about the internuclear axis, that is, the same vector component of angular momentum, $m_l h/2\pi$, in the direction of the bond axis. The LCAO approximation

$$\Psi = \psi_A + \gamma\psi_B$$

can still be made, but γ is no longer equal to ± 1 since the electronegativity of the two atoms is different.

Consider the bonding MO for the HCl molecule. We can write

$$\Psi = \psi(H:1s) + \gamma\psi(Cl:3p_x)$$

Since the chlorine atom is more electronegative than the hydrogen atom, the electron will spend more time in the region of the Cl nucleus and $\gamma > 1$. The larger γ, the greater is the polarity of the bond and the more unsymmetrical the MO. The electronic structure may be written

$$H(1s) + Cl(1s^2 2s^2 2p^6 3s^2 3p^5) = HCl[KL(\sigma 3s)^2(\sigma 3p)^2(\pi_y 3p)^2(\pi_z 3p)^2]$$

Electrons which occupy three types of orbitals are present in the HCl molecule. The K and L orbitals contain entirely atomic *inner-shell* electrons, while the $(3s)^2$, $(3p_y)^2$, and $(3p_z)^2$ electrons are *valence-shell non-bonding* electrons (often called *lone-pair* electrons) which are mainly atomic in character. Only the $\sigma 3p$ orbital containing two valence-shell bonding electrons is an effective *molecular* orbital, and it is this orbital that provides the chemical bond between the atoms.

Nitric oxide is frequently used as a free-radical trap or scavenger in photochemical studies. The formation of its molecular orbitals may be represented as

$$N(1s^2 2s^2 2p^3) + O(1s^2 2s^2 2p^4) \rightarrow$$

$$NO[KK(\sigma 2s)^2(\sigma^* 2s)^2(\sigma 2p)^2(\pi_y 2p)^2(\pi_z 2p)^2(\pi_y^* 2p)]$$

or, more realistically, by using Mulliken's terminology

$$\rightarrow NO[KK(z\sigma)^2(y\sigma)^2(x\sigma)^2(w\pi)^4(v\pi)]$$

Since $(z\sigma)^2$, $(x\sigma)^2$, and $(w\pi)^4$ are bonding and $(y\sigma)^2$ and $(v\pi)$ are valence-shell antibonding, the bond order is $2\frac{1}{2}$ and there is one unpaired electron in the $v\pi(\pi_y^* 2p)$ orbital. This accounts for the paramagnetic behavior of NO and for its high reactivity with free radicals which also possess odd electrons.

Heteronuclear diatomic molecules such as NO, CO, CN, BO, and BN have sufficiently similar nuclei to permit the use of a homonuclear correlation diagram. However, for molecules with unlike nuclei, such as the hydrogen halides, LiH, BeH, and CH, this is not satisfactory, and special techniques applicable to heteromolecules must be employed.

3-1C   Wave-Mechanical Picture of Absorption and Emission of Electromagnetic Radiation by Simple Molecules

We discussed in Sec. 2-7A the nature of the interaction of light with the electrons of an atom and the rules which governed excitation. The wave-mechanical treatment of the absorption process in molecules follows the

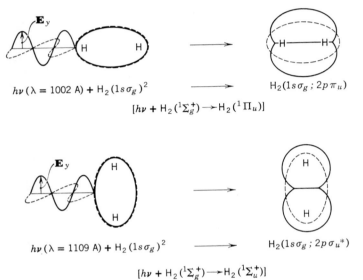

$h\nu\,(\lambda = 1002\ \text{A}) + H_2\,(1s\sigma_g)^2 \qquad\longrightarrow\qquad H_2(1s\sigma_g\,;\,2p\pi_u)$

$$[h\nu + H_2\,({}^1\Sigma_g^+)\longrightarrow H_2\,({}^1\Pi_u)]$$

$h\nu\,(\lambda = 1109\ \text{A}) + H_2\,(1s\sigma_g)^2 \qquad\longrightarrow\qquad H_2(1s\sigma_g\,;\,2p\sigma_u{}^*)$

$$[h\nu + H_2\,({}^1\Sigma_g^+)\longrightarrow H_2\,({}^1\Sigma_u^+)]$$

Fig. 3-23   The wave-mechanical picture of absorption of 1002 and 1109 A Lyman radiation by molecular hydrogen; one electron moves on absorption of light to a higher orbit with a nodal plane at right angles to the electronic vector of the quantum. After Bowen,[7] p. 111.

same pattern. The probability of absorption or emission of radiation by molecules is also proportional to the dipole transition strength. However, in dealing with molecules the spatial relationship between the electric vector of the quantum and the internuclear axis becomes important. Thus, as shown in Fig. 3-23, the absorption of 1109 A radiation with its electric vector *parallel* to the internuclear axis of the hydrogen molecule forces one σ_g electron into oscillation about a nodal plane perpendicular to the molecular axis. This produces a wave function of the familiar hourglass-shaped $2p$ orbital. The transition is

$$H_2(1s\sigma_g)^2 + h\nu\,(1109\ \text{A}) \to H_2(1s\sigma_g\,;\;2p\sigma_u{}^*)$$

or
$$H_2(^1\Sigma_g^+) + h\nu \ (1109 \ A) \rightarrow H_2(^1\Sigma_u^+)$$

When the electric vector of the quantum is perpendicular to the molecular axis the cloud of the absorbing electron is displaced above and below the axis, forming a nodal plane intersecting the axis and parallel to it. This is the $1s\sigma_g$; $2p\pi_u$ state, which is more energetic than the $1s\sigma_g$; $2p\sigma_u{}^*$ state (see Table 3-3) and requires 1002 A radiation.

$$H_2(1s\sigma_g)^2 + h\nu \ (1002 \ A) \rightarrow H_2(1s\sigma_g; \ 2p\pi_u)$$

or
$$H_2(^1\Sigma_g^+) + h\nu \ (1002 \ A) \rightarrow H_2(^1\Pi_u)$$

One approach to the calculation of absolute intensities of bands follows that of Mulliken, who presented the theory of absolute intensities of electronic transitions in molecular spectra in a series of papers starting in 1939;[15] see also Mulliken and Rieke.[16] The subject is well discussed and summarized in Herzberg[1] and Kauzmann.[8]

Mulliken's general procedure is to consider the total spectrum associated with a molecular electronic transition as being analogous to (and having approximately the same absolute intensity as) a single line associated with a similar single electronic transition in an atom. Thus a continuous molecular spectrum corresponds to a very broad atomic line, while a molecular spectrum with vibrational and rotational structure corresponds to an atomic line with fine structure. The absolute total strength of a molecular electronic transition is defined as the integral of the intensity over all the resulting band lines and the whole of the continuum. This is similar to obtaining absolute intensities for electronic transitions in atoms.

The *total strength per molecule* is usually obtained experimentally by utilizing absorption spectra, preferably continuous. With gases spectra are often taken at high pressures so that a discrete gaseous spectrum will become almost continuous. The total strength of all the absorption lines and/or continuum is divided by the total population of all the initial states to obtain the strength per molecule.

The total strength of a transition determined by this method is practically independent of temperature. Thus, a temperature change redistributes the molecules among the various appropriate vibrational and rotational levels of the ground state, but this has little effect because the electronic transition probability is practically independent of the vibrational or rotational level which the molecule occupies at the time of absorbing a photon.

With these general remarks we shall proceed to consider theoretical and experimental equations for the calculation of absolute absorption and emission intensities, and the mean lifetimes of excited states.

3-1C-1   The Theory of Light Absorption by Molecules

According to the wave-mechanical picture, the probability of light absorption by molecules is governed by the magnitude of dipole strength D or the square of the transition moment integral $\mathbf{m}$, as in the atomic systems:

$$D = \mathbf{m}^2 = \left(\int \Psi'_m \mathbf{M} \Psi'_n \, d\tau \right)^2 \tag{2-22}$$

The summation in the dipole moment operator $\mathbf{M}$ (Σer_i) is carried out over all electrons as before with the atomic case, but r_i is now the distance of the ith electron from the center of positive charge of the molecule.

Ψ'_m and Ψ'_n represent the total electronic wave functions of the initial and final states, respectively. Mulliken and Rieke have determined values of D for a series of simple molecules;[16] for molecules of even moderate complexity simplification of the method is necessary to overcome the prohibitive complexity of the more rigorous solution. Thus in these cases it is assumed that the wave functions can be factored into single electron functions, that only one electron is excited, and that the distribution of all other electrons in the excited state can be described by their ground-state wave functions. In these conditions the transition moment integral becomes

$$\mathbf{m} = \int \psi_m^* \mathbf{M} \psi_n \, d\tau$$

where the wave functions ψ_m and ψ_n refer to the appropriate functions for the ground-state and excited-state orbitals of the single electron undergoing change. Although the results are approximate for this method of solution, much useful qualitative information on the probability of the transitions has been obtained by using this approach.

Theory points to the following relationship between the dipole strength of the transition D and the Einstein probability for absorption B_{mn} (see Sec. 2-7A-1).

$$B_{mn} = \left(\frac{8\pi^3 e^2}{3h^2 c} \right) G_n D \tag{3-37}$$

where G_n is the degeneracy of the nth state, that is, the number of suitable orbitals in the excited state that belong to the final energy level and with which any one suitable orbital of the ground state can combine; e is the charge on the electron, and the other symbols have their usual meaning.

The f number or *oscillator strength* is frequently employed in describing the absolute intensity of an electronic transition. It arises in classical dispersion theory in the expression for the molar refraction R of a substance:

$$R = \frac{M(n^2 - 1)}{d(n^2 + 2)} = \frac{Ne^2}{3\pi m_e} \sum \frac{f_{mn}}{v_{mn}^2 - v^2} \qquad (3\text{-}38)$$

where M is the gram-molecular weight of the substance; d is the density (grams/cm³); n is the refractive index; N is Avogadro's number; the summation is over all excited states n (including continuum states) to which transition from the normal state m occurs. The quantity v_{mn} is the frequency of the absorption band having a mean oscillator strength f_{mn}, and v is the actual frequency of the light used.

It follows from Eq. 3-38 that, if one allows the frequency of the incident light to approach the value for a specific absorption band v_{mn}, the refractive index should increase, the increase being greatest for strong absorption bands. This increase is observed experimentally, the phenomenon being called dispersion. Indeed f numbers are often referred to as the *effective number of dispersion electrons*. The total *oscillator strength* of an absorption band can be regarded as the effective number of electrons set into oscillation about their equilibrium positions in their respective normal modes when a group of molecules is placed in a radiation field (e.g., light of frequency v). Thus, in terms of classical mechanics one interprets the frequency of absorption of a spectral band as the normal mode frequency of a classical oscillating electron, and the oscillator strength as a measure of the absorption band relative to that of a classical three-dimensional harmonic oscillator.

The useful relationship between classical *oscillator strength* f_{mn} and the quantum-mechanical dipole strength D of an electronic absorption band is

$$f_{mn} = \left(\frac{8\pi^2 m_e c g_n}{3he^2}\right) \omega_{mn} D \qquad (3\text{-}39)$$

where ω_{mn} is the frequency in cm⁻¹. The identical expression holds for emission except that g_n is replaced by the degeneracy of the lower state, g_m (Kauzmann,[8] p. 646).

Substituting 3-37 into 3-39, we relate the oscillator strength to the Einstein transition probability of absorption, B_{mn}:

$$f_{mn} = \left(\frac{m_e hc^2 \omega_{mn}}{\pi e^2}\right) B_{mn} \qquad (3\text{-}40)$$

A further useful relationship exists between the oscillator strength and the experimentally determined integrated molar extinction coefficient of an absorption band:

$$f_{mn} = \left[\frac{2303 m_e c^2}{\pi N e^2}\right] F \int_{\omega_1}^{\omega_2} \epsilon \, d\omega = 4.32 \times 10^{-9} F \int_{\omega_1}^{\omega_2} \epsilon \, d\omega \qquad (3\text{-}41)$$

where the integration extends over the entire band related to the transition from state $m \to n$; N is Avogadro's number, and F constitutes a correction factor near unity related to the refractive index of the medium in which the absorbing molecule is dissolved. Lewis and Kasha[17] chose $F = \mathbf{n}^2$, but Rubinowicz[18] derives $F = 9\mathbf{n}/(\mathbf{n}^2 + 2)^2$. In actual practice it is common to take $F = 1$ in the application of the equation; however, for large $\mathbf{n}$ values the F values may be significantly different from unity (e.g., 0.69 for $\mathbf{n} = 1.6$, using the Rubinowicz relation).

We see from Eq. 3-41 that the oscillator strength for a normal mode frequency is directly proportional to the area under the curve of the corresponding absorption band.

The magnitude of f, and hence that of ϵ, is restricted by theory; the Kuhn-Thomas *sum rule*, derived from classical or wave mechanics for a single emission electron, states

$$\sum f_i = 1 \qquad (3\text{-}42)$$

where the summation extends over all absorptions (see Kauzmann,[8] p. 651). It follows from 3-42 that for the strongest electronic transition, absorption or emission, the oscillator strengths are of the order of unity. As a crude but useful approximation, the area of the average absorption band in solution can be characterized in terms of the half-width of the absorption band, $\Delta\omega_{1/2}$. This is the width at which $\epsilon = \frac{1}{2}\epsilon_{\max}$, and, assuming a band symmetrical about $\epsilon_{\max}$, we have

$$\int \epsilon_\omega \, d\omega \cong \epsilon_{\max} \Delta\omega_{1/2} \qquad (3\text{-}43)$$

The absorption bands of many molecules in solution have half-widths of the order of 5000 cm^{-1}. Thus, taking an oscillator strength of unity and inserting 3-41 into 3-43, we find $\epsilon_{\max} \cong 5 \times 10^4$. This is an approximate theoretical upper limit to values for $\epsilon_{\max}$. Typical f numbers include 10^{-6} to 10^{-8} for rare earth ions in the visible region, 10^{-4} for Cu^{2+}, Cr^{3+}, Fe^{3+}, and ions of similar transition metals, and about 3×10^{-2} for the absorption responsible for the deep purple color of MnO_4^- ion. The long-wavelength absorption bands of the aliphatic aldehydes and ketones have maxima in the region around 2700–2900 A and $\epsilon_{\max}$ of about 10–30. These correspond to oscillator strengths in the range 2×10^{-4} to 6×10^{-4}.

Often experimental oscillator strengths calculated from refractive index values (3-38) or absorption spectra data (3-41) are compared with theoretical f numbers obtained by substituting dipole strengths calculated by wave mechanics into 3-39. However, caution should be exercised when comparing f numbers calculated from liquid-phase spectral data with theoretical oscillator strengths calculated for isolated molecules, as the electronic transition may be appreciably altered in the condensed phase.

In the second of his series of papers on absolute intensities of electronic transitions, Mulliken[19] calculated oscillator strengths for the transition

$$H_2(1s\sigma_g)^2;\ {}^1\Sigma_g^+ \rightarrow H_2(1s\sigma_g;\ 2p\sigma_u)^1\Sigma_u^+$$

at $\omega = \omega_{max} = 90,000\ cm^{-1}$ (1110 A). He used both MO and valence-bond approximations for the wave functions appearing in the dipole strength D. The f numbers were 0.68 and 0.49, respectively, and Mulliken suggests that the true value falls between. The large calculated oscillator strength (compared to the "maximum" of unity) indicates a very strong transition probability, which is indeed observed in hydrogen at 1109 A.

3-1C-2   Emission of Radiation by Excited Molecules

The Einstein probability of spontaneous emission is given by wave mechanics as

$$A_{nm} = \left(\frac{64\pi^4\omega_{nm}^3 e^2}{3h}\right) g_m D_{nm} \tag{3-44}$$

where A_{nm} is as defined previously, the fraction of the atoms in the initial excited state n returning per second to the ground state m, of degeneracy g_m. The dipole strength D_{nm} (or the square of the dipole moment integral $|\mathbf{m}_{nm}|^2$) determines the probability of emission, just as it did for electric dipole absorption. Combining 3-44 and 3-39,

$$A_{nm} = \left(\frac{8\pi^2\omega_{nm}^2 e^2}{m_e c}\right)\left(\frac{g_m}{g_n}\right) f_{mn} \tag{3-45}$$

which relates the probability of spontaneous emission to the classical oscillator strength, f_{mn}.

Since A_{nm} is the number of times per second that an excited molecule emits light of frequency ω_{nm} and returns to the ground state, for the important special case that this is the *only mode* of decay we have

$$\frac{1}{A_{nm}} = \tau_0 \tag{3-46}$$

The units of τ_0 are seconds per transition $n \rightarrow m$, and τ_0 is thus the *mean lifetime* of the excited state n. Assuming a maximum oscillator strength of unity, the lower limit to τ_0 becomes about 10^{-8} sec, for emission of electric dipole radiation in the visible. Since transition probabilities for magnetic dipole and electric quadrupole transitions are factors of about 10^{-5} and 10^{-8} as small as A_{nm} for electric dipole transitions (Herzberg,[1] p. 21), the mean lifetimes for emission of magnetic dipole and electric quadrupole radiation are much higher, of the order of 10^{-3} and 1 sec, respectively. These states are termed *metastable*. We can relate the *mean radiative lifetime* of an excited state, τ_0, to the experimentally determined integral of ϵ versus ω through the use of 3-41, 3-45, and 3-46:

$$\tau_0 = \left[\frac{g_n N}{g_m 8\pi\, 2303 c}\right] \bigg/ F \int_{\omega_1}^{\omega_2} \epsilon\, d\omega$$

$$= \frac{g_n}{g_m} \frac{3.47 \times 10^8}{\omega^2} \bigg/ F \int_{\omega_1}^{\omega_2} \epsilon\, d\omega \qquad (3\text{-}47)$$

F is commonly taken as unity (see preceding discussion of Eq. 3-41), and the other symbols are as defined previously. In their pioneering studies of the triplet state Lewis and Kasha[17] derived lifetimes of a variety of photo-excited molecules by using these techniques. τ_0 calculated from 3-47 is equal to the actual lifetime τ of the excited molecule only when the quantum yield of fluorescence, φ_f, is 1. For all other cases $\tau = (\tau_0)\varphi_f$. It is worth noting that the value of the degeneracy factor g_n/g_m in 3-47 depends on whether the transition is allowed or forbidden. Thus, while Lewis and Kasha used a value of 3 for the triplet $\rightarrow$ singlet transition, Robinson and Frosch[20] point out that because of the forbidden nature of the transition the appropriate factor depends on the degeneracy factor associated with the allowed transitions from which the intensity is "borrowed." Thus for the $^3B_{1u} \rightarrow {}^1A_{1g}$ transition in benzene they use the factor 2.

Many absorption bands in solution have half-widths of about 5000 cm^{-1}. Treating them as triangles of height ϵ_{max}, we find that, as a rough approximation, for absorptions in the near ultraviolet ($\omega \sim 3 \times 10^4$ cm^{-1}) Eq. 3-47 reduces to

$$\tau_0 \,(\text{sec}) \sim \frac{10^{-4}}{\epsilon_{max}} \qquad (3\text{-}48)$$

This is a useful expression to remember for arriving at an order-of-magnitude estimate of the radiative lifetimes of excited molecules.

3-1C-3   Molecular Selection Rules

The transition probabilities between different electronic states of a molecule are governed by selection rules analogous to those for atomic transitions. These rules arise through a consideration of the conditions which determine the size of the transition moment integral, **m** of Eq. 2-22, as in the case of the atomic systems. The general rules that apply to most cases are stated below without justification (cf. Herzberg,[1] p. 240, and Kauzmann,[8] p. 654, for details).

In cases of weak coupling between electron spin and orbital angular momenta, that is, the Russell-Saunders type observed for light nuclei [cf. Sec. 2-6; also Herzberg,[1] p. 241, Hund's cases (a) and (b)],

$$\Delta \Lambda = 0, \pm 1$$

$$\Delta S = 0$$

Transitions are permitted only between states of the same multiplicity. Intercombinations such as singlet $\leftrightarrow$ triplet transitions are forbidden. Additional rules involve the symmetry of the wave functions in the two electronic states.

1. Odd terms combine only with even and vice versa. Thus $u \to g$ and $g \to u$ are allowed, but $u \not\leftrightarrow u$ and $g \not\leftrightarrow g$. In other words, a dipole must be created or destroyed in the transition.

2. Positive terms combine only with positive terms and negative with negative. Thus $(+) \leftrightarrow (+)$, $(-) \leftrightarrow (-)$, but $(+) \not\leftrightarrow (-)$.

These rules are summarized in Table 3-5. For the strong spin-orbital interaction encountered with heavier nuclei these rules are not valid and are replaced by

$$\Delta \Omega = 0, \pm 1$$

except that $\Delta \Omega \neq 0$ for $\Omega'' = 0 \leftrightarrow \Omega' = 0$, and other restrictions.

TABLE 3-5 Allowed[a] Electronic Transitions for Light Nuclei (no spin-orbit momenta interaction)[b]

Homonuclear Diatomic (Equal Nuclear Charge)	Heteronuclear Diatomic (Unequal Nuclear Charge)
$\Sigma_g^+ \leftrightarrow \Sigma_u^+$	$\Sigma^+ \leftrightarrow \Sigma^+$
$\Sigma_g^- \leftrightarrow \Sigma_u^-$	$\Sigma^- \leftrightarrow \Sigma^-$
$\Pi_g \leftrightarrow \Sigma_u^+, \Pi_u \leftrightarrow \Sigma_g^+$	$\Pi \leftrightarrow \Sigma^+$
$\Pi_g \leftrightarrow \Sigma_u^-, \Pi_u \leftrightarrow \Sigma_g^-$	$\Pi \leftrightarrow \Sigma^-$
$\Pi_g \leftrightarrow \Pi_u$	$\Pi \leftrightarrow \Pi$
$\Pi_g \leftrightarrow \Delta_u, \Pi_u \leftrightarrow \Delta_g$	$\Pi \leftrightarrow \Delta$
$\Delta_g \leftrightarrow \Delta_u$	$\Delta \leftrightarrow \Delta$
$\cdots$	$\cdots$

[a] Presuming that the rule $\Delta S = 0$ is obeyed.
[b] Taken from Herzberg,[1] p. 243.

3-1D   The Relative Intensity of the Bands in
Molecular Spectra; the Franck-Condon Principle

We have seen that the total integrated absorption over a band for a given transition is a constant characteristic of a given molecule (Eqs. 3-41 and 3-47) and is relatively independent of the temperature, state of the molecule, and the other variables, barring gross perturbations. However, the distribution of intensities between the various structured bands and continua within the absorption region can alter with conditions and is determined by the relative positioning of the potential energy surfaces which characterize the ground state and the excited electronic states of the molecule. The factors which govern the relative intensities of bands are conveniently considered in terms of the Franck-Condon principle.

In Sec. 3-1B-1 we diagrammed the origin of band progressions (Fig. 3-12) and band sequences (Fig. 3-13) and examined a schematic energy-level diagram for an absorption band system similar to iodine gas (Fig. 3-14). Such diagrams provide no clue, however, as to the *intensity* distribution of lines in such spectra as that of $I_2(g)$. The intensities may be understood qualitatively in terms of potential energy curves for the ground state and excited electronic state involved, and of the important Franck-Condon principle. This principle states that the time required for absorption of a quantum of light and the resultant transition of an electron to an excited state is so short (about 10^{-15} sec) compared to the period of vibration of the molecule (about 10^{-13} sec) that during the act of absorption and excitation the nuclei do not alter appreciably their relative positions (i.e., internuclear distance r) or their kinetic energies.

As a consequence of the Franck-Condon principle electronic transitions between two potential energy surfaces can be represented by vertical lines connecting them. This is shown in Fig. 3-24, which gives potential energy curves for the ground state and first excited state of a hypothetical diatomic molecule similar to iodine [see Fig. 3-33 for the actual curves for $I_2(g)$]. Quantized vibrational energy levels are shown as horizontal lines with the shapes of the vibrational wave functions $\psi_{v'}$ and $\psi_{v''}$ superimposed on them. The wave functions are for a typical "particle in a box" solution for a harmonic oscillator, except for $v' = j$, where the model is a system with only one infinite wall with r extending to infinity. The latter states with $v' > i$ are non-quantized. (See Fig. 3-9, which gives probability *density* distributions $\psi_v \psi_v{}^*$, for a harmonic oscillator.)

With this information we can interpret qualitatively the molecular absorption spectrum shown in the right of Fig. 3-24. At room temperature most diatomic molecules are in their 0th vibrational state, and the most favored transitions is from $v'' = 0$. The vertical line originates at the

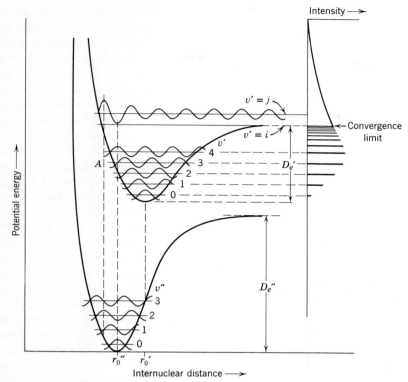

Fig. 3-24   The transitions between potential energy curves for an electronically excited and ground-state diatomic molecule (Type III). After Bowen,[7] p. 86.

midpoint of $v'' = 0$ since $\psi_{v''}$ is a maximum there (cf. Sec. 3-1A-2). Wave mechanics further shows that the probability of transition to a particular vibrational level v' in the excited electronic state is determined largely by the product of the vibrational wave functions for the two states $\psi_{v'}\psi_{v''}$ (actually by the magnitude of the *overlap integral*, which in turn is largely governed by $\psi_{v'}\psi_{v''}$; see Herzberg,[1] pp. 199 and 391).

Consider a transition from $v'' = 0$. The maximum values for $\psi_{v'}\psi_{v''=0}$ occur in the region where $v' = 3, 4, 5$. These should be the most probable transitions, and reference to Fig. 3-24 shows that the absorption bands originating from them, the $3 \leftarrow 0$, $4 \leftarrow 0$, $5 \leftarrow 0$ bands (v' is given first), have the greatest intensities. Rotational fine structure is not shown in this figure. The wave function at $v' = 0$ is very small at values of r' where $\psi_{v''=0}$ is a maximum (i.e., at the equilibrium internuclear distance r_0''); hence $(\psi_{v'=0})(\psi_{v''=0})$ is very small and the spectral line for the 0–0 transition is weak.

Finally consider the transition $(v' = j) \leftarrow (v'' = 0)$, the $j \leftarrow 0$, transition. There is excellent overlap of the two wave functions, but the sign of $\psi_{v'=j}$ oscillates rapidly in this region of overlap with the net result that the negative values of the integral substantially cancel the positive ones and the $j \leftarrow 0$ transition probability is small. However, for $(v' = j) \leftarrow (v'' = 1$ or $2)$ transitions, there is good overlap of positive wave functions. Thus, when the $v'' = 1$ and 2 levels are also populated, as is assumed in the example, continuous absorption is observed. The continuum arises from j being one of an infinite number of non-quantized states above the dissociation limit of the excited state, $v' = i$. After vertical Franck-Condon transitions to these states the molecule is highly compressed, and on the next vibration it dissociates into two atoms which carry off as non-quantized kinetic energy the potential energy in excess of the dissociation energy of the excited state, D_e'.

In terms of classical mechanics, as it was first formulated by J. Franck,[21] the Franck-Condon principle states that transitions tend to occur between those vibrational levels of two electronic states for which the nuclear configurations are the same (i.e., $r'' = r'$). Furthermore, transitions tend to originate at the turning points in each vibration where the vibrational energy level intersects the potential energy surface of the molecule. Here the nuclear kinetic energy is a minimum since the nuclei are stationary or moving slowly, and the molecule spends most of its time at these points.

Implicit in our discussion is the assumption that the transition probability from $v' \leftrightarrow v''$ is independent of r, over the range involved in one vibration.

A molecule excited to point A in Fig. 3-24 has far more *total* energy than necessary for dissociation into two atoms, D_e'', yet barring special conditions it can exist for the relatively long time of 10^{-8} sec before reradiating and returning to the ground state. This suggests that the energy of the excited electron cannot instantaneously (10^{-15} sec) be converted into kinetic energy of the nuclei by *external* perturbations unless a phenomenon such as predissociation or internal conversion occurs. This example is cited as evidence of the difficulty of directly converting electronic energy into nuclear kinetic energy.[22]

3-1D-1   Typical Absorption Band Spectra

Following the approach of Herzberg,[1] three types of absorption band spectra are illustrated in Figs. 3-24 and 3-25. Spacing between vibrational levels has been made the same in the examples of Fig. 3-25 to simplify the presentation. Actually, the separation varies with the molecule and electronic state involved.

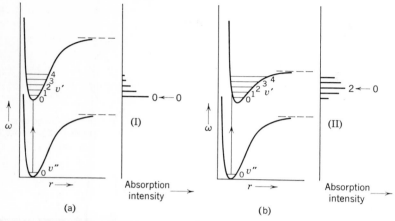

Fig 3-25 Typical potential energy curves for different types, I and II, of band spectra.

Type I: The wholly banded Type I spectrum (Fig. 3-25a) with maximum absorption intensity in the $0 \leftarrow 0$ band arises from transitions between electronic states with similar Franck-Condon curves in which the equilibrium internuclear distances r_0 are about equal. As actual examples, for the oxygen molecule the $^1\Sigma_g^+ \leftarrow {}^3\Sigma_g^-$ transitions in the visible (about 7600 A) and the $^1\Delta_g \leftarrow {}^3\Sigma_g^-$ transition in the infrared result in the weak "atmospheric oxygen bands." These violate the selection rules but occur to a small extent as a result of collisional perturbations of the symmetry properties of the molecule. Figure 3-26 shows a spectrum of the atmospheric O_2 band near 7650 A, including a dramatic example of the isotope effect. Figure 3-27 shows the potential energy curves for the oxygen molecule, with the transition resulting in this band indicated.

Type II: If r_0' for the excited state is displaced somewhat to larger values, a Type II band intensity distribution results, as shown in Fig. 3-25b. The $2 \leftarrow 0$ transition has the maximum intensity, which is reasonable in terms of the Franck-Condon curves for the states involved. Carbon monoxide shows such a band intensity distribution in the region 1545–1368 A and below, as seen in Fig. 3-28.

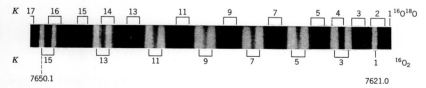

Fig. 3-26   The atmospheric O_2 band near 7650 A. From Herzberg,[1] p. 167; originally from Babcock and Herzberg.[44]

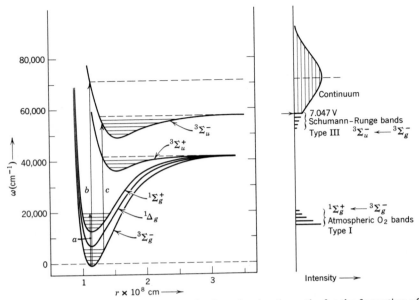

Fig. 3-27   Franck-Condon curves for the O_2 molecule; the paths for the formation of the atmospheric O_2 absorption bands, the Schumann-Runge bands, and the O_2 continuum are shown. Relative absorption band intensities within each transition are shown, but the intensities of the two electronic transitions are not to scale, the $^3\Sigma_u^- \leftarrow {}^3\Sigma_g^+$ being far more intense than the $^1\Sigma_g^+ \leftarrow {}^3\Sigma_g^-$. From Herzberg,[1] pp. 194, 195.

Type III: Still further displacement of r_0' from the ground state r_0'' leads to a Type III absorption spectrum in which the bands merge into a continuum. Figure 3-24, which we consider previously, shows such a spectrum and the Franck-Condon curves for the ground and excited state involved. The visible spectrum of iodine vapor (Figs. 3-15 and 3-30) arising from the $^3\Pi_{0u}^+ \leftarrow {}^1\Sigma_g^+$ transition is a classic example. Another is the strong Schumman-Runge band system of the oxygen molecule. Weak absorption bands start as about 2000 A and, gaining in strength, extend to the far ultraviolet with a strong continuum starting at about 1759 A. This absorption (Figs. 3-26 and 3-40) is due to the transition $^3\Sigma_u^- \leftarrow {}^3\Sigma_g^-$ (Fig. 3-27) and is a limiting factor in spectroscopic and photochemical work in air.

3-1D-2   Continuous Absorption Spectra

Continuous absorption spectra arise from transitions between two states one of which is non-quantized and thus has a continuous range of energy values. Continua in atomic spectra occur as a result of photoionization

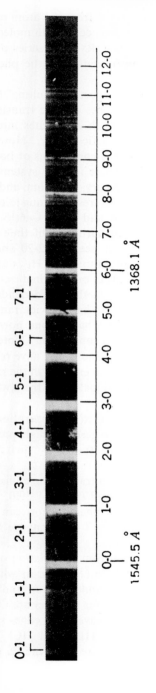

Fig. 3-28 Absorption spectrum of the CO molecule; the main series of absorption bands is indicated below the spectrogram; a very weak series, originating from the first excited vibrational level of the ground state, is indicated above. From Herzberg,[1] p. 37; originally from Hopfield and Birge.[45]

processes where the excited electron ejected from the atom may possess a range of kinetic energies. A similar process occurs with molecules and has been observed for O_2 and N_2. These have Rydberg series of bands with adjoining continua resulting from the formation of the photoionization products O_2^+ and N_2^+.

Far more prevalent are continuous spectra resulting from photodissociation of the molecule. Most of these involve transitions from a stable ground state to an upper state which dissociates into two atoms that can carry off varying amounts of kinetic energy. However, several cases are known in which the lower state is continuous or both the upper and the lower states are continuous. These include systems containing vapors of certain metal atoms such as mercury, cadmium, and zinc. Thus, under conditions of absorption at high pressures, continua join the mercury resonance lines $6(^3P_1) \leftarrow 6(^1S_0)$ at 2537 A and $6(^1P_1) \leftarrow 6(^1S_0)$ at 1849 A. These are ascribed to absorption occurring during the lifetime of a collision between two normal $^1S_0$ mercury atoms; see Fig. 2-20 and Sec. 2-9C. The collision results in the formation of an unstable Hg_2 molecule in the ground state, the energy of which depends upon the kinetic energy vectors of the colliding atoms; such stabilization as there is depends on van der Waals forces. Since the kinetic energies can have a wide range of values, transitions to the stable upper state Hg_2^* having one normal and one excited atom, either $^3P_1$ or $^1P_1$, result in a continuum. Note in Fig. 2-20 that certain of the upper states of the Hg_2^* molecules have relatively deep potential wells, corresponding to dissociation energies in the range of 1 ev; they have quantized vibrational and rotational levels from which fluorescence may occur.

A similar phenomenon has been observed in absorption spectra of mixtures of these metal atoms with inert gases at high pressures. Absorption is presumably from ground-state transient "quasi" molecules, such as Hg-He, formed at the instant of collision.

The precise effects of central and non-central atomic collisions in these systems are discussed in detail by Herzberg[1] (pp. 394–399). The subject is pertinent in photochemistry, since the phenomenon can be a major contributing factor in "pressure broadening" of resonance lines emitted by arcs employed in photochemical studies.

Continuous absorption spectra arising from dissociation of the excited states important in photochemistry include (1) those in which the continuum joins the convergence limit of a banded region and (2) those in which only a continuum is observed. Among the later are the ultraviolet spectra of the hydrogen halides. The long-wavelength edges start at about 3270, 2650, and 2500 A for gaseous HI, HBr, and HCl, respectively. Presumably the sole important transitions are from the $^1\Sigma$ ground state

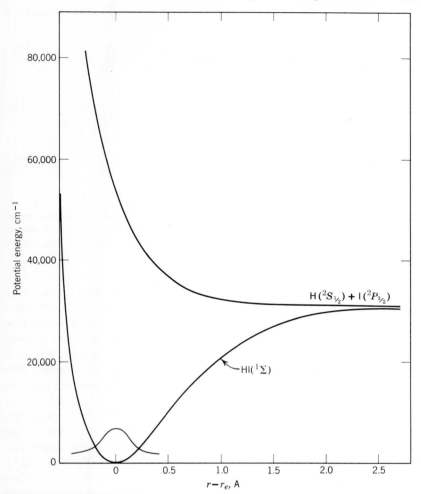

Fig. 3-29   Potential energy curves for ground and repulsive excited state of HI. From Goodeve and Taylor;[23] see Fig. 3–36 also.

to completely repulsive upper states that dissociate immediately into normal hydrogen atoms and halogen atoms, as shown by the potential energy curves for HI in Fig. 3-29.[23]

It may be seen in Fig. 3-30 that fluorine, chlorine, and bromine all show strong continua in the visible or ultraviolet region. Presumably they result at least in part from the allowed transition $^1\Pi_u \leftarrow {}^1\Sigma_g^+$. This is analogous to the hydrogen halides in that the $^1\Pi_u$ state is completely repulsive. With iodine this transition must be very weak, as it was not observed in the

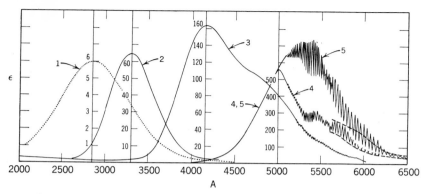

Fig. 3-30   Absorption spectra of the halogens: (1) $F_2(g)$, 25°; (2) $Cl_2(g)$, 18°; (3) $Br_2(g)$, 25°; (4) $I_2(g)$, 70–80°; (5) $I_2(g)$ plus 1 atm air, 70–80°; the weak banded region in Cl_2 which converges to the continuum at 4785 A is not visible with the scale chosen. Curve (1) from Steunenberg and Vogel;[26] (2) from Gibson and Bayliss;[46] (3), (4), and (5) determined by Mrs. Veronique McMillan.[222]

study by Mathieson and Rees.[24] Instead they postulated two other repulsive states, $^3\Pi_{1u}$ to explain the weak red absorption and $^3\Sigma_u^+$ for a very weak absorption at about 2700 A. The continuous absorption spectra and their calculated spectra based on this assignment are in good agreement. The main continuum of iodine, however, adjoins the convergence limit at 4990 A of the well-known visible band system. This spectrum is ascribed to the transition $^3\Pi_{0u}^+ \leftarrow {}^1\Sigma_g^+$. Bromine and chlorine also undergo the latter transition but show correspondingly much weaker absorption band systems converging at 5110 and 4785 A, respectively, with adjoining weak continua. A very weak absorption attributed to the $^3\Pi_{0^+u} \leftarrow {}^1\Sigma_g^+$ transition is reported by Rees[25] to occur in the long-wavelength region of the main absorption continuum of $F_2 ({}^1\Pi_u \leftarrow {}^1\Sigma_g^+)$. Presumably the heavy mass of the iodine molecule permits a relaxation of the singlet $\leftrightarrow$ triplet selection rule. This rule apparently becomes more effective as the molecular weight decreases. This is analogous to the decrease in probability of the transition $^3P_1 \rightarrow {}^1S_0$ (as reflected in the drop in absorption coefficients of the respective atomic absorption resonance lines) going through the group mercury, cadmium, and zinc.

Rees used accurate data on the continuous absorption spectrum of molecular fluorine obtained by Steunenberg and Vogel[26] to calculate potential energy curves for both excited states, $^1\Pi_u$ and $^3\Pi_{0^+u}$, and to obtain a value of 37.1 ± 0.85 kcal/mole for the dissociation energy of F_2 in the ground state (going to two normal fluorine atoms). Steunenberg and Vogel found a maximum ϵ of 6.00 liters/mole-cm at 2845 A. However, the long tail which extends slightly into the visible accounts for the very pale yellow color of gaseous and liquid fluorine; see Fig. 3-30.

3-1D-3 Diffuse Molecular Spectra; Predissociation

In addition to continuous spectra where intensity is a smooth function of wavelength, and band spectra with sharp rotational and vibrational structure, *diffuse band spectra* also are observed. These include vapor-phase electronic absorption spectra in which the molecule shows well-defined rotational and vibrational structure up to a certain frequency at which the rotational structure suddenly becomes blurred (the lines are broadened and the bands become diffuse). This phenomenon was first discovered in the absorption spectrum of the S_2 molecule by Henri and Teves;[27] who used the term *predissociation spectrum* to describe the diffuse region.

Bonhoeffer and Farkas[28] and Kronig[29] explained the effect in terms of a radiationless transition (also called a *non-adiabatic* transition) from a stable excited state of the molecule into a continuous electronic state of the same energy. Blurring of the rotational spectrum occurs when the time between excitation to a given vibrational level of that stable excited state and the radiationless transfer to the dissociation continuum of the other state (this is τ, the mean lifetime of the quantized state) is of the order of the rotational period of the molecule ($\sim 10^{-11}$ sec). Under these circumstances quantization of the rotational levels in this vibrational band breaks down, resulting in the "washing out" of the fine structure. In less extreme cases when τ is somewhat longer than 10^{-11} sec the rotational lines are simply broadened until at $\tau \sim 10^{-9}$ sec predissociation will not be definitely evident from the spectrum.

The increase in line broadening as the mean lifetime of the excited state decreases is a consequence of the uncertainty principle, as we saw earlier with line broadening in atomic spectra (Sec. 2-7B-1). Thus $\Delta E \cong h/\tau$, and combining this with $\Delta E = h \, \Delta \nu$ we have

$$\Delta \nu \cong \frac{1}{\tau} \sim \gamma$$

where $\Delta \nu$ is the frequency range of the energy level of the excited stable state, τ is the lifetime in that level, and γ is the probability in unit time of a radiationless transition to the state with continuous energy levels. A large value of γ (short lifetime) gives a large $\Delta \nu$ and hence a broad spectral line.

A better understanding of this phenomenon can be had by considering a specific example. The absorption spectrum of gaseous S_2 (Fig. 3-31)

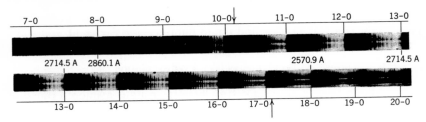

Fig. 3-31   Absorption spectrum of gaseous S_2 vapor; the arrows indicate the positions at which the bands become diffuse. From Herzberg,[1] p. 38.

has the following characteristics: (1) sharp band structure exists in the region from about 4100–2799 A; (2) at this point the fine structure becomes blurred but the gross features remain down to 2715 A, where rotational lines start to become sharper; (3) at 2615 A the line structure disappears altogether. The region 2799–2715 A is pressure sensitive, with fine structure reappearing as the pressure is decreased, but the blurring at 2615 A and below is pressure independent.

Potential energy curves for the ground state and three excited states of S_2 are shown in Fig. 3-32. The only allowed transition in the near ultraviolet is $^3\Sigma_u^- \leftarrow {}^3\Sigma_g^-$, and the banded spectrum from 4100 to 2799 A

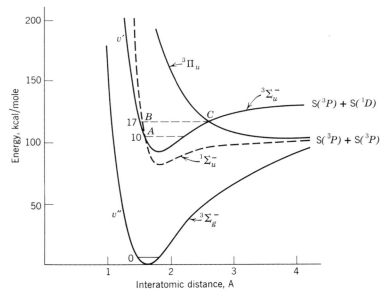

Fig. 3-32   Potential energy curves for the S_2 molecule. From Bowen,[7] p. 95, based on data of Lochte-Holtgreven.[30]

corresponds to rotational structure superimposed on the vibrational changes $v' = 9, 8, 7, \ldots 0 \leftarrow v'' = 0$. Absorption of 2799 A radiation corresponds to a transition which intersects at $v' = 10$, very near the intersection of the $^3\Sigma_u^-$ curve with $^1\Sigma_u^-$ at point A. At wavelengths shorter than 2799 A the electronic transitions terminate at the $^3\Sigma_u^-$ state at one of the vibrational levels $v' = 10$ to $v' = 17$ in the region $A - B$ above the intersection of the curves for the two excited electronic states. During the period of a vibration when the nuclei reach the intersection A, there is an opportunity for a radiationless transfer to the state represented by the dotted curve, $^1\Sigma_u^-$.

Such non-adiabatic transitions lead directly to dissociation into two ^3P sulfur atoms. However, the transition probability γ is small in this case (at intersection A) because the transfer of curves is forbidden by selection rules. Thus at low pressures the lines in the region $v' = 10$ to $v' = 17$ are sharp. But collisions with other molecules perturb the energy levels in the system so that at higher pressures the selection rule singlet $\leftrightarrow$ triplet breaks down, and some non-adiabatic transitions occur. These decrease the lifetime τ for the $^3\Sigma_u^-$ state and thus increase rotational line breadth in this region. This secondary effect is called *induced predissociation*. It is also important in the case of the halogens. Thus a chlorine molecule excited to the $^3\Pi_{0u}^+$ state may, as a result of perturbations induced by a collision, pass over to the repulsive $^1\Pi_u$ level and dissociate into two normal atoms. When v' reaches 17 at $\lambda = 2615$ A (point B, Fig. 3-32) vibrations of the photoexcited molecule start to carry it through the crossover point C, and the radiationless transfer $^3\Pi_u \leftarrow {}^3\Sigma_u^-$ can occur, leading directly to dissociation into two normal sulfur atoms. This transition, *spontaneous predissociation*, is allowed by the selection rules, and the spectrum below 2615 A is *non*-pressure sensitive, so that blurring occurs even at low pressures.

Although predissociation is relatively rare with diatomic molecules, the potential energy curves $^3\Pi_u$ and $^1\Sigma_u^-$ for S_2 in Fig. 3-32 are illustrative of two general types of perturbations that may lead to indirect photodissociation of other diatomic molecules, as well as S_2. These include chlorine and other halogens showing banded spectra. A prime question now is, given these types of perturbations, what are the factors governing the probability of radiationless transitions, γ, at the crossover points of the Franck-Condon curves?

We shall discuss this topic first in terms of classical mechanics and then briefly by wave-mechanical concepts.

1. Kronig[29] has derived a general set of selection rules for perturbations which include the special case of predissociation. (See also the review by Sponer[31].) In essence these rules state that any transition involving the

emission or the absorption of radiation can occur *without* radiation except, that, in a radiationless transfer, $(+) \leftrightarrow (-)$, $g \leftrightarrow u$, the opposite of transitions with radiation. Thus the rules in Table 3-5 for allowed electronic transitions also apply to predissociation with the exceptions just cited. In the case of S_2, for example, $^3\Sigma_u^- \rightarrow {}^1\Sigma_u^-$ is forbidden because of the change in multiplicity, but $^3\Sigma_u^- \rightarrow {}^3\Pi_u$ is allowed because $\Delta S = 0$ and $u \rightarrow u$ (the latter transition with radiation would be forbidden, as in that case $g \rightarrow u$ is the rule).

2. The transition probability depends on the shapes of the two curves at the crossover points. If they approach gradually over a relatively long range of r, γ is much greater than if they intersect at an acute angle. Thus, the *other factors being equal*, γ would be greater at crossover point A, Fig. 3-32, than at point C.

3. The higher the velocity of the system at the crossover point the smaller is the value of γ. Thus the chance of the non-adiabatic transition $^3\Sigma_u^- \rightarrow {}^1\Sigma_u^-$ is less starting at $v' = 15$ than at $v' = 11$, since in the former case the nuclei will be moving much faster at the time they reach the configuration at the crossover point A. This is reflected in the rotational fine structure for S_2, which becomes blurred (at elevated pressures) starting at 2799 A, corresponding to intersection A just above $v' = 10$, but which starts becoming sharper again at 2715 A ($v' = 13$).

Predissociation is explained in wave mechanics in terms of the coupling that exists when the quantized energy levels of a given electronic state overlap in energy the continuous range of energy levels of another state in the same system. This coupling arises from the non-diagonal matrix components of the Hamiltonian which connects the continuum with quantized states of equal energy, and which determines the probability of a radiationless transfer between these two states. From this matrix element one can separate a factor which depends only upon the vibrational motion of the nuclei of the molecule and then show that the transition probability depends upon the magnitude of the overlap integral of the vibrational eigenfunctions of the continuous and the discrete states.

In some systems the region of overlap of vibrational wave functions is somewhat larger than the classical point of intersection of two Franck-Condon curves. This would suggest that the region where possible transitions can occur would be greater than predicted by classical mechanics, and indeed radiationless transitions have been found to occur *below* the actual intersection point of two Franck-Condon curves. Thus, in an interesting example, apparently unique for diatomic molecules, Herzberg and Mundie[32] observed for S_2 that some rotational line broadening sets in at $v' = 10$, just below the crossover point A (Fig. 3-32), but maximum blurring occurred at $v' = 11$ just above the intersection. (This effect is evident on close examination of Fig. 3-31, the absorption spectrum of S_2 vapor.) They explain this in terms of the passage *through* the potential "hill" formed by the two intersecting curves at point A. There is sufficient overlap of wave functions *below* the crossover point that some transfer between curves can occur and predissociation result, in apparent violation of classical mechanics. Such a passage through a potential barrier is analogous to the well-known "tunnel-effect" employed in interpreting α-particle decay in radioactive nuclei, and in other systems.

It should be remembered that a "classical" potential energy curve only exists as a sharply defined concept if it is allowable to separate electronic from vibrational energies. At "curve-crossing" points this assumption breaks down, and the curves fade into ill-defined areas. In the photochemistry of the polyatomic molecules, collisionally induced predissociation is a most important mechanism of internal energy transfer. An excellent review of predissociation phenomena was written by Sponer (1959) to which the reader is referred for further discussion.[31]

3-2   PHOTOPHYSICAL PROCESSES OF ELECTRONICALLY EXCITED DIATOMIC MOLECULES

The elementary reactions of excited diatomic molecules include those discussed for excited atoms plus photodissociation either directly or by predissociation. Molecular iodine is a useful model, and its several primary processes form the basis of the following brief discussion which first deals chiefly with vapor-phase processes and then considers briefly effects in solution. Details are to be found in the treatise of Pringsheim.[33]

3-2A   Fluorescence of Diatomic Gases

We have seen that molecular electronic absorption spectra reflect changes in vibrational and rotational modes and are thus far more complex than atomic "line" spectra. Similarly molecular fluorescence spectra are characterized by the appearance of bands. In order for such fluorescence bands to appear, the initial act of absorption must be in the discontinuous region; no fluorescence results from absorption in the continuum.

The selection rules for fluorescence from a harmonic oscillator are $\Delta v = \pm 1$ and $\Delta J = 0, \pm 1$, so that the bands of a typical diatomic molecule either have exclusively doublet character (as with the green fluorescence of iodine) or consist of singlets and doublets as with Na_2. The occurrence of overtones in which $\Delta v > \pm 1$ leads to complex spectra characterized by highly irregular intensities of lines.

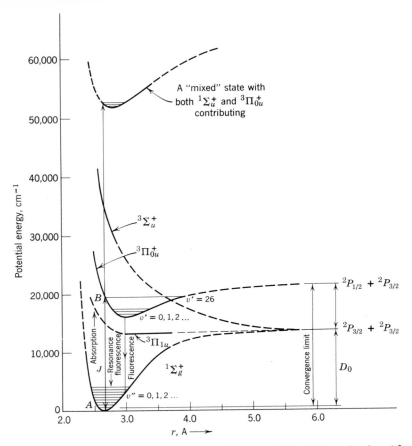

Fig. 3-33   Potential energy diagram for several states of the $I_2(g)$ molecule.   After Mathieson and Rees.[24]

The visible fluorescence band system of iodine, first investigated critically by Wood,[34] has been widely studied.   It is readily produced by excitation with the 5461 A green line of mercury, and the multitude of lines in the fluorescence spectrum fall in a region ideally suited for experimental work. The bands arise from the transitions[11]

$$^3\Pi_{0u}^+(v' = 26) \rightarrow {}^1\Sigma_g^+(v'' = 1, 2, 3, \ldots, 39)$$

as can be deduced from the potential energy curves of Mathieson and Rees[24] shown in Fig. 3-33.

Examination by spectrographs of high resolving power reveals that only doublets are found in the resonance spectrum.   The band spectrum has been studied out to 9087 A.[35] This near-infrared radiation is emitted in the transition $(v' = 26) \rightarrow (v'' = 39)$. The main lines in the progression of doublets are given by the equation

$$\omega \; (\text{cm}^{-1}) = 18307.50 - 213.7977v'' + 0.614045v''^2$$

$$+ \; 0.000931961v''^3 + 0.00001866v''^4 \qquad (3\text{-}49)$$

and the doublet separation by $\delta\omega = 5.168 - 0.194v''$. Analysis of Eq. 3-49 leads to values for the constants of the iodine molecule. It is interesting that the large moment of inertia of the I_2 molecule permits transitions in which J'' is as large as 135. Pringsheim[33] points out that at constant vapor density the fluorescence yield for $I_2(g)$ is independent of temperature nearly up to the temperature at which dissociation becomes appreciable. Fluorescence ceases at 4990 A where the continuum begins, and absorption of a quantum gives

$$I_2 + h\nu(\lambda < 4990) \rightarrow I(^2P_{\frac{1}{2}}) + I(^2P_{\frac{3}{2}})$$

A second resonance band system of $I_2(g)$ is observed in the region 1760–2000 A. It is fully discussed by Pringsheim[33] and Mathieson and Rees[24] and will not be covered here.

TABLE 3-6 Location of Absorption and Fluorescence Bands of O_2, S_2, Se_2, and Te_2[a]

Element:	O_2	S_2	Se_2	Te_2
Absorption, A	<1900	2548–4000	3238–4180	3831–6200
Fluorescence, A	<2000–3870	2800–5650	3050–4910	4200–6600

[a] After Pringsheim,[33] p. 177.

"Resonance spectra" have been observed for vapors of the alkali metals and, as first proposed by Pringsheim in 1921, have been shown to arise from molecules of the type Na_2, KNa, K_2, Li_2, Rb_2, and Cs_2. Elements in the sixth column of the periodic table show fluorescence, and Table 3-6 gives the approximate location of their absorption and fluorescence bands.

Certain emission lines appearing in the "tails" of comets have been ascribed to primary processes in which relatively stable free radicals and ions formed by solar radiation absorb and re-emit fluorescence radiation.[36] These radicals and ions include OH, CH, NH, CN, C_2, CO^+, and N_2^+.

Resonance fluorescence is observed with simple gases at low pressure [e.g., $I_2(g)$ at 10^{-2} mm] but not at high pressures or in liquids. (More complex molecules rarely show resonance fluorescence, even when in the gaseous state.) The rationales behind this behavior can be seen by considering the I_2 potential energy curves in Fig. 3-33. Absorption corresponds to the transition $A \rightarrow B$, which occurs in about 10^{-15} sec. After existing in the excited state ${}^3\Pi_{0u}^{+}$ for a short time the molecule at low pressures emits radiation and drops back to the ground state S_0 via $B - A$, emitting resonance fluorescence in the process. However, in iodine-containing systems at usual gas pressures or in the liquid state the excited molecule may suffer many collisions during its lifetime so that it may be degraded rapidly to the lower vibrational levels of the excited state from which it may fluoresce.*

More energy is involved in the absorption act than in emission, so that, as Stokes observed empirically in 1852, fluorescence bands are centered at longer wavelengths than the corresponding absorption bands. In a very few cases absorption occurs from a higher vibrational level of the ground level $v'' = 0$. This leads to low-intensity "anti-Stokes" lines, since the observed fluorescence is at a shorter wavelength than the exciting radiation.

Molecules in the excited singlet state may also undergo radiationless intersystem crossings and pass over to lower-lying triplet levels (T_1) before they can fluoresce. Since the transition $T_1 \rightarrow S_0$ is "forbidden," the triplet state is metastable and the relatively long-lived radiation that is finally emitted is known as phosphorescence (or chemical luminescence). This important phenomenon, much more probable for complex molecules, can most readily be observed with many organic compounds dissolved in rigid "glasses" at low temperature. We shall discuss these processes in detail in our consideration of the photochemistry of polyatomic molecules.

In contrast to fluorescence, which involves absorption of a photon and a lifetime of about 10^{-8} sec of the resulting quantized excited state, both the Rayleigh and Raman effects involve very short-lived transitions (about 10^{-15} sec) to non-quantized levels of the absorbing molecule (i.e., transitions from A to somewhere below B, e.g., J, Fig. 3-33). In both of the latter cases "absorption" results in a temporary distortion of the oscillations of the electrons in the molecule, and in 10^{-15} sec the molecule returns to its original electronic configuration. In most cases the return is to the lowest vibration level, A, $v'' = 0$, and the scattered radiation has the same wavelength as the incident radiation. This is Rayleigh scattering. However, occasionally the electronically distorted molecule returns to a higher vibrational level, say $v'' = 1$, and the frequency of the emitted light will be

---

* However, quenching of the electronic energy of the excited molecule may occur on collision also, or the molecule may undergo collisionally induced predissociation into atoms; see Sec. 3-3C.

reduced by the difference in vibrational energy levels corresponding to $E_{v''=1} - E_{v''=0}$. This effect gives rise to so-called *Raman lines*.

Rayleigh scattering can be viewed as an "elastic collision" between a photon and a molecule, and the intensity of scattered light, I_s, is

$$I_s \propto \frac{I_0(\mathbf{n_1} - \mathbf{n_2})^2 r^6}{n\lambda^4} \tag{3-50}$$

where $(\mathbf{n_1} - \mathbf{n_2})$ = difference in refractive index between the particles and dispersing medium,

r = radius of the spherical particle ($r <$ 500 A for Rayleigh effect),

n = number of scattering particles per unit volume.

The dependence of Rayleigh scattering upon direction is obtained by multiplying Eq. 3-50 by the factor $(1 + \cos^2 \theta)$, where θ is the angle between the direction of the incident beam and the scattered light. The inverse λ^4 dependence of Rayleigh scattering is responsible for many colorful effects, such as the red sunsets and blue sky, and is used to determine the size and shapes of colloidal particles in the proper size range (i.e., r less than 500 A).

Unlike lines in a fluorescent spectrum, a Raman line is not characterized by a single, fixed difference in frequency, $\Delta\omega$, between the exciting and the emitted radiation. These frequency differences correspond to differences in vibrational energy levels of molecules in the ground state. Thus, homopolar diatomic molecules, for example, N_2, O_2, and H_2, which are inactive toward infrared absorption (no permanent dipole moment), are Raman active so that quantities such as moment of inertia, interatomic distance, force constants, and ω_e can be determined. The selection rules for transitions are $\Delta v = \pm 1$, 0 and $\Delta J = 0$, ± 2. When $\Delta v = +1$, we have a Stokes line, and $\Delta v = -1$ gives an anti-Stokes line.

3-2B   Photophysical Energy Transfer Processes; Gases at Low Pressures

Diatomic molecules in excited vibronic states may, on collision, lose vibrational and rotational energy as well as electronic and translational energy, which we have seen may be transferred by excited atoms. For example, at low pressures (0.02 mm), iodine shows resonance fluorescence originating at the $v' = 26$ level. This is shown schematically on the potential energy curves, Fig. 3-33 (transition $B \rightarrow A$), and experimentally in the spectra of Arnot and McDowell,[37] Fig. 3-34. The upper half (a) shows the resonance fluorescence bands arising from the $(v' = 26) \rightarrow (v'' = 1, 2, 3, 4, 5, 6)$ transitions in pure iodine at about 0.02 mm pressure.

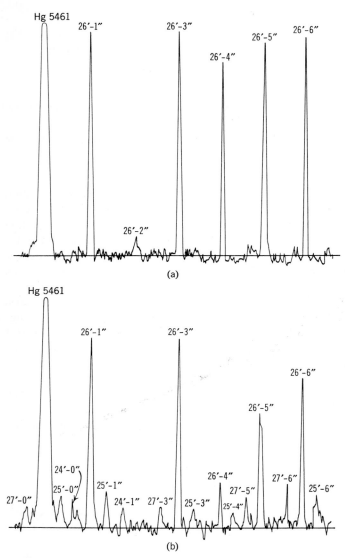

Fig. 3-34   A portion of the fluorescence spectrum (a) of the iodine molecule; in (b) the transfer bands are seen when 0.5 mm of neon are added. From Arnot and McDowell.[37]

At these low pressures the molecule, which is excited electronically in about 10^{-15} sec, usually remains unperturbed by collisions until its natural lifetime is reached, about 10^{-8} sec, and it fluoresces from the *same* vibronic level to which it was excited.

With the addition of 0.5 mm of neon (Fig. 3-34b) new lines appear with $v' = 25$ and 24, as a result of loss of one or two quanta of vibrational energy by *transferring collisions* before emission by the excited iodine. It is interesting that bands with $v' = 27$ also appear. This "anti-Stokes" fluorescence illustrates that energy can also be transferred *to* the photo-excited iodine molecule, although these events are of lowered probability.

From qualitative calculations, it appears that cross sections for such energy-transferring collisions of excited iodine, σ_T^2, with simple gases, are up to 100 times the usual collision cross sections, σ_{AB}^2 calculated from the kinetic collision frequency equation 6-31.[37,38,39] Effective cross sections for transfer to rare gases increase with atomic weight[33] and may be as high as 25 times σ_{AB}^2. Stevens[130] has pointed out, however, that the apparent superefficiency of the process is likely to be an artifact which results from the assumed radiative lifetime of the excited I_2 molecule ($\tau_0 \sim 10^{-8}$ sec) and the assumption of equality of size of the excited and ground-state I_2 molecules. If both species involved in a collision have energy levels in resonance, it seems possible that transfer could occur over several molec-ular diameters (certainly it seems to do so in liquids and solids). Results on energy transfer in other diatomic gases, such as S_2, Se_2, Te_2, $HgCl$, $HgBr$, and HgI, are found in Pringsheim.[33]

The theoretical aspects of the intermolecular (as well as *intra*-molecular in complex molecules) transfer of vibrational energy are beyond the scope of this book (see the article by Stevens and Boudart[38]). However, the information derived from experiment and theory can be summarized in the following terms:

1. The effectiveness of intermolecular energy exchange is directly related to the resonance existing between energy levels in the excited molecule or atom and those in the colliding molecule. Thus for maximum efficiency in a transfer or quenching collision (collision of the second kind) the change in translational energy should be minimized.

2. Rotational energy exchange occurs with $\Delta J = 0, \pm 2$, in accord with theory and more readily than vibrational exchange, where usually $\Delta v = \pm 1$.

3. Deactivation of an excited molecule occurs by a series of successive collisions during each of which certain amounts of vibrational and rotational energy are exchanged. If both species have energy levels in resonance, transfer can apparently extend over several molecular diameters.

Another type of energy exchange, charge transfer (e.g., $He^+ + He = He + He^+$) for ions and molecules, has been discussed by Kondratiev.[40] Space limitations prohibit considering it here, but it is of importance in flames, electric discharges, and radiation chemistry.

3-3 THE PHOTOCHEMISTRY OF THE SIMPLE MOLECULES

In the remaining section of this chapter the photochemistry of the simple inorganic molecules is reviewed briefly. It will be helpful in our considerations to obtain first an overall view of the competitive reactions which

TABLE 3-7   The Reaction Paths of an Electronically Excited Simple Molecule

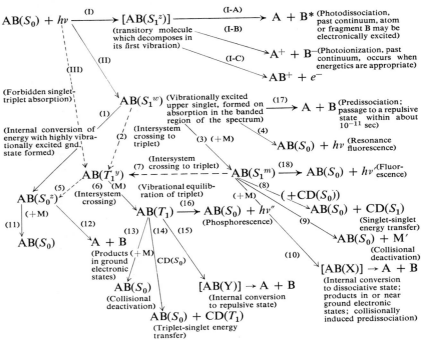

occur with the simple excited molecules. These reactions are summarized in Table 3-7. Excitation of the molecule AB, assumed to be in a singlet ground state (S_0), may result in direct photodissociation (I) if the wavelength of the absorbed light lies within the region of continuous absorption by AB. The bond usually is cleaved homolytically, process I-A; one of the two netural atoms or fragments may be formed in an excited electronic state. For certain types of diatomic molecules, for example, the halides of gallium, indium, and thallium, irradiated in the far ultraviolet, ion products may be formed, process I-B. Photoionization (I-C) sets in as the dominant primary step at the very short wavelengths where the energy of the absorbed quantum corresponds to the ionization potential of the molecule AB.

Irradiation of AB in the region of rotational line blurring may lead to products A and B by way of process II and a rapid crossover to a repulsive state in about 10^{-11} sec, reaction 17. Absorption within the sharp banded region of the spectrum gives in process II an excited singlet state $AB(S_1^w)$ in an upper vibrational level of vibrational quantum number w. In process III the absorption within the very weak forbidden band of AB, at somewhat longer wavelengths than the first allowed band, may excite AB directly to the first excited triplet state, $AB(T_1^y)$.

Which of the multitude of reactions the excited molecule $AB(S_1^w)$ undergoes is determined by many factors: the radiative lifetime of the molecule, the nature of the potential energy surfaces, the number of collisions with other molecules, the nature of the molecules with which it collides, etc. At low pressures resonance fluorescence may be emitted, process 4, while at slightly higher pressures collisions may remove vibrational energy in reaction 3 and fluorescence emission with $v' < v$ may result, reaction 18.

Ground electronic state products A and B can arise from one of many paths of reaction of the upper singlet state $AB(S_1^w)$: the partially vibrationally equilibrated upper singlet $AB(S_1^m)$ may be formed by collisional deactivation 3, and then the molecule may cross over to a repulsive excited state which leads to A and B, reaction 10; it may undergo intersystem crossing to an excited triplet T_1^y by 7 and ultimately dissociate from a repulsive state to which the triplet might pass, paths 6 and 15. Alternative routes 1 and 5 form initially a highly vibrationally excited ground electronic state which may dissociate quickly in reaction 12 or be deactivated in 11 if the collision frequency is high.

If another type of molecule CD is present in the system and the energies of its lowest excited singlet and triplet states are below those for the corresponding states in AB, then singlet-singlet or triplet-triplet energy transfer may occur efficiently through reactions 8 and 14, respectively.

If the triplet excited molecule $AB(T_1)$ has a potential energy surface which does not intersect that of a dissociative state, and it is neither collisionally deactivated nor involved in electronic energy transfer to some acceptor molecule, then after a considerable delay, about 10^{-3} sec, it will emit phosphorescence of frequency v'' such that $v'' < v' < v$, path 16.

When one adds to the many paths shown in Table 3-7 the actual complication of stepwise vibrational deactivation, $S_1{}^w \rightarrow S_1{}^v \rightarrow S_1{}^u \rightarrow S_1{}^t \rightarrow S_1{}^s \rightarrow \cdots$, and different efficiencies for each reaction from each vibrational position, a surprisingly complex labyrinth of reaction paths is seen to be available to even the very simplest excited molecule.

3-3A   The Photochemistry of the Simple Inorganic Hydrides

3-3A-1   The Hydrogen Halides

The hydrogen halides show continuous absorption which has its onset at about 2500 A for HCl, 2650 A for HBr, and 3270 A for HI.[47] The

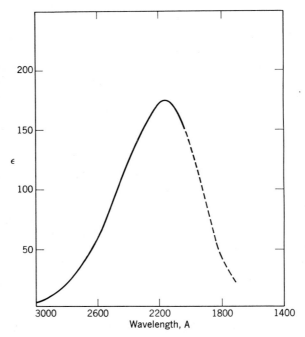

Fig. 3-35   Absorption spectrum of HI. From Romand.[49]

absorption spectrum of HI is shown in Fig. 3-35. Mulliken[48] has studied the low-lying electronic states of the hydrogen halides and derived the potential energy diagram for HI shown in Fig. 3-36. The original excitation of the HI molecule probably involves the promotion of a non-bonding halogen electron to one of several higher molecular orbitals. For HI the electronic states formed are all dissociative; the $^3\Pi_1$ and $^1\Pi$ states form atoms in their normal ground electronic states $H(^2S_{1/2})$ and $I(^2P_{3/2})$, whereas the $^3\Pi_{0+}$ state forms an excited $^2P_{1/2}$ iodine atom.

The photochemistry of the hydrogen halides has been studied extensively over the years.[50] Recent work substantiates the earlier view that the primary split of the HI molecule into atoms, process 3-51, occurs with a

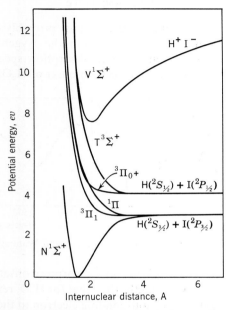

Fig. 3-36   Potential energy curves for the lowest electronic states of HI. After Mulliken.[48b]

quantum yield of near unity at both 2537 and 1849 A.[51]

$$HX(^1\Sigma^+) + h\nu \rightarrow [HX(X)] \rightarrow H(^2S_{1/2}) + X(^2P_{3/2}) \qquad (3\text{-}51a)$$

$$[HX(Y)] \rightarrow H(^2S_{3/2}) + X(^2P_{1/2}) \qquad (3\text{-}51b)$$

The fraction of iodine atoms formed in the $^2P_{1/2}$ state at various wavelengths is not completely clear, although from the relative positions of the maxima for the $^3\Pi_1$, $^3\Pi_{0+}$, and $^1\Pi$ states Martin and Willard[51] suggest that the maximum in the $^1\Pi$ transition will occur at the shortest wavelength region of the band, the $^3\Pi_{0+}$ will be favored at intermediate wavelengths, and the $^3\Pi_1$ will occur at the longest wavelengths. Thus production of the excited $I(^2P_{1/2})$ atoms may be favored somewhat near the center of the band and normal $I(^2P_{3/2})$ atoms at both extremes of the band. In all cases the very large excess energy of the quantum over the H-X bond dissociation energy is reflected in the "hot" atom reactions.[52] Thus at 1849 A up to 84 kcal/mole excess kinetic energy may be associated with the hydrogen atom. See the discussion of Sec. 6-7B-3.

3-3A-2 The Photochemistry of the Group Six Hydrides: H_2O, H_2O_2, H_2S, H_2Se, and H_2Te

The first absorption band in these compounds probably corresponds to the promotion of a non-bonding p-electron on the oxygen family element to a higher σ^* molecular orbital.[58] The absorption spectrum of water vapor is shown in Fig. 3-37. The absorption onset of H_2O_2 vapor extends

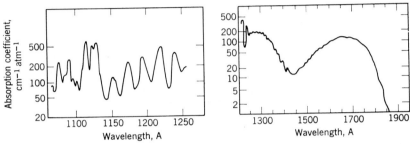

Fig. 3-37   The absorption spectrum of water vapor. From Watanabe and Zelikoff.[53]

to longer wavelengths; see Fig. 3-38. The absorption onset for H_2S, H_2Se, and H_2Te shifts to longer wavelengths than that for H_2O, reflecting, at least in part, the lower affinity of the non-bonding electron to the heavier atom; see Fig. 3-39. Some structure is evident in the first two absorption bands of water. Below 1250 A banded structure is dominant. The band at 1240 A has been attributed to the $^1B_1 \leftarrow {}^1A_1$ transition.[60] (See Sec. 4-2 for discussion of electronic state designations.)

There is considerable evidence that the photolysis of water in all wavelength regions leads to hydrogen and OH radicals.[54,57,61-67,77,78] The following primary processes are probably significant:

$$H_2O + h\nu \rightarrow H(^2S_{1/2}) + OH(^2\Pi) \qquad (3\text{-}52a)$$

$$H(^2S_{1/2}) + OH(^2\Sigma^+) \qquad (3\text{-}52b)$$

$$H_2 + O(^1D) \qquad (3\text{-}53)$$

Reaction 3-52a becomes possible energetically at wavelengths less than 2420 A, and it is probably the major reaction in the longer-wavelength absorption bands; the primary quantum yield of hydrogen atom formation is near unity.[65] At wavelengths less than 1356 A process 3-52b becomes

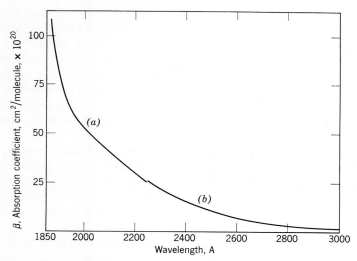

Fig. 3-38   The absorption spectrum of H_2O_2 vapor; the absorption coefficient β is defined by $\beta = 2.303 \log (I_0/I)/nl$, where n is the concentration in molecules/cubic centimeter and l the path in centimeters. From Volman,[54] originally from Refs. 55 (curve a) and 56 (curve b).

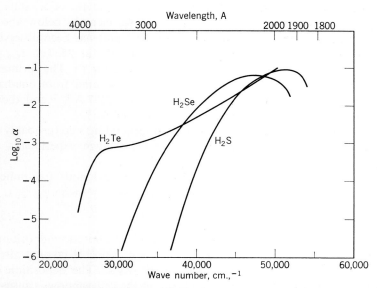

Fig. 3-39   The absorption spectrum of H_2S, H_2Se, and H_2Te; the absorption coefficient $\alpha = [\log (I_0/I)]/\rho(\text{atm})l(\text{cm})$. From Rollefson and Burton,[50b] p. 179; originally from Goodeve and Stein.[59]

possible energetically, and indeed the 3062 A 0-0 band of the fluorescence of the $OH(^2\Sigma^+) \rightarrow OH(^2\Pi)$ transition is seen on irradiation of water vapor within the second continuum[61c] and the 1240 A band.[66] It is interesting to note that the rotational energy of the OH fragments was found to be greatly in excess of the thermally equilibrated species; radicals with rotational quantum numbers in the range 18–22 were abundant in the photolysis at 1216 A. If the excited state retains some non-linearity, then considerable spin can be imparted to the OH fragment as the "hot" hydrogen atom separates.

McNesby, Tanaka, and Okabe[67] have demonstrated that some H_2 is formed in H_2O photolysis at 1236 A even when C_2D_4 is present to scavenge hydrogen atoms. They suggest that primary process 3-53 occurs with $\varphi_{53}/\varphi_{52} \cong 0.3$ at 1236 A; a small contribution from it to the photolysis of water in the first two continua cannot be confirmed or excluded at this writing.

Volman[54] in his summary of the photochemistry of hydrogen peroxide favors a photodissociative primary process:

$$H_2O_2 + h\nu \rightarrow 2\ OH(^2\Pi_{3/2\ or\ 1/2}) \tag{3-54a}$$

$$OH(^2\Pi_{3/2\ or\ 1/2}) + OH(A\,^2\Sigma^+) \tag{3-54b}$$

The electronic excitation of one of the OH radicals to the $A\,^2\Sigma^+$ state is energetically feasible and appears to occur at wavelengths below about 2025 A, since the 3064 A fluorescence of the $^2\Sigma^+$ state has been observed under those conditions.[56] In gas-phase experiments at 2537 A $\varphi_{54a} = 0.85 \pm 0.2$, or unity within the experimental error.[68] The primary quantum yield of 3-54 in aqueous solution, as measured from one-half the yield of scavengeable OH radicals, is near 0.5 at 2537 A[69–73] and about 0.3 at 3130;[74] 3-54 occurs measurably even at 3650 A.[75]

A small contribution from an oxygen-atom-generating step (probably in a secondary reaction) is needed to explain exchange experiments in aqueous solution.[69,71]

All evidence points to the occurrence of the analogous free-radical splits in H_2S photolysis in the 2550–2000 A region,[76,79,82] with $\varphi_{55} \cong 1$.

$$H_2S + h\nu \rightarrow H + SH \tag{3-55}$$

It is reasonable to assume that H_2Se and H_2Te photodecompositions follow this pattern also, although Goodeve and Stein[59,83] favored intramolecular hydrogen formation in their early work. The deposition of selenium and tellurium in mirror-like form on the cell windows causes a serious experimental difficulty, especially since photocatalytic reactions may occur on the irradiated deposits.[84]

3-3A-3   The Photochemistry of the Group Five Hydrides: NH_3, PH_3, N_3H, and NH_2NH_2

The absorption spectrum of ammonia, Fig. 5-11, shows banded structure overlying at least three continua in the range 1050–2200 A.[85] Bands in the 1680–2170 A region are broad and consistent with a predissociative upper electronic state. Bands in the 1670–1160 region are all very sharp. The upper electronic states in all regions are thought to be planar.[85e,f] Since the ground state is non-planar, absorption of ultraviolet light always forms an electronically excited molecule which is also vibrationally excited in an out-of-plane bending mode; the intensity maximum occurs at about $v' = 7$-9 in all series. Presumably the transitions are associated with an electron in a non-bonding nitrogen orbital promoted to a Rydberg orbital (essentially a higher atomic nitrogen orbital). At 1225–1231 A photoionization begins.[85f,86]

There is abundant evidence that hydrogen atoms are produced at all wavelengths in ammonia photolysis.[50,67,87–98] The NH_2 radical has been observed in NH_3 photolysis and characterized by absorption spectroscopy[87,88] and ESR.[92] In addition to NH_2 formation, NH has been identified in the photolysis of NH_3 at the shorter wavelengths; in photolyses below 1550 A, the $^3\Sigma^-$ state of NH was found,[94,96,97] while at 1165, 1236, and 1295 A there was emission from the $^1\Pi$ state.[98]

The probable primary processes in ammonia photoysis are, in summary:

$$NH_3 + h\nu \rightarrow NH_2 + H(^2S_{1/2}) \qquad (3\text{-}56)$$
$$\searrow NH(^3\Sigma^-) + 2H(^2S_{1/2}) \qquad (3\text{-}57a)$$
$$\nearrow NH(^1\Pi) + H_2 \qquad (3\text{-}57b)$$

Process 3-56 dominates at all wavelengths. The product NH_2 is probably formed in its ground state ($^2B_1$) at wavelengths greater than 2130 A and probably also at the shorter wavelengths. The energetics allow NH_2 to be in the excited state ($^2A_1\Pi_u$) at wavelengths below 2130 A, and although the emission bands of the excited NH_2 were reported for photolyses in the 1400–1600 A range,[61b] this observation has not been confirmed.

McNesby, Tanaka, and Okabe[67] scavenged hydrogen atoms formed in NH_3 photolysis by using C_2D_4 and estimated that at least 96% of the primary split of NH_3 follows 3-56 at 1849 A, while at 1236 A molecular hydrogen formation in 3-57b accounts for about 14% of the total. The energetics are favorable for 3-57a and 3-57b at wavelengths shorter than 1420 and 1360 A, respectively.[57] The possible primary process, $NH_3 + h\nu \rightarrow NH(^3\Sigma^-) + H_2(^1\Sigma_g^+)$, violates the spin conservation rule, and so the alternative reaction forming hydrogen atoms, process 3-57a, has been favored. The quantum yield of NH_3 disappearance at 1849 A may approach unity at low pressures;[89] at 1470 A and above 15 mm pressure a value of 0.45 ± 0.1 has been reported.[91]

Phosphine photolysis has received little attention since the early work of Melville.[99] The absorption shows some banded structure at the long wavelengths (2360, 2320, 2295, 2280 A) and is continuous from the region 2250–1850 A. The quantum yield of hydrogen formation in the long-wavelength absorption region is equal to about 0.56, independent of the pressure and the temperature. The flash photolysis studies of Ramsay[100] and Norrish and Oldershaw[101] show evidence of PH_2 formation in 3-58, analogous to NH_3 photolysis.

$$PH_3 + h\nu \rightarrow PH_2 + H \qquad\qquad (3\text{-}58)$$

$$PH(A^3\Pi) + H + H \qquad\qquad (3\text{-}59a)$$

$$PH(^3\Sigma^-) + H + H \qquad\qquad (3\text{-}59b)$$

Below 2000 A, spectroscopic evidence is found for PH in both the $^3\Pi$ and $^3\Sigma^-$ states.[102] If these species arise from a singlet excited state of PH_3, then, following spin conservation, molecular hydrogen cannot be formed in 3-59a and 3-59b.

Hydrazoic acid, N_3H, absorption onset occurs at about 2250 A, and the quantum yields of decomposition at 1990 A are about 2 at low pressures.[103] More recent work[104–108] confirms the earlier suggestion[103] that the major primary split of the molecule occurs thus:

$$N_3H + h\nu \rightarrow N_2 + NH \qquad\qquad (3\text{-}60)$$

Hydrazine absorbs at somewhat longer wavelengths than NH_3, and its absorption bands below 2200 A appear diffuse.[109] The photolysis at 1990 A was studied by Wenner and Beckman,[111] who reported a quantum yield of decomposition of hydrazine of about unity at low pressures. There is evidence of hydrogen atom formation when irradiation is made with a zinc spark (2100, 2064, 2025 A),[110] and flash studies disclose the formation of the NH_2 radical.[109] Two primary processes have been suggested:

$$NH_2NH_2 + h\nu \rightarrow H + NHNH_2 \qquad\qquad (3\text{-}61)$$

$$NH_2 + NH_2 \qquad\qquad (3\text{-}62)$$

The more recent spectroscopic work and the weakness of the NH_2-NH_2 band in hydrazine favor 3-62; however, 3-61 is the choice of many early researchers.[110–114] It is not possible to distinguish clearly between the alternatives from the early work, and the extent of 3-61 remains uncertain.

The researchers in the older studies of the photolysis of $CH_3NHNHCH_3$[115] and $(CH_3)_2NNH_2$[116] chose the N-H bond split as the primary act, although again the evidence is not overwhelming.

3-3B   The Photochemistry of Oxygen and the Simple Oxides and Sulfides

3-3B-1   Oxygen, O_2, and O_3

The absorption spectrum of oxygen in the various regions of the ultraviolet is summarized in Fig. 3-40. In addition to these bands there is a very weak absorption responsible for the Fraunhofer lines in the solar spectrum at 7590–7650 and 6870–6920 A; see Fig. 3-26. This absorption in oxygen corresponds to a very forbidden transition, $O_2(^3\Sigma_g^-) + h\nu \rightarrow O_2(^1\Sigma_g^+)$. This transition can be pictured together with others in the energy level diagram for several of the electronic states of O_2 shown in Fig. 3-27. Absorption within the forbidden Herzberg band, originating near 2454 A, gives the forbidden transition $O_2(^3\Sigma_g^-) + h\nu \rightarrow O_2(^3\Sigma_u^+)$, which violates the $(-) \leftrightarrow (+)$ rule. The shallow potential well of the $^3\Sigma_u^+$ state is displaced to larger internuclear distances than the ground state, and promotion to this state results in rapid dissociation:

$$O_2(^3\Sigma_g^-) + h\nu \rightarrow O_2(^3\Sigma_u^+) \rightarrow 2\ O(^3P) \tag{3-63a}$$

Absorption in the Schumann-Runge bands from 1759–1950 A causes excitation to one of the vibrational levels of the $O_2(^3\Sigma_u^-)$ state. Note that this state crosses the energy curve for the $^3\Pi_u$ state and allows a mechanism for predissociation of the excited molecule to ground-state oxygen atoms. Therefore, when light is absorbed in the 1759–1950 A region, the following reaction sequence is likely to occur:

$$O_2(^3\Sigma_g^-) + h\nu \rightarrow O_2(^3\Sigma_u^-) \rightarrow O_2(^3\Pi_u) \rightarrow 2\ O(^3P) \tag{3-63b}$$

Note in Fig. 3-40d that the Schumann-Runge bands converge to a continuum at about 1759 A. This corresponds to the onset of dissociation of the $O_2(^3\Sigma_u^-)$ state to an excited $O(^1D)$ and normal $O(^3P)$ atoms.

$$O_2(^3\Sigma_g^-) + h\nu \rightarrow [O_2(^3\Sigma_u^-)] \rightarrow O(^1D) + O(^3P) \tag{3-63c}$$

The f-value of the 1290–1750 A region, $0.16 - 0.23$,[124] is consistent with the allowed character of this transition.

Below 1300 A the absorption changes form as vibrational structure reappears. The energy requirements at wavelengths below 1342 A are suitable for the dissociation:

$$O_2(^3\Sigma_g^-) + h\nu \rightarrow O(^2P) + O(^1S) \tag{3-63d}$$

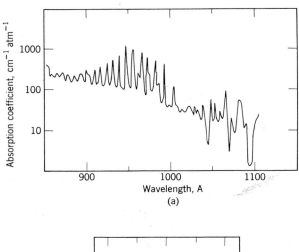

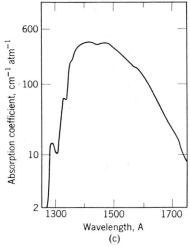

Fig. 3-40 Absorption spectrum of O_2. Part (a) from Watanabe and Marmo;[118] (b) and (c) from Inn;[117] (d) from Ref. 57.

and below 923 A, the process:

$$O_2(^3\Sigma_g^-) + h\nu \rightarrow 2\,O(^1S) \tag{3-63e}$$

The quantum yield of ozone formation at 2070 A, within the 1650–1900 A range, 1470 A, and at 1295 A, is near 2.0 and suggests a perfect efficiency of oxygen atom formation following excitation.[120,121,122] Excellent reviews of the photochemistry of oxygen are available[54,57] to which the reader is referred for more detailed information.

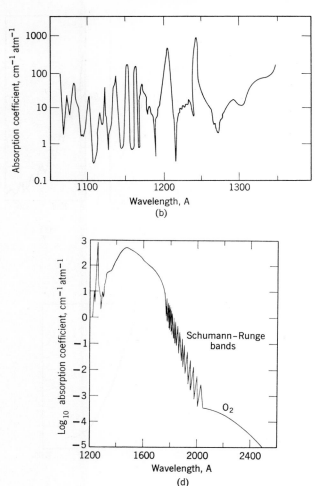

(b)

(d)

The first two absorption bands for ozone are shown in Fig. 3-41. The origin of the bands is somewhat more obscure than in the case of O_2.[123,124] The detailed photochemistry is a matter for some conjecture as well. Table 3-8 is useful as a guide to the nature of the possible products in the photolysis in the various wavelength regions. In his review of ozone photochemistry Leighton[125] suggested that the visible band of ozone is probably a singlet-triplet excitation followed by formation of ground-state products:

$$O_3(S_0) + h\nu \rightarrow O_3(T_1) \rightarrow O_2(^3\Sigma_g^-) + O(^3P) \tag{3-64a}$$

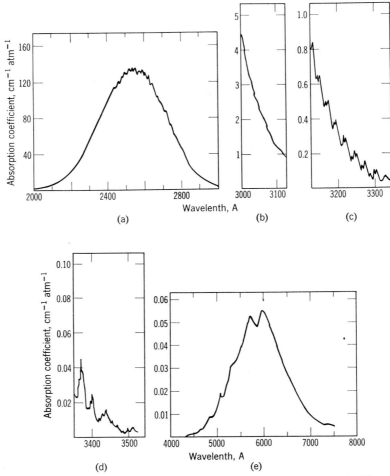

Fig. 3-41   Absorption spectrum of O_3. From Inn and Tanaka.[119]

At wavelengths shorter than 5900 A process 3-64b is allowed energywise but is forbidden by the spin rule.

$$O_3(S_1) + h\nu \rightarrow O_3(T_1) \rightarrow O_2(^1\Delta_g) + O(^3P) \qquad (3\text{-}64b)$$

In the strong ultraviolet band an allowed singlet-singlet transition is suggested. If this is the case, decomposition into two singlet products is favored by the spin rule:

$$O_3(S_0) + h\nu \rightarrow O_3(S_1) \rightarrow O_2(^1\Delta_g) + O(^1D) \qquad (3\text{-}64c)$$

$$\searrow$$

$$O_2(^1\Sigma_g^+) + O(^1D) \qquad (3\text{-}64d)$$

TABLE 3-8 Wavelengths (A) below Which It Is Energetically Possible to Produce the Indicated Species from O_3 Photolysis[a]

Species	$O_2(^3\Sigma_g^-)$[b]	$O_2(^1\Delta_g)$	$O_2(^1\Sigma_g^+)$	$O_2(^3\Sigma_u^+)$	$O_2(^3\Sigma_u^-)$
$O(^3P)$[b]	11,400	5900[c]	4600[c]	2300	1700
$O(^1D)$	4,100[c]	3100	2600	1670[c]	1500[c]
$O(^1S)$	2,340[c]	1960	1790	1290[c]	1080[c]

[a] From McNesby and O'Kabe.[57]
[b] Ground state.
[c] Forbidden transition.

That $O(^1D)$ atoms are formed by photolysis in the ultraviolet band is consistent with the O_3 flash photolysis results of McGrath and Norrish.[126,127] There is some question of the magnitude of the primary efficiency of ozone decomposition since an "energy chain" reaction is operative in this system,[54,57,125] but a high efficiency is suggested by the continuous nature of the absorption. In the visible band ($\lambda < 5900$) the energy chain is absent, and the quantum yield of ozone decomposition is 2.0; a primary quantum yield of near unity for 3-64a is likely[128] for these conditions.

3-3B-2 The Oxides of Sulfur and Nitrogen: SO_2, SO_3, N_2O, NO, and NO_2

Sulfur dioxide shows much fine structure in its first strong absorption band (second region of absorption), shown in Fig. 3-42. Photodissociation of SO_2 into SO and oxygen is not possible energetically until about 2180 A; it is evident from all the facts that the photochemistry of SO_2 in this absorption region is that of the reactions of the electronically excited SO_2 other than unimolecular decomposition. A very weak first absorption region, not shown in Fig. 3-42, originates at 3880 A with a maximum at 3740 A.[129] There is a third region of absorption at 2400–1800 A. The nature of the electronic states has been considered by Walsh[123] and Mulliken.[131] The excited SO_2 molecule fluoresces from each of the three excited states.[132,133,134] Fluorescence from the second excited state follows Stern-Volmer quenching (see Sec. 6-7C). A magnetic field effect was observed with SO_2 excited in the first electronic state[135] and was attributed to its triplet character. The radiative lifetime of the first state found by integrated absorption, $\tau_0 \cong 1.3 \times 10^{-2} - 2.2 \times 10^{-3}$ sec, is also suggestive of a triplet state; in solid SO_2 at 77°K the phosphorescence lifetime of this state is $5 \pm 1 \times 10^{-4}$ sec.[134] The integrated absorption of the second band suggests a natural radiative lifetime of 2×10^{-7} sec, and probably it is a singlet state.

The reactions of electronically excited SO_2 have been studied in pure SO_2,[136] SO_2—O_2,[136,140] SO_2-hydrocarbon,[138,139] and other more complex mixtures.[141-143] Hall[136] found that, at 3130 A in pure SO_2, sulfur and SO_3 form with a quantum efficiency of about 10^{-2}, and in SO_2—O_2 mixtures only SO_3 forms with about the same quantum yield.[136,137] Dainton and Ivin[138] reported that excited SO_2 reacts with hydrocarbons (RH) to form, overall, sulfinic acids (RSO_2H) with quantum efficiencies that vary from

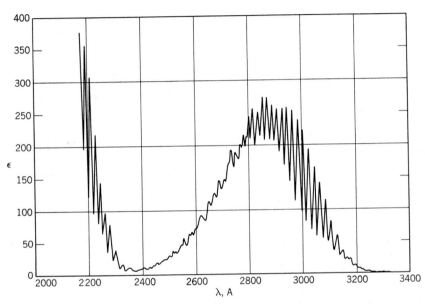

Fig. 3-42 The absorption spectrum of $SO_2(g)$, 25°. Spectra determined by Mrs. Veronique McMillan.[222]

0.26 for reaction with pentane to 0.006 with methane. The possible involvement of SO_2 photolysis in particulate formation in SO_2-polluted atmospheres has been considered.[125,141,143,206]

Various speculations on the mechanisms of the excited SO_2 molecule reactions have been made; Johnston and dev Jain[139] favored the involvement of the triplet state formed from an excited singlet about 1% of the time by intersystem crossing. Obviously some interesting intermediates such as SO_4 probably are involved in the SO_2—O_2 system.

The photochemistry of SO_3 has been studied little. The older work shows that absorption occurs in the ultraviolet region with weak diffuse bands superimposed on a continuum extending to about 3100 A, where structure ends.[144] The minimum energies necessary to effect the molecular splits 3-65 and 3-66 are available at about 3440 and 3000 A, respectively.

$$SO_3 + h\nu \to SO_2 + O(^3P) \qquad (3\text{-}65)$$

$$SO + O_2(^3\Sigma_g^-) \qquad (3\text{-}66)$$

At 2750 A decomposition of SO_3 was observed, but it is not clear which of the processes is important here.[145] At wavelengths less than 2240 A the $O(^1D)$ atom can be a product of 3-65. $SO(v'' = 0, 1, 2, 3)$ has been observed in SO_3 flash photolysis at short wavelengths, but whether it is formed in 3-66 or through the exothermic reaction, $O(^1D) + SO_2 \to SO + O_2$, is uncertain.[220]

The spectrum of N_2O is given in Fig. 3-43; it shows diffuse bands superimposed on strong continua, suggestive of transitions to short-lived repulsive or dissociative upper states; a possible exception is the band centered at about 1450 A. The two possible fragmentation steps 3-67 and 3-68 are energetically allowed at all wavelengths absorbed by N_2O, assuming ground-state products.

$$N_2O + h\nu \to N_2 + O \qquad (3\text{-}67)$$

$$N + NO \qquad (3\text{-}68)$$

Some effort in N_2O photolysis studies has been directed toward estimating the relative importance of these alternative steps and the nature of the excitation in the products formed. If the spin conservation rule is applied and the dissociative upper state is a singlet, then reactions 3-67a and 3-67b represent the probable products in the 1800 A band.

$$N_2O + h\nu \to N_2(^1\Sigma_g^+) + O(^1D) \qquad (3\text{-}67a)$$

$$N_2(^1\Sigma_g^+) + O(^1S) \qquad (3\text{-}67b)$$

Decomposition reactions 3-67c and 3-68a, possible energetically, are spin forbidden from an excited singlet N_2O but could occur from a triplet by intersystem crossing.

$$N_2O + h\nu \to N_2(^1\Sigma_g^+) + O(^3P) \qquad (3\text{-}67c)$$

$$NO(X^2\Pi) + N(^4S) \qquad (3\text{-}68a)$$

In experiments at 1470 A two additional energy and spin allowed processes could occur from an excited singlet.

$$N_2O + h\nu \to N_2(^3\Sigma_u^+) + O(^3P) \qquad (3\text{-}67d)$$

$$NO(X^2\Pi) + N(^2D) \qquad (3\text{-}68b)$$

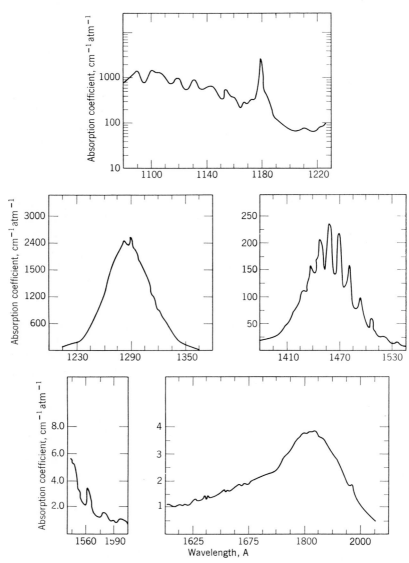

Fig. 3-43   The absorption spectrum of nitrous oxide, N_2O.   From Zelikoff, Watanabe, and Inn.[146]

At 1236 another allowed process could contribute:

$$N_2O + h\nu \rightarrow NO(X^2\Pi) + N(^2P) \qquad (3\text{-}68c)$$

Other reactions are possible if the N_2O decomposition occurs from a triplet excited state.[57]

The combined results of Zelikoff and Aschenbrand[149a] and Castellion and Noyes[150] suggest strongly that 3-67a is dominant in both the 1849 and 1470 A regions with $\varphi_{67} = 1.0$. However, McNesby and Okabe point out that at least the partial participation of 3-68 is likely, especially at the shorter wavelengths, in view of several other observations: (1) NH_3 has been reported as a product in N_2O photolyses in H_2;[151] (2) the β band of NO fluorescence was observed when N_2O was irradiated at wavelengths greater than 1200 A;[152] (3) $^{15}N^{15}N$ formation occurred in $^{15}N^{14}NO$ photolyses at 1236 A. Doering and Mahan[153] estimated that 3-68 occurs to the extent of about 12% at 1236 A.

Nitrous oxide is often used as an actinometer in the vacuum ultraviolet where $\Phi_{N_2} = 1.44 \pm 0.04$ at 1849 A[150,154] and 1470 A;[149a] $\Phi_{N_2} = 1.18$,[155] 1.34 ± 0.04[153a] at 1238 A. (See Sec. 7-4B-1.) Presumably the yield of N_2 above unity results from the secondary reaction, $O + N_2O \rightarrow O_2 + N_2$, which competes with $O + N_2O \rightarrow 2 NO$.

Nitric oxide, NO, shows sharp bands in the 1500–2300 A region (Fig. 3-44) which have been classified as α, β, γ, δ, and ϵ systems.[147,148,157,158] The potential energy diagram of the states from which these originate is shown in Fig. 3-45. Although there is no evidence of predissociation from the absorption spectrum in the 1500–2300 A region,[156] the fluorescence emission bands from the β, γ, and ϵ systems are missing above $\nu' = 7, 4$, and 3, respectively.[159] Since lowered intensity of fluorescence emission is a much more sensitive criterion of predissociation than broadening of absorption lines (see Sec. 6-2), this has been interpreted by some workers as evidence that a crossover to some dissociative or repulsive state occurs in this region above 1910 A.

The photochemistry of NO in the long-wavelength bands at 2265 and 2144 A has been studied to some extent. There is insufficient energy here to dissociate the nitric oxide molecule, and the other reactions of the excited molecule are observed. Kleinberg and Terenin[164] followed the fluorescence of NO when irradiated with 2265 and 2144 A Cd-arc lines; these correspond to the $0'$, $0''$, and $1'$, $0''$ bands of the γ system of NO; see Fig. 3-44. They added various gases (He, Ne, Ar, H_2, N_2, CO, CO_2, CH_4, C_2H_4, H_2O, C_2H_5OH, hexane, and cyclohexane) and noted the efficiency of the gas in altering the vibrational distribution in the excited molecules and also the facility of the gas in lowering the intensity of fluorescence. All gases altered the distribution by deactivating a portion

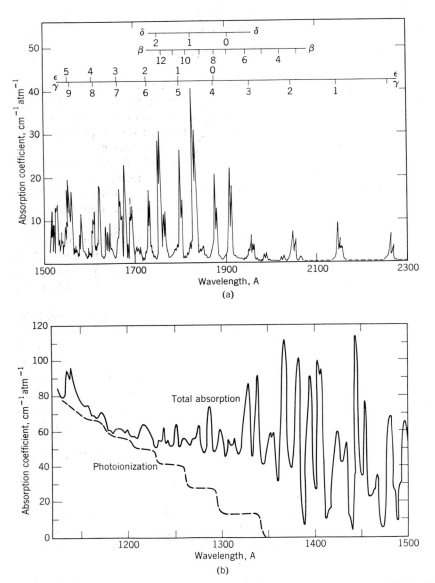

Fig. 3-44   The absorption spectrum of nitric oxide, NO. From McNesby and Okabe;[57] originally from Watanabe.[160]

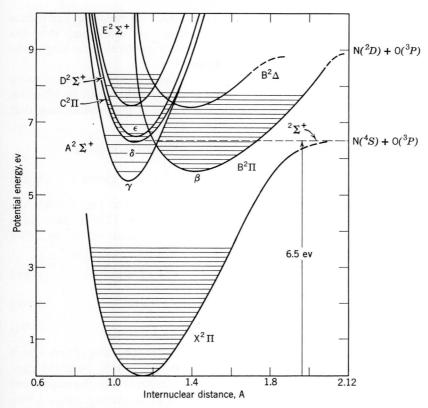

Fig. 3-45   Potential energy diagram for nitric oxide, NO. From McNesby and Okabe.[57]

of the $v' = 1$ vibrationably excited state, as one would expect. However, extinction of the lines was observed only with CO_2, CO, C_2H_4, H_2O, and C_2H_5OH. Kleinberg and Terenin believed that this was the result of a chemical reaction of the excited molecule with the added gas in these cases. Moore, Wulf, and Badger[163] also found that nitric oxide excited at 2144 and 2265 A decomposed, ultimately forming N_2O_3. McGee and Heicklen[175a] have confirmed the excited-molecule mechanism for NO excited at 2144 and 2265 A. The mechanism which was operative in pure NO was the following:

$$NO + h\nu \rightarrow NO(A^2\Sigma) \tag{3-69}$$

$$NO(A^2\Sigma) + NO \rightarrow N_2 + O_2 \tag{3-69a}$$

$$N_2O + O \tag{3-69b}$$

McGee and Heicklen[175b] also showed that $NO(A^2\Sigma)$ molecules can induce the decomposition of ethylene to acetylene and hydrogen; thus the original suggestion of Kleinberg and Terenin of chemical quenching of the $NO(A^2\Sigma)$ molecule by ethylene is confirmed.

Flory and Johnston[162] studied NO photolysis at low pressures, using a mercury arc from which the 1832 A line was believed to be effective. They concluded from the pressure independence of the product rates that a predissociation mechanism was operative:

$$NO(X^2\Pi) + h\nu \rightarrow NO(A^2\Sigma) \rightarrow NO(B^2\Pi; \ v' > 7)$$
$$\downarrow$$
$$N(^4S) + O(^3P) \qquad \text{(3-70a)}$$

Underlying the banded region below 1500 A (see Fig. 3-44b), the continua 1230–1400 A and the continuum below 1230 A have been attributed to the transition to an upper state which dissociates by 3-70b and 3-70c, respectively:

$$NO(X^2\Pi) + h\nu \rightarrow N(^2D) + O(^3P) \qquad \text{(3-70b)}$$
$$N(^2P) + O(^3P) \qquad \text{(3-70c)}$$
$$NO^+ + e^- \qquad \text{(3-71)}$$

Below 1343 A photoionization occurs, 3-71.[160] The absorption which results in photoionization has been plotted in Fig. 3-44b. Note the stepwise nature of the ionization; Watanabe attributes this to the population of various vibrational levels of the NO^+ ion in its ground state. Using 1236 A radiation, Zelicoff and Aschenbrand[149b] noted that the ion neutralization reaction can lead to dissociation products following 3-71:

$$NO^+ + e^- \rightarrow [NO^{\ddagger}] \rightarrow N + O$$
$$\xrightarrow{(+M)}$$
$$NO \ (+M)$$

Macdonald[161] first measured the nitric oxide decomposition using an aluminum spark (1860, 1930, 1990 A) and found the quantum yield for NO disappearance to be 1.45. Apparently reactions 3-69 and/or 3-70 occur with nearly perfect efficiency.

Nitrogen dioxide, NO_2, absorbs over most of the visible and ultraviolet spectrum; a portion of the band, as resolved from that of the dimer N_2O_4 by Hall and Blacet,[165] is shown in Fig. 3-46. The multitude of sharp bands in the visible become more and more diffuse starting at about 3700 A. Norrish[169] found that NO_2 fluoresced noticeably when excited at 4358 A, only weakly at 4047 A, and hardly at all when excited at 3660 A. Neuberger and Duncan[170] observed some fluorescence on excitation with $\lambda >$ ~3950 A but found none on irradiating at 3660 A.

Much of the interest in NO_2 photolysis has centered on establishing the wavelength for the onset of photodissociation. This becomes energetically possible at wavelengths below about 3945 A; however, see the discussion which follows on this point. The answer to this question is of practical concern in the evaluation of the rate of ozone production and other air

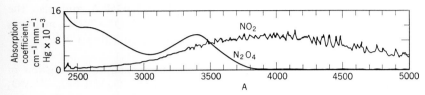

Fig. 3-46   Absorption spectrum of nitrogen dioxide, NO_2, and dinitrogen tetroxide, N_2O_4, at 25° corrected to pure compound spectra. From Hall and Blacet.[165]

pollutants from oxygen atoms released into the polluted atmosphere through NO_2 photolysis in the sunlight. Leighton has treated this subject in considerable detail.[125]

The limiting quantum yields of oxygen production in the photolysis of nitrogen dioxide at room temperature are 0.97 at 3130 A, 0.92 at 3660 A, 0.36 at 4047 A and 0.00 at 4358 A.[125] At both the lower wavelengths, 3660 and 3130 A, the absorption spectrum of nitrogen dioxide is diffuse, while fluorescence is weak or absent. Also, by means of $^{18-18}O_2$ tracer techniques, Blacet, Hall, and Leighton[167] have shown that scrambling in the oxygen and transfer of ^{18}O to nitrogen dioxide occur when mixtures of $^{18-18}O_2$ enriched oxygen and nitrogen dioxide are irradiated at 3130 A. From this evidence, the primary process in the photolysis of nitrogen dioxide is complete dissociation at 3130 A and probably virtually complete dissociation at 3660 A.

$$NO_2 + h\nu \rightarrow NO(X^2\Pi) + O(^3P) \qquad (3\text{-}72)$$

At the longer wavelengths, 4047 and 4358 A, the absorption spectrum shows discrete structure and the molecule fluoresces. Blacet *et al.*[167] found in one run that no scrambling occurred when a mixture of NO_2 and oxygen enriched in $^{18-18}O_2$ was irradiated at 4047 A. Also, the addition of inert gases was more effective in quenching the nitrogen dioxide photo-decomposition at 4047 A than at 3130 A. On this basis, Blacet *et al.* subsequently postulated an activated molecule mechanism to explain oxygen formation at 4047 A.[167]

Sato and Cvetanovic,[168] however, in studying the photooxidation of 1-butene by nitrogen dioxide, found that the same addition products, α-butene oxide and butanal, were formed at several ultraviolet wavelengths, including 4047 A. Furthermore, the ratio of their yields was the same at all these wavelengths. They found no reaction at 4358 A. They point out that this would be difficult to understand if free oxygen atoms were not involved at all the wavelengths used, including 4047 A but not 4358 A. Recently Pitts, Sharp, and Chan[166] redetermined the quantum yields of oxygen in NO_2 photolyses at 3130, 3660, 3800, 4047, and 4358 A and also the ^{18}O-scrambling which occurred in the photolysis of NO_2—$^{18-18}O_2$ mixtures at these wavelengths. The results are summarized in Table 3-9.

TABLE 3-9 Quantum Yields and Yields of Scrambling as a Function of Wavelength and Intensity at 24° in the Photolysis of NO_2 and NO_2—$^{18-18}O_2$ Mixtures[a]

λ, A	I_0, einsteins/sec	Q_m, % abs.	ppt[b], einstein abs.	Φ_{O_2}
3130	1.92×10^{-8}	82	8.4×10^5	0.97
3130	0.96×10^{-8}	88	8.7×10^5	0.97
3130	0.48×10^{-8}	95	8.5×10^5	0.97
3660	3.0×10^{-8}	80	8.1×10^5	0.92
3800	0.4×10^{-8}	85	7.2×10^5	0.82
4047	0.95×10^{-9}	96	3.0×10^5	0.36
4047	0.95×10^{-9}	96	2.9×10^5	0.36
4358	9.0×10^{-8}	79	$<0.05 \times 10^5$	<0.005

[a] Taken from Pitts, Sharp, and Chan.[166]
[b] Units of parts per thousand of scrambling produced per einstein of light absorbed.

Compare the values for 3800, 4047, and 4358 A. It is reasonably certain that the $^{18-18}O_2$ scrambling to $^{18}O^{16}O$ occurs by way of O_3 formation from oxygen atoms from NO_2 photolysis [for example, $NO_2 + h\nu \rightarrow NO + O$, $O + O_2(+ M) \rightarrow O_3(+ M)$, $O_3 + NO \rightarrow NO_2 + O_2$]. Accepting this, it is apparent from the data of Table 3-9 that oxygen atoms are still formed by NO_2 photolysis in the millimeter pressure range at 4047 A, although with a lowered efficiency. Tables 3-10 and 3-11 show the effects of temperature on the Φ_{O_2} and oxygen scrambling for experiments at 4047 and 4358 A.

At temperatures of 293° the photodecomposition of NO_2 is nearly perfectly efficient even at 4047 A, although unimportant at 4358 A. Since an einstein of light quanta at 4047 A corresponds to only 70.6 kcal/mole

TABLE 3-10 Quantum Yields of Oxygen as a Function of Temperature at Several Wavelengths in NO_2 Photolysis

Temperature, °C	Φ_{O_2}		
	3660 A	4047 A	4358 A[a]
23	0.95	0.36	(0.005)
23	0.92	0.35	(0.005)
71	1.02	0.41	(0.012)
71	0.95	0.42	(0.014)
133	0.99	0.50	(0.018)
133	0.97	0.52	(0.018)
223	1.00	0.70	(0.035)
223	[b]	0.71	(0.030)
293	[b]	0.90	[b]
293	[b]	0.92	[b]

[a] These small yields of oxygen are probably due to photolysis by a trace component of 4047 A radiation in the 4358 A "line."
[b] Not determined.

and the likely dissociation energy of NO_2 is at least 71.8 kcal/mole, dissociation might not be expected to occur at this wavelength. However, the marked temperature dependence of the quantum yield of oxygen production and oxygen exchange offers a real clue to the problem. Pitts et al.[166] found that they could explain the results quantitatively if they took into account the vibrational and rotational energies of the NO_2 molecule and the change of these with temperature. The fraction of the molecules which have the additional 1.2 kcal/mole of internal energy necessary to

TABLE 3-11 Yield of Scrambling as a Function of Temperature in $NO_2—^{18-18}O_2$ Photolysis

Temperature, °C	ppt[a]/einstein abs.	
	4047 A	4358 A[b]
23	3.0×10^5	(0.05×10^5)
44	3.8×10^5	
98		(0.17×10^5)
134	6.6×10^5	

[a] See footnote b, Table 3-9.
[b] See footnote a, Table 3-10.

overcome the barrier to dissociation on absorption of a 4047 A quantum was about 36% at $25°$, 50% at $133°$, 70% at $223°$, and 90% at $293°$; presumably the quantum yields as a function of temperature in Table 3-10 reflect this internal energy distribution.

The preceding interpretation of the temperature dependence of the quantum yield is based upon the following presuppositions. First, the state to which the molecule is excited must be a bound state with a quite similar N—O distance to that in the ground state. If the upper state is a repulsive one, dissociation can take place only if the energy of the quantum exceeds the dissociation energy. Second, it is assumed that all the rotational energy of the NO_2 molecule in the ground electronic state is available for the breakage of the ON . . . O bond. The exact nature of this energy conversion process can only be inferred, since little is known about the excited electronic states of NO_2. However, if we assume an energy-level scheme such as that proposed in Fig. 3-47, and further assume that absorption of a 4047 A quantum of radiation excites the molecule into the $^2B_2$ state and that once in this state the molecule can cross over to the close-lying $^2A_1$ state, then the availability of the rotational energy for bond dissociation may be understood (see also the treatment of Marcus[172]).

Evidence for such a nearby repulsive electronic state or one with a shallow potential well is provided by predissociation at ~3700 A. Green and Linnett[171] have also suggested that the upper $^2A_1$ state is linear. The rotational energy about the axis of least moment of inertia will then be converted into vibrational energy of the degenerate bending modes in the activated complex. Coriolis interaction mixes these bending vibrations with the antisymmetric stretching mode, and in this way part of the rotational energy in the ground-state molecule can become available for the breaking of the ON . . . O bond. The remainder of the rotational energy arises from rotation about axes perpendicular to the O—N—O axis. Through centrifugal stretching, this rotational energy can also excite the stretching vibrations and hence contribute to bond dissociation.

In a similar but independent study involving isotopic scrambling experiments at various pressures, Ford and Jaffee[174b] also report that oxygen atoms are important in NO_2 photolysis at 4047 A. However, they propose that the reaction occurs by an excited molecule mechanism and that the reaction, $NO_2^* + NO_2 \rightarrow N_2O_3 + O$, is the source of the atomic oxygen.

In summary, efficient photodissociation of NO_2 in the millimeter pressure range occurs by process 3-72 at wavelengths shorter than 4047 A, and apparently even at this wavelength provided that there is sufficient internal energy in the molecule to make up the energy deficiency of the quantum. At the longer wavelengths excitation to the $^2B_1$ or $^2B_2$ states is followed

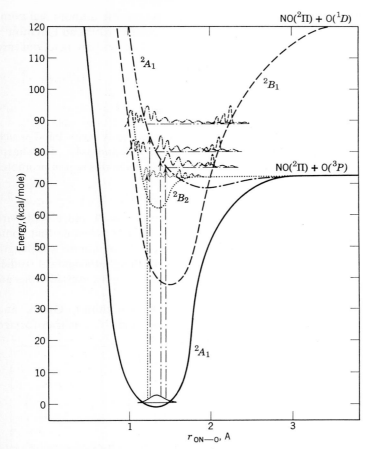

Fig. 3-47   Approximate potential energy diagram for some probable electronic states of NO_2. From Pitts, Sharp, and Chan.[166]

only by fluorescence, deactivation, or conceivably other excited-molecule reactions which do not lead to molecular dissociation.

Sato and Cvetanovic[173] have found a change in the electronic state of oxygen on photolysis at the shorter wavelengths. 1-Butene was photo-oxidized, using NO_2 photolysis at 3261, 2537, and 2288 A. Between 2537 and 2288 A a change in the mechanism of oxygen atom attack occurred, and it is likely that the primary reaction for these conditions is

$$NO_2 + h\nu \rightarrow NO(X^2\Pi) + O(^1D) \tag{3-72a}$$

As in all cases discussed in this book we have restricted our attention to those directly concerned with the nature of the primary photochemical processes. Since this is such an important system the authors feel compelled to refer the reader to the detailed studies of Ford[174] and Leighton[125] in which mechanisms of NO_2 photolysis and secondary reactions are evaluated.

3-3B-3   The Oxides and Sulfides
of Carbon: CO, CO_2, C_3O_2, CS_2, and COS

Carbon monoxide, CO, absorbs light in a relatively weak band which extends from about 1150 to 1500 A; see Figs. 3-28 and 3-48. The sharpness of the structure is obvious. Absorption of light in this region promotes the transition

$$CO(X^1\Sigma^+) + h\nu \rightarrow CO(A^1\Pi) \tag{3-73}$$

Careful study shows that the vibrational levels $v' = 9$ and $v' = 10$ are spectrally weakened in the $CO(A^1\Pi)$ state, and it is probable that some transition to another state occurs at this point. The minimum wavelength necessary to dissociate CO is 1110 A; since all the photochemical studies to date have been made at 1165 A or larger wavelengths, excited-molecule reactions alone can be important in them.

In the first photochemical study of CO by Faltings, Groth, and Harteck,[176] 1295 A Xe radiation was employed, and CO was transformed

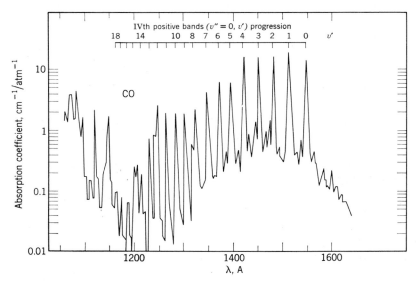

Fig. 3-48 Absorption spectrum of carbon monoxide; since the bands are very sharp, the extinction coefficients are only accurate to about 50% at the spikes. From McNesby and Okabe.[57]

to CO_2 and C_3O_2, presumably by mechanism 3-73 followed by these reactions:

$$CO(A^1\Pi) + CO \rightarrow CO_2 + C \qquad (3\text{-}73a)$$

$$C + CO \rightarrow C_2O \qquad (3\text{-}73b)$$

$$C_2O + CO \rightarrow C_3O_2 \qquad (3\text{-}73c)$$

At wavelengths less than 2179 A reaction 3-73a is exothermic, although it is forbidden by the spin rule if the carbon atom is in the ^3P state. If $\lambda < 1780$ A, the $C(^1D)$ state is a possible product of 3-73a; if $\lambda < 1477$ the $C(^1S)$ state is possible.

A rather unusual wavelength dependence of the quantum yield of CO disappearance was found by Groth and co-workers. Wavelength 1470 A was ineffective in causing chemical change, while the quantum yield of CO disappearance at 1295 A was 0.8 ± 0.4; surprisingly the yield at 1236 A dropped to about 0.01. Groth, Pessara, and Rommel[177] rationalized this result in terms of the participation of different excited states of CO. Since the 1295 A radiation falls in the region of the spectrally weakened vibrational levels, transition to a long-lived excited state may occur efficiently on excitation here, and excited-molecule reactions would be probable as found. At 1236 A, however, no perturbation is evident in the spectrum and the molecule is short-lived with low probability of any reaction requiring collisions at the low pressures.

Excited CO molecule reactions with hydrogen[178] and methane[157] have been observed.

Carbon dioxide absorbs light in at least three regions of the far ultraviolet: absorption bands of intermediate intensity appear at about 1700–1400 A and 1400–1200 A, with a stronger band below 1200 A. Each of these regions consists of diffuse vibrational bands overlying absorption continua with maxima near 1450, 1350, and 1120 A; see Fig. 3-49.

At wavelengths less than 1650 A there is sufficient energy per quantum to cause reaction 3-74a; through decomposition of an excited singlet, conceivably $CO_2(^1\Delta_g)$,[131] the spin is conserved.

$$CO_2 + h\nu \rightarrow CO(X^1\Sigma^+) + O(^1D) \qquad (3\text{-}74a)$$

$$CO(X^1\Sigma^+) + O(^1S) \qquad (3\text{-}74b)$$

$$CO(a^3\Pi) + O(^3P) \qquad (3\text{-}74c)$$

At wavelengths below 1273 A, reaction 3-74b is possible energetically, and below 1070 A, 3-74c may occur. If a triplet excited CO_2 is involved at the longer wavelengths, then $CO(X^1\Sigma^+)$ and $O(^3P)$ may form at $\lambda < 2240$ A without spin rule violation.

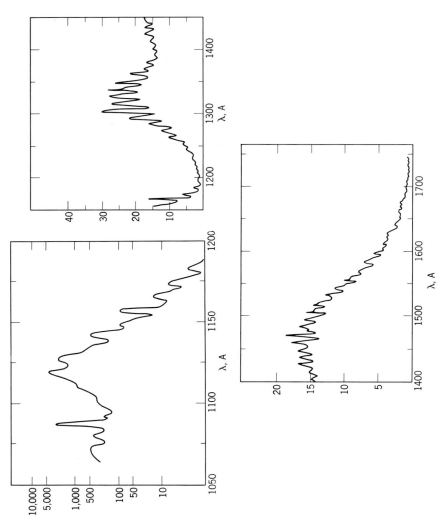

Fig. 3-49   Absorption spectrum of carbon dioxide. From Inn, Watanabe, and Zelicoff.[179]

The primary quantum yield of CO_2 decomposition in 3-74 is probably near unity,[121] at least over most of the first two bands, 1236–1500 A. However, Jucker and Rideal[91] reported $\Phi_{CO} \cong 2$, and they suggested an excited-molecule mechanism for the reaction, Mahan[181] disproved this hypothesis by finding Φ_{CO} independent of pressure when the 1470 A light used was completely absorbed. He found $\Phi_{CO} = 1.2 \pm 0.1$ at 1236 A, in general agreement with Groth and co-workers. In flashes at high intensity the O_2/CO ratio is near 0.5,[78,183] but at low intensity of 1470 A Ung and Schiff[182] reported a large deficiency of oxygen in the products; ozone formation could not account for the results. Much of the chemistry of the secondary reactions in CO_2 photolysis at low intensity is unclear at this writing.

Carbon suboxide ($O{=}C{=}C{=}C{=}O$) photolysis has been of special interest to researchers because it seemed to offer a unique route to the low-temperature preparation and study of carbon atoms.[184] Its absorption onset occurs at about 3250 A with $\lambda_{max} = 2650$ A, $\epsilon_{max} = 94$ liters/mole-cm.[185] The reactive entity formed on photolysis of carbon suboxide is now thought to be C_2O rather than a carbon atom;[185,186] the probable primary process is likely to be

$$C_3O_2 + h\nu \rightarrow CO + C_2O \qquad (3\text{-}75)$$

The thermochemical data[187,188] and the specificity of attack of the reactive fragment on $C{=}C$ double bonds in preference to $C{-}H$ insertion favor 3-75.

The absorption of COS and CS_2 occurs at increasingly longer wavelengths than that of CO_2. Note the energy changes at 25° for the following reactions (each substance in ground state):

$$CS_2 \rightarrow CS + S, \quad 109 \text{ kcal/mole}$$

$$COS \rightarrow CO + S, \quad {\sim}71$$

$$COS \rightarrow CS + O, \quad {\sim}163$$

From this information and by analogy with CO_2 photolysis one would predict that the favored primary steps in CS_2 and COS photolyses within the first absorption band would occur from an excited singlet state by 3-76 and 3-77a, respectively.

$$CS_2 + h\nu \rightarrow CS + S(^1D) \qquad (3\text{-}76)$$

$$COS + h\nu \rightarrow CO + S(^1D) \qquad (3\text{-}77a)$$

$$\searrow$$

$$CS + O(^1D) \qquad (3\text{-}77b)$$

Nalbandyan[192] and Kondratiev and Yakovleva[189] proved the occurrence of 3-76 by identifying and following CS radical concentrations photometrically in CS_2 or COS photolyses with a hydrogen discharge tube; at the very short wavelengths employed 3-77b occurred measurably. Kondratiev and Yakovleva[189] found that CS decayed only very slowly and by a heterogeneous path. Dyne and Ramsay[190] substantiated the occurrence of 3-76 and reported the rather surprising gas-phase lifetime of CS of about 30 min. Callear and Norrish[193] studied the vibrational distribution of CS formed in the flash photolysis of CS_2. It was suggested that the high vibrational excitation observed in CS (up to $v'' = 4$) originated in the secondary photolysis of the CS product with subsequent crossover to the vibrationally excited ground state.

Strausz, Knight, and Gunning[191] have photolyzed COS in the 2290–2550 A region and presumably demonstrated the occurrence of 3-77a by the stereospecificity of addition of the $S(^1D)$ atoms to olefin double bands and by the deactivation of $S(^1D)$ to $S(^3P)$ with loss of stereospecificity.[223]

3-3C Photochemistry of the Halogens and Some Simple Halogen Atom-Containing Compounds

3-3C-1 Cl_2, Br_2, and I_2

The absorption spectra of the halogens can be seen in Fig. 3-30. They show considerable diffuse vibrational structure at the longer wavelengths; this structure is seen to converge to a limit which is then followed by continuous absorption. The onset of the continuum occurs at 4785 A for Cl_2, 5100 A for Br_2, and 4989 A for I_2. The banded region for Cl_2 occurs where there is a very weak absorption, and it is not visible with the scale chosen for Fig. 3-30. The absorption maxima and the ϵ_{max} for the halogens show a regular rise with increase in atomic number: F_2, 2845 A, $\epsilon = 6$; Cl_2, 3300 A, $\epsilon = 66$; Br_2, 4200 A, $\epsilon = 200$; I_2, 5200 A, $\epsilon = 950$ liters/mole-cm. The smallness of the ϵ values reflects some forbidden character of the transition which becomes progressively more allowed as one moves to the heavier atoms. Indeed the transition responsible for these bands is presumed to be a singlet-triplet promotion symbolized by 3-78,[48c] where X is chlorine, bromine, or iodine:

$$X_2(^1\Sigma_g^+) + h\nu \rightarrow X_2(^3\Pi_u) \qquad (3-78)$$

There are several near-lying triplet states to which excitation may occur.[203,204,205]

All available evidence suggests that the act of absorption of a quantum of light by a halogen molecule, over most of the spectral range absorbed by the halogens, results largely in the formation of halogen atoms; however, at very low pressures $I_2(g)$ fluoresces as was described in Secs. 3-2A and 3-2B. If the absorption occurs in the continuum of the spectrum, dissociation occurs from the original state on the first vibration of the excited molecule; one normal ($^2P_{3/2}$) and one excited ($^2P_{1/2}$) halogen atom may be formed in this case.

$$X_2(^1\Sigma_g^+) + h\nu \rightarrow X_2(^3\Pi_{0^+u}) \rightarrow X(^2P_{3/2}) + X(^2P_{1/2}) \qquad (3\text{-}78a)$$

If absorption occurs within the vibrationally structured region, but at wavelengths which are of sufficient energy to break the bond (ΔE_{298}° for $X_2(g) \rightarrow 2X(g)$, 4989 A for Cl_2; 6284 A for Br_2; 8037 A for I_2), and, if the molecule is not already in a dissociative state, it undergoes collisionally induced predissociation for systems at reasonable pressures by crossing over to a repulsive or dissociative state; in this case two ground-state ($^2P_{3/2}$) atoms are formed.

$$X_2(^1\Sigma_g^+) + h\nu \rightarrow X_2(^3\Pi_{0^+u})$$
$$\searrow \qquad \downarrow (+M)$$
$$X_2(^3\Pi_{1u}) \rightarrow 2X(^2P_{3/2}) \qquad (3\text{-}78b)$$

Consider the photochemistry of bromine in illustration of these processes. Kistiakowsky and Sternberg[194] studied the photobromination of ethylene at wavelengths ranging from 4820 to 6800 A and found that the primary quantum efficiency of photodissociation was the same (presumably unity) at all wavelengths. The efficiency of dissociation was nearly perfect even in experiments at 6800 A, where the quantum energy (42.0 kcal/mole) is less than that necessary for bond rupture (45.5 kcal/mole). At 6800 A the extinction coefficient for Br_2 was temperature dependent, and absorption of light of this wavelength was shown to be by molecules possessing vibrational energy. The energy which was insufficient to dissociate a Br_2 molecule in the $v'' = 0$ state added to that already in the vibrationally excited molecule to give dissociation.

In Fig. 3-50 the approximate potential energy curves of Kistiakowsky and Sternberg for some of the excited states of Br_2 are shown; the ground-state curve is not pictured. The six ellipses in the figure represent the positions reached by bromine molecules immediately after absorption of the radiation of the wavelength shown; allowance was made for the width of the transmission band of the filters used in the experiments, the Frank-Condon principle, and the vibrational energy distribution of the absorbing molecule. Note that each of the positions reached on absorption of 4820, 5435, 5940, 6140, and 6800 A are such that dissociation will occur. However, the 7150 A excited molecule will not dissociate since it lies within the trough of the $^3\Pi_{1u}$ potential energy curve; a molecule in this position will only rarely be activated sufficiently by collision to dissociate, but it will usually lose vibrational quanta on collision and be deactivated.

The results of photolyses of the halogens in solution show a very interesting relation between the apparent quantum efficiency of halogen atom formation in 3-78a or 3-78b and the wavelength and the viscosity of the solvent. Booth and Noyes,[195] through the use of an iodine atom

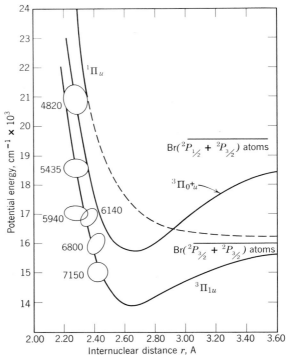

Fig. 3-50 Potential energy diagram of the lowest excited states in the Br_2 molecule. From Kistiakowsky and Sternberg.[194a,b]

scavenger technique, found that the apparent φ_{78} for I_2 at 4358 A varied from 0.66 for hexane ($\eta = 0.0029$) to 0.036 for a very viscous solvent ($\eta = 1.8$ poise). In a simple model which was surprisingly successful in correlating these results, the authors assumed that dissociation was perfectly efficient in all solvents and at all wavelengths of sufficient energy of the quantum. They further assumed that the viscous drag of the separating atoms in the solvents lowered the kinetic energy of the atoms and made more likely the chance that the two separating atoms would find their original partners before leaving the vicinity of the solvent "cage" in which they were formed.[196] Meadows and Noyes[197] studied I_2 photodissociation in hexane and 1,3-hexafluorobutadiene at various wavelengths, and thus varied the kinetic energy of the separating iodine atoms. The apparent quantum efficiency of iodine atom formation in hexane at 25°, φ_{78}, was 0.83 at 4047 A, 0.66 at 4358 A, 0.46 at 5461 A, 0.36 at 5790 A, 0.14 at 6430 A, and 0.11 at 7350 A. The simple theory explained the trend qualitatively;[196] the atoms of higher kinetic energy, formed at the shorter wavelengths, have an increased chance of separation. Although serious limitations exist on the quantitative aspects of the theory, the simple picture obviously has some elements of truth.

Different techniques used by three different laboratories gave consistent estimates of the apparent φ_{78} for I_2 in CCl_4 solution at 25°. Lampe and Noyes[198] estimated $\varphi_{78} = 0.14$, using 4368 A; Marshall and Davidson[199] found $\varphi_{78} = 0.19$ for $\lambda > 5000$ A; Strong and Willard[200] obtained $\varphi_{78} = 0.13 \pm 0.04$, using the full visible spectrum.

In attempts at quantitative treatment of solution-phase photolysis of halogens allowance must be made for this apparent decrease in φ_{78} from unity as the viscosity and the wavelength increase. These effects would be expected to be somewhat less important with the smaller bromine and chlorine atoms.

There has been no evidence for a change in mechanism or product distribution as a result of the formation of two possible states of the halogen atom, $^2P_{3/2}$ and $^2P_{1/2}$, although this would be expected. Thus Filseth and Willard[202] have studied the reaction of I_2 with C_3H_8 at wavelengths 5125 and 4790 A; these wavelengths lie above and below the convergence limit of I_2 (4995 A). In each case the ratio of iso-C_3H_7I/ n-C_3H_7I formed was the same within the experimental error. Since the reaction, $I + RH \rightarrow HI + R$, is very endothermic and too slow to be significant under these conditions, the authors suggest that it occurs by way of a halogen atom-hydrocarbon complex:

$$I + RH \rightleftharpoons RH \cdots I$$

$$I + RH \cdots I \rightarrow I_2 + RH$$
$$\searrow$$
$$RI + HI$$

There is another feature of the photochemistry of the halogens which should be mentioned. Molecular iodine excited by 1849 A radiation has been found to react with hydrogen and hydrocarbons.[201] The major reaction appears to be represented by $I_2^* + RH \rightarrow RI + HI$; it does not proceed through dissociation of I_2 and subsequent reaction of iodine atoms. At low pressures the yields are low, increasing to a maximum at pressures where the average time between collisions is small compared to the fluorescence lifetime of the iodine molecule.

3-3C-2   The Nitroxyl and Carbonyl Halides: NOCl, NOBr, etc.

The absorption spectrum of NOCl (Fig. 3-51) shows about six bands with continuous absorption over most of the visible and ultraviolet ranges. NOBr also shows continuous absorption.[212]

The photochemistry of NOCl was first investigated quantitatively by Kistiakowsky.[207] He found the quantum yield of NOCl decomposition equal to 2.0 over the entire range from 3650 to 6300 A. One favored

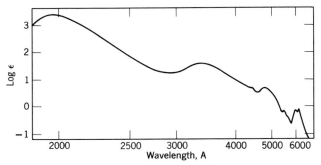

Fig. 3-51   Absorption spectrum of nitrosyl chloride, NOCl. From Goodeve and Katz.[208]

alternative in the original interpretation of the NOCl photolysis, based largely on the appearance of structure at the longer wavelengths and inaccurate early thermal data for NOCl → NO + Cl, involved an excited-molecule mechanism at the longer wavelengths; a free-radical primary step at the shorter wavelengths was consistent with the absence of an effect of added N_2 on the decomposition.

Natanson[211] confirmed that the quantum yield of NOCl disappearance was 2.0 over the range 4090–5460 A, and he showed further that it was independent of a 14-fold change in [NOCl] and a 50-fold excess of N_2 or CO_2. Goodeve and Katz[208] reported that there was no significant structure in NOCl absorption at long wavelengths, and that the original observations were in error because of NO_2 impurity. Re-evaluations of the photolysis data[208] in view of these results and more accurate thermal data[210] now favor the dissociative primary process 3-79 over the entire visible and near ultraviolet bands; the quantum energy is sufficient at any wavelengths below about 7600 A.

$$NOCl + h\nu \rightarrow NO(X^2\Pi) + Cl(^2P_{3/2,1/2}) \qquad (3\text{-}79)$$

Basco and Norrish[212] studied the flash photolysis of NOCl and NOBr at wavelengths less than 2600 A. They found that the highly vibrationally excited molecule $NO(X^2\Pi, v'' \leq 11)$ was an important product for isothermal flash conditions. The excitation of the NO product was not removed by filtering the flash with acetic acid, but was absent in the products from a flash filtered through Pyrex. They consider two alternative mechanisms for this product excitation. The first mechanism, which they favor, assumes the direct formation of $NO(X^2\Pi, v'' \leq 11)$ state in the primary act; presumably absorption produces an instantaneous repulsion between the halogen and nitrogen atoms so that the N—O distance is highly compressed with respect to the equilibrium position in the new state. With this choice of mechanism the fraction of the excess energy which may appear as vibrational energy, δ, assuming conservation of momentum, is given by

$$\delta = \frac{m_1 m_3}{(m_1 + m_2)(m_2 + m_3)} \tag{3-80}$$

where m_1, m_2, and m_3 are the masses of the oxygen, nitrogen, and halogen atoms, respectively. The observed maximum excitation, 55 kcal/mole, is somewhat too high (about 13 kcal/mole) to fit this picture quantitatively, but the simple model is in qualitative accord with the facts.

The alternative scheme, involving the intermediate formation of the excited $NO(^4\Pi)$ state from a triplet, will also fit the facts (X = Cl or Br):

$$NOX(S_0) + h\nu \rightarrow NOX(S_1)$$

$$NOX(S_1) \rightarrow NOX(T_1)$$

$$NOX(T_1) \rightarrow NO(^4\Pi) + X(^2P)$$

$$NO(^4\Pi) + M \rightarrow NO(^2\Pi, v'' > 0) + M$$

The photolyses of numerous other simple inorganic halogen compounds have been studied to some extent. The efficient splitting of a halogen atom is the accepted primary event in the photolysis of ICl,[214] $COCl_2$,[213] $ClCN$, $BrCN$, ICN,[215] ClO, BrO, IO,[216] and Cl_2O.[217] The absorption onset of the XCN compounds occurs for ClCN, BrCN, and ICN at about 2270, 2460, and 3100 A, respectively. Fluorescence of the CN radical is observed from the $B^2\Sigma^+$ excited state on irradiation of ICN with 1854–1935 A light, favoring process 3-81b, but none is seen when light with $\lambda > 2025$ A is used; apparently the CN radical is formed in its ground state $(X^2\Sigma^+)$ for these conditions (process 3-81a):

$$XCN + h\nu \rightarrow X + CN(X^2\Sigma^+) \tag{3-81a}$$

$$\searrow$$

$$X + CN(B^2\Sigma^+) \tag{3-81b}$$

The relatively transient halogen monoxides, ClO, BrO, and IO, show extensive predissociation as observed by absorption after the flash photolysis of X_2-O_2 mixtures; they probably decompose in the continuous region by the reaction[216]

$$XO(^2\Pi) + h\nu \to X(^2P_{3/2}) + O(^1D) \tag{3-82}$$

The spectrum of Cl_2O is continuous over its entire absorption region, 8500–2200 A,[217] and decomposition by 3-83 appears to occur:

$$Cl_2O + h\nu \to ClO + Cl \tag{3-83}$$

Chlorine dioxide, ClO_2, absorbs from 5225 to 2700 A, with rotational fine structure evident up to 3753 A, where diffuseness enters.[218] Presumably the photodecomposition may occur by 3-84a in the predissociation region and 3-84b in the continuum:

$$ClO_2 + h\nu \to ClO + O(^3P) \tag{3-84a}$$
$$\searrow$$
$$ClO + O(^1D) \tag{3-84b}$$

Terenin and Popov[219] (1932) discovered that the photodissociation of the halides of thallium occurs in the vacuum ultraviolet by the ionization into halide and Tl^+ ions:

$$TlX + h\nu \to Tl^+ + X^- \tag{3-85}$$

PROBLEMS

1. $H^{35}Cl$ and $D^{35}Cl$ absorb light in the infrared. (a) Calculate the approximate wavelengths (in cm^{-1}) of the absorption maxima which correspond to the expected rotational energy changes $J = 0 \to J = 1 \to J = 2$ for these two molecules.

(b) Calculate the approximate wavelengths (in cm^{-1}) of the absorption maxima in the rotational-vibrational spectrum of $H^{35}Cl$ and $D^{35}Cl$ expected for $\Delta v = 1$ and $J = 0 \to J = 1 \to J = 2 \to J = 1 \to J = 0$. Use your data from (a) where possible. The internuclear distances in both HCl and DCl are 1.27 A; $\nu = 8.66 \times 10^{13}$ sec^{-1} for $H^{35}Cl$.

2. Calculate the minimum energy difference (in cm^{-1}) between vibrational levels of a diatomic molecule such that the ratio of the number of molecules in the vibrational level $v = 1$ to the number in the level $v = 0$ will be less than 0.10 at all temperatures below 700°K. (Most diatomic molecules have ΔE_v greater than 1200 cm^{-1}.)

3. (a) Calculate the ratio of the number of molecules in rotational levels with $J = 1, 4, 8, 12, 16, 24, 48$ to the number in the rotational level $J = 0$ for the lowest vibrational level of gaseous bromine $^{79}Br^{79}Br$ at 300°K. Br_2 has an internuclear distance of 2.28 A.

(b) From your results for Problems 2 and 3a, what can you conclude about the states normally occupied by Br_2 molecules at 300°K?

4. From the data of Fig. 3-40 and a knowledge of the products of dissociation of O_2 at the convergence limit, calculate the approximate spectroscopic dissociation energy of O_2 (to form two ground-state atoms).

5. You are to attempt to determine the relative importance of the two possible primary processes 1 and 2 in SO_3 photolysis at 2804 A.

$$SO_3 + h\nu \rightarrow SO + O_2 \tag{1}$$

$$SO_2 + O \tag{2}$$

Give the reasoning used in arriving at your plan.

6. How might you differentiate between the two alternative explanations of the formation of the vibrationally excited ground-state NO molecules in the photolysis of NOCl at the short wavelengths? See Sec. 3-3C-2.

REFERENCES TO CHAPTER 3

1. G. Herzberg, *Spectra of Diatomic Molecules*, 2nd Edition, D. Van Nostrand Co., Princeton, N.J., 1950.
2. M. Czerny, *Z. Physik*, **34**, 227 (1925).
3. L. Pauling and E. B. Wilson, *Introduction to Quantum Mechanics*, McGraw-Hill Book Co., New York, 1935, p. 68.
4. P. M. Morse, *Phys. Rev.*, **34**, 57 (1929).
5. E. S. Imes, *Astrophys. J.*, **50**, 251 (1919).
6. C. A. Coulson, *Valence*, Oxford University Press, 1952.
7. E. J. Bowen, *Chemical Aspects of Light*, 2nd Ed., The Clarendon Press, Oxford, 1946.
8. W. Kauzmann, *Quantum Chemistry*, Academic Press, New York, 1957.
9. K. S. Pitzer, *Quantum Chemistry*, Prentice-Hall, Englewood Cliffs, N.J., 1953.
10. J. E. Lennard-Jones, *Trans. Faraday Soc.*, **25**, 668 (1929).
11. R. S. Mulliken, *Revs. Modern Phys.*, **4**, 1 (1932).
12. C. A. Coulson, *Trans. Faraday Soc.*, **33**, 1479 (1937).
13. J. J. Hopfield, *Phys. Rev.*, **35**, 1133; *ibid.*, **36**, 784 (1930).
14. Y. Tanaka, *Sci. Papers Inst. Phys. Chem. Research (Tokyo)*, **39**, 465 (1942).
15. R. S. Mulliken, *J. Chem. Phys.*, **7**, 14 (1939).
16. R. S. Mulliken and C. A. Rieke, *Repts. Progr. in Phys.*, **8**, 231 (1941).
17. G. N. Lewis and M. Kasha, *J. Am. Chem. Soc.*, **67**, 994 (1945).
18. A. Rubinowicz, *Repts. Progr. in Phys.*, **12**, 233 (1948–9).
19. R. S. Mulliken, *J. Chem. Phys.*, **7**, 20 (1939).
20. G. W. Robinson and R. P. Frosch, Symposium on Reversible Photochemical Processes, Duke University, April, 1962.
21. J. Franck, *Trans. Faraday Soc.*, **21**, 536 (1926).
22. J. Franck and H. Levi, *Z. Physik. Chem.*, **B27**, 409 (1935).
23. C. F. Goodeve and A. W. C. Taylor, *Proc. Roy. Soc. (London)*, **A152**, 221 (1935); *ibid.*, **A154**, 181 (1936).
24. L. Mathieson and A. L. G. Rees, *J. Chem. Phys.*, **25**, 753 (1956).

25. A. L. G. Rees, *J. Chem. Phys.*, **26**, 1567 (1957).
26. R. K. Steunenberg and R. C. Vogel, *J. Am. Chem. Soc.*, **78**, 901 (1956).
27. V. Henri and M. C. Teves, *Nature*, **114**, 894 (1924); *Compt. Rend.*, **179**, 1156 (1924).
28. K. F. Bonhoeffer and L. Farkas, *Z. physik. Chem.*, **A134**, 337 (1928).
29. R. de L. Kronig, *Z. Physik*, **50**, 347 (1928).
30. W. Lochte-Holtgreven, *Z. Physik*, **103**, 395 (1936).
31. H. Sponer, *Radiation Research*, Suppl. **1**, 558 (1959).
32. G. Herzberg and L. G. Mundie, *J. Chem. Phys.*, **8**, 263 (1940).
33. P. Pringsheim, *Fluorescence and Phosphorescence*, Interscience Publishers, New York, 1949.
34. R. W. Wood, *Phil. Mag.*, **12**, 499 (1906).
35. D. H. Rank, *J. Opt. Soc. Am.*, **36**, 239 (1946).
36. P. Swings, *Astrophys. J.*, **95**, 270 (1942).
37. C. Arnot and C. A. McDowell, *Can. J. Chem.*, **36**, 114 (1958).
38. B. Stevens and M. Boudart, *Ann. N.Y. Acad. Sci.*, **67**, 570 (1956-7).
39. J. C. Polanyi, *Can. J. Chem.*, **36**, 121 (1958).
40. V. N. Kondratiev, *Energy Exchange in Interactions between Ions and Molecules*, *Royal Inst. of Chem. (London)*, Lectures, Monographs, Reports, No. 3, 1 (1960).
41. W. J. Moore, *Physical Chemistry*, 3rd Edition, Prentice-Hall, Englewood Cliffs, N.J., 1962.
42. J. Curry, L. Herzberg, and G. Herzberg, *Z. Physik*, **86**, 348 (1933).
43. W. West, Ed., *Technique of Organic Chemistry*, Vol. IX, *Chemical Applications of Spectroscopy*, Interscience Publishers, New York, 1956.
44. H. D. Babcock and L. Herzberg, *Astrophys. J.*, **108**, 167 (1948).
45. J. J. Hopfield and R. T. Birge, *Phys. Rev.*, **29**, 922 (1927).
46. G. E. Gibson and N. S. Bayliss, *Phys. Rev.*, **44**, 188 (1933).
47. (a) J. R. Bates, J. O. Halford, and L. C. Anderson, *J. Chem. Phys.*, **3**, 415, 531 (1935); (b) J. H. Raley, F. F. Rust, and W. E. Vaughan, *J. Am. Chem. Soc.*, **70** 2767 (1948).
48. (a) R. S. Mulliken, *Phys. Rev.*, **50**, 1017 (1936); (b) *ibid.*, **51**, 310 (1937); (c) *ibid.*, **57**, 500 (1940); (d) *J. Chem. Phys.*, **8**, 382 (1940).
49. J. Romand, *Ann. Phys.*, **4**, 529 (1949).
50. For excellent reviews of the literature up to 1940 see (a) W. A. Noyes, Jr., and P. A. Leighton, *The Photochemistry of Gases*, Reinhold Publishing Corp., New York, 1941; (b) G. K. Rollefson and M. Burton, *Photochemistry and the Mechanism of Chemical Reactions*, Prentice-Hall, Englewood Cliffs, N.J., 1939.
51. R. M. Martin and J. E. Willard, *J. Chem. Phys.*, **40**, 2999 (1964).
52. (a) R. A. Ogg, Jr., and R. R. Williams, Jr., *J. Chem. Phys.*, **11**, 214 (1943); (b) *ibid.*, **13**, 586 (1945); (c) R. R. Williams, Jr., and R. A. Ogg, Jr., *J. Chem. Phys.*, **15**, 691 (1947); (d) H. A. Schwarz, R. R. Williams, Jr., and W. H. Hamill, *J. Am. Chem. Soc.*, **74**, 6007 (1952); (e) R. J. Carter, W. H. Hamill, and R. R. Williams, Jr., *J. Am. Chem. Soc.*, **77**, 6457 (1955); (f) J. R. Nash, R. R. Williams, Jr., and W. H. Hamill, *J. Am. Chem. Soc.*, **82**, 5974 (1960).
53. K. Watanabe and M. Zelikoff, *J. Opt. Soc. Am.*, **43**, 753 (1953).
54. D. H. Volman, "Photochemical Gas Phase Reactions in the Hydrogen-Oxygen System," *Advances in Photochemistry*, Vol. I, ed. by W. A. Noyes, Jr., G. S. Hammond, and J. N. Pitts, Jr., Interscience Publishers, a division of John Wiley & Sons, New York, 1963, p. 43.
55. R. B. Holt, C. K. McLane, and O. Oldenberg, *J. Chem. Phys.*, **16**, 225, 638 (1948).
56. H. C. Urey, L. H. Dawsey, and F. O. Rice, *J. Am. Chem. Soc.*, **51**, 1371 (1929).

57. J. R. McNesby and H. Okabe, "Vacuum Ultraviolet Photochemistry," *Advances in Photochemistry*, Vol. III, ed. by W. A. Noyes, Jr., G. S. Hammond, and J. N. Pitts, Jr., Interscience Publishers, a division of John Wiley & Sons, New York, 1964, p. 157.
58. S. F. Mason, *Quart. Revs. (London)*, **15**, 287 (1961).
59. C. F. Goodeve and N. O. Stein, *Trans. Faraday Soc.*, **27**, 393 (1931).
60. J. W. C. Johns, *Can. J. Phys.*, **41**, 209 (1963).
61. (a) A. Terenin and H. Neujmin, *Nature*, **134**, 255 (1934), (b) *J. Chem. Phys.*, **3**, 436 (1935); (c) H. Neujmin and A. Terenin, *Acta Physicochim. U.R.S.S.*, **5**, 465 (1936).
62. W. Groth and H. Suess, *Naturwissen.*, **26**, 77 (1938).
63. W. Groth, *Z. Elektrochem.*, **45**, 262 (1939).
64. M. C. Chen and H. A. Taylor, *J. Chem. Phys.*, **27**, 857 (1957).
65. C. A. Barth and H. E. Suess, *Z. Physik*, **158**, 85 (1960).
66. I. Tanaka, T. Carrington, and H. P. Broida, *J. Chem. Phys.*, **35**, 750 (1961).
67. J. R. McNesby, I. Tanaka, and H. Okabe, *J. Chem. Phys.*, **36**, 605 (1962).
68. D. H. Volman, *J. Chem. Phys.*, **17**, 947 (1949).
69. J. P. Hunt and H. Taube, *J. Am. Chem. Soc.*, **74**, 5999 (1952).
70. J. L. Weeks and M. S. Matheson, *J. Am. Chem. Soc.*, **78**, 1273 (1956).
71. J. H. Baxendale and J. A. Wilson, *Trans. Faraday Soc.*, **53**, 344 (1957).
72. D. H. Volman, J. C. Chen, and L. W. Swanson, *J. Am. Chem. Soc.*, **81**, 756 (1959).
73. D. H. Volman and J. C. Chen, *J. Am. Chem. Soc.*, **81**, 4141 (1959).
74. F. S. Dainton, *J. Am. Chem. Soc.*, **78**, 1278 (1956).
75. J. F. Gibson, D. J. E. Ingram, M. C. R. Symons, and M. G. Townsend, *Trans. Faraday Soc.*, **53**, 914 (1957).
76. B. de B. Darwent and V. J. Krasnansky, *Seventh Symposium (International) on Combustion*, Butterworths Scientific Publications, London, 1959, p. 3.
77. A. Y.-M. Ung and R. A. Back, *Can. J. Chem.*, **42**, 753 (1964).
78. G. Black and G. Porter, *Proc. Roy. Soc. (London)*, **A266**, 185 (1962).
79. G. S. Forbes, J. E. Cline, and B. C. Bradshaw, *J. Am. Chem. Soc.*, **60**, 1431 (1938).
80. G. Herzberg, *Trans. Faraday Soc.*, **27**, 402 (1931).
81. W. H. Avery and G. S. Forbes, *J. Am. Chem. Soc.*, **60**, 1005 (1938).
82. B. de B. Darwent and R. Roberts, *Proc. Roy. Soc. (London)*, **A216**, 344 (1953).
83. N. O. Stein, *Trans. Faraday Soc.*, **29**, 583 (1933).
84. (a) D. J. G. Ives and R. W. Pittman, *J. Chem. Soc.*, **1948**, 766; (b) R. W. Pittman, *J. Chem. Soc.*, **1949**, 1811.
85. (a) A. B. F. Duncan, *Phys. Rev.*, **47**, 822 (1935); (b) *ibid.*, **50**, 700 (1936); (c) K. Watanabe, *J. Chem. Phys.*, **22**, 1564 (1954); (d) F. I. Vilesov, B. L. Karbatov, and A. N. Terenin, *Doklady Akad. Nauk S.S.S.R.*, **122**, 94 (1958); (e) A. E. Douglas and J. M. Hollas, *Can. J. Phys.*, **39**, 479 (1961), (f) A. D. Walsh and P. A. Warsop, *Trans. Faraday Soc.*, **57**, 345 (1961).
86. W. C. Walker and G. L. Weissler, *J. Chem. Phys.*, **23**, 1540 (1955).
87. G. Herzberg and D. A. Ramsay, *J. Chem. Phys.*, **20**, 347 (1952).
88. K. Dressler and D. A. Ramsay, *Phil. Trans. Roy. Soc. (London)*, **A251**, 553 (1958–59).
89. C. C. McDonald, A. Kahn, and H. E. Gunning, *J. Chem. Phys.*, **22**, 908 (1954).
90. H. Gesser, *J. Am. Chem. Soc.*, **77**, 2626 (1955).
91. H. Jucker and E. K. Rideal, *J. Chem. Soc.*, **1957**, 1058.
92. S. N. Foner, E. L. Cochran, V. A. Bowers, and C. K. Jen, *Phys. Rev. Letters*, **1**, 91 (1958).
93. A. Serewicz and W. A. Noyes, Jr., *J. Phys. Chem.*, **63**, 843 (1959).
94. O. Schnepp and K. Dressler, *J. Chem. Phys.*, **32**, 1682 (1960).

95. R. Srinivasan, *J. Phys. Chem.*, **64**, 679 (1960).
96. K. D. Bayes, K. H. Becker, and K. H. Welge, *Z. Naturforsch.*, **17a**, 676 (1962).
97. F. Stuhl and K. H. Welge, *Z. Naturforsch.*, **18a**, 900 (1963).
98. K. H. Becker and K. H. Welge, *Z. Naturforsch.*, **18a**, 600 (1963).
99. H. W. Melville, *Proc. Roy. Soc. (London)*, **A139**, 541 (1933).
100. D. A. Ramsay, *Nature*, **178**, 374 (1956).
101. R. G. W. Norrish and G. A. Oldershaw, *Proc. Roy. Soc. (London)*, **A262**, 1 (1961).
102. K. H. Becker and K. H. Welge, unpublished work quoted in Ref. 57.
103. A. O. Beckman and R. G. Dickinson, *J. Am. Chem. Soc.*, **52**, 124 (1930).
104. B. A. Thrush, *Proc. Roy. Soc. (London)*, **A235**, 143 (1956).
105. E. D. Becker, G. C. Pimentel, and M. Van Thiel, *J. Chem. Phys.*, **26**, 145 (1957).
106. M. Van Thiel and G. C. Pimentel, *J. Chem. Phys.*, **32**, 133 (1960).
107. H. A. Papazian, *J. Chem. Phys.*, **32**, 456 (1960).
108. L. F. Keyser and G. W. Robinson, *J. Am. Chem. Soc.*, **82**, 5245 (1960).
109. D. A. Ramsay, *J. Phys. Chem.*, **57**, 415 (1953).
110. E. A. B. Birse and H. W. Melville, *Proc. Roy. Soc. (London)*, **A175**, 164 (1940).
111. R. R. Wenner and A. O. Beckman, *J. Am. Chem. Soc.*, **54**, 2787 (1932).
112. R. A. Ogg, Jr., P. A. Leighton, and F. W. Bergstrom, *J. Am. Chem. Soc.*, **56**, 318 (1934).
113. C. H. Bamford, *Trans. Faraday Soc.*, **35**, 568 (1939).
114. J. C. Elgin and H. S. Taylor, *J. Am. Chem. Soc.*, **51**, 2059 (1929).
115. W. L. Kay and H. A. Taylor, *J. Chem. Phys.*, **10**, 497 (1942).
116. J. D. Overman and E. O. Wiig, *J. Am. Chem. Soc.*, **68**, 320 (1946).
117. E. C. Y. Inn, *Spectrochim. Acta*, **7**, 65 (1955–6).
118. K. Watanabe and F. F. Marmo, *J. Chem. Phys.*, **25**, 965 (1956).
119. E. C. Y. Inn and Y. Tanaka, "Ozone Chemistry and Technology," *Advances in Chemistry*, No. 21, American Chemical Society, Applied Publications, 1959, p. 263.
120. (a) E. Warburg, *Sitzber. Preuss. Akad Wiss., Physik-Math. Kl.*, 216 (1912); (b) E. Warburg, *Z. Elektrochem.*, **27**, 133 (1921).
121. W. Groth, *Z. Physik. Chem. (Leipzig)*, **B37**, 307 (1937).
122. W. E. Vaughan and W. A. Noyes, Jr., *J. Am. Chem. Soc.*, **52**, 559 (1930); (b) O. R. Wulf and E. H. Melvin, *Phys. Rev.*, **38**, 330 (1931).
123. A. D. Walsh, *J. Chem. Soc.*, **1953**, 2266.
124. D. W. O. Heddle, *J. Chem. Phys.*, **32**, 1889 (1960).
125. P. A. Leighton, *Photochemistry of Air Pollution*, Academic Press, New York, 1961, p. 47.
126. (a) W. D. McGrath and R. G. W. Norrish, *Proc. Roy. Soc. (London)*, **A242**, 265 (1957); (b) W. D. McGrath and R. G. W. Norrish, *Z. Physik. Chem. (Frankfurt)*, **15**, 245 (1958).
127. R. G. W. Norrish, *Proc. Chem. Soc.*, **1958**, 247.
128. E. Castellano and H.-J. Schumacher, *Z. Physik. Chem. (Frankfurt)*, **34**, 198 (1962).
129. N. Metropolis and H. Beutler, *Phys. Rev.*, **57**, 1078 (1940).
130. B. Stevens, *Can. J. Chem.*, **37**, 831 (1959).
131. R. S. Mulliken, *Can. J. Chem.*, **36**, 10 (1958).
132. W. Lotmar, *Z. Physik*, **83**, 765 (1933).
133. R. G. W. Norrish and A. P. Zeelenberg, *Proc. Roy. Soc. (London)*, **A240**, 293 (1957).
134. K. F. Greenough and A. B. F. Duncan, *J. Am. Chem. Soc.*, **83**, 555 (1961).
135. A. E. Douglas, *Can. J. Phys.*, **36**, 147 (1958).
136. T. C. Hall, Jr., "Photochemical Studies of NO_2 and SO_2," Ph.D. Thesis, University of California, Los Angeles, 1953.

137. G. Kornfeld, and E. Weegmann, Z. Elektrochem., **36**, 789 (1930).
138. F. S. Dainton and K. J. Ivin, Trans. Faraday Soc., **46**, 374, 382 (1950).
139. H. S. Johnston and K. dev Jain, Science, **131**, 1523 (1960).
140. E. R. Gerhard and H. F. Johnstone, Ind. Eng. Chem., **47**, 972 (1955).
141. E. A. Schuck, H. W. Ford, and E. R. Stephens, Rept. No. 26, Air Pollution Foundation, San Marino, Calif., 1958.
142. E. A. Schuck and G. J. Doyle, Rept. No. 29, Air Pollution Foundation, San Marino, Calif., 1959.
143. (a) N. A. Renzetti and G. J. Doyle, J. Air Pollution Control Assoc., **8**, 293 (1959); (b) N. A. Renzetti and G. J. Doyle, Intern. J. Air Pollution, **2**, 327 (1960).
144. E. Fajans and C. F. Goodeve, Trans. Faraday Soc., **32**, 511 (1936).
145. G. Kornfeld, Trans. Faraday Soc., **33**, 614 (1937).
146. M. Zelikoff, K. Watanabe, and E. C. Y. Inn, J. Chem. Phys., **21**, 1643 (1953).
147. H. Sun and G. L. Weissler, J. Chem. Phys., **23**, 1372 (1955).
148. G. W. Bethke, J. Chem. Phys., **31**, 662 (1959).
149. (a) M. Zelikoff and L. M. Aschenbrand, J. Chem. Phys., **22**, 1680, 1685 (1954); (b) ibid., **25**, 674 (1956).
150. G. A. Castellion and W. A. Noyes, Jr., J. Am. Chem. Soc., **79**, 290 (1957).
151. J. W. Zabor and W. A. Noyes, Jr., J. Am. Chem. Soc., **62**, 1975 (1940).
152. P. K. Sen-Gupta, Nature, **136**, 513 (1935).
153. (a) J. P. Doering and B. H. Mahan, J. Chem. Phys., **34**, 1617 (1961); (b) ibid., **36**, 1682 (1962).
154. R. M. Martin and J. E. Willard, J. Chem. Phys., **40**, 2999 (1964).
155. W. Groth and H. Schierholz, Planetary Space Sci., **1**, 333 (1959).
156. M. H. J. Wijnen, J. Chem. Phys., **24**, 851 (1956).
157. F. F. Marmo, J. Opt. Soc. Am., **43**, 1186 (1953).
158. G. Herzberg, A. Lagerquist, and E. Miescher, Can. J. Phys., **34**, 622 (1956).
159. Y. Tanaka, J. Chem. Phys., **21**, 788 (1953).
160. K. Watanabe, J. Chem. Phys., **22**, 1564 (1954).
161. J. Y. Macdonald, J. Chem. Soc., **1928**, 1.
162. (a) P. J. Flory and H. L. Johnston, J. Am. Chem. Soc., **57**, 2641 (1935); (b) J. Chem. Phys., **14**, 212 (1946).
163. G. E. Moore, O. R. Wulf, and R. M. Badger, J. Chem. Phys., **21**, 2091 (1953).
164. A. V. Kleinberg and A. N. Terenin, Doklady Akad. Nauk S.S.S.R., **101**, 1031 (1955).
165. T. C. Hall, Jr., and F. E. Blacet, J. Chem. Phys., **20**, 1745 (1952).
166. J. N. Pitts, Jr., J. H. Sharp, and S. I. Chan, J. Chem. Phys., **39**, 238 (1963); ibid., **40**, 3655 (1964); J. N. Pitts, Jr., and J. H. Sharp, Abstracts, 142nd Meeting, American Chemical Society, Atlantic City, September, 1962, p. 10v.
167. F. E. Blacet, T. C. Hall, Jr., and P. A. Leighton, J. Am. Chem. Soc., **84**, 4011 (1962).
168. S. Sato and R. J. Cvetanovic, Can. J. Chem., **36**, 279 (1958).
169. R. G. W. Norrish, J. Chem. Soc., **1929**, 1158, 1611.
170. D. Neuberger and A. B. F. Duncan, J. Chem. Phys., **22**, 1693 (1954).
171. M. Green and J. W. Linnett, Trans. Faraday Soc., **57**, 1 (1961).
172. R. A. Marcus, J. Chem. Phys., **20**, 359 (1952).
173. S. Sato and R. J. Cvetanovic, Can. J. Chem., **36**, 1668 (1958).
174. (a) H. W. Ford, Can. J. Chem., **38**, 1780 (1960); (b) H. W. Ford and S. Jaffe, J. Chem. Phys., **38**, 2935 (1963).
175. (a) J. J. McGee and J. Heicklen, Aerospace Corporation, El Segundo, Calif., Rept. No. TDR-269 (4240-20)-2, prepared for Ballistics Systems and Space Systems Divisions, Air Force Systems Command; (b) ibid., Rept. No. TDR-269 (4240-20)-3.

176. K. Faltings, W. Groth, and P. Harteck, *Z. Physik. Chem.*, **B41**, 15 (1938).
177. W. Groth, W. Pessara, and H. J. Rommel, *Z. Physik. Chem. (Frankfurt)*, **32**, 192 (1962).
178. W. Groth, *Z. Physik. Chem. (Leipzig)*, **B37**, 315 (1937).
179. E. C. Y. Inn, K. Watanabe, and M. Zelikoff, *J. Chem. Phys.*, **21**, 1648 (1953).
180. J. W. Linnett, *The Electronic Structure of Molecules*, John Wiley & Sons, New York, 1964.
181. B. H. Mahan, *J. Chem. Phys.*, **33**, 959 (1960).
182. A. Y. M. Ung and H. I. Schiff, *Abstracts Sixth Informal Photochemistry Conference*, University of California, Davis, June, 1964.
183. M. H. Bortner, V. D. Povard, and A. L. Myerson, *J. Opt. Soc. Am.*, **50**, 172 (1960).
184. K. Bayes, *J. Am. Chem. Soc.*, **83**, 3712 (1961).
185. K. D. Bayes, *J. Am. Chem. Soc.*, **84**, 4077 (1962).
186. R. T. Mullen and A. P. Wolf, *J. Am. Chem. Soc.*, **84**, 3214 (1962).
187. H. B. Palmer and T. J. Hirt, *J. Am. Chem. Soc.*, **84**, 113 (1962).
188. C. MacKay, P. Polak, H. E. Rosenberg, and R. Wolfgang, *J. Am. Chem. Soc.*, **84**, 308 (1962).
189. V. N. Kondratiev and A. Yakovleva, *J. Phys. Chem. (U.S.S.R.)*, **14**, 853 (1940). *C. A.*, **35**, 3903.[9]
190. P. J. Dyne and D. A. Ramsay, *J. Chem. Phys.*, **20**, 1055 (1952).
191. (a) O. P. Strausz and H. E. Gunning, *J. Am. Chem. Soc.*, **84**, 4080 (1962); (b) A. R. Knight, O. P. Strausz, and H. E. Gunning, *J. Am. Chem. Soc.*, **85**, 1207 (1963); (c) *J. Am. Chem. Soc.*, **85**, 2349 (1963); (d) A. R. Knight, O. P. Strausz, S. M. Malm, and H. E. Gunning, *J. Am. Chem. Soc.*, **86**, 4243 (1964).
192. A. B. Nalbandyan, *J. Phys. Chem. (U.S.S.R.)*, **14**, 598 (1940); *C. A.*, **35**, 2073.[3]
193. A. B. Callear and R. G. W. Norrish, *Nature*, **188**, 53 (1960).
194. (a) G. B. Kistiakowsky and J. C. Sternberg, *J. Chem. Phys.*, **21**, 2218 (1953); see also (b) *J. Chem. Phys.*, **22**, 1949 (1954); (c) C. A. McDowell, *Nature*, **175**, 860 (1955).
195. D. Booth and R. M. Noyes, *J. Am. Chem. Soc.*, **82**, 1868 (1960).
196. R. M. Noyes, *Z. Elektrochem.*, **64**, 153 (1960).
197. L. F. Meadows and R. M. Noyes, *J. Am. Chem. Soc.*, **82**, 1872 (1960).
198. F. W. Lampe and R. M. Noyes, *J. Am. Chem. Soc.*, **76**, 2140 (1954).
199. R. Marshall and N. Davidson, *J. Chem. Phys.*, **21**, 2086 (1953).
200. R. L. Strong and J. E. Willard, *J. Am. Chem. Soc.*, **79**, 2098 (1957).
201. (a) A. G. Harris and J. E. Willard, *J. Am. Chem. Soc.*, **76**, 4678 (1954); (b) T. A. Gover and J. E. Willard, *J. Am. Chem. Soc.*, **82**, 3816 (1960).
202. S. V. Filseth and J. E. Willard, *J. Am. Chem. Soc.*, **84**, 3806 (1962).
203. (a) W. G. Brown, *Phys. Rev.*, **38**, 1179 (1931); (b) *ibid.*, **39**, 777 (1932).
204. (a) O. Darbyshire, *Proc. Roy. Soc. (London)*, **A159**, 93 (1937); (b) *J. Chem. Phys.*, **4**, 747 (1936).
205. A. L. G. Rees, *Proc. Phys. Soc. (London)*, **59**, 998, 1008 (1947).
206. J. Harkins and S. W. Nicksic, *Paper* No. 37, Symposium on Air Pollution, Division of Water, Air, and Waste Chemistry, 148th Meeting American Chemical Society, Chicago, September, 1964 p. 16y.
207. G. B. Kistiakowsky, *J. Am. Chem. Soc.*, **52**, 102 (1930).
208. C. F. Goodeve and S. Katz, *Proc. Roy. Soc. (London)*, **A172**, 432 (1939).
209. J. W. Linnett, *J. Am. Chem. Soc.*, **83**, 2643 (1961).
210. (a) C. R. Bailey and A. B. D. Cassie, *Proc. Roy. Soc. (London)*, **A145**, 336 (1934); (b) P. G. Ashmore and J. Chanmugam, *Trans. Faraday Soc.*, **49**, 265 (1953).
211. G. L. Natanson, *Acta Physicochim. U.R.S.S.*, **11**, 521 (1939).

212. N. Basco and R. G. W. Norrish, *Proc. Roy. Soc. (London)*, **A268**, 291 (1962).
213. (a) M. Bodenstein, W. Brenschede, and H.-J. Schumacher, *Z. Physik. Chem.*, **B40**, 121 (1938); (b) M. Bodenstein, S. Lehner, and C. Wagner, *Z. Physik. Chem.*, **B3**, 459 (1929); (c) F. Almasy and T. Wagner-Jauregg, *Naturwissen.*, **19**, 270 (1931); (d) G. K. Rollefson and C. W. Montgomery, *J. Am. Chem. Soc.*, **55**, 142 (1933); (e) C. W. Montgomery and G. K. Rollefson *J. Am. Chem. Soc.*, **55**, 4025 (1933); (f) G. K. Rollefson and C. W. Montgomery, *J. Am. Chem. Soc.*, **55**, 4036 (1933); (g) M. S. Kharasch and H. C. Brown, *J. Am. Chem. Soc.*, **62**, 454 (1940), (h) M. H. J. Wijnen, *J. Am. Chem.* **83**, 3014 (1961).
214. (a) G. G. Palmer and E. O. Wiig, *J. Am. Chem. Soc.*, **74**, 2785 (1952); (b) M. I. Christie, R. S. Roy, and B. A. Thrush, *Trans. Faraday Soc.*, **55**, 1149 (1959).
215. (a) R. M. Badger and S.-C. Woo, *J. Am. Chem. Soc.*, **53**, 2572 (1931); (b) A. Yakovleva, *Acta Physicochim. U.R.S.S.*, **9**, 665 (1938).
216. R. A. Durie and D. A. Ramsay, *Can. J. Phys.*, **36**, 35 (1958).
217. (a) M. Bodenstein and G. Kistiakowski, *Z. Physik. Chem.*, **116**, 371 (1925); (b) C. F. Goodeve and J. I. Wallace, *Trans. Faraday Soc.*, **26**, 254 (1930); (c) W. Finkelnburg, H.-J. Schumacher, and G. Stieger, *Z. Physik. Chem.*, **B15**, 127 (1931); (d) F. H. C. Edgecombe, R. G. W. Norrish, and B. A. Thrush, *Proc. Roy Soc. (London)*, **A243**, 24 (1957).
218. (a) W. Finkelnburg and H.-J. Schumacher, *Z. Physik. Chem.*, Bodenstein-Festband, 704 (1931); (b) H. C. Urey and H. Johnston, *Phys. Rev.*, **38**, 2131 (1931); (c) F. J. Lipscomb, R. G. W. Norrish, and G. Porter, *Nature*, **174**, 785 (1954).
219. A. Terenin and B. Popov, *Physik. Z. Sowjetunion*, **2**, 299 (1932).
220. R. G. W. Norrish and G. A. Oldershaw, *Proc. Roy. Soc. (London)*, **A249**, 498 (1959).
221. G. R. Harrison, R. C. Lord, and J. R. Loofbourow, *Practical Spectroscopy*, Prentice-Hall, Englewood Cliffs, N.J., 1948, p. 282.
222. Spectra determined by Mrs. Veronique McMillan; see, for details, Ref. 424 of Chapter 5.
223. Recent results from the H. E. Gunning research group show that both singlet and triplet sulfur atoms may add stereospecifically to olefins; see the discussion in Sec. 5-9D.

4

Primary Photophysical
Processes of Polyatomic Molecules

In contrast to diatomic molecules, non-linear polyatomic molecules have more electronic energy levels and closer spacing between them, $3n - 6$ additional fundamental modes of vibration per electronic level, and one more principal axis of inertia. These factors lead to a greater overlapping of energy levels of the various electronic states (see Fig. 4-1). This in turn has a pronounced effect on the photochemistry of complex molecules compared to that of simple diatomic molecules. For example, the probabilities of *radiationless* transitions such as intersystem crossing and internal conversion are greatly enhanced.

Structural effects become highly significant in the photophysical and photochemical processes of polyatomic molecules. Thus anthracene is a classic example of a highly fluorescing molecule, yet the related compound, phenazine, is never fluorescent.[1] In the vapor, methyl *n*-propyl ketone

Phenazine

photodissociates readily at 3130 A and 120°, by both free-radical and intramolecular processes, yet methyl propenyl ketone ($CH_3COCH = CHCH_3$) is remarkably stable under these conditions (Sec. 5-2).

Environmental effects on photoprocesses of polyatomic molecules have been extensively investigated. Profound differences in the overall photochemistry occur, for example, in going from the vapor phase to a condensed system. Thus photolysis of acetone vapor leads to fragmentation into free radicals and carbon monoxide, but in a hydrogen-atom-donating solvent such as isopropyl alcohol photoreduction occurs and pinacol is formed. Deactivation by solvent, and "cage" effects, are significant. Thus the quantum yield of CO in pure liquid acetone at 25° and 3130 A is about 0.001; it is about 0.1 in the vapor phase at 25°, and unity at 120°.

In order to develop a rationale to explain such overall observations it is essential to differentiate primary from secondary reactions and, insofar as possible, to evaluate the relative efficiencies of the primary photophysical and primary photochemical processes. We shall consider photophysical processes in this chapter and photochemical processes in Chapter 5. These photophysical processes are classified in Table 4-1 using hypothetical polyatomic molecules, ABC, and the following symbology (employed throughout the text):

$S_0, S_1, S_2, \ldots$ = Singlet electronic states

$T_1, T_2, \ldots$ = Triplet electronic states

Superscript 0 = Lowest vibrational level (i.e., $v = 0$)

No superscript = The molecule is *thermally equilibrated* (at 25° most molecules are in the $v = 0$ state)

Superscript v = Excess vibrational energy.

Classically, photophysical processes 2 through 14 in Table 4-1 have tended to be a prime concern of the molecular spectroscopist interested, *per se*, in establishing, experimentally and theoretically, energy levels, molecular and electronic structures, and probabilities of radiative and non-radiative transitions between electronic states. Photochemists, on the other hand, until recently tended to concentrate more on reactions 5-1 to 5-10 in Table 5-1, the primary photochemical processes of polyatomic molecules. This has been largely because of the dearth of reliable spectroscopic data and theory applicable to the determination of the actual *overall photochemistry* of a given system and not because of a lack of interest or desire on the part of photochemists to correlate the findings of molecular spectroscopy with the photochemistry of polyatomic molecules. Clearly, in order to understand the total photochemistry or photobiology of a given system one must understand the act of absorption and elucidate the nature and extent of the subsequent photophysical, as well as photochemical, processes. These compete for each quantum absorbed and are one limit to the overall yield of product. Furthermore, if different electronic states have different reactivities it is highly important to know their energies, populations, transition probabilities (lifetimes), and electronic configurations.

Unfortunately, the unambiguous assignment of the types and energies of the lowest excited states responsible for absorption in the visible and ultraviolet regions from analysis of experimentally determined absorption spectra is often difficult. Furthermore, until recently, there have been few

TABLE 4-1 Photophysical Processes of Polyatomic Molecules

Absorption of Radiation and Promotion to First Excited Singlet

$ABC(S_0) + h\nu_1 \rightarrow ABC(S_1^{v'})$ (1)

Photophysical Processes:

$ABC(S_1^{v'}) \overset{(M)}{\rightsquigarrow} ABC(S_1^{v}) \ldots \overset{(M)}{\rightsquigarrow} ABC(S_1)$ Vibrational and rotational relaxation. (2)

$ABC(S_1) \longrightarrow ABC(S_0) + h\nu_1'$ *Fluorescence.* (3)

$ABC(S_1) \rightsquigarrow ABC(S_0^{v})$ Non-radiative internal conversion (IC) to highly vibrationally excited ground state. (4)

$ABC(S_1) \rightsquigarrow ABC(T_1^{v})$ Non-radiative intersystem crossing (ISC) to vibrationally excited triplet state. (5)

$ABC(S_1) \xrightarrow{+D(S_0)} ABC(S_0) + D(S_1)$ Singlet electronic energy transfer. (6)

$ABC(T_1^{v}) \overset{(M)}{\rightsquigarrow} ABC(T_1)$ (7)

$ABC(T_1) \longrightarrow ABC(S_0) + h\nu_2$ *Phosphorescence:* radiative intersystem crossing. (8)

$ABC(T_1) \rightsquigarrow ABC(S_0^{v})$ Non-radiative intersystem crossing. (9)

$ABC(T_1) \xrightarrow{+D(S_0)} ABC(S_0) + D(T_1)$ Triplet electronic energy transfer. (10)

$ABC(T_1) \xrightarrow{+h\nu''} ABC(T_2^{v})$ Triplet–triplet absorption. (11)

Absorption of Radiation and Promotion to Higher Excited States

$ABC(S_0) + h\nu_3 \rightarrow ABC(S_2^{v'})$ (12)

Photophysical Processes:

$ABC(S_2^{v}) \overset{(M)}{\rightsquigarrow} ABC(S_2^{0}) \rightsquigarrow ABC(S_1^{v'}) \overset{(M)}{\rightsquigarrow} ABC(S_1)$ Non-radiative internal conversion; thermal equilibration. (13)

$ABC(S_0) + 2h\nu \longrightarrow ABC(S_1)$ True biphotonic absorption encountered at laser intensities; to be distinguished from successive absorption as in 11.[293,294] (14)

reliable experimental or theoretical estimates of the molecular and electronic structures of these states and of the transition probabilities between them.

However, in the last decade there has been a great advance in our knowledge of the relative and absolute probabilities of these photoprocesses and of the nature of the transient intermediates involved, in particular, molecules in their triplet states. Furthermore, during this period a wide variety of new and novel photoreactions of great synthetic and theoretical interest has been discovered, and currently "organic photochemistry" is one of the most exciting areas in organic chemistry. Parallel to this development, molecular orbital theory has been applied to the point where it is of great utility in the theoretical and applied aspects of the electronic structure of polyatomic molecules. Such progress is highly encouraging and suggests that application of spectroscopic theory and experiment to the photochemistry of complex molecules is fulfilling its promise.

In this chapter we shall discuss the characteristic features of the primary photophysical processes of organic molecules in terms of the fundamental spectroscopic, kinetic, and chemical properties of the excited state. No attempt is made here to delineate a special area and call it "organic photochemistry." We prefer to think in terms of the photochemistry of organic molecules as in Chapter 5; this classification includes organic photochemistry but is not as restrictive in its implications. We shall illustrate the nature of the primary photophysical processes by using "model" compounds of general interest for which the salient experimental facts are reasonably well known and are correlated with modern theory. Naphthalene is a typical example of an aromatic molecule having its lowest excited states $^1(\pi, \pi^*)$ and $^3(\pi, \pi^*)$ in character, and benzophenone is a "model" aromatic carbonyl compound with its lowest excited singlet state $^1(n, \pi^*)$ and lowest triplet $^3(n, \pi^*)$.

The manifold of lower excited states of a representative organic molecule is shown in the modified Jablonski diagram,[2] Fig. 4-1. Each electronic state is depicted with its associated vibrational and rotational levels approximately equally spaced for ease of presentation. Actually, as the vibrational quantum numbers v increase, the spacing diminishes until at last the levels blend into a virtual continuum, resulting in a "smear" of energy states. For convenience and visual clarity in presentation of other figures we may not specifically show this band of vibrational and rotational levels associated with each electronic state, but their relationship to isoenergetic radiationless transition of organic molecules is important and should be kept in mind.

In this particular representation of the manifold of excited states the initial ground state is at the left. The various possible physical radiative

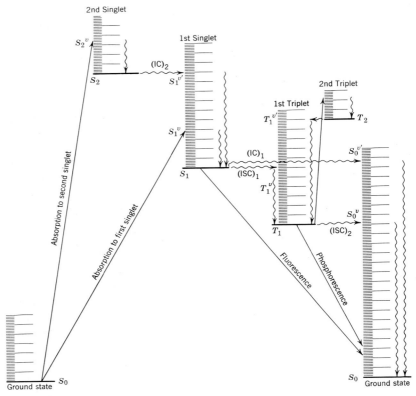

Fig. 4-1 Excited states and photophysical transitions between these states in a "typical" organic molecule. Radiative transitions between states are given by solid lines, radiationless processes by wavy lines; IC = internal conversion, ISC = intersystem crossing. Vertical wavy lines are vibrational relaxation processes. Vibrational and rotational levels are shown approximately equally spaced for convenience in presentation. Actually they blend into a continuum at large quantum numbers. Higher electronic states exist but are omitted for convenience. Photodissociation and possible relationless transitions from upper vibrational levels of the excited states have been omitted for simplicity of presentation.

(straight lines) and non-radiative (wavy lines) transitions between electronic states, starting with the act of absorption, are shown sequentially going from left to right with the excited molecule finally returning to the same thermally equilibrated ground state, S_0, it started from. It is important to note that radiationless transitions between electronically excited states are *isoenergetic*; hence they are shown as horizontal lines (they are not shown this way on many diagrams, and we feel this technique is confusing). Vertical wavy lines represent vibrational relaxation processes. None of the primary *photochemical* acts listed in Chapter 5, Table 5-1, is shown because, depending on the type of molecule and its environment, different processes may originate from different states (or the same state). For simplicity, possible radiationless transitions from upper vibrational levels of the excited states are omitted. These may be significant in certain systems, particularly in the gas phase.

Our discussion will generally follow the order indicated in Fig. 4-1 and Table 4-1, that is, absorption of light, radiative and non-radiative transitions, energy-transfer processes, and the chemical reactivities of excited states. Chapter 5 is devoted to a survey of the photochemistry of polyatomic molecules and includes the absorption spectra and estimates of the types and efficiencies of primary photochemical processes of the major classes of organic compounds. Simple inorganic compounds were discussed in Chapter 3, and the photochemistry of ions in solution is treated briefly in Secs. 4-4A and 4-4B.

General monographs dealing with the photochemistry of polyatomic molecules include Refs. 3–9. Reviews and critical discussions of various aspects of the subject include the following: spectroscopy and photochemistry, Refs. 10–16; primary processes, Refs. 17–22; "organic photochemistry," Refs. 23–27. Recently chapters by experts in these several areas have appeared and should be consulted for the details of a particular subject.[28] The "vocabulary" of photochemistry also has been discussed in an attempt to clarify the meaning of terms common to photochemistry and spectroscopy.[29]

Space limitations preclude a detailed discussion of the spectroscopy of polyatomic molecules. Thus we shall confine our remarks to the areas of prime concern to photochemists and present those aspects of spectroscopy that seem most significant to this field. Our treatment is largely qualitative and is based on the more quantitative theory for atoms and diatomic molecules considered in Chapters 2 and 3. We trust that the reader will be encouraged to consult the excellent monographs and reviews on the theory and applications of electronic spectroscopy[30–38] and molecular orbital methods for treating the spectra and structure of polyatomic molecules.[39–43]

4-1 NOTATION FOR EXCITED STATES

Various types of notation may be employed when describing an electronic transition of a polyatomic molecule. This has led to considerable difficulties on the part of the researcher not fully versed in the terminology of the spectroscopist (see Ref. 29 for a discussion of the problem). We shall consider first the types of transitions encountered in diatomic molecules and review the systems of notation commonly employed. Subsequently other types of notation will be introduced when appropriate to the system being considered.

An international agreement has been reached upon a convention for the description of radiative transitions between molecular states. *The symbol for the upper state is always written first and that for the lower state last regardless of whether the process is absorption or emission.* The direction of the transition is indicated by an arrow. We shall follow this convention when the states involved are known and it seems useful to use symmetry notation[44,45] or Mulliken state symbols[46,47] to describe the transition. However, in accord with common practice among chemists and many spectroscopists, when detailed characterization of excited states is either unavailable or unnecessary, enumerative notation[29] or molecular orbital representations[11–13,48] will be employed, and we shall write the absorbing or emitting state first.[30] Thus the arrow is from left to right. For example, the transition responsible for the first absorption band of formaldehyde can be described as $^1A_2 \leftarrow {}^1A_1$, $Q \leftarrow N$, $^1u \leftarrow {}^1A$, $\sigma^2\pi^2p_y^2 \rightarrow \sigma^2\pi^2p_y\pi^*$ or simply $n \rightarrow \pi^*$ (see Table 4-5 and Sec. 4-2C).

In the enumerative notation, singlets are labeled S_0, S_1, S_2, etc., in order of increasing energy (Fig. 4-1) with S_0 the ground state. Triplets are labeled T_1, T_2, T_3, etc. Mulliken employs different capital letters to represent states, N (normal) being the ground state, and V, Q, R, for example, refering to excited states.

One can also describe electronic transitions in terms of the initial and final orbitals occupied by the single electron involved in the transition.[48] This is a relatively simple system and is commonly employed, but it is less precise than symmetry notation, for example, and does not emphasize the important role of *electron correlation* (electron interaction, Ref. 30, p. 92). In simple molecules one often expresses the transitions in terms of all the MO's (molecular orbitals) involved, and the state symbols may be included. In complex molecules often only the initial and final MO's of the single electron are specified (e.g., $n \rightarrow \pi^*$).

4-2 MOLECULAR ORBITAL TREATMENT OF ABSORPTION OF RADIATION

We shall begin by considering three types of electronic transitions well characterized for diatomic molecules. We shall then extend the treatment to consider polyatomic molecules of photochemical interest where assignment of excited states and types of transitions is necessarily much less definite.

4-2A   Simple Molecules

4-2A-1   Charge-Transfer Spectra; $V \leftarrow N$ Transitions

The promotion of one electron from a *bonding* MO to an *antibonding* MO is always allowed for a diatomic molecule. Using Mulliken's notation, the transition is classed as $V \leftarrow N$, where V stands for a state with large ionic character. The Lyman absorption band of molecular hydrogen at 1109 A is a $V \leftarrow N$ transition (see Fig. 3-23). It is a highly intense, intramolecular, charge-transfer spectrum. The transition may be symbolized as

$$V \leftarrow N \qquad\qquad \text{(Mulliken)}$$

$$^1\Sigma_u^+ \leftarrow {}^1\Sigma_g^+ \qquad\qquad \text{(Symmetry notation)}$$

$$\sigma_g{}^2 \rightarrow \sigma_g\sigma_u \ (\text{or } \sigma1s^2 \rightarrow \sigma1s\sigma^*1s) \qquad \text{(MO)}$$

or simply

$$\sigma \rightarrow \sigma^* \qquad \text{(MO)}$$

With the symmetry notation, a state is described in terms of the behavior of the electronic wave function under the symmetry operations of the point group to which the molecule belongs. The characters of the one-electron orbitals are determined by inspection of the character table; the product of the characters of the singly occupied orbitals gives the character of the *molecular* wave function. In the Lyman transition the net angular momentum about the molecular axis is zero in both states; hence they are Σ in character (see Fig. 3-23 for the MO picture of this transition). The electrons are paired in the ground and excited states, so both are singlets (indicated by the superscript on the left side of the principal symbol). In the ground state the molecular wave function of H_2 is symmetric with respect to inversion through a center of symmetry and hence is g (*gerade*); in the excited state it is antisymmetric, u (*ungerade*).

Mulliken introduced the term *charge transfer* to denote the transfer of an electron from one atom to the other in going from a "normal" ground state to an "ionic" excited state. This is seen more clearly by the valence-bond picture of the $V \leftarrow N$ transition for hydrogen, which portrays it as

$$H:H + h\nu(1109 \text{ A}) \rightarrow H^+H^-$$

Charge-transfer spectra arising from this type of transition are observed with many diatomic molecules, including oxygen and the halogens; characteristically they are very intense.

4-2A-2 $Q \leftarrow N$ and $R \leftarrow N$ Transitions

These are transitions in which an electron is promoted from a *non-bonding*, localized, essentially AO (atomic orbital) to an antibonding MO. In the case of the hydrogen halides the $Q \leftarrow N$ transition is

$$\mathrm{HX}(\sigma^2 \pi_y{}^4) + h\nu \rightarrow \mathrm{HX}(\sigma^2 \pi_y{}^3 \sigma^*)$$

where the π_y orbital is essentially a p_y type of non-bonding AO (an n orbital) with its axis perpendicular to the molecular axis. Thus the simplest notation for the transition is $n \rightarrow \sigma^*$.

In $Q \leftarrow N$ transitions the transition moment is at right angles to the molecular axis, and the bands (e.g., for the hydrogen halides) typically have low intensities (as do $n \rightarrow \pi^*$ transitions in polyatomic molecules). Both $Q \leftarrow N$ and $V \leftarrow N$ transitions occur without a change in the principal quantum number and are *valence shell* transitions.

In Rydberg transitions, $R \leftarrow N$, a change in the principal quantum number does occur. The electron is promoted from a bonding MO to an MO of sufficiently high energy that the excited orbital is essentially atomic in character. This results in an atomic-like absorption spectrum of high absolute intensity, usually lying in the vacuum ultraviolet region.

4-2B   Types of Molecular Orbitals in Organic Molecules

In this section we shall consider the process of absorption of radiation by organic molecules, citing, as particular examples, ethylene, 1,3-butadiene, benzene, formaldehyde, and benzophenone. The spectroscopy and photochemistry of these important classes of compounds are being actively studied; furthermore, they have significant molecular and electronic structural differences which result in characteristic and widely different photochemistry. Thus they serve as particularly useful "model" compounds.

Transitions of non-conjugated organic molecules resulting from absorption of light usually involve the promotion of a single electron from a σ, π, or n orbital in the ground state to an *antibonding* π^* or σ^* orbital which is vacant in the ground state. These orbitals are shown for hydrocarbons in Fig. 4-2 and for formaldehyde in Figs. 4-3 and 4-4.

Just as with diatomic molecules, a σ orbital is symmetrical about the molecular axis and has zero component of angular momentum. The π MO is symmetrical about the bond axis with a plane of symmetry in the skeletal plane of the molecule. It has one component of angular momentum. In conjugated organic molecules (e.g., 1,3-butadiene, Fig. 4-2) there are additional delocalized π orbitals extending over all the atoms involved in conjugation.

In molecules containing a heteroatom (O, N, I, etc.) the highest filled MO in the ground state is the n orbital. Such orbitals are essentially atomic in character, $2p_y$ for the oxygen atom. Since p_y orbitals are perpendicular to the molecular axis (e.g., C—O axis in H_2CO), there is little overlap with other MO's; hence they are virtually *non-bonding*.

4-2C Types of Electronic Transitions in Organic Molecules

The most common transition in organic molecules (one or more may occur for every molecule having bonding π electrons) is promotion of an electron from a bonding π MO to an antibonding π^* orbital. These $\pi \rightarrow \pi^*$ transitions are classified as $V \leftarrow N$, and with unsaturated hydrocarbons they are the only type to consider in the visible and ultraviolet regions.

In common with $V \leftarrow N$ transitions of diatomic molecules, $\pi \rightarrow \pi^*$ transitions of polyatomic molecules have high intensities unless they are forbidden by selection rules based on molecular symmetry. For example, the "long" wavelength bands of benzene and naphthalene arise from the symmetry-forbidden $^1L_b \leftarrow {}^1A$ (Platt notation)[44] transition, and their ϵ_{max} values are about 220 and 280 liter/mole/cm, respectively. However, the longest wavelength band of anthracene results from an *allowed* $^1L_a \leftarrow {}^1A$ transition, and $\epsilon_{max} \cong 8000$ liter/mole/cm. In each of these three cases the transition is classed as $\pi \rightarrow \pi^*$.

The simplest unsaturate, ethylene, has its λ_{max} at 1625 A with $\epsilon_{max} \cong 10,000$. The double bond can be treated as being made up of two electrons in a σ-shaped orbital (Fig. 4-2) and two in a π_u orbital. Absorption at the 1625 A band results from the transition of one electron from the π_u bonding MO to the π_g^* antibonding MO.

The π^* orbital in ethylene (and the σ^* MO for the $\sigma_g \rightarrow \sigma_u^*$ transition in hydrogen at 1109 A, Fig. 3-23) has a nodal plane (zero electron-density plane) through the center of the molecule and perpendicular to the molecular axis (i.e., to the xy-plane). It is characteristic of such absorption bands of high intensity that the electron moves from a lower MO to an upper MO with one more nodal plane (or surface) than the lower. Such an electric dipole transition has a large transition moment, and for light absorption to be most efficient in ethylene, for example, the electric vector of the quantum must lie along the C—C bond axis.[10] Such polarization effects in absorption (and emission) have been well verified experimentally in a number of kinds of molecules oriented in crystals or stretched films.

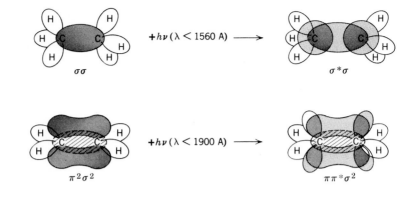

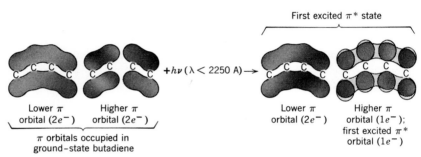

Fig. 4-2 Approximate molecular orbitals of C_2H_6, C_2H_4, and C_4H_6 in their ground and first excited states.

1,3-Butadiene illustrates the effect of conjugation in shifting the $\pi \rightarrow \pi*$ band to longer wavelengths than ethylene, $\lambda_{max} = 2170$ A versus 1650 A, and increasing its intensity, $\epsilon_{max} \cong 21,000$ versus $\sim15,000$. Excitation of the first band is from a π_g orbital (with one nodal plane, Fig. 4-2) to a π_u* orbital with two nodal planes.

In molecules containing a heteroatom such as oxygen or nitrogen the highest filled orbitals in the ground state are generally the non-bonding, essentially atomic n orbitals; the lowest unfilled orbitals are $\pi*$.[11-13,48] Thus, for example, the transitions of lowest energy are considered to be $n \rightarrow \pi*$ in most carbonyl compounds, nitrogen heterocyclics, quinones, etc.

Such $n \rightarrow \pi*$ transitions are generally responsible for the longest wavelength band in the absorption spectra of molecules with heteroatoms. Hence, although weak in intensity, they are extremely important in chemical and biological systems. For example, they absorb above 3000 A, the approximate lower limit of solar radiation reaching the earth's surface. Furthermore in many cases (n, π^*) states are the lowest excited singlet and triplet states of these molecules with heteroatoms. Since in solution most unimolecular processes involve the lowest excited singlet or triplet state, these (n, π^*) states determine the chemistry of the excited state. We shall discuss this crucial point in detail later.

Formaldehyde is a useful model for the higher aliphatic aldehydes and ketones; molecular symmetry properties result in helpful diagnostic simplifications when assigning its observed absorption bands to specific electronic transitions, and the assignments seem about as reliable as those for any known organic molecule containing a heteroatom such as oxygen. However, even in this structurally simplest of carbonyl compounds the classification of the second absorption band, an intense one at 1800 A, is in doubt with both $n \rightarrow \sigma^*$ and $\pi \rightarrow \pi^*$ classifications having been proposed. (See the papers of Kasha,[11–13] Platt,[44] Robinson,[14] Mulliken,[46] McMurray,[302] Duncan,[49] and Sidman,[45] and the reviews of Mason[35] and Jaffe and Orchin[30] for discussion of the spectroscopy of formaldehyde and the higher homologs.)

The long-wavelength band of formaldehyde (Fig. 5-1) is an example of an $n \rightarrow \pi^*$ transition which is symmetry forbidden, but as with benzene, vibrational interaction permits a weak transition. Thus in the vapor phase ϵ_{max} is only ~ 18 liter/mole/cm at $\lambda_{max} = 3040$ A. In the higher aliphatic aldehydes and ketones the transition is not forbidden by molecular symmetry, but the bands are still weak ($\epsilon_{max} \sim 15$). To explain this, Platt[44] has introduced the concept of *local symmetry*, in which the symmetry about the oxygen atom with its n and $2p\pi$ orbitals is considered most important in the $n \rightarrow \pi^*$ transition. Furthermore, the energies of the $n \rightarrow \pi^*$ transition of carbonyl compounds are grouped remarkably close together; that is, conjugative effects are generally small. This suggests that the concept of the upper orbital being a π^* *molecular* orbital is a gross oversimplification. The excitation seems to stay virtually localized on the heteroatom. This is even more pronounced in the triplets than in the singlets.[50] This important point is not made clear in Fig. 4-4, which is illustrative of the MO's involved but does not give an accurate picture of electron densities in the excited states.*

An $n \rightarrow \pi^*$ transition can be classified more precisely as $Q \leftarrow N$, $^1A_2 \leftarrow {}^1A_1$, or $^1u \leftarrow {}^1A$ by the notations of Mulliken, group theory, or Platt.[29]

The other transition of general importance in the photochemistry of

---

* Freeman and Klemperer utilized the Stark effect to determine that the dipole moment of formaldehyde in the first excited state is 1.48 ± 0.07 **D** and in the same direction as the ground state, where it is 2.34 ± 0.02 **D**.[303]

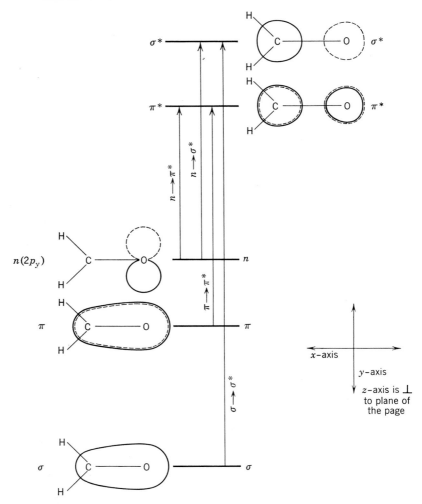

Fig. 4-3   Molecular orbitals and their approximate energy levels in formaldehyde. Adapted from Kasha.[11]

carbonyl compounds is the $V \leftarrow N$ transition. In the aliphatic compounds this is an intense band with the maximum in the vacuum ultraviolet (e.g., for formaldehyde and acetaldehyde, respectively, $\epsilon_{max} \simeq 18,000$ and $10,000$ at 1749 and 1816 A, respectively). With the exception of formaldehyde the transition is generally classified as $\pi \rightarrow \pi^*$.

The MO's approximate energy levels, and several transitions of importance for formaldehyde are shown in Fig. 4-3. Figure 4-4 is a pictorial

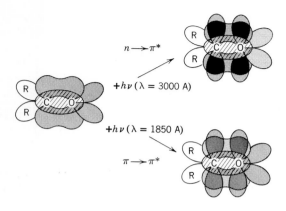

$n \longrightarrow \pi^*$

$+h\nu\,(\lambda = 3000\ \text{A})$

$+h\nu\,(\lambda = 1850\ \text{A})$

$\pi \longrightarrow \pi^*$

Fig. 4-4 Pictorial representation of the molecular orbitals for the carbonyl group in the ground state and after $n \to \pi^*$ or $\pi \to \pi^*$ transitions. Adapted from Cram and Hammond.[51]

representation of the MO's involved in $n \to \pi^*$ and $\pi \to \pi^*$ transitions of a "typical" carbonyl group.

When a carbonyl group is conjugated with a C=C group, the highest π orbital in the ground state is raised and the lowest π^* orbital in the excited state is lowered (relative to the respective π and π^* orbitals in the non-conjugated C=O group). However, the lone-pair orbitals (and the σ orbitals) are not greatly affected. As a consequence the $n \to \pi^*$ and $\pi \to \pi^*$ absorption bands of α,β-unsaturated carbonyl compounds (and of course aromatic ketones and aldehydes) are shifted significantly to longer wavelengths and overlap to a greater extent. The $\pi \to \pi^*$ band in particular becomes experimentally much more accessible (e.g., $\lambda_{max} = 2200$ A and $\epsilon_{max} = \cong 15{,}000$ for the $V \leftarrow N$ transition of crotonaldehyde). Woodward[52] formulated a set of empirical rules relating λ_{max} of this $V \leftarrow N$ transition for various solvents and substituent groups that has proven highly useful in the structure proof of complex α,β-unsaturated carbonyl compounds (steroids, etc.).

The spectra of aromatic hydrocarbons have been widely studied theoretically (see References in Tables 4-2 and 4-3) and experimentally (e.g., see Shull[54] and Mason[35]). Three main bands have been classified by Clar,[53] chiefly on an intensity basis, as $\alpha(\epsilon \sim 10^2,\ f \sim 0.001)$, $p(\epsilon \sim 10^4, f \sim 0.1)$, and $\beta(\epsilon \sim 10^5, f \sim 1)$. The wavelengths of the origins of the singlet α and p, and first triplet, t, bands and the maxima of the β bands are given in Table 4-2 for a variety of aromatic hydrocarbons.[35]

TABLE 4-2   Wavelengths (in A) of the Origins of the Singlet α and p Bands and the First Triplet, t, Band, and the Maxima of the β Band for Several Aromatic Hydrocarbons[a]

| Hydrocarbon | Singlets[b] | | | Triplets[c] | Ref. |
	α	p	β	t	
Benzene	2640	2068	1830	3400	54
Naphthalene	3145	2885	2210	4695	55
Anthracene	...	3785	2545	6700	56
Tetracene	...	4710	2740	9755	57
Pentacene	4280	5755	3100	13000	15
Phenanthrene	3445	2945	2547	4630	59
Chrysene	3600	3190	2670	5050	60
Picene	3760	3285	2865	...	
1,2-Benzanthracene	3850	3590	2900	6060	60
1,2-5,6-Dibenzanthracene	3950	3510	3000	5460	60
Triphenylene	3425	2870	2595	4200	60
Coronene	4100	3415	3050	5154	61

[a] Data from Mason; triplet data from references given.[35]
[b] Data of Clar.[53] The approximate intensities of the bands are α ($\epsilon \sim 10^2$, $f \sim 0.001$), p ($\epsilon \sim 10^4, f \sim 0.1$), and β ($\epsilon \sim 10^5, f \sim 1$).
[c] Data for alcohol–glass solutions at low temperature given where available.

TABLE 4-3   Effect of "Conjugative" Groups on the $0 \rightarrow 0$ Band of Benzene[a]

Compound	Frequency, cm^{-1}	Wavelength, A
Benzene	38,089	2625
Isopropylbenzene	37,601	2659
Cyclohexylbenzene	37,590	2660
Cyclopentylbenzene	37,435	2671
Cyclopropylbenzene	36,861	2713
Phenylacetylene	36,370	2750
Styrene	34,761	2877

[a] W. W. Robertson, J. F. Music, and F. A. Matsen, *J. Am. Chem. Soc.*, **72**, 5260 (1950). Adapted from Ref. 30.

The absorption spectra of several of these are shown in Fig. 5-26, while the effects of "conjugative" groups on the 0—0 absorption band in benzene are given in Table 4-3.

Considerations of molecular symmetry play an important role in characterizing the electronic spectra of "simple" polyatomic molecules (recall the cases of formaldehyde and benzene) and are equally useful when attempting to classify the bands observed with aromatic hydrocarbons. For example, Coulson[62] utilizes the concepts of MO's and molecular symmetry to explain readily the origin of the α, p, and β bands (and a fourth band, β') of naphthalene and to show the polarization of each band. The p band is ascribed to a one-electron jump (as we considered earlier), but the α and β bands "cannot be so described, and we are obliged to speak of an excited state in which excitation is no longer represented in terms of a single electron jump." This may occur in the spectra of both atoms and molecules and is described as *configuration interaction*. But, as Coulson notes, such interaction is particularly pronounced and effective in conjugated π-electron systems. The approach Coulson describes is the basis of a general characterization that can be used to develop the major aspects of the electronic spectra of almost all π-electron hydrocarbons.[62]

The effect of replacing one or more of the carbon atoms in a π-electron hydrocarbon with a nitrogen atom has been treated by several theoretical methods. We shall simply note that for pyridine the characterization of the α $(2500\,\text{A}, f = 0.03, \epsilon = 2100)$, p $(1950\,\text{A}, f = 0.20)$, and β $(1760\,\text{A}, f = 1.36)$ bands can be obtained from the same treatment as the aromatic hydrocarbons.[62] The presence of the heteroatom nitrogen increases the band intensities relative to benzene but has surprisingly little effect on the wavelengths of the α, p, and β bands (see benzene, Table 4-2).

The most significant effect of the nitrogen atom is to introduce into the aromatic molecule the lone-pair, n, electrons. This results in a $^1(n, \pi^*)$ band that in polar solvents is masked by the $\pi \rightarrow \pi^*$ transition (α band). The band is evident in the vapor-phase spectrum[48,63] and in non-polar solvents as the long-wavelength tail on the (π, π^*) band.[64] The great differences in the spectroscopy and photochemistry of pyridine and benzene are obviously not indicated by a casual inspection of the two absorption spectra. However, the $n \rightarrow \pi^*$ transition in pyridine, for example, differs from $\pi \rightarrow \pi^*$ transitions in two significant and experimentally observable ways. The first is easily demonstrated; changing from a nonpolar solvent (e.g., hexane) to a polar solvent (ethanol) results in a shift of the (n, π^*) band to shorter wavelengths (*blue shift*), and the (π, π^*) band to longer wavelengths (*red shift*). In the case of pyridine (see above) the polar solvent caused a blue shift of the (n, π^*) band and a red shift of the (π, π^*) band, resulting in complete masking of the $n \rightarrow \pi^*$ transition by the $\pi \rightarrow \pi^*$ transition.

TABLE 4-4 Summary of Symmetry and State Notations Used for the Polyacenes by Various Authors[a]

Representation of V_h (or D_{2h}) (for singlets)	Ham-Ruedenberg Notation[b] (for singlets)	Platt State Symbols[c]	Moffitt State Notation[d] (for singlets)	Benzene States in D_{6h}	Clar's Upper State (for singlets)[e]	Mulliken and Rieke (for singlets)[f]	Coulson Excited-State Configuration[g] (naphthalene)	Pariser Notation[h] Benzene	Pariser Notation[h] Polyacene
A_{1g}	SS	^1A (for ground state)		$^1A_{1g}$		N (ground state)		$^1A_{1g}$	$^1A_{1g}^-$
B_{1g}	AA	$^1B_a, {}^3B_a$	X	$^1E_{1u}, {}^3E_{1u}$	...	$V_4(B_{2u})$	S_1R_2	$^1E_{1u}^+, {}^3E_{1u}^+$	$^1B_{2u}^+, B_{2u}^+$
B_{2u}	AS	$^1L_a, {}^3L_a$	U	$^1B_{1u}, {}^3B_{1u}$	p	V_2	P_2Q_2	$^1B_{1u}^+, {}^3B_{1u}$	$^1B_{2u}^+, {}^2B_{2u}^+$
B_{3u}	SA	$^1B_b, {}^3B_b$	Y	$^1E_{1u}, {}^3E_{1u}$	β	$V_3(B_{3g})$	R_1Q_2	$^1E_u^+, {}^3E_u^+$	$^1B_{3u}^-, {}^3B_{3u}^+$
		$^1L_b, {}^3L_b$	V	$^2B_{2u}, {}^3B_{2u}$	α	$V_1(B_{2u})$	S_1Q_2	$^1B_{2u}^-, {}^3B_{2u}^-$	$^1B_{3u}^-, {}^3B_{3u}^-$

[a] Table from Kearns.[66]
[b] Ref. 67.
[c] Ref. 68.
[d] Ref. 69.
[e] Ref. 53.
[f] Ref. 47.
[g] Ref. 62b.
[h] Ref. 70.

This "solvent shift" (see below) is one of the most convenient and widely used means of determining the character of an absorption band. In the case of acetone λ_{max} for the $n \to \pi^*$ transition varies with solvent as follows: hexane (2790 A), chloroform (2770 A), ethanol (2720 A), methanol (2700 A), and water (2645 A).[30]

The solvent shifts may be explained in the following way.[31,48] Polar solvents are more strongly hydrogen bonded to the ground state than to the excited (n, π^*) state (where only one n electron is available). Thus the energy of the ground state is lowered more than that of the excited state, resulting in a greater energy requirement for the transition and consequently a blue shift. The red shift of the (π, π^*) band in ketones is a more complex phenomenon to explain (see Ref. 30, p. 188), but it is believed that the more polar (relative to the ground state) excited state is stabilized by polar solvents to a greater extent than the ground state, and a red shift results.

A second effect of the nitrogen atom in the aromatic ring is to change the polarization of the transition. In the $\pi \to \pi^*$ transitions of the aromatic hydrocarbons the electric vector lies in the plane of the molecule, but there is also an $n \to \pi^*$ transition in pyridine and it is polarized perpendicularly to the molecular plane. For example, polarization of the $\pi \to \pi^*$ and $n \to \pi^*$ phosphorescence spectra has been used by El-Sayed and Brewer[65] to establish the character of the emitting singlet and triplet states in several N-heterocyclics.

We should now mention one other system of notation that is useful and is often encountered, particularly with aromatic molecules, the *Platt notation*. It is based on the conceptually simple perimeter model description of excited states.[44a] In this system ground states are labeled A, the excited states involved in certain very high intensity transitions are labeled B, and the excited states produced in partially forbidden transitions (i.e., those in which selection rules are violated) are labeled L and C. The notation is derived from selection rules appropriate for imaginary monocyclic aromatic systems. States to which transitions are forbidden because of a large change in angular momentum are L states. Transitions to C states are parity forbidden; that is, they violate the $g \leftrightarrow g$, $u \leftrightarrow u$ selection rule. In common aromatics other than benzene these selection rules break down, and transitions to L and C states occur but at lower intensities relative to B states.

Table 4-4 summarizes the symmetry and state notations used for the polyacenes by various authors,[66] while Table 4-5 gives an example of nomenclatures employed for ethylene, benzene, and formaldehyde.[29]

TABLE 4-5   Examples of Nomenclatures for Several Important Transitions in Polyatomic Molecules[a]

	Ethylene	Benzene	Formaldehyde[b]
	$\lambda_{max} = 1650$ A; $\epsilon_{max} \cong 15{,}000$	$\lambda_{max} = 2560$ A; $\epsilon_{max} \cong 160$	$\lambda_{max} = 3040$ A; $\epsilon_{max} \cong 18$
Group theory	$^1B_{1u} \leftarrow {}^1A_{1g}$	$^1B_{2u} \leftarrow {}^1A_{1g}$	$^1A_2 \leftarrow {}^1A_1$
Mulliken state[c]	$V \leftarrow N$	$V \leftarrow N$	$Q \leftarrow N$
Platt[d]	$^1B \leftarrow {}^1A$	$^1L_b \leftarrow {}^1A$	$^1u \leftarrow {}^1A$
Molecular orbital	$\sigma^2\pi^2 \rightarrow \sigma^2\pi\pi^*$	e	$\sigma^2\pi^2 p_y{}^2 \rightarrow \sigma^2\pi^2 p_y\pi^*$
Kasha[f]	$\pi \rightarrow \pi^*$	$\pi \rightarrow \pi^*$	$n \rightarrow \pi^*$

[a] Table modified from Pitts, Wilkinson, and Hammond.[29]
[b] Note: p_y in formaldehyde symbolizes a non-bonding orbital on the oxygen atom. Data in vapor phase by V. McMillan.
[c] See Ref. 47.
[d] See Ref. 44a.
[e] Degeneracy of both the occupied and unoccupied benzene π orbitals, and the fact that configuration interaction removes the degeneracies, render the transition too complicated to describe in terms of a single configuration.
[f] See Ref. 48.

4-2D   Selection Rules

Several of the selection rules have analogs in those we have cited for atoms and diatomic molecules; others, such as those dealing with molecular symmetry, do not. Excellent discussions of these "rules" are given by Mason,[35] Kasha,[11–13] and Platt.[44b] We shall summarize the rules briefly here.[29]

Spin-forbidden. Radiative transitions involving a change of spin, or multiplicity, are strongly forbidden, and in the absence of a perturbing environment can be observed only by careful measurements in favorable cases.

For example, the singlet-triplet transitions in ethylenic compounds generally have $\epsilon_{max} \ll 1$. The fact that spin-forbidden transitions can be observed at all involves the phenomenon of *spin-orbit coupling*. Basically, spin-orbit coupling is the interaction between an electron's spin magnetic moment and its orbital magnetic moment. This interaction introduces a term into the Hamiltonian operator which operates on both spin and space variables. In the presence of this spin-orbit coupling operator, the zero-order wave functions of the system, which are originally pure singlets and triplets, are mixed to a small extent. These new wave functions of mixed multiplicity lead to the possibility of singlet-triplet transitions because the triplet state is no longer pure triplet but has some singlet character mixed with it. Thus the mixed triplet wave function is

$$\psi_T{}' = \psi_T{}^0 + \lambda_{TS}\psi_S{}^0 \tag{4-1}$$

where the zero superscript refers to a pure zero-order state, and λ_{TS} is the mixing coefficient. It can be shown that the transition moment integral $\int \psi_S{}' \mathbf{M} \psi_T{}' \, d\tau$ is non-zero; hence the transition is partially allowed. The mixing coefficient λ_{ij} is an inverse function of the energy difference between the states i and j. Thus, when $E_i - E_j$ is small, the states i and j are strongly coupled.

In addition to providing an explanation of singlet-triplet absorption, mixing of excited electronic states in polyatomic molecules also plays an important role in the phenomena of intensity "borrowing" (see below), intersystem crossing, and internal conversion.

Symmetry-forbidden. Transitions are forbidden for which the transition moment vanishes because of the symmetry properties of the integrand. To be non-zero, the function $\psi_i \mathbf{M} \psi_f$ must be totally symmetric; since ψ_i is normally totally symmetric, the transition will be allowed only if the product $\mathbf{M}\psi_f$ is symmetric. Because the three components of the dipole operator ordinarily transform differently under the covering operations of the various point groups, a transition may be allowed with polarization along one or two axes but forbidden with polarization along the other(s). In molecules which have centers of symmetry the general selection rule can be stated by saying that only $u \leftrightarrow g$ and $g \leftrightarrow u$ transitions are allowed, the *Laporte rule*. Transitions between states of similar parity, that is, $g \leftrightarrow g$ and $u \leftrightarrow u$, are sometimes said to be *parity-forbidden*.

Symmetry-forbidden transitions are usually easily observable but are characterized by low intensity. Failure of the selection rule to hold rigorously is due to the fact that purity of the symmetry of various states is modified by vibrational motions having different symmetries. The effect may be especially pronounced if the molecule has allowed transitions to excited states having energies fairly close to the energy of the excited state involved in the forbidden transition. An example is found in the forbidden $^1B_{2u} \leftarrow {}^1A_{1g}$ (λ_{max} 2640 A, $\epsilon_{max} = 204$) and $^1B_{1u} \leftarrow {}^1A_{1g}$ ($\lambda_{max} = 2070$ A, $\epsilon_{max} = 7400$) transitions of benzene. These transitions are fairly intense because they "borrow intensity" from the allowed transition, $^1E_{1u} \leftarrow {}^1A_{1g}$ ($\lambda_{max} = 1790$ A); that is, the wave functions of the $^1B_{2u}$ and $^1B_{1u}$ states mix with the wave function of the $^1E_{1u}$ state.

Platt has discussed the application of selection rules to the spectra of conjugated organic molecules, in particular condensed ring systems.[44b] He cites the various kinds of forbiddenness and then compares them with the corresponding selection rules for atomic systems. His treatment is useful, and the following statements are taken directly from his article:

"If we think of a perfectly allowed $\pi \rightarrow \pi^*$ transition as having an oscillator strength F_A of the order of unity, then any other transition will have its oscillator strength F given as to order of magnitude by

$$F = f_s f_o f_m f_p F_A$$

where the f factors differ from unity as follows for the different kinds of forbiddenness which have been distinguished so far:

f_s, spin-forbidden transition, involving change of multiplicity, 10^{-5} for second-row elements.

f_o, overlap-forbidden, involving change of position of electronic charge, 10^{-2} for $n \rightarrow \pi^*$ transitions of second-row heteroatoms.

f_m, momentum-forbidden or 'orbitally forbidden,' involving large change of linear or angular momentum, 10^{-1} to 10^{-3} for condensed ring systems.

f_p, parity-forbidden transition, initial and final states both even or both odd, 10^{-1} for condensed ring systems."

4-2E   Assignment of Electronic Transitions

Unequivocal assignment of an observed electronic transition as due to promotion of an electron from one specific MO to another, for example, $n \rightarrow \pi^*$ and $\pi \rightarrow \pi^*$ transition, is difficult for simple molecules, let alone for more complex species with complicated absorption spectra having overlapping bands, etc. Theoretical calculations alone are rarely sufficient except in certain special cases where there is a particular symmetry in the skeletal structure of the molecule.

With molecules having a plane of symmetry the orientation of the transition moment can be determined experimentally in several ways.[5,7,12] In some cases one measures the absorption of polarized light by a suitably oriented molecular crystal of known structure. Another approach is to irradiate an isotropic distribution of molecules in a rigid "glass" medium with polarized monochromatic radiation and determine the polarization of the emitted fluorescence or phosphorescence relative to the incident beam.[65]

The single-crystal technique presents three chief problems. First, organic crystals often have very complex structures, and relative orientations of crystal planes to molecular axes are not known. Second, electronic transitions in crystals may be drastically altered by strong intermolecular interactions. Third, tiny amounts of impurities can serve as energy traps with the consequence that one sees emission from the impurity.

Other bases for identifying transitions in polyatomic molecules include reasonable agreement between theory and experiment on the location and intensities of absorption bands; analysis of the vibrational structure of the band (e.g., the calculations on formaldehyde); and the method of controlled perturbations in which one substitutes deuterium atoms in place of hydrogen atoms, CH in place of nitrogen, or introduces functional groups at key positions in the molecule and observes the changes in the spectrum.

Assignment of a transition in a complex molecule containing a heteroatom as $n \rightarrow \pi^*$ rather than $\pi \rightarrow \pi^*$ is usually done in terms of a set of empirical or semiempirical criteria. Kasha[12] summarizes them as follows (several have already been mentioned; see above):

1. Absence of (n, π^*) band in hydrocarbon analogs.
2. Disappearance of band in acid media (proton presumably coordinates with the "basic" lone-pair electrons responsible for the transition).
3. Blue shift of absorption spectrum in polar solvents; (π, π^*) bands show a red shift.
4. Conjugative-substituent blue shift.
5. Low absolute absorption intensity relative to $\pi \rightarrow \pi^*$ transitions.
6. Unique polarization of absorption and emission spectra.
7. Low transition energy so that bands are found at longest wavelengths.

It is clear that the present approach to assigning observed bands in complex absorption spectra to transitions involving specific MO's is sufficiently empirical that many such assignments must be viewed with considerable caution awaiting new and more definite theoretical and experimental evidence as to their validity.

Various types of molecular energy-level diagrams have been devised to present spectroscopic information of the type we have considered and a word about these seems in order.* The nature and amount of information presented in any particular diagram depend upon what is experimentally known and/or theoretically calculated and the points one wishes to make. Thus a Grotrian type (e.g., Fig. 2-10) is a *state diagram* that shows pictorially the energies of the experimentally determined *energy states* relative to the ground state, and the observed transitions between these states.

Molecular energy states are determined experimentally; the interpretation of the mechanisms of the observed transitions is made in terms of some model, for example, one based on MO theory and molecular symmetry

---

* The authors are indebted to Professor C. A. Coulson and Dr. F. Wilkinson for interesting discussions on this matter.

properties. If good agreement is reached between experimentally observed transitions and those calculated from a given theory one may be somewhat confident in applying the theory to the important calculations of the changes in electronic charge distribution and possibly bond strengths occurring on excitation.

An *MO energy-level* diagram may be used to show, in an approximate way, the distribution of electrons in the MO's of any one of the lower excited states. A one-electron radiative or non-radiative transition is represented by transferring an electron from one MO to another (e.g. Fig. 4-3 for formaldehyde).

Such a diagram is a highly useful complement to the Grotrian type, provided the assumptions inherent in its formulation are clearly understood and a clear distinction between theoretical calculation and experimental observation is maintained. Unfortunately, diagrams are often shown which, to someone not expert in spectroscopy, are a confusing blend of experimental fact (e.g., wavelength of a radiative transition) with theoretical calculation (e.g., specifying a given transition as $n \rightarrow \pi^*$ and then showing the actual *states*). Furthermore, most MO energy-level diagrams, as a simplification, neglect electron interaction, yet this may be very important, even reversing the expected order of energy of MO's. The magnitude of the effect may be unknown, but the fact that it exists should, if possible, be indicated on the diagram or kept well in mind by the reader.

The *state* diagram, Fig. 4-1, is for a hypothetical organic molecule and does not show MO's. Enumerative notation is used. Since most organic molecules in their ground states have their electrons paired, the ground state is a singlet, S_0. The act of absorption (or emission) is shown as solid lines to the lowest excited singlet S_1^v and the second excited singlet S_2^v.

The only radiative absorptions shown are singlet-singlet and triplet-triplet; singlet-triplet radiative transitions may occur, but they violate the selection rule $\Delta S = 0$ and are usually extremely weak in absorption unless a perturbing influence (e.g., O_2 or a heavy atom) is present. Triplet states lie below their corresponding singlet states (the molecular version of "Hund's rule" for atoms, see Table 4-2) and may be populated by intersystem crossing (Sec. 4-7). They may play a very important role in the photochemistry of the system.

After excitation to S_1^v the excited molecule has a variety of possible fates, including photochemical reactions. These are not shown in Fig. 4-1. Primary photophysical processes of (n, π^*) and (π, π^*) excited states (including energy transfer) are discussed later in this chapter; primary photochemical processes are treated in Chapter 5.

4-3   EMPIRICAL RELATIONSHIPS BETWEEN MOLECULAR STRUCTURE AND ULTRAVIOLET ABSORPTION SPECTRA OF ORGANIC COMPOUNDS

Of prime concern in photochemistry is the absorption spectrum of the compound under investigation. Many of these spectra are given for specific examples in Chapter 5. Here we shall cite some general relationships, largely empirical, that might be useful in examining the effect of structure on absorption spectra. References 71–78 are useful catalogs and indexes of absorption spectra in the visible and ultraviolet; Ref. 80 reviews the vacuum ultraviolet.

Useful relationships between molecular structure and the color of organic compounds were formulated empirically by the early dye chemists, who observed that characteristic absorption bands could be ascribed to specific groups of atoms in the absorbing molecule, called *chromophores* ("color carriers"). The location of these bands was often virtually independent of the structure of the rest of the molecule. Two chief types were recognized, the "two-atom" kind (e.g., the carbonyl group responsible for the absorption of aliphatic aldehydes and ketones) and the "many-atom" kind, such as benzene or porphyrin rings.

Certain substituents, called *auxochromes*, appreciably intensify and shift the absorption. A shift to the red (longer wavelengths) is called *bathochromic*, and to the blue (shorter wavelengths) *hypsochromic*. When the effect of the auxochrome is very large (e.g., when an auxochrome is conjugated to a chromophore) and strong new bands appear, the distinction between auxochrome and chromophore loses its significance.

For example, with acetophenone it is difficult to define whether acetyl or phenyl is the auxochrome. Nagakura and Tanaka[79] have utilized MO theory to explain this case in terms of the transfer of charge that accompanies excitation. With acetophenone (as with ortho and para directing groups other than acetyl) they suggest that during the electronic transition charge flows from the acetyl group ("donor") to the phenyl ring ("acceptor"). Thus they refer to the spectrum as an *intramolecular charge-transfer spectrum*. With meta directing substituents such as NO_2, the phenyl ring becomes the donor, and during the excitation of nitrobenzene charge is pictured as being transferred from the phenyl ring to the NO_2. Such "charge-transfer" effects appear to have important implications with regard to the photochemical reactivities of the excited states of substituted benzophenones and butyrophenones (Secs. 4-11 and 5-2B). Table 4-6 shows the λ_{max} and ϵ_{max} values for the ^1L_a (*primary*) and ^1L_b

TABLE 4-6   Spectra of Monosubstituted Benzenes[a,b]

R	Primary Band (^1L_a)		Secondary Band (^1L_b)		
	λ_{max}, mμ	ϵ_{max}	λ_{max}, mμ	ϵ_{max}	$\lambda_{sec}/\lambda_{pri}$
H	203.5	7,400	254	204	1.25
NH_3^+	203	7,500	254	160	1.25
CH_3	206.5	7,000	261	225	1.25
I	207	7,000	257	700	1.24
Cl	209.5	7,400	263.5	190	1.25
Br	210	7,900	261	192	1.24
OH	210.5	6,200	270	1450	1.28
OCH_3	217	6,400	269	1480	1.24
SO_2NH_2	217.5	9,700	264.5	740	1.22
CN	224	13,000	271	1000	1.21
CO_2^-	224	8,700	268	560	1.20
CO_2H	230	11,600	273	970	1.19
NH_2	230	8,600	280	1430	1.22
O^-	235	9,400	287	2600	1.22
$NHCOCH_3$	238	10,500	...	...	...
$COCH_3$	245.5	9,800	...	...	...
CHO	249.5	11,400	...	...	...
NO_2	268.5	7,800	...	...	...

[a] From Jaffe and Orchin,[30] p. 257.
[b] Water as solvent, trace of MeOH added for solubility where necessary.

(*secondary*) bands (Platt notation) of several monosubstituted benzenes.[30]*

Table 4-7 lists some of the more important chromophoric and auxo-chromic groups. It gives the approximate frequencies (cm^{-1}), wavelengths, and extinction coefficients of their absorption bands when they are attached to an alkane or when they are alone as a stable molecule. "Typical" examples are included. Many of the values are approximations and should be regarded as such,[31] particularly values of ϵ_{max}. Nevertheless, a number of useful illustrations of $\sigma \rightarrow \sigma^*$, $\pi \rightarrow \pi^*$, and $n \rightarrow \pi^*$ transitions are included (e.g., note the bathochromic shift of CH_3Cl, CH_3Br, and CH_3I, where $\lambda_{max} = 1725$, 2040, and 2577 A).

Several chromophoric groups absorbing in the vacuum ultraviolet have not been listed in Table 4-7. Some individual spectra are in Chapters 3 and 5, and Kaye[80] has published an extensive and highly useful compilation of vacuum ultraviolet spectra, including the pioneering works of Platt and of Pickett and their co-workers.

---

* Note that several photochemically important ^1L_b bands from $n \rightarrow \pi^*$ transitions are omitted (e.g., acetophenone, benzaldehyde).

TABLE 4-7   Chromophores and Auxochromes[a]

Group	Example	ω_{max}, 10^3 cm^{-1}	λ_{max}, A	Approximate ϵ, liters/ mole-cm
$\diagdown C{=}C \diagup$	$H_2C{=}CH_2$	55	1825	250
		57.3	1744	16,000
		58.6	1704	16,500
		62	1620	10,000
$—C{\equiv}C—$	$H—C{\equiv}C—CH_2—CH_3$	58	1720	2500
$\diagdown C{=}O \diagup$	H_2CO	34	2950	10
		54	1850	Strong
$\diagdown C{=}S \diagup$	$CH_3—\overset{\overset{S}{\|}}{C}—CH_3$	22	4600	Weak
$—NO_2$	$CH_3—NO_2$	36	2775	10
		47.5	2100	10,000
$—N{=}N—$	$CH_3—N{=}N—CH_3$	28.8	3470	15
		>38.5	<2600	Strong
⬡		39	2550	200
		50	2000	6300
		55.5	1800	100,000
$—Cl$	CH_3Cl	58	1725	...
$—Br$	CH_3Br	49	2040	1800
$—I$	CH_3I	38.8	2577	...
		49.7	2010	1200
$—OH$	CH_3OH	55	1830	200
		67	1500	1900
$—SH$	C_2H_5SH	43	2320	160
$—NH_2$	CH_3NH_2	46.5	2150	580
		52.5	1905	3200
$—S—$	$CH_3—S—CH_3$	44	2280	620
		46.5	2150	700
		49.3	2030	2300
$C{=}C—C{=}C$	$H_2C{=}CH—CH{=}CH_2$	48	2090	25,000
⬡⬡		32	3110	250
		37	2700	5000
		45	2210	100,000

(*Table continued on p. 266*)

TABLE 4-7 *Continued*

Group	Example	ω_{max}, 10^3 cm^{-1}	λ_{max}, A	Approximate ϵ, liters/ mole-cm
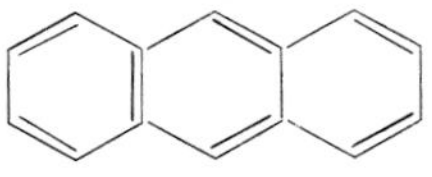 (anthracene structure)		28 40	3600 2500	6000 150,000
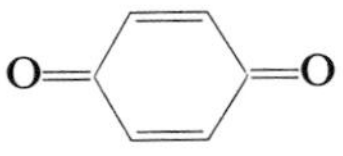 O=(ring)=O		23 34 40	4400 3000 2500	20 1000 15,000
C=C—C=O	H₂C=C—C—H (with O above)	30 47.5	3330 2100	20 12,000
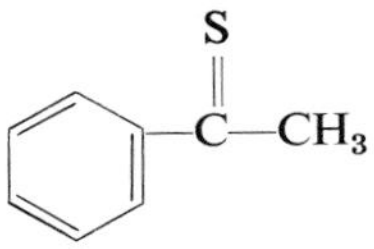 (phenyl)—C(=S)—CH₃		16.5	6000	...
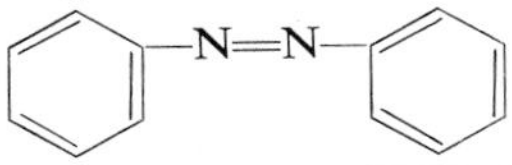 (phenyl)—N=N—(phenyl)		22.5 31 43	4400 3200 2300	500 20,000 10,000

[a] From Bauman,[31] p. 318, original data from Kamlet and Ungnade[73] or Duncan and Matsen.[37]

Solvent effects may play an important role in the character of the absorption spectra, as we have already seen for $n \rightarrow \pi^*$ transitions. This in turn may have a significant effect on the photochemical reactivity of the excited state[268] (Secs. 4-11 and 5-9).

The absorption spectrum of an organic compound may be strongly affected by its physical state. Thus λ_{max} for anthracene (Fig. 4-9) shifts progressively further to the red in going from the vapor to solution in dioxane to the solid state. Bayliss[82] has derived an expression for the red shift occurring on solvation and shows that it increases with the polarity of the solvent.

Leermakers and Thomas[274] have observed that silica gel-cyclohexane and silica gel-benzene matrices, if of sufficiently short path length, are highly transparent in the near ultraviolet and provide an excellent medium for the determination of quite well-resolved electronic absorption spectra of organic molecules. In typical systems, red shifts, in going from pure cyclohexane solvent to cyclohexane-silica gel, for transitions are well over 100 A (as compared to about 30 A for ethanol). Blue shifts in $n \rightarrow \pi^*$ transitions of the absorbed species are also of greater magnitude than the corresponding shifts in ethanol solvent. This technique also should be applicable to photochemical investigations. For example, Holmogorov et al. observed the doublet EPR signal of hydrogen atoms abstracted from

TABLE 4-8 Empirical Rules for Calculating Absorption Maxima of Dienes and α,β-Unsaturated Carbonyl Systems in Ethanol[a]

System[b]	Structure	λ_{max}, mμ	$\alpha =$				$\beta =$		$\gamma, \delta =$
			R[c]	OH	Cl	Br	R[c]	OH	R[c]
Diene[d,e]		217[f]	5	...	17	17	...	...	...
α,β-Unsaturated ketones[d,g]		215	10	35	...	23	10	35	...
α,β-Unsaturated aldehyde[d,g]		209	11	...	...	...	11	...	...
α,β-Unsaturated esters or acids[d,g]		197	10	...	...	...	10	35	...
Dienone[d,g]		245	10	35	15	23	12	...	18

[a] From Jaffe and Orchin,[30] pp. 218–219.
[b] If any of the conjugated systems is part of a ring system:
   1. The ring residue at each position is regarded as an alkyl group.
   2. If the diene system is in one six-membered ring (homoannular diene), add 39 mμ.
   3. If C—C double bond is exocyclic to a five- or six-membered ring or endocyclic in a five- or seven-membered ring, add 5 mμ.
   4. If a [3.1.1]bicyclo system is part of the conjugated system, add 15 mμ.
[c] Substituent R may be only alkyl (or a ring residue) in the diene system but in addition can be OAc or OR in the other systems.
[d] If the conjugation is extended by a C=C, add 30 mμ.
[e] No solvent correction necessary.
[f] In the steroid compounds, the preferred value is 214 mμ.
[g] For solvent corrections see Table 4-9.

CH$_3$OH by photoexcited triphenylamine molecules and stabilized by absorption on silica gel.[282] Similar strong spectral shifts have been observed for ketones dispersed in solid KBr matrices.[281]

As indicated earlier, Woodward[52] devised a set of useful rules relating the nature of the substituent on an α,β-unsaturated ketone to the position of the λ_{max} of its intense $V \leftarrow N$ band. A number of similar empirical rules have been developed for calculating λ_{max} for other conjugated molecules;[83] these are presented in Table 4-8. With these, and the

TABLE 4-9   Solvent Corrections for the $V \leftarrow N$ Band of Several α,β-Unsaturated Ketones[a]

	Correction, $m\mu$[b]	
Solvent	Woodward[c]	Fieser and Fieser[d]
Methanol	−1	0
Chloroform	0	+1
Ether	+6	+7
Hexane	+7	+11
Water	...	−8
Dioxane	...	+5

[a] Table from Jaffe and Orchin,[30] p. 207.
[b] Corrections should be added to the λ_{max} in the solvent in the left column to obtain the λ_{max} in ethanol.
[c] Ref. 52.
[d] Ref. 83.

additional corrections for solvent shifts in the $V \leftarrow N$ band given in Table 4-9, one can estimate with good accuracy, particularly in view of the generality of the rules, λ_{max} for a large number of conjugated molecules.

4-4   ABSORPTION SPECTRA OF IONS

The photochemistry and spectroscopy of inorganic ions in solution have been extensively investigated and reviewed[84–93] (see also Table 4-11 and the references therein). Here we shall simply comment briefly on the general empirical features of absorption spectra and quantum yields of primary processes of several characteristic types of ions. No discussion of theory is given (e.g., see Refs. 88, 89, and 92), and no attempt is made to be comprehensive.

4-4A   Electron-Transfer Spectra

Electronic transitions resulting in the transfer of an electron from one ion in a molecule to another ion (or to the solvent) are responsible for much of inorganic photochemistry. A typical example of a vapor-phase *charge-transfer* (electron-transfer) type of spectrum is the strong continuous absorption band of the gaseous alkali halides around 2000–2500 A, for example, CsI.[94] The ground state of CsI is essentially ionic and the excited state covalent, the reverse of the $V \leftarrow N$ charge-transfer spectrum of chlorine. The more covalent excited state is unstable (all potential energy curves for the upper states are repulsive), and the overall result of absorption of radiation is the formation of the neutral atoms,

$$CsI + h\nu \ (2085 \ A) \rightarrow Cs + I$$

Rather good evidence for the actual transfer of an electron from the absorbing ion in aqueous solution in such an electronic transition is shown in Table 4-10. The absorption maxima for a series of cations and anions

TABLE 4-10   Free Energies of Electron Transfer and λ_{max} for Several Ions[a]

Typical Ions for Electron Transfer	λ_{max}, A[b]	$\Delta F°$, kcal/mole, for $X^n + H^+ \rightarrow X^{n+1} + \frac{1}{2}H_2$
F⁻	1500 (191 kcal)	+94
Cl⁻	1900 (150)	56
Br⁻	1995 (143)	44
I⁻	2320 (123)	29
Co²⁺	2200 (130)	42
Fe²⁺	2850 (100)	18
V²⁺	3500 (81)	−5
Cr²⁺	3800 (75)	−9

[a] Adapted from table by Marcus.[84]
[b] The extinction coefficients of the halide ions are in the range $\epsilon = 5000–12,000$.

presumably having charge-transfer type of spectra are compared with the free energy change for the reaction, $X^n + H^+ \rightarrow X^{n+1} + \frac{1}{2}H_2$. The most electronegative ion is F^- ($\Delta F = +94$ kcal/mole), which has its absorption maximum at the shortest wavelength, 1500 A (corresponding to 191 kcal/einstein). Conversely the process $Cr^{2+} + H^+ \rightarrow Cr^{3+} + \frac{1}{2}H_2$ is exothermic by 10 kcal and Cr^{2+} absorbs farthest toward the visible, λ_{max} being 3800 A (the tail of this band is responsible for the color of the chromous ion). The other ions, Cl^-, Br^-, I^-, Co^{2+}, Fe^{2+}, and V^{2+}, fall in between, with a decrease in electron affinities correlating well with a shift towards the visible of the absorption maximum of the ion. The absorptions are intense, ϵ_{max} ranging from 5000 to 12,000 for the halide ions.

Several factors, including the observed photochemistry, have suggested that the water hydrating the ion was involved in the electronic transition, which was written as

$$X^n H_2O + h\nu \rightarrow [X^{n+1}H_2O^-]$$

The latter species has been presumed to dissociate or react by several paths, for example,

$$[X^{n+1}H_2O^-] \xrightarrow{(H^+)} X^{n+1} + H_2O + H$$
$$\searrow X^{n+1} + OH^- + H$$

However, the electron probably does not go to a single water molecule but may go into the ligand field of all of them.

Evidence for water being involved in the primary absorption is the large calculated distance the excited electron moves in a transition. Kauzmann[40] derives the following approximate expression for this distance, D (in angstrom units):

$$D = \sqrt{f\lambda/1080}$$

where $f =$ the oscillator strength, and $\lambda =$ the wavelength of the absorption maximum in angstrom units. For $f = 0.2$ (corresponding to $\epsilon \cong 10^4$) and $\lambda = 2000$ A, D becomes about 0.6 A. This is sufficiently large to imply that orbitals from coordinated water molecules are involved.

Recent work suggests that when aqueous inorganic ions absorb ultraviolet light of sufficient energy an actual photo-detachment of an electron occurs, and the ejected electron becomes hydrated. The hydrated electron has been tentatively identified through flash photolysis of aqueous solutions of ions and pulse radiolysis of water; in each case the reducing entity formed has the same absorption spectrum with $\lambda_{max} \cong 7200$ A.[286,287] The ultraviolet irradiation of low-temperature aqueous alkaline glasses containing 10^{-4} M $Fe(CN)_6^{4-}$ produces a species with ESR (narrow singlet) and optical spectra ($\lambda_{max} \cong 5850$ A) identical with those attributed to trapped electrons formed on absorption of ionizing radiation by a similar glass.[288,289] Furthermore, the reducing species produced photochemically or by ionizing radiation exhibit similar relative rate constants for reaction with added scavenger (N_2O, H^+, acetone, etc.). Summarized in Table 4-11 are the estimates of the limiting yields of hydrated electron reaction with added solutes at high scavenger concentration.

Typical cations which undergo photoreduction through an electron-transfer process (and their λ_{max} values) include Hg^{2+} (1800 A), Cu^{2+} (2000 A), Pb^{2+} (2085 A), Fe^{3+} (2300 A), and Ce^{4+} (~ 3200 A). They absorb strongly ($\epsilon_{max} \sim 10^4$ at λ_{max}), and in aqueous solution the electron donor is apparently the water of hydration, for example,

$$X^n \cdot H_2O + h\nu \rightarrow [X^{n-1} \cdot H_2O^+]$$

$$[X^{n-1} \cdot H_2O^+] \xrightarrow{OH^-} X^{n-1} + H_2O + OH$$
$$\searrow X^{n-1} + OH + H^+$$

TABLE 4-11 Limiting Quantum Yields φ_0 of Hydrated Electron Reaction at High Scavenger Concentration[a]

Reaction	Wavelength, A	ϕ_0	Reference
$I^- + h\nu \rightarrow I + e^-(aq)$	2537	0.23	290
	2537	0.29	291, 292
	Ultraviolet	...	254
$Br^- + h\nu \rightarrow Br + e^-(aq)$	1849	0.34	242
	1849	0.67 (0.31)[b]	292
	2288	0.5	292
	Ultraviolet	...	254
$Cl^- + h\nu \rightarrow Cl + e^-(aq)$	1849	0.43	242
	1849	0.98 (0.46)[b]	292
$OH^- + h\nu \rightarrow OH + e^-(aq)$	1849	0.11	242
	1849	0.5 (0.15)[b]	292
	Ultraviolet	...	254
$SO_4^{2-} + h\nu \rightarrow SO_4^- + e^-(aq)$	1849	0.71	242
$Fe(CN)_6^{4-} + h\nu \rightarrow Fe(CN)_6^{3-} + e^-(aq)$	2140	0.88	157
	2288	0.89	157
	2537	1.00	157
	2537	0.67	143
	2650	0.40	157
	Ultraviolet	...	254
$CNS^- + h\nu \rightarrow CNS + e^-(aq)$	Ultraviolet	...	254
$Fe^{2+} + h\nu \rightarrow Fe^{3+} + e^-(aq)$	2537	0.062	143

[a] Summary of data collected by Dainton.[58]
[b] Jortner et al.[292] used 10^{-2} M methanol as an actinometer with $\Phi_{H_2} = 0.65$; the values in brackets are those calculated using $\Phi_{H_2} = 0.30$, which Dainton and Fowles[242] believe to be a more reliable value.

When these cations are complexed with various anions to form *ion pairs*, their absorption spectra shift toward the visible, the magnitude of the shift being almost directly proportional to the decrease in electron affinity of the anion. Thus λ_{max} for $Fe^{3+}Cl^-$, $Fe^{3+}Br^-$, and $Fe^{3+}SCN^-$ are 3200, 3800, and 4600 A, respectively.[86] This suggests that in the ion pair the anion is the electron donor and the primary act of absorption involves, for example,

$$Fe^{3+}Cl^- + h\nu \rightarrow [Fe^{2+}Cl]$$

followed by numerous reactions of the intermediate, including dissociation

$$Fe^{2+}Cl \rightarrow Fe^{2+} + Cl$$

The following ion pairs were found capable of photochemically initiating polymerization of vinyl compounds,[95] presumably by radical formation through processes analogous to the above: $Fe^{3+}OH^-$, $Fe^{3+}Cl^-$, $Fe^{3+}C_2O_4^{2-}$, $Fe^{3+}HCitr^{2-}$, $Pb^{2+}Cl^-$, and $Ce^{4+}OH^-$.

It is interesting to note that fluorescence studies with organic dyes show an efficiency of quenching in the order $I^- > CNS^- > Br^- > Cl^- > C_2O_4^{2-} > SO_4^{2-} > NO_3^- > F^-$. This is close to the order of their decreasing λ_{max}, so that the fluorescence quenching efficiency of these ions seems related to the ease of charge transfer from the ion.

4-4B   Other Types of Transitions in Ions

Absorption in ions such as MnO_4^- (4200–7000 A, $f = 0.03$) and CrO_4^{2-} (3100–4500 A, $f = 0.09$) probably involves electrons in bonding orbitals between metal and oxygen atoms, or in the case of the NO_3^- ion (2600–3200 A, $f = 10^{-4}$), between the nitrogen and oxygen atoms.

In the transition-metal cations such as Cu^{2+} and Co^{2+}, the oscillator strengths of the visible bands are of the order of 10^{-4} ($\epsilon_{max} \sim 5$). They are weak, as they are probably due to multiplet transitions involving d electrons. Such transitions are forbidden by Laporte's rule (Sec. 4-2D) but perturbations by solvent, etc., permit the weak absorptions observed. The absorption bands are sensitive to environment. Complexing the hydrated cations Cu^{2+} and Co^{2+}, for example, causes rather large shifts in their absorption maxima and increases their intensity. For example, for Cu^{2+}, $\lambda_{max} = 8100$ A, $\epsilon_{max} = 10$, whereas for $Cu(NH_3)_4^{2+}$, $\lambda_{max} = 6000$ A and $\epsilon_{max} = 50$ (see the articles by McClure[88,89] and by Ballhausen[92] for details of spectra of transition metal ions).

The trivalent rare earth ions offer a contrasting example of spectra essentially unaffected by environment, presumably because the transitions involve the deep-lying $4f$ orbitals (the absorption of hydrated Nd^{3+} ion is virtually unchanged by complexing it with EDTA).[40] Their visible absorption spectra consist of numerous sharp but weak lines with oscillator strengths of $f = 10^{-6}$ or less ($\epsilon \ll 0.05$). Transitions are weak, as they violate Laporte's rule prohibiting transitions between multiplet levels [$La^{3+}(f^0)$, $Ce^{3+}(f^1)$, $Yb^{3+}(f^{13})$, and $Lu^{3+}(f^{14})$ have no multiplet structure and do not absorb in the visible region].

4-5   ABSORPTION OF RADIATION BY CRYSTALLINE SOLIDS

The photoreactions of solids is an area of great importance which, unfortunately, is generally beyond the scope of this book. However, we shall deal with one important aspect, radiative and radiationless transitions in organic solids, in Sec. 4-10B.

We should mention here, however, that theoretical and experimental considerations of absorption spectra, luminescence, and energy-transfer processes in organic crystals have been greatly complicated by the need for extremely pure crystals and the exceptional experimental difficulty in obtaining them.* Thus Schnepp (1963)[98] states, "The fluorescence spectra of naphthalene and anthracene which have been studied for the past ten years are the result of impurities and are thus not a property of the pure crystal. Consequently, all fluorescence measurements must be carefully examined before they can be accepted as final." Similar re-evaluations apply to phosphorescence from aromatic hydrocarbon crystals, where considerations of the rapid migration and relatively long lifetimes of triplet excitations (which would favor triplet-triplet annihilation) have led Sternlicht, Nieman, and Robinson[106] to question whether phosphorescence ever occurs from absolutely pure crystals.

Finally, it is significant that Broude, Pachomova, and Prichotjko[107] discovered the fine structure and polarization ratios in absorption spectra of benzene, naphthalene, and anthracene to be affected greatly (e.g., "induced" splitting, frequency and intensity shifts) by the strain introduced when their crystals were cooled while in contact with a quartz plate. Ferguson and Schneider[108] examined a series of anthracene crystals and found that splitting of the electronic origin line varied from almost zero in some crystals to 60 cm^{-1} in others.

These observations are cited because of the perspective they give on the problems faced by investigators in this challenging field and because of their implications when considering many aspects of the photochemistry of the organic solid state.

4-6 FLUORESCENCE

In a polyatomic molecule with n atoms the potential energy function plotted versus interatomic distance generates a hypersurface with $3n - 6$ dimensions. A hyperspace of 66 dimensions would be necessary to represent completely the vibrational motions of the nuclei in an anthracene molecule. We simplify this by considering only the function along a single "critical coordinate"; this gives the curves in Fig. 4-5.

---

* Recent reviews with references to the original literature on organic crystals include the following: absorption spectra of molecular crystals, Refs. 89b, 96, 97, 98; luminescence and energy transfer, 99–105. References for liquid and solid solutions are in Sec. 4-10.

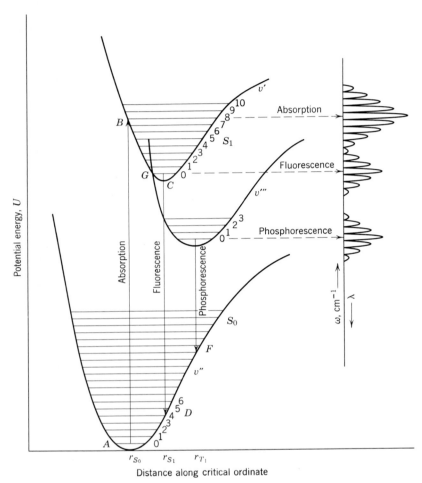

Fig. 4-5 Potential energy diagram, giving the shape of the hypersurface along a critical coordinate for the ground state S_0 and the first excited singlet S_1 and triplet T_1 states of a representative organic molecule in solution. G is a point of intersystem crossing, $S_1 \rightarrow T_1$. For convenience in representation the distances r were chosen $r_{S_0} < r_{S_1} < r_{T_1}$ so the spectra are spread out. Actually, in complex, fairly symmetrical molecules $r_{S_0} \cong r_{S_1} < r_{T_1}$ and the 0—0 absorption and fluorescence bands almost coincide, but phosphorescence bands are significantly displaced to the longer wavelengths.

Although absorption, $A \rightarrow B$, raises the molecule to a vibrationally as well as an electronically excited state, the emission of resonance fluorescence $B \rightarrow A$, often observed in diatomic gases at low pressures (Sec. 3-2A), is rare. Often the absorption bands are weak (particularly in the $S_0 \rightarrow S_1$ transition), so that pressures of 50 mm or more are necessary to observe fluorescence.[5] In gases at such pressures and in condensed systems the excited molecule collides many times with other molecules during its lifetime, and the molecule vibrationally equilibrates quickly, dropping usually to the zeroth vibrational level at room temperature. The detailed mechanism of this intermolecular vibrational energy transfer is not clearly understood but apparently it proceeds through a series of collisions rather than in one total interchange of energy (Sec. 3-2A).

The resulting fluorescence bands correspond to the transitions ($v' = 0$) $\rightarrow (v'' = v'', \ldots, 2, 1, 0)$, their relative intensities depending on the shapes and location of the Franck-Condon curves along the critical coordinate. In highly conjugated aromatic molecules excitation in the π-electron system does not alter greatly the interatomic distances, and there is pronounced overlap of absorption and fluorescence bands.[1]

In a liquid, contact with other molecules is maintained at all times so that a molecule such as anthracene with a singlet-singlet radiative lifetime of about 10^{-8} sec may be perturbed about 10^4 times before it emits fluorescence. Thus, in solution resonance fluorescence never appears, only transitions originating from the lowest vibrational levels, usually the $v' = 0$ level ($C \rightarrow D$, Fig. 4-5).

In gases the 0—0 transition in absorption and fluorescence bands should ideally coincide, with the bands shading respectively towards higher and lower frequencies (Stokes' law), as shown on the right side of Fig. 4-5. In solution, however, relaxation effects are important. Lippert et al.[295] have shown that the separation between absorption and fluorescence band maxima is small at low temperatures because molecular movements are frozen, and also at high temperatures because of violent motions. At intermediate temperatures, however, the 0—0 band separation may be large because the excited molecule relaxes into a new environment before radiating.

The distance between peaks in a fluorescence spectrum, Fig. 4-5 (see also Fig. 4-6), is a direct measure of the energy differences between the vibrational levels of the *ground state* of the fluorescing molecule. Conversely, the absorption spectrum gives the spacings of the vibrational levels in the excited state of the molecule. If, as is often the case, the spacings between the vibrational levels of the ground and excited states are similar, the fluorescence and absorption spectra bear a *mirror-image* relationship to each other. (See the excellent discussions by Bowen and Wokes,[1] Förster,[18b] and Pringsheim.[94])

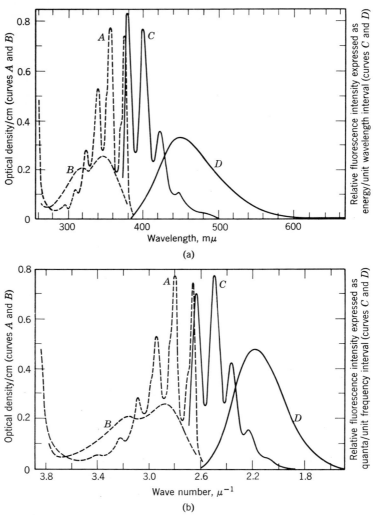

Fig. 4-6   Absorption and fluorescence spectra of anthracene in ethanol [17.2 (*A*) and 1.0 μg/ml (*C*), respectively]; absorption and fluorescence spectra of quinine bisulfate in 0.1*N* sulfuric acid [25 (*B*) and 1.0 μg/ml (*D*), respectively]. In (a) fluorescence and absorption data are plotted as a function of wavelength; in (b) the data are plotted versus wave number. Note that the "mirror image" symmetry is most evident in method (b), and it is the recommended method of plotting fluorescence yields and absorption. From Parker and Rees.[109]

In Fig. 4-6 the absorption spectrum of anthracene in ethanol (17.2 micrograms/ml) is compared with its fluorescence emission spectrum (1.0 microgram/ml). This figure is an excellent example of mirror-image symmetry and serves to illustrate a standard form of presentation of fluorescence and excitation spectra proposed by Parker and Rees.[109] They argue in favor of plotting quanta emitted per unit frequency interval versus frequency. By plotting fluorescence data in this way, one obtains a value for the integrated area under the emission curve that is directly proportional to the true fluorescence efficiency of the substance. By comparing this value with the corresponding area obtained under identical conditions for a standard substance (fluorescence "actinometer") of known absolute fluorescence quantum yield (e.g., quinine sulfate, where φ_f is 0.55[110]) one can readily obtain the unknown absolute quantum yield (cf. Sec. 7-5C-1). Recently this proposal was set forth in detail by a group of internationally recognized experts.[111]

4-6A Effect of Wavelength on the Quantum Yield of Fluorescence

Let us first consider absorption in the first band (e.g., to S_1^v, Fig. 4-1). It is observed experimentally that in liquid solutions fluorescence spectra and quantum yields, φ_f, are generally independent of the wavelength of exciting light. This suggests that vibrational relaxation must be fast relative to emission, perhaps 10^{-11} to 10^{-12} sec versus 10^{-8} to 10^{-9} sec.

As an example, Weber and Teale[114] site 26 organic compounds of widely varying structures with absolute fluorescence quantum yields ranging from unity down to 0.03. In dilute solutions all show this invariance of φ_f over a wide range of exciting wavelengths down to 2100 A. These authors point out that tautomerism, molecular association, and the presence of more than one absorbing system *within the same* molecule result in changes in φ_f with wavelength and may be detected by taking such *excitation spectra* (see below).

Two types of primary processes also could change φ_f: photochemical reactions or radiationless transitions from vibrationally excited levels of the S_1 state. These could be significant if their rates are of the same order or are faster than the vibrational relaxation processes $S_1^v \rightsquigarrow S_1$. These may be important considerations, particularly in gas-phase studies, where vibrational quenching by collisional deactivation is much less rapid than in liquids.

Finally, the fact that a compound has φ_f independent of wavelength does not preclude a constant fraction of the photoexcited molecules from undergoing photochemical reactions (or internal conversion) via a vibrationally excited ground state. Thus in some systems in which φ_f

(and φ_p) are independent of wavelength of excitation it may be incorrect to suggest, as has been proposed, that the emitting state is the *only* one which is important in photochemical reactions.

When excitation is to a second (or higher) excited state, S_2 (Fig. 4-1), fluorescence is *solely from the lowest excited state*, S_1. Thus Kasha[11,48] states that "the emitting electronic level of a given multiplicity is the lowest excited level of that multiplicity." Azulene was considered to be an exception to this rule; it has been reported to emit fluorescence only from the S_2 state.[112,113] Although these original measurements now appear to have been in error,* other exceptions may exist.

While fluorescence occurs only from the first excited level, it does not follow that in all cases of excitation to upper electronic states φ_f is independent of wavelength.[304] Thus, in quantitative studies of pure liquid benzene and some alkyl benzenes from 2700 to 1600 A, Braun, Kato, and Lipsky[275] report that the *internal conversion efficiencies* (the efficiency with which the absorbing molecule internally converts to the emitting state S_1') are *significantly* less than unity. Furthermore, *no emission* or internal conversion to the emitting state S_1 is observed from benzene or any alkyl benzene studied in the vapor phase for excitation in the long-wavelength side of the second absorption band and extending into the far ultraviolet. They proposed that upper electronic states undergo photochemical change with unit quantum efficiency in the vapor or alternatively internally convert to the ground electronic state without resultant photochemistry.

Subsequently, Pitts, Foote, and Wan[276] reported that the quantum yield of disappearance of benzene vapor is indeed 0.000 in the first absorption band but is approximately unity on irradiation in the second and third bands (see Sec. 5-7C). Whether the photochemical reaction occurred directly from the upper electronic states or a highly vibrationally excited state could not be deduced from their preliminary data, but the photochemical results offer good confirmation of the proposal of Lipsky and co-workers, which was based solely on spectroscopic data (see Sec. 4-10A for a discussion of energy-transfer processes with benzene).

A useful consequence of the constancy of φ_f with exciting wavelength in solutions is that under the proper experimental conditions the fluorescence excitation spectrum of a solute in a very dilute solution corresponds closely to its absorption spectrum in more concentrated solutions. Thus, as Parker points out,[115] the rate of emission of fluorescence is given by

$$I_f = [I_0(1 - e^{-\epsilon cl})\varphi_f] \tag{4-2}$$

---

* Unpublished studies of G. W. Robinson suggest that the fluorescence attributed to azulene was from an impurity.

where I_f = total fluorescence emitted per unit time, I_0 = total flux of exciting light, c = concentration of solute, l = optical depth of solution (cm), ϵ = molar extinction coefficient of solute, and φ_f = quantum yield of fluorescence. In very dilute solutions the absorption is small, and Eq. 4-2 reduces to

$$I_f = (I_0 2.3\epsilon c l \varphi_f) \tag{4-3}$$

In a given dilute solution, if φ_f is independent of wavelength and I_0 is held constant as the wavelength of exciting light is varied, then I_f is proportional

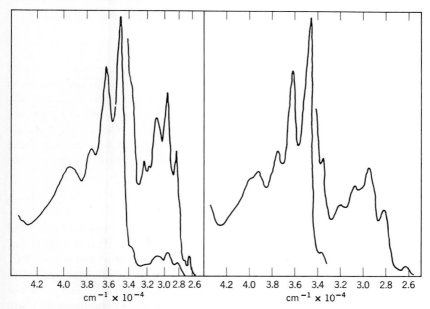

Fig. 4-7   Excitation (left) and absorption (right) spectra of 1,2-benzanthracene in ethanol. The total fluorescence emitted was taken over the region 4080–4450 A. From Parker.[115,116]

to ϵ, and total fluorescence at a given wavelength will vary with the extinction coefficient.

Figure 4-7 compares the fluorescence excitation spectrum of a very dilute solution of 1,2-benzanthracene in ethanol with its absorption spectrum (determined by conventional means in a much more concentrated solution).[115,116] Clearly spectrofluorimetry makes it possible to obtain absorption spectra of solutes at much lower concentrations than conventional absorption techniques. Furthermore, as Parker points out, the absorption spectrum of one fluorescent compound can be determined in a mixture of absorbing species by determining the total fluorescence emitted at the fluorescence frequencies characteristic of that compound. The analytical and photochemical applications of this highly useful technique are clear.[117]

Parker has adapted his spectrofluorimeter to measure longer-lived emission such as phosphorescence and delayed emission. Use of this spectrophosphorimeter, particularly in conjunction with accurate measurement of the intensity of the exciting light, has led to better understanding of the mechanism of radiative and non-radiative transitions between excited states.[115] Haugen and Marcus[118] also have described a spectrofluorophosphorimeter of elegant design and wide versatility.

4-6B   Radiative Lifetimes

It is useful to consider the lifetime of an excited state relative to the rates of competing intramolecular (as well as intermolecular) deactivation processes, such as internal conversion and intersystem crossing. Actually one must take care to differentiate between the "average life" of a molecule in an excited state and its mean "radiative lifetime." Consider a molecule in excited state S_1, Fig. 4-1. In the special case that fluorescence is the *sole mode of decay* (i.e., $\varphi_f = 1.00$) the *mean radiative lifetime* τ_0 (or simply the *natural lifetime*) is given by

$$\tau_0 = \frac{1}{A_{nm}} \qquad (3\text{-}46)$$

where A_{nm} is the Einstein probability of spontaneous emission, and the units of τ_0 are seconds per transition (see Sec. 3-1C-2). The average life of an excited state is determined, however, by the sum of the rates of *all* processes depopulating that state. Thus, in cases where other unimolecular or bimolecular processes compete with fluorescence (i.e., where φ_f is not unity), the *observed* radiative lifetime τ, determined experimentally, will be proportionately less than the mean radiative lifetime.

We saw in Secs. 3-1C-1 and 2 that the radiative lifetime of an excited state bears an inverse relation to the transition probability of absorption to that state. Thus, as an approximation for molecules absorbing in the near ultraviolet we found that

$$\tau_{\text{calc}} \text{ (sec)} \cong \frac{10^{-4}}{\epsilon_{\max}} \qquad (3\text{-}48)$$

Strongly absorbing compounds have short radiative lifetimes. For example, the first singlet $\pi \to \pi^*$ transition of anthracene originating at about 3785 A is allowed and has $\epsilon_{\max} =$ about 10^4. This corresponds to a *calculated* natural radiative lifetime of about 10^{-8} sec. Benzophenone absorbs in approximately the same region, but the transition is $n \to \pi^*$ and is forbidden, so that $\epsilon_{\max}$ is only 150 at 3325 A; τ of this $^1(n, \pi^*)$

state is calculated as about 10^{-6} sec, 100 times longer than the $^1(\pi, \pi^*)$ state of anthracene. Benzophenone is an example where the calculation is misleading; the *actual* lifetime of $(C_6H_5)_2CO$ singlet in solution must be much less than 10^{-6} sec (about 10^{-8} to 10^{-9} sec) because φ intersystem crossing is unity (see below). Saturated aldehydes and ketones have ϵ_{max} of the order of 10–20 for the $S_0 \rightarrow S_1$ transition, so the natural radiative lifetime of these $^1(n, \pi^*)$ states is *calculated* to be relatively long, approximately 10^{-5} sec.

The long lifetimes of $^1(n, \pi^*)$ states relative to $^1(\pi, \pi^*)$ states have an important correlation with observed differences in the photochemistry of these substance. For example, radiationless transitions to the triplet state are favored by the longer lifetimes of the (n, π^*) state. We shall consider this in more detail later.

4-6C Effect of Physical State

Not only are the fluorescence efficiency and the shape of the fluorescence spectrum affected by the physical state of the molecule, the *nature* of the luminescence of organic molecules may also be profoundly affected. Thus at low temperatures in solid solutions of clear "glasses" many complex aromatic compounds phosphoresce as well as fluoresce. We shall discuss this important subject in the next section, confining our remarks here to fluorescence.

The quantum yield of fluorescence of an organic compound is usually highly dependent on its physical state. Pure liquids have very low efficiencies because of self-quenching effects. For example, the fluorescence of pure crystalline anthracene, evident just below its melting point, vanishes on liquefaction.[94] Figure 4-8 shows the effect of the physical state of a polyatomic molecule upon its fluorescence spectrum. Spectra are shown schematically for (a) benzene vapor at high pressure, (b) solid at $-180°C$, (c) solid at $0°C$, (d) liquid at $0°C$, (e), (f), (g) in solution in ethanol, 30%, 10%, and 4%, respectively. Vibrational band structure is shown by the vapor and the solid at $-180°$ with the bands of the solid shifted appreciably to the red, a general phenomenon. Solvent effects are interesting in that as the solution becomes progressively more dilute the positions of the bands shift back to the blue until with 4% benzene in ethanol (curve g) they fall almost directly below those of the vapor (curve a), and the spectrum, though lacking fine structure, resembles that of the vapor. It is interesting that in dropping from $-180°$ to $-259°C$ (not shown on Fig. 4-8) there is an increase in fine structure in the absorption bands, but no improvement in resolution occurs in the fluorescence spectrum.[94] Just as in the vapor, the fluorescence spectrum of crystalline benzene is independent of the

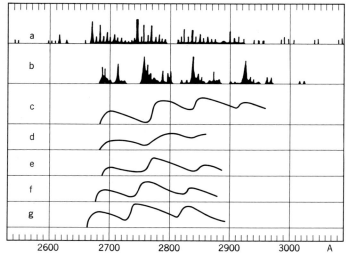

Fig. 4-8   Effect of physical state on the fluorescence spectrum of benzene. (a) Vapor;
(b) solid at −180°C; (c) solid at 0°C; (d) liquid at 0°C; (e), (f), (g) 30, 10, and 4%
solutions, respectively, in ethanol; Taken directly from Pringsheim,[94] p. 402; originally
from Kronenberger and Pringsheim.[120]

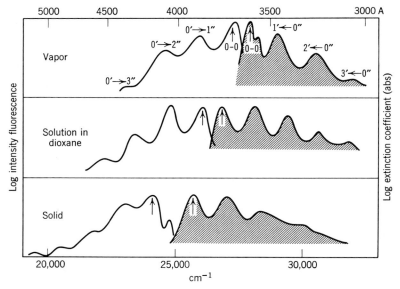

Fig. 4-9   Absorption (shaded curves) and fluorescence spectra of anthracene in vapor,
solution, and solid phases. Arrows indicate the 0—0 bands. Note the red shift and
increased separation of the 0—0 bands in going to the solid phase. Other vibronic
bands are shown for the vapor. From Bowen,[5] p. 162.

wavelength of the light absorbed. The same emission spectrum was obtained by using the ultraviolet continuum from a hydrogen discharge tube, the full mercury arc, and monochromatic 2537 A radiation.

Figure 4-9 shows both the absorption and the emission spectra of anthracene in three physical states.[5] Both spectra shift toward the red in going to condensed media. Furthermore, the gap between the two respective 0—0 bands increases from about 150 cm^{-1} in the vapor to 300 cm^{-1} and 750 cm^{-1} for the solution and the crystal, respectively.

4-7 THE TRIPLET STATE

It is interesting, and somewhat surprising, that the highly significant role of the triplet state in the spectroscopy of organic molecules has become apparent only in the last two decades. Indeed, general understanding and appreciation of the importance of triplets as intermediates in *photochemical* reactions began as late as 1960. Today studies of triplet phenomena are most active, ranging from pure spectroscopy to key areas of molecular biology. We shall start with a brief review of the history of some of the fascinating deductive and experimental efforts in molecular spectroscopy that led to the conclusion that the phosphorescence of complex organic molecules arises from triplet states.

Historically the first spectroscopic assignment of a singlet-triplet transition in a "complex" organic molecule appears to have been that of Snow and Allsop, who in 1934 suggested it for a weak absorption band of ethylene.[121] In a chemical sense Bäckström[122] as early as 1934 suggested that the hydrogen-abstracting species in the photoreduction of benzophenone by alcohols was, in his terms, the "biradical":

$$(C_6H_5)_2CO + h\nu \rightarrow \quad \begin{matrix} C_6H_5 \\ \diagdown \\ \diagup \\ C_6H_5 \end{matrix} \dot{C}-\dot{O}$$
(I)

This species, (I), we now identify as the benzophenone triplet, but this does not affect the validity or timeliness of Bäckström's original arguments.

It was, however, the pioneering spectroscopic studies starting in the late 1930's of Lewis and his collaborators in the U.S. and Terenin in the U.S.S.R. that demonstrated the generality and significance of triplet states of complex molecules. We shall consider these after first reviewing the nature of the triplet state.

We discussed earlier for atoms and diatomic molecules the spectroscopic origin of triplet states and their relationship to the corresponding singlet states. Similar considerations apply to polyatomic organic molecules.

Most of those that are chemically stable contain an even number of electrons which are paired, and their ground states are singlet. Photoexcitation raises one electron to a higher quantum state in which its spin can remain antiparallel to its "partner," so that the multiplicity is still singlet, or it may become parallel to its partner, so that the multiplicity is three, and a set of triplet energy levels is formed.

The coupling of electron spin and orbital angular momentum is strong in heavy atoms such as mercury (Sec. 2-7A-1), and there is an appreciable energy gap between these levels (cf. the separation of the $^3P_2$, $^3P_1$, and $^3P_0$ states of mercury, Fig. 2-10). However, most organic molecules are made up of atoms in the first row. These are relatively light; consequently spin-orbit coupling is small, and the three levels in effect merge into a single triplet state.

Hund's rule (Sec. 2-6) applies to polyatomic molecules as well as atoms, so that triplet states have lower energies than their corresponding singlet states (compare S_0, S_1, and T_1 in Fig. 4-1). Recently, however, cases are claimed in which S_1 lies *below* T_1 because of strong coupling between excited states.

Furthermore, the atomic selection rule prohibiting a change in multiplicity in a radiative transition between states (Sec. 2-7A-1) also applies to organic molecules. The total electron spin angular momentum S is independently quantized, and its value must be conserved in a radiative transition. Thus in most organic molecules the only strong absorption and emission are singlet-singlet in character, the transition $S_0 + h\nu \rightarrow T_1$ being prohibited.

However, we saw that, as the atomic number of the excited atom increased, coupling between the spin angular momentum and the orbital angular momentum vectors began to occur (j-j coupling), and the selection rules for spin conservation in radiative atomic transitions broke down. Similarly the introduction of a heavy atom into the skeleton of an absorbing molecule or the solvent may cause a breakdown of the spin conservation rule for molecules, facilitate a change in multiplicity, and permit weak $S_0 \rightarrow T_1$ absorption to be observed. (However, this is not a necessary criterion; cf. Sec. 4-2D concerning singlet-triplet mixing.)

4-7A Phosphorescence and the Triplet State*

The technique of observing the luminescent afterglow of organic molecules by dispersing them and "fixing" them in a rigid medium

---

* For excellent historical reviews and discussions see Pringsheim,[94] Ermolaev,[103] and Kasha and McGlynn.[123] Note that Pringsheim uses the term "slow fluorescence" for the phenomenon that Lewis and Kasha, and Terenin and Ermolaev, describe as phosphorescence. We use the latter terminology.

originated in 1895, when Wiedemann and Schmidt observed that liquid
dye solutions showing only normal fluorescence could be made to give
off a luminescent "afterglow" by the addition of gelatin.[124]

Since then the technique of studying the luminescence of organic
compounds by distributing them in rigid matrices such as boric acid glass
for room-temperature studies, or in solvents such as a mixture of ether,
pentane, and alcohol (EPA) to make clear, "glass-like" solid solutions at
liquid-nitrogen temperatures, has become widely employed.[125,126]

It has been generally known that three distinct types of luminescence
could occur in complex molecules and that molecular environment was
crucial in determining the relative extent of each type. Thus, at room
temperature most organic compounds did not fluoresce strongly as pure
liquids or in liquid solutions, and no luminescent afterglow was observed
except in unusual circumstances (e.g., biacetyl vapor or in solution).
However, when the system was cooled and clear, glassy solutions were
formed, in addition to normal fluorescence, which usually was enhanced,
the following two distinct types of afterglow were generally identified:

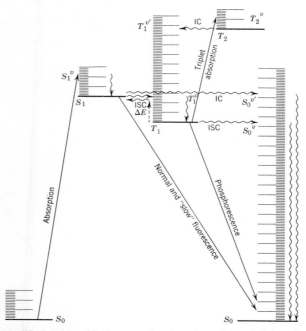

Fig. 4-10 Modified Jablonski diagram showing the origin of "slow fluorescence,"
phosphorescence, and triplet-triplet absorption. Radiationless transitions are indicated
by wavy lines (IC = internal conversion, ISC = intersystem crossing). T_1 is Jablonski's
"metastable state."

1. A long-lived emission (molecular "slow fluorescence") having the same spectrum as normal fluorescence but with a relatively long lifetime (up to 1 sec or more) that was *temperature dependent* (recall that the natural lifetime of normal fluorescence is *not*). At low temperature such "slow fluorescence" could be effectively "trapped" in that the exciting light could be removed, the emission would cease, and then on warming up the system rapidly the luminescence could be emitted as a bright flash of light (*thermoluminescence*).

2. A relatively long-lived molecular "phosphorescence" emission with a natural life *independent* of temperature and with a spectrum always displaced to the red from fluorescence. This emission was rarely observed in liquids (again, biacetyl is a notable exception), but was a general phenomenon with organic compounds in "glassy" solvents at low temperature.

In 1935 Jablonski rationalized these three types of luminescence by introducing into the usual molecular energy-level diagram a "metastable" state, described as a tautomeric form of the ground state, which lay just below the lowest excited singlet level and from which the longer-wavelength, relatively long-lived phosphorescence originated.[2] See Fig. 4-10.

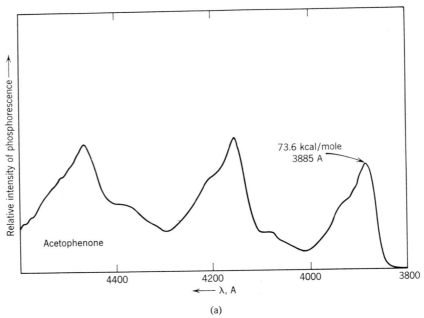

(a)

Fig. 4-11 Phosphorescence spectra in hydrocarbon solvents. From Herkstroeter, Lamola, and Hammond.[150]

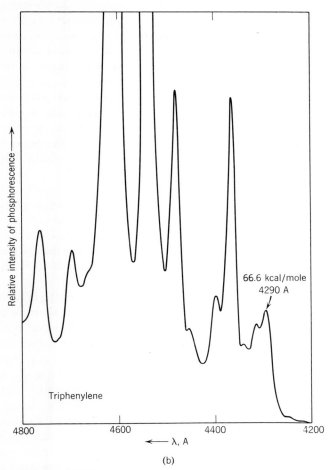

(b)

His theory was essentially that which is held today except that his proposed "metastable" state is now accepted as being the lowest triplet level
in the molecule.

In 1941 Lewis, Lipkin, and Magel proved that molecular phosphorescent
spectra were uniquely distinct from fluorescent spectra.[126]   By intense
irradiation of a sample of fluorescein in EPA glass at − 180° they were able
to put 80% of the absorbing molecules into the lowest triplet state and
demonstrate the phenomenon we know as triplet-triplet absorption
$(T_1 + h\nu \rightarrow T_2)$.

The authors offered two alternative explanations of the nature of the
"P state" (phosphorescing state).   One was that it might be a highly

vibrationally excited level of the ground state. They also said, "The second reasonable assumption is that in the P state the atomic configuration is the same as in the N state (ground electronic state), but that one is an electromer of the other, such as a triplet state (biradical), which has a low probability of returning to the normal state because of quantum inhibitions."[126]

In 1943, Terenin advanced his reasons for the concept of the triplet (biradical) nature of the metastable (phosphorescent) state of aromatic molecules.[127] Then in 1944 Lewis and Kasha[128] published a comprehensive study of the molecular phosphorescence of almost one hundred compounds and established the generality and significance of this type of emission for many types of organic molecules. Furthermore, they presented strong arguments that Jablonski's "metastable state" was indeed the lowest triplet.

Figure 4-11 (pp 286–287) shows the phosphorescence spectra of typical hydrocarbon and carbonyl compounds recently determined in hydrocarbon solvents at 77°K by Herkstroeter, Lamola, and Hammond.[150] Spectra such as these were used to establish accurately the triplet-state energies of a series of selected sensitizers for experiments on triplet energy transfer in solution (Table 4-13, Sec. 4-8A). The position of the 0—0 band, which establishes the $T_1 \rightarrow S_0$ energy difference, is indicated.

Let us now discuss the observed luminescence phenomena in terms of the Jablonski diagram, Fig. 4-10, equating T_1, the lowest triplet, to his "metastable state" (see also Fig. 4-5, the potential energy curves for states S_0, S_1, and T_1, and Fig. 4-1). Consider the lowest singlet-singlet transition, $S_0 \rightarrow S_1^v$, in an aromatic molecule at $-190°C$ dissolved in a clear glassy solvent (e.g., EPA). After excitation to the lowest singlet S_1^v (and vibrational equilibration), the molecule can, after about 10^{-8} to 10^{-9} sec, emit normal fluorescence, return to a highly vibrationally excited ground state, $S^v \rightarrow S_0^{v'}$ by internal conversion (IC), or undergo an intersystem crossing (ISC), passing over to the lower-lying triplet state T_1^v, where it will equilibrate rapidly to T_1. A molecule in the lowest triplet state T_1 is effectively "trapped" there, since radiative return to the ground state, $T_1 \rightarrow S_0^v$, is forbidden, and in order to fluoresce the molecule must acquire thermal energy equal to $\Delta E(S_1 \rightarrow T_1)$, which is improbable at low temperatures; see Fig. 4-10. It remains there until it (1) emits the forbidden radiation, molecular phosphorescence, which is at a longer wavelength than normal fluorescence, since $\Delta E(T_1 \rightarrow S_0) < \Delta E(S_1 \rightarrow S_0)$; (2) acquires enough thermal energy to go back to the S_1 state and emit "slow fluorescence"; or (3) undergoes another intersystem crossing, this time to a highly vibrationally excited ground state S_0^v, which subsequently rapidly undergoes vibrational equilibration to the ground state S_0. Thus under favorable conditions (i.e, low temperatures, rigid medium, absence of quenchers) emission of phosphorescence often can compete favorably with "slow fluorescence" and intersystem crossing.

Although the natural radiative lifetime of phosphorescence is independent of temperature, the actual observed rate of decay of the triplet state is the sum of all competing processes, phosphorescence, intersystem crossing back to the excited state S_1, intersystem crossing to the ground state S_0^v, and bimolecular reactions with other substances. To the extent that the latter occur, the observed lifetime will be shorter than the natural lifetime, and, if the temperature is varied, the phosphorescence lifetime will *appear* to be temperature dependent.

4-7B Magnetic Properties of the Triplet State

A direct identification of the phosphorescent state with the triplet state is by determination of its paramagnetism. In the ground state of most organic molecules, all the electrons are "paired" and the molecule is diamagnetic. However, a polyatomic molecule in the triplet state would be expected to be paramagnetic, since it would have two electrons with parallel spins; these could interact strongly with an external magnetic field.

Lewis and Calvin[129] and later Lewis, Calvin, and Kasha[130] observed that a specimen of fluorescein in boric acid glass became paramagnetic under intense continuous irradiation. They estimated the steady-state concentration of fluorescein in the triplet state and from the measured paramagnetism calculated a value of its absolute paramagnetic susceptibility that was in reasonable agreement with theory.

In a definitive experiment, Evans (1955)[131] confirmed and extended these observations. He showed that the lifetimes of the phosphorescent decay of fluorescein (I), 1-hydroxy-2-naphthoic acid (II), and triphenylene (III),

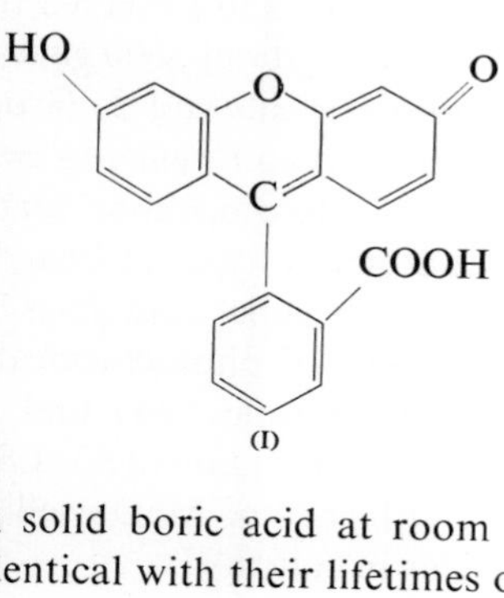

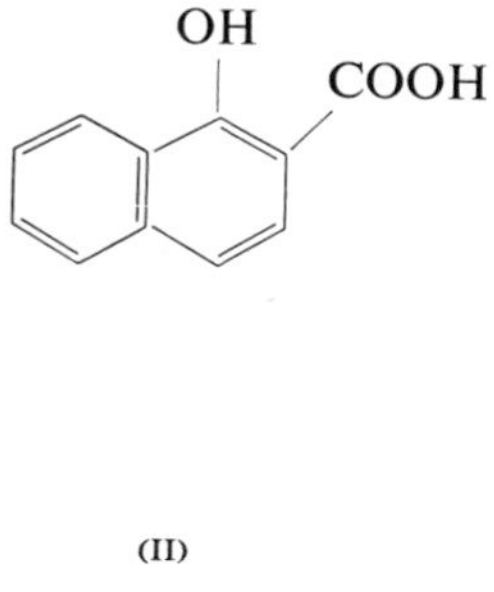

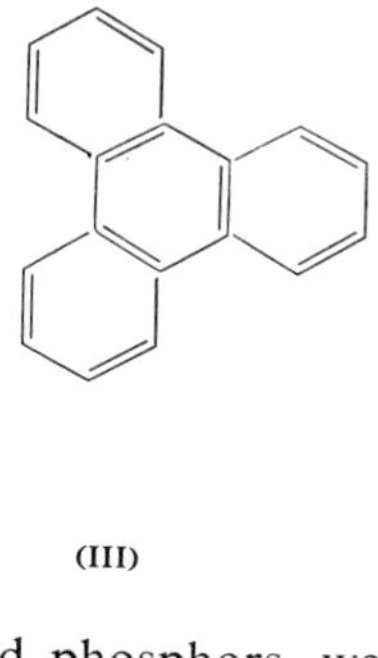

in solid boric acid at room temperature as boric acid phosphors, were identical with their lifetimes of decay of paramagnetism.[131] This is shown in Fig. 4-12 for triphenylene. The exponential nature of the decay of the phosphorescence and the paramagnetism is good evidence that both arise in a unimolecular process of a triplet state rather than from a slow recombination of an electron and radical (or two free radicals) formed photochemically. Thus, the observed phosphorescent decay of triphenylene (Fig. 4-12) follows the expression $I = I_0 \exp(-t/11.5)$ with $t = $ time in seconds. For recombination of electrons and free radicals in similar organic compounds in glasses at low temperature[132,133] the expression has the form $I = I_0/t^m$, where $m \sim 1$.

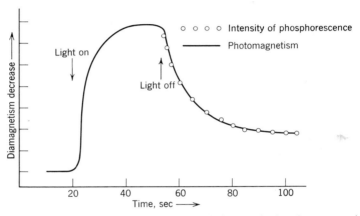

Fig. 4-12   Comparison of photomagnetism and decay of phosphorescence in triphenylene in boric acid "glass" at room temperature. From Evans.[131]

Subsequently the triplet state of naphthalene was unambiguously detected by Hutchison and Mangum,[134] who irradiated the compound in the form of a single crystal of a solid solution in durene and observed the resulting electron spin resonance (ESR) signal at $g = 2$ (about 3000 gauss), corresponding to the transition $\Delta m = \pm 1$. Van der Waals and de Groot have carried out ESR studies at lower magnetic field strengths where $g = 4$ (about 1500 gauss) and have shown triplet-triplet ESR transitions corresponding to $\Delta m = \pm 2$ in naphthalene and other aromatic hydrocarbons.[135] A similar technique was used by Piette, Sharp, Kuwana, and Pitts to detect triplet resonance in irradiated solid solutions of photochemically "abnormal" aromatic ketones, such as p-phenylbenzophenone and p-aminobenzophenone[136,265] (see Secs. 4-11 and 5-9A). Low-field ESR techniques also have been used by Farmer, Gardner, and McDowell to demonstrate unequivocally triplet energy transfer in solids.[137]

4-7C   Spectroscopic Studies of the Triplet State

Porter and Windsor (1953)[138] first applied the technique of flash spectroscopy[139-141] to the photolysis of aromatic molecules in solution and, in a wide variety of polynuclear compounds, photographed transient absorption spectra which could be attributed to absorption from the lowest triplet level. Figure 4-13 is taken from their original paper and shows the

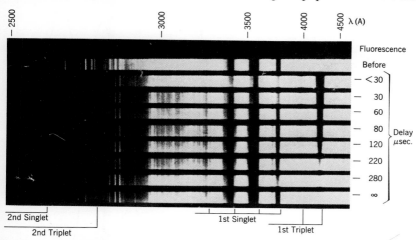

Fig. 4-13   Triplet-triplet absorption by flash photolysis of $10^{-5} M$ anthracene in hexane. From Porter and Windsor.[138a]

rise and decay of bands due to absorption by the anthracene triplet. In a series of subsequent researches utilizing flash spectroscopic techniques, Porter and his co-workers established the generality of aromatic triplets as intermediates in the gas phase as well as in solution.[141,142]

There have been several detailed low-temperature studies of triplet-triplet absorption in rigid media (EPA), including those of McClure[60] and Craig and Ross.[144] Values of the rate of triplet decay, as determined by the decrease in $T_1 \rightarrow T_2$ absorption, were in substantial agreement with those made by determining the rate of decay of phosphorescence.

Figure 4-14 shows the triplet-triplet absorption spectra of a number of compounds, including anthracene, taken in the relatively simple but elegant low-temperature irradiation cell of Craig and Ross.[144]

Triplet-singlet emission in fluid solutions has been reported by Parker and Hatchard.[145] Using a highly sensitive spectrophosphorimeter, they investigated quantitatively the delayed luminescence from ethanol and glycerol solutions of eosin and found two bands, one attributable to

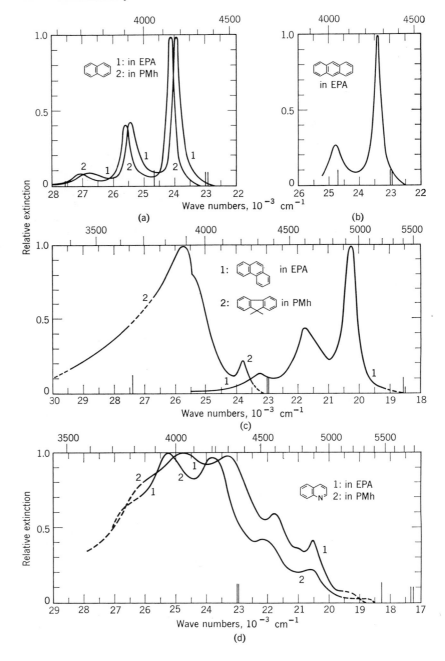

(a)

(b)

(c)

(d)

Wave numbers, 10^{-3} cm^{-1}

Relative extinction

1: in EPA
2: in PMh

in EPA

1:    in EPA
2:    in PMh

1: in EPA
2: in PMh

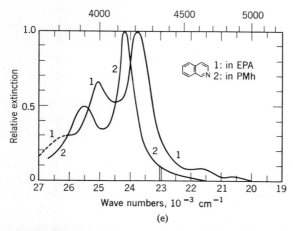

(e)

Fig. 4-14   Triplet-triplet absorption spectra of naphthalene (a), anthracene (b), phen-anthrene (c)-1, fluorene (c)-2, quinoline (d), and isoquinoline (e) in rigid matrices at 77°K. Dotted lines indicate reduced accuracy of determination. Long vertical lines along the bases of the figures show the positions of mercury lines. From Craig and Ross.[144]

$T_1 \rightarrow S_0$ emission (phosphorescence) and one to delayed fluorescence arising from $T_1 \rightarrow S_1$ thermal activation followed by $S_1 \rightarrow S_0 + h\nu$.[145]*

4-8   INTRAMOLECULAR PRIMARY PHYSICAL PROCESSES OF (n, π^*) AND (π, π^*) STATES

Having established the identity of the phosphorescent state with the lowest spectroscopic triplet state in an organic molecule, we shall now consider the possible paths for the dissipation of the energy of the excited singlet produced in the act of absorption. We will *assume that no photo-chemical reaction is involved*; we will deal only with primary photo-physical processes in our discussions in this section.

We should preface our remarks by noting that during the last ten to fifteen years there has been a great deal of controversy in the literature on primary photophysical processes. This of course reflects an active and

---

* An interesting discovery from Parker's detailed eosin studies is that the quantum yield of formation of the triplet state of the dye in a given solvent, φ_T, remains fairly constant when temperature and viscosity vary over a wide range. Furthermore, although the triplet yield φ_T is less in ethanol than in the more viscous glycerol at $-20°$, it appears that the rate of the *radiationless* $T_1 \rightsquigarrow S_0$ intersystem crossing is virtually the same in both solvents.[115] Viscosity independence of this process also has been suggested for anthracene.[146]

challenging research area. However, it also reflects the great experimental problems encountered in obtaining reliable experimental values of such important quantities as absolute quantum yields of fluorescence and phosphorescence, rates of radiationless decay of triplets, etc. Reported experimental values have fluctuated widely and, in many cases, still are not established.

We have tried to formulate a reasonably coherent picture of the important aspects of the subject and, where serious disagreement in theory or experiment occurs, to note it and include our evaluation of the problem from the viewpoint of the photochemist.

Naphthalene and benzophenone have been chosen to illustrate liquid- and solid-phase spectroscopic and photochemical phenomena because they represent two broad classes of aromatic compounds with widely different spectroscopic and photochemical properties, those having their lowest excited states (π, π^*), and those with (n, π^*). Furthermore, the parent compounds and many derivatives have been widely studied and furnish excellent examples of the effects of molecular structure on the chemistry of the excited state. We should note, however, that there is a substantial disagreement in reported values of φ_f for naphthalene, 0.55^{155} versus $0.29,^{103}$ although there is excellent agreement on φ_p for benzophenone, 0.73^{155} and $0.74.^{103}$ We shall use φ_f for naphthalene $= 0.29$ because this value was determined by the same techniques as the other quantum yields in Table 4-12. The lower value also seems best for naphthalene in view of the great difficulties experienced in removing the impurity, β-naphthalene. Thus, in "pure" crystals the latter substance apparently acts as a triplet exciton trap, giving off delayed fluorescence that could be mistaken for normal fluorescence and lead to high values (see Refs. 99 and 106 for discussion).

4-8A Energy Levels and Lifetimes of (n, π^*) and (π, π^*) States

We have already noted that, with the exception of benzene and naphthalene (where the transition is forbidden by molecular symmetry), the first $\pi \rightarrow \pi^*$ absorption bands of aromatic hydrocarbons are intense in relation to the $n \rightarrow \pi^*$ transitions of aromatic carbonyl compounds. Thus the (π, π^*) states generally have correspondingly *shorter* lifetimes than (n, π^*) states. Furthermore, the energy differences $\Delta E(S_1 \rightarrow T_1)$ between the lowest excited (π, π^*) singlet and triplet states are generally much larger in the aromatic hydrocarbons than the (n, π^*) states of the carbonyl systems. We shall see that these facts have strong bearing on the pronounced differences in the observed spectroscopy and photochemistry of these two major classes of compounds.

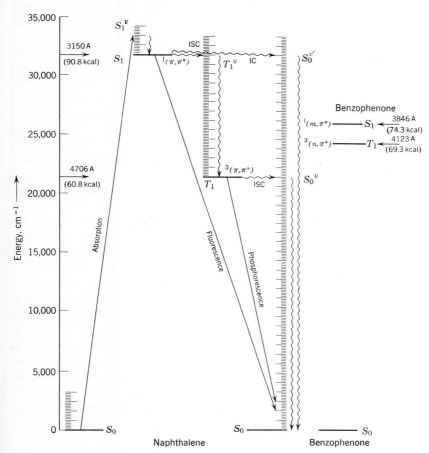

Fig. 4-15 Energy level diagram and transitions for naphthalene with levels of the S_1 and T_1 benzophenone indicated.

The possible primary photophysical processes of naphthalene and the absolute values of the energies of the lowest excited states of naphthalene and benzophenone are shown in Fig. 4-15. The $S_1 \rightarrow T_1$ energy gaps are typical in magnitude for normal aromatic hydrocarbons compared to normal aromatic ketones. Thus, values of $\Delta E(S_1 \rightarrow T_1)$ are 8500, 10,490, 11,400, and 7200 cm^{-1} for benzene, naphthalene, anthracene, and phenanthrene, compared to only 1800 and 1650 cm^{-1} for the aromatic ketones benzophenone and acetophenone, respectively.

There are, however, important exceptions to these generalizations. Thus, $\Delta E(S_1 \rightarrow T_1)$ is as small as 5000 cm^{-1} for the aromatic hydrocarbon triphenylene (see Sec. 4-7B) and as large as 5575 and 6445 cm^{-1} for the aromatic ketones p-phenylbenzophenone and β-acetylnaphthalene. We shall see that these "abnormal" aromatic compounds also show unique spectroscopic and photochemical behavior that can be attributed to the differences in the energies and reactivities of their excited states as compared to those of normal aromatic hydrocarbons and carbonyl compounds (Sec. 4-11).

Listed in Table 4-12 are the spectroscopic properties of a series of aromatic compounds with (π, π^*) and (n, π^*) excited states. The absolute values of φ_p and φ_f of the pure compound are given along with the energies of the S_1 and T_1 states and the lifetimes of observed phosphorescence. These results, cited by Ermolaev,[103] are for alcohol-ether as the rigid solvent at 77°K. The table is divided into triplet energy *donors* and triplet energy *acceptors* in sensitized phosphorescence experiments. We need not concern ourselves with the distinction here (see Sec. 4-10B-3 and Table 4-26 for quantum yields of *sensitized* phosphorescence, $\varphi_p{}^s$).

In Table 4-13 are the triplet-state energies of a variety of compounds determined from the 0″—0′ band of their phosphorescence spectra at 77°. These compounds are used as sensitizers for chemical and spectroscopic studies of triplet energy transfer in solution, the important technique developed particularly by Hammond and his associates.[156,260] In order to obtain a consistent set of energy levels to apply to their solution studies, which were generally in benzene, Herkstroeter, Lamola, and Hammond used hydrocarbon solvents throughout their spectroscopic work and thus avoided possibly significant solvent shifts. For comparison, included in Table 4-13 are some literature values for polar solvents, including the set of values of Ermolaev (Table 4-12). The agreement between the two sets of results is excellent.

4-8B Radiationless Transitions; Intersystem Crossing and Internal Conversion

Let us now consider an aromatic molecule dispersed in a rigid solvent at 77°K. Absorption raises it to its first excited singlet state $S_1{}^v$ (refer to Fig. 4-15). We will continue to assume that *no photochemical process* occurs at this wavelength and no bimolecular quenching such as triplet energy transfer occurs. The molecule first very rapidly equilibrates vibrationally to the zeroth vibrational level, $S_1{}^0$. The electronically excited molecule $S_1{}^0$ now has the following ways to redistribute its energy: (1) fluorescence $(S_1{}^0 \rightarrow S_0 + h\nu_1)$; (2) radiationless *internal conversion* (IC) to a highly vibrationally excited ground state $(S_1{}^0 \rightsquigarrow S_0{}^{v'})$; (3) radiationless *intersystem crossing* (ISC) to the lower triplet state $(S_1{}^0 \rightsquigarrow T_1{}^v)$.

TABLE 4-12 Spectroscopic Properties of a Series of Aromatic Compounds in Alcohol-Ether Glass at 77°K (Included Are Energies of Lowest Singlet and Triplet States, Absolute Quantum Yields of Phosphorescence and Fluorescence, and Observed Lifetime of Phosphorescence)[a]

Compound	E_{T_1}, kcal/mole	T_1, cm^{-1}	S_1, cm^{-1}	τ (phos), sec (observed)	φ_p/φ_f	φ_p	φ_f[c]
"Energy Donors"							
Benzaldehyde	71.3	24,950	26,750	1.5×10^{-3}	>1000	0.49	0.00
Benzophenone	69.3	24,250	26,000	4.7×10^{-3}	>1000	.74	.00
Acetophenone	73.6	25,750	27,500	2.3×10^{-3}	>1000	.62	.00
Ethyl phenyl ketone	74.8	26,150	28,000	3.8×10^{-3}	>1000	...	...
p-Chlorobenzaldehyde	70.8	24,750	...	...	>1000	...	...
o-Chlorobenzaldehyde	69.6	24,350	...	...	>1000	...	...
m-Iodobenzaldehyde	70.8	24,750	26,250	6.5×10^{-4}	>1000	.64	.00
Anthrone	71.9	25,150	27,000	1.5×10^{-3}	>1000	...	...
Xanthrone	70.9	24,800	27,000	2×10^{-2}	>1000	...	...
Anthraquinone	62.8	21,950	...	...	>1000	...	...
Triphenylamine	70.0	24,500	29,000	7×10^{-1}	15	...	...
Carbazole	70.3	24,600	29,500	7.6	0.55	...	...
Phenanthrene	62.0	21,700	28,900	3.3	1.1	.13$_5$	.12
"Energy Acceptors"[b]							
Naphthalene	60.8	21,250	31,750	2.3	0.09	.03	.29
Octodeuteronaphthalene	61.2	21,400	31,850	9.5	0.21	.06	.28
1-Methylnaphthalene	60.0	21,000	31,450	2.1	0.05	.02$_3$	.43
1-Chloronaphthalene	59.2	20,700	31,360	2.9×10^{-1}	5.2	.16	.03
1-Bromonaphthalene	59.0	20,650	31,280	1.8×10^{-2}	164	.14	.00
1-Iodonaphthalene	58.6	20,500	31,000	2.0×10^{-3}	>1000	.20	.00
Quinoline	62.0	21,700	31,900	1.4	1.9	.10	.05$_3$
Biphenyl	65.7	23,000	33,500	3.1	0.8	.17	.21
Decadeuterobiphenyl	66.0	23,100	33,650	11.3	1.9	.34	.18

[a] Adapted from a review article by Ermolaev[103] (see this article for original references).
[b] These compounds demonstrate sensitized phosphorescence.[103]
[c] The quantum yield of fluorescence of 9,10-di-n-propylanthracene is 1.00 under these conditions. λ_{excit} = 3030, 3340, or 3650 A.

TABLE 4-13 Triplet-State Energies from Phosphorescence Spectra in Rigid Hydrocarbon Solvents at 77°K[a]

	Triplet Energy,[b] E_{T_1}, kcal/mole	
Compound	Hydrocarbon Solvent[c]	Polar Solvent[d]
Propiophenone	74.6	
Xanthone	74.2[e] in MP	70.9[f]
Acetophenone	73.6	76.3,[g] 73.6[f]
1,3,5-Triacetylbenzene	73.3	
Isobutyrophenone	73.1	
1,3-Diphenyl-2-propanone	72.2	
Benzaldehyde	71.9	71.3[f]
Triphenylmethyl phenyl ketone	70.8	
Carbazole	70.1	70,[h] 70.3[f]
Diphenylene oxide	70.1	
Triphenylamine	70.1	70.1,[h] 70.0[f]
Dibenzothiophene	69.7	69.3
o-Dibenzoylbenzene	68.7	
Benzophenone	68.5	69.2, 69.3[f]
4,4′-Dichlorobenzophenone	68.0	
p-Diacetylbenzene	67.7	
Fluorene	67.6	
9-Benzoylfluorene	66.8	
Triphenylene	66.6	67.2[i]
p-Cyanobenzophenone	66.4	
Thioxanthone	65.5	
Phenylglyoxal	62.5	
Anthraquinone	62.4[e]	63.3,[g] 62.8[f]
Phenanthrene	62.2	61.8,[i] 62.0[f]
α-Naphthoflavone	62.2	
Flavone	62.0[e] in IPMC	
Ethylphenylglyoxalate	61.9	63.0[e]
4,4′-Bis(dimethylamino)benzophenone	61.0[e]	62[h]
Naphthalene	60.9	61,[h] 60.8[f]
β-Naphthyl phenyl ketone	59.6	
β-Naphthaldehyde	59.5[e]	
β-Acetonaphthone	59.3[e]	59.5[e]
α-Naphthyl phenyl ketone	57.5[e]	57.7[e]
α-Acetonaphthone	56.4[e]	58[h]
α-Naphthaldehyde	56.3	56.3
5,12-Naphthacenequinone	55.8	55.8 in EA
Biacetyl	54.9[e]	57.2[e]
Acetylpropionyl	54.7[e]	57.2[e]
Benzil	53.7[e]	57.3[e]
Fluorenone	53.3	
Pyrene	48.7	

[a] Data of Herkstroeter, Lamola, and Hammond;[150] values of Ermolaev[103] were added to their table.

[b] These values refer to the maximum of the 0″–0′ band of the phosphorescence measured spectrophotometrically at 77°K.

[c] In MCIP (methyl cyclohexane-isopentane 5:1 by volume) unless otherwise noted.

[d] In EPA (ether–isopentane–ethanol 5:5:2) unless otherwise noted.

[e] Measured spectrographically, MP = 3-methyl pentane, IPMC = isopentane–methyl cyclohexane 1:5.

[f] Ermolaev,[103] alcohol–ether at 77°K.

[g] Parker and Hatchard.[154]

[h] Lewis and Kasha.[128]

[i] McClure[147] (value for 0″–0′ band head).

Since vibrational deactivation, $T_1^v \rightsquigarrow T_1^0$, is very fast ($k \approx 10^{12}$ sec^{-1}) compared to intersystem crossing, after the latter transition occurs, the molecule quickly drops to the lowest triplet vibrational level T_1^0. Once in this level three processes are possible. If the triplet molecule should acquire additional thermal energy equal to $\Delta E(S_1^0 \rightarrow T_1^0)$, it can be raised to T_1^v and then pass back to the S_1^0 state, $T_1^v \rightsquigarrow S_1^0$, from which it can emit "slow" fluorescence or undergo internal conversion to the ground state (or return again to T_1^v). At 77°K this is very inefficient (nor is it apparently as efficient as the reverse downhill step, $S_1^0 \rightsquigarrow T_1^0$, at room temperature), and one or both of two other modes of return to the ground state by the "trapped" triplet molecule must occur. These are the spin-forbidden radiative intersystem crossing, $T_1^0 \rightarrow S_0 + h\nu_2$, *phosphorescence*, and non-radiative intersystem crossing to a highly vibrationally excited ground state, $T_1^0 \rightsquigarrow S_0^v$, followed by rapid vibrational relaxation, $S_0^v \rightsquigarrow S_0^0$.*

Recalling our assumption that *no primary photochemical act occurred*, we can specify the fate of the quanta absorbed as the sum of the yields of four primary photophysical processes, where $\varphi_{\mathrm{ISC}}(T_1 \rightsquigarrow S_0)$, it must be recalled, is the yield of non-radiative return from the triplet to the ground state (Robinson and Frosch[113] refers to this as "tunneling") and $\varphi_{\mathrm{IC}}(S_1 \rightsquigarrow S_0)$ is the yield of internal conversion.

$$\varphi_f + \varphi_p + \varphi_{\mathrm{ISC}}(T_1 \rightsquigarrow S_0) + \varphi_{\mathrm{IC}}(S_1 \rightsquigarrow S_0) = 1.00 \qquad (4\text{-}4)$$

We should note several points about Eq. 4-4. First, we assumed no photochemical process and no "external" quenching. Second, the expression for the overall yield is true at ordinary temperatures in solution or gas phases [if a photochemical act(s) does occur, add the term $\varphi_D =$ summation of the photochemical primary quantum yields]. However, the relative yields of the four quantities will be altered because of environmental changes, temperature, change in state, solvent perturbation, etc.

In the light of these possible primary processes, let us examine the data in Table 4-12 with particular reference to naphthalene and benzophenone in rigid solvents at 77°K. Certain generalizations emerge at once. The most obvious is that the normal aromatic carbonyl compounds (e.g., benzophenone, acetophenone, benzaldehyde) have high quantum yields of phosphorescence and do not fluoresce significantly (i.e., the ratio $\varphi_p/\varphi_f > 1000$). However, the unsubstituted aromatic hydrocarbons generally show both fluorescence and phosphorescence. Presumably the fluorescence occurs in the unsubstituted hydrocarbons mainly because the large

---

* We shall henceforth drop the superscript zero, and the absence of a superscript will imply vibrational equilibration.

$S_1 \rightarrow T_1$ energy gap lowers the probability of the $S_1 \rightsquigarrow T_1$ nonradiative transition. Benzophenone, however, has a relatively long singlet lifetime, $\sim 10^{-6}$ sec, and a small energy difference that facilitates the intersystem crossing, $S_1 \rightsquigarrow T_1$. This results in essentially complete depopulation of the first excited singlet state before significant fluorescence can occur.

If, for the moment, we *assume* that no internal conversion $S_1 \rightsquigarrow S_0^{v'}$ occurs (and no photochemical reaction), then approximately 70 % of the naphthalene molecules in the S_1 state and 100 % of the benzophenone singlet molecules undergo intersystem crossing to their respective $^3(\pi, \pi^*)$ and $^3(n, \pi^*)$ states.

We can now inquire as to the fate of the naphthalene in its $^3(\pi, \pi^*)$ state. The quantum yield of phosphorescence of naphthalene in the rigid solvent at 77°K is only 0.03 (Table 4-12). Hence, if we assume that there are no bimolecular quenching processes (or triplet-triplet annihilation) and no thermal reactivation back to the S_1 state, then an efficient radiationless transition, the intersystem crossing $T_1 \rightsquigarrow S_0^v$, must occur with 96 % probability.

The species S_0^v is a highly vibrationally excited molecule in its ground electronic state which, if we eliminate possible chemical reactions (this is an assumption for this part of the discussion only), must exchange its vibrational energy with the solvent and return to its vibrationally equilibrated ground state or immediately return to the state T_1. The latter process results in no overall charge and will be neglected in subsequent discussions. Thus the energy of the quanta which go through this sequence of radiationless transitions, $S_1 \rightsquigarrow T_1^v \rightsquigarrow T_1 \rightsquigarrow S_0^v \rightsquigarrow S_0$, simply winds up as thermal excitation of the solvent.

With benzophenone, matters are quite different. There is probably no significant internal conversion at 77°K since the quantum yield of the intersystem crossing $S_1 \rightsquigarrow T_1$, $\varphi_{ISC}(S_1 \rightarrow T_1)$, is 0.99 in liquids at 25°C (Table 4-17).[177] Thus about three-fourths of the molecules reaching the triplet state phosphoresce in rigid solvents at 77°K. The remaining one-fourth are quenched by some bimolecular process (including triplet energy transfer or annihilation) or undergo radiationless intersystem crossing to the highly vibrationally excited ground state S_0^v, which then, in the absence of photochemical reactions, undergoes vibrational equilibration. Just as with the $S_1 \rightsquigarrow T_1$ transition, the magnitude of the energy gap, in this case $\Delta E(T_1 \rightarrow S_0)$, apparently plays a significant role in establishing the rate of radiationless decay, $T_1 \rightsquigarrow S_0^v$.

One illustration of this effect is to consider a series of cyclic polyenes in which the $T_1 \rightarrow S_0$ energy gap ranges from 14,700 cm^{-1} for anthracene up to 21,600 cm^{-1} for phenanthrene. The corresponding radiationless lifetimes, defined as the reciprocal of the first-order rate constant, k, increase from <0.1 to 3.3 sec respectively[144] in EPA at $77°K$, as shown in Table 4-14. These data of Craig and Ross, with their own values for benzene, are treated by Robinson and Frosch,[113] and the implications are discussed critically in terms of relating the "vibrational factors" between the low-lying π-electron states with the $T_1 \to S_0$ energy gap. They assume that, in each case but benzene, the natural radiative lifetime $\tau_p \geqslant 10$ sec, so

TABLE 4-14   Estimated Rate Constants k and Non-Radiative Lifetimes for the Radiationless $T_1 \leadsto S_0$ Transition versus Magnitude of Energy Gap, $\Delta E(T_1 \to S_0)$ for Several Cyclic Aromatic Hydrocarbons[a]

Compound	Energy Gap, $\Delta E(T_1 \to S_0)$, cm^{-1}	Rate Constant k, sec^{-1}	Non-radiative Lifetime k^{-1}, sec
Anthracene	14,700	>10	<0.1
1,2-Benzanthracene	16,500	3.3	0.3
Pyrene	16,800	1.4	0.7
1,2-5,6-Dibenzanthracene	18,300	0.71	1.4
Chrysene	19,800	0.38	2.6
Naphthalene	21,300	0.40 (0.42)[b]	2.5
Phenanthrene	21,600	0.30 (0.26)[b]	3.3
Benzene	29,565	0.024	42

[a] The data, except for benzene, are from Craig and Ross.[144] The molecules are in rigid solvents at $77°K$. The assumption is made by Robinson and Frosch that, except for benzene, the natural triplet radiative lifetimes are $\geqslant 10$ sec, so that the observed phosphorescence lifetimes are essentially the non-radiative lifetimes. With benzene, k^{-1} is calculated from a phosphorescence radiative lifetime of 26 sec, and an observed overall lifetime of 16 sec. The table is modified somewhat from that in the paper by Robinson and Frosch.[113]

[b] For comparison these are values from Ermolaev,[103] Table 4-12 of this book.

that the *observed* phosphorescence lifetimes are a good approximation to the actual radiationless lifetimes of triplet decay. From their values (Table 4-14) there is, empirically at least, a smooth curve relationship between the magnitude of $\Delta E(T_1 \to S_0)$ and the increased radiationless lifetime of the triplet state, k^{-1}. Coronene and triphenylene are exceptions.[157] In the two cases where data are available, naphthalene and phenanthrene, the agreement with Ermolaev's values for k is excellent.

Let us now consider briefly other experimental evidence bearing on the relative rates and yields of radiationless versus radiative transitions in rigid solvents at low temperature. In such studies, perturbations are introduced into the normally very weak triplet $\to$ singlet transition, and the effect on phosphorescence emission ($T_1 \to S_0 + h\nu_2$) and absorption

$(S_0 + h\nu_2 \to T_1)$ is observed. The perturbations are of two general types, *intramolecular*, in which for example, a halogen atom is substituted for a hydrogen atom in an aromatic compound (e.g., naphthalene versus iodonaphthalene) and *intermolecular*, in which the perturbing atom, ion, or molecule (e.g., paramagnetic metal ions such as Cu^{2+}, Co^{2+}, paramagnetic molecules such as nitric oxide and oxygen, or heavy-atom solvents such as propyl iodide) is present in solution (liquid or solid) along with the absorbing species.

4-8B-1   Intramolecular Perturbation

In 1949 McClure examined the phosphorescence lifetimes, τ_p, of a series of halogen-substituted aromatic compounds in rigid glass at $-190°C$ and observed a regular, strong decrease in τ_p of naphthalene substituted by chlorine, bromine, and iodine, respectively.[147] The effect has been correlated with theory in terms of intramolecular heavy-atom spin-orbit coupling; as the atomic number of the perturbing halogen atom increases, the breakdown of the spin conservation rule for both radiative and non-radiative transitions[148,149] occurs. The values of Ermolaev in Table 4-12 illustrate this heavy-atom effect; the observed phosphorescence lifetimes in seconds for naphthalene and its 1-substituted derivatives are H (2.3), CH_3 (2.1), Cl (0.29), Br (0.018), and I (0.002).

Strong intramolecular perturbation of the triplet state may also occur when certain metal ions are chelated to an organic molecule. The degree of perturbation has been measured in several ways; decrease in phosphorescence lifetimes in rigid glassy solvents, decrease in conversion of a large percentage of the molecules to their triplet state by triplet-triplet absorption following an intense flash, and enhancement of singlet-triplet absorption $(S_0 + h\nu \to T_1)$.

The results of various investigations since the original work of Yusta and Weissman[158] in 1949 are somewhat contradictory in detail, depending in part upon which technique was employed. However, the strong quenching effect of chelated (and unchelated) ions of the transition metals is noteworthy. Thus Becker and Kasha[159] state that porphyrin-like molecules with diamagnetic central chelated metal ions (e.g., Mg^{2+} and Zn^{2+}) showed strong fluorescence but no phosphorescence in rigid EPA at low temperatures. The opposite was true when the chelated ion was one of the paramagnetic transition metal ions, Cu^{2+} or Ni^{2+}.

In controlled experiments in which the triplet concentration was monitored directly, using fast absorption spectroscopic techniques, Pekkarinen and Linschitz[160] and Livingston and Fujimore[161] observed dramatic effects for several porphyrins in solutions at room temperature.

Thus, tetraphenylporphine (TPP) and zinc tetraphenylporphine (ZnTPP) had sufficiently long-lived triplets that the rates of the several physical quenching processes could readily be followed and compared with the rate constants for chlorophyll a and b.[162] All four proved strikingly similar. Apparently, neither the side groups nor the introduction of the diamagnetic metal ion had a significant effect on the triplet quenching processes. However, on substitution of the transition metal ions Cu^{2+} and Co^{2+} (to make CuTPP and CoTPP) no triplet absorption was observed after the initial flash. These "negative" results are interpreted to mean that, although triplet CuTPP and CoTPP species are formed by the flash, the presence of the Cu^{2+} and Co^{2+} drastically reduces the triplet lifetimes so that they are shorter than the time resolution of the experiments (about 10^{-5} sec).

It is interesting that one of the important chemical differences between the natural porphyrins chlorophyll and hemin (from hemoglobin) is that the former has diamagnetic magnesium as its central metal ion while the latter has paramagnetic iron. Perhaps certain of the pronounced differences in the "biphotochemical" behavior of these related porphyrins[163] may be due, as Livingston and Pugh suggest,[164] to large differences in the lifetimes of their respective triplet states.

Interest in the reversible photochemical processes of chlorophyll, and in porphyrin photochemistry in general, is widespread, and the field is very active today. For example, it now appears that the reversible photobleaching of chlorophyll may involve a charge transfer between the pigment and a molecule of solvent or some other reductant complexed with it.

Excellent discussions of the photochemistry, photobiology, and spectroscopy of reversible photoprocesses of these and other biologically interesting substances, such as intermediates in the visual process (e.g., retenine, the chromophore of the visual pigment rhodopsin), are given in several articles in Ref. 165, and in the published proceedings of the IV International Photobiology Congress held at Oxford University in July, 1964.[277]

The magnetic properties of a chelated ion now seem *not* to be the key factor in the effectiveness of the ion as a "catalyst" for promoting intersystem crossing (they certainly are *not* in the case of non-chelated ions in the solvent, as we shall see). Thus Evans[166] has observed that when manganous ion is complexed with 9-anthronyl acetone well-defined long-wavelength absorption bands appear. These correspond very closely to those of the ligand in the presence of oxygen and presumably are $S_0 \rightarrow T_1$ bands arising as a result of the perturbing effect of the manganous ion. However, no comparable effect is observed (i.e., no $S_0 \rightarrow T_1$ absorption bands appear) when the complexed ion is gadolinium or dysprosium, both of which have approximately the same ionic radius and *larger* magnetic moments ($Dy^{3+} = 10.5$; $Gd^{3+} = 7.9$; $Mn^{2+} = 5.9$ Bohr magnetons). Ease of valency change of the central ion, with associated charge transfer, seems of chief importance.

4-8B-2   Intermolecular Perturbations

Pronounced environmental (heavy-atom) effects have been shown for the $^3B_{1u} \rightarrow {}^1A_{1g}$ phosphorescence of benzene dispersed in crystalline rare-gas "solvents" at $4.2°K$. Dramatic examples from Robinson's laboratories are shown in Table 4-15. The *observed* phosphorescence lifetime of benzene,

TABLE 4-15   Effect of Crystalline Rare-Gas Solvent at $4.2°K$ on Phosphorescence Lifetimes and on Ratio of Quantum Yield of Fluorescence to Total Triplet-Singlet Intersystem Crossing Quantum Yield[a]

	Crystalline Solvent			
	CH_4	Ar	Kr	Xe
Observed phosphorescence lifetime, τ_p, sec[b]				
Benzene, C_6H_6	16	16	1	0.07
Perdeuterobenzene, C_6D_6	22	26	1	0.07
Ratio of quantum yield of fluorescence, φ_f, to corrected[c] quantum yield of phosphorescence, $\varphi_p{}'$				
Benzene, $\varphi_f/\varphi_p{}'$	0.6	≈ 0.05	0	0
Naphthalene, $\varphi_f/\varphi_p{}'$	0.6	≈ 0.05	0	0

[a] From Wright, Frosch, and Robinson.[167]   See also Refs. 113 and 168.
[b] Ref. 167.
[c] $\varphi_p{}' = \varphi_p + \varphi_{ISC}(T_1 \rightsquigarrow S_0)$ (i.e., $\varphi_p{}' = $ the sum of radiative and non-radiative triplet–singlet intersystem crossing quantum yields).

τ_p, drops from 16 sec with crystalline argon as a solvent to 0.07 sec in xenon.[113,167,168] Furthermore, the ratio of the quantum yield of fluorescence, φ_f, to the "corrected quantum yield of phosphorescence," $\varphi_p{}'$ [where $\varphi_p{}' = \varphi_{ISC}(T_1 \rightsquigarrow S_0) + \varphi_p$; that is, $\varphi_p{}'$ is the *sum* of the radiative and non-radiative $T_1 \rightarrow S_0$ processes], drops from 0.6 with crystalline methane as solvent to 0.05, 0, and 0 with argon, krypton, and xenon, respectively, as crystalline solvents.

Let us consider the implications of the relative values of these primary yields of benzene under the "ideal" conditions of Robinson and co-workers (4.2°K, rare-gas solvent).*[113,167,168] They point out the following:

1. "Tunneling" [i.e., intersystem crossing, ISC($T_1 \rightsquigarrow S_0$)] from the zero-point level of the lowest triplet to a high vibrational level of the ground state has been indicated recently by the "deuterium effect" on the phosphorescence lifetimes of naphthalene[169] and benzene.[167,168] *"There seems little doubt that tunneling is of general importance for the long-lived states of many complex molecules."*

2. *"The quantum ratio of fluorescence to phosphorescence is highly sensitive to environment."* Thus in solid krypton and argon solvents the fluorescence yields are negligible, and phosphorescence is strong ($\varphi_f/\varphi_p' \approx 0$). However, in solid methane the fluorescence yields are comparable to phosphorescence yields, and the ratio $\varphi_f/\varphi_p' \approx 0.6$.

Robinson and Frosch have considered in detail the several roles of the solvent in radiationless processes in these dense media.[113] In their opinion in the simplest case the crystalline solvent acts as a "collection of phonon oscillators coupled to the molecule, into which energy in the form of lattice vibrations may ultimately flow." The solvent does not alter the probability of radiationless intersystem transitions ($S_1 \rightsquigarrow T_1$ or $T_1 \rightsquigarrow S_0$). However, in more complex cases, such as solvents containing heavy atoms, this probability may be modified through several effects, the magnitude of the change depending on "the availability of solvent electronic states, the electrostatic interaction between solute and solvent, and the strength of the spin-orbit coupling in the solvent." They also point out that, as the zero-order energy levels of the excited electronic states of the solvent approach those of the solute, interaction increases until it is difficult to differentiate the electronic states of the solute from those of the total system (solvent and solute).[113]

We should note, however, the theoretical paper dealing with radiationless transitions by Gouterman.[170] He approaches the problem from a point of view that is different from Robinson's. Gouterman develops a semiclassical theory in which the molecular system (solute at infinite dilution in rigid solid solution) interacts with the harmonic oscillators of the *phonon* field of the solid lattice. This is analogous to *radiative* transitions in which the molecular system interacts with the harmonic oscillators of the *photon* field, and he develops expressions for non-radiative transitions that depend primarily on the characteristics of the solute molecule and are analogous to the classical Einstein coefficients A and B for radiative transitions.

---

* See also the deuterium effect reported by Ermolaev[103] for naphthalene and biphenyl, Table 4-12.

Robinson considers the problem of *intramolecular* non-radiative transitions in dense media as being essentially equivalent to the *"intermolecular"* process of electronic energy transfer between dilute unlike molecules in similar environments, that is, dilute solid solutions, and treats them both as radiationless transitions between non-stationary degenerate electronic states of the overall system.

Both authors develop equations which account for various characteristics of radiationless transitions, including their fast rates, temperature dependence, etc., and discuss them in detail.

McGlynn and co-workers have reviewed the literature and status of *intermolecular* perturbations and presented results on the phosphorescence spectra and decay times of naphthalene and all its α-monohalogenated derivatives at −190° in EPA and in "cracked glasses." The latter consisted of the halonaphthalene solute in various propyl halide solvents (propyl chloride, propyl bromide, and propyl iodide) in the mole ratio 2:5 solute to solvent.[171] Phosphorescence lifetimes decreased as the spin-orbit coupling factor of either the internal or external halogen increased. They conclude "that definite weak complexes of a charge-transfer nature form, that there is a genuine heavy-atom effect, and that this effect is saturative." Phosphorescence decays were non-exponential, and possible causes, including oxygen effects, were discussed.

Phosphorescence lifetimes also may vary widely in solid solutions when the solvents do *not* contain heavy atoms. Thus, while propyl bromide was perhaps the most effective of twenty-one different solvents in reducing τ_p of substituted phthalimides, large decreases also were observed in certain non-halogenated solvents.[172] In support of this finding McGlynn *et al.*[171] point out that the lifetimes of benzene triplet in rigid solvents at −190° are as follows: in EPA, 7 sec;[173] in dioxane, 5 sec;[173] in alcohol, 3.3 sec;[174] in water, 0.95 sec;[174] and in CCl₄, 0.66 sec.[174]

Graham-Bryce and Corkhill have noted the effect of different solvents, plus 1 part in 21 by volume of added ethyl iodide, on the phosphorescence of several isomeric dinitronaphthalenes, N,N-dimethylaniline, fluorescein, and coumarin[175] in glassy solid solutions at 77°K. In each case the added ethyl iodide decreased the phosphorescence lifetime and increased its quantum yield.

Several recent studies have contributed greatly to our knowledge of the quantitative aspects of the rates of radiative versus non-radiative decay. Ermolaev (1963)[103] studied the quantum yields of ordinary and sensitized phosphorescence of naphthalene and biphenyl and their deuterated analogs and states that the *radiationless degradation of electronic excitation in simple aromatic molecules in rigid solvents at low temperatures occurs only via the triplet state* (i.e., *internal* conversion, $S_1 \rightsquigarrow S_0^{v'}$, does not take place). Proceeding on this basis, he calculated the rate constants for radiative and radiationless transitions (k_p and k, respectively) from the triplet state to the ground state listed in Table 4-16. The natural lifetimes of the triplet molecules, $1/k_p$, are also included.

It is evident from comparing the rate constants for phosphorescence and intersystem crossing in Table 4-16 and the results of Robinson *et al.* that radiationless decay ("tunneling" in Robinson's terminology[113]) is a major process with most aromatic molecules at low temperature in rigid glasses.* We should note, however, that this is contradictory to the view that radiationless transitions in aromatic compounds in rigid solvents at low temperature generally do *not* occur.[11]†

Forster and Dudley have determined the fluorescence and phosphorescence yields and triplet lifetimes for a series of halogenated fluorescein dyes in rigid EPA solution.[176] They find that the lifetimes decrease progressively as the number of halogen atoms is increased in both the bromine and iodine series of derivatives, and that iodine is the more effective in reducing φ_p. They suggest that their decrease in fluorescence yields with increased halogen substitution may be due to enhanced internal conversion, $S_1 \rightarrow S_0^v$, rather than increased $S_1 \rightsquigarrow T_1$ intersystem crossing.

An important contribution to the entire problem of estimating the efficiency of intersystem crossing under conditions of general interest in photochemistry, room temperature and fluid solutions, has been made recently by Lamola and Hammond.[177] They have developed a simple chemical method for measurement of the quantum yield of intersystem crossing.‡ The substance to be studied is used as a sensitizer in some well characterized *cis* ↔ *trans* isomerization, and under appropriate conditions the quantum yield of isomerization becomes a direct measure of the φ_{ISC}. (See Sec. 6-7C for a discussion of the principles and kinetic treatment.)

Table 4-17 includes the values of φ_{ISC} for a variety of different

---

* Ermolaev[103] notes, however, that "in contradiction to the opinion expressed by Robinson,[168] naphthalene does not show radiationless degradation from the triplet state; our data (see Table 4-16) indicate the rate constant of the radiationless transition $T_1 \rightsquigarrow S_0$ for $C_{10}D_8$ is six times as great as that of the corresponding radiative transition."

† Kasha defines an *intersystem crossing ratio* $\chi = \varphi_p/\varphi_f$ that is based in part on his results[11] that $\varphi_p + \varphi_f = 1.0$ in rigid glasses at low temperatures for triphenylene, phenanthrene, chrysene, and naphthalene. His values for the sum of these absolute φ's do not agree with those of Ermolaev, Table 4-12, who finds, for example, for naphthalene $\varphi_p + \varphi_f = 0.32$.

‡ φ_{ISC} is the ratio of the number of molecules crossing over to the triplet state to the total number of molecules that originally populated the excited singlet state.

TABLE 4-16 Calculated Rate Constants for Radiative and Non-Radiative Intersystem Crossing to the Ground State, and Calculated "Natural" Phosphorescence Lifetimes for Aromatic Molecules in Alcohol-Ether at 77°K[a]

Compound	k_p, sec^{-1} $T_1 \rightarrow S_0 + h\nu'$	k, sec^{-1} $T_1 \leadsto S_0$	τ_{calc}, sec[b]
m-Iodobenzaldehyde	1.0×10^3	5.5×10^2	1.0×10^{-3}
Benzaldehyde	3.4×10^2	3.5×10^2	2.9×10^{-3}
Acetophenone	2.8×10^2	1.7×10^2	3.6×10^{-3}
Benzophenone	1.6×10^2	5.0×10^2	6.2×10^{-3}
Ethyl phenyl ketone	$\sim 1.5 \times 10^2$	$\sim 1.2 \times 10^2$	$\sim 6.7 \times 10^{-3}$
1-Iodonaphthalene	1.0×10^2	4.0×10^2	1.0×10^{-2}
1-Bromonaphthalene	7.0	4.3×10^1	1.4×10^{-1}
4-Phenyl-4'-methoxy-benzophenone	2.3	1.3	4.3×10^{-1}
4-Phenylbenzophenone	1.6	1.7	6.2×10^{-1}
4-(p-Methoxyphenyl)-benzophenone	1.0	1.0	1.0
Triphenylamine	8.6×10^{-1}	5.7×10^{-1}	1.2
1-Nitronaphthalene	8.6×10^{-1}	2.0×10^1	1.2
1-Chloronaphthalene	5.7×10^{-1}	1.7	1.7
1-Naphthaldehyde	3.8×10^{-1}	1.2×10^1	2.6
Quinoline	7.7×10^{-2}	6.6×10^{-1}	1.3×10^1
Carbazole	6.9×10^{-2}	6.3×10^{-2}	1.5×10^1
2-Naphthyl methyl ketone	5.1×10^{-2}	9.8×10^{-1}	2.0×10^1
Phenanthrene	4.6×10^{-2}	2.6×10^{-1}	2.2×10^1
Biphenyl	3.7×10^{-2}	2.9×10^{-1}	2.7×10^1
Decadeuterobiphenyl	3.7×10^{-2}	5.1×10^{-2}	2.7×10^1
1-Fluoronaphthalene	3.6×10^{-2}	6.3×10^{-1}	2.8×10^1
1-Methylnaphthalene	2.0×10^{-2}	4.5×10^{-1}	5.0×10^1
1-Naphthol	1.6×10^{-2}	5.1×10^{-1}	6.3×10^1
Naphthalene	1.6×10^{-2}	4.2×10^{-1}	6.3×10^1
Octadeuteronaphthalene	1.6×10^{-2}	9.0×10^{-2}	6.3×10^1

[a] From Ermolaev;[103] see this review for original references. Calculation made assuming that no internal conversion, $S_1 \leadsto S_0$, occurred.
[b] Calculated natural radiative lifetime if $T_1 \leadsto S_0$ did not occur (i.e., $\tau_{\text{calc}} = 1/k_p$).

aromatic compounds. They range from unity for benzophenone and aceto-phenone to 0.15 for 1-naphthylamine. Of interest is the aromatic hydro-carbon triphenylene, which has an unusually small $\Delta E(S_1 \rightarrow T_1)$ energy gap (see above), and we note that φ_{ISC} is 0.95 in contrast to naphthalene, where φ_{ISC} is 0.39.

TABLE 4-17   Quantum Yields for Intersystem Crossing in Solution[a] at 29°C[b]

Compound	φ_{ISC}	Compound	φ_{ISC}
Naphthalene	0.39	Fluorenone	0.93
Triphenylene	0.95	Benzil	0.92
Chrysene	0.67	9,10-Anthraquinone	0.88
1,2-5,6-Dibenzanthracene	0.89	1-Methylnaphthalene	0.48
Phenanthracene	0.76	2-Methylnaphthalene	0.51
Fluorene	0.31	Acenaphthene	0.47
Benzene	0.24	1-Fluoronaphthalene	0.63
Diphenylamine	0.38	1-Naphthol	0.27
Triphenylamine	0.88	1-Methoxynaphthalene	0.26
Carbazole	0.36	1-Naphthyl acetate	0.29
Acetophenone	0.99	1-Naphthoic acid	0.20
Benzophenone	0.99	1-Naphthonitrile	0.17
p-Methylbenzophenone	1.03	1-Naphthylamine	0.15
p-Bromobenzophenone	1.01	Quinoline	$\begin{cases} 0.16^c \\ 0.32^d \end{cases}$
2-Acetonaphthone	0.84		

[a] Solvent was benzene unless otherwise specified.
[b] Unpublished observations of Lamola and Hammond.[177]
[c] Ethanol solution.
[d] Dry benzene solution.

It is important to note that comparison of the absolute quantum yields of phosphorescence for a series of compounds does not necessarily give a true picture of their relative efficiencies of intersystem crossing. Thus, for example, φ_p of naphthalene is greater than φ_p of 1-methylnaphthalene (0.03 versus 0.02_3), but φ_{ISC} of naphthalene is *less* than φ_{ISC} 1-methyl-naphthalene (0.39 versus 0.48).

Finally, if we combine the data on φ_{ISC} in solution with the quantum yields of fluorescence in solution summarized by Bowen* and presented in

---

* See Bowen's chapter, "Photochemistry of Aromatic Hydrocarbons in Solution," Ref. 152, for details of fluorescence measurements and the primary photochemical processes of aromatic hydrocarbons in solution.

TABLE 4-18   Quantum Yields of Fluorescence of Aromatic Hydrocarbons in Solution at Ordinary Temperature[a]

Hydrocarbon	Solvent	φ_f
Acenaphthene	Hexane	0.31
Anthracene	Hexane	0.31
	Benzene	0.28
	Benzene	0.29
	Ethanol	0.27
Anthracene, 2-methyl	Ligroin	0.32
Anthracene, 9-methyl	Ligroin	0.35
Anthracene, 9,10-dimethyl	Benzene	0.81
	Ligroin	1.0
Benzene	Hexane	0.04
Coronene	Chloroform	0.3
Biphenyl	Ligroin	0.23
Durene	Ligroin	0.5
Fluorene	Hexane	0.54
	Ethanol	0.54
Naphthalene	Hexane	0.10
	Ethanol	0.19
Perylene	Benzene	0.98
Phenanthrene	Ligroin	0.15
	Ethanol	0.1
	Ethanol	0.2
Rubrene	Benzene	1.0
Stilbene	Ligroin	0.27
p-Terphenyl	Ligroin	1.0
Toluene	Hexane	0.23
Triphenyl methane	Hexane	0.23
Xylenes	Hexane	0.3

[a] From Bowen;[152] see this review for original references.

Table 4-18, we can estimate the efficiency by which the singlet state is depopulated by radiationless processes other than intersystem crossing. Thus *if no photochemical reaction occurs* we can write

$$\varphi_X + \varphi_{IC}(S_1 \rightsquigarrow S_0) + \varphi_{ISC} + \varphi_f = 1.0$$

where φ_X represents radiationless processes that depopulate the S_1 state, *other* than internal conversion [e.g., bimolecular reactions such as formation of pyrene dimer (see above)]. If $\varphi_X = 0.00$, then with naphthalene in hydrocarbon solvents near room temperature we would predict that about one-half of the excited molecules undergo internal conversion (1.00 − 0.39 − 0.10). Actually this is a very qualitative business, since φ_f and φ_{ISC} can vary with solvent, and particularly because φ_X is probably far from zero. Yet the calculations do suggest that in *fluid solutions at room temperature* radiationless internal conversion from the first excited singlet state may be a major process for many aromatic molecules. This appears to be in direct contrast to the situation in rigid solvents at low temperature (see above).

Clearly the role of radiationless transitions, particularly internal conversions to the ground state, is one of the most controversial and significant questions currently facing molecular spectroscopists and photochemists. Elucidation of absolute quantum yields of intersystem crossing in fluid solutions by Lamola and Hammond represents a major contribution in this field. Other significant advances include the strong evidence recently acquired of photochemical reactions occurring in the vibrationally excited ground state. Thus, evidence has been presented which has been interpreted by Srinivasan as indicative of an intermediate vibrationally excited ground electronic state of 1,3,5-cycloheptatriene in the gas-phase photoinduced rearrangement of this compound to toluene.[278] The principal argument is that the reaction is quenched as the pressure of inert gas is increased, a phenomenon which may be explained by collisional deactivation of vibrationally excited 1,3,5-cyclohexatriene before rearrangement. The argument for identifying this vibrationally excited species as a ground rather than electronically excited state rests on the assumption that only one electronically excited state is involved. The arguments are compelling if this assumption is accepted. However, since, as Ullman has noted, 1,3,5-cyclohexatriene is in equilibrium with norcaradiene, the formation of two chemically distinct singlets is not improbable, and the conclusion is subject to reservation.

Evidence interpreted as supporting an intermediate vibrationally excited ground state in fluid solution has been obtained by Ullman and Henderson[279] for the reversible phototautomerization I ⇌ II. Since direct irradiation of II (population of S_{II}^*) gives I and III, whereas irradiation of I fails to give III, S_{II}^* cannot be an intermediate in the reaction I → II.

(I)   (II)   (III)

However, the reaction proceeds predominately *via* S_I^* without intermediacy of T_I, since a quantum yield reduction of only 11% is obtained with complete quenching of T_I. Therefore, S_I^* may give S_{II}^0 without the intermediacy of other electronically excited species.

Sensitization and quenching experiments show that T_I can also be a precursor to II. Intermediacy of T_{II} is considered improbable by the absence of the sensitized non-vertical excitation $S_I^0 \rightarrow T_{II}$, a process which has been reported to occur in a number of reactions in which an exothermic rearrangement of the reactant triplet can take place.[260c] Therefore, T_I probably also leads to S_{II}^0 without the intermediacy of other electronically excited species.

These results may be interpreted on the basis of an intermediate vibrationally excited ground state formed from S_I^* and T_I. The effect of the variation of solvent on the quantum yield is as expected for this mechanism. Likewise, a vibrationally excited ground-state intermediate appears probable for reaction II → I, since intermediate excited states of I are excluded by energy considerations. The solvent and temperature effects on quantum yield are in accordance with this interpretation.

The intermediate vibrationally excited ground-state hypothesis can be circumvented by assuming that the processes $S_I^* \rightarrow T_{II}$ and $T_I \rightarrow S_{II}^*$ occur in the forward reaction and that an intermediate structurally distinct from I and II is involved in the reverse reaction. It is difficult for us to rationalize the significant participation of the rearrangement reactions of a highly vibrationally excited ground-state molecule of reasonable complexity in the solution phase, since vibrational relaxation is so very rapid in the solution phase; see Sec. 6-7A-5.

With regard to the radiationless transitions in the vapor phase, we note that long-term, quantitative vapor-phase studies of the aliphatic aldehydes and ketones in the laboratories of Blacet, Noyes, and Steacie (see Chapter 5) have shown that, in the words of Noyes, "Transfer to the ground state without either dissociation or fluorescence (and presumably phosphorescence, when it occurs) must account for the removal of many of the molecules from the lowest singlet and triplet levels, since the sum of primary photochemical yield and fluorescence yield is usually far from unity."[17,19] However, with regard to aromatic hydrocarbons, Ishikawa and Noyes have shown that internal conversion does not seem to be important in the vapor-phase photoprocesses of benzene at 2537 A (see Sec. 4-10A).[210]

We will close this section by noting that much of the present confusion in the literature of the past decades has arisen from the dearth of reliable *absolute* quantum yield data. Although these may be difficult to obtain experimentally, particularly in the solid state (scattering problems, etc.), the effort is well worthwhile, as only through acquisition of accurate values can a satisfactory understanding of the relative importance of the several primary processes be achieved.*

4-9 INTERMOLECULAR PHOTOPHYSICAL PROCESSES OF EXCITED STATES

In this section we shall consider intermolecular reactions of excited singlet and triplet states with emphasis on these properties in fluid solutions.†

4-9A Delayed Emission

Some of the most fundamental information concerning the reactions of excited molecules in solution has come from the study of the spectra, lifetimes, and intensity dependence of delayed emission. This topic has been reviewed critically by Parker;[115] we will only outline the major features of the subject.

Increasing the concentration of certain dilute fluorescing solutions may lead to changes in the absorption spectrum *or* the fluorescence spectrum. Thus, as the concentration of certain dye solutions is increased, the absorption spectrum shows a strong concentration dependency, while over the same range the fluorescence spectrum is unchanged in shape or lifetime, although the overall fluorescence yield may be lowered. This phenomenon may be explained by the equilibrium

$$S_0 + S_0 \rightleftharpoons (S_0)_2$$

and the assumption that the dimer $(S_0)_2$ does not fluoresce.

Increasing the concentration of a dilute solution of pyrene, however, has no effect on the absorption spectrum, so no dimers seem to be formed (cryogenic data support this statement). However, the violet fluorescence is replaced at longer wavelengths by a structureless blue emission,[178] as seen in Fig. 4-16.

---

* Medinger and Wilkinson have conducted a detailed study of the mechanism of fluorescence quenching of certain anthracene derivatives, which included quantitative measurements of triplet concentrations by flash spectroscopy. They found that with these compounds the quantum yield of triplet formation (φ_T) plus the quantum yield of fluorescence was essentially unity.[296] Labhart, however, using a different technique, found that $\varphi_T = 0.55 \pm 0.10$ for 1,2-benzanthracene in hexane at room temperature.[297] Since $\varphi_f = 0.20$ under these conditions (determined by Eigenmann[299]) and no photochemical reaction occurs, approximately 25% of the molecules excited to the first singlet apparently undergo the radiationless $S_1 \rightsquigarrow S_0$ internal conversion to the ground state.

† We will, however, defer the important topic of energy transfer to Sec. 4-10.

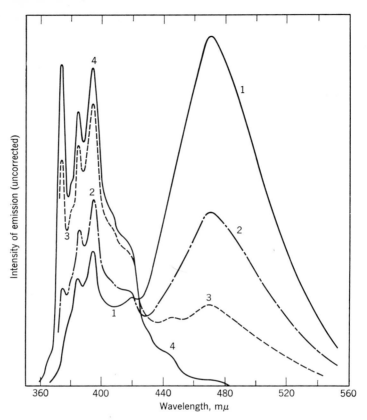

Fig. 4-16 Fluorescence of pyrene in ethanol as a function of concentration, showing the emission band of the excited dimer at the longer wavelength. (1) $3 \times 10^{-3}\,M$, (2) $1 \times 10^{-3}\,M$, (3) $3 \times 10^{-4}\,M$, (4) $2 \times 10^{-6}\,M$. The instrumental sensitivity settings for curves 1 and 4 were approximately 0.6 and 3.7 times the setting for curves 2 and 3. The short-wavelength ends of the spectra in the more concentrated solutions are distorted by self-absorption. From Parker[115] and Hatchard.[179]

The fluorescence spectrum may be explained by the Förster-Kasper mechanism[178] in terms of an excited dimer $(S_0S_1)^*$ formed by combination of an excited singlet molecule S_1 and an unexcited one S_0.

$$S_0 + S_1 \rightarrow (S_0S_1)^*$$

The new fluorescence band arises from the radiative transition

$$(S_0S_1)^* \rightarrow (S_0)_2 + h\nu'$$

after which $(S_0)_2$ rapidly dissociates into two ground-state molecules. Birks and Munro report the lifetime of the pyrene monomer, τ_M, to equal 3.4×10^{-7} sec, while that of the dimer, τ_D, is 4×10^{-8} sec.[180]

The formation of mixed singlet excited dimers, from an excited singlet of one species, A*, reacting with a molecule of another species in its ground state, D, has been demonstrated by Birks and Christophorou.[181] It is explained in terms of the Förster-Kasper mechanism:

$$A + h\nu \rightarrow A*$$

$$A* + D \rightarrow (AD)* \rightarrow (AD) + h\nu'$$
$$\searrow$$
$$A + D$$

A different type of delayed emission is observed in the vapor-phase luminescence of certain aromatic hydrocarbons such as anthracene and phenanthrene.[183] The absorption spectrum remains unchanged, as does the spectral contour of the emission spectrum, except that as the concentration of the aromatic hydrocarbon is increased a relatively long-lived component (lifetime of the order of milliseconds versus about 10^{-8} sec for normal fluorescence) appears in the fluorescence spectrum. This delayed fluorescence was first explained by Williams in terms of the dissociation of the excited dimer $(S_0S_1)*$ followed by fluorescence:

$$S_0 + h\nu \rightarrow S_1$$

$$S_0 + S_1 \rightarrow (S_0S_1)* \rightarrow S_1 + S_0$$
$$\searrow$$
$$S_0 + h\nu'$$

which, when taken with other competing processes, gives a mechanism yielding the observed long-lifetime fluorescence.[19]

Stevens and his associates have extended this idea[182,184–186] and recently have reviewed the phenomenon of delayed fluorescence in aromatic vapors in terms of the dissociation of the species $(S_0S_1)*$. They proposed the term *excimer*, to distinguish the electronically excited dimeric species $(S_0S_1)*$ formed by the process

$$S_0 + S_1 \rightarrow (S_0S_1)*$$

from the excited dimer produced directly by light absorption from the ground-state dimer found in certain dye molecules in solution.

Delayed fluorescence in fluid solutions has recently been observed with a number of aromatic hydrocarbons. For example, although most of the blue emission from the excited dimer of pyrene in fluid solution is relatively short lived, Stevens and Hutton[182] found a component with identical spectral distribution but a significantly longer lifetime. They did not observe the monomer band in the delayed emission. Subsequently, however, this band was also observed.[179]

Before considering the possible explanations for the delayed fluorescence observed in fluid solutions, let us follow the treatment of Parker[115] and summarize the experimental observations.

The three types of delayed emission in fluid solutions are *triplet-singlet phosphorescence, E-type delayed fluorescence, and P-type delayed fluorescence* (the notation is that of Parker[115]). The E-type includes delayed fluorescence that is *directly* excited and a recently discovered *sensitized delayed fluorescence*. P-type delayed fluorescence shows the band of the monomer and may also contain another delayed emission band due to an excited dimer.

The several types can be differentiated experimentally by their dependence on the rate of absorption of exciting light, I_a, and the temperature dependence of their emission (also, of course, by the unique nature of the phosphorescence spectrum). Thus, the intensity of both phosphorescence and E-type delayed fluorescence is (for low rates of absorption) proportional to the first power of I_a, the intensity of P-type delayed fluorescence is proportional to the square of the rate of absorption (i.e., I_a^2) and decays exponentially. The intensity of phosphorescence *increases* as the temperature is lowered, becoming most intense in rigid media at low temperatures (Sec. 4-7A). The intensity of E-type delayed fluorescence *decreases* exponentially as the absolute temperature is lowered. P-type delayed fluorescence does not obey the exponential temperature law and approaches zero in a completely rigid medium.

We have already considered the mechanistic aspects of triplet-singlet emission and E-type delayed fluorescence in rigid solvents. The latter is simply the Jablonski-Lewis "slow fluorescence" arising from reactivation from the triplet level to the singlet, followed by emission of fluorescence (Sec. 4-7A, Fig. 4-10). The delayed fluorescence from pyrene monomer and dimer has now been shown to be of the P-type; furthermore, the generality of the phenomenon has been demonstrated by Parker and Hatchard,[115,187,188] who found it with carefully deoxygenated alcoholic solutions of anthracene, phenanthrene, naphthalene, pyrene, acenaphthene, fluoranthene, and 3,4-benzpyrene.[115] Since the intensity of delayed emission is proportional to the square of the rate of light absorption, P-type delayed fluorescence cannot be accounted for by formation of an excited dimer (excimer). Instead Parker and Hatchard rationalize their data by the following mechanism, in which a bimolecular triplet-triplet quenching reaction yields a new excited species that carries off the electronic energy from both triplets:

$$A + h\nu \rightarrow A^*$$

$$A^* - \begin{cases} \rightarrow A \\ \rightarrow A + h\nu' \\ \rightarrow {}^3A \end{cases}$$

$${}^3A \rightarrow A$$

$${}^3A + {}^3A \rightarrow X(+ A)$$

$$X - \begin{cases} \rightarrow A(+ A) \\ \rightarrow A^*(+ A) \end{cases}$$

A kinetic treatment of this mechanism predicts an intensity dependence of delayed fluorescence on I_a that is consistent with the Parker mechanism. The intensity effect could not be reconciled with a Williams type of mechanism, which we saw was applicable to "excimer" formation in the gas phase.

In addition to the three types of delayed fluorescence cited above, Parker and Hatchard also report a *sensitized* delayed fluorescence in fluid solutions. Thus, on irradiating 10^{-3} M solutions of phenanthrene (donor) containing anthracene (acceptor) in the concentration range of 10^{-6} to 10^{-7} M, they observed quite intense anthracene delayed emission, but the normal (short-lived) emission was only that from phenanthrene. They propose two mechanisms to account for their results, both of which they suggest are operative in the phenanthrene-anthracene system:

$$P + h\nu \rightarrow P^* \rightarrow {}^3P$$

$${}^3P + A \rightarrow P + {}^3A$$

followed by either

$${}^3A + {}^8A \rightarrow A_2^* \rightleftharpoons A_2^{**} \rightarrow A^* + A$$

or

$${}^3A + {}^3P \rightarrow AP^* \rightleftharpoons AP^{**} \rightarrow A^* + P$$

The generality of this important process has been shown with other donor-acceptor pairs, and the implications of triplet quenching as a source of "high chemical potential" are discussed by Parker.

4-9B   Other Intermolecular Perturbations

Pronounced enhancements of the rates of both radiative and non-radiative triplet-singlet intersystem crossings in organic molecules in liquid solutions also may be achieved by adding to the system molecular oxygen (or nitric oxide) or certain of the transition-metal ions.

Oxygen is a particularly effective quencher of organic triplets in a solution. Furthermore *it is exceedingly difficult to remove readily the last traces of oxygen from solution (liquid or solid) by conventional degassing techniques* (see Sec. 6-5D). Thus, as an unsuspected impurity it has been a major source of the confusion that has also plagued the determination of rate constants of the radiationless first-order decay of triplets, k_1 (i.e., the non-radiative $T_1 \rightsquigarrow S_0$ process, "tunneling"). A prime example is anthracene. The overall rate of decay of anthracene triplet in liquid solutions where phosphorescence is negligible, $-d[T_1]/dt$, is the sum of several first- and second-order processes, namely,

$$\frac{-d[T_1]}{dt} = k_1[T_1] + k_2[T_1]^2 + k_3[C_0][T_1] + k_4[M][T_1] \qquad (6\text{-}26)$$

where $[C_0] =$ total anthracene concentration and $[M]$ is the concentration of impurity (e.g., dissolved oxygen) or added "catalyst" (e.g., Cu^{2+}). By use of rapid-flash kinetic spectroscopy the value of the sum of all the terms first order in T_1 has been obtained by several investigators. If all traces of impurity were removed, no catalyst was added, and $k_3[C_0]$ was essentially zero, the observed first-order rate constant would be equal to the true k_1.

In practice it is extremely difficult to remove the last traces of oxygen from solution by conventional degassing techniques. Thus, as Linschitz, Steel, and Bell[189b] point out, the reported value for k_1 for anthracene has dropped from 1300 sec^{-1} (Porter and Wright[190]) to 580 sec^{-1} (Pekkarinen and Linschitz[160]) to their latest results of 75 ± 75 sec^{-1} in pyridine and hexane.[189b] The latter value includes the $k_3[C_0]$ term, so k_1 is certainly small.

Jackson and Livingston have reported values of the true k_1 in agreement with this, for example, 160 and 110 sec^{-1} in hexane and tetrahydrofuran, respectively.[191] They also point out that over the range from 0.3 to about 500 centipoise the rate of the radiationless $T_1 \rightsquigarrow S_0$ transition appears reasonably *independent of viscosity*, but then seems to decrease as the viscosity increases, the lower limit of k_1 being at approximately 3×10^5 centipoise (glycerol at $-25°$).[191]

The dramatic drop in values for k_1 is apparently due to improvements in removing dissolved oxygen, thus reducing the pseudo first-order term $k_4[M][T_1]$, which, under the condition of these experiments, is included along with $k_1[T_1]$. Thus, in their latest work Linschitz, Steel, and Bell found that, instead of trap-to-trap distillation, improvement was obtained by subjecting the anthracene solutions to repeated cycles, of freezing pumping, and thawing with vigorous agitation by an enclosed magnetic stirrer. Solutions were sealed off only after three consecutive cycles gave a "stick vacuum."[189b]

Of course impurities other than oxygen also contribute to $[M]$ in the $k_4[M][T_1]$ term, and to the extent that these are effective quenchers of triplets they also contribute to the size of the *apparent* first-order constant versus the true k_1. The admonition "keep it clean" certainly may be applied with fervor to solvents used in kinetic quenching studies such as these! We might also note that the slowest first-order decay rates in solution are still about three orders of magnitude greater than those observed in organic crystals: it may be that impurities are produced by photoreactions of the solute.

The perturbing effect of oxygen is shown spectroscopically by the studies of Evans on the singlet-triplet absorption spectra of a wide variety of organic molecules (aromatic, heterocyclic, olefins, and acetylenes) in the presence of up to 100 atm of oxygen.[192,166] He observed well-defined absorption bands which disappeared on the removal of oxygen. The longest-wavelength absorption band coincides almost exactly with the shortest wavelength phosphorescence band in those cases where phosphorescence emission spectra have been determined. Studies by Tsubomora and Mulliken[193] and Evans[194] on oxygen enhancement of forbidden $S_0 \rightarrow T_1$ absorption bands indicate that charge-transfer states involving complexes between the oxygen and the organic molecule (perhaps $A^+ \cdot O_2^-$) are important in some systems, and the breaking down of the $S_0 \rightarrow T_1$ selection rule is not directly connected with the paramagnetism of the oxygen.

In principle, heavy atoms in the solvent (e.g., bromobenzene[193] or ethyl iodide[123]) might in an *intermolecular* process perturb solute organic molecules in their triplet states and bring about a relaxation of the spin conservation rule, as we have just seen for certain chelated metal ions and for oxygen and NO. Such an effect has been reported for liquid ethyl iodide as a solvent.[123] However, in more recent work no pronounced effect due to heavy-atom catalysis (spin-orbit coupling) of radiationless inter-system crossing has conclusively been shown in *liquids*. For example, Livingston and Tanner[195] observed no marked effect of carbon disulfide or bromobenzene on the lifetimes of the triplet state of anthracene.

Recently, considerable effort has been made to evaluate the mechanism of intermolecular triplet quenching by metal ions. Thus Porter and Wright point out that *diamagnetic* ions such as Zn^{2+} and Ga^{3+} have no measurable quenching effect on the triplet state of naphthalene in water.[190,196] On the other hand, certain *paramagnetic* ions such as Ni^{2+} and Fe^{2+} have a pronounced intermolecular catalytic quenching effect on triplets. For some time this effect was considered to be due to the perturbing effect of their inhomogeneous magnetic fields. A similar explanation was advanced to explain quenching by the paramagnetic molecules oxygen and nitric oxide. However, on the basis of recent experimental studies, among them those in which triplet concentrations were followed directly by fast absorption spectroscopy,[196] it appears that for unchelated metal ions there is no direct correspondence between the triplet quenching constants of the organic molecule and the magnetic moments of the metal ions. Similarly, the strong quenching action of oxygen is apparently not directly related to its paramagnetic properties. Identical conclusions were reached by others[192,193,166] who studied comparable phenomena by observing the effects of perturbing species on the intensity of singlet-triplet absorption.

Porter and Wright[196] propose that the essential difference between paramagnetic and diamagnetic ions and molecules is that the former have a multiplicity greater than 1. Their effectiveness is then due to their ability to promote the spin-forbidden change triplet $\rightarrow$ singlet by maintaining spin conservation as a whole. Thus, as they observe, the collisional process

$$A^*(triplet) + Q(singlet) \rightarrow A(singlet) + Q(singlet)$$

is forbidden by spin conservation rules, but the analogous processes may be "allowed" if the multiplicity of Q is greater than singlet.

TABLE 4-19   Typical Triplet Quenching Constants[a]

	Rate Constant for Quenching, k, liters/mole-sec	Type of Quencher
Group 1	$\sim 10^{10}$	O_2, NO, aromatic triplet
Group 2	$\sim 5 \times 10^7$	Metal ions of first transition series
Group 3	$\sim 2 \times 10^5$	Ions of lanthanide rare earths

[a] From Porter and Wright.[196]

Porter and Wright further suggest that the mechanism involves a short-lived complex as an intermediate and that the relative quenching abilities of the various types of quenchers are related to their complexing ability (and lifetime of complex) as shown in Table 4-19. They propose that the decrease in quenching ability is parallel to the decrease in availability of the electrons in the quencher for loose bonding in the "complex," that is, maximum overlap for the p electrons of $O_2 > d$ orbitals of solvated ions of transition metals $> f$ orbitals of solvated rare earth ions. The idea of such a collision complex seems attractive, and recent theoretical treatments involve this intermediate.[197,198]

Certain parallels between singlet and triplet quenching were observed by Linschitz and Pekkarinen,[189d] who suggest that the various "chemical mechanisms" proposed for fluorescence quenching may also apply to heavy-metal "catalysis" of triplet-singlet conversion. In particular, they suggest that the intermediate may be a charge-transfer complex between the excited molecule and the metal ion. Presumably this complex then undergoes a radiationless transition to the ground state. Theoretical considerations are in accord with this hypothesis.[193] Recent studies of the uncatalyzed and copper ion-catalyzed decay of anthracene triplets in organic solvents also support the hypothesis.[189]

In conclusion one should note that certain *diamagnetic* substances have quenching efficiencies as high as that of oxygen itself,[199] so that the presence of initially unpaired electrons is not essential for all triplet quenchers. For example, triplet energy transfer to ground-state organic molecules is a very effective quenching process. Thus, although paramagnetic chelated compounds are powerful quenchers of benzophenone triplets[200,201] (of the order of oxygen), naphthalene, for example, is also very effective because of the process

$$(C_6H_5)_2CO(T_1) + \text{Naphthalene } (S_0) \rightarrow$$

$$(C_6H_5)_2CO(S_0) + \text{Naphthalene } (T_1)$$

(This is discussed in detail in Sec. 4-10B-3.)

4-10 INTERMOLECULAR ELECTRONIC ENERGY-TRANSFER PROCESSES

Transfer of electronic energy involves the species absorbing the radiation, the photosensitizer or *donor*, and the species accepting the energy, the *acceptor*. The absorption and emission act may be localized in a single atom or molecule, or, as in molecular crystals with strong "coupling," the entire crystal may act as the absorber and emitter.

Experimentally, electronic energy transfer may manifest itself in several ways, including sensitized fluorescence or phosphorescence, concentration depolarization of fluorescence, photoconduction, and the formation of triplet acceptor molecules observed by flash spectroscopy or ESR techniques. In addition to these photophysical effects, the acceptor molecule may be altered chemically by spin inversion, dissociation, dimerization, or isomerization.

These various aspects of energy transfer, electronic and vibrational, intermolecular and intramolecular, and occurring in solid, liquid, and gaseous phases, are of great importance to photochemical and photo-biological systems and in vast areas of radiation chemistry and biology. The awareness of this fact and the tremendous amount of current research in all aspects of energy transfer are evidenced, for example, by symposia such as the *Faraday Society Discussion* No. 27, 1959, on "Energy Transfer with the Special Reference to Biological Systems."* Reviews of electronic energy transfer are to be found in these published symposia, in the review of electronic energy transfer in solution by Wilkinson,[202] in articles such as those of Hammond and co-workers[260] and in the important book of Reid.[7]

It is beyond the scope of this book to consider in detail the many aspects of the field or to attempt complete literature surveys. We shall simply pick several examples which have a direct bearing on photochemical problems and for which the data seem both cogent and reliable. We trust that these will afford valuable references and techniques for application to future problems in photochemistry. We have already considered several aspects of the problem, particularly intramolecular transfer by radiationless transitions, for example, in dense media where electronic excitation of the absorbing molecule is transferred and ultimately converted to vibrational energy of the surroundings (Sec. 4-9).

Our prime emphasis in photochemistry is on electronic and associated vibrational transfer, rather than on purely vibrational intramolecular and intermolecular transfer. We considered the latter topic briefly for diatomic molecules in Chapter 3, and some of the same points can, as approximations, be carried over to polyatomic molecules. Various aspects of vibrational transfer in polyatomic molecules have been reviewed by Herzfeld,[203] Stevens and Boudart,[204] and Stevens,[205] and these works contain surveys of the literature in this field to about 1957.

Results and implications of mass spectrometric studies of energy exchange in interactions between ions and molecules have been discussed

---

* Other symposia in which electronic energy transfer was an important topic of discussion and papers were published include the International Congress of Radiation Research, August, 1958 (Academic Press, New York, 1959); the Conference on Comparative Effects of Radiation, Puerto Rico, February, 1960 (*Comparative Effects of Radiation*, edited by M. Burton, J. S. Kirby-Smith, and J. L. Magee, John Wiley, New York, 1960); the Symposium on Light and Life held in March, 1960 (edited by W. D. McElroy and B. Glass, Johns Hopkins Press, Baltimore 1961); the Symposium on Reversible Photochemical Processes, Duke University, April, 1962 (papers published in the December 1962 issue of *J. Phys. Chem.*), the International Conference on Luminescence, New York University, 1964 (edited by H. P. Kallman and G. M. Spruch, John Wiley, New York, 1962), the 4th International Photobiology Congress at Oxford, July, 1964 (*Recent Advances in Photobiology*, edited by E. J. Bowen, Blackwells, 1965), and the International Conference on Organic Photochemistry (published by I.U.P.A.C. as *Organic Photochemistry*, Butterworths, London, 1965).

by Kondratiev.[206] He considers the charge-transfer type

$$A^+ + B \rightarrow A + B^+ \quad \text{or} \quad A^- + B \rightarrow A + B^-$$

and chemical reactions between colliding species such as

$$A^+ + B \rightarrow C^+ + D$$

These processes, while of great importance in mass spectroscopy, radiation chemistry, and photochemistry in the vacuum ultraviolet region, cannot be considered in detail here.

A most important area of energy transfer is that of organic molecules in ordered laminar lattices such as the crystalline pigment chlorophyll. This field, which includes, of course, photoconduction of organic molecules, is beyond the scope of this book. Recent reviews are included in the published proceedings of the several symposia cited in the footnote on p. 322.

4-10A   Intermolecular Electronic Energy Transfer in the Vapor Phase

The concept of energy transfer between an electronically excited atom and an atom of another species in its ground state was first advanced by Franck in 1922. He further pointed out that the efficiency of transfer should increase as the difference in electronic energy levels of the excited atom approached the electronic energy gap in the unexcited atom, that is, as the system approached "resonance." As we saw in Chapter 2, Franck's predictions were rapidly confirmed by the experiments of Cario and Franck in which the fluorescence of thallium vapor was sensitized by $Hg(^3P_1)$ atoms. Soon the phenomenon of "sensitized atomic fluorescence" was established for a number of systems.*

The vapor-phase sensitized fluorescence of polyatomic molecules was first systematically studied in 1935 by Prilezhaeva, who irradiated the gaseous mixtures aniline-indigo and aniline-benzene and observed, on absorption of light by aniline, the fluorescence of indigo and benzene.[207,208] Subsequently, Noyes and his students have carefully studied various aspects of vapor-phase energy-transfer processes, for example, sensitized fluorescence, phosphorescence, or decomposition in several systems[17] including acetone-biacetyl,[209a-d] benzene-biacetyl,[210] and benzene-methyl iodide[211] (the first-named molecule is the photosensitizer or *donor*, and the second-named the *acceptor*). Benzene also has been employed as a photosensitizer to excite fluorescence from β-naphthylamine[212] and anthracene.[213]

---

* Atom-molecule energy transfer is considered under mercury-sensitized reactions, Chapter 2.

In the work at Noyes' laboratory energy transfer in the system acetone-biacetyl was confirmed by (1) an increase in the phosphorescence-fluorescence ratio[209b] and (2) diminished acetone photodecomposition and phosphorescence.[209c] See Sec. 6-7C. Diethyl ketone also can act as a donor to biacetyl, as evidenced by the decreased photodecomposition of diethyl ketone and the enhanced phosphorescence of biacetyl.[214] The theoretical and experimental aspects of energy dissipation in such vapor-phase systems have been discussed by Noyes.[19]

As other illustrative examples we note that electronic energy transfer to olefins in the gas phase was demonstrated in 1950 by Dainton and Ivin, who found that olefins quenched the photoreaction between sulfur dioxide and paraffins to produce sulfinic acids.[215] Subsequently Cundall and Palmer[216] showed the SO_2-sensitized *cis-trans* isomerization of butene-2, and Greenhough and Duncan demonstrated that triplet SO_2 was the transferring species.[217] Cundall and Palmer[216] also showed that benzene photoexcited at 2537 A could induce the isomerization of both *cis*- and *trans*-2-butene.

Ishikawa and Noyes[210] recently made an admirably thorough study of primary photophysical and photochemical processes in the vapor-phase system benzene-biacetyl irradiated at 2537 A. They demonstrated the benzene-sensitized phosphorescent emission of biacetyl and, as they state, with reasonable certainty its sensitized decomposition. Their research represents a sound experimental and mechanistic approach to the many spectroscopic and kinetic aspects of photochemical and energy-transfer processes in mixtures of polyatomic gases, and we shall use it as an example.

First, they studied the absorption and emission spectra and photochemistry of *pure* benzene and *pure* biacetyl irradiated at 2537 A. Some 2654 A radiation also was passed by their filter.* This is presently unavoidable, however, if reasonably high intensities of 2537 A are to be obtained, and in their work proper account was taken of this second component.

They studied the effects of the variables, temperature, pressure, light intensity, and the presence of an "inert" gas, cyclohexane, which is similar to benzene in some of its kinetic properties.

The combination benzene-biacetyl is useful because, although biacetyl absorbs strongly at 2537 A, which lies in its second absorption region (2200–3100 A), its absolute emission yield there, φ_e, is very small compared

---

* Five centimeters of chlorine gas at 1 atm + 10 cm of cobalt-nickel sulfate solution (24 grams of $NiSO_4 \cdot 6H_2O$ Merck Reagent and 4.5 grams of $CoSO_4 \cdot 7H_2O$ Baker analyzed in 200 ml distilled water), supplemented with a Corning 9863 filter when emission measurements were made.

to that in its first absorption band (3500–4670 A). This is shown in Table 4-20, where φ_e at 2537 A is less than 10^{-4}, compared to 0.15 at 4358 A and 4050 A. In establishing the character and magnitude of the benzene-sensitized emission of biacetyl the following observations were made. Irradiation of pure biacetyl at 2537 A produces no emission visible to the

TABLE 4-20 Absolute Emission Yields φ_e for Biacetyl at Various Wavelengths and Pressures[a,b]

Irradiating Wavelength, A	Biacetyl Pressure, mm			
	5	10	20	40
4358	0.15	0.15	0.15	0.15
4050	0.15	0.15	0.15	0.15
3650	0.051	0.086	0.12	0.13
3340	0.0052	0.010	0.021	0.042
3130	0.0004	0.001	0.004	0.011
3020	0.0001	0.0003	0.001	0.003
2537	<0.0001	0.0002	0.0003	0.0004

[a] This table is taken directly from Ishikawa's dissertation.[210b]
[b] φ_e is the absolute emission yield at room temperature, that is, $\varphi_e = (I_p + I_f)/I_a$, where I_p and I_f are, respectively, the number of photons emitted per milliliter per second as phosphorescence and as fluorescence, and I_a is the number of photons absorbed by biacetyl per milliliter per second. The absorption bands of biacetyl are 4670–3500 A and 3100–2200 A.

eye, as the absolute yield is only 4×10^{-4} at 25° and 40 mm biacetyl. However, addition of 20 mm of benzene to 0.1 mm of biacetyl gave a visible emission at wavelengths longer than 5000 A.

The benzene-sensitized emission from irradiation at 2537 A was shown to be identical with that of pure biacetyl vapor irradiated at 4358 A at the onset of its first absorption band (Fig. 4-17). Furthermore, it appeared to be entirely phosphorescence—little or no fluorescence could be observed (Fig. 4-18).

Oxygen was shown to have a dramatic effect in quenching the long-wavelength emission of pure biacetyl (which is consistent with its being phosphorescent in nature). This is shown in Fig. 4-19.

In order to prove that the biacetyl emission from irradiation of the system benzene-biacetyl at 2537 A results from energy transfer and not simply from collisional stabilization of excited biacetyl molecules, a series of irradiations with cyclohexane-biacetyl mixtures was carried out at

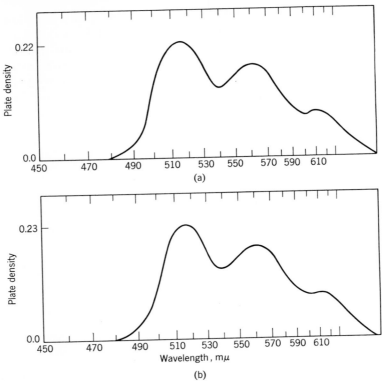

Fig. 4-17 Comparison of microdensitometer tracings of emission spectrum of (a) pure biacetyl vapor (40 mm) irradiated 6.5 hr at 4358 A with sensitized emission from a mixture of (b) benzene (30 mm) and biacetyl (0.2 mm) irradiated 288 hr at 2537 A. Note identity of the spectra. From Ishikawa and Noyes.[210]

2537 A and longer wavelengths. It is evident from the results in Table 4-21 that in irradiations at 2537 A (where cyclohexane is transparent) no biacetyl emission is induced by addition of the cyclohexane. While this finding is confirmation of the transfer idea, the authors point out that there is, however, "a very slight doubt about this conclusion because excited biacetyl molecules may be saved by benzene but not by cyclohexane."

Runs were also made on benzene-biacetyl mixtures irradiated at 3130, 3650, and 4358 A, where benzene is transparent, and compared with results on cyclohexane-biacetyl and pure biacetyl taken under similar conditions. The effect of the added benzene on both the absolute emission yield, Table 4-21, and the photodecomposition, Table 4-22, was the same as that of the "inert" gas cyclohexane. The term "inert" may be somewhat

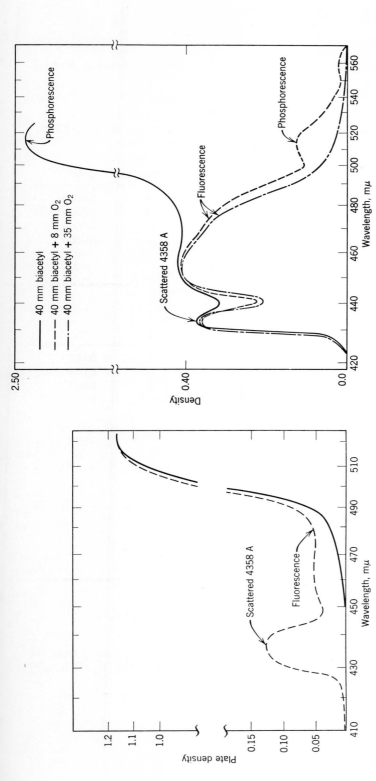

Fig. 4-19 Quenching of phosphorescence of biacetyl vapor by addition of oxygen. Excitation was by mercury 4358 A line. From Ishikawa and Noyes.[210]

Fig. 4-18 Microdensitometer tracing of emission in fluorescence region of pure biacetyl vapor (broken line), 40 mm and 6.5 hr irradiation at 4358 A, and a mixture of benzene (30 mm) and biacetyl (0.2 mm) irradiated 288 hr at 2537 A (solid line). Little if any fluorescence is in the sensitized emission. From Ishikawa and Noyes.[210]

327

TABLE 4-21   Effect of Foreign Gases on the Absolute Biacetyl Emission Yield at Various Wavelengths[a]

Temperature: 29 ± 1°C

(1) Incident Wavelength: 2537 A

| Biacetyl Pressure: 30 mm | | Biacetyl Pressure: 0.11 mm | |
Cyclohexane Pressure, mm	φ_e	Cyclohexane Pressure, mm	φ_e
0	0.0004 ± 0.0001	0	0.0000
10	0.0005 ± 0.0001	5	0.0000
20	0.0006 ± 0.0001	10	0.0000
40	0.0005 ± 0.0001	20	0.0000

(2) Incident Wavelength: 3130 A

Biacetyl Pressure: 30 mm

Cyclohexane Pressure, mm	φ_e	Benzene Pressure, mm	φ_e
0	0.007	0	0.007
12	0.009	12	0.009
20	0.010	32	0.012
40	0.014	40	0.016

(3) Incident Wavelength: 3650 A

Biacetyl Pressure: 0.16 mm

Cyclohexane Pressure, mm	φ_e
0	0.0025[b]
7	0.060
14	0.080
21	0.11
35	0.14
45	0.15
62	0.15

[a] From Ishikawa and Noyes.[210b]

[b] The emission yield of biacetyl at 0.16 mm was estimated from the results reported by Henriques and Noyes[300] and by Almy and Gillette.[301]

| Biacetyl Pressure: 7.0 mm | | Biacetyl Pressure: 7.5 mm | |
Cyclohexane Pressure, mm	φ_e	Benzene Pressure, mm	φ_e
0	0.067	0	0.073
5	0.094	5.5	0.11
10	0.12	10	0.12
20	0.15	20	0.14
36	0.15	38	0.15
50	0.15	50	0.15

(4) Incident Wavelength: 4358 A
Biacetyl Pressure: 10 mm

Cyclohexane Pressure, mm	φ_e	Benzene Pressure, mm	φ_e
0	0.15	0	0.15
17	0.15	20	0.15
30	0.15	31	0.15
43	0.15	40	0.15

misleading, since both the benzene and cyclohexane have a definite effect in *increasing* the emission yield of biacetyl at 3130 and 3650 A. Presumably the inert gas acts to reduce the yield of the competing process, photo-dissociation, by siphoning off through collisions some of the excess vibrational energy of the electronically excited biacetyl molecules.

In addition to sensitized phosphorescence as the photophysical manifestation of energy transfer, Ishikawa and Noyes found a *benzene-sensitized decomposition* of biacetyl. The overall quantum yields of product formation as a function of the pressure of added benzene are shown in Fig. 4-20. The sensitized quantum yield of product formation, Φ^s, is defined as

$$\Phi^s = \frac{\text{No. of molecules formed from energy acceptors}}{\text{No. of photons absorbed by energy donors}}$$

The sensitized yield of CO is only about 0.05 at 30° but is substantial at 60°C, for example, $\Phi_{CO}^s = 0.27$ for 10 mm benzene and 40 mm biacetyl. (Actually the yields are similar to the quantum yields for pure biacetyl at 3130 A.) Φ_{CO}^s is pressure dependent at 60°C, dropping to 0.16 at 30 mm added benzene.

On the basis of their results, some of which we have cited above, Ishikawa and Noyes have developed or extended presently reported,

TABLE 4-22 Foreign Gas Effect on Quantum Yields of the Products in the Photolysis of Biacetyl[a]

Incident Wavelength: 2537 A
Biacetyl Pressure: 40 mm
Exposure: 1.80×10^4 sec

Temperature, °C	$I_a^{\text{Biacetyl}} \times 10^{-12}$,[b] quanta/cc-sec	Cyclohexane Pressure, mm	Quantum Yield (Φ)		
			CO	CH_4	C_2H_6
30	2.50	0	0.65	0.020	0.21
30	2.50	40	0.64	...	0.21
30	2.50	60	0.62	...	0.21
60	2.18	0	0.97	0.075	0.31
60	2.15	40	0.94	0.085	0.27
60	2.19	60	0.91	0.090	0.27

Incident Wavelength: 3130 A
Biacetyl Pressure: 40 mm
Exposure: 2.52×10^4 sec

Temperature, °C	$I_a^{\text{Biacetyl}} \times 10^{-12}$,[b] quanta/cc-sec	Benzene Pressure, mm	Cyclohexane Pressure, mm	Quantum Yield (Φ)		
				CO	CH_4	C_2H_6
30	2.26	0	0	0.069	...	0.013
30	2.62	60	0	0.070	...	0.012
30	2.90	0	60	0.072	...	0.012
60	2.90	0	0	0.24	0.035	0.052
60	2.90	60	0	0.24	0.033	0.053
60	3.00	0	60	0.23	0.036	0.047

[a] From Ishikawa and Noyes.[210b]
[b] I_a^{Biacetyl} is the number of photons absorbed by biacetyl per milliliter per second.

detailed mechanisms for the photolysis of both pure biacetyl and benzene–biacetyl mixtures. Here we shall note the energy-transfer aspect of their work, commenting briefly, however, also on pure benzene. Figure 4-21 shows the energies of the lower electronic states of benzene and biacetyl and indicates the possible transitions between them, while Table 4-23 lists the reactions and classifies them.

Both benzene and biacetyl absorb at 2537 A, but the latter process is not shown in Fig. 4-21 or Table 4-23, since we are dealing here with energy transfer in which electronic energy is supplied by benzene. We should note,

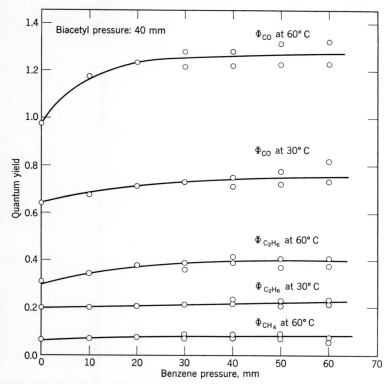

Fig. 4-20   Quantum yields for the benzene-sensitized photodecomposition of biacetyl at 2537 A.   From Ishikawa and Noyes.[210]

however, that absorption at 2537 A by pure biacetyl is to a vibrationally excited, second electronic state,

$$B(S_0, {}^1A_g) + h\nu(\lambda = 2537 \text{ A}) \rightarrow B(S_2^v, {}^1A_u)$$

from which dissociation apparently occurs, giving products

$$B(S_2^v) \rightarrow \text{Dissociation products}$$

some of whose yields are shown at *zero* benzene pressure in Fig. 4-20.

Primary processes in benzene vapor following absorption to a low vibrational level of the first singlet state (S_1, ${}^1B_{2a}$), reactions 1-6, Table 4-23, are generally those observed in dilute solid solutions at 77°K except that neither photodissociation, photodimerization, or phosphorescence occurs, and reaction 6 must be included to account for slight self-quenching of fluorescence.

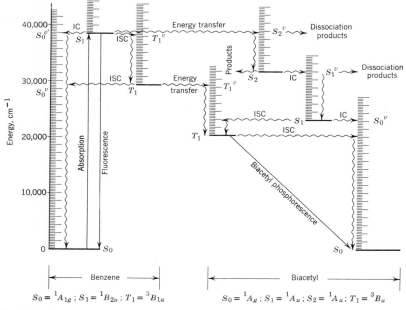

Fig. 4-21   Electronic states and transitions between them in the system benzene-biacetyl irradiated at 2537 A. Biacetyl also absorbs directly 2537 A radiation, but this transition and state T_2 are omitted for clarity. From Ishikawa and Noyes.[210]

Fluorescence from biacetyl excited by 2537 A radiation has an absolute yield, $\varphi_f = 0.22 \pm 0.04$, at 29° and 20 mm pressure with a mean wavelength of 2900 ± 50 A. The vapor-phase value of 0.22 (which drops to 0.19 at 41.5 mm pressure) may be compared to 0.11 in hexane solution, found by Bowen and Williams,[218] and 0.25 ± 0.04 in rigid EPA at 77°K, obtained by Gilmore, Gibson, and McClure.[155]

Benzene does not phosphoresce in the gas phase, and, in contrast to other aromatic hydrocarbons, no triplet-triplet absorption has been found (although major efforts have been made to see it). However, by analogy with naphthalene and anthracene, and to explain the induced emission of biacetyl phosphorescence, the triplet must be included in the mechanism.

Ishikawa and Noyes assume that internal conversion, process 3, $S_1 \rightsquigarrow S_0^{v'}$, is negligible (but point out this may not be the case) and calculate the rate constants of the several processes shown in Table 4-23. In addition they evaluated a constant for the quenching of benzene fluorescence by biacetyl and oxygen, finding $k_q = 7.4 \times 10^{10}$ and 6.4×10^{10} liters/mole/sec, respectively. They then calculated the mean lifetime of

TABLE 4-23   Primary Processes and Electronic Energy Transfer in the Vapor-Phase System Benzene-Biacetyl Irradiated at 2537 A. (Certain rate constants are included.)[a]

Benzene Absorption

(1) $C_6H_6(S_0) + h\nu \ (\lambda = 2537 \text{ A}) \longrightarrow C_6H_6(S_1)$

Fluorescence

(2) $C_6H_6(S_1) \longrightarrow C_6H_6(S_0) + h\nu'$; $k_2 = 1.6 \times 10^6 \text{ sec}^{-1}$
Radiative $\tau_f = 6.2 \times 10^{-7} \text{ sec}$

Internal Conversion, IC

(3) $C_6H_6(S_1) \underset{\text{IC}}{\leadsto} [C_6H_6(S_0^{v'})] \leadsto C_6H_6(S_0)$; $k_3 = \text{small}$

Intersystem Crossing, ISC

(4) $C_6H_6(S_1) \underset{\text{ISC}}{\leadsto} [C_6H_6(T_1^v)] \underset{\text{IC}}{\leadsto} C_6H_6(T_1)$; $k_4 = 4.7 \times 10^6 \text{ sec}^{-1}$

(5) $C_6H_6(T_1) \underset{\text{ISC}}{\leadsto} C_6H_6(S_0^v) \leadsto C_6H_6(S_0)$

Quenching

(6) $C_6H_6(S_1) + C_6H_6(S_0) \longrightarrow 2C_6H_6(S_0)$; $k_6 = 10^9 \text{ liters/mole/sec}$

Intermolecular Electronic Energy Transfer

Singlet $\longrightarrow$ Singlet

(7) $C_6H_6(S_1) + B(S_0) \longrightarrow C_6H_6(S_0) + B(S_2) \text{ [or } (S_2^v)]$

Triplet $\longrightarrow$ Triplet

(8) $C_6H_6(T_1) + B(S_0) \longrightarrow C_6H_6(S_0) + B(T_1) \text{ [or } T_1^v]$

Biacetyl

Dissociation

(9) $B(S_2) \longrightarrow \text{Products}$

Intersystem Crossing

(10) $B(S_2) \leadsto B(T_2)$

(11) $B(T_2) \leadsto [B(S_0^{v'})] \leadsto B(S_0)$

Phosphorescence

(12) $B(T_1) \longrightarrow B(S_0) + h\nu''$

Intersystem Crossing

(13) $B(T_1) \leadsto [B(S_0^v)] \leadsto B(S_0)$

---

[a] Table adapted from Ishikawa and Noyes.[210]

fluorescence in benzene-biacetyl and benzene-oxygen mixtures to be 1.4×10^{-7} sec in both cases (in contrast to the natural radiative lifetime, $\tau_f = 6.2 \times 10^{-7}$ sec). The calculation of these important rate constants is an excellent example of the highly useful information that can be obtained by careful studies of this type.

Both singlet-singlet (7) and triplet-triplet (8) electronic energy transfer seem to occur in this system. The former is assumed responsible for the sensitized decomposition (Fig. 4-20), and the latter for the sensitized phosphorescence.

Biacetyl quenching of benzene in its first excited state, $C_6H_6(S_1)$, is postulated to excite the biacetyl to its second excited singlet, $B(S_2)$, because (a) there is sufficient energy, (b) the sensitized emission is purely phosphorescence, and if the first singlet were formed, $B(S_1)$, some fluorescence should also be emitted (as occurs in direct irradiation of pure biacetyl at 4358 A), and (c) the sensitized emission yield is a maximum at low biacetyl pressures. Biacetyl dissociation from the lowest vibrational level of state S_2 (reaction 9 of Table 4-23) was proposed because the sensitized quantum yields resemble those for the direct photolysis at 3130 A, near the onset of the second absorption band (hence at low vibrational levels of the second excited state).

The yield of dissociation is not large enough to account for the fate of all the excited biacetyl produced by the quenching of excited benzene. The internal conversion process $B(S_2)$ -⋀⋙ $B(S_1^v)$ must be small, since for reasons cited in the preceding paragraph little or no biacetyl in the *lowest singlet* seems present in this system. The direct internal conversion process $B(S_2)$ -⋀⋙ $B(S_0^v)'$ seems unlikely because of the large $S_2 \rightarrow S_0$ energy gap. Thus the sequence of radiationless transitions, reactions 10 and 11, are proposed.

Triplet-triplet quenching, process 8, which is allowed by the Wigner spin conservation rule, furnishes a reasonable explanation of the sizable yield of sensitized biacetyl emission of pure phosphorescence, which was as high as 0.12. Direct population of the lowest biacetyl triplet is thus possible without having to invoke a process involving the first singlet state.

On the basis of their mechanism for sensitized emission Ishikawa and Noyes derived the following expression for the sensitized yield of phosphorescence $\varphi_p{}^s$, where $I_p{}^B$ is the intensity of sensitized biacetyl phosphorescence and $I_a{}^{C_6H_6}$ is the intensity of light absorbed by benzene:

$$\varphi_p{}^s = \frac{I_p{}^B}{I_a{}^{C_6H_6}} = \frac{k_{12}}{k_{12} + k_{13}} \times \frac{k_8[B]}{k_8[B] + k_5}$$
$$\times \frac{k_4}{k_2 + k_6[C_6H_6] + k_3 + k_4 + k_7[B]} \quad (4\text{-}5)$$

At constant benzene pressure of 20 mm this reduces to Eq. 4-6 when the values for the rate constants and extinction coefficients are inserted and concentrations are in moles per liter:

$$\varphi_p^{\ s} + \frac{2.00 \times 10^{-5}}{[B]^2 + 1.50 \times 10^{-4}[B] + 6.22 \times 10^{-11}} \tag{4-6}$$

The excellent fit between yields calculated from 4-6 and the experimental values, Table 4-24, is good confirmative evidence for this mechanism.

TABLE 4-24 Comparison of Observed and Calculated Sensitized Emission Yields for Gaseous Benzene-Biacetyl Mixtures Irradiated at 2537 Å[a]

Biacetyl Concentration [B], moles/liter $\times 10^5$	Pressure Biacetyl, mm	Quantum Yield of Sensitized Phosphorescence, $\varphi_p^{\ s}$	
		Observed[b]	Calculated[c]
0.536	0.1	0.120	0.120
10.7	2.0	0.078	0.078
32.2	6.0	0.043	0.043
42.9	8.0	0.034	0.035

[a] From Ishikawa and Noyes.[210]
[b] The pressure of benzene was 20 mm and $t = 28°C$ in these runs.
[c] Calculations based on Eq. 4-6.

If one assumes that every collision between triplet benzene and singlet biacetyl gives an efficient transfer, then, since $\varphi_f = 0.22$ for pure benzene and no photodecomposition occurs, the yield of triplet biacetyl should be 0.78, if one further assumes no internal conversion of singlet benzene, S_1, and no intersystem crossing of triplet benzene. The sensitized yield of biacetyl phosphorescence should be, then, 0.78 times the phosphorescence yield in pure biacetyl, $(0.78) \times (0.15) = 0.12$, in agreement with the observed value of 0.12. Ishikawa and Noyes point out this suggests that the benzene internal conversion process, $S_1 \leadsto S_0^v$, is small, but since experimental error is large no definite conclusion can be reached.[210]

In ending this discussion of the "model" energy-transfer system benzene-biacetyl we should also note that Ishikawa and Noyes, using a low-pressure Hg 2537 Å *resonance lamp*, found qualitative evidence suggesting that the interesting energy-transfer process

$$Hg(^3P_1) + C_6H_6(S_0) \rightarrow Hg(^1S_0) + C_6H_6(T_1)$$

may occur.*

4-10B   Energy Transfer in Condensed Systems

In the vapor phase, electronic energy transfer occurs as a result of collisions between the excited donor and the acceptor. However, in liquids and solids the donor-acceptor pair are normally much closer together than in gases, and, in addition to "short-range" exchange via collisions, several other types of energy transfer have been shown experimentally to occur. These include long-range "dipole-dipole" transfer of the type first quantitatively treated by Förster, which, he estimates, may be effective at distances up to 50–100 A, and shorter-range "triplet-triplet" transfer.

In both pure crystals and dilute solid solutions, the mechanism for singlet-singlet transfer is considered to involve excitons (in certain cases "localized excitons" and "surface excitons"), and it now appears that shorter-range "triplet excitons" and triplet-triplet annhilation are important processes in organic solids as well as solutions (Sec. 4-9A).

We shall focus our discussion here chiefly on the experimental evidence for these phenomena, in part because the theories are in a state of flux and in part because they are beyond the scope of this book. However, we shall review references to the latest theory and deal with some theoretical considerations in a tentative sense. (See Ref. 202 for a recent review by Wilkinson on transfer in the liquid phase.)

4-10B-1   Experimental Evidence for Singlet-Singlet
Electronic Energy Transfer in Liquid Solutions

In 1924 Perrin[219] extended Franck's idea of electronic energy transfer in atomic systems to explain the recently discovered phenomenon of concentration depolarization of molecular fluorescence.[220] This was observed when a solution containing a fluorescing dye was irradiated with polarized light[221] (see Refs. 1, 18b, and 94 for reviews). At low solute concentrations the resulting fluorescence was also polarized, but as the concentration increased it became progressively more depolarized, even in viscous solvents, showing that it was not a collision-induced process. The

---

* Note the difference in symbology with the two S_0's; in the case of mercury the 0 is the value of a quantum number, J, while for benzene the 0 simply refers to the ground-state singlet.

effect also was shown not to be due to the so-called "trivial" process in which light emitted as a photon by the fluorescing molecule is reabsorbed by a second solute molecule and then re-emitted. Perrin, therefore, proposed the existence of a long-range, radiationless, molecular electronic energy-transfer process.*

In the next twenty-five years transfer was proposed in several systems.[222-228] Among the most carefully confirmed cases to date for solutions of aromatic hydrocarbons (in which solute dimerization is minimized relative to the fluorescing dyes previously employed) are those of Bowen and Brocklehurst[229] and Bowen and Livingston[230] in the early 1950's. In essence they took liquid solutions containing two different solutes in which the emission spectrum of the donor D overlapped the absorption spectrum of the acceptor A (the conditions for Förster type transfer) and showed that the fluorescence of D is quenched and the fluorescence of A is sensitized.† Fluorescent intensities of the following pairs of solutes were determined: 1-chloroanthracene-perylene,[229-230] 1-chloroanthracene-rubrene,[230] 9-phenylanthracene-9,10-dichloroanthracene,[229] and cyanoanthracene-rubrene[230] (the first-named is the donor). It was shown by spectroscopic and kinetic quenching data, particularly detailed for the first-named pair, that singlet-singlet electronic energy transfer is much more efficient than can be explained by the trivial process, that is, emission and reabsorption.

Evidence for transfer in the pair 1-chloroanthracene-perylene is particularly compelling, since here the donor which initially absorbs the radiation has a *low* intrinsic fluorescence intensity and the acceptor a high intrinsic fluorescence intensity. In Fig. 4-22 are shown the fluorescence efficiencies of benzene solutions containing 1-chloroanthracene-perylene mixtures in the constant ratio 5:1, plotted against increasing concentration of perylene, the acceptor. The total combined emission, curve 1, rises with concentration, despite increased concentration quenching. Furthermore, the perylene fluorescence, curve 2, rises rapidly with concentration, whereas the donor fluorescence, curve 3, falls. The rapid rise in perylene fluorescence yield above the low limiting efficiency of the donor, 1-chloro-anthracene, is excellent evidence that energy absorbed by donors must be

---

* In considering electronic energy transfer we should note at the start that experimentally in liquid or solid solutions only *average* values for donor-acceptor inter-molecular distances (R_{DA}) are known and there is some doubt as to the significance of an *average* value for R_{DA} when dealing with individual events of energy transfer. A further complication is the possibility that in some systems solute-solute attractive forces are stronger than solute-solvent forces, causing a shortening of the *actual* donor-acceptor distance.

† In their papers Bowen *et al.* use the symbol A to represent the *donor* molecule.

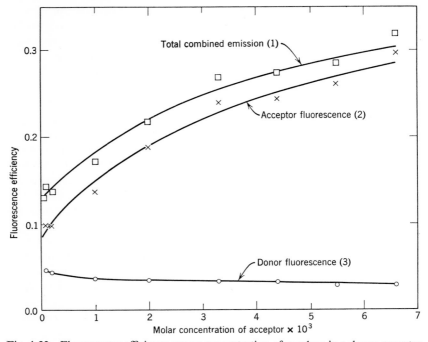

Fig. 4-22   Fluorescence efficiency versus concentration of perylene in a donor-acceptor mixture of 1-chloroanthracene-perylene, mole ratio 5:1 in benzene solvent. From Bowen and Brocklehurst.[229]

directly transferred to normal perylene molecules in a time short compared to that of their normal degradative processes. As the authors point out, "this is an example where a poorly fluorescent molecule can efficiently 'sensitize' the fluorescence of another of higher efficiency."[229]

As a further critical check the phenomenon was shown not to be due to the formation of donor-acceptor dimers on the basis of the concentration dependence of the fluorescence and by the validity of the Beer-Lambert law in the mixed solutions. Furthermore, the rate of interaction was independent of viscosity of the solvent and calculated to be faster by at least a factor of ten than a diffusion-controlled process.[230]

The latter point is one often cited for various liquid systems and is based on calculating the specific reaction rate of a diffusion-controlled process, k_{diff}, by the Debye equation[231] (for a discussion see Sec. 6-7A-6). Calculated values of k_{diff} for benzene and chloroform at 20° are 1.0×10^{10} and 1.1×10^{10} liter/mole/sec, respectively. The value approximately 10^{10} is useful to remember for the bimolecular rate constant of a diffusion-controlled process in mobile liquids at room temperature.

The diffusion rate equation of Debye[231] (with the Bäckström-Sandros modification,[232] Sec. 6-7A-6) has been confirmed empirically for the self-quenching of fluorescence of the solutions of hydrocarbons studied by Bowen, Brocklehurst,[229] and Livingston.[230] With regard to energy transfer, these authors make the significant point that empirical values of the rate constants for self-quenching do not exceed those calculated by the Debye equation, yet the observed rate constants for sensitized fluorescence via energy transfer *exceed the calculated maxima by factors ranging from* 15 *to* 30, depending on the solvent and the particular solute donor-acceptor pair. Thus, "energy exchange between unlike aryl-hydrocarbons is not a diffusional process, although self-quenching of these hydrocarbon solutions appears to be the result of simple diffusion-controlled bimolecular reactions." They point out, however, that the latter point "should not be generalized because self-quenching in chlorophyll solutions is a quadratic rather than linear function of concentration and is independent of the viscosity of the solvent."[230]

The system 1-chloroanthracene-perylene also was studied by Bowen and Brocklehurst in a rigid glassy solvent of tetrachloro- and pentachloro-ethanes at 77°K. As the concentration of the acceptor, perylene (which absorbs only weakly at 3650 A), was increased, a large rise in the total fluorescence emission, and in the fluorescence of perylene, was observed. The curves for the solid solution were similar to those in Fig. 4-22 for the liquid system.[233] The effects show that singlet electronic excitation energy absorbed by the 1-chloroanthracene is transferred to the perylene by a non-radiative process which appears to be the same in the solid phase at 77°K as in liquids at room temperature.

4-10B-2   Theory of Electronic Energy Transfer

Singlet-singlet non-radiative electronic energy transfer of the type described in the above liquid-phase experiments has been referred to as long-range dipole-dipole transfer (*dd*), inductive resonance, or simply "classical resonance." Theoretical analysis of the phenomenon for two allowed (electric dipole) transitions in organic molecules was developed chiefly by Förster.[18,101,226,234]

In a more generalized treatment, Dexter[235] included the case of an allowed transition in the donor and a forbidden transition in the acceptor, which is typical of electronic energy transfer in inorganic solids. He further considered exchange effects which occur in triplet-triplet transfer (see Dexter,[235] Reid,[7] and Robinson and Frosch[113] for discussions and a review of previous literature).

Before considering the experimental evidence for triplet-triplet transfer and its important chemical applications, we shall comment briefly on these three types of interactions, which Dexter classifies as due to (1) overlapping of the electric dipole fields of the donor and the acceptor, *dd* transfer (in the terminology used for crystalline phosphors these are called sensitizer or absorber and activator or emitter, respectively), (2) the overlapping of the dipole field of the donor with the quadrupole field of the acceptor (*dq* transfer), and (3) exchange effects. These transfer mechanisms are listed in order of decreasing strength of the interaction. Dexter derives expressions for transfer probabilities for each case and calculates that they give rise to "sensitization" of about 10^3–10^4, 10^2, and 30 lattice sites, respectively, surrounding each donor (sensitizer) in typical "sensitized" solids.*

Treatment of these three cases is applicable to liquid systems, and Dexter's equation for case 1, dipole-dipole transfer (*dd* transfer of singlets), is identical with that derived first by Förster (Eq. 4-7). The primary differences between solid and liquid systems "seem to lie in the relative smallness of the index of refraction in liquid solutions and in the relative smallness of the Stokes' shifts in the liquids."[235]

The effective ranges of these three types of transfer drop off as $1/R^6$ for *dd* transfer, $1/R^8$ for *dq* transfer, and in an even faster but more complex fashion for exchange interaction. Thus, while Förster estimates that *dd* transfer may occur up to 50–100 A separation, exchange transfer operates over very short ranges, of the order of the normal collision diameters of the interacting molecules, about 10–15 A. Thus the rate constants for 100% effective triplet-triplet transfer in liquid solutions should not exceed those calculated for a bimolecular, diffusion-controlled process ($k_{diff} \simeq 10^{10}$ liters/mole/sec). This is true, for example, in the liquid systems benzophenone-biacetyl[232] and benzophenone-naphthalene[142b] (see Sec. 4-10B-3). Another way of emphasizing the short-range nature of these exchange forces is to point out that if the intermolecular donor-acceptor distance is increased by only one molecular diameter the transfer probability drops by a factor of about 100. We should keep in mind, however, that the relatively long radiational lifetime of the triplets facilitates many exchanges, but over a shorter distance than singlets (see below).

Direct quadrupole transitions are weaker by a factor of about 10^{-7} to 10^{-8} than electric dipole transitions. [The factor for atoms is $(a/\lambda)^2$, where a = radius of the atom and λ the wavelength of the absorbed light.] However, the probability of a radiationless electric dipole-quadrupole energy-transfer process, *dq*, is only a factor of about 10 less than for a

---

* Note, however, that the long lifetime of triplet excitons must be considered (see Sec. 4-10B-3).

wholly "allowed" *dd* transfer. Thus transfer can readily occur from a donor to an acceptor if the latter has a quadrupole transition in the suitable frequency range, even though direct absorption by the acceptor atom or molecule is only about 10^{-7} to 10^{-8} as strong as an allowed transition.[235]

Förster's equation[7,101,235] for the number of intermolecular dipole-dipole transitions per second, the transfer rate constant, $k_{D^* \to A}$, is

$$k_{D^* \to A} = \frac{9000 \ln 10 \kappa^2 \varphi_f}{128\pi^6 n^4 N \tau_D R_{DA}^6} \int_0^\infty f_D(\nu)\epsilon_A(\nu) \frac{d\nu}{\nu^4} \qquad (4\text{-}7)$$

where R_{DA} is the intermolecular distance between donor and acceptor, τ_D is the actual mean lifetime of the excited state (i.e., of the emission), N is Avogadro's number, n is the solvent refractive index, κ^2 is an orientation factor (about 2/3), φ_f is the quantum yield of fluorescence, $f_D(\nu)$ is the spectral distribution of the fluorescence of the donor (in quanta and normalized to unity), $\epsilon_A(\nu)$ is the molar extinction coefficient of the acceptor as a function of ν, and ν is the frequency in centimeters^{-1}.

Qualitatively, one assumes that energy available for transfer by the donor is that which would otherwise be emitted radiatively. The transfer probability is thus stated in terms of the strengths of the individual transitions and the energy overlap of the emission band of the donor and the absorption band of the acceptor (the quantity within the integral in Eq. 4-7). A further assumption is that the transfer time is long relative to vibrational internal conversion processes, so that transfer is from the lower vibrational levels of the first excited singlet state of the donor.

If one defines the quantity R_0 as the radius at which the probability of transfer equals that for spontaneous decay, then at that distance $1/\tau_D = k_{D^* \to A}$, and substituting in Eq. 4-7 we find

$$R_0^6 \approx \frac{9000 \ln 10 \kappa^2 \varphi_f}{128\pi^6 n^4 N} \int_0^\infty f_D(\nu)\epsilon_A(\nu) \frac{d\nu}{\nu^4} \qquad (4\text{-}8)$$

As indicated earlier, singlet-singlet transfer is calculated to occur up to 50–100 A. Bowen and Brocklehurst[229] found experimentally that such transfer occurred in hydrocarbon solutions in the concentration range 10^{-2} to 10^{-3} M (similar to Förster's dye solutions). This corresponds to an *average* experimental distance of about 50 A, in good agreement with Förster's equation. More recent data by Ware,[244] shown in Table 4-25, offer further confirmation of the Förster theory for singlet-singlet transfer.

TABLE 4-25 Experimental Values of Critical Distances for Singlet-Singlet Transfer Compared with the Critical Distances from Förster's Theory[a]

Pair[b]	$k_{D^* \to A}$ (theor.), (moles/liter)$^{-1}$ sec^{-1}	$k_{D^* \to A}$ (exp.), (moles/liter)$^{-1}$ sec^{-1}	R_0 (theor.), A	R_0 (exp., A
Anthracene-perylene	2.3×10^{10}	1.2×10^{11}	31	54
Perylene-rubrene	2.8×10^{10}	1.3×10^{11}	38	65
9,10-Dichloroanthra-cene-perylene	1.7×10^{10}	8.0×10^{10}	40	67
Anthracene-rubrene	7.7×10^{9}	3.7×10^{10}	23	39
9,10-Dichloroanthra-cene-rubrene	8.5×10^{9}	3.1×10^{10}	32	49

[a] Data from Ware;[244] table from Wilkinson.[202]
[b] The first-named compound is the energy donor.

4-10B-3   Triplet Energy Transfer in Solid Solutions

During the last two decades, as we have seen, the importance of the role of the triplet state in the spectroscopy and photochemistry of polyatomic molecules has become increasingly apparent. Among the latest developments, and perhaps most significant to chemists, is the discovery and specific utilization in chemical reactions of radiationless transfer of triplet energy in solutions and in solids in which a donor molecule ("sensitizer") in its lowest triplet state transfers energy to an acceptor (quencher) molecule in its singlet ground state, raising it to its triplet level and quenching the donor to its ground singlet state. Such a process is in accord with the Wigner spin conservation rule, since the total spin momentum of the entire system is conserved. It may be written

$$D(T_1) + A(S_0) \to D(S_0) + A(T_1)$$

A requirement for such a "spin transfer" process is that the triplet level of the acceptor lies below (or near) the triplet level of the donor.

The first spectroscopic evidence for such triplet transfer is that of Terenin and Ermolaev, who observed sensitized phosphorescence in frozen binary solutions of aromatic compounds[237-240] and who in 1956 elucidated the general aspects of intermolecular energy transfer between triplet states[241] in solids (see the recent reviews by Ermolaev[103] and Terenin[283]). Thus phosphorescence spectra of naphthalene, α-methylnaphthalene, α-chloronaphthalene, and biphenyl were excited by transfer of energy originally absorbed as light by various donors such as benzaldehyde, benzophenone, acetophenone, ethyl phenyl ketone, o-hydroxybenzaldehyde, benzoin, diphenylamine, and carbazole. The rigid solvent was an ethanol-ether mixture at 77°K.

The sensitized emission by the acceptors was shown to be identical with that produced by direct excitation. This is evident in Fig. 4-23b, where the phosphorescence spectra of benzophenone and naphthalene alone may be compared to the emission of a mixture of the two in a glassy solvent at $-180°$ irradiation at 3660 A, where *only the benzophenone absorbs* (Fig. 4-23a). The latter point is significant, since in the mixture of solutes the naphthalene triplets from which sensitized phosphorescence arose could not have been formed by a radiative process either by direct absorption or by the "trivial" process of reabsorbing phosphorescence emitted by benzophenone, or as a result of a singlet-singlet non-radiative energy transfer, since the naphthalene singlet lies above that of benzophenone.

The mechanism of the process is shown in Fig. 4-24. Benzophenone absorbs 3660 A radiation and is raised to the first excited singlet state, S_1, a $^1(n, \pi^*)$ state. It efficiently undergoes $S_1 \rightsquigarrow T_1$ intersystem crossing ($\varphi_{\text{ISC}} = 0.99$, Table 4-17; $\varphi_p = 0.74$, Table 4-12), populating the triplet state, $^3(n, \pi^*)$. The latter has a relatively long radiative lifetime, about 5×10^{-6} sec, and during this period exchange interaction with neighboring naphthalene molecules in their ground singlet states raises them to their triplet levels and quenches the benzophenone:

$$(C_6H_5)_2CO \ ^3(n, \pi^*) + \bigcirc\bigcirc (S_0) \rightarrow$$

$$(C_6H_5)_2CO(S_0) + \bigcirc\bigcirc \ ^3(\pi, \pi^*)$$

It is interesting that under the experimental conditions in Fig. 4-23 the sensitized quantum yield of naphthalene phosphorescence was 0.07 (Table 4-26), greater than the value of 0.03 for naphthalene excited directly in its own absorption region (Table 4-12, Ref. 103).

Concurrently with population of the acceptor triplet level by exchange transfer there must be a diminished concentration of donor triplets, and this should be observed in a decreased lifetime of donor phosphorescence, τ_p^D. This was demonstrated by the authors, who also cited good spectroscopic evidence that the entire phenomenon was *not* due to donor-acceptor dimer formation[103,241] [it will be recalled that a similar proposal was made as an alternative to *dd* (singlet-singlet) transfer in solution].

We should note parenthetically that utilization of low-field (zero-field splitting) ESR techniques enabled Farmer, Gardner, and McDowell to confirm energy transfer between triplet benzophenone and naphthalene in glassy solutions of the two in EPA at 77°K, irradiated at 3660 A.[137] The ESR spectrum of triplet naphthalene was clearly observed at $\Delta m \pm 2$,

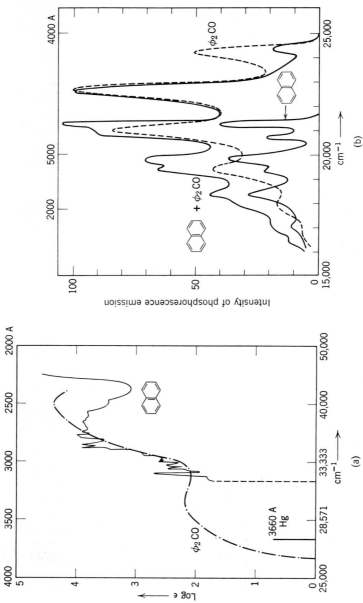

Fig. 4-23 (a) Absorption spectra of benzophenone (ethanol, 20°C) and naphthalene (ethanol + methanol, −180°). (b) Phosphorescence emission spectra at −190° in ether + ethanol, under steady irradiation at 3660 A. Benzophenone, 2×10^{-2} M; benzophenone + naphthalene, 2×10^{-2} M and 3.2×10^{-1} M, respectively; concentration of pure naphthalene (solid line) not known. From Terenin and Ermolaev.[241]

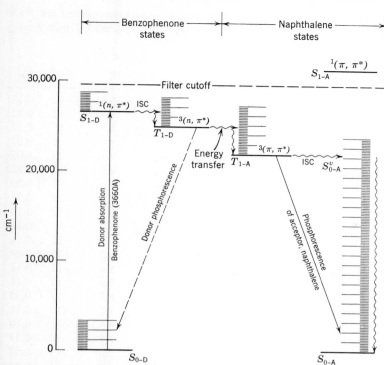

Fig. 4-24 Energy level diagram showing absorption of radiation by benzophenone and triplet energy transfer to naphthalene.

and at the same time a much reduced spectrum of the ketyl radical, $(C_6H_5)_2\dot{C}OH$, was noted.

The latest values of Ermolaev and Terenin on the quantum yields of sensitized phosphorescence $\varphi_p{}^s$ of a variety of donor-acceptor pairs are shown in Table 4-26.[103] They define the quantity $\varphi_p{}^s$ as

$$\varphi_p{}^s = \frac{I_{p-A}}{I^0_{p-D} - I_{p-D}} \tag{4-9}$$

where I_{p-A} and I_{p-D} are the quantum intensities of the phosphorescence of the acceptor and donor molecules, respectively, and I^0_{p-D} is that for the donor when no acceptor is present. Also included in this table are calculated values for the "spheres of action of quenching"* and the distance R between the centers of the donor-acceptor pair of molecules (assuming that they are both spheres).

---

* The sphere of instantaneous energy transfer from the donor in the triplet state to the acceptor in the ground state, which raises the acceptor to a triplet state from which it may phosphoresce. See Ref. 103.

TABLE 4-26 Quantum Yields of Sensitized Phosphorescence and the Radii and "Spheres of Action" of Quenching by Donor → Acceptor Triplet Energy Transfer[a]

No.	Donor	Acceptor	Vol. $\times 10^{21}$, cm^3	R, Å	φ_p^s
1	Benzaldehyde	Naphthalene	6.8	12	0.13
2	Benzaldehyde	1-Chloronaphthalene	7.0	12	0.22
3	Benzaldehyde	1-Bromonaphthalene	7.2	12	0.27
4	Benzophenone	Naphthalene	8.6	13	0.07
5	Benzophenone	1-Methylnaphthalene	9.5	13	0.07
6	Benzophenone	1-Chloronaphthalene	9.5	13	0.12
7	Benzophenone	1-Bromonaphthalene	8.6	13	0.20
8	Benzophenone	1-Iodonaphthalene	8.6	13	0.35
9	Benzophenone	Quinoline	7.2	12	0.14
10	Acetophenone	Naphthalene	6.0	11	0.10
11	p-Chlorobenzaldehyde	Naphthalene	6.7	12	0.14
12	p-Chlorobenzaldehyde	1-Bromonaphthalene	6.2	11	0.49
13	o-Chlorobenzaldehyde	Naphthalene	5.4	11	0.11
14	m-Iodobenzaldehyde	Naphthalene	5.8	11	0.11
15	m-Iodobenzaldehyde	1-Bromonaphthalene	5.7	11	0.30
16	Xanthone	Naphthalene	9.2	13	0.11
17	Anthraquinone	Naphthalene	5.9	11	0.10
18	Anthraquinone	1-Bromonaphthalene	7.6	12	0.27
19	Triphenylamine	Naphthalene	9.3	13	0.07
20	Carbazole	Naphthalene	14	15	0.08
21	Phenanthrene	Naphthalene	10	13	0.30
22	Phenanthrene	1-Chloronaphthalene	11	14	0.73
23	Phenanthrene	1-Bromonaphthalene	11	14	0.99

[a] From the review by Ermolaev[103]; calculated from the data of Ermolaev.[153] All measurements were made in alcohol–ether mixture at 90° or 77°K. For Nos. 1–16, the 3650 Å mercury line was used for excitation, and for Nos. 12–23, the 3340 Å line. The quantum yield of sensitized phosphorescence φ_p^s is calculated from Eq. 4-9.

It is evident from the results in Table 4-26 that the effective transfer distance is about 11–15 Å in these rigid solutions at 77°K. This experimental value is greater by a power of 10 than that calculated by assuming the Förster equation (that gave a value of 1.1 Å, assuming interaction of two electric dipoles for the pair benzophenone + naphthalene[103]). This is a major feature of Ermolaev and Terenin's conclusion that, as we have indicated above, the phenomenon of sensitized phosphorescence should be interpreted in terms of relatively short-range exchange-resonance interactions. As we saw earlier, these have been treated theoretically by Dexter, who noted that the probability of energy transfer drops off experimentally much faster for this type of interaction than for the electric dipole-dipole case. Thus, Ermolaev notes, one can "treat the situation as if the triplet donor molecule in exchange-resonance interactions had a quite well delimited sphere of action, and when an acceptor molecule enters it, instantaneous energy transfer from the former to the latter molecule would take place."

Terenin (1958)[237] first pointed out that the close intermolecular distances in crystal lattices should facilitate triplet-triplet exchange transfer and proposed that triplet energy "can be handed over and propagated along an array of closely packed molecules as efficiently as by the exciton mechanism valid for the singlet state." This means that a "triplet exciton" must also be taken into account, and the role of triplet excitons and the migration of triplet excitons in crystals and in solutions (see Parker's work in fluids, Sec. 4-9A) is being actively investigated (see the recent reviews of Windsor[99]).

Some definitive work on the role of triplet excitons in crystalline solids has been carried out by Robinson and coworkers[106,245,247] (see also Sec. 4-5). They studied the emission at $4.2°K$ of crystals of perdeuteronaphthalene doped with 0.5 % naphthalene[247] (the S_1 and T_1 energy levels of $C_{10}H_8$ are about 100 cm^{-1} lower than in $C_{10}D_8$, so the $C_{10}H_8$ "impurity" acts as a weak trap) and perdeuterobenzene similarly "doped" with C_6H_6. In the latter case Nieman and Robinson[245] found a value of 12 ± 1 cm^{-1} for the triplet exciton interaction. This corresponds to about 10^{12} nearest-neighbor transfers of triplet energy during the lifetime of the triplet state.*

Another example of the migration of triplet excitons is provided by a study of the phosphorescence of benzophenone crystals doped with naphthalene.[248] From data on the variation of transfer efficiency with concentration of naphthalene Cadas et al. calculated that one naphthalene molecule can be excited by 10^3 donor molecules.

The luminescence of organic compounds incorporated into rigid plastics (e.g., polymethylmethacrylate, PMM) has been studied recently. Windsor[99] has found that the triplet lifetimes of aromatic hydrocarbons are about a factor of 2 lower in PMM at room temperature than in rigid EPA at $77°K$. Quenching of the phosphorescence by the slow diffusion of O_2 into the plastic was noted over a period of several months. Recently Melhuish has reported values of φ_f and φ_p for a similar system (aromatic hydrocarbons in PMM).

---

* Robinson[246] and Parker[115] both recently considered the biochemical implications of triplet energy transfer. Clearly triplet energy-transfer processes provide an important possible mechanism for "uphill" photoprocesses (e.g., in chlorophyll).

Oster and Oster[250] have made a detailed series of studies in this general area, including the effect of binding dye molecules on the luminescence of polymers. They have observed the benzophenone-sensitized phosphorescence of naphthalene in PMM at room temperature and the emission from the pyrene dimer in polycarbonate. Thus they rule out material diffusion as a means of energy transfer.

Finally we should mention one other type of transfer, triplet-singlet, in which triplet energy from the donor raises the acceptor molecule to its singlet state, from which it can fluoresce. Förster[251] pointed out that the selection rule forbidding the radiative $T_1 \rightarrow S_1$ transition in a donor molecule does not prohibit *radiationless* energy transfer to an acceptor molecule, raising it to its first excited singlet state, if there is an overlap of the phosphorescence band of the donor and the absorption band of the acceptor (and if the transition in the acceptor molecule is allowed). Such a process has been demonstrated in rigid solutions at 90°K by Ermolaev and Sveshnikova,[252] who have reported that, for example, triphenylamine as a donor transferred triplet energy to an acceptor, such as chrysoidine, resulting in "sensitized afteremission" (sensitized delayed fluorescence). Parker and Hatchard[253] reported a similar phenomenon in phenanthrene (donor) and anthracene (acceptor) in liquid solution; however, this case involved bimolecular quenching of two triplet species (Sec. 4-9A). The important implications with regard to "energy storage," uphill photochemical processes, etc., have been discussed by both groups.

4-10B-4 Triplet Energy Transfer in Fluid Solutions

Exchange interaction resulting in triplet energy transfer in liquid solutions was demonstrated in 1958 by Bäckström and Sandros, who proposed two types of quenchers of biacetyl phosphorescence.[243] One group consisted of atom donors which "chemically quench" by transferring the hydrogen atom to the abstracting species triplet biacetyl. The second class consisted of certain unsaturated and aromatic compounds which in a sense "physically" quench the phosphorescence of biacetyl (the donor) by a transfer of excitation, causing a triplet $\rightarrow$ singlet transition in the donor and the reverse in the acceptor. These authors pointed out that this idea for liquids was essentially the same as the earlier proposal of Terenin and Ermolaev for solid solutions and also stressed the need that the triplet level of the donor lie above that of the acceptor. Thus the biacetyl triplet is at about 56 kcal/mole, and they demonstrated that strong quenchers had $E_{T_1} < 56$ kcal; those with $E_{T_1} > 56$ kcal had low quenching constants, and chrysene with $E_{T_1} = 57$ kcal/mole occupied an intermediate position.

As a "chemical" check on this triplet transfer process they irradiated a benzene solution of biacetyl and anthracene in a region where anthracene did not absorb and found a photosensitized formation of dianthracene with a yield, however, of only about 1 %. Presumably this arose from triplet anthracene formed by exchange energy transfer. (However, it should be noted that on direct irradiation of anthracene the photodimer seems to be formed only from excited singlets.) Later research by Hammond and co-workers, often with benzophenone as sensitizer (donor), has dramatically emphasized the chemical utility of triplet energy transfer, as we shall see shortly.

Subsequently Bäckström and Sandros published a more detailed paper on the transfer of triplet-state energy in fluid solutions, this time using benzophenone, whose triplet level lies 4000 cm^{-1} above that of biacetyl, to sensitize the biacetyl phosphorescence.[232] It is apparent that with the proper energy relationships between donor and acceptor biacetyl can act either as a donor or an acceptor in triplet energy transfer.

On the assumption (which seems well confirmed) that triplet-state energy transfer is a diffusion-controlled process, they calculated the mean lifetime of benzophenone in its triplet state, obtaining the following values at 20°: $\tau_{T_1} = 1.9 \times 10^{-6}$ sec in benzene, and 5.7×10^{-8} sec in the hydrogen atom-donating solvent isopropanol (4.6×10^{-8} sec at 25°). The latter figure was in agreement with a previous value calculated from the kinetics of a photochemical reaction involving the triplet state of benzophenone.

Good evidence for triplets in fluid solutions and for exchange transfer of triplet energy is found in the work of Porter and Wilkinson[142,255] carried out concurrently with, but independently of, Bäckström and Sandros. They utilized various techniques of flash kinetic spectroscopy to photograph both the neutral and the ionized form of the transient ketyl radical, $(C_6H_5)_2\dot{C}OH$, in solutions of benzophenone in alcohol and obtained a pK of 9.2 ± 0.1 for the equilibrium $(C_6H_5)_2\dot{C}\!-\!OH \rightleftharpoons C_6H_5)_2\dot{C}\!-\!O^- + H^+$. Although the flash duration was too long to identify unequivocally the transient triplet of benzophenone (presumably the hydrogen atom-abstraction species and the precursor of the ketyl radical), they proved its presence by adding naphthalene to the system.* By flash-photolyzing a solution of benzophenone in benzene with added naphthalene they showed that naphthalene completely quenches the formation of ketyl radicals; concurrently triplet naphthalene is formed. This was demonstrated both spectroscopically and kinetically. A number

---

* Bell and Linschitz,[256] using a flash photolysis system with a shorter decay constant, have detected the triplet of benzophenone and followed its reactions as well as those of the ketyl radical.

of other donor-acceptor pairs, including phenanthrene-naphthalene, triphenylene-naphthalene, phenanthrene-1-bromonaphthalene, and biacetyl-1,2-benzanthracene, were shown to undergo triplet energy transfer.[142]

Chemical evidence for energy transfer was obtained when two degassed solutions of benzophenone in isopropyl alcohol, one also containing $2 \times 10^{-3} M$ naphthalene, were irradiated identically with 3660 A radiation. A good yield of benzopinacol was obtained in the first solution, but *no* product was formed in the benzophenone solution to which naphthalene was added.*

Recently an abundance of chemical evidence for triplet energy transfer has been presented by Hammond and co-workers.[260] For example, they used various carbonyl compounds as sensitizers (donors) and unsaturates such as piperylene ($CH_2\!\!=\!\!CH\!\!-\!\!CH\!\!=\!\!CH\!\!-\!\!CH_3$), 1,2-dichloroethylene, and 2-pentene as acceptors. By studying the sensitized *cis* $\rightleftharpoons$ *trans* isomerization they showed that the results form a coherent pattern if it is assumed that the key step in the photochemical reactions is a transfer of triplet excitation. Apparently transfer is diffusion controlled and seems to occur on every collision between a triplet donor and singlet acceptor if the transfer is *exothermic*. Endothermic transfers also can occur, but the efficiency generally drops as the degree of endothermicity increases; however, it may vary in a complex manner. On the basis of this hypothesis the authors were able to deduce, by their photochemical energy-transfer techniques, values for the lowest triplet states of a number of compounds which had not been clearly established spectroscopically.

More recently Hammond *et al.*[260c] showed in extensive studies of direct and sensitized photochemical *cis-trans* isomerization that all their results can be understood if it is assumed that transfer of triplet excitation may involve excitation of acceptors to *non-spectroscopic* as well as spectroscopic states. They refer to the former as "phantom triplets," and their definitive article discusses in detail evidence for their existence as well as the mechanisms for *cis-trans* photoisomerizations (Sec. 5-9C-1).

Utilization of triplet transfer in solution is of great interest chemically

---

* The quenching of photoreduction by naphthalene has been well documented by Hammond, Turro, and Leermakers[257] and Moore and Ketchum,[258] who have studied the triplet-triplet transfer from benzophenone in fluid solutions under a variety of conditions. Electrochemical evidence for liquid-phase triplet energy transfer in benzophenone-naphthalene was reported by Pitts, Kuwana, and Marchetti, who showed that photopotentials produced on irradiating benzophenone in alcohol at room temperature were effectively quenched by addition of naphthalene to the solution.[259] Presumably triplet transfer from benzophenone to naphthalene quenched the formation of ketyl and other radicals for which the triplet benzophenone is the precursor (either directly or indirectly), and which are responsible for the photopotentials.

for several reasons. The first, the ability to initiate photochemical reactions in molecules which do not absorb directly in a convenient wavelength range (e.g., the mono-olefins, which are transparent down to about 2200 A), has been utilized for decades and is not unique to triplet transfer. However, in addition, one now has some understanding of the *nature* of the process, and this can shed light on a variety of significant phenomena, for example, estimation of the energy levels of the triplet states of both donors and acceptors and clarification of the mechanisms of photochemical reactions and the process of excitation transfer.

A second consequence of triplet transfer is that molecules whose triplet state are *not* appreciably populated by direct absorption $S_0 \rightarrow S_1$ because the excited singlet states do not decay appreciably via the triplet state may be populated by triplet transfer. For example, the quantum yield of the benzophenone-sensitized decomposition of ethyl pyruvate is *twice* that obtained by direct photolysis.[261]

Finally triplet transfer provides a convenient means of producing triplet species, such as that of the methylene radical $CH_2\uparrow\uparrow$, and comparing their spectrocopic and chemical properties with those of the corresponding singlet species, $CH_2\uparrow\downarrow$ formed by direct photolysis under suitable conditions.

A nice example of utilizing the transfer of triplet energy to elucidate certain details of a mechanism of a thermal organic reaction is the use of benzophenone to photosensitize the dimerization of cyclopentadiene.[262] Thermally this diene undergoes the Diels-Alder reaction at room temperature to give exclusively endodicyclopentadiene[263,264] (I).

(I)

The photosensitized process, which presumably proceeds through triplets, may be illustrated using 1,3-butadiene as follows:

$$D(S_0) + h\nu \rightarrow D(S_1) \xrightarrow{\text{ISC}} D(T_1)$$

$$D(T_1) + CH_2{=}CH{-}CH{=}CH_2 \longrightarrow D(S_0) + \overset{\downarrow}{C}H_2{-}CH{=}CH{-}\overset{\downarrow}{C}H_2$$

$$\overset{\downarrow}{C}H_2{-}CH{=}CH{-}\overset{\downarrow}{C}H_2 + CH_2{=}CH{-}CH{=}CH_2 \longrightarrow$$

$$CH_2{-}CH{\cdots}CH{\cdots}CH_2\downarrow$$
$$|$$
$$CH_2{-}CH{\cdots}CH{\cdots}CH_2\downarrow$$
$$\downarrow$$
$$\text{Dimers}$$

Irradiation of cyclopentadiene with a 400 watt Hanovia immersion lamp and with benzophenone, acetone, benzil, or 2,3-pentanedione as donor produced *endo*-dicyclopentadiene, *exo*-dicyclopentadiene (II), and *trans*-(3, 0, 3, 0) tricyclo-2,7-decadiene (III), in about equal amounts.

(II)   (III)

These results suggest different paths for the photosensitized dimerization, which presumably involves a triplet intermediate, and the thermal Diels-Alder, which *may* involve a different species.[261]

A final point here is to emphasize the experimental ease with which these triplet transfers were carried out. The usual apparatus and glassware of the synthetic chemist are employed, with a commercially available immersion type of mercury lamp replacing the heating mantle!

4-11   "INTRAMOLECULAR" ELECTRONIC ENERGY-TRANSFER PROCESSES

In certain substituted aromatic ketones and aldehydes an interesting type of *intramolecular* transfer of energy seems to occur. Thus, for example, in *p*-phenylbenzophenone[136,236,265,267,268] and β-acetonaphthaldehyde[260,266] the first excited singlet state is (n, π^*) as expected, but the lowest triplet seems to be (π, π^*) in character. Confirmation of the latter point includes the fact that for *p*-phenylbenzophenone, for example, Ermolaev and Terenin find the absorption spectrum is similar to that of benzophenone itself but the phosphorescence spectrum in structure and relatively longer lifetime resembles that of *p*-hydroxybiphenyl, in which the lowest triplet is (π, π^*).[236,151] Furthermore ESR studies by Piette, Sharp, and co-workers on irradiated solid solutions of it in EPA at 77°K [as well as the *p*-NH$_2$ and *p*,*p*'-bis-dimethylamino derivatives (see Sec. 5-9A)] show a low field resonance (at about 1500 gauss) corresponding to $\Delta m = \pm 2$ and presumably due to formation of a triplet state.[136] The decay time of the resonance when the irradiation was terminated was about 0.3 sec and equal to that of the observed phosphorescence decay. This is about 50 times the τ_p of "normal" benzophenones and falls in the range of $\pi \rightarrow \pi^*$ phosphorescence lifetimes. Pitts and co-workers[136,265] and independently Porter and co-workers[267,268] also showed that "abnormal" benzophenones such as the *p*-phenyl and *p*-NH$_2$ derivatives do not efficiently photopinacolize in hydrogen atom-donating solvents in which benzophenone does. This suggests that they have a much weaker hydrogen atom-abstracting ability than normal aromatic ketones, compatible with greater delocalization of excitation in a $^3(\pi, \pi^*)$ state than in $^3(n, \pi^*)$, where it is substantially much more localized in the heteroatom, oxygen. Furthermore, substitution alters the electron density on the oxygen atom in the excited state, and this has a great effect on the reactivity of the ketone. (See Sec. 5-9A for discussion.) Pitts and co-workers have reported similar large effects for the photochemical intramolecular hydrogen-atom abstraction (photocyclo-elimination) in substituted butyrophenones[280,281,298] (see Sec. 5-2).

Other observations of a chemical nature were first made by Hammond and Leermakers, who found that irradiation of β-acetonaphthone in optically active 2-octanol led to no racemization of the alcohol; they concluded that the failure of this compound to photopinacolize is not due simply to reversal of the hydrogen-atom abstraction reaction.[266] Thus they proposed that the lowest triplet of reactive aldehydes and ketones has the (n, π^*) configuration, although it is (π, π^*) in such abnormal unreactive species.

Presumably the sequence of events in these cases is

$$S_0 + h\nu_1 \to S_1{}^1(n, \pi^*) \underset{1}{\rightsquigarrow} T_1{}^3(n, \pi^*) \underset{2}{\rightsquigarrow} T_1{}^3(\pi, \pi^*) \longrightarrow S_0 + h\nu_2$$

$$S_0{}^v \rightsquigarrow S_0$$

with step 2 being designated *intramolecular energy transfer*.[236]

An interesting case of intramolecular electronic energy transfer occurs in 4-(1-naphthylalkyl)-benzophenone:[269]

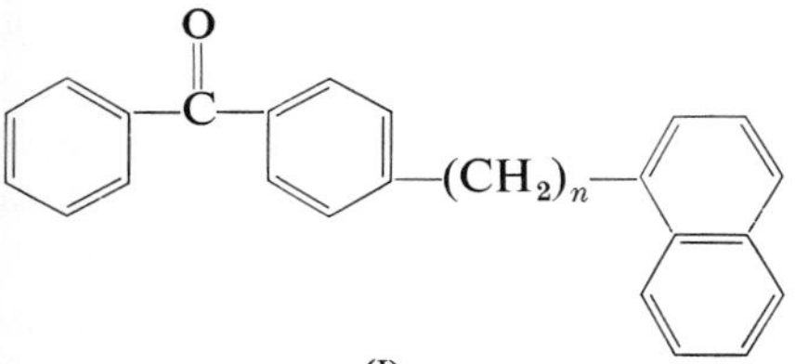

(I)

The absorption spectrum of (I) shows that the molecule contains two independent absorbing systems, the benzophenone moiety and the naphthalene moiety. Using light absorbed only by the benzophenone moiety, Leermakers and colleagues demonstrated by emission spectra that efficient transfer of triplet excitation from the benzophenone moiety to the naphthalene moiety occurs.[269] Because the singlet energy level of naphthalene is higher than that of benzophenone, singlet energy transfer from the latter to the first is unlikely. On the other hand, when (I) is excited with light absorbed by the naphthalene moiety, efficient transfer of singlet excitation to the benzophenone moiety occurs. Apparently, the rate of triplet energy transfer is not influenced by the length of the methylene chain, whereas a decrease in the efficiency of singlet transfer is observed as the chain increases from $n = 1$ to $n = 3$.

An intramolecular *singlet-singlet* transfer of high efficiency occurs with (II). Thus Schnepp and Levy showed that irradiation of the naphthyl group leads to fluorescence characteristic of the anthracene moiety even when the "insulating" chain contains three CH_2 groups.[284]

$$\text{—CH}_2\text{CH}_2\text{CH}_2\text{—}$$

$$+ \, h\nu_{\text{abs}} \qquad \qquad + \, h\nu_{\text{emitted}}$$

(II)

An example of singlet-singlet transfer of particular importance in photobiology is cited by Weber.[285] Irradiation of dihydrodiphosphopyridine nucleotide (DPNH) in the region where the adenine moiety absorbs results in a highly efficient intramolecular transfer to the nicotinamide portion of the molecule, which then emits its characteristic fluorescence.

Another interesting and useful intramolecular energy-transfer process occurs in the rare earth chelates. Stable complexes of the trivalent ions lanthanum through lutecium (excepting Ce^{3+}) all have remarkably similar properties, including absorption spectra, which for a given ligand are virtually identical. Their emission spectra, however, are complex, containing both molecular fluorescence and phosphorescence and "line" emission characteristics of the lanthanide ions. These spectra differ significantly from ion to ion in character and total luminescence yield (from approximately unity to 10^{-4}) in such a manner that highly useful information can be obtained concerning energy migration in complex molecules, as well as the resonance energy levels of the ions themselves.

This phenomenon has been reviewed by Crosby, Whan, and Freeman[270] in terms of their energy-level diagram, Fig. 4-25. We shall indicate briefly their treatment, using their diagram. After absorption to the first excited singlet S_1, the chelate may undergo the several molecular radiative and non-radiative processes we have discussed for organic molecules (i.e., fluorescence, phosphorescence, intersystem crossing) and in addition undergo a radiationless transition from the triplet system to a low-lying state derived from the $4f$ electronic configuration of the coordinated rare earth ion.[271] If the state is a "resonance level" (e.g., state d in Fig. 4-25) a radiative "line" emission characteristic of the particular ion may occur. Otherwise, deactivation to the ground state may proceed by a series of radiationless transitions. Energy migration from non-resonance levels (e.g., states a, b, c, e, and f, Fig. 4-25) can only be non-radiative in character. In order to excite the characteristic line emission from a coordinated rare earth ion, the resonance level of the ion must be equal to or lie lower than the lowest triplet, level T_1, in the complex. Thus, as the authors point out, "The luminescence observed from a specific chelated rare earth ion is a sensitive function of the position of the lowest triplet energy level of the complex relative to a resonance level of the ion. Consequently, it is possible to control the emission from a given ion by varying the ligand and therefore the position of the triplet state of the complex." Two interesting examples

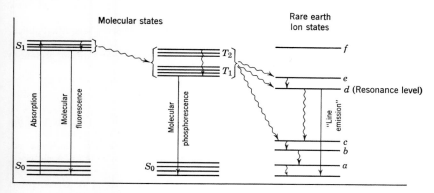

Fig. 4-25 Representative energy level diagram for a rare earth chelate having low-lying $4f$ electronic states. Wavy lines are non-radiative transitions, solid arrows radiative transitions. Taken essentially directly from Crosby, Whan, and Freeman.[270]

are cited by the authors. The luminescence of dysprosium trisdibenzoyl-methide consists of molecular phosphorescence and fluorescence, but dysprosium trisbenzoylacetonate emits primarily the bright line emission characteristic of rare earth ion Dy^{3+}. Emission from trivalent europium usually consists of two lines, but with the appropriate chelating agent only emission from the lowest resonance level is observed. Specific examples of using this ingenious technique either to fix the triplet levels of the molecule or to clarify the emission spectrum of a trivalent rare earth ion are cited.[270,271]

It would seem that this type of molecule might demonstrate laser activity, and indeed this is the case. Thus Lempicki and Samuelson[272] first observed stimulated emission at 6129 A from a 10^{-2} M solution of europium benzoylacetonate. The solution was a 3:1 mixture of methanol and ethanol at $-150°C$. Similar results have been observed by Schimits-chek[273] and Windsor.[99] Currently this field is, so to speak, active!

REFERENCES TO CHAPTER 4

1. E. J. Bowen and F. Wokes, *The Fluorescence of Solutions*, Longmans, Green and Co., London, 1953.
2. A. Jablonski, *Z. Physik*, **94**, 38 (1935).
3. W. A. Noyes, Jr. and P. A. Leighton, *The Photochemistry of Gases*, Reinhold Publishing Corp., New York, 1941.
4. G. K. Rollefson and M. Burton, *Photochemistry*, Prentice-Hall, Englewood Cliffs, N.J., 1939.
5. E. J. Bowen, *Chemical Aspects of Light*, 2nd Edition, Oxford University Press, Oxford, 1946.
6. C. R. Masson, V. Boekelheide, and W. A. Noyes, Jr., "Photochemical Reactions," *Catalytic, Photochemical, and Electrolytic Reactions*, Vol. II, 2nd Edition, *Technique of Organic Chemistry*, ed. by A. Weissberger, Interscience Publishers, New York, 1956.
7. C. Reid, *Excited States in Chemistry and Biology*, Butterworths Scientific Publications, London, 1957.
8. E. W. R. Steacie, *Atomic and Free Radical Reactions*, 2nd Edition, Reinhold Publishing Corp., New York, 1954.
9. A. Schönberg, *Präparative Organische Photochemie*, Springer, Berlin, 1958.
10. E. J. Bowen, *Quart. Revs. (London)*, **4**, 236 (1950).
11. M. Kasha, *Radiation Research*, Suppl. **2**, 243 (1960).
12. M. Kasha, "The Nature and Significance of $n \rightarrow \pi^*$ Transitions," *Light and Life*, ed. by W. B. McElroy and B. Glass, Johns Hopkins Press, Baltimore, 1961.
13. M. Kasha, "Molecular Photochemistry," *Comparative Effects of Radiation*, ed. by M. Burton, J. Kirby-Smith, and J. Magee, John Wiley & Sons, New York, 1960, p. 72.
14. G. W. Robinson, *Light and Life*, ed. by W. B. McElroy and B. Glass, Johns Hopkins Press, Baltimore, 1961.
15. G. Porter, *Proc. Chem. Soc.*, **1959**, 291.
16. C. Reid, *Quart. Revs. (London)*, **12**, 205 (1958).
17. W. A. Noyes, Jr., G. B. Porter, and J. E. Jolley, *Chem. Rev.*, **56**, 49 (1956).
18. (a) T. Förster, *Z. Elektrochem.*, **56**, 716 (1952); (b) *Fluoreszenz Organischer Verbindungen*, Vandenhoeck and Ruprecht, Göttingen, 1951.
19. (a) W. A. Noyes, Jr., *Festschrift Arthur Stoll*, Birkhäuser A. G., Basel, 1958, p. 64; (b) Academie Das Ciências de Lisboa, May, 1964; see also Ref. 268b.
20. R. M. Hochstrasser and G. B. Porter, *Quart. Revs. (London)*, **14**, 146 (1960).
21. J. P. Simons, *Quart. Revs. (London)*, **13**, 3 (1959).
22. J. N. Pitts, Jr., *J. Chem. Educ.*, **34**, 112 (1957).
23. P. de Mayo, *Advances in Org. Chem.*, **2**, 367 (1960).
24. P. de Mayo and S. T. Reid, *Quart. Revs. (London)*, **15**, 393 (1961).
25. G. O. Schenck and R. Steinmetz, *Bull Soc. Chim. Belges*, **71**, 781 (1962).
26. G. S. Hammond and N. J. Turro, *Science*, **142**, 1541 (1963).
27. P. A. Leermakers and G. F. Vesley, *J. Chem. Educ.*, **41**, 535 (1964).
28. *Advances in Photochemistry*, Vols. I, II, and III, ed. by W. A. Noyes, Jr., G. S. Hammond, and J. N. Pitts, Jr., Interscience Publishers, a division of John Wiley & Sons, New York, 1963, 1964.
29. J. N. Pitts, Jr., F. Wilkinson, and G. S. Hammond, "The 'Vocabulary' of photochemistry," *Advances in Photochemistry*, Vol. I, ed. by W. A. Noyes, Jr., G. S. Hammond, and J. N. Pitts, Jr., Interscience Publishers, a division of John Wiley & Sons, New York, 1963, p. 1.

30. H. H. Jaffe and M. Orchin, *Theory and Applications of Ultraviolet Spectroscopy*, John Wiley & Sons, New York, 1962.
31. R. P. Bauman, *Absorption Spectroscopy*, John Wiley & Sons, New York, 1962.
32. W. West, Ed., *Chemical Applications of Spectroscopy*, Vol. IX, *Technique of Organic Chemistry*, Interscience Publishers, New York, 1956.
33. J. N. Murrell, *Theory of the Electronic Spectra of Organic Molecules*, John Wiley & Sons, New York, 1964.
34. J. W. Linnett, *The Electronic Structure of Molecules*, John Wiley & Sons, New York, 1964.
35. S. F. Mason, *Quart. Revs. (London)*, **15**, 287 (1961).
36. W. West, "Introductory Survey of Molecular Spectra," *Chemical Applications of Spectroscopy*, Vol. IX, ed. by W. West, *Technique of Organic Chemistry*, Interscience Publishers, New York, 1956, Chapters 1 and 6.
37. A. B. F. Duncan and F. A. Matsen, "Electronic Spectra in the Visible and Ultraviolet Regions," *Chemical Applications of Spectroscopy*, Vol. IX, ed. by W. West, *Technique of Organic Chemistry*, Interscience Publishers, New York, 1956, Chapter 5.
38. J. N. Murrell, *Quart. Revs. (London)*, **15**, 191 (1961).
39. C. A. Coulson, *Valence*, Oxford University Press, Oxford, Second Edition, 1961.
40. W. Kauzmann, *Quantum Chemistry*, Academic Press, New York, 1957.
41. A. Streitwieser, *Molecular Orbital Theory for Organic Chemists*, John Wiley & Sons, New York, 1961.
42. J. D. Roberts, *Molecular Orbital Calculations*, W. A. Benjamin, New York, 1961.
43. G. Herzberg, *Molecular Spectra and Molecular Structure*, 2nd Edition, Van Nostrand, Princeton, N.J., 1950.
44. (a) J. R. Platt, *J. Chem. Phys.*, **18**, 1168 (1950); (b) *J. Opt. Soc. Am.*, **43**, 252 (1953); (c) *Radiation Biology*, Vol. III, ed. by A. Hollaender, McGraw-Hill Book Co., New York, 1956, Chapter 2.
45. J. W. Sidman, *Chem. Revs.*, **58**, 689 (1958).
46. (a) R. S. Mulliken, *J. Chem. Phys.*, **7**, 20 (1939); (b) *ibid.*, **23**, 1997 (1955).
47. R. S. Mulliken and C. A. Rieke, *Rept. Progress in Phys.*, **8**, 231 (1941).
48. M. Kasha, *Discussions Faraday Soc.*, **9**, 14 (1950).
49. R. S. Holdsworth and A. B. F. Duncan, *Chem. Revs.*, **41**, 311 (1947).
50. G. W. Robinson and G. S. Hammond, private communication.
51. D. J. Cram and G. S. Hammond, *Organic Chemistry*, 2nd Edition, McGraw-Hill Book Co., New York, 1964.
52. R. B. Woodward, *J. Am. Chem. Soc.*, **63**, 1123 (1941).
53. E. Clar, *Aromatische Kohlenwasserstoffee*, Springer-Verlag, Berlin, 1952.
54. H. Schull, *J. Chem. Phys.*, **17**, 295 (1949).
55. J. Ferguson, T. Iredale, and J. A. Taylor, *J. Chem. Soc.*, **1954**, 3160.
56. M. R. Padhye, S. P. McGlynn, and M. Kasha, *J. Chem. Phys.*, **24**, 588 (1956).
57. S. P. McGlynn, M. R. Padhye and M. Kasha, *J. Chem. Phys.*, **23**, 593 (1955).
58. F. S. Dainton, private communication.
59. Y. Kanda and R. Shimada, *Spectrochim. Acta*, **15**, 211 (1959).
60. D. S. McClure, *J. Chem. Phys.*, **19**, 670 (1951).
61. E. J. Bowen and B. Brocklehurst, *J. Chem. Soc.*, **1955**, 4320.
62. (a) C. A. Coulson, *Bull. Photoelectric Spectrometry Group*, No. 13, 358 (1961); (b) *Proc. Phys. Soc. (London)*, **60**, 257 (1948).
63. J. H. Rush and H. Sponer, *J. Chem. Phys.*, **20**, 1847 (1952).
64. H. P. Stephenson, *J. Chem. Phys.*, **22**, 1077 (1954).
65. M. A. El-Sayed and R. G. Brewer, *J. Chem. Phys.*, **39**, 1623 (1963).

66. D. R. Kearns, *J. Chem. Phys.*, **36**, 1608 (1962).
67. N. S. Ham and K. Ruedenberg, *J. Chem. Phys.*, **25**, 1 (1956).
68. J. R. Platt, *J. Chem. Phys.*, **17**, 484 (1949).
69. W. Moffit, *J. Chem. Phys.*, **22**, 320 (1954).
70. R. Pariser, *J. Chem. Phys.*, **24**, 250 (1956).
71. R. A. Friedel and M. Orchin, *Ultraviolet Spectra of Aromatic Compounds*, John Wiley & Sons, New York, 1951.
72. American Petroleum Institute, Ultraviolet Spectra, API Project No. 44 and Manufacturing Chemists Association, B. J. Zwolinski and A. Danti, Texas A. and M. College, College Station, Texas.
73. *Organic Electronic Spectral Data*, Vol. I, 1946–1952, ed. by M. J. Kamlet; Vol. II, 1953–1955, ed. by H. E. Ungnade; Vol. III, 1956–1957, ed. by O. H. Wheeler and L. A. Kaplan, Interscience Publishers, New York.
74. H. M. Hershenson, *Ultraviolet and Visible Absorption Spectra, Index for 1930-1954*, Academic Press, New York, 1956; *Index for 1955-1959*, Academic Press, New York, 1961.
75. L. Lang, Ed., *Absorption Spectra in the Ultraviolet and Visible Region*, Vols. I and II, Academic Press, New York, 1961.
76. L. E. Keuntzel, Ed., American Society of Testing Materials LASTM, IBM coded cards of ultraviolet-visible spectra, ASTM, 1916 Race Street Philadelphia, Pa.
77. L. N. Ferguson, *Chem. Revs.*, **43**, 385 (1948).
78. C. Karr, Jr., *Appl. Spectroscopy*, **13**, 15–25, 40–45 (1959); *ibid.*, **14**, 146–153 (1960), and later publications; tabulates spectra of polynuclear aromatic hydrocarbons and heterocyclics.
79. S. Nagakura and J. Tanaka, *J. Chem. Phys.*, **22**, 236 (1954); S. Nagakura, *J. Chem. Phys.*, **23**, 1441 (1955).
80. W. I. Kaye, *Appl. Spectroscopy*, **15**, 89 (1961); *ibid.*, **15**, 130 (1961).
81. J. R. Platt, *Systematics of the Electronic Spectra of Conjugated Molecules*, John Wiley & Sons, New York, 1964.
82. N. S. Bayliss, *J. Chem. Phys.*, **18**, 292 (1950).
83. L. F. Fieser and M. Fieser, *Steroids*, Reinhold Publishing Corp., New York, 1959.
84. R. J. Marcus, *Science*, **123**, 399 (1956).
85. E. Orgel, *Quart. Revs. (London)*, **8**, 422 (1954).
86. N. Uri, *Chem. Revs.*, **50**, 375 (1952).
87. E. Rabinowitch, *Revs. Modern Phys.*, **14**, 112 (1942).
88. D. S. McClure, *Radiation Research Suppl.*, **2**, 218 (1960).
89. D. S. McClure, *Solid State Phys.*, **9**, 399 (1959); (b) *ibid.*, **8**, 1 (1959).
90. W. A. Runciman, "Absorption and Fluorescence Spectra of Ions in Crystals," *Repts. Progr. in Phys.*, **21**, 30 (1958).
91. T. M. Dunn, "The Visible and Ultraviolet Spectra of Complex Compounds," in *Modern Coordination Chemistry*, Interscience Publishers, New York, 1960, p. 229.
92. C. J. Ballhausen, *Introduction to Ligand Field Theory*, McGraw-Hill Book Co., New York, 1962.
93. A. Adamson, *Proceedings Symposium on Reversible Photochemical Processes*, Duke University, April, 1962.
94. P. Pringsheim, *Fluorescence and Phosphorescence*, Interscience Publishers, New York, 1949.
95. M. G. Evans, M. Santappa, and N. Uri, *J. Polymer Sci.*, **7**, 243 (1951).
96. H. C. Wolf, "The Electronic Spectra of Aromatic Molecular Crystals," *Solid State Phys.*, **9**, 1 (1959).

97. A. S. Davydov, *Theory of Molecular Excitons* (translated by M. Kasha and M. Oppenheimer), McGraw-Hill Book Co., New York, 1962.
98. O. Schnepp, *Ann. Rev. Phys. Chem.*, **14**, 35 (1963).
99. M. W. Windsor, "Luminescence and Energy Transfer in the Organic Solid State", *Physics and Chemistry of the Organic Solid State*, Vol. II, ed. by D. Fox, M. M. Labes, and A. Weissberger, Interscience Publishers, a division of John Wiley & Sons, New York, 1965, p. 343.
100. T. Förster, "Transfer Mechanisms of Electronic Excitation Energy," *Radiation Research*, Suppl. **2**, 326 (1960).
101. T. Förster, "Excitation Transfer," *Comparative Effects of Radiation*, ed. by M. Burton, J. Kirby-Smith, and J. Magee, John Wiley & Sons, New York, 1960, p. 300.
102. H. P. Kallman and G. M. Spruch, eds., *Luminescence of Organic and Inorganic Materials*, John Wiley & Sons, New York, 1962.
103. V. L. Ermolaev, *Uspekhi Fiz. Nauk*, **80**, 3 (1963), English translation; *Soviet Physics*, Uspeki, Nov.–Dec., 1963, p. 333.
104. R. M. Hochstrasser, *Revs. Modern Phys.*, **34**, 531 (1963).
105. *Proceedings Organic Crystal Symposium*, National Research Council of Canada, Ottawa, Oct., 1962.
106. H. Sternlicht, G. C. Nieman, and G. W. Robinson, *J. Chem. Phys.*, **38**, 1326 (1963).
107. (a) W. L. Broude, O. S. Pachamova, and A. F. Prichotjko, *Opt. i Spektr.*, **2**, 323 (1951); (b) W. L. Broude and A. F. Prichotjko, *Opt. i Spektr.*, **7**, 102 (1956).
108. J. Ferguson and W. G. Schneider, *J. Chem. Phys.*, **28**, 761 (1958).
109. C. A. Parker and W. T. Rees, *Analyst*, **85**, 587 (1960).
110. W. H. Melhuish, *New Zealand J. Sci. Technol.*, **B37**, 142 (1955).
111. J. H. Chapman, T. Förster, G. Kortüm, E. Lippert, W. H. Melhuish, G. Nebbia, and C. A. Parker, *Z. Anal. Chem.*, **197**, 431 (1963).
112. C. Viswanath and M. Kasha, *J. Chem. Phys.*, **24**, 574 (1956).
113. G. W. Robinson and R. P. Frosch, *Proceedings Symposium on Reversible Photochemical Processes*, Duke University, April, 1962; *J. Chem. Phys.*, **38**, 1187 (1963).
114. G. Weber and F. W. J. Teale, *Trans. Faraday Soc.*, **54**, 640 (1958).
115. C. A. Parker, "Phosphorescence and Delayed Fluorescence," *Advances in Photochemistry*, Vol. II, ed. by W. A. Noyes, Jr., G. S. Hammond, and J. N. Pitts, Jr., Interscience Publishers, a division of John Wiley & Sons, New York, 1964, p. 306.
116. C. A. Parker, *Nature*, **182**, 1002 (1958).
117. C. A. Parker and W. J. Barnes, *Analyst*, **82**, 606 (1957); *ibid.*, **85**, 3 (1960).
118. G. R. Haugen and R. J. Marcus, *Appl. Optics*, **3**, 1049 (1964).
119. A. Kronenberger, *Z. Physik.*, **63**, 494 (1930).
120. A. Kronenberger and P. Pringsheim, *Z. Physik*, **40**, 75 (1927).
121. C. P. Snow and C. B. Allsop, *Trans. Faraday Soc.*, **30**, 93 (1934).
122. H. L. J. Bäckström, *Z. Physik. Chem.*, **B25**, 99 (1934).
123. M. Kasha and S. P. McGlynn, *Ann. Rev. Phys. Chem.*, **7**, 403 (1956).
124. E. Wiedemann and G. C. Schmidt, *Ann Physik*, **56**, 201 (1895).
125. S. I. Vanilov and W. L. Lewschin, *Z. Physik*, **35**, 920 (1926).
126. G. N. Lewis, D. Lipkin, and T. T. Magel, *J. Am. Chem. Soc.*, **63**, 3005 (1941).
127. A. Terenin, *Acta Physicochim. U.R.S.S.*, **18**, 210 (1943); *Zhur. Fiz. Khim.*, **18**, 1 (1944).
128. G. N. Lewis and M. Kasha, *J. Am. Chem. Soc.*, **66**, 2100 (1944).
129. G. N. Lewis and M. Calvin, *J. Am. Chem. Soc.*, **67**, 1232 (1945).
130. G. N. Lewis, M. Calvin, and M. Kasha, *J. Chem. Phys.*, **17**, 804 (1949).

131. D. F. Evans, *Nature*, **176**, 777 (1955).

132. P. Debye and J. Edwards, *J. Chem. Phys.*, **20**, 236 (1953).

133. H. Linschitz, M. Berry, and D. Schweitzer, *J. Am. Chem. Soc.*, **76**, 5833 (1954).

134. C. A. Hutchinson, Jr. and B. W. Mangum, *J. Chem. Phys.*, **29**, 952 (1958); *ibid.*, **34**, 908 (1961).

135. J. H. van der Waals and M. S. de Groot, *Mol. Phys.*, **2**, 333 (1959); M. S. de Groot and J. H. van der Waals, *Mol. Phys.*, **3**, 190 (1960).

136. L. H. Piette, J. H. Sharp, T. Kuwana, and J. N. Pitts, Jr., *J. Chem. Phys.*, **36**, 3094 (1962); J. H. Sharp, Ph.D. Thesis, University of California, Riverside, 1963.

137. J. B. Farmer, C. L. Gardner, and C. A. McDowell, *J. Chem. Phys.*, **34**, 1058 (1961).

138. (a) G. Porter and M. W. Windsor, *J. Chem. Phys.*, **21**, 2088 (1953); (b) *Discussions Faraday Soc.*, **17**, 178 (1954).

139. R. G. W. Norrish and G. Porter, *Nature*, **164**, 658 (1949).

140. R. G. W. Norrish, *Am. Scientist*, **50**, 131 (1962).

141. G. Porter, "Flash Photolysis," *Investigation of Rates and Mechanisms of Reactions*, Vol. VIII, Part II, 2nd Edition, *Technique of Organic Chemistry*, ed. by S. L. Friess, E. S. Lewis, and A. Weissberger, Interscience Publishers, a division of John Wiley & Sons, New York, 1963.

142. (a) G. Porter and F. Wilkinson, *Trans. Faraday Soc.*, **57**, 1686 (1961); (b) *Proc. Roy. Soc. (London)*, **A264**, 1 (1961).

143. P. L. Airey, unpublished work.

144. D. P. Craig and I. G. Ross, *J. Chem. Soc.*, **1589** (1954).

145. C. A. Parker and C. G. Hatchard, *Trans. Faraday Soc.*, **57**, 1894 (1961).

146. G. Jackson, R. Livingston, and A. C. Pugh, *Trans. Faraday Soc.*, **56**, 1635 (1960).

147. D. S. McClure, *J. Chem. Phys.*, **17**, 905 (1949).

148. D. S. McClure, *J. Chem. Phys.*, **20**, 682 (1952).

149. M. Mizushima and S. Koide, *J. Chem. Phys.*, **20**, 765 (1952).

150. W. G. Herkstroeter, A. A. Lamola, and G. S. Hammond, *J. Am. Chem. Soc.*, **86**, 4537 (1964).

151. V. L. Ermolaev and A. N. Terenin, *J. Chim. Phys.*, **55**, 698 (1958).

152. E. J. Bowen, "The Photochemistry of Aromatic Hydrocarbon Solutions," *Advances in Photochemistry*, Vol. I, ed. by W. A. Noyes, Jr., G. S. Hammond, and J. N. Pitts, Jr., Interscience Publishers, a division of John Wiley & Sons, New York, 1963, p. 23.

153. V. L. Ermolaev, *Doklady Acad. Nauk SSSR*, **139**, 348 (1961); *Soviet Phys. Doklady*, **6**, 600 (1962).

154. C. A. Parker and C. G. Hatchard, *Analyst*, **87**, 664 (1962).

155. E. H. Gilmore, G. E. Gibson, and D. S. McClure, *J. Chem. Phys.* **20**, 829 (1952); *ibid.*, **23**, 399 (1955).

156. G. S. Hammond, N. J. Turro, and A. Fischer, *J. Am. Chem. Soc.*, **83**, 4674 (1961), and subsequent papers in the series.

157. M. Shirom and G. Stein, *Nature*, **204**, 778 (1964).

158. P. Yusta and S. J. Weissman, *J. Chem. Phys.*, **17**, 1182 (1949).

159. R. S. Becker and M. Kasha, *J. Am. Chem. Soc.*, **77**, 3669 (1955); *The Luminescence of Biological Systems*, ed. by H. Johnson, American Association for the Advancement of Science, Washington, D.C., 1955, p. 25.

160. L. Pekkarinen and H. Linschitz, *J. Am. Chem. Soc.*, **82**, 2407 (1960); *ibid.*, 2411 (1960).

161. R. Livingston and E. Fujimori, *J. Am. Chem. Soc.*, **80**, 5610 (1958).

162. H. Linschitz and K. Sarkaren, *J. Am. Chem. Soc.*, **80**, 4826 (1958).
163. E. Rabinowitch, "Primary Photochemical and Photophysical Processes in Photosynthesis," *Discussions Faraday Soc.*, **27**, 161 (1959).
164. R. Livingston and A. C. Pugh, "The Role of the Triplet State Reactions Sensitized by Chlorophyll," *Discussions Faraday Soc.*, **27**, 144 (1959). See this for references to earlier work as a review.
165. *Proceedings Symposium on Reversible Photochemical Processes*, Duke University, April, 1962; published in *J. Phys. Chem.*, **66**, 2423–2577 (1962).
166. D. F. Evans, *J. Chem. Soc.*, 1987 (1961).
167. M. R. Wright, R. P. Frosch, and G. W. Robinson, *J. Chem. Phys.*, **33**, 934 (1960).
168. G. W. Robinson, *J. Mol. Spec.*, **6**, 58 (1961).
169. C. A. Hutchison, Jr. and B. W. Mangum, *J. Chem. Phys.*, **32**, 1261 (1960).
170. M. Gouterman, *J. Chem. Phys.*, **36**, 2845 (1962).
171. S. P. McGlynn, M. J. Reynolds, G. W. Daigre, and N. D. Christodoyleas, *Proceedings Symposium on Reversible Photochemical Processes*, Duke University, April, 1962; *J. Phys. Chem.*, **66**, 2499 (1962). See this paper for a literature survey of earlier references.
172. E. N. Viktorova, I. A. Zhmyreva, V. P. Kolobkov, and A. A. Saganenko, *Optika i Spektroskopiya*, **9**, 349 (1960).
173. Y. Kanda and R. Shimada, *Spectrochim. Acta* **17**, 7 (1961).
174. B. Y. Sveshnikov and A. A. Petrov, *Doklady Akad. Nauk U.S.S.R.*, **71**, 46 (1950).
175. I. J. Graham-Bryce and J. M. Corkhill, *Nature*, **186**, 965 (1960).
176. L. S. Forster and D. Dudley, *J. Phys. Chem.*, **66**, 838 (1962).
177. We are indebted to Professor G. S. Hammond and Dr. A. A. Lamola for these unpublished observations.
178. T. Förster and K. Kasper, *Z. Elektrochem.*, **59**, 977 (1955).
179. C. A. Parker and C. G. Hatchard, *Trans. Faraday Soc.*, **59**, 284 (1963); *Nature*, **190**, 165 (1961).
180. J. B. Birks and I. H. Munro, in *Luminescence of Organic and Inorganic Materials*, ed. by H. P. Kallman and G. M. Spruch, John Wiley & Sons, New York, 1962, p. 230.
181. J. B. Birks and L. G. Christophorou, *Nature*, **196**, 33 (1962).
182. B. Stevens and E. Hutton, *Nature*, **186**, 1045 (1960).
183. R. Williams, *J. Chem. Phys.*, **28**, 577 (1958).
184. B. Stevens and E. Hutton, *Proceedings Symposium on Reversible Photochemical Processes*, Duke University, April, 1962.
185. B. Stevens, *Nature*, **192**, 725 (1961).
186. B. Stevens and P. J. McCartin, *Mol. Phys.* **3**, 425 (1960).
187. C. A. Parker and C. G. Hatchard, *Proc. Chem. Soc.*, **1962**, 147.
188. (a) C. A. Parker and C. G. Hatchard, *Proceedings Symposium on Reversible Photochemical Processes*, Duke University, April, 1962; (b) *J. Phys. Chem.*, **66**, 2506 (1962).
189. (a) H. Linschitz and C. Steel, *Proceedings Symposium on Reversible Photochemical Processes*, Duke University, April, 1962; (b) H. Linschitz, C. Steel, and J. A. Bell, *J. Phys. Chem.*, **66**, 2574, (1962); (c) C. Steel and H. Linschitz, *J. Phys. Chem.*, **66**, 2577 (1962); (d) H. Linschitz and L. Pekkarinen, *J. Am. Chem. Soc.*, **82**, 2411 (1960).
190. G. Porter and M. R. Wright, *J. Chim. Phys.*, **55**, 705 (1958).
191. G. Jackson and R. Livingston, *J. Chem. Phys.*, **35**, 2182 (1961).
192. D. F. Evans, *J. Chem. Soc.*, **1957**, 1351.
193. H. Tsubomora and R. S. Mulliken, *J. Am. Chem. Soc.*, **82**, 5966 (1960).

194. D. F. Evans, *Proc. Roy. Soc. (London)*, **A255**, 55 (1960).
195. R. Livingston and D. W. Tanner, *Trans. Faraday Soc.*, **54**, 765 (1958).
196. G. Porter and M. R. Wright, *Discussions Faraday Soc.*, **27**, 18 (1959).
197. J. N. Murrell, *Mol. Phys.*, **3**, 319 (1960).
198. G. J. Hoijtink, *Mol. Phys.*, **3**, 67 (1960).
199. E. Fujimori and R. Livingston, *Nature*, **180**, 1036 (1957).
200. W. M. Moore, G. S. Hammond, and R. P. Foss, *J. Am. Chem. Soc.*, **83**, 2789 (1961).
201. G. S. Hammond, W. P. Baker, and W. M. Moore, *J. Am. Chem. Soc.*, **83**, 2795 (1961).
202. F. Wilkinson, "Electronic Energy Transfer between Organic Molecules in Solution," *Advances in Photochemistry*, Vol. III, ed. by W. A. Noyes, Jr., G. S. Hammond, and J. N. Pitts, Jr., Interscience Publishers, a division of John Wiley & Sons, New York, 1964.
203. K. F. Herzfeld, *High Speed Aerodynamics and Jet Propulsion*, I, Sec. H, Princeton University Press, Princeton, N. J., 1955.
204. B. Stevens and M. Boudart, *Ann. N. Y. Acad. Sci.*, **67**, 570 (1957).
205. B. Stevens, *Can. J. Chem.*, **36**, 96 (1958).
206. V. N. Kondratiev, *Roy. Inst. Chem.*, No. 3, (1960).
207. N. A. Prilezhaeva, *Acta Physicochim. U.S.S.R.*, **1**, 785 (1935).
208. N. A. Prilezhaeva, *Acta Physicochim. U.S.S.R.*, **7**, 163 (1937).
209. Earlier papers include (a) M. S. Matheson and J. W. Zabor, *J. Chem. Phys.*, **7**, 536 (1939); (b) H. Okabe and W. A. Noyes, Jr., *J. Am. Chem. Soc.*, **79**, 801 (1957); (c) J. Heicklen and W. A. Noyes, Jr., *J. Am. Chem. Soc.*, **81**, 3858 (1959); (d) J. Heicklen, *J. Am. Chem. Soc.*, **81**, 3863 (1959).
210. (a) H. Ishikawa and W. A. Noyes, Jr., *J. Am. Chem. Soc.*, **84**, 1502 (1962); (b) H. Ishikawa, Doctoral Dissertation, University of Rochester, 1962; (c) *J. Chem. Phys.*, **37**, 583 (1962).
211. J. T. Dubois and W. A. Noyes, Jr., *J. Chem. Phys.*, **19**, 1512 (1951).
212. J. T. Dubois, *J. Phys. Chem.*, **63**, 8 (1959).
213. B. Stevens, *Discussions Faraday Soc.*, **27**, 34 (1959).
214. D. S. Weir, *J. Am. Chem. Soc.*, **83**, 2629 (1961).
215. F. S. Dainton and K. J. Ivin, *Trans. Faraday Soc.*, **46**, 374, 382 (1950).
216. (a) R. B. Cundall and T. F. Palmer, *Trans. Faraday Soc.*, **56**, 1211 (1960); (b) see the recent review of the kinetics of *cis-trans* isomerizations by R. B. Cundall, *Progress in Reaction Kinetics*, ed. by G. Porter, Macmillan Company, New York, 1964, p. 208.
217. K. F. Greenhough and A. B. F. Duncan, *J. Am. Chem. Soc.*, **83**, 555 (1961).
218. E. J. Bowen and A. H. Williams, *Trans. Faraday Soc.*, **35**, 765 (1939).
219. J. Perrin, 2 me Conseil de Chim. Solvay, Gouthier-Villars, Paris, 1925.
220. E. Gaviola and P. Pringsheim, *Z. Physik*, **24**, 24 (1924).
221. J. Perrin, *Compt. Rend.*, **184**, 1097 (1924); J. Perrin and M. Choucroun, *Compt. Rend.*, **189**, 1213 (1929).
222. E. J. Bowen, E. Mikiewicz, and F. W. Smith, *Proc. Phys. Soc., (London)*, **62A**, 26 (1949).
223. J. Franck and R. Livingston, *Revs. Modern Phys.*, **21**, 505 (1949).
224. E. J. Bowen, *Symp. Soc. Exp'tl. Biol.*, **1951**, 152.
225. M. Moodie and C. Reid, *J. Chem. Phys.*, **20**, 1510 (1952).
226. T. Förster, *Z. Elektrochem.*, **53**, 93 (1949); *Z. Naturforsch.*, **4a**, 321 (1949).
227. W. F. Watson and R. Livingston, *J. Chem. Phys.*, **18**, 802 (1950).
228. L. N. M. Duysens, *Nature*, **168**, 548 (1951).
229. E. J. Bowen and B. Brocklehurst, *Trans. Faraday Soc.*, **49**, 1131 (1953).

230. E. J. Bowen and R. Livingston, *J. Am. Chem. Soc.*, **76**, 6300 (1954).
231. P. Debye, *Trans. Electrochem. Soc.*, **82**, 265 (1942).
232. H. L. J. Bäckström and K. Sandros, *Acta Chem. Scand.*, **14**, 48 (1960).
233. E. J. Bowen and B. Brocklehurst, *Trans. Faraday Soc.*, **51**, 774 (1955).
234. T. Förster, *Ann. Phys. (Leipzig)*, **2**, 55 (1948).
235. D. L. Dexter, *J. Chem. Phys.*, **21**, 836 (1953).
236. V. Ermolaev and A. Terenin, *Sov. Phys., Uspekhi*, **3**, 423 (1960); *Uspekhi Fiz. Nauk*, **71**, 137 (1960).
237. A. Terenin, E. Putzeiko, and I. Akimov, *Discussions Faraday Soc.*, **27**, 83 (1959).
238. A. Terenin and V. Ermolaev, *Doklady Acad. Sci. U.S.S.R.*, **85**, 547 (1952).
239. V. Ermolaev and A. Terenin, *S. I. Vavilov Memorial Volume*, ed. by Academy of Science, U.S.S.R., 1952, p. 137.
240. V. Ermolaev, *Doklady Acad. Sci. U.S.S.R.*, **102**, 925 (1955).
241. A. Terenin and V. Ermolaev, *Trans. Faraday Soc.*, **52**, 1042 (1956).
242. F. S. Dainton and P. Fowles, to be published.
243. H. L. J. Bäckström and K. Sandros, *Acta Chem. Scand.*, **12**, 823 (1958).
244. W. Ware, *J. Am. Chem. Soc.*, **83**, 4374 (1961).
245. G. C. Nieman and G. W. Robinson, *J. Chem. Phys.*, **39**, 1298 (1963).
246. G. W. Robinson, *Proc. Natl. Acad. Sci. U.S.*, **49**, 521 (1963).
247. M. A. El-Sayed, M. T. Wauk, and G. W. Robinson, *Mol. Phys.*, **5**, 205 (1962).
248. J.-P. Cadas, C. Courpron, R. Lochet, and A. Rousset, *Compt. Rend.*, **254**, 2490 (1962).
249. W. H. Melhuish, *J. Opt. Soc. Am.*, **54**, 183 (1964).
250. G. Oster and G. K. Oster, *Luminescence of Organic and Inorganic Materials*, ed. by H. P. Kallman and G. M. Spruch, John Wiley & Sons, New York, 1962, p. 186.
251. T. Förster, *Discussion Faraday Soc.*, **27**, 7 (1959); *Z. Elektrochem*, **64**, 157 (1960).
252. V. L. Ermolaev and E. B. Sveshnikova, *Izv. Akad. Nauk, SSSR, ser. Fiz.*, **26**, 29 (1962); abstracts 11th conference on luminescence (Minsk, September, 1962), *Akad. Nauk, SSSR*, pp. 25, 26.
253. C. A. Parker and C. G. Hatchard, *Proc. Roy. Soc. (London)*, **A269**, 574 (1962).
254. M. S. Matheson, W. A. Mulac, and J. Rambani, *J. Phys. Chem.*, **67**, 2613 (1963).
255. G. Porter, Tilden Lecture, December, 1958; reprinted *Proc. Roy. Soc. (London)*, **1959**, 291.
256. J. A. Bell and H. Linschitz, *J. Am. Chem. Soc.*, **85**, 528 (1963).
257. G. S. Hammond, N. J. Turro, and P. A. Leermakers, *J. Phys. Chem.*, **66**, 1144 (1962).
258. W. M. Moore and M. Ketchum, *J. Am. Chem. Soc.*, **84**, 1368 (1962).
259. J. N. Pitts, Jr., T. Kuwana, and A. Marchetti, *5th International Symposium on Free Radicals*, Uppsala, July, 1961; published by Almquist and Wiksell, Uppsala, Sweden, 1961, p. 51.
260. (a) G. S. Hammond, N. J. Turro, and P. A. Leermakers, *Proceedings Symposium on Reversible Photochemical Processes*, Duke University, April, 1962; (b) see the review of G. S. Hammond and N. J. Turro for details and literature references, *Science*, **142**, 1541 (1963); (c) G. S. Hammond, J. Saltiel, A. A. Lamola, N. J. Turro, J. S. Bradshaw, D. O. Cowan, R. C. Counsell, V. Vogt, and C. Dalton, *J. Am. Chem. Soc.*, **86**, 3197 (1964).
261. G. S. Hammond, P. A. Leermakers, and N. J. Turro, *J. Am. Chem. Soc.*, **83**, 2395 (1961).
262. N. J. Turro and G. S. Hammond, *J. Am. Chem. Soc.*, **84**, 2841 (1962).
263. K. Alder and G. Stein, *Ann.*, **504**, 216 (1933).

264. P. D. Bartlett and I. S. Goldstein, *J. Am. Chem. Soc.*, **69**, 2553 (1947).
265. J. N. Pitts, Jr., H. W. Johnson, Jr., and T. Kuwana, *Proceedings Symposium in Reversible Photochemical Processes*, Duke University, April, 1962, p. 195; *J. Phys. Chem.*, **66**, 2456 (1962).
266. G. S. Hammond and P. A. Leermakers, *J. Am. Chem. Soc.*, **84**, 207 (1962).
267. A. Beckett and G. Porter, *Trans. Faraday Soc.*, **59**, 2051 (1963).
268. (a) G. Porter and P. Suppan, *Pure Appl. Chem.*, **9**, 499 (1964); (b) International Conference on Organic Photochemistry, Strausberg, July, 1964; *Organic Photochemistry*, I.U.P.A.C., Butterworth, London, 1965.
269. P. A. Leermakers, G. W. Byers, A. A. Lamola, and G. S. Hammond, *J. Am. Chem. Soc.*, **85**, 2670 (1963).
270. G. A. Crosby, R. E. Whan, and J. J. Freeman, *Proceedings Symposium on Reversible Photochemical Processes*, Duke University, April, 1962; *J. Phys. Chem.*, **66**, 2493 (1962).
271. G. A. Crosby, R. E. Whan, and R. M. Alire, *J. Chem. Phys.*, **34**, 743 (1961).
272. A. Lempicki and H. Samuelson, *Phys. Letters*, **4**, 133 (1963).
273. E. J. Schimitschek, *Appl. Phys. Letters*, **3**, 117 (1963).
274. P. A. Leermakers and H. T. Thomas, *J. Am. Chem. Soc.*, **87**, 1620 (1965).
275. C. L. Braun, S. Kato, and S. Lipsky, *J. Chem. Phys.*, **39**, 1645 (1963).
276. J. N. Pitts, Jr., J. K. Foote, and J. K. S. Wan, *J. Photochem. and Photobiol.*, **4**, 323 (1659). IVth International Photobiology Congress, Oxford, July, 1964; published as *Recent Progress in Photobiology*, ed. by E. J. Bowen, Blackwells, 1965, p. 357.
277. IVth International Photobiology Congress, Oxford, July, 1964, proceedings published as *Recent Progress in Photobiology*, ed. by E. J. Bowen, Blackwells, 1965.
278. R. Srinivasan, *J. Am. Chem. Soc.*, **84**, 3982 (1962).
279. E. F. Ullman and W. A. Henderson, Jr., *J. Am. Chem. Soc.*, **86**, 5050 (1964).
280. J. N. Pitts, Jr., L. D. Hess, E. J. Baum, E. A. Schuck, J. K. S. Wan, P. A. Leermakers, and G. F. Vesley, IVth International Congress of Photobiology, Oxford, July, 1964; published as *Recent Progress in Photobiology*, ed. by E. J. Bowen, Blackwells, 1965, p. 23; *J. Photochem. and Photobiol.*, **4**, 305 (1965).
281. J. K. S. Wan, E. J. Baum, and J. N. Pitts, Jr., Symposium on Structure and Photochemistry of Excited States, 149th Meeting American Chemical Society, Detroit, April, 1965; J. K. S. Wan, R. N. McCormick, and J. N. Pitts, Jr., unpublished work.
282. V. E. Holmgorov, E. V. Baranov, and A. N. Terenin, *Doklady Akad. Nauk, SSSR*, **149**, 142 (1963); **152**, 1399 (1963).
283. A. Terenin, *Recent Progress in Photobiology*, ed. by E. J. Bowen, Blackwells, 1965, p. 3.
284. O. Schnepp and M. Levy, *J. Am. Chem. Soc.*, **84**, 172 (1962).
285. G. Weber, *Nature*, **180**, 1409 (1957); *J. Chim. Phys.*, **55**, 878 (1958).
286. E. J. Hart and J. W. Boag, *J. Am. Chem. Soc.*, **84**, 4090 (1962).
287. L. M. Dorfman and I. A. Taub, *J. Am. Chem. Soc.*, **85**, 2370 (1963).
288. R. Collins, unpublished work; communication from F. S. Dainton to the authors.
289. J. Russell, unpublished work; communication from F. S. Dainton to the authors.
290. F. S. Dainton and S. R. Logan (to be published).
291. J. Jortner, M. Ottolenghi, and G. Stein, *J. Phys. Chem.*, **66**, 2029 (1962); *ibid.*, **66**, 2037 (1962); *ibid.*, **66**, 2042 (1962).
292. J. Jortner, M. Ottolenghi, and G. Stein, *J. Phys. Chem.*, **68**, 247 (1964).
293. S. Z. Weisz, A. B. Zahlan, J. Gilreath, R. C. Jarnagin, and M. Silver, *J. Chem. Phys.*, **41**, 3491 (1964).

294. W. L. Peticolas and K. E. Rieckhoff, *J. Chem. Phys.*, **39**, 1347 (1963).
295. E. Lippert, W. Lüder, and F. Moll, *Spectrochim. Acta*, **10**, 858 (1959).
296. T. Medinger and F. Wilkinson, *Trans. Faraday Soc.*, **61**, 620 (1965).
297. H. Labhart, *Helv. Chim. Acta*, **47**, 2279 (1964).
298. E. J. Baum, J. K. S. Wan, and J. N. Pitts, Jr., Abstracts, 149th Meeting American Chemical Society, Detroit, April, 1965; E. J. Baum, Doctoral Dissertation, University of California, Riverside, 1965.
299. Dr. Eigenmann (CIBA, Aktiengesellschaft, Basel), quoted in Ref. 297.
300. F. C. Henriques and W. A. Noyes, Jr., *J. Am. Chem. Soc.*, **62**, 1038 (1940).
301. G. M. Almy and P. R. Gillette, *J. Chem. Phys.*, **11**, 188 (1943).
302. H. L. McMurry, *J. Chem. Phys.*, **9**, 231, 241 (1941).
303. D. E. Freeman and W. Klemperer, *J. Chem. Phys.*, **40**, 604 (1964).
304. In their theoretical paper Robinson and Frosch[113] state that under high-energy excitation to higher states the relative quantum yields of phosphorescence to fluorescence, φ_p/φ_f should show either no change or an increase, but never a decrease, when compared to the value of the ratio obtained on excitation to S_1. Actually conflicting data exist. O'Dwyer *et. al.*[305] reported that the ratio of intensities I_p/I_f increased markedly on excitation of chrysene to higher states. However, recently Amako, Ikemura, and Saito[306] found that the ratios I_p/I_f for chrysene, triphenylene, phenanthrene, and naphthalene were unchanged when excitation was to the S_2 and S_3 states. The latter result implies that in these molecules intersystem crossing between higher excited singlet and triplet states is slow relative to internal conversion between the singlet states.
305. M. F. O'Dwyer, M. Ashraf El-Bayoumi, and S. J. Strickler, *J. Chem. Phys.*, **36**, 1395 (1962).
306. Y. Amako, T. Ikemura, and N. Saito, private communication.

5

Photochemistry of the Polyatomic Molecules

Many of the possible primary photochemical processes which occur on excitation of molecules are summarized in Table 5-1. Examples of each of these classes of primary reactions will be seen in the review of primary processes considered in this chapter. In addition to the primary processes which we observed in our considerations of the photochemistry of the simple molecules in Chapter 3, that is, dissociation into free radicals (process 1), photosensitized reactions (7), photoionization (8), and "internal" electron transfer (10), the more complex molecules show an interesting pattern of other chemical reactions of the electronically excited molecule: for example, intramolecular decomposition into molecules (2), intramolecular rearrangement (3), photoisomerization (4), hydrogen-atom abstraction (5), and photodimerization (6).

The quantitative theoretical prediction of the nature and the efficiency of the possible primary processes which occur as the immediate result of light absorption is not yet possible for even very simple molecules. However, from the survey of the current information on primary processes given in this chapter, one will find that various systematic patterns and correlations exist between chemical structure and photochemical reaction modes. These correlations are sufficiently clear in several classes of compounds that in view of them one can make reasonable predictions as to the nature and extent of primary processes to be expected in related compounds which have not yet been studied directly. Furthermore these correlations form the logical basis for the development of more quantitative theories of photochemical reactions.

In the first sections of this chapter the accent will be placed on the consideration of the various fragmentation modes of excited molecules. In Sec. 5-9, photoreduction, photodimerization, molecular photosensitization, and other non-dissociative, intermolecular chemical reactions of the excited state will be reviewed with special emphasis on the well-studied reactions of the carbonyl compounds.

It is impossible to present here a critical discussion and evaluation of the literature leading to the primary processes summarized and still maintain a reasonable brevity of text. In the summary the electronically excited molecules, M*, or the more clearly designated states, singlet (S_1, S_2, . . .), triplet (T_1, T_2, . . .), etc., are indicated only for those molecules for which

TABLE 5-1 Primary Photochemical Processes

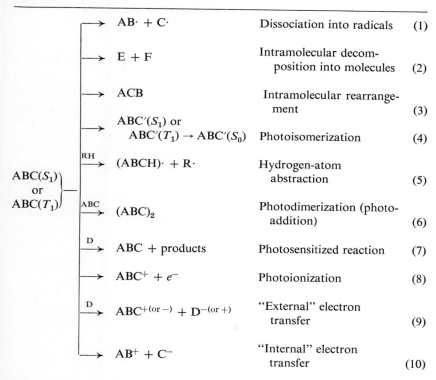

AB· + C·	Dissociation into radicals	(1)
E + F	Intramolecular decomposition into molecules	(2)
ACB	Intramolecular rearrangement	(3)
ABC'(S_1) or ABC'(T_1) → ABC'(S_0)	Photoisomerization	(4)
(ABCH)· + R·	Hydrogen-atom abstraction	(5)
(ABC)$_2$	Photodimerization (photoaddition)	(6)
ABC + products	Photosensitized reaction	(7)
ABC$^+$ + e^-	Photoionization	(8)
ABC$^{+(or-)}$ + D$^{-(or+)}$	"External" electron transfer	(9)
AB$^+$ + C$^-$	"Internal" electron transfer	(10)

the electronic states are of sufficient lifetimes that fluorescence, phosphorescence, collisional deactivation, internal conversion, or other direct manifestation of the excited states is experimentally observable. In cases where the importance of the excited molecules is unknown or where the excited molecule reacts during one of its first vibrations, the transient excited states are not shown. Absorption spectra of typical molecules of a given family or, in other cases, the regions of absorption of light are given; the nature of the original electronic excitation, the current best estimate of the primary quantum efficiencies, φ, for the different decomposition or rearrangement modes, and the molar extinction coefficients,

$\epsilon = [\log_{10} (I_0/I)/cl]$ (liters/mole-cm), are given also for selected wavelengths where available. Reference is given only to the pertinent current literature from which data were taken and in which earlier work is reviewed. No reference to the state of the absorbing molecule is made when the data were obtained in the vapor-phase studies; the liquid- and solid-phase studies are so indicated.

5-1 PRIMARY PHOTODISSOCIATIVE PROCESSES IN THE ALDEHYDES

The simple aldehydes show the characteristic weak absorption band of the carbonyl group in the 3400–2300 A region; see Figs. 5-1 and 5-2. The absorption of CH_2O is shifted to slightly longer wavelengths, and because of its simplicity of structure, considerably more vibrational and rotational structure is resolvable in its spectrum. The similarity of this absorption band for the simple aldehydes is evident in the spectra of acetaldehyde and propionaldehyde in Fig. 5-1 and the butyraldehydes in Fig. 5-2. The band is presumed to have its origin in a "forbidden" $n \rightarrow \pi^*$, singlet-singlet transition involving the promotion of a non-bonding $2p$-electron of the oxygen atom to the carbonyl group antibonding π orbital. (See Secs. 4-2C and 6-2.) The onset of a second absorption band is seen in the spectra below 2200 A. Near 1800 and 1600 A aldehydes show maxima of strong absorption bands which may relate to the allowed $\pi \rightarrow \pi^*$ and $n \rightarrow \sigma^*$ transitions respectively. There is a further very weak absorption

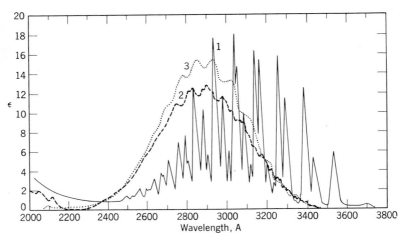

Fig. 5-1   Absorption spectra for (1) formaldehyde [$CH_2O(g)$], ~75°; (2) acetaldehyde [$CH_3CHO(g)$], 25°; (3) propionaldehyde [$C_2H_5CHO(g)$], 25°.[424]

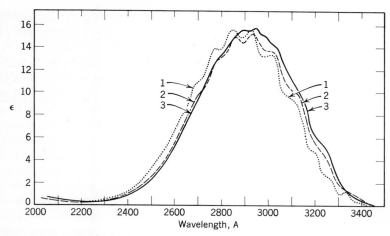

Fig. 5-2 Absorption spectra for (1) propionaldehyde [$C_2H_5CHO(g)$], 25°; (2) n-butyraldehyde [$n\text{-}C_3H_7CHO(g)$], 25°; (3) isobutyraldehyde [iso-$C_3H_7CHO(g)$], 25°.[424]

band near 4000 A ($\epsilon = 10^{-3}$) which has been attributed to a doubly "forbidden" $n \to \pi^*$, single-triplet transition.

Most of the photochemical studies of the aldehydes have been made in the 3300–2500 A region; for a few of the compounds, studies have extended to the Schumann-ultraviolet region. The data of the following survey suggest that the major primary dissociative modes of the aldehydes can be generalized by a few simple processes: reaction I, forming the free radicals R and HCO; reaction II, forming stable hydrocarbon and carbon monoxide molecules; and a third process, peculiar to aldehydes with a γ-hydrogen atom (sometimes called "Norrish Type II split" or photo-elimination), forming enol-aldehyde and olefin molecules in the primary act. Of course in the usual system the enol-aldehyde isomerizes to the keto form of the aldehyde, and the intermediate enol form is detected only in experiments of special design.

$$RCHO + h\nu \to R + HCO \qquad (I)$$
$$\searrow$$
$$RH + CO \qquad (II)$$

$$R_2CHCR_2CR_2CHO + h\nu \to R_2C{=}CR_2 + CR_2{=}C\overset{\displaystyle OH}{\underset{\displaystyle H}{\Big\langle}} \qquad (III)$$

R represents a hydrogen atom or alkyl or aryl organic groups which need not be the same. Process I is important at all wavelengths; process II is unimportant at 3130 A but increases in importance toward the shorter wavelengths. For the simple aliphatic aldehydes which have been tested, the ratio of φ_{II}/φ_I is approximately a constant for a given wavelength of absorbed light: 3130 A, $\varphi_{II}/\varphi_I \cong 0.001-0.05$; 2804 A, 0.34; 2654 A, 0.95; 2537 A, 1.22. For all aldehydes which contain γ-hydrogen atoms, III is important at all wavelengths. For a consideration of the details of process III, see Sec. 5-2. Processes of relatively low efficiency are found in certain long-chain aldehydes which result in the formation of radicals by a bond-cleavage down-chain from the energy-absorbing carbonyl group. (For examples in the following summary, see the processes for propionaldehyde, n-butyraldehyde, isobutyraldehyde, 2-methylbutanal, and pivaldehyde.) These reactions may not occur from electronically excited states of the molecules. They may result from the decomposition of a highly vibrationally excited molecule (or primary radical product) in its ground electronic state; such vibrationally excited molecules may be formed by the internal conversion of the original electronic excitation. Usually such processes are efficiently quenched at high gas pressures or in the liquid phase, since vibrational equilibration is rapid for these conditions. By analogy with the primary processes in the γ-hydrogen-containing ketones, a fourth primary process which forms cyclobutanol derivatives may occur in γ-hydrogen-containing aldehydes. Little work has been done to evaluate this possibility at this writing. A possible primary split of excited aldehyde molecules into an acyl radical and a hydrogen atom has been suggested, but it appears to be of relatively minor importance; hydrogen and biacetyl yields in the flash photolysis of the aldehydes are suggestive of such a process.[1]

The nature of the excited electronic states of the molecules which decompose by processes I, II, and III is still uncertain in most cases. Fluorescence studies with acetaldehyde[2] show that dissociation occurs from an excited triplet almost exclusively at 3340 A (probably by process I). At 3130 A, dissociation by process I from vibrationally excited levels of the electronically excited singlet state begins to occur in addition to triplet dissociation. At 2537 A, process II becomes important, and here dissociation from the upper vibrational levels of a short-lived excited singlet state seems likely. With n-butyraldehyde photodecomposition at 3340 A, process III probably occurs from an excited triplet state; this is suggested strongly by the observation that the triplet emission from added biacetyl is excited by energy transfer from excited aldehyde with a concurrent decrease in the quantum yield of ethylene.[3] On the other hand, the products of I at 3340 A seem unaffected by the presence of biacetyl and are presumed to arise from the decomposition of an excited singlet state. However, it is likely that process III also occurs through the decomposition of an excited singlet state in photolyses at the shorter wavelengths.[4]

The mode of dissociation of the aldehydes may depend strongly on the degree of vibrational excitation of the excited singlet or triplet formed, so that the measured efficiencies of the primary processes really apply for only those conditions of wavelength, temperature, and pressure employed in the particular experiment, and extrapolation to entirely different conditions cannot be made with any assurance of success. In many cases in the following summary, the efficiencies of the primary processes have been estimated from experiments with added iodine as a free radical trap. Because of the facility with which iodine deactivates excited molecules, these estimates are shown as lower limits to the actual values.

1. Formaldehyde:[5-9,488] absorption spectrum under low resolution shown in Fig. 5-1; 3660A, $\epsilon \cong 0.07$; 3130 A, $\varphi_1 + \varphi_2 \cong 1$, $\varphi_1 \cong \varphi_2$, $\epsilon \cong 3.2$ (195°); CD_2O similar although $\varphi_1 + \varphi_2$ is somewhat less than unity at the longer wavelengths; emission is only from the $^1A_2$ excited state, although the $^3A_2$ state has been observed in absorption; M* may be the $^1A_2$, $^3A_2$ or other electronically excited states, or the $^1A_1$ highly vibrationally excited ground-state molecule formed by internal conversion.[755] Low-temperature irradiation of CH_2O (1%) in an argon matrix using a hydrogen discharge produced ESR signals consistent with the occurrence of process 1; secondary photolysis of trapped HCO radicals occurred to form highly excited hydrogen atoms ($HCO + h\nu \rightarrow H + CO$).[672,673]

$$CH_2O(^1A_1) + h\nu \rightarrow CH_2O(^1A_2) \rightarrow CH_2O(^1A_1) + h\nu'$$
$$\downarrow$$
$$M^* \rightarrow HCO + H \qquad\qquad (1)$$
$$\searrow$$
$$H_2 + CO \qquad\qquad (2)$$

2. Acetaldehyde:[2,10-14] absorption spectrum shown in Fig. 5-1; 3130 A, $\varphi_1 \geqslant 0.20$ $(0.8)^{12}$, $\varphi_2 \cong 0.001$, $\epsilon = 6.3(109°)$; 2804 A, $\varphi_1 \geqslant 0.39$, $\varphi_2 \geqslant 0.15$; 2654 A, $\varphi_1 \geqslant 0.36$, $\varphi_2 \geqslant 0.28$; 2537 A, $\varphi_1 \cong 0.38$, $\varphi_2 \cong 0.66$; 2380 A, $\varphi_1 \geqslant 0.31$, $\varphi_2 \geqslant 0.37$; CH_3CDO similar; full mercury-arc irradiation of acetaldehyde in methyl cyclohexane at 77°K gave small amounts of CO and CH_4.[674]

$$CH_3CHO + h\nu \rightarrow M^*(+N) \rightarrow M(+N')$$
$$M + h\nu'$$
$$CH_3 + HCO \qquad\qquad (1)$$
$$CH_4 + CO \qquad\qquad (2)$$

3. Trifluoroacetaldehyde:[3,15] first absorption band, 3500–2450 A, $\lambda_{max} =$ 3020 A; 3340 A, $\epsilon = 3.03(56°)$; 3130 A, $\varphi_1 \geqslant 0.14$, $\varphi_2 \cong 0.02$, $\epsilon = 6.97$.

$$CF_3CHO + h\nu \rightarrow M^*(+N) \rightarrow M(+N')$$

$$M + h\nu'$$

$$CF_3 + HCO \tag{1}$$

$$CF_3H + CO \tag{2}$$

4. Propionaldehyde:[3,16,17] absorption spectrum shown in Fig. 5-1; 3130 A, $\varphi_1 \geqslant 0.48$, $\varphi_2 \cong 0.022$, $\varphi_3 \cong 0.003$, $\varphi_4 \cong 0.00$; $\epsilon = 8.88(32°)$; 2804 A, $\varphi_1 \geqslant 0.53$, $\varphi_2 \geqslant 0.13$, $\varphi_3 \cong 0.01$, $\varphi_4 \cong 0.007$, $\epsilon = 13.35$; 2654 A, $\varphi_1 \geqslant 0.28$, $\varphi_2 \geqslant 0.34$, $\varphi_3 \cong 0.013$, $\varphi_4 \cong 0.012$, $\epsilon = 8.35$; 2537 A, $\varphi_1 \geqslant 0.28$, $\varphi_2 \geqslant 0.37$, $\varphi_3 \cong 0.013$, $\varphi_4 \cong 0.039$; 2380 A, $\varphi_4 \cong 0.080$; 1870 A, $\varphi_1 \cong 0.12$, $\varphi_2 \cong 0.51$, $\varphi_3 \cong 0.06$, $\varphi_4 \cong 0.31$.

$$CH_3CH_2CHO + h\nu \rightarrow M^*(+N) \rightarrow M(+N')$$

$$M + h\nu'$$

$$C_2H_5 + HCO \tag{1}$$

$$C_2H_6 + CO \tag{2}$$

$$C_2H_4 + CH_2O \tag{3}$$

$$CH_3 + CH_2CHO \tag{4}$$

5. Pentafluoropropionaldehyde:[3,18] in full ultraviolet of mercury arc, $\overline{\varphi_1} > \overline{\varphi_2}$; ϵ, 8.87 (3340 A), 15.25 (3130 A), 7.87 (2804 A), 3.26 (2652 A).

$$CF_3CF_2CHO + h\nu \rightarrow M^*(+N) \rightarrow M(+N')$$

$$M + h\nu'$$

$$C_2F_5 + HCO \tag{1}$$

$$C_2F_5H + CO \tag{2}$$

6. n-Butyraldehyde:[3,17,19,20,489] absorption spectrum shown in Fig. 5-2; 3340 A, process 3 important and has its origin in excited triplet molecule, $\epsilon = 1.32$; 3130 A, $\varphi_1 \geqslant 0.35$, $\varphi_2 \cong 0.017$, $\varphi_3 = 0.16$, $\varphi_4 \cong 0.005$, $\epsilon = 9.85$ (32°); 2804 A, $\varphi_1 \geqslant 0.28$, $\varphi_2 \geqslant 0.11$, $\varphi_3 \cong 0.27$, $\varphi_4 \cong 0.006$, $\epsilon = 12.73$;

2654 A, $\varphi_1 \geqslant 0.28$, $\varphi_2 \geqslant 0.25$, $\varphi_3 \cong 0.38$, $\varphi_4 = 0.010$, $\epsilon = 7.25$; 2537 A, $\varphi_1 \cong 0.31$, $\varphi_2 \cong 0.33$, $\varphi_3 \cong 0.30$, $\varphi_4 \cong 0.015$; 1870 A, $\varphi_1 \cong 0.34$, $\varphi_2 \cong 0.13$, $\varphi_3 \cong 0.24$, $\varphi_4 \cong 0.25$, $\varphi_5 \cong 0.04$.

$$CH_3CH_2CH_2CHO + h\nu \rightarrow M^*(+N) \rightarrow M(+N')$$

$$M + h\nu'$$

$$n\text{-}C_3H_7 + HCO \tag{1}$$

$$C_3H_8 + CO \tag{2}$$

$$C_2H_4 + CH_3CHO \tag{3}^{21}$$

$$CH_3 + CH_2CH_2CHO \tag{4}$$

$$C_3H_6 + CH_2O \tag{5}$$

7. Heptafluoro-n-butyraldehyde:[18] in full ultraviolet of mercury arc, $\overline{\varphi}_1 > \overline{\varphi}_2$; no analog to the aldehyde primary process III (process 3 of $n\text{-}C_3H_7CHO$ above) occurs here.

$$CF_3CF_2CF_2CHO + h\nu \rightarrow n\text{-}C_3F_7 + HCO \tag{1}$$

$$C_3F_7H + CO \tag{2}$$

8. Isobutyraldehyde:[3,17,19,20] absorption spectrum shown in Fig. 5-2; 3340 A, $\epsilon = 1.27 (32°)$; 3130 A, $\varphi_1 \geqslant 0.72$, $\varphi_2 \cong 0.03$, $\varphi_3 \cong 0.006$, $\epsilon = 10.30$; 2804 A, $\varphi_3 \cong 0.012$, $\epsilon = 12.69$; 2654 A, $\varphi_1 \geqslant 0.43$, $\varphi_2 \geqslant 0.40$, $\varphi_3 \cong 0.036$, $\epsilon = 6.70$; 2537 A, $\varphi_3 \cong 0.072$; 1870 A, $\varphi_1 \cong 0.30$, $\varphi_2 \cong 0.18$, $\varphi_3 \cong 0.29$, $\varphi_4 \cong 0.23$.

$$(CH_3)_2CHCHO + h\nu \rightarrow M^*(+N) \rightarrow M(+N')$$

$$M + h\nu'$$

$$\text{iso-}C_3H_7 + HCO \tag{1}$$

$$C_3H_8 + CO \tag{2}$$

$$CH_3 + CH_3CHCHO \tag{3}$$

$$C_3H_6 + CH_2O \tag{4}$$

9. *Pivaldehyde:*[22,23] full mercury arc, $\varphi_1 \cong \varphi_2$, φ_3 small; 2537 A, $\varphi_3 \cong$ 0.10.

$$(CH_3)_3CCHO + h\nu \rightarrow tert\text{-}C_4H_9 + HCO \tag{1}$$

$$iso\text{-}C_4H_{10} + CO \tag{2}$$

$$CH_3 + (CH_3)_2CCHO \tag{3}$$

10. *2-Methylbutanal:*[24,25] 3130 A, $\varphi_1 \geqslant 0.60$, $\varphi_2 \cong 0.003$, $\varphi_3 = 0.17$, $\varphi_4 \cong 0.04$, $\epsilon = 10.2$ (25°).

$$CH_3CH_2CH(CH_3)CHO + h\nu \rightarrow M^*(+N) \rightarrow M(+N')$$

$$\downarrow$$

$$sec\text{-}C_4H_9 + HCO \tag{1}$$

$$n\text{-}C_4H_{10} + CO \tag{2}$$

$$C_2H_4 + CH_3CH_2CHO \tag{3}[21]$$

$$CH_3 + C_3H_6CHO \tag{4}$$

11. *n-Valeraldehyde:*[26] full mercury arc, processes 1 and 3 major, 4 and 5 minor, extent of process 2 uncertain.

$$CH_3CH_2CH_2CH_2CHO + h\nu \rightarrow n\text{-}C_4H_9 + HCO \tag{1}$$

$$n\text{-}C_4H_{10} + CO \tag{2}$$

$$C_3H_6 + CH_3CHO \tag{3}[21]$$

$$CH_3 + C_3H_6CHO \tag{4}$$

$$C_2H_5 + C_2H_4CHO \tag{5}$$

12. *Isovaleraldehyde:*[27] full mercury arc, $\varphi_3/(\varphi_1 + \varphi_2) \cong 0.7$.

$$(CH_3)_2CHCH_2CHO + h\nu \rightarrow iso\text{-}C_4H_9 + HCO \tag{1}$$

$$iso\text{-}C_4H_{10} + CO \tag{2}$$

$$C_3H_6 + CH_3CHO \tag{3}[21]$$

13. *Acrolein:*[28,29,656] first absorption band, 3850–2400 A, $\lambda_{max} = 3330$ A, $\epsilon = 18$; excited-molecule mechanism leading to polymer formation

dominant; at 30°, $\Phi_{polymer} = 0.39$ (3660 A), 2.3 (3130 A), 1.0 (3020 A), 10 (2804 A), 19 (2654, 2537 A); φ_1 and φ_2 small at all wavelengths.

$$CH_2{=}CHCHO + h\nu \rightarrow M^*(+M) \rightarrow \text{polymer}$$

$$\begin{cases} CH_2{=}CH + HCO \\ \text{or } CH_2{=}CHCO + H \end{cases} \tag{1}$$

$$CH_2{=}CH_2 + CO \tag{2}$$

14. Crotonaldehyde:[30-33,656] first absorption band 3850–2600 A, $\lambda_{max} = 3280$, $\epsilon = 16$; vapor-phase photoisomerization to 3-butenal by process 5 reported to be important for full mercury arc, $\overline{\varphi_5} \cong 0.1$,[33] but not found to occur by later investigators in gas phase[656] or solution phase;[697] excited-molecule mechanism with deactivation dominant at 25°; polymer formation small; 3660 A, $\Phi_{polymer} = 0.02$; Φ_{CO} near zero at 25°; at 245° and 36 mm, $\Phi_{CO} = 0.012$ (3130 A), 0.048 (2804 A), 0.13 (2654 A), 0.27 (2537 A), 0.55 (2380 A); CH_4 and 2-C_4H_8 among the products at short wavelengths; at elevated temperatures and 2654–2537 A, $\Phi_{CO} > 1$, processes 1–4 possible, but extent of each not clear.[656]

$$CH_3CH{=}CHCHO + h\nu \rightarrow M^*(+N) \rightarrow M(+N')$$

$$CH_3CH{=}CH + HCO \tag{1}$$

$$CH_3CH{=}CHCO + H \tag{2}$$

$$CH_3 + CH{=}CHCHO \tag{3}$$

$$C_3H_6 + CO \tag{4}$$

$$CH_2{=}CHCH_2CHO \tag{5}$$

15. Cyclopropylaldehyde:[556,569] 3130 A, 25°, $\Phi_{CO} = 0.12$ (90 mm), 0.58 (4 mm); 120°, $\Phi_{cyclo\text{-}C_3H_6} = 0.063$ ($I_a = 2.73 \times 10^{-12}$), 0.23 ($I_a = 0.37 \times 10^{-12}$ einstein/cc-sec); 160°, $\Phi_{cyclo\text{-}C_3H_6} = 0.22$; $\varphi_3 \cong 0.35$, independent of temperature and I_a; probable important primary processes are 1, 2, and 3; the extent of 1 and 2 is uncertain.

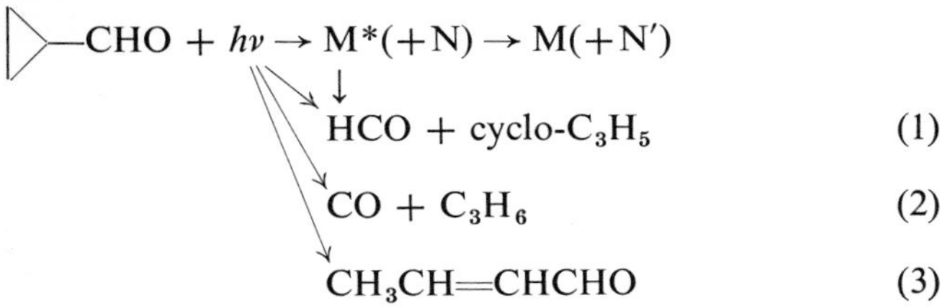

$$\triangleright{-}CHO + h\nu \rightarrow M^*(+N) \rightarrow M(+N')$$

$$HCO + \text{cyclo-}C_3H_5 \tag{1}$$

$$CO + C_3H_6 \tag{2}$$

$$CH_3CH{=}CHCHO \tag{3}$$

16. Glycidaldehyde:[570] first absorption region, $\lambda_{max} = 2950$ A, $\epsilon = 16.6$; second band below 2500 A; 3130 A, $\varphi_1 \cong 0.1$, $\varphi_3 \cong 0.71$ (77°, 27 mm), 0.2 (77°, 85 mm), $\varphi_4 \cong 0.05$; 2654 A, $\varphi_3 \cong 0.8$ (120°, 16 mm).

$$CH_2\!\!-\!\!CH\!\!-\!\!CHO + h\nu \rightarrow CH_2\!\!-\!\!CH + HCO$$

$$\text{(with O bridges)}$$

$$CH_3 + CO \qquad (1)$$

$$\left[\begin{array}{c} CH_2\!\!-\!\!CH_2 \\ | \quad\quad | \\ O\!\!-\!\!-\!\!C\!\!=\!\!O \end{array}\right]^{\ddagger}_{(+M)} \xrightarrow{} \begin{array}{c} CH_2\!\!-\!\!CH_2 \\ | \quad\quad | \\ O\!\!-\!\!-\!\!C\!\!=\!\!O \end{array} \qquad (2)$$

$$CH_2CH_2 + CO_2 \qquad (3)$$

$$CH_3CHO + CO \qquad (4)$$

17. Glyoxal:[34–36,605] first band 4600–3400 A, second band 3200–2300 A; 4358 A, $\varphi_2 \cong 0.6$, $\varphi_1 \cong 0.01$; presumably process 2 occurs from a triplet excited state with violation of the spin conservation rule; 1 may occur from a vibrationally excited ground state formed by intersystem crossing; 3 may occur through triplet-triplet excited molecule interactions; 3660 A, $\varphi_1/\varphi_2 \cong 0.03$, deactivation is important at usual pressures, $\varphi_3 \cong 0.0$; 3130 A, $\varphi_1 \cong 0.15$, $\varphi_2 \cong 0.85$, $\varphi_3 \cong 0.0$, $\epsilon = 22.5$ (150°); 2537 A, $\varphi_1/\varphi_2 \cong 0.19$; below 2537 $\varphi_3 \neq 0$.

$$(HCO)_2 + h\nu \rightarrow M^*(+N) \rightarrow M(+N')$$

$$M + h\nu'$$

$$H_2 + 2CO \qquad (1)$$

$$CH_2O + CO \qquad (2)$$

$$2HCO \qquad (3)$$

18. Benzaldehyde:[37,38] in hexane first band 3800–3100 A; second band 3100–2700 A, $\lambda_{max} = 2820$ A, $\epsilon \cong 1600$; 3130 A, φ_1 and φ_2 very small at 25°; chain decomposition at elevated temperatures; relative importance of processes 1 and 2 unknown; in hydroxylic solvents, hydrogen-atom abstraction by the oxygen atom of the carbonyl (in the triplet excited state) leads to reduction products of benzaldehyde (anisaldehyde is similar; contrast with 1-naphthaldehyde below), see also the nitro-benzaldehydes in Sec. 5-5H.

$$C_6H_5CHO + h\nu \rightarrow M^*(+N) \rightarrow M(+N')$$

$$C_6H_5 + HCO \qquad (1)$$

$$C_6H_5CO + H \qquad (2)$$

19. α-Naphthaldehyde:[39] spectrum shows two $\pi \rightarrow \pi^*$ maxima, 2120 A ($\epsilon = 32{,}000$), and 3120 A ($\epsilon = 6500$); no photoreduction found in the usual hydrogen-donor solvents at 3130 A; it is reduced at 3130 A, using the very good hydrogen-donor, tributylstannane; in this compound the lowest triplet state derived from the $\pi \rightarrow \pi^*$ promotion requires extensive electronic reorganization for the carbonyl of the excited molecule to abstract hydrogen; thus this process is much less efficient than that observed for the triplet of the $n \rightarrow \pi^*$ promoted systems such as benzaldehyde; see above.

5-2 PRIMARY PHOTODISSOCIATIVE PROCESSES IN THE KETONES

The absorption characteristics of the ketones are similar to those described for the aldehydes and reflect the presence of the carbonyl group. See the spectra of Fig. 5-3. The common absorption band in the near ultraviolet (maximum near 2800 A) is again related to a "forbidden" singlet-singlet, $n \rightarrow \pi^*$ transition involving the non-bonding electrons of the oxygen atom. The substitution of an alkyl group for the aldehyde acyl hydrogen-atom shifts the absorption band to slightly shorter wavelengths; presumably this is a consequence of a larger resonance effect of the alkyl substituent which raises the π^* level to a greater extent than the n level is raised by the inductive effect of the substituent. The singlet

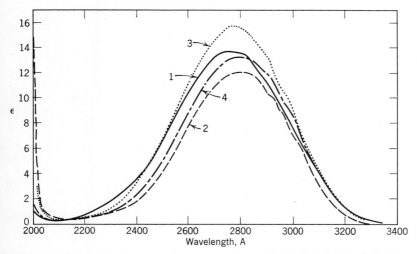

Fig. 5-3 Absorption spectra for (1) acetone [$CH_3COCH_3(g)$], 25°; (2) diethyl ketone [$C_2H_5COC_2H_5(g)$], 25°; (3) methyl ethyl ketone [$CH_3COC_2H_5(g)$], 25°; (4) methyl-*n*-butyl ketone [$CH_3CO(CH_2)_3CH_3(g)$], 25°.[424]

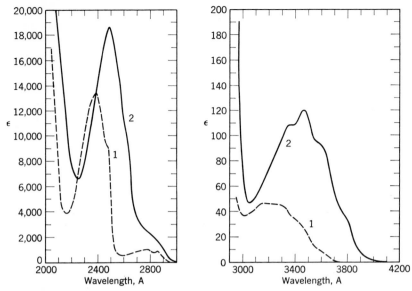

Fig. 5-4   Absorption spectra for (1) acetophenone ($CH_3COC_6H_5$) in cyclohexane, 25°; (2) benzophenone ($C_6H_5COC_6H_5$) in cyclohexane, 25°.[424]

$n \rightarrow \pi^*$ transition in aromatic ketones lies at still longer wavelengths; see Fig. 5-4.

From a study of the following summary it can be seen that primary photodissociative processes IV and V in the ketone photolysis form free radicals and stable products in a fashion analogous to processes I and III of the aldehydes; there appears to be no analog of primary process II in the aldehydes, although in the cyclic ketones this type of process is a possible alternative (see discussion following). Another intramolecular rearrangement, VI, forming cyclobutanol derivatives, has been observed in recent years and may be important in all ketones (and aldehydes) containing γ-hydrogen atoms

$$RCOR' + h\nu \rightarrow R + COR' \qquad (IVa)$$
$$\searrow RCO + R' \qquad (IVb)$$

$$R_2CHCR_2CR_2COR' + h\nu \rightarrow R_2C{=}CR_2 + CR_2{=}C \overset{\displaystyle OH}{\underset{\displaystyle R'}{\diagdown}} \qquad (V)$$

$$\searrow \quad \underset{\displaystyle \underset{|}{CR_2}{-}CR_2}{\overset{\displaystyle OH}{\overset{\diagup}{CR_2{-}C{-}R'}}} \qquad (VI)$$

The R's may be hydrogen atoms or different alkyl or aryl groups; structural variations in R and R' may alter the efficiency of the primary process significantly.

The photochemistry of the ketones is the most thoroughly studied of any class of compounds. Several interesting relationships between molecular structure of the ketone and the efficiency of the alternative primary processes IV, V, and VI, and other modes of reaction of the excited molecules, are considered in the following sections of this chapter. The non-dissociative processes which involve intermolecular reduction of ketone, photocyclodimerization, carbonyl cycloaddition to unsaturated molecules, and photosensitized reactions of ketones are described in Sec. 5-9.

5-2A   Primary Process IV; the Norrish "Type I"; Free Radical Splits in Ketone Photolysis

When both R and R' in the ketone RCOR' are aryl groups, all dissociative modes of the excited ketone molecule are unimportant. If R and R' are different alkyl groups, both of the alternative processes of bond cleavage (represented by IVa and IVb) occur, but a preference is shown for the process involving the rupture of the weakest bond when the absorbed light is of long wavelength. For example, in methyl ethyl ketone photolysis, two possible primary steps occur:

$$CH_3COC_2H_5 + h\nu \rightarrow CH_3CO + C_2H_5 \qquad (1)$$

$$\searrow$$

$$CH_3 + COC_2H_5 \qquad (2)$$

However, the ratio of φ_1/φ_2 varies significantly with the energy of the absorbed quantum; at 3130 A, $\varphi_1/\varphi_2 \cong 40$; at 2654 A, $\varphi_1/\varphi_2 \cong 5.5$; at 2537 A, $\varphi_1/\varphi_2 \cong 2.4$. Less selectivity of the excited ketone is shown between 1 and 2 as the energy of the quantum increases.[62,63]

The excess energy carried off by the newly formed acyl radicals (R'CO, RCO in IVa and IVb) increases with increase in energy of the absorbed quantum; this results in the formation of a larger fraction of the RCO radicals which is non-thermally equilibrated; these "hot" radicals undergo decomposition, $RCO^{\ddagger} \rightarrow R + CO$, in an early vibration following formation. For example, in the vapor-phase photolysis of acetone at 3130 A about 7% of the acetyl radicals formed in the primary act decompose rapidly and cannot be thermally equilibrated under usual conditions. However, in acetone photolysis at 2537 A, using the same conditions of temperature and pressure, about 22% of the acetyl radicals are non-vibrationally equilibrated and fragment quickly after the primary act.

The pronounced influence of structural variations on the efficiencies of free radical formation in processes IVa and IVb is evident in the data from a series of related ketones containing the cyclopropyl group; see

TABLE 5-2 Quantum Yields of CO Production for Cyclopropyl Ketones at 3130 A and 120°[a]

Ketone	Φ_{CO}
(A) CH_3CO—◁ 	0.04
(B) CH_3COCH_2—◁ 	0.88
(C) $CH_3COCH_2CH_2$—◁ 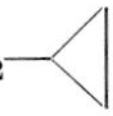	0.70
(D) 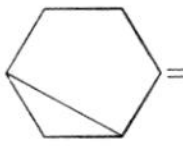 [bicyclic]=O	0.009[b]
(E) 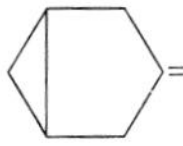 [bicyclic]=O	0.76[b]

[a] From Refs. 497, 504, 514.
[b] Under the same conditions for the analogous cyclopentenones, [structure]=O and [structure]=O, Φ_{CO} = 0.004 and 0.87, respectively.[504,514]

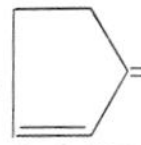

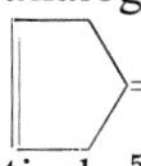

Table 5-2. The major primary photochemical reaction of gaseous methyl cyclopropyl ketone is the rearrangement to methyl propenyl ketone:

$$CH_3CO—◁ + h\nu \rightarrow CH_3COCH{=}CHCH_3$$

At 2654–2537 A the quantum yield of the process is 0.3. Quantum yields of the free radical splits, processes IVa and IVb, total from 0.03 (25°) to 0.11 (170°) at this wavelength region. These results suggest that the energy absorbed by the carbonyl chromophore may be transferred intramolecularly to the cyclopropyl ring with high efficiency compared to the cleavage of C—C bonds adjacent to the carbonyl chromophore. The nature of the electrical interaction between the small ring and the carbonyl group has been described as a type of hyperconjugation which results from orbital overlap of the bent bonds of the small ring with the π orbitals of the attached carbonyl group.[80] Hess and co-workers[497,504,514] determined the values of Φ_{CO} at 3130 A and 120° for a series of related cyclopropyl ketones and used these as measures of the efficiencies of free radical splits. The results, summarized in Table 5-2, suggest a major influence of molecular structure in the processes. Apparently the insertion of a methylene group(s) between the carbonyl chromophore and cyclopropyl ring lowers the orbital overlap between the carbonyl group and the cyclopropyl ring and greatly enhances the free radical splits (IVa and IVb). The fact that Φ_{CO} for ketone C of Table 5-2 is lower than that of ketone B is attributed to the competition from the intramolecular process V in this case, and the expected olefin, methylene cyclopropane, is a product. (See Sec. 5-2B.) With the bicyclic ketone D, analogous to the methyl cyclopropyl ketone A, intramolecular rearrangement to 3-methyl-2-cyclopentenone is the important process. However, ketone E, analogous to ketone B, also photodissociates with high efficiency, giving CO and 1,4-pentadiene as major products and vinyl cyclopropane as a minor product. A similar bicyclic ketone, thujone F, behaves similarly photochemically when irradiated in cyclohexane and isopropyl alcohol solutions; CO elimination with chain rupture is the major process.[578]

There are some very interesting effects on the photoexcited ketone molecule and its primary processes when substitution is made of fluorine or chlorine atoms for hydrogen. "Down-chain" photodissociation of a chlorine atom substituted on a carbon alpha to the carbonyl group occurs efficiently, but the analogous chlorine atom split is absent in the β-substituted ketones. See the data for monochloroacetone and 4-chloro-2-butanone in the summary of data which follows. Fluorine atom substitution for hydrogen lengthens the lifetime of the excited ketone molecules, and collisional deactivation and other non-dissociative processes become more important than with the unsubstituted ketone analogues; compare acetone and the fluorinated derivatives of acetone in the data summary which follows.

5-2B   Primary Process V; the Norrish "Type II" Split in Ketones

Rice and Teller[756] and Noyes and Davis[40] have considered alternative mechanisms for the Norrish "Type II" split of ketones, which we have symbolized as process V. Present evidence favors strongly their suggestion of a cyclic, six-membered-ring intermediate:[487]

$$R_2CHCR_2CR_2\overset{O}{\overset{\|}{C}}R' + h\nu \rightarrow \begin{matrix} CR_2 & \overset{H\cdots O}{\diagdown} & CR' \\ & R_2C\cdots C\dot{R}_2 & \end{matrix} \rightarrow \begin{matrix} CR_2 \\ \| \\ CR_2 \end{matrix} + \begin{matrix} HO & R' \\ \diagdown & \diagup \\ C \\ \| \\ CR_2 \end{matrix} \quad (V)$$

The initial products of the reaction are an olefin and the enol form of a ketone.[487] Although the proposed cyclic intermediate allows a convenient representation of the process, alternative stepwise processes are possible. In theory the spatial arrangement and the charge distribution within the carbonyl group in the excited π^* state both favor bond formation between γ-hydrogen atoms and the carbonyl oxygen.[41] There is no known case of an aliphatic ketone with γ-hydrogen atoms not participating in the photo-cycloelimination (or simply photoelimination) process V; γ-hydrogen atoms next to a double bond are not transferred in unsaturated ketones; see hex-5-ene-2-one, p. 399 in the summary. The interposition of an oxygen (and probably other atoms) in the α or β position of the carbon chain (as with $CH_3COCH_2OCH_3$) does not eliminate process V provided that γ-hydrogen atoms are present, as one would anticipate from the relatively unchanged geometry of the transition state. There appears to be a qualitative relation between the number of γ-hydrogen atoms in the ketone and the quantum efficiency of primary process V, but many other factors are also important, and no simple relationship between the quantum efficiency of process V and structure has been derived at this writing.

The "Type II" split in ketones occurs with a good efficiency when one of the alkyl groups is replaced by an aromatic ring, as in butyrophenone,[497-499] or by a cycloalkyl group, as in menthone.[108] The quantum yield of the "Type II" process in butyrophenone is strongly affected by certain *ortho* and *para* substituents; see Table 5-3. $\Phi_{C_2H_4}$ drops from 0.40 in butyro-phenone to 0.00 in both *o*-and *p*-hydroxy derivatives. The reactivities of the *para*-substituted butyrophenones toward intramolecular hydrogen atom abstraction can be compared with their ESR resonances, the 0—0 bands of their lowest triplet states, and their phosphorescence lifetimes, in Table 5-3. Baum, Wan, and Pitts suggest that at least two factors affect the chemical reactivity of the excited states: (1) the nature of the ground triplet, which appears to be $^3(n, \pi^*)$ in the reactive and $^3(\pi, \pi^*)$ in the non-reactive butyrophenones; and (2) the electron-donating ability of the substituent groups; in the case of the p-OH and p-NH$_2$ derivatives, the negative charge on the excited carbonyl oxygen is increased and hence the hydrogen atom-abstracting ability is reduced; however, see the discussion in Sec. 5-9A.

TABLE 5-3 Quantum Yields of Ethylene Formation, Triplet Levels (0–0 Band), and EPR Resonances for Butyrophenone and Several Derivatives[a]

Substituent	$\Phi_{C_2H_4}$[b]	Triplet Level[c]		EPR Resonance,[d] Gauss		Phosphorescence First-Order Decay Time, τ, sec[e]
		mμ	ev	Band Position	Band Width	
None	0.42	383	3.24	1413 (weak)	27.89	0.002
p-Methyl	0.39	388	3.20	...	...	0.009[f]
p-Fluoro	0.29	373	3.32	...	...	0.004
p-Methoxy	0.10	390	3.18	1362 (strong)	17.71	0.051
p-Hydroxy	0.00	403	3.08	1362 (strong)[g]	18.58	0.084
o-Hydroxy	0.00	...	...	...	...	...
p-Amino	0.00	443	2.80	1392 (strong)[g]	17.71	0.084

[a] From Refs. 497–499.
[b] Benzene solvent, 3130 A, 25°.
[c] 1:4 MeOH—EtOH at −190°.
[d] 0.1 M in isopropyl alcohol at −190°C, full arc.
[e] In alcohol glass at −190°C; τ = the reciprocal of the first-order rate constant for the decay.
[f] In 2-pentene at −190°C.
[g] In glacial acetic acid at −190°C; these resonances shift and become weak and broad; the phosphorescence lifetimes are significantly shorter than those of the resonance signal.

The non-reactivity of the o-hydroxy derivative seems due to the favored occurrence of the reversible abstraction of the hydroxyl-H atom to form a photo enol rather than abstraction of a γ-hydrogen atom to give the "Type II" split.[497–499] Similar ideas have been advanced to explain the behavior of "abnormal" ortho-substituted benzophenones (Secs. 4-11, 5-9A).

Some subtle but interesting effects have been observed in the occurrence of process V. For example, a small activation energy difference exists between the transfer of hydrogen and deuterium from the γ-position of a ketone as process V occurs at the longer wavelengths.[79] See the data for 2-pentanone-4,5,5-d_3, p. 397.

The significance of the γ-hydrogen transfer mechanism in the photochemistry of 20-ketosteroids has been reviewed by Chapman.[501] This photochemical synthetic route has claimed increasingly more interest on the part of organic chemists in the field of natural products. The Norrish "Type II" or the photocycloelimination process is of such general character that it may serve in the future as a means of structure proof for γ-hydrogen containing ketones and as a useful synthetic route to certain special compounds.

In the photolysis of methyl isopropyl ketone at 2537 A acetaldehyde and propylene are major products. Zahra and Noyes[503] suggest that they are formed by a Norrish "Type III" split involving transfer of a β-hydrogen atom.

$$CH_3COCH(CH_3)_2 + h\nu \rightarrow CH_3CHO + C_3H_6 \qquad (Va)$$

The reaction is highly sensitive to wavelength; at 3130 A it is negligible compared to free radical splits IVa and IVb. Presumably Va occurs either through a cyclic four-center transition state or through a five-member transition state (analogous to the six-member transition state of process V) involving the intramolecular abstraction of the β-hydrogen atom by the oxygen with subsequent rearrangement of the initial product (CH$_3$COH) to acetaldehyde. It appears that a similar reaction occurs in the vapor-phase photolysis of α-hydroxymethyl ethyl ketone at 3130 A. The yield of the major product, acetaldehyde, is independent of the temperature in the range 40–150°, and an intramolecular photocycloelimination mechanism seems reasonable.[504]

$$CH_3COCH(OH)CH_3 + h\nu \rightarrow 2CH_3CHO \qquad (Vb)$$

Either a cyclic four- or five-member transition state may be involved, as in Va. Coyle, Peterson, and Heicklen[505] suggest that photodecomposition of 4-methyl-4-methoxy-2-pentanone proceeds through competitive four-, six-, and seven-membered cyclic transition states; see the summary data on p. 397. Elucidation of the details of the mechanism of "Type III" splits such as Va and Vb and the determination of the generality of these reactions remain to be accomplished at this writing.

The nature of the excited states which participate in primary process V has been a subject of considerable controversy. The relative independence of φ_V to the experimental variables of temperature, pressure, added oxygen, and iodine, and the results of experiments with added biacetyl, suggest the possible participation of the first excited singlet electronic state in process V. Michael and Noyes[77] observed that addition of biacetyl quenches only inefficiently the "Type II" split in the photolysis of methyl-n-butyl ketone both at 3130 and 2537 A and suggested that both the energy transfer process and the "Type II" process occur via a singlet excited state of the ketone. However, Ausloos and Rebbert[500] report that at 3130 A the "Type II" process in methyl-*n*-propyl ketone is quenched relatively efficiently by the addition of biacetyl and that the light emitted by various ketone-biacetyl mixtures containing 1 mm of oxygen is identical to that emitted by pure ketones alone. Thus they conclude that the energy-transfer process gives only triplet excited biacetyl and that, consequently, primary process V occurs in methyl-*n*-propyl ketone via an excited triplet state at 3130 A. Their conclusion is supported by studies of ketone-aldehyde mixtures at 3130 A in which they show that the "Type II" process of *n*-butyraldehyde is sensitized by triplet acetone.[489] At this writing the available evidence favors the triplet excited state as the precursor for process V in many ketones and aldehydes excited by absorption at 3130 A. However, the participation of the excited singlet as well as the triplet states in process V, especially in experiments at the shorter wavelengths (2537 A), is possible. Recently Wagner and Hammond[757] studied the inhibition of process V at 3130 A in methyl-*n*-propyl and methyl-*n*-butyl ketones in piperylene solutions (up to 8M), and they concluded that *both* singlet and triplet states of these molecules are involved in both cases; however, the triplet state is a more important source of V in methyl-*n*-propyl ketone [$\varphi_V(T_1) \cong 0.22$; $\varphi_V(S_1) \cong 0.04$] than in methyl-*n*-butyl ketone [$\varphi_V(T_1) \cong 0.08$; $\varphi_V(S_1) \cong 0.18$].

5-2C Primary Process VI; Intramolecular Reduction of the Carbonyl Group

A primary intramolecular rearrangement involving reduction of the carbonyl group and the formation of a cyclic carbinol is common to simple aliphatic ketones with γ-hydrogen atoms, process VI. It provides a reasonable synthetic route to a group of cyclobutanol derivatives otherwise difficult to prepare. One possible mechanism of process VI in ketones may be illustrated for the case of the *n*-propyl ketones.

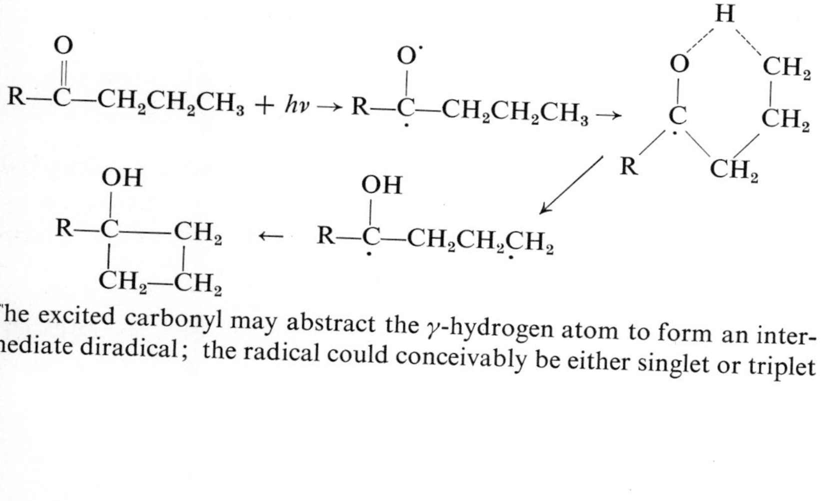

The excited carbonyl may abstract the γ-hydrogen atom to form an intermediate diradical; the radical could conceivably be either singlet or triplet in nature, depending on the multiplicity of the original reactive state of the ketone and the efficiency of intersystem crossing. Thus the timing of the cyclobutane ring formation might be very fast (singlet diradical) or relatively slow (triplet diradical). This mechanism is consistent with the studies of Yang and co-workers. They photolyzed ketones with a δ-ϵ double bond and γ-hydrogen atoms in solution-phase experiments and found photoreduction and cyclization of A to occur with the formation of the two cyclic alcohols B and C; presumably an allyl radical intermediate allows either a four- or a six-membered ring to be formed.[509]

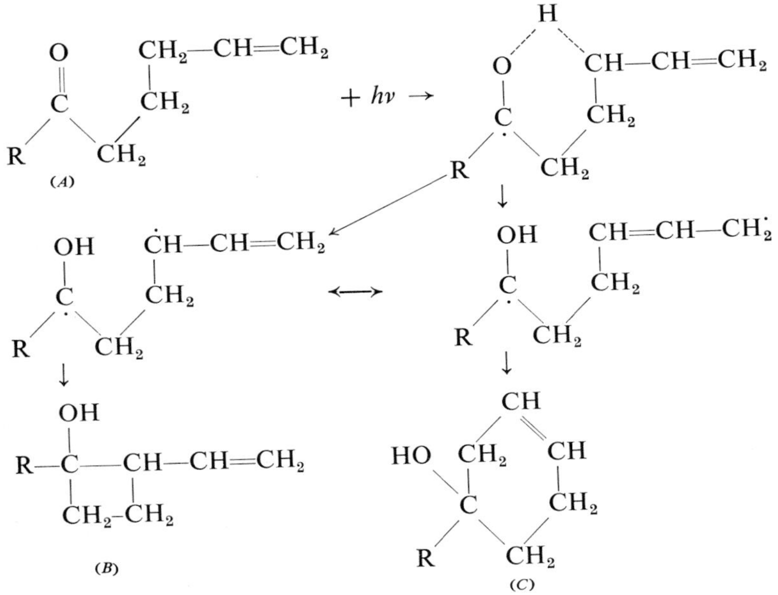

On the other hand, irradiation of 2,6-dimethyl-oct-7-en-3-one, D, in a 10% cyclohexane solution gives the following products:[510]

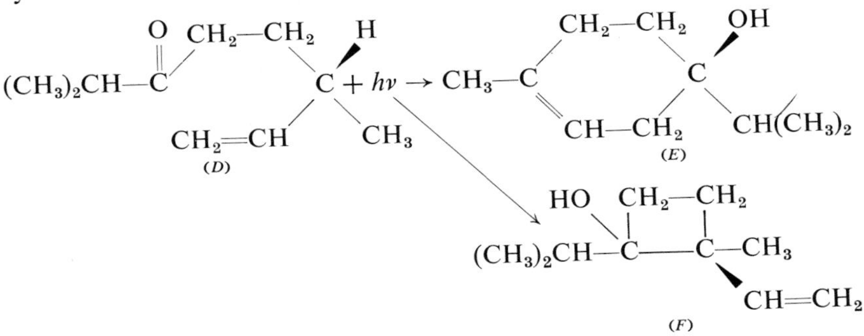

Formation of E with retention of configuration is not likely via an allyl radical intermediate. Thus Schulte-Elte and Ohloff suggest that a concerted, intramolecular, six-center process is responsible for the formation of E, and a similar four-center one-step process leads to F with stereospecific removal of the allyl γ-hydrogen atom.[510] However, the Yang mechanism can explain these results equally well provided that the time required for ring closure is short compared to the time for rotation about the C—C bond.

The light-induced rearrangement of *trans*-1,4-diphenyl-3,4-epoxybutan-1-one has been shown recently to afford dibenzoylethane and an alcohol whose structure was designated as G.[80]

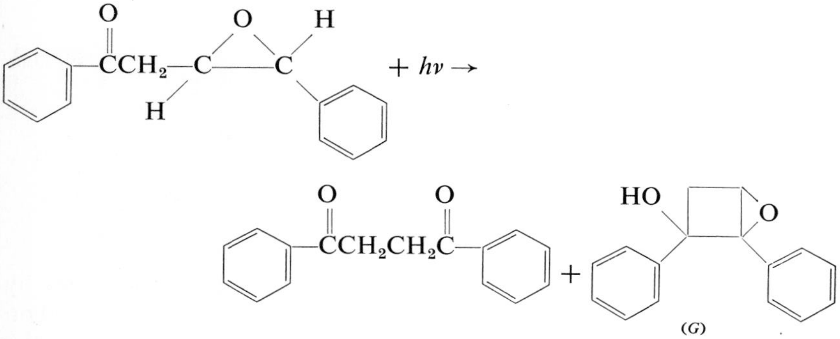

The formation of the epoxycyclobutane may be considered to be analogous to the formation of cyclobutanols from the irradiation of aliphatic ketones containing γ-hydrogens, process VI. The formation of dibenzoylethane, however, cannot be rationalized by a concerted mechanism and is only compatible with Yang's stepwise mechanism.

Note that the analog to cyclobutanol formation in a primary process occurs for the very large ring cyclic ketones; here abstraction of hydrogen atoms does not occur from the γ-hydrogen atoms, which are physically inaccessible to the carbonyl oxygen, but from a carbon atom across the ring which can be in close proximity to the abstracting group. For example, irradiation of cyclodecanone, H, at 2537 A gives the isomeric bicyclic alcohols I and J in 42 and 10% yields, respectively.[105]

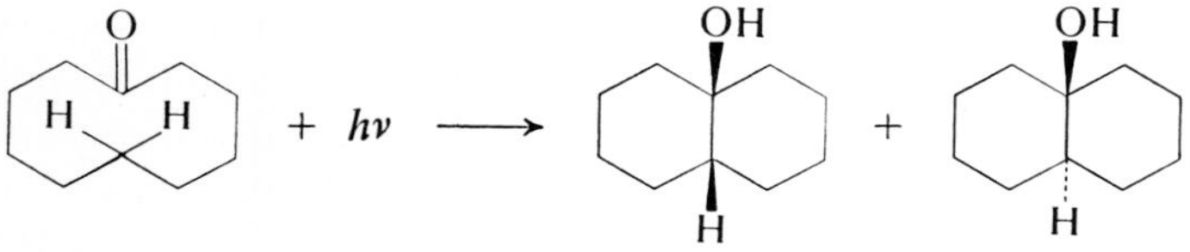

Certain α,β-unsaturated cyclic ketones also undergo skeletal rearrangement with reduction of the carbonyl chromophore. For example, Wheeler and Eastman found that when liquid umbellulone K was irradiated with monochromatic 2537 A radiation 10% conversion to L was observed.[511]

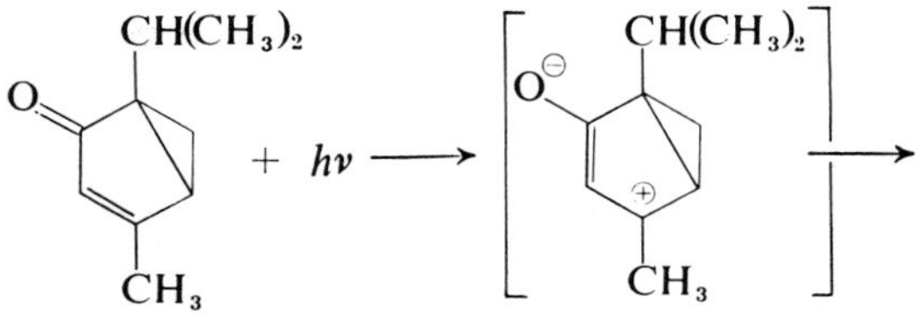

(K)

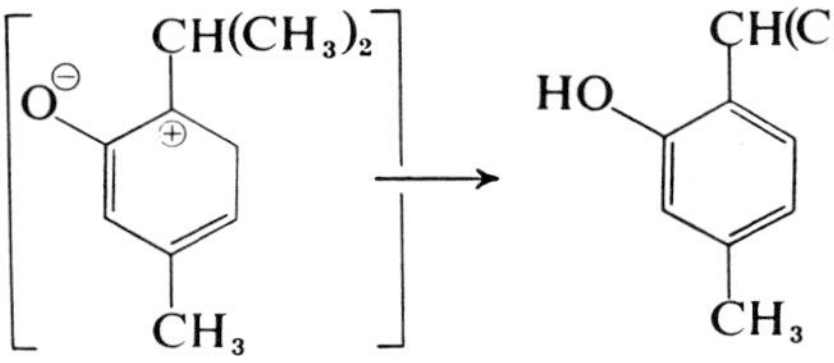

(L)

The intramolecular reduction of the carbonyl group can be rationalized by using Chapman's approach;[501] a positive charge is eventually developed on the β-carbon atom and a negative charge on the carbonyl oxygen in the excited state, as shown in the reaction sequence above.

The 1,2-diketones undergo primary process VI with high efficiency in solution. For example, in ethanol at 4358 A and 25°, 2,7-dimethyl-4,5-octanedione forms compound M with a quantum yield near unity.[574]

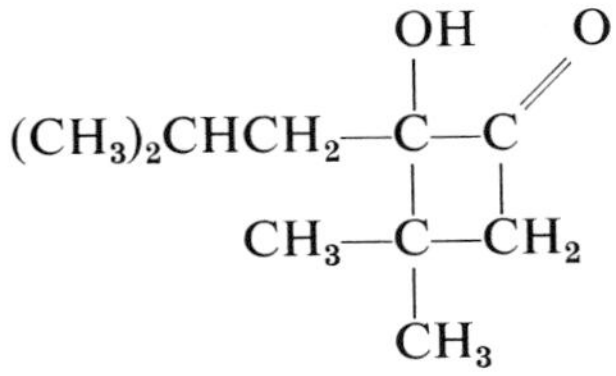

(M)

At first sight it seems attractive to suggest that primary processes V and VI in ketone photolysis occur as alternative reaction paths which involve the same intermediates. However, the effects of temperature, pressure, and added O_2, I_2, etc., are not completely compatible with this explanation; for example, see the data for methyl-*n*-propyl ketone, p. 396 in the summary. φ_{VI} is somewhat more sensitive to pressure, temperature, and added oxygen than φ_V; as the pressure of gas is increased, the significance of VI increases, and it is very important in solution-phase photolyses. Ausloos and Rebbert[42] interpret these results as an indication that process VI in gas-phase photolysis involves the decomposition from the lower vibrational levels of an upper electronic state of undefined multiplicity. The reaction of cyclobutanol formation in solution may proceed through the triplet in many cases since it can be sensitized by triplet benzophenone.[574]

5-2D Primary Processes in the Cyclic Ketones

The modes of photodecomposition of the cyclic ketones have been interpreted differently by various workers. The alternatives may be appreciated by consideration of the results for cyclohexanone photolysis. The major products, cyclopentane, carbon monoxide, 5-hexenal, and 1-pentene, are formed with quantum efficiencies which are relatively insensitive to radical scavengers (O_2, NO, etc.), temperature, pressure, etc. By analogy with the free radical-forming process IV common to the aliphatic ketones, one may suggest that the probable primary process in the cyclic ketones is the cleavage of a C—C bond adjacent to the absorbing carbonyl, forming a diradical.

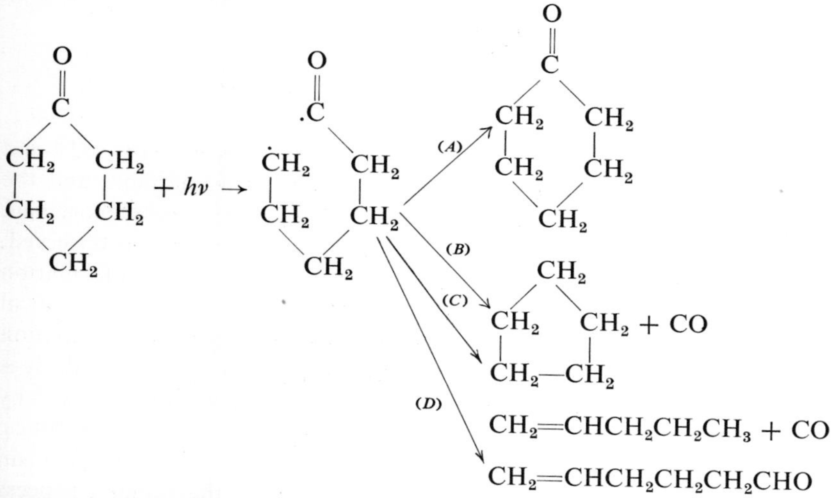

Evidence suggests that the dissociative processes in the vapor state occur from an excited singlet state so that, if ring cleavage occurs, the two odd electrons in the intermediate diradical should be paired, and a very rapid intramolecular combination or disproportionation involving the radical ends would be expected. The radical formed in the photolysis would lead quickly (within the period of a molecular vibration or so) to the reformation of the original ketone (path *A*, combination), cyclopentane and CO (path B, displacement of CO with cyclization), 1-pentene and CO (path C, disproportionation with displacement), or 5-pentenal (path D, disproportionation). Presumably a fifth path forming the ketene, $CH_3CH_2CH_2CH_2CH=C=O$, would be expected as well. The alternative explanation of the product yields is that final products are formed essentially in an intramolecular concerted process which does not involve the intermediate diradical. Because of the expected rapidity of the diradical reactions of self-combination and disproportionation it is impossible to test these mechanism alternatives with the usual radical scavenger techniques.

The two possible mechanisms involving the concerted and free radical paths of formation of the unsaturated aldehyde have been championed by various workers. The diradical mechanism of path D above has been considered. Srinivasan and coworkers[100,516] favor the concerted path involving the transfer of a β-hydrogen atom to the carbonyl group via a four-center configuration:

$$\begin{array}{c} O \\ \parallel \\ C \\ \diagup \quad \diagdown \\ (CH_2)_n \quad H \quad CH_2 \\ \diagdown \quad \diagup \\ C \\ \mid \\ H \end{array}$$

With increasing size of the ring, freedom to rotate about the C—C bond increases and the distance between the carbonyl chromophore and the β-hydrogen atom of the intermediate would be considerably shortened, resulting in a higher efficiency of the isomerization process, as is observed. On the other hand, Quinkert and co-workers[508] explain ketene formation in cyclic ketone photolysis through the disproportionation of the diradical formed by ring cleavage, and presumably they would explain the formation of the aldehyde by the analogous free radical path D above. Again it is difficult to differentiate between alternatives at this writing. Purely by analogy with the dominance of the radical split in the aliphatic ketones, one is tempted to show some preference to the free radical mechanism of these reactions; however, the difference between the primary process alternatives is largely academic, and the products can be considered to be formed in the primary act for most purposes.*

---

* The stereochemistry of the products of the photolyses of pure *cis*- and pure *trans*-2,6-dimethylcyclohexanone were recently studied by Pritchard and co-workers.[700] The results strongly favor the choice of primary process involving ring cleavage with diradical formation. See the discussion of compound 69 of this section.

The intramolecular carbonyl reduction of the large cyclic ketones with ring contraction was discussed in Sec. 5-2C. A different, interesting reaction of ring contraction has been observed recently in pure liquid-phase photolysis of cyclohexanone, cycloheptanone, and cyclooctanone. In the photolysis of pure liquid cyclohexanone, methyl cyclopentanone is formed with a quantum efficiency of 0.03 at 3130 A. Srinivasan and Cremer[538] suggest that this process represents a primary reaction which occurs in a concerted, one-step rearrangement. The photolysis of cyclo-hexanone-2,2,6,6-d_4 gave only the product of structure E. Thus of the two possible concerted rearrangement paths 1 and 2, only the path involving the intermediate F was consistent with the observed isotope distribution in the product.

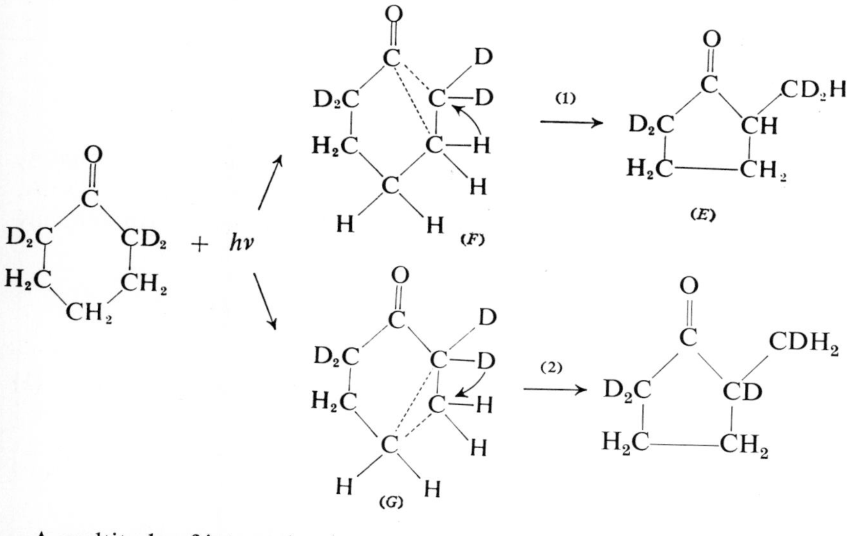

A multitude of interesting intramolecular skeletal rearrangements occur in the unsaturated cyclic ketones, the bicyclic and tricyclic ketones, the epoxyketones, and the steroids. Some examples of these reactions are given in the following summary. The reader is referred to the comprehensive reviews for additional discussion of these processes and the interesting "mechanistic" photochemistry which can be used to rationalize the reactions of these compounds.[501,637,80,120,493]

1. Ketene:[43–46,640–3] first absorption region, 3700–2600 A, $\lambda_{max} = 3300$ A, $\epsilon = 12$; 3650 A, $\varphi_1 = 0.27$ (27°, 5 × 10⁻⁵ M), 0.22 (27°, 5 × 10⁻⁴ M), $\epsilon = 3.82$; 3340 A, $\varphi_1 = 0.72$ (37°, 26 mm), 0.21 (37°, 385 mm); 3130 A, $\varphi_1 = 1.0$ (37°, <50 mm), 0.59 (37°, 751 mm); 2700 A, $\varphi_1 = 1.0$ (independent of temperature, pressure, I_a); in the vapor phase the product

CH_2 is formed largely as a singlet from 2700–2900 A, but presumably it can be deactivated to a lower-lying triplet state by collisions with inert molecules; recent work suggests that a large fraction of the CH_2 radicals are formed as triplets for photolyses at the longer wavelengths;[644,701,702] the fractions of methylene triplet ($\cdot CH_2 \cdot$) formed, presumably from the dissociation of triplet ketene in process 2, at various wavelengths have been estimated to be: 15% (2804 A),[702] 15–20% (3130 A),[702,701] 30% (3340 A),[702] 40% (3660 A),[702] and greater than 50% (3460–3820 A).[644]

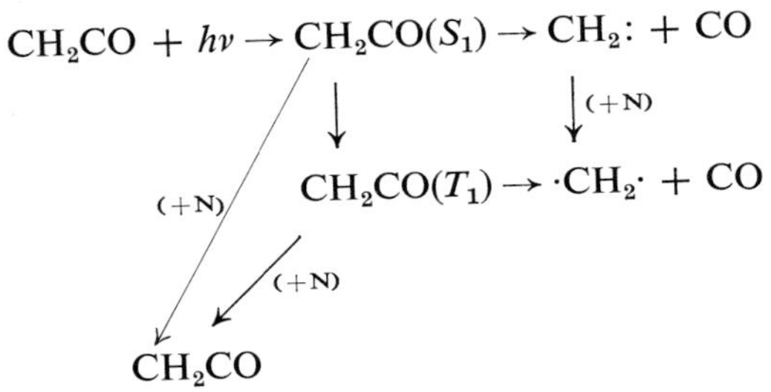

$$CH_2CO + h\nu \rightarrow CH_2CO(S_1) \rightarrow CH_2{:} + CO \tag{1}$$

$$CH_2CO(T_1) \rightarrow \cdot CH_2{\cdot} + CO \tag{2}$$

$$CH_2CO$$

2. *Methyl ketene:*[47,640-3,707] first absorption region, 3900–2800 A, $\lambda_{max} \cong 3500$ A, $\epsilon \cong 12$; 3650 A, $\varphi_1 = 0.0043$ (low pressure, 24°); 3130 A, $\varphi_1 \cong 1.0$ (low pressure, 24°); $CH_3CH^{\ddagger}$ and $C_2H_4^{\ddagger}$ represent vibrationally excited species.

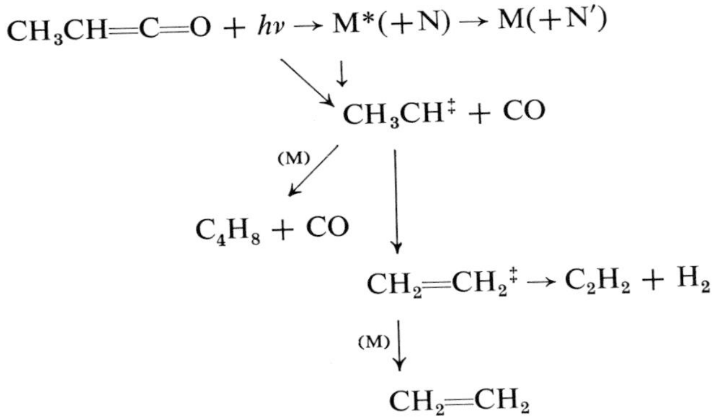

$$CH_3CH{=}C{=}O + h\nu \rightarrow M^*(+N) \rightarrow M(+N')$$

$$CH_3CH^{\ddagger} + CO \tag{1}$$

$$C_4H_8 + CO$$

$$CH_2{=}CH_2^{\ddagger} \rightarrow C_2H_2 + H_2$$

$$CH_2{=}CH_2$$

3. *Dimethyl ketene:*[48,640-3] first absorption region, 4350–3000 A, $\lambda_{max} = 3640$ A, $\epsilon \cong 10$; second region, 2600–2200 A, $\lambda_{max} = 2380$ A, $\epsilon \cong 200$; 3660 A, $\varphi_1 = 0.001$ (31°, 8×10^{-3} M); $\varphi_1 = 0.04$ (31°, 7×10^{-5} M); 2537 A, $\varphi_1 = 1.0$ (independent of temperature, pressure).

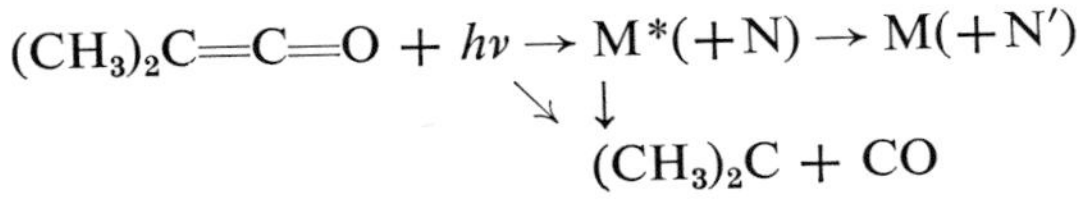

$$(CH_3)_2C{=}C{=}O + h\nu \rightarrow M^*(+N) \rightarrow M(+N')$$

$$(CH_3)_2C + CO \tag{1}$$

4. Acetone:[49–53] first absorption region shown in Fig. 5-3; 3130 A, most dissociation is from the triplet electronic state; $\varphi_2/(\varphi_1 + \varphi_2) = 0.07$ (25°, ~100 mm); $\varphi_1 + \varphi_2 = 1.0$ (above 100°), $\epsilon = 2.86$; 2537 A, dominant dissociation from the first excited singlet state; $\varphi_2/(\varphi_1 + \varphi_2) = 0.22$ (25°); $\varphi_1 + \varphi_2 = 1.0$ (above 100°), $\epsilon = 7.7$; below 2537 A, $\varphi_3 \neq 0$; 1900–1600 A, $\varphi_3 \cong 0.03$; in solutions of perfluoromethylcyclobutane, 2537 A, 26°, $\Phi_{CO} \cong 10^{-4}$; solvent quenching believed important. Process 1 occurs on irradiation of acetone at 77°K as ESR signal of CH_3 is observed.[675] Other values of ϵ (25°): 3341 A, <0.1; 3025 A, 6.32; 2893 A, 10.3; 2804 A, 12.4; 2652 A, 11.2; CD_3COCD_3 similar photochemical behavior. $CH_3CO^{\ddagger}$ represents a non-thermally equilibrated radical.

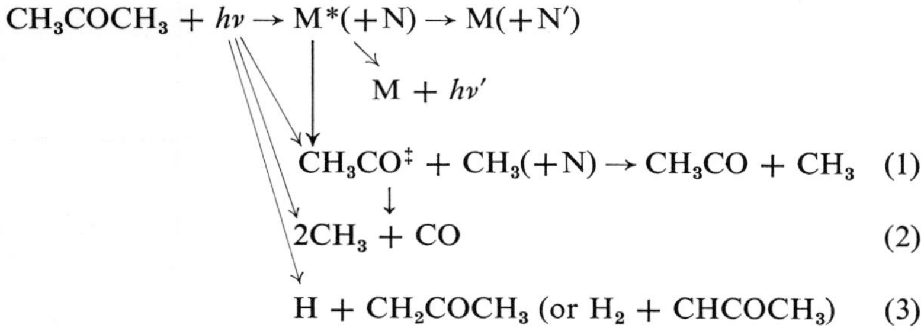

$$CH_3COCH_3 + h\nu \to M^*(+N) \to M(+N')$$

$$M + h\nu'$$

$$CH_3CO^{\ddagger} + CH_3(+N) \to CH_3CO + CH_3 \quad (1)$$

$$2CH_3 + CO \quad (2)$$

$$H + CH_2COCH_3 \ (\text{or} \ H_2 + CHCOCH_3) \quad (3)$$

5. 1,3-Difluoroacetone:[708] $\lambda_{max} = 2850$ A, $\epsilon = 28.5$; 3130 A, $\epsilon \cong 15$; $\varphi_1 \cong 1$ for temperatures above 100°.

$$CFH_2COCFH_2 + h\nu \to CFH_2 + COCFH_2 \quad (1)$$

6. 1,1,1-Trifluoracetone:[54,51,490] first absorption band 3400–2600, $\lambda_{max} = 2850$ A; second band 2600–2000 A, $\lambda_{max} = 2400$ A; 3130 A, $\varphi_1 > \varphi_2$; φ_1, φ_2 very small at 25°; $\varphi_1 + \varphi_2 \cong 1.0$ above 200°; values of ϵ (25°), 3341 A, 0.61; 3130 A, 3.95; 3025 A, 6.55; 2894 A, 8.35; 2804 A, 8.15; 2654 A, 5.58; 2537 A, 3.2.

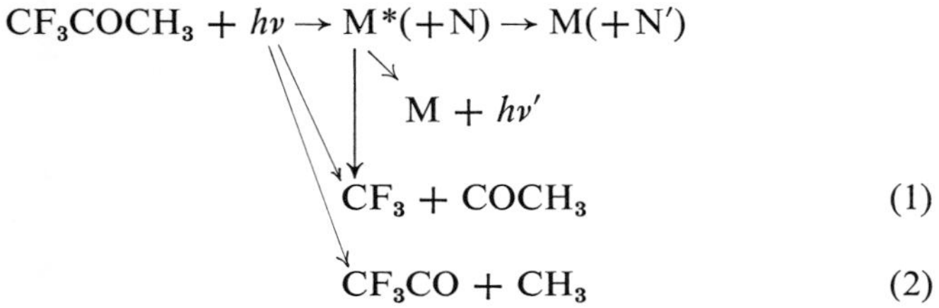

$$CF_3COCH_3 + h\nu \to M^*(+N) \to M(+N')$$

$$M + h\nu'$$

$$CF_3 + COCH_3 \quad (1)$$

$$CF_3CO + CH_3 \quad (2)$$

7. Hexafluoroacetone:[51] 3130 A, $\varphi_1 = 1.0$ (temperatures > 200°), $\Phi_{CO} = 0.065$ (27°, 99 mm), 0.64 (107°, 97 mm); emission from both excited singlet and triplet states is observed at the lower temperatures;[709] $\varphi_f =$ 0.009 (25°), 0.051 ($-78°$); $\varphi_p = 0.025$ (25°), 0.51 ($-78°$); values of ϵ (25°): 3341 A, 2.6; 3130 A, 7.0; 3025 A, 8.1; 2804 A, 5.6; 2652 A, 2.8; 2537 A, 1.4.

$$CF_3COCF_3 + h\nu \rightarrow M^*(+N) \rightarrow M(+N')$$

$$M + h\nu'$$

$$CF_3 + COCF_3 \tag{1}$$

8. Monochloroacetone:[55] first absorption band, 3300–2400 A, $\lambda_{max} =$ 2900 A; 3130 A, $\varphi_1 + \varphi_2 \cong 1.0$, $\varphi_2 \leqslant 0.15$. CH_2Cl and CH_3 formation unimportant for these conditions.

$$ClCH_2COCH_3 + h\nu \rightarrow Cl + CH_2COCH_3 \tag{1}$$

$$HCl + CHCOCH_3 \tag{2}$$

9. 1,3-Dichloro-1,1,3,3-tetrafluoroacetone:[56,57] first absorption band, 3600–2400 A, $\lambda_{max} \cong 3050$ A, $\epsilon \cong 38$; process 1 dominant at 3130 A; process 2 possible at 2537 A.

$$ClF_2CCOCF_2Cl + h\nu \rightarrow M^*(+N) \rightarrow M(+N')$$

$$(ClF_2CCO^\ddagger) + CF_2Cl$$

$$2ClF_2C + CO \tag{1}$$

$$Cl + F_2CCOCF_2Cl \tag{2}$$

10. 1,1,3-Trichloro-1,3,3-trifluoroacetone:[58] spectrum similar to that for ClF_2CCOCF_2Cl. 3130 A, process 1 dominant but 2 possible at higher temperatures; $\epsilon = 56.7$; 2537 A, 1 dominant and 2 possible; $\epsilon = 9.4$.

$$Cl_2FCCOCF_2Cl + h\nu \rightarrow (Cl_2FCCO) + CF_2Cl$$

$$Cl_2FC + CF_2Cl + CO \tag{1}$$

$$Cl + C_3Cl_2F_3O \tag{2}$$

11. Hexachloroacetone:[59] 3130 A, $\Phi_{CO} \cong 0.5$ (183°, independent of pressure), 3.1 (325°); process 1 favored but 2 possible by analogy with $ClCH_2COCH_3$.

$$Cl_3CCOCCl_3 + h\nu \rightarrow M^*(+N) \rightarrow M(+N)$$

$$CCl_3 + COCCl_3 \qquad (1)$$

$$Cl + Cl_2CCOCCl_3 \qquad (2)$$

12. Methoxyacetone:[60] 3130 A, $\varphi_1 = 0.32$ (25°), 0.38 (106°); $\varphi_2 + \varphi_3 \cong$ 0.06 (106°); $\epsilon = 6.49$ (25°).

$$CH_3COCH_2OCH_3 + h\nu \rightarrow M^*(+N) \rightarrow M(+N')$$

$$CH_3COCH_3 + CH_2O \qquad (1)^{21}$$

$$CH_3CO + CH_2OCH_3 \qquad (2)$$

$$CH_3 + COCH_2OCH_3 \qquad (3)$$

13. Methyl ethyl ketone:[61-63] first absorption band shown in Fig. 5-3; second region below 2000 A; 3130 A, $\varphi_1 + \varphi_2 \cong 1.0$ (temperatures >100°), $\varphi_1/\varphi_2 = 40$ (100°), 21 (175°); 2654 A, $\varphi_1/\varphi_2 = 5.5$ (100°); 2537 A, $\varphi_1/\varphi_2 = 2.4$; 1850–2000 A, $\varphi_1 + \varphi_2 = 1.0$.

$$CH_3COC_2H_5 + h\nu \rightarrow CH_3CO + C_2H_5 \qquad (1)$$

$$CH_3 + COC_2H_5 \qquad (2)$$

14. 4-Chloro-2-butanone:[64] 3130 A, $\varphi_1 + \varphi_2 \cong 0.3$, $\varphi_3 \cong 0.0$.

$$ClCH_2CH_2COCH_3 + h\nu \rightarrow ClCH_2CH_2 + COCH_3 \qquad (1)$$

$$ClCH_2CH_2CO + CH_3 \qquad (2)$$

$$Cl + CH_2CH_2COCH_3 \qquad (3)$$

15. 3-Chloro-2-butanone:[64] 3130 A, $\varphi_1 \cong 0.5$, $\varphi_2 + \varphi_3 \cong 0.02$.

$$CH_3CHClCOCH_3 + h\nu \rightarrow Cl + CH_3CHCOCH_3 \qquad (1)$$

$$CH_3CHCl + COCH_3 \qquad (2)$$

$$CH_3CHClCO + CH_3 \qquad (3)$$

16. 3-Hydroxy-2-butanone:[504] 3130 A, acetaldehyde is the major product of the vapor-phase photolysis at 40°; $\varphi_1 = 0.35$, independent of temperature (40–150°); $\Phi_{CO} = \Phi_{CH_4} = 1.2$ at 150°; X may be a four- or five-membered cyclic transition state leading to the transient CH_3COH species.

$$CH_3COCH(OH)CH_3 + h\nu \rightarrow [X] \rightarrow 2CH_3CHO \tag{1}$$

17. Diethylketone:[65–72,710] first absorption band shown in Fig. 5-3; 3130 A, $\varphi_1 + \varphi_2 \cong 1.0$, $\varphi_2/(\varphi_1 + \varphi_2) \cong 0.09$ (35°), 0.15 (70°), 0.3 (150°); decomposition from first excited triplet state leads to processes 1 and 2; 2650 A, $\varphi_1 + \varphi_2 = 1.0$, $\varphi_2/(\varphi_1 + \varphi_2) \cong 0.24$ (35°); 2537 A, $\varphi_1 + \varphi_2 = 1.0$ decomposition of first excited singlet probably responsible for 1 and 2 here. In liquid phase, $\Phi_{CO} \cong 1$ (95°), 0.23 (0°); in solution of perfluorodimethylcyclobutane, $\varphi_1 + \varphi_2 \cong 0.01$ (26°); $CH_3CD_2COCD_2CH_3$ similar photochemically. $C_2H_5CO^\ddagger$ is a non-thermally equilibrated radical.

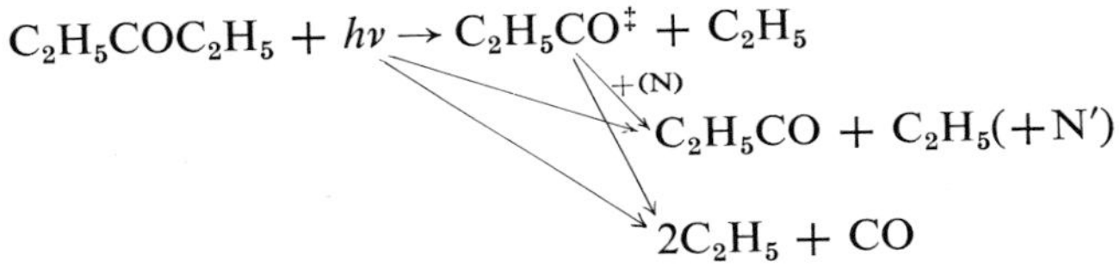

$$C_2H_5COC_2H_5 + h\nu \rightarrow C_2H_5CO^\ddagger + C_2H_5$$
$$+ (N)$$
$$\searrow C_2H_5CO + C_2H_5(+N') \tag{1}$$
$$\searrow 2C_2H_5 + CO \tag{2}$$

18. Perfluorodiethyl ketone:[73] 3340 A, $\epsilon = 14.3$; 3130 A, $\varphi_1 + \varphi_2 \cong$ 0.15 (27°, pressure → ∞), 1.0 (27°, pressure → 0), $\epsilon = 22.3$; 2640 A, $\varphi_1 + \varphi_2 = 0.3$ (27°, pressure → ∞), 1.0 (27°, pressure → 0), $\epsilon = 3.50$.

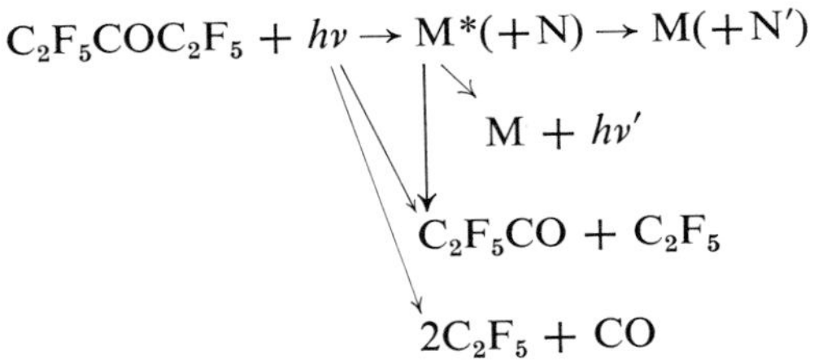

$$C_2F_5COC_2F_5 + h\nu \rightarrow M^*(+N) \rightarrow M(+N')$$
$$\searrow M + h\nu'$$
$$\searrow C_2F_5CO + C_2F_5 \tag{1}$$
$$\searrow 2C_2F_5 + CO \tag{2}$$

19a. Methyl n-propyl ketone:[42,74–78,657] full mercury arc, $\bar{\varphi}_{1a} + \bar{\varphi}_{1b} = \bar{\varphi}_2$; 3130 A, $\varphi_2 = 0.24$,[77] 0.31,[78] 0.27,[657] 0.25,[738] $\varphi_3 = 0.108$ (28°, 3.2 cm), 0.028 (28°, 0.13 cm), 0.044 (150°, 1.5 cm); decomposition by process 2 has been suggested to occur from a lower vibrational level of the first excited singlet state, while 1 may involve the lowest triplet;[77] 2537 A, $\varphi_1 \geqslant 0.22$ (temperatures > 120°), $\varphi_2 = 0.39$; 2537–2650 A, $\varphi_3/\varphi_2 = 0.12$ (28°, 1.5 cm); in liquid phase, 3130 A, −65°, $\varphi_3/\varphi_2 = 0.42$; at 76°, 0.45; little change in these ratios using 2537 A. Enol-acetone observed as initial product of 2, through infrared absorption.[487]

$$CH_3COCH_2CH_2CH_3 + h\nu \rightarrow CH_3CO + CH_2CH_2CH_3 \quad (1a)$$

$$CH_3 + COCH_2CH_2CH_3 \quad (1b)$$

$$C_2H_4 + CH_3C(OH){=}CH_2 \quad (2)$$

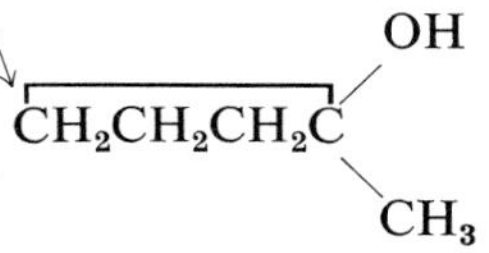

$$\overset{\displaystyle OH}{\underset{\displaystyle CH_3}{\overline{CH_2CH_2CH_2}C}} \quad (3)$$

19b. 2-Pentanone-4,5,5-d_3:[78]   3130 A, $\varphi_{2a} + \varphi_{2b} = 0.28$; $\varphi_{1a} + \varphi_{1b} = 0.58$; $\varphi_{2b}/\varphi_{2a} = 2.00$ (305°K, low ketone pressure), 2.72 (305°K, high ketone pressure), 2.60 (306°K, fixed ketone pressure), 1.42 (420°K); 2537–2654 A, $\varphi_{2a} + \varphi_{2b} = 0.41$; $\varphi_{1a} + \varphi_{1b} = 0.42$; $\varphi_{2b}/\varphi_{2a} = 0.90$ (306°K, low ketone pressure), 1.00 (308°K, high ketone pressure); 1700–1900 A, $\varphi_{2b}/\varphi_{2a} = 0.65$.

$$CH_3COCH_2CHDCD_2H + h\nu \rightarrow CH_3CO + CH_2CHDCD_2H \quad (1a)$$

$$CH_3 + COCH_2CDHCD_2H \quad (1b)$$

$$DHC{=}CDH + CH_3C(OD){=}CH_2 \quad (2a)$$

$$CD_2{=}CDH + CH_3C(OH){=}CH_2 \quad (2b)$$

20. 4-Methyl-4-methoxy-2-pentanone:[505]   3130 A, photolysis in heptane, ethanol, or allyl alcohol, $\varphi_1 = 0.25$, $\varphi_2 = 0.04$, $\varphi_3 = 0.17$; presumably processes 1, 2, and 3 involve four-, six-, and seven-membered cyclic transition states, respectively; free radical processes appear to be unimportant.

$$CH_3COCH_2C(CH_3)_2OCH_3$$
$$+ h\nu \rightarrow CH_3COCH{=}C(CH_3)_2 + CH_3OH \quad (1)$$

$$CH_3COCH_3 + CH_2{=}C(CH_3)OCH_3 \quad (2)^{21}$$

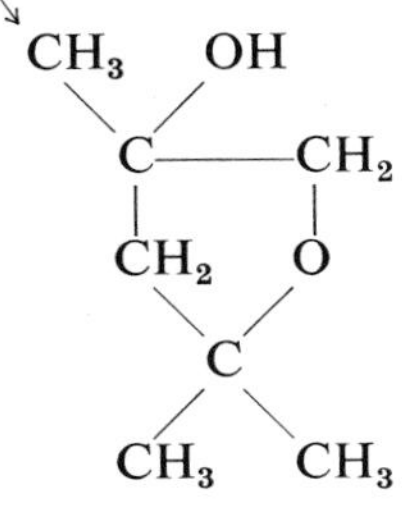

$$
\begin{array}{c}
\overset{\displaystyle CH_3}{\underset{\displaystyle CH_2}{\diagdown}}\;\;\overset{\displaystyle OH}{\underset{\displaystyle O}{\diagup}} \\
C\text{------}CH_2 \\
| \qquad\quad | \\
CH_2 \qquad O \\
\diagdown\quad\diagup \\
C \\
\diagup\quad\diagdown \\
CH_3 \qquad CH_3
\end{array}
\qquad (3)
$$

21. trans-Methyl propenyl ketone:[79,504] 3130 A, $\varphi_2 + \varphi_3 = 0.00$ (25°, 18 mm), 0.1 (275°, 18 mm); φ_1 significant; 2380 A, $\varphi_2 + \varphi_3 \cong 0.015$ (60°, 19 mm), 1.0 (275°, 10 mm).

$$\textit{trans-}CH_3COCH{=}CHCH_3 + h\nu \rightarrow M^*(+N) \rightarrow \textit{cis-} \text{ or } \textit{trans-}M(+N') \tag{1}$$

$$M + h\nu'$$

$$\dot{C}H_3 + \dot{C}OCH{=}CHCH_3 \tag{2}$$

$$CH_3\dot{C}O + \dot{C}H{=}CHCH_3 \tag{3}$$

22. Methyl isopropyl ketone:[74,492,503] 1 and 2 are the only important processes at 3130 A; $\varphi_1 > \varphi_2$; 2537 A, 127°, $\varphi_1 + \varphi_2 \leqslant 0.78$, $\varphi_3 \leqslant 0.33$.

$$CH_3COCH(CH_3)_2 + h\nu \rightarrow CH_3\dot{C}O + \dot{C}H(CH_3)_2 \tag{1}$$

$$\dot{C}H_3 + \dot{C}OCH(CH_3)_2 \tag{2}$$

$$CH_3CHO + C_3H_6 \tag{3}$$

23. Methyl n-butyl ketone:[40,77,81-83] first absorption band shown in Fig. 5-3; 3130 A, $\varphi_1 + \varphi_2 \geqslant 0.06$, $\varphi_3 = 0.45$,[40] 0.46,[83] 0.42;[77] 2537 A, $\varphi_1 + \varphi_2 \geqslant 0.08$, $\varphi_3 = 0.30$. Reaction 3 may involve decomposition from low vibrational levels of first excited singlet at both 3130 and 2537 A, although participation of the triplet state at 3130 A cannot be excluded. The electronic state which is the precursor to 1 and 2 is not clear. Experiments with 2-hexanone-5,5-d_2 suggest enol-acetone intermediate first formed in 3 and, by analogy, in other Norrish Type II processes.

$$CH_3COCH_2CH_2CH_2CH_3 + h\nu \rightarrow M^*(+N) \rightarrow M(+N')$$

$$CH_3\dot{C}O + n\text{-}C_4H_9 \tag{1}$$

$$\dot{C}H_3 + \dot{C}OC_4H_9 \tag{2}$$

$$CH_3C(OH){=}CH_2 + C_3H_6 \tag{3}$$

24. Ethyl n-propyl ketone:[738] 3130 A, $\varphi_1 + \varphi_2 \cong 0.57$ (150°), $\varphi_3 = 0.20$ (60–150°)

$$C_2H_5COCH_2CH_2CH_3 + h\nu \rightarrow C_2H_5\dot{C}O + n\text{-}C_3H_7 \tag{1}$$

$$\dot{C}_2H_5 + \dot{C}OC_3H_7 \tag{2}$$

$$C_2H_5COCH_3 + C_2H_4 \tag{3}^{21}$$

25. Heptafluoropropyl ethyl ketone:[711] 3130 A, $\epsilon = 20.8$, $\varphi_1 \cong 1$ (353–635°K).

$$C_3F_7COC_2H_5 + h\nu \rightarrow (R + R'CO) \rightarrow C_3F_7 + CO + C_2H_5 \qquad (1)$$

26. Hex-5-ene-2-one:[84] very stable to light; 3130 A, $\varphi_1 + \varphi_2 = 0.005$ (139°), $\varphi_3 = 0.005$ (139°); no intramolecular allene and enol-acetone formation here (analog to process 3 of methyl-*n*-butyl ketone).

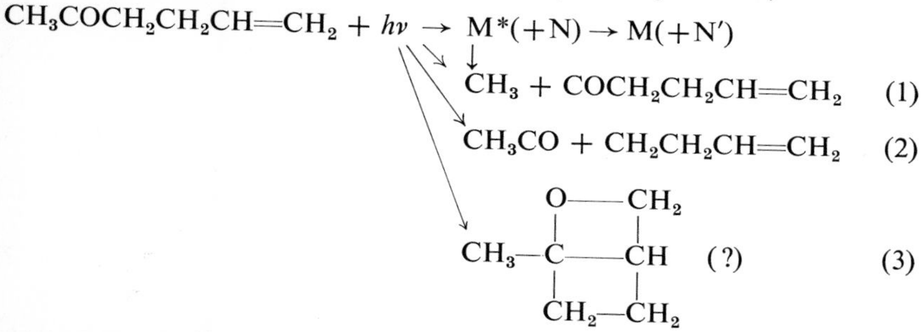

$$CH_3COCH_2CH_2CH{=}CH_2 + h\nu \rightarrow M^*(+N) \rightarrow M(+N')$$

$$\dot{C}H_3 + \cdot COCH_2CH_2CH{=}CH_2 \qquad (1)$$

$$CH_3\dot{C}O + \cdot CH_2CH_2CH{=}CH_2 \qquad (2)$$

$$
\begin{array}{c}
O\!-\!-\!CH_2 \\
| \quad\quad | \\
CH_3\!-\!C\!-\!-\!CH \quad (?) \qquad (3)\\
| \quad\quad | \\
CH_2\!-\!CH_2
\end{array}
$$

27. 4-Methyl-3-hexen-2-one:[513] this ketone, 3,4-dimethyl-3-penten-2-one, and 4,5-dimethyl-3-hexene-2-one all show no change on irradiation in ether solution, using Pyrex-filtered mercury arc.

$$CH_3COCH{=}C(CH_3)CH_2CH_3 + h\nu \rightarrow \text{no observable change}$$

28. 5-Methyl-3-hexen-2-one:[513] irradiation with Pyrex-filtered mercury arc in ether solution gave 75% yield of *A*; 3-hexen-2-one behaved similarly but *cis* and *trans* isomers of the product form.

$$CH_3COCH{=}CHCH(CH_3)_2 + h\nu \rightarrow CH_3COCH_2CH{=}C(CH_3)_2$$
$$(A)$$

29. 5,5-Dimethyl-3-hexen-2-ones:[512,591] Pyrex-filtered mercury-arc irradiation of *A* (R = H) in ether solution showed *cis-trans* isomerization to photostationary state and slow rearrangement to *B* (38% yield); for similar conditions *A* (R = CH₃) gave *B* (55% yield); product *C* also forms in liquid-phase photolysis for R = CH₃, presumably by a Norrish "Type II" intermediate.

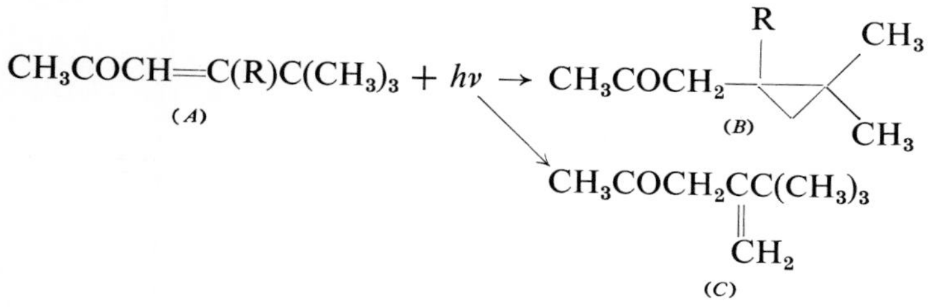

$$CH_3COCH{=}C(R)C(CH_3)_3 + h\nu \rightarrow CH_3COCH_2{-}\!\!\!\overset{R \quad\quad CH_3}{\underset{CH_3}{\triangle}}$$
$$(A) \qquad\qquad\qquad (B)$$

$$CH_3COCH_2CC(CH_3)_3$$
$$\overset{\|}{CH_2}$$
$$(C)$$

30. Methyl sec-butyl ketone:[74] full mercury arc, process 3 dominant.

$$CH_3COCH(CH_3)C_2H_5 + h\nu \rightarrow CH_3CO + CH_3CHC_2H_5 \qquad (1)$$

$$CH_3 + COCH(CH_3)C_2H_5 \qquad (2)$$

$$CH_3COC_2H_5 + C_2H_4 \qquad (3)^{21}$$

31. Methyl isobutyl ketone:[85] 3130 A, $\varphi_1 + \varphi_2 \cong 0.15$, $\varphi_3 \cong 0.35$ (120°).

$$CH_3COCH_2CH(CH_3)_2 + h\nu \rightarrow M^*(+N) \rightarrow M(+N)$$

$$CH_3CO + CH_2CH(CH_3)_2 \qquad (1)$$

$$CH_3 + COCH_2CH(CH_3)_2 \qquad (2)$$

$$CH_3COCH_3 + C_3H_6 \qquad (3)^{21}$$

32. 3,4-Epoxy-4-methyl-2-pentanone:[80,522] irradiation in gas or solution phase gives *A* in 2–12% yield; minor products are CH_3CHO, $(CH_3)_2CO$, $CH_3COC_2H_5$, $CH_3COCH(CH_3)_2$, and 2-butenyl acetate (in part from the photolysis of *A*).

$$(CH_3)_2C\underset{O}{\underline{\diagdown\diagup}}CHCOCH_3 + h\nu \rightarrow CH_3COCH(CH_3)COCH_3$$
$$(A)$$

33. Methyl n-amyl ketone:[657] 3130 A, 120°, $\varphi_1 + \varphi_2 = 0.10$, $\varphi_3 = 0.40$; in pure liquid, 25°, $\varphi_1 + \varphi_2 = 0.003$, $\varphi_3 = 0.23$.

$$CH_3COCH_2CH_2CH_2CH_2CH_3 + h\nu \rightarrow CH_3CO + n\text{-}C_5H_{11} \qquad (1)$$

$$CH_3 + COC_5H_{11} \qquad (2)$$

$$CH_3COCH_3 + CH_2{=}CHCH_2CH_3 \qquad (3)^{21}$$

34. 4-Methyl-2-hexanone:[86] 3130 A, $\varphi_3/\varphi_4 = 0.32$ (44°), 0.33 (84°), 0.36 (150°), 0.38 (258°); $\varphi_5/(\varphi_3 + \varphi_4 + \varphi_5) = 0.10$ (44°), 0.11 (84°), 0.13 (150°), 0.15 (258°); 2537 A, $\varphi_3 + \varphi_4 = 0.40$ (independent of temperature, pressure), $\varphi_5/(\varphi_3 + \varphi_4 + \varphi_5) = 0.18$; 1900 A, $\varphi_3/\varphi_4 = 0.49$ (44°); $\varphi_5/(\varphi_3 + \varphi_4 + \varphi_5) = 0.29$.

$$CH_3COCH_2CH(CH_3)C_2H_5 + h\nu \rightarrow CH_3CO + CH_2CH(CH_3)C_2H_5 \quad (1)$$

$$CH_3 + COCH_2CH(CH_3)C_2H_5 \quad (2)$$

$$CH_3COCH_3 + \textit{cis}\text{-2-}C_4H_8 \quad (3)^{21}$$

$$CH_3COCH_3 + \textit{trans}\text{-2-}C_4H_8 \quad (4)^{21}$$

$$CH_3COCH_3 + 1\text{-}C_4H_8 \quad (5)^{21}$$

35. Methyl neopentyl ketone:[85] 3130 A, $\varphi_1 + \varphi_2 = 0.04$ (120°), $\varphi_4 = 0.23$ (120°); 2654 A, $\varphi_1 + \varphi_2 = 0.08$, $\varphi_4 = 0.24$ (120°); 0.39 (250°), φ_3 low but not zero.

$$CH_3COCH_2C(CH_3)_3 + h\nu \rightarrow M^*(+N) \rightarrow M(+N')$$

$$\downarrow$$

$$CH_3CO + CH_2C(CH_3)_3 \quad (1)$$

$$CH_3 + COCH_2C(CH_3)_3 \quad (2)$$

$$(CH_3)_3C + CH_2COCH_3 \quad (3)$$

$$CH_3COCH_3 + (CH_3)_2C{=}CH_2 \quad (4)^{21}$$

36. Di-n-propyl ketone:[87,108b,738] 3130 A, $\varphi_1 = 0.31$,[87] 0.37,[108b] $\varphi_2 = 0.21$ (55–160°, 8–115 mm), $\epsilon = 7.5$.

$$(CH_3CH_2CH_2)_2CO + h\nu \rightarrow M^*(+N) \rightarrow M(+N')$$

$$\downarrow$$

$$n\text{-}C_3H_7 + COCH_2CH_2CH_3 \quad (1)$$

$$CH_3COCH_2CH_2CH_3 + C_2H_4 \quad (2)^{21}$$

37. n-Propyl isopropyl ketone:[738] 3130 A, $\varphi_1 + \varphi_2 = 0.77$ (60°), 0.68 (100°), 0.71 (150°): $\varphi_3 = 0.09$ (60°), 0.11 (100°), 0.16 (150°).

$$CH_3CH_2CH_2COCH(CH_3)_2 + h\nu \rightarrow n\text{-}C_3H_7 + COCH(CH_3)_2 \quad (1)$$

$$n\text{-}C_3H_7CO + CH(CH_3)_2 \quad (2)$$

$$CH_3COCH(CH_3)_2 + C_2H_4 \quad (3)^{21}$$

38. Diisopropyl   ketone:[88]   3130 A, $\varphi_1 = 1.0$ (50–150°), $\epsilon = 9.05$; $[(CH_3)_2CD]_2CO$ has a similar photochemical behavior.[90]

$$[(CH_3)_2CH]_2CO + h\nu \rightarrow (CH_3)_2CH + COCH(CH_3)_2 \tag{1}$$

39. Perfluoro-di-n-propyl ketone:[90] 3130 A, $\varphi_1 = 1.0$ (temperature $\geqslant 107°$, pressure = 5–80 mm), 0.65 (27°, 140 mm); no process analogous to 2 in di-*n*-propyl ketone photolysis.

$$(CF_3CF_2CF_2)_2CO + h\nu \rightarrow M^*(+N) \rightarrow M(+N')$$
$$\searrow \downarrow$$
$$CF_3CF_2CF_2 + COCF_2CF_2CF_3 \tag{1}$$

40. Methyl n-hexyl ketone:[76] full mercury arc, isooctane solution, major processes are 2 and 3; free radical process 1 suggested by analogy with other ketones.

$$CH_3CO(CH_2)_5CH_3 + h\nu \rightarrow CH_3CO + (CH_2)_5CH_3 \tag{1}$$
$$\searrow$$
$$CH_3COCH_3 + CH_2{=}CHCH_2CH_2CH_3 \tag{2}[21]$$
$$CH_3\overset{\frown}{C}(OH)CH_2CH_2CHCH_2CH_2CH_3 \tag{3}$$

41. n-Propyl n-butyl ketone:[738] 3130 A, $\varphi_1 + \varphi_2 = 0.10$ (150°), 0.07 (110°), 0.05 (75°); $\varphi_3 = 0.25$ (150°), 0.24 (110°), 0.24 (75°); $\varphi_4 = 0.035$ (150°), 0.029 (110°), 0.024 (75°).

$$n\text{-}C_4H_9COCH_2CH_2CH_3 + h\nu \rightarrow n\text{-}C_4H_9 + COC_3H_7 \tag{1}$$
$$\searrow$$
$$n\text{-}C_4H_9CO + n\text{-}C_3H_7 \tag{2}$$
$$C_3H_6 + CH_3COC_3H_7 \tag{3}[21]$$
$$n\text{-}C_4H_9COCH_3 + C_2H_4 \tag{4}[21]$$

42. n-Propyl isobutyl ketone:[738] 3130 A, $\varphi_1 + \varphi_2 = 0.24$ (150°), 0.20 (110°), 0.16 (75°); $\varphi_3 = 0.15$ (150°), 0.16 (110°), 0.17 (75°); $\varphi_4 = 0.055$ (150°), 0.053 (110°), 0.060 (75°).

$$\text{iso-}C_4H_9COCH_2CH_2CH_3 + h\nu \rightarrow \text{iso-}C_4H_9 + COC_3H_7 \tag{1}$$
$$\searrow$$
$$\text{iso-}C_4H_9CO + n\text{-}C_3H_7 \tag{2}$$
$$C_3H_6 + CH_3COC_3H_7 \tag{3}[21]$$
$$\text{iso-}C_4H_9COCH_3 + C_2H_4 \tag{4}[21]$$

43. n-Propyl sec-butyl ketone:[738] 3130 A, $\varphi_1 + \varphi_2 = 0.36$ (150°), 0.44 (75°); $\varphi_3 + \varphi_4 = 0.12$ (150°), 0.078 (75°); $\varphi_3 \cong \varphi_4$ (75–150°).

$$sec\text{-}C_4H_9COCH_2CH_2CH_3 + h\nu \rightarrow sec\text{-}C_4H_9 + COC_3H_7 \qquad (1)$$

$$sec\text{-}C_4H_9CO + n\text{-}C_3H_7 \qquad (2)$$

$$C_2H_4 + C_2H_5COC_3H_7 \qquad (3)^{21}$$

$$sec\text{-}C_4H_9COCH_3 + C_2H_4 \qquad (4)^{21}$$

44. n-Propyl tert-butyl ketone:[738] 3130 A, $\varphi_1 + \varphi_2 = 0.54$ (150°), 0.57 (110°), 0.63 (75°); $\varphi_3 = 0.12$ (150°), 0.093 (110°), 0.073 (75°).

$$tert\text{-}C_4H_9COCH_2CH_2CH_3 + h\nu \rightarrow tert\text{-}C_4H_9 + COC_3H_7 \qquad (1)$$

$$tert\text{-}C_4H_9CO + n\text{-}C_3H_7 \qquad (2)$$

$$tert\text{-}C_4H_9COCH_3 + C_2H_4 \qquad (3)^{21}$$

45. Methyl n-heptyl ketone:[76] conditions as for ketone 40.

$$CH_3CO(CH_2)_6CH_3$$
$$+ h\nu \rightarrow CH_3CO + (CH_2)_6CH_3 \qquad (1)$$

$$CH_3COCH_3 + CH_2{=}CHCH_2CH_2CH_2CH_3 \qquad (2)^{21}$$

$$CH_3C(OH)CH_2CH_2CHCH_2CH_2CH_2CH_3 \qquad (3)$$

46. Di-tert-butyl ketone:[91] full mercury arc, $\bar{\varphi}_1 \cong 1$ (temperature $> 100°$).

$$[(CH_3)_3C]_2CO + h\nu \rightarrow (CH_3)_3C + COC(CH_3)_3 \qquad (1)$$

47. Diisobutyl ketone:[91] full mercury arc, $\bar{\varphi}_1 \cong 0.19$, $\bar{\varphi}_2 \cong 0.37$.

$$[(CH_3)_2CHCH_2]_2CO + h\nu \rightarrow M^*(+N) \rightarrow M(+N')$$
$$\downarrow$$
$$(CH_3)_2CHCH_2 + COCH_2CH(CH_3)_2 \qquad (1)$$

$$CH_3COCH_2CH(CH_3)_2 + C_3H_6 \qquad (2)^{21}$$

48. Di-sec-butyl ketone:[91] full mercury arc, $\bar{\varphi}_1 \cong 0.37$, $\bar{\varphi}_2 \cong 0.29$.

$$[CH_3CH_2CH(CH_3)]_2CO +$$
$$h\nu \rightarrow M^*(+N) \rightarrow M(+N')$$
$$\downarrow$$
$$CH_3CH_2CHCH_3 + COCH(CH_3)C_2H_5 \qquad (1)$$

$$C_2H_5COCH(CH_3)C_2H_5 + C_2H_4 \qquad (2)^{21}$$

49. Polymethyl vinyl ketone:[92-94] solid film, 3130 A, $\varphi_1 \geqslant 0.04$ (25°), $\geqslant 0.07$ (50°), $\geqslant 0.03$ (80°); $\varphi_2 \cong 0.03$ (25–80°); the free-radical process 1 and the intramolecular split 2 of the polymer are shown involving terminal groups only to simplify the presentation; random cleavage of the polymer is expected in the actual case. X and Y represent terminal groups.

$$X-[CH_2CH(COCH_3)]_n-Y +$$

$$hv \rightarrow X-CH_2\dot{C}H-[CH_2CH(COCH_3)]_{n-1}-Y + CH_3\dot{C}O \qquad (1)$$

$$X-CH_2C(COCH_3)=CH_2 + CH_3COCH_2[CH_2CH(COCH_3)]_{n-2}-Y \qquad (2)$$

50. Methyl cyclopropyl ketone:[95,497,514] 3130 A, $\varphi_1 + \varphi_2 \cong 0.04$ (120°); 2654–2537 A, $\varphi_1 + \varphi_2 \cong 0.12$ (170°), $\varphi_3 \cong 0.34$; X may be a diradical, $CH_3CO\dot{C}HCH_2CH_2\cdot$, or an enol, $CH_3C(OH)=CHCH=CH_2$, intermediate.

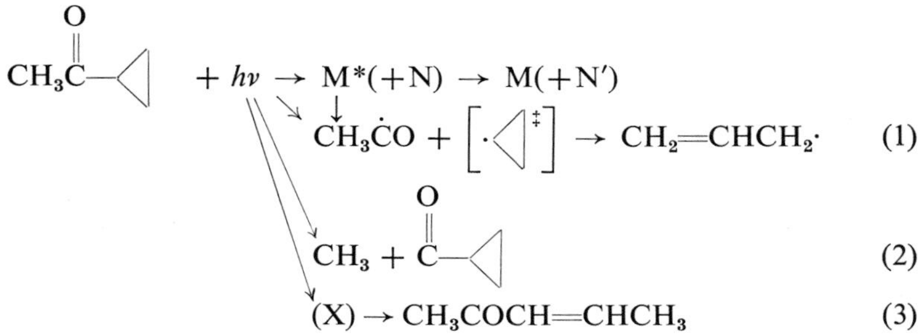

51. Diphenylcyclopropenone:[573] irradiation in solution results in decarbonylation.

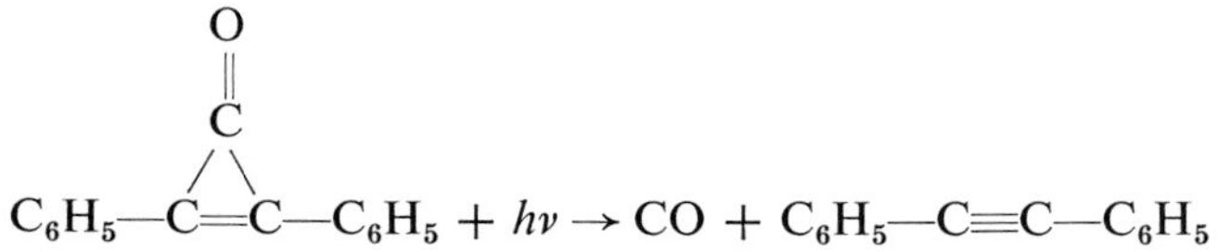

52. 3-Cyclopropyl-2-propanone:[497,504,514] 3130 A 120°, $\varphi_1 + \varphi_2 \cong 0.88$, φ_3 small; contrast this result with the efficiencies of the analogous processes in methyl cyclopropyl ketone. No cyclopropane derivatives formed as products; products identified include CO, CH_4, C_2H_6, 1-C_4H_8, 1-C_5H_{10}, 1,7-octadiene, and $CH_3COCH_2CH_2CH=CH_2$.

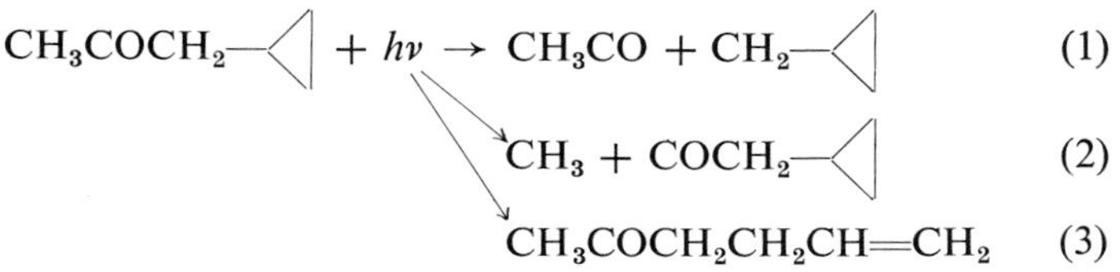

53. 4-Cyclopropyl-2-butanone:[497,504,514] 3130 A, 120°, 30 mm, $\varphi_1 + \varphi_2 \cong$ 0.70, pressure sensitive; process 3 occurs with a small efficiency, about 0.06; other products identified (larger than C_2) contain the cyclopropyl group; e.g., the quantum yields of cyclopropylethane, cyclopropyl-ethylene, 1-cyclopropylpropane, and 1,4-dicyclopropylbutane are 0.27 0.02, 0.15, and 0.09, respectively; contrast this result with that for compound 52.

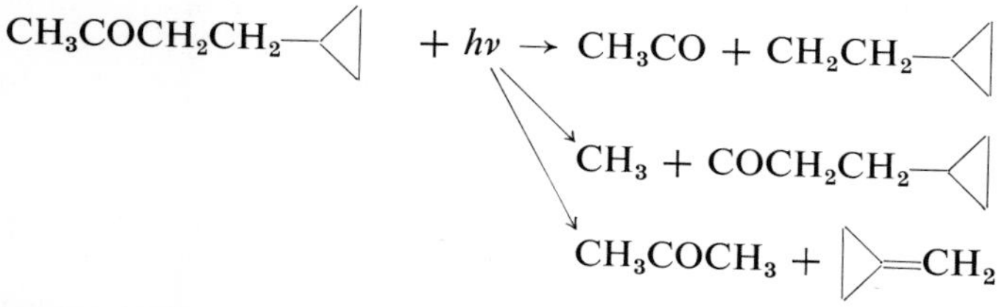

$$CH_3COCH_2CH_2{-}\triangleleft \; + \; h\nu \; \rightarrow \; CH_3CO + CH_2CH_2{-}\triangleleft \quad (1)$$

$$CH_3 + COCH_2CH_2{-}\triangleleft \quad (2)$$

$$CH_3COCH_3 + \triangleright{=}CH_2 \quad (3)^{21}$$

54. Dicyclopropyl ketone:[504,515] major net reaction 1 occurs; free radical split unimportant.

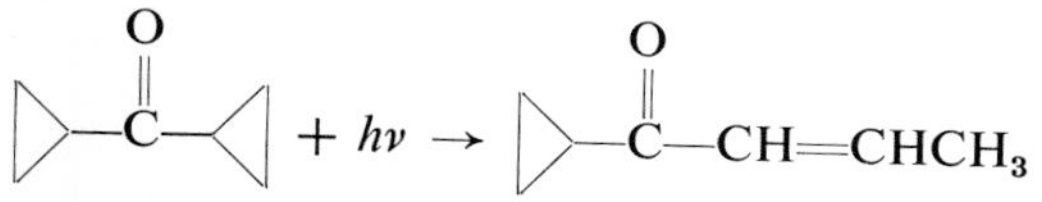

$$\triangleright{-}\overset{O}{\underset{\|}{C}}{-}\triangleleft \; + \; h\nu \; \rightarrow \; \triangleright{-}\overset{O}{\underset{\|}{C}}{-}CH{=}CHCH_3 \quad (1)$$

55. Methyl cyclobutyl ketone:[96] 2654 A, $\varphi_1 + \varphi_2 = 0.36$ (170°).

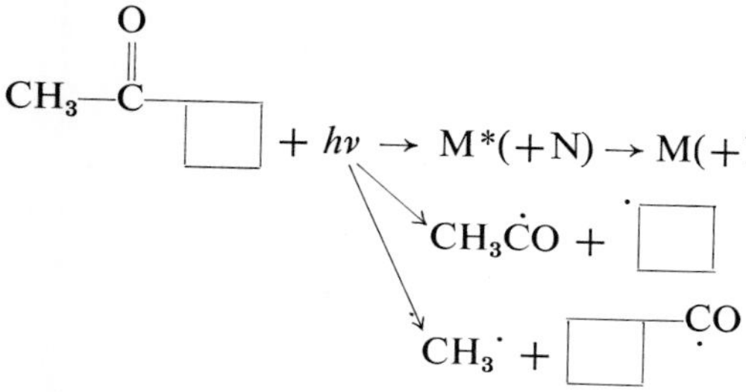

$$CH_3{-}\overset{O}{\underset{\|}{C}}{-}\square \; + \; h\nu \; \rightarrow \; M^*(+N) \rightarrow M(+N')$$

$$CH_3\dot{C}O + \square \quad (1)$$

$$CH_3^{\cdot} + \square{-}\overset{CO}{\underset{\cdot}{}} \quad (2)$$

56. 1-Acetylcyclohexene:[591,592] presumably net process 1 occurs with 50% yield in liquid-phase photolysis; however, in highly purified solvents reaction 1 could not be detected.

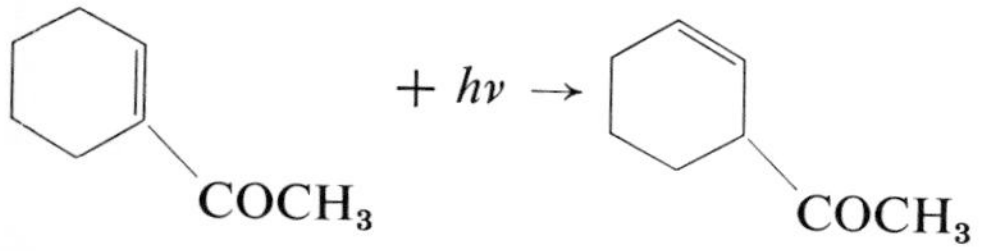

$$\text{(cyclohexene-COCH}_3\text{)} \; + \; h\nu \; \rightarrow \; \text{(cyclohexadiene-COCH}_3\text{)} \quad (1)$$

57. α-Ionone:[593] irradiation of *trans* form in ethanol solution leads to *cis-trans* isomerization and subsequent isomerization by Norrish "Type II" process to product *A*; reaction occurs with R = OH, CH$_3$, or OCH$_3$.

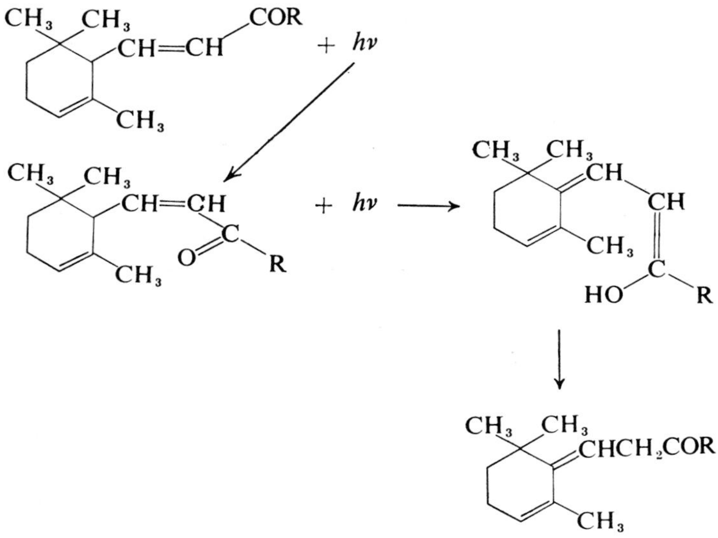

(A)

58. Cyclobutanone:[97–100,111] first absorption region in hexane solution, 3250–2400 A, $\lambda_{max} = 2800, 2900$ A, $\epsilon \cong 19$. Processes 1 and 3, involving intermediate diradical formation, and processes 2 and 4, forming final products directly in a concerted step, are alternatives which have been suggested (see discussion of cyclic ketones, p. 389). If 1 is important, then 3 and 5 may conceivably arise from that fraction of the highly vibrationally excited intermediate formed in 1 which dissociates in an early vibration. Full mercury arc, φ_3/φ_5 (or $\varphi_4/\varphi_5) \cong 0.67$; 3130 A, $\varphi_3 \cong 0.35$, $\varphi_5 \cong 0.51$, $\varphi_2 \leqslant 0.004$; 2654 A, $\varphi_3 \cong 0.53$, $\varphi_5 \cong 0.53$.

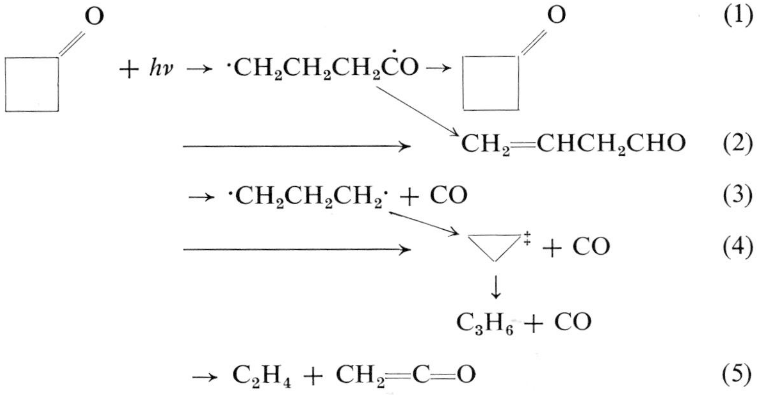

59. Cyclopentanone:[97,98,100–103,111,516,518] first absorption region, 2400–3250 A, $\lambda_{max} = 3000$ A, $\epsilon \cong 17$. Processes 2 and 4 are possible alternatives to 1 and 3; all decomposition modes appear to arise from the first excited singlet state; 1 or 2 formed from low vibrational levels, 5 from higher vibrational levels, and 3 or 4 from intermediate levels. Full mercury arc, φ_3/φ_5 (or φ_4/φ_5) $\cong 0.61$; 3130 A, $\varphi_2 + \varphi_4 + \varphi_5 = 0.72$ (independent pressure, 124°), at 124°, $\varphi_2/(\varphi_4 + \varphi_5) = 1.08$ (106 mm), 0.75 (53 mm), 0.16 (12 mm); $\varphi_5/\varphi_4 = 1.8$ (106 mm), 2.2 (53 mm), 1.8 (12 mm); 2654 A, $\varphi_4 \cong 0.48$, $\varphi_5 \cong 0.13$ (independent of temperature, 100–150 mm); 2537 A, $\varphi_4 \cong 0.63$, $\varphi_5 \cong 0.11$.

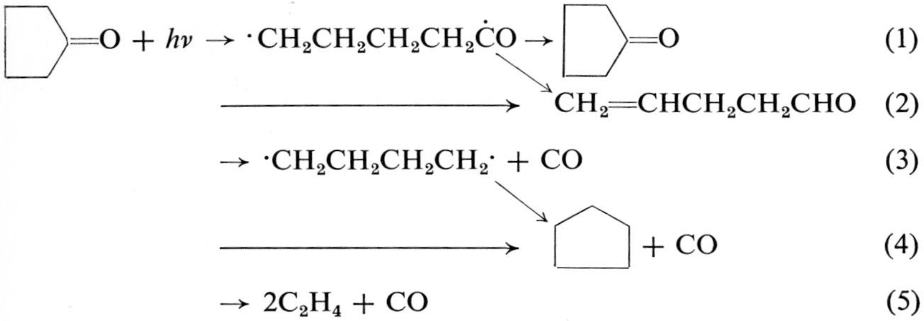

$$\text{[cyclopentanone]}{=}O + h\nu \rightarrow \cdot CH_2CH_2CH_2CH_2\dot{C}O \rightarrow \text{[cyclopentanone]}{=}O \quad (1)$$

$$\longrightarrow \quad CH_2{=}CHCH_2CH_2CHO \quad (2)$$

$$\rightarrow \cdot CH_2CH_2CH_2CH_2\cdot + CO \quad (3)$$

$$\longrightarrow \quad \text{[cyclobutane]} + CO \quad (4)$$

$$\rightarrow 2C_2H_4 + CO \quad (5)$$

60. 2,3-Cyclopentenone:[504,514] 3130 A, 120°, very stable, $\varphi_1 = 0.004$; contrast with compounds 61, 73, and 74.

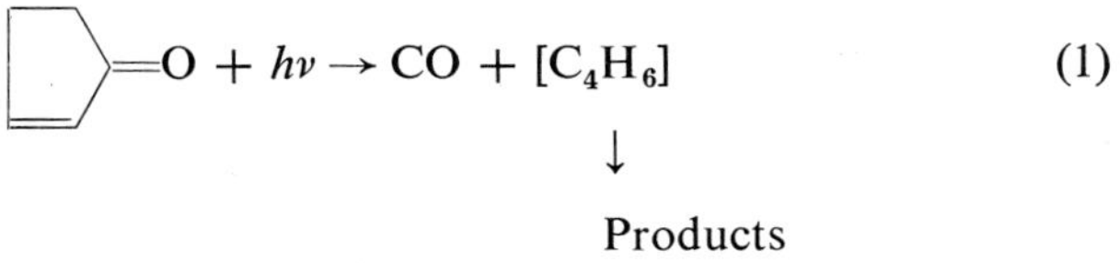

$$\text{[cyclopentenone]}{=}O + h\nu \rightarrow CO + [C_4H_6] \quad (1)$$

$$\downarrow$$

$$\text{Products}$$

61. 3,4-Cyclopentenone:[504,514] 3130 A, $\varphi_1 = 0.87$, independent of temperature (60–195°); contrast with compounds 60, 73, and 74.

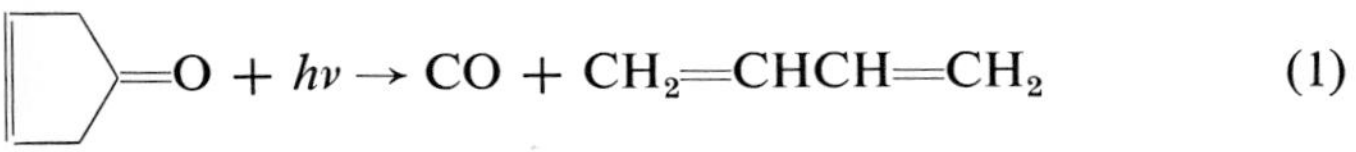

$$\text{[cyclopentenone]}{=}O + h\nu \rightarrow CO + CH_2{=}CHCH{=}CH_2 \quad (1)$$

62. 2-Methylcyclopentanone:[103] 3130 A, $\varphi_4/\varphi_3 = 2.1$ (25–100°, 4–6 mm); alternative free radical processes 1 and 2 and intramolecular processes 3 and 4 exist; probably hexenals are also formed by analogy with cyclopentanone. *2-Ethylcyclopentanone* forms ethylcyclobutane in an analogous fashion.[107]

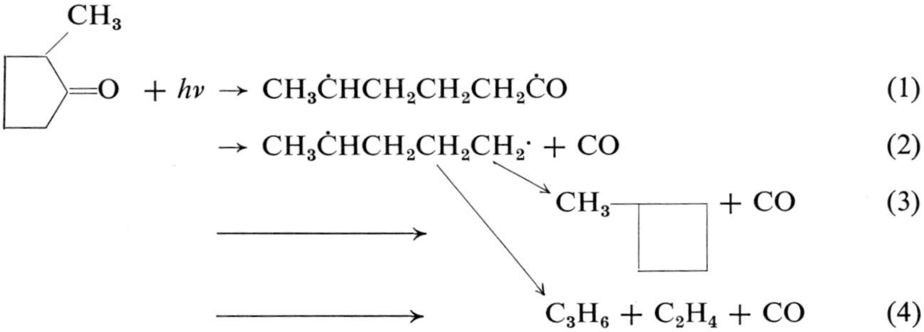

$$\text{(cyclopentanone with CH}_3\text{)}{=}O + h\nu \rightarrow CH_3\dot{C}HCH_2CH_2CH_2\dot{C}O \qquad (1)$$

$$\rightarrow CH_3\dot{C}HCH_2CH_2CH_2\cdot + CO \qquad (2)$$

$$\searrow CH_3{-}\square + CO \qquad (3)$$

$$\xrightarrow{\qquad} C_3H_6 + C_2H_4 + CO \qquad (4)$$

63. 3-Methylcyclopentanone:[103] 3130 A, $\varphi_4/\varphi_3 = 1.29$ (25–100°, 4–6 mm); alternatives as before.

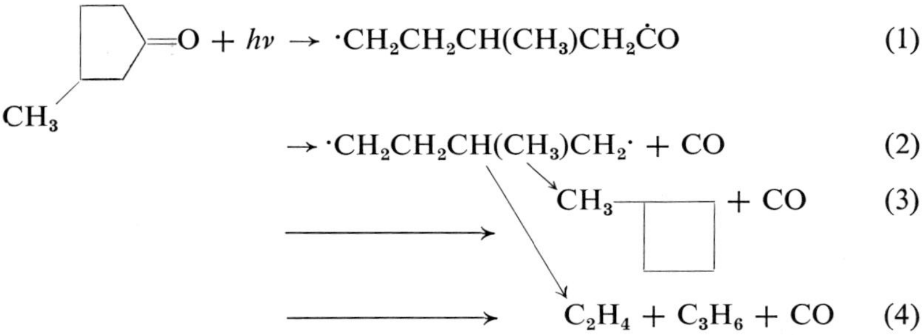

$$\text{(cyclopentanone with CH}_3\text{)}{=}O + h\nu \rightarrow \cdot CH_2CH_2CH(CH_3)CH_2\dot{C}O \qquad (1)$$

$$\rightarrow \cdot CH_2CH_2CH(CH_3)CH_2\cdot + CO \qquad (2)$$

$$\searrow CH_3{-}\square + CO \qquad (3)$$

$$\xrightarrow{\qquad} C_2H_4 + C_3H_6 + CO \qquad (4)$$

64. Bicyclo[3.2.0]heptanone-3:[109] mercury arc, filtered by Pyrex, 80°, 15 mm ketone, CO_2 (150 mm); alternative primary step 1 or steps 2 and 3 likely; $\varphi_2/\varphi_3 \leqslant 0.05$; increase in λ or pressure favors 2 over 3.

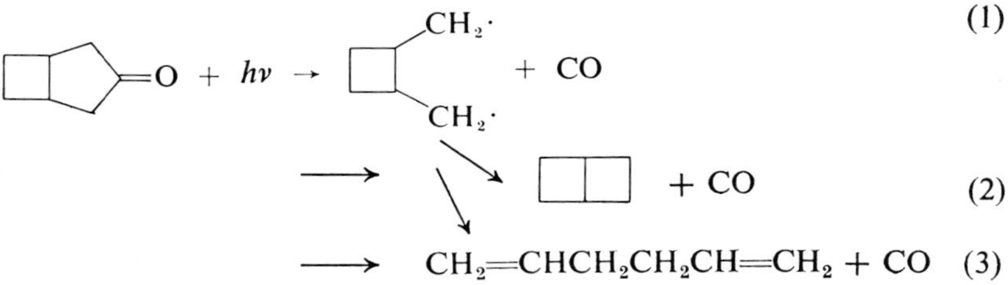

$$\text{(bicyclic ketone)}{=}O + h\nu \rightarrow \text{(cyclobutane with } CH_2\cdot, CH_2\cdot) + CO \qquad (1)$$

$$\xrightarrow{\qquad} \searrow \text{(bicyclic)} + CO \qquad (2)$$

$$\xrightarrow{\qquad} CH_2{=}CHCH_2CH_2CH{=}CH_2 + CO \qquad (3)$$

65. 2-Indanones:[583] irradiation of reactant in solution of hydrogen donor gives products shown: $R = H$, A is major product, 5% B; $R = C_6H_5$, yield of B is 80% (both *cis* and *trans* isomers); CO is also formed with B.

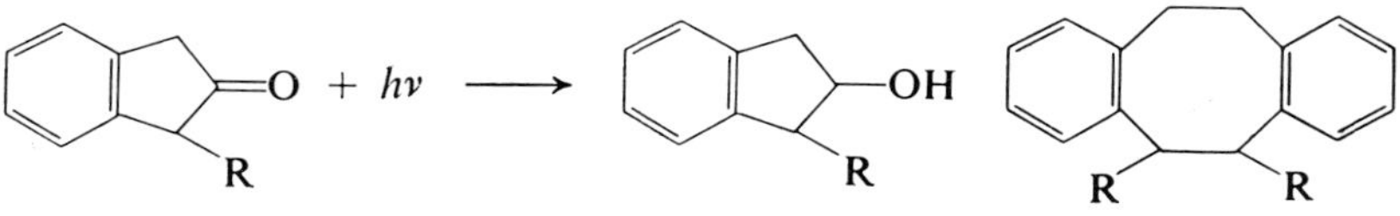

$$\text{(indanone)}{=}O + h\nu \xrightarrow{\qquad} (A) \qquad (B)$$

66. *Cyclohexanone:*[97,98,100,104–106,538] first absorption region, 2400–3250 A, $\lambda_{max} = 2900$ A, $\epsilon \cong 11$; alternative primary steps forming diradicals and molecules can explain the present data. Full mercury arc, φ_6/φ_3 [or $\varphi_6/(\varphi_4 + \varphi_5)$] $\cong 0.02$; 3130 A, 300°, $\varphi_3 + \varphi_6 = 0.91$, $\varphi_6/\varphi_3 \cong 0.02$, $\varphi_2 \cong 0.17$ (4–5 mm, 29°), 0.13 (5–47 mm, 100°), $\varphi_7 \cong 0$; in pure liquid state, $\varphi_2 = 0.26$, $\varphi_7 = 0.03$; 2654 A, 100–300°, $\varphi_1/\varphi_3 \cong 0.03$, $\varphi_3 + \varphi_6 = 0.78$; 2537 A, 100–300°, $\varphi_3 + \varphi_6 \cong 0.81$, $\varphi_6/\varphi_3 \cong 0.03$; in hydrocarbon solvent, 2 important; in H$_2$O, caproic acid is a product;[112] in cyclohexanol solution, cyclohexanone pinacol forms.[113]

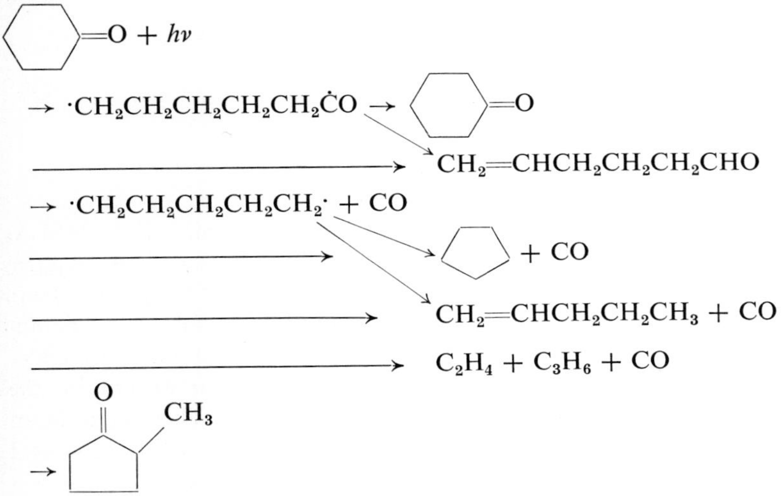

$$\to \cdot CH_2CH_2CH_2CH_2CH_2\dot{C}O \to \quad \bigcirc\!\!=\!O \qquad (1)$$

$$\longrightarrow CH_2\!=\!CHCH_2CH_2CH_2CHO \quad (2)$$

$$\to \cdot CH_2CH_2CH_2CH_2CH_2\cdot + CO \qquad\qquad (3)$$

$$\longrightarrow \quad \bigcirc + CO \qquad (4)$$

$$\longrightarrow CH_2\!=\!CHCH_2CH_2CH_3 + CO \quad (5)$$

$$\longrightarrow C_2H_4 + C_3H_6 + CO \qquad (6)$$

$$(7)$$

67. *2-Methylcyclohexanone:*[106,108,538] full mercury arc, pure liquid, *trans*-5-heptenal major product; 3130 A, liquid phase $\varphi_2 \cong 0.48$; quenching of process 2 occurs as heptenal builds up. Alternatives 1 and 2 exist; the formation of predominantly *trans* isomer of heptenal has been interpreted to favor intramolecular process 2;[538] both *cis* and *trans* isomers have been observed in recent work, and process 1 is favored;[700] other processes analogous to those of cyclohexanone must also occur to form methylcyclopentane, carbon monoxide, hexenes, and lower olefins. No process analogous to 7 of cyclohexanone is found.

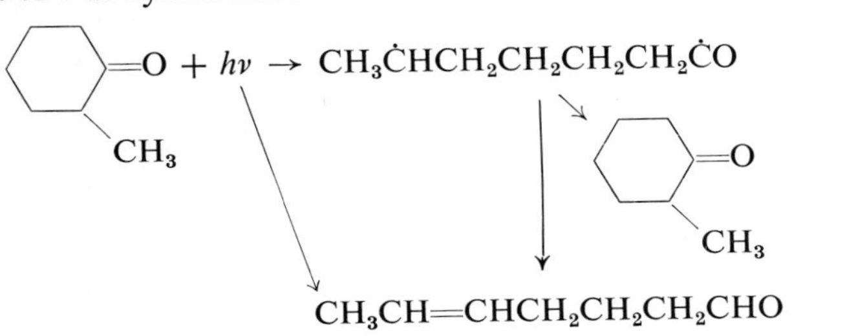

$$\to CH_3\dot{C}HCH_2CH_2CH_2CH_2\dot{C}O \qquad (1)$$

$$CH_3CH\!=\!CHCH_2CH_2CH_2CHO \qquad (2)$$

68. 3-Methylcyclohexanone:[109,538] irradiation with full mercury arc in pure liquid state gives 3-methyl-5-hexenal as the major isomeric product; 5-methyl-5-hexenal not observed; $\varphi_2/\varphi_3 \cong 2$; qualitative data for *4-methylcyclohexanone* are not inconsistent with a similar mechanism of photolysis.

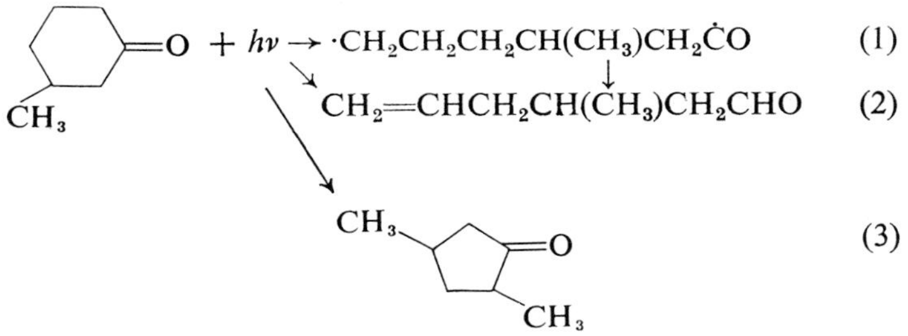

$$\text{(structure)} =O + h\nu \rightarrow \cdot CH_2CH_2CH_2CH(CH_3)CH_2\dot{C}O \quad (1)$$

$$CH_2{=}CHCH_2CH(\dot{C}H_3)CH_2CHO \quad (2)$$

$$\text{(structure)} \quad (3)$$

69. cis- and trans-2,6-Dimethylcyclohexanone:[700] *cis* form, $\lambda_{max} = 2858$ A, $\epsilon = 18.8$; $\epsilon_{3130} = 6.1$; *trans* form, $\lambda_{max} = 2952$ A, $\epsilon = 27.8$, $\epsilon_{3130} = 15.9$; 3130 A vapor-phase photolysis at 100° of either of the pure isomers yields the following products in *both cis* and *trans* forms: the reactant ketone, 2-heptene (*trans/cis* = 2), 1,2-dimethylcyclopentane (*trans/cis* = 1), and 2-methyl-5-heptenal; the product distribution cannot be the result of photolysis of the photoisomerized reactant. The results favor strongly the rupture of the ring and diradical formation in process 1 rather than the concerted mechanism of product formation.

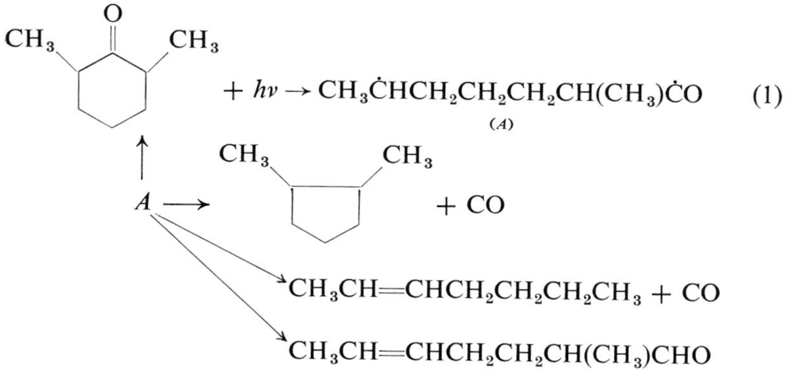

$$\text{(structure)} + h\nu \rightarrow CH_3\dot{C}HCH_2CH_2CH_2CH(CH_3)\dot{C}O \quad (1)$$
$$(A)$$

$$A \longrightarrow \text{(structure)} + CO$$

$$CH_3CH{=}CHCH_2CH_2CH_2CH_3 + CO$$

$$CH_3CH{=}CHCH_2CH_2CH(CH_3)CHO$$

70. Menthone:[108] full mercury arc, vapor at 80°, process 1 dominant; other processes analogous to those of cyclohexanone likely also.

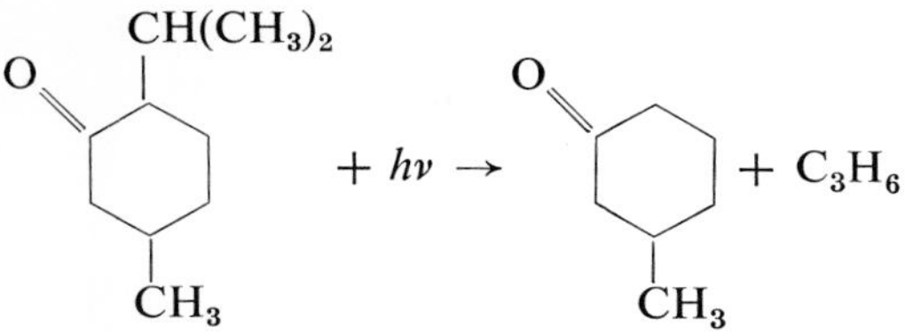

(1)[21]

71. Norcamphor:[110] 3130 A, 80°, 80 mm, process 1 or processes 2 and 3 occur; the occurrence of 4 or 5 may explain aldehydic product; $\varphi_2/\varphi_3 \cong 0.1$.

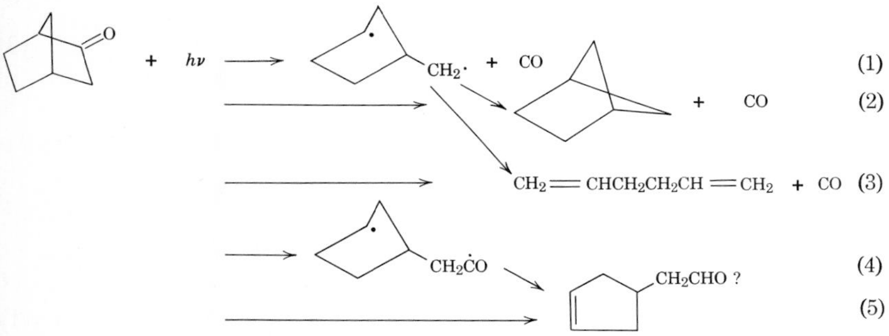

72. d,l-Camphor:[110] mercury arc, gas phase, process 1 or processes 2 and 3 occur; $\varphi_3 > \varphi_2$. 3130 A, alcohol solution, the products are largely campholenic aldehyde (*A*) and 1,2,2-trimethyl-3-cyclopentenyl methyl ketone (*B*).[101,579,580]

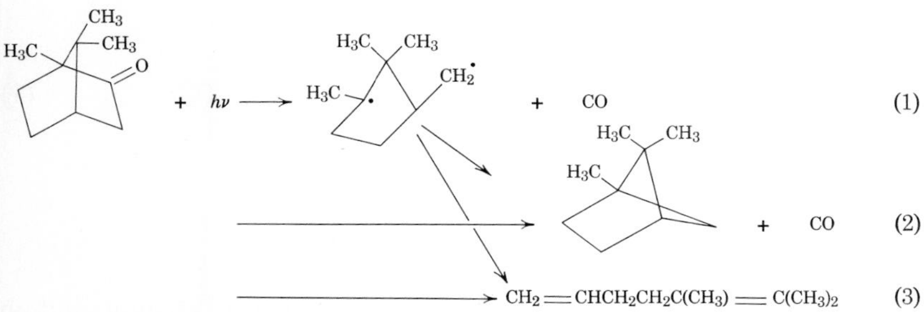

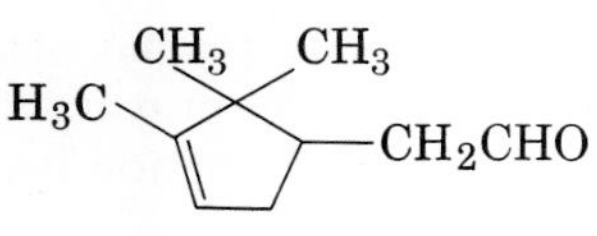

(*A*)

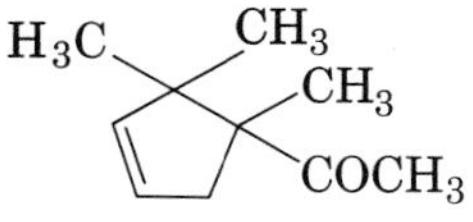

(*B*)

73. *Bicyclo[3.1.0]hexane-2-one:*[497,504,514] 3130 A, 120°, $\varphi_1 + \varphi_2 = 0.009$; process 3 major reaction; $\varphi_3 = 0.25$, independent of temperature.

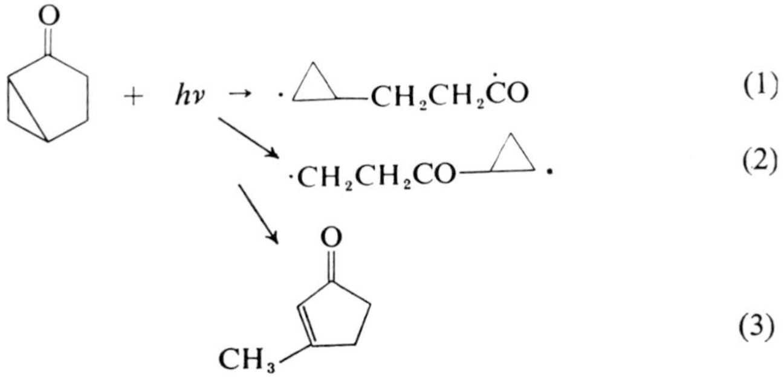

O
+ hν →
·CH₂CH₂ĊO
(1)
·CH₂CH₂CO
(2)
O
CH₃
(3)

74. *Bicyclo[3.1.0]hexane-3-one:*[497,504,514] 3130 A, 120°, $\varphi_1 = 0.76$; $\varphi_2 \ll \varphi_1$.

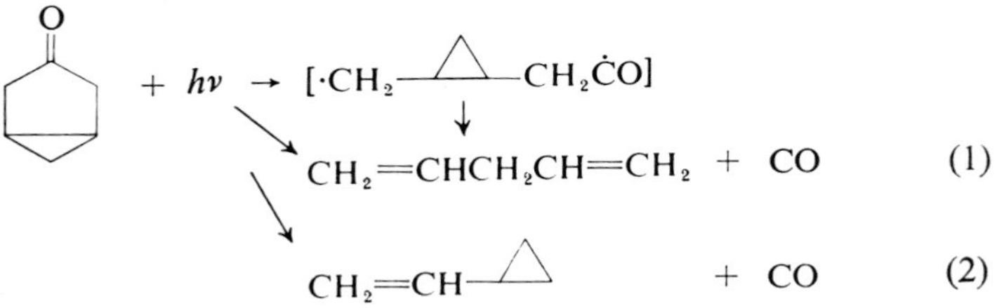

O
+ hν → [·CH₂ CH₂ĊO]
CH₂=CHCH₂CH=CH₂ + CO
(1)
CH₂=CH + CO
(2)

75. *Thujone:*[578] in cyclohexane and propyl alcohol solutions, 1 is the major net reaction.

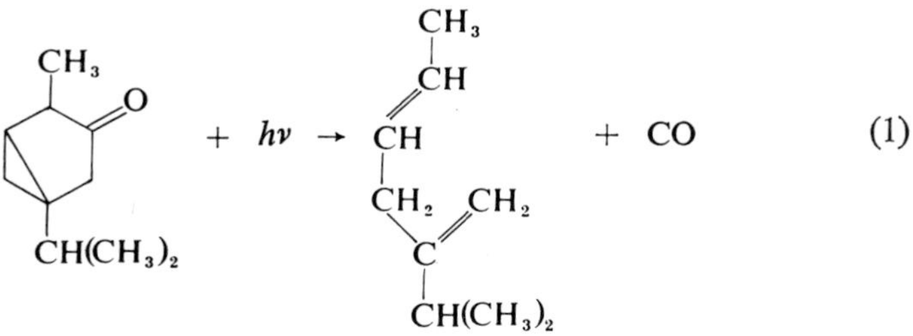

CH₃
O
CH(CH₃)₂
+ hν →
CH₃
CH
CH
CH₂ CH₂
C
CH(CH₃)₂
+ CO
(1)

76. *d-Cyclocamphanone:*[581] irradiation in 1% methanol or ethanol solution (under N_2) leads to the overall changes shown; 2 is the major path of the reaction; 1 is minor. The first sequence is similar to that observed for dehydronorcamphor; it has been proposed that the primary step is the cleavage of the 1-2 C—C bond followed by bond formation between C-1 and the carbonyl oxgyen atom.

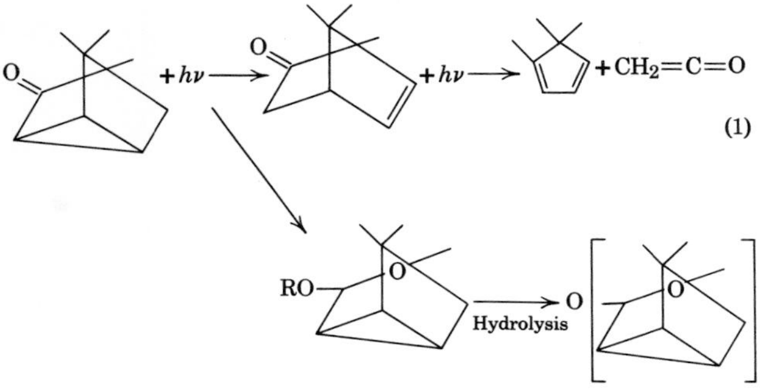

(1)

(2)

7. Isophorone oxide:[522] irradiation in C_6H_6, ether, and acetic acid with R = CH_3 gave 9:1 mixture of product *A* to product *B* in 10% yield; with R = C_6H_5, a 15% yield of *A* resulted and no detectable *B*. See also Ref. 584 for a discussion of the photochemistry of the steroidal epoxy-ketones.

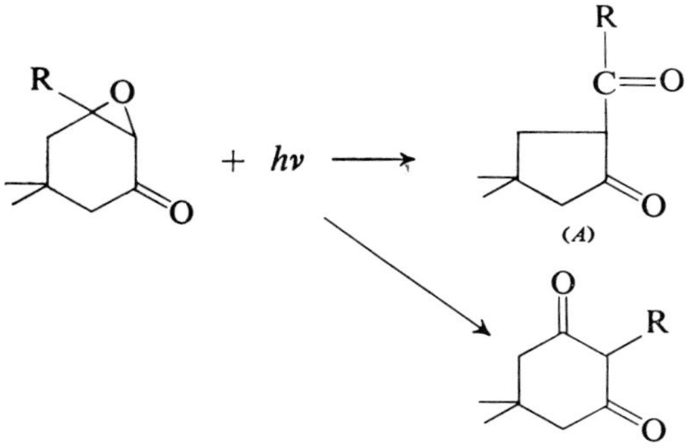

78. 2,3-Diphenylindenone oxide:[585, 712] high-pressure mercury-arc irradiation (3200–3900 A) in deoxygenated benzene solution gives a red-colored product, presumably the valence tautomer *B*; irradiation of *B* in visible light (λ > 4500 A) reforms *A*.

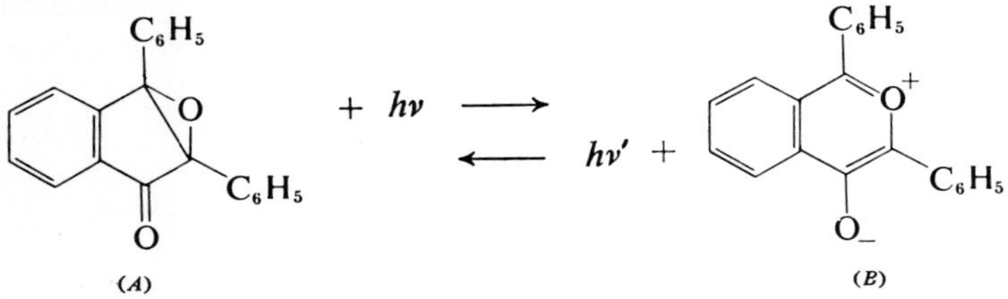

79. Dehydronorcamphor:[506,507,508] photolysis in solutions of ether, dioxane, or cyclohexane with Pyrex-filtered mercury arc, product *A* formed primarily initially; subsequent photolysis of *A* leads to process 2; direct conversion of dehydronorcamphor to products of 2 through an alkyl-acyl radical-pair formation by rupture of bond *a* has been suggested also.

80. Verbenone:[586] irradiation in cyclohexane solution gives chrysanthenone *A* among other products, including esters, acids, and amides when solvents were ethanol, wet ether, and ammonia in ether, respectively.

81. Carvone:[595] irradiation in sunlight (Pyrex-filtered) in 95% ethanol causes the net intramolecular addition reaction to form a 10% yield of carvonecamphor *A*.

82. 6,6-Diphenylbicyclo[3.1.0]hex-3-en-2-one:[380,692] the irradiation of aqueous dioxane solutions for $\lambda > 3100$ A, 1 is the major overall reaction.

83. 4a,β,8α-Dimethyl-5,6,7,8-tetrahydro-2(4aH)-naphthalenone:[588]   Pyrex-filtered, mercury-arc irradiation in 45% acetic acid solution at 20° forms the main product *B* via intermediate cyclopropyl ketone *A* (29%); the spiro ketone *C* also forms.

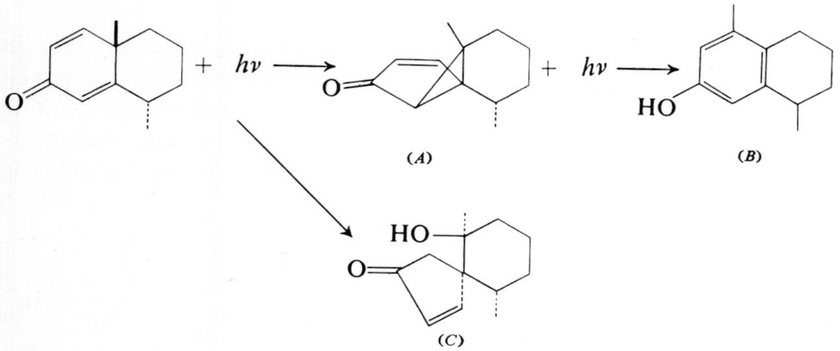

(A)

(B)

(C)

84. 3,4a-Dimethyl-5,6,7,8-tetrahydro-2(4aH)-naphthalenone:[587]   irradiation in dioxane gives the major product *A*; in glacial acetic acid, product *B* predominates; apparently intermediates involved are very sensitive to solvent; formation of *A* presumably involves at least three distinct photochemical rearrangements with cyclopropyl ketones as the intermediates.

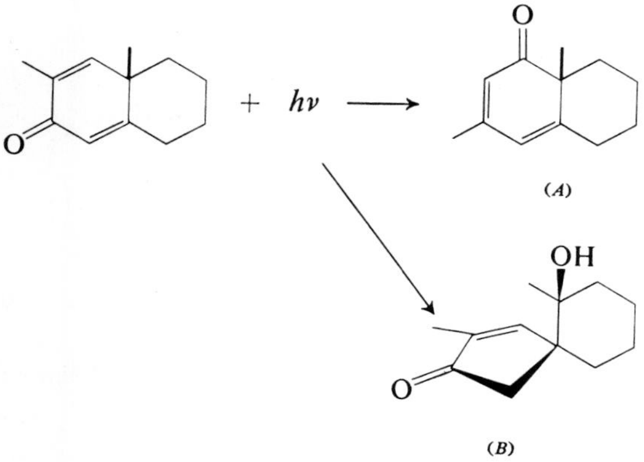

(A)

(B)

85. 6-Acetoxy-6-methylcyclohexa-2,4-dienone:[590]   Pyrex-filtered mercury-arc irradiation in a suitable oxygen-free refluxing solvent (water-ether, cyclohexylamine) results in ring fission to form acids or amides; reaction gives good yields and is general for β-substituted cyclohexadienones.

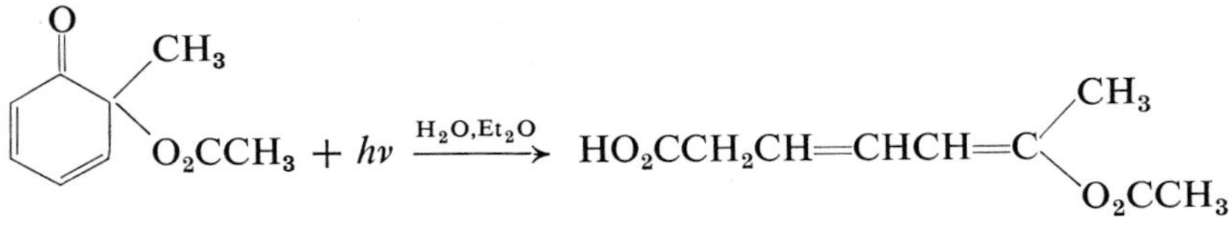

$$O_2CCH_3 + h\nu \xrightarrow{H_2O,Et_2O} HO_2CCH_2CH{=}CHCH{=}C\begin{smallmatrix}CH_3\\O_2CCH_3\end{smallmatrix}$$

86. 4,4-Diphenylcyclohexadienone:[380,521,692] irradiation ($\lambda > 3100$ A) in aqueous dioxane forms B in 80% yield, independent of the wavelength in the range 4200–3100 A; on the basis of studies of photoreactions of A alone and in mixtures of A with acetophenone or naphthalene, isomerization through the triplet state seems most probable. Further photolysis of B leads to C.

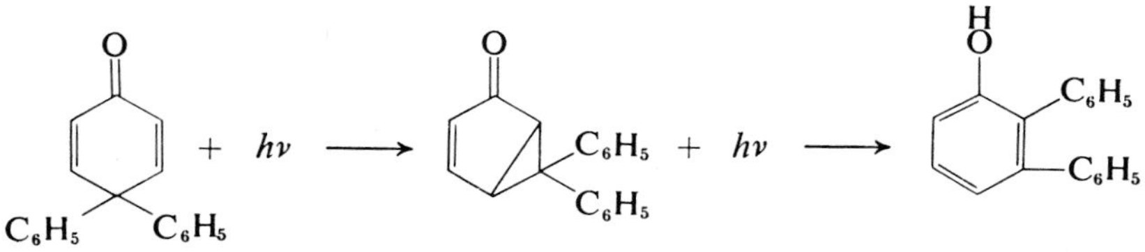

87. 2,6-Di-t-butyl-4-hydroxy-4-phenyl-2,5-cyclohexadiene-1-one:[519] Pyrex-filtered mercury-arc irradiation in dilute dioxane solution gives 20% yield of product A.

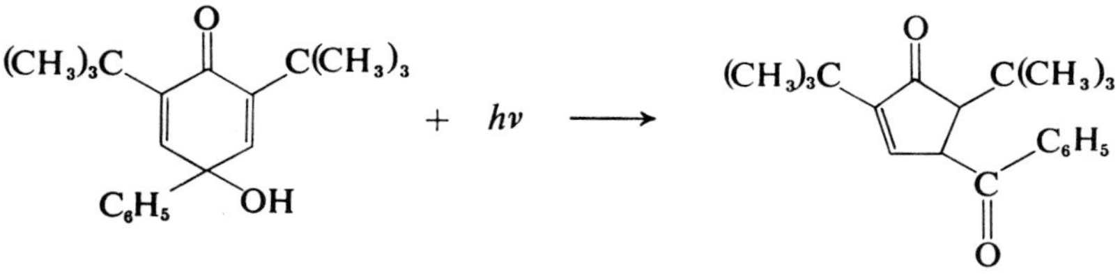

88. 4,6-Dimethyl-2-pyrone:[599] irradiation in methanol leads to net photo-isomerization with ring fission.

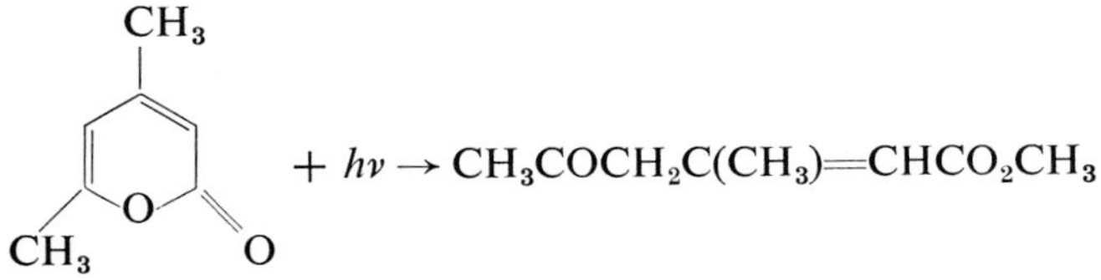

$$+ h\nu \rightarrow CH_3COCH_2C(CH_3){=}CHCO_2CH_3$$

89. 2,6-Dimethyl-4-pyrone:[598,600] full mercury-arc irradiation of the solid or solutions of *A* gives largely dimer formation *B*; irradiation of a 0.2% aqueous solution of *A* in the absence of air gives about 1% of product *C*.

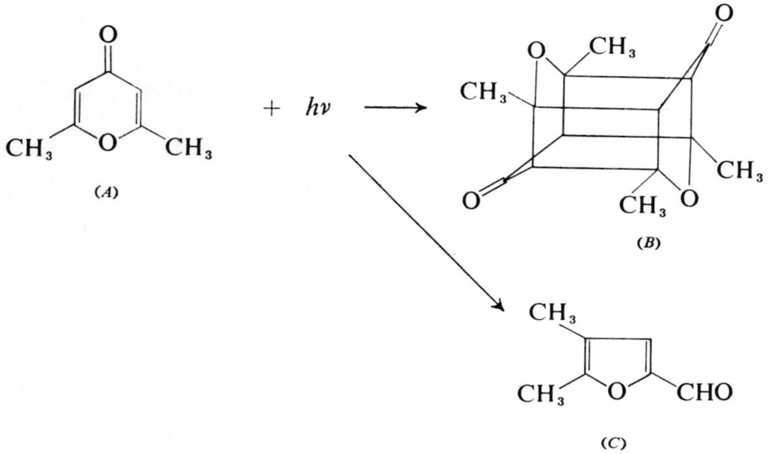

90. Cycloheptanone:[99,538] 3130 A, $\log \epsilon \cong 0.86$, $\varphi_4 \cong 0.14$, $\varphi_2 \cong 0.15$ (70–100°, 9–12 mm); unexplained process leading to C_3H_6. Processes 1 and 3 alternatives to 2 and 4. The pure liquid-phase photolysis gives process 5 as well as 2 and cycloheptanol.

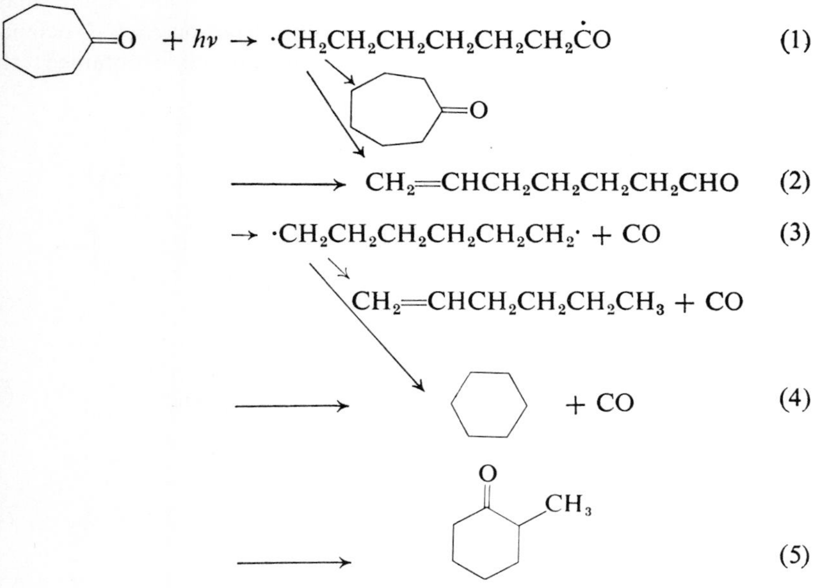

$$\bigcirc\hspace{-0.5em}=O \; + \; h\nu \; \rightarrow \; \cdot CH_2CH_2CH_2CH_2CH_2CH_2\overset{\cdot}{C}O \tag{1}$$

$$\longrightarrow \; CH_2{=}CHCH_2CH_2CH_2CH_2CHO \tag{2}$$

$$\rightarrow \; \cdot CH_2CH_2CH_2CH_2CH_2CH_2\cdot \; + \; CO \tag{3}$$

$$CH_2{=}CHCH_2CH_2CH_2CH_3 \; + \; CO$$

$$\longrightarrow \; \bigcirc \; + \; CO \tag{4}$$

$$\longrightarrow \tag{5}$$

91. 3,5-Cycloheptadienone:[571,572] irradiation in ether solution gives 1,3,5-trienes in 95% yield; no cyclic hydrocarbons are formed; R = H or CH_3.

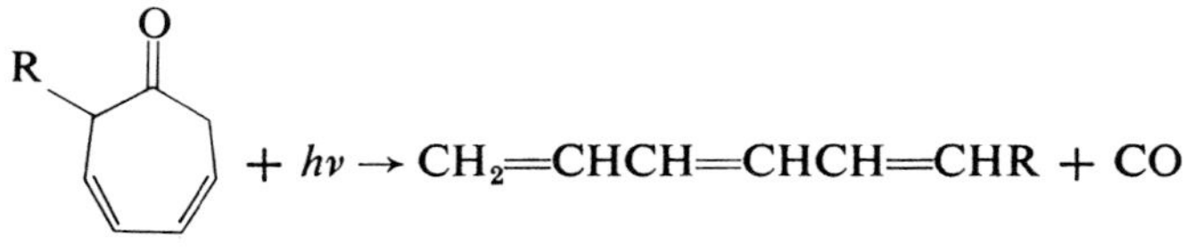

$$+ \ h\nu \rightarrow CH_2{=}CHCH{=}CHCH{=}CHR + CO$$

92. 5-Methoxy-2,4-cycloheptadienone:[572] irradiation in ether solution with full mercury arc gives *A*.

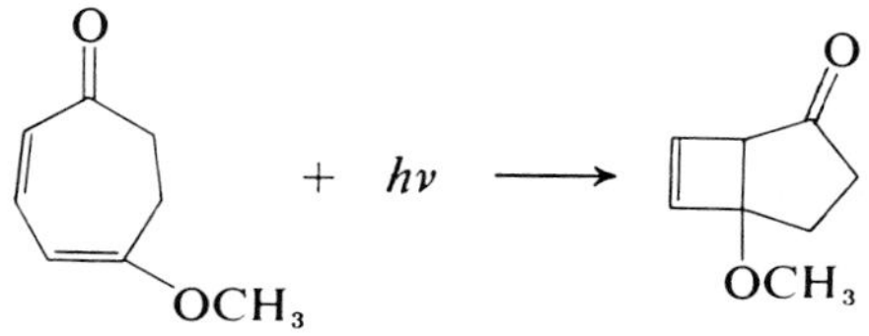

93. Cyclooctanone:[105,538] in cyclohexane solution, 2537 A, reduction products, cyclooctanol, and unidentified bicyclooctanol formed; triplet-state hydrogen-atom abstraction reactions likely; in pure liquid-phase photolysis, a mixture of products, including *trans*-octenal, 7-octenal, 2-*n*-propylcyclopentanone, and 2-methylcycloheptanone, is obtained; the following primary steps are probable:

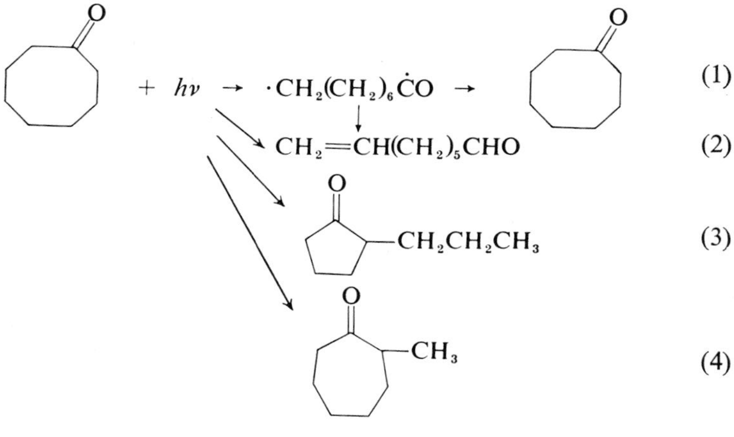

$$+ \ h\nu \rightarrow \ \cdot CH_2(CH_2)_6\dot{C}O \rightarrow \qquad (1)$$

$$CH_2{=}CH(CH_2)_5CHO \qquad (2)$$

(3)

(4)

94. 10-Ketobicyclo[5.2.1]decane:[582] irradiation in cyclopentane solution leads to the overall processes shown; products *A* and *B* form with 65 and 15% yields, respectively; free radical split adjacent to the carbonyl has been suggested as the primary process.

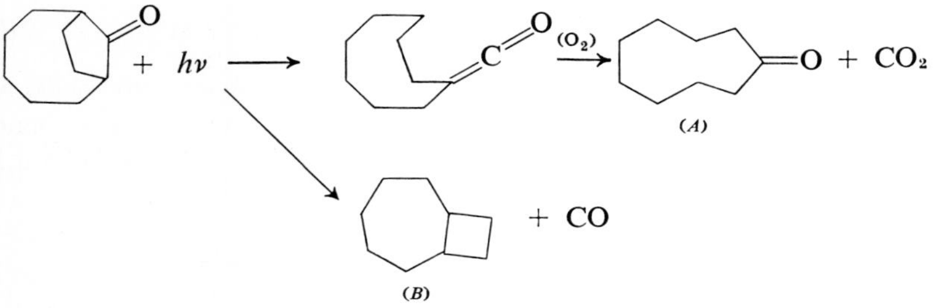

(A)

(B)

95. 2,4,6-Cyclooctatrienone:[520] on irradiation in hexane solution, product *A* formed in 30% yield; in methanol solution, *B* is the major product.

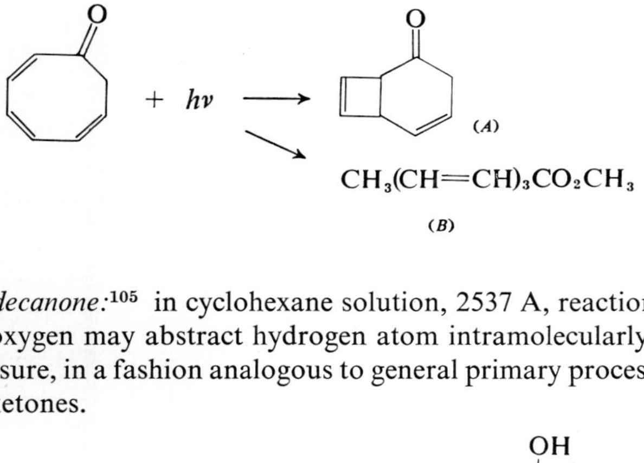

(A)

$$CH_3(CH{=}CH)_3CO_2CH_3$$

(B)

96. Cyclodecanone:[105] in cyclohexane solution, 2537 A, reaction 1 major; carbonyl oxygen may abstract hydrogen atom intramolecularly, followed by ring closure, in a fashion analogous to general primary process VI of the aliphatic ketones.

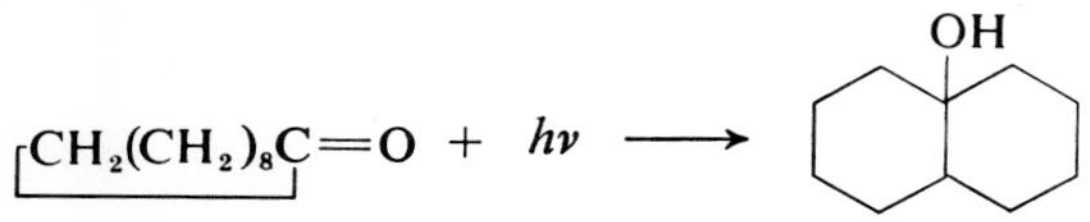

$$[CH_2(CH_2)_8\underline{C}{=}O + h\nu \longrightarrow$$

(1)

97. Acetophenone (methyl phenyl ketone):[113–115] absorption spectrum shown in Fig. 5-4; full mercury arc, steps 1 and 2 likely; step 3 possible but not clear; no decomposition in hydrocarbon-glass at 77°K. Irradiation in hydrogen containing solvents leads to reduction products through triplet reaction.

$$CH_3COC_6H_5 + h\nu \rightarrow M^*(+N) \rightarrow M(+N')$$

$$CH_3CO + C_6H_5 \tag{1}$$

$$CH_3 + COC_6H_5 \tag{2}$$

$$H + CH_2COC_6H_5 \;\; (?) \tag{3}$$

98. Trifluoromethyl phenyl ketone:[116] first absorption band, 3900–3000 A; second band, 3000–2600 A; third band, 2600–2100 A; fourth band, below 2100 A; 3660 A, $\varphi_1 > \varphi_2$, $\varphi_1 + \varphi_2 \geqslant 0.004$ (280°), $\epsilon = 6.2$; 3130 A, $\varphi_1 + \varphi_2 \geqslant 0.002$ (157°), $\geqslant 0.18$ (304°), $\epsilon = 74$.

$$CF_3COC_6H_5 + h\nu \rightarrow M^*(+N) \rightarrow M(+N')$$

$$CF_3 + C_6H_5CO \tag{1}$$

$$CF_3CO + C_6H_5 \tag{2}$$

99. n-Propyl phenyl ketones:[497,499] 3130 A, processes 1, 2, and 3 occur in benzene at 25°; φ_3 small; butyrophenone, $\varphi_2 = 0.42$; φ_2 for substituted butyrophenones: *p*-methyl-, 0.39; *p*-fluoro-, 0.29; *p*-methoxy-, 0.10; *p*- and *o*-hydroxy, 0.00; *p*-amino-, 0.00.

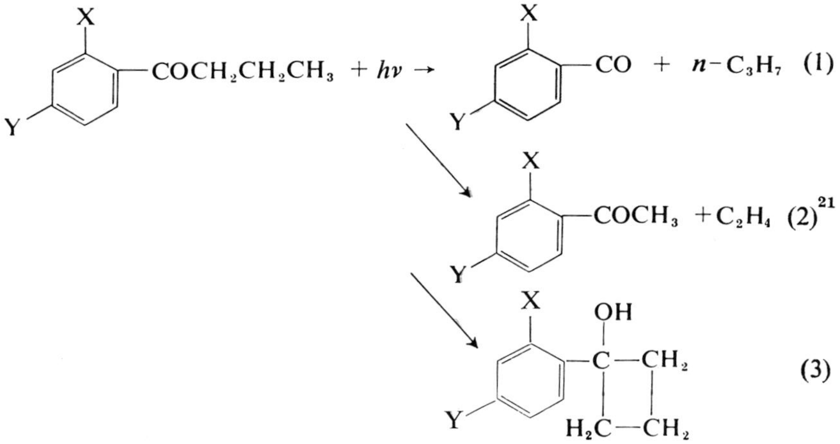

100. trans-β-Benzoyl-α-methylacrylic acid:[594] irradiation of solution in sunlight formed product *B* on short exposure and product *C* on prolonged exposure; possibly a Norrish "Type II" process is involved in the $A \rightarrow C$ transformation.

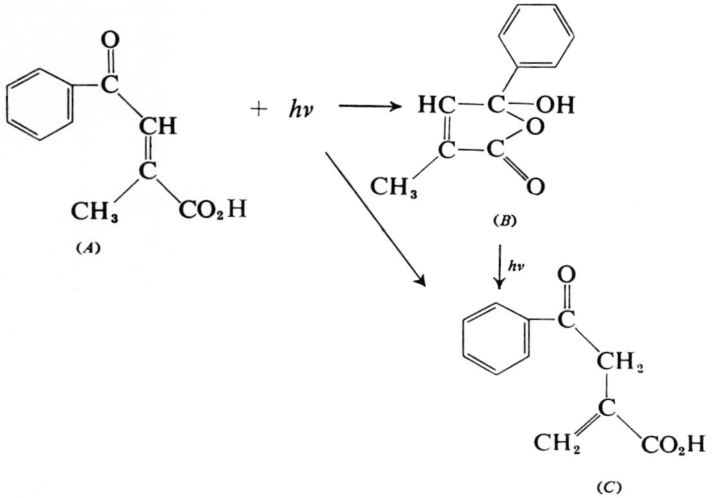

101. *Benzophenone* (*diphenyl ketone*):[113,117] absorption spectrum shown in Fig. 5-4; full mercury arc, φ_1 small. In hydrogen-containing solvents, reaction of triplet excited state leads to reduction products (benzopinacol).[118,119,533,539–544] See Sec. 5-9A.

$$C_6H_5COC_6H_5 + h\nu \rightarrow M^*(+N) \rightarrow M(+N')$$
$$\searrow \downarrow$$
$$C_6H_5 + C_6H_5CO \qquad (1)$$

102. *Biacetyl*:[49,121–126,713] absorption spectrum shown in Fig. 5-5; 4358 A, at room temperature decomposition by process 1 occurs by the uncommon process of interaction of *two excited molecules* (in the first excited triplet state); at 100° and above, first-order decomposition of the excited triplet species takes place with an activation energy of about 15 kcal. Emission seen from first excited singlet and triplet states; intersystem crossing from the lowest vibrational level of the first excited singlet to the first excited triplet may occur 99% of the time in the absence of perturbing gases. $\varphi_1 + \varphi_2 \cong 0.001$ (28°, low I_a; increases proportional to I_a), ~ 0.04 (100°), ~ 0.4 (198°); 3660 A, dissociation from both first excited singlet and triplet states may occur; $\varphi_1 + \varphi_2 \cong 0.03$ (28°, function of pressure), ~ 0.17 (75°), ~ 0.22 (100°); 3130 A, dissociation from second and first excited singlet possible here; $\varphi_1 + \varphi_2 \geqslant 0.10$ (150°), $\varphi_2/(\varphi_1 + \varphi_2) \cong 0.35$; 2804 A, $\varphi_1 + \varphi_2 \geqslant 0.22$ (150°), $\varphi_3 \leqslant 0.01$; 2654 A, $\varphi_1 + \varphi_2 \geqslant 0.36$ (150°); $\varphi_2/(\varphi_1 + \varphi_2) \cong 0.61$; 2537 A, dissociation is from second excited singlet; $\varphi_1 + \varphi_2 \geqslant 0.44$ (150°), $\varphi_3 \leqslant 0.02$; 2380 A, $\varphi_1 + \varphi_2 \geqslant 0.5$ (150°), $\varphi_3 \leqslant 0.04$; $CH_3CO^{\ddagger}$ is a non-thermally equilibrated radical. Photolysis

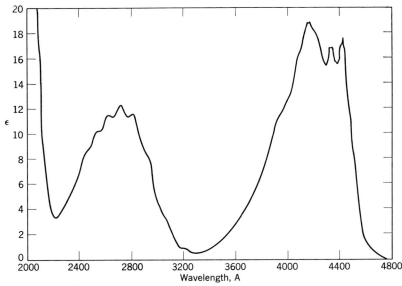

Fig. 5-5   Absorption spectrum for biacetyl $[CH_3COCOCH_3(g)]$, 25°.[424]

in 2-propanol with sunlight source gives acetone, and 3,4-dihydroxy-3,4-dimethyl-2,5-hexanedione.

$$CH_3COCOCH_3 + h\nu \rightarrow M^*(+N) \rightarrow M(+N')$$

$$M + h\nu'$$

$$2CH_3CO^{\ddagger}(+N) \rightarrow 2CH_3CO(+N') \quad (1)$$

$$2CH_3 + 2CO \quad (2)$$

$$CH_3COCH_3 + CO \quad (3)$$

103. 2,3-Pentanedione:[574] irradiation with a sunlamp (Pyrex filter) in benzene solution gave *A* and its dimer.

$$CH_3CH_2COCOCH_3 + h\nu \rightarrow \underset{\substack{| \\ CH_2—CH_2 \\ (A)}}{\overset{\substack{O \quad\;\; OH \\ \| \quad\;\; | }}{C——C—CH_3}} \searrow \text{Dimer}$$

104. 3,4-Hexanedione:[125] in propanol solution in sunlight, carbonyl reduction by way of triplet likely; process 1 important (analogous to ketone general process VI); products are 4-hydroxy-3-hexanone (*A*), 23%; 2-ethyl-2-hydroxycyclobutanone (*B*), 23%; 4-oxo-3-hexanol-proprionate, 54%; in cyclohexane in sunlight, *A*, 25% and *B*, 60%.

$$CH_3CH_2COCOCH_2CH_3 + h\nu \rightarrow C_2H_5 \overset{OH}{\underset{}{\rule{0pt}{0pt}}}\!\!\square\!\!\overset{O}{\diagup} \qquad (1)$$

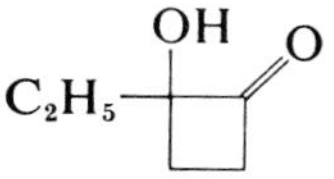

105. 4,5-Octanedione:[125] in butanal solution, 2537 A, process 1 important; products are 2-hydroxy-3-methyl-2-propylcyclobutanone (82%), 5-hydroxy-4-octanone (8.7%), 5-oxo-4-octanolbutyrate (7.7%).

$$CH_3CH_2CH_2COCOCH_2CH_2CH_3 + h\nu \rightarrow n\text{-}C_3H_7 \overset{OH}{\underset{CH_3}{\rule{0pt}{0pt}}}\!\!\square\!\!\overset{O}{\diagup} \qquad (1)$$

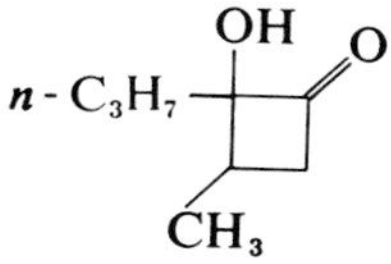

106. 2,7-Dimethyl-4,5-octanedione:[574] in ethanol solution at 25°, 4358 A, $\varphi_1 = 1.1 \pm 0.1$.

$$(CH_3)_2CHCH_2COCOCH_2CH(CH_3)_2 + h\nu \rightarrow (CH_3)_2CHCH_2 \overset{OH}{\underset{CH_3}{\rule{0pt}{0pt}}}\!\!\square\!\!\overset{O}{\diagup} \qquad (1)$$

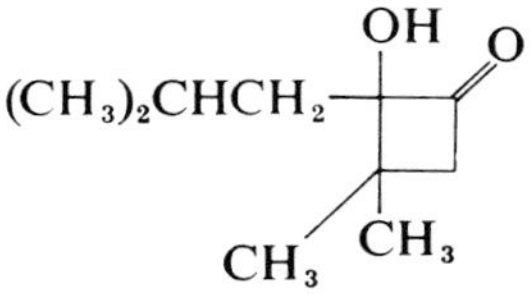

107. 5,6-Decanedione:[125,574] in cyclohexane solution in sunlight, process 1 is important; in ethanol solution at 25°, 4358 A, $\varphi_1 = 1.0 \pm 0.1$.

$$CH_3CH_2CH_2CH_2COCOCH_2CH_2CH_2CH_3 + h\nu \rightarrow n\text{-}C_4H_9 \overset{OH}{\underset{C_2H_5}{\rule{0pt}{0pt}}}\!\!\square\!\!\overset{O}{\diagup} \qquad (1)$$

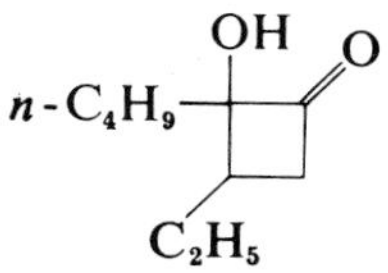

108. Tetramethyl-1,3-cyclobutanedione:[575,576,577,714] the final products of the photolysis are very dependent on the nature of the solvent employed; overall process 1 is important in benzene; a small amount of dimethyl ketene is also formed in benzene solution; process 2 occurs in 5–15% ethanol solution; ethyl isobutyrate has its origin in the reaction of dimethyl ketene with ethanol. At least two photolytic paths are possible: (a) a bis-fragmentation without decarbonylation to give dimethyl ketene; (b) decarbonylation to produce the intermediate tetramethylcyclopropanone or a diradical of this composition; the reaction is not sensitized by triplet benzophenone and presumably involves the (n, π^*) state.

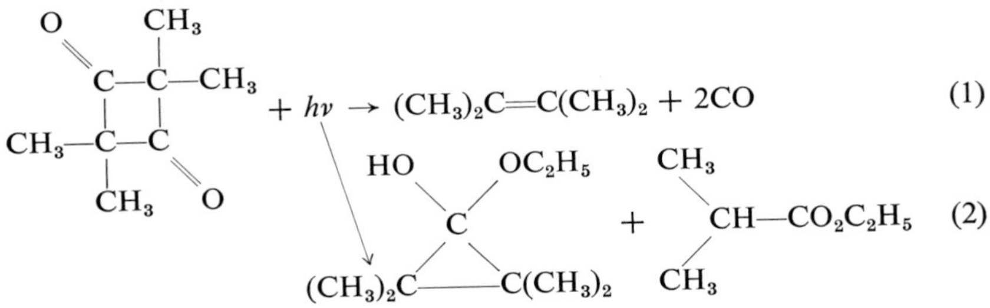

$$+ h\nu \rightarrow (CH_3)_2C=C(CH_3)_2 + 2CO \qquad (1)$$

$$+ \qquad \qquad \qquad \qquad (2)$$

109. Dispiro[5.1.5.1]tetradecane-7,14-dione:[577] irradiation in degassed benzene gives *A* (61% yield); overall reaction 1 probably proceeds through ring rupture; with O_2 added the major reaction products (moles) from 1 mole of reactant are: acetone (1.5), CO (0.8), CO_2 (0.4), tetramethylethylene oxide (0.07).

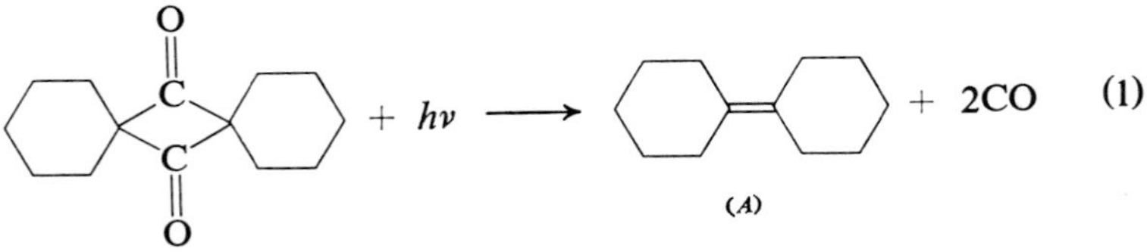

$$+ h\nu \longrightarrow \qquad + 2CO \qquad (1)$$

(A)

110. 1,2-Cyclodecanedione:[574] irradiation with sunlamp (Pyrex filter) in benzene solution gave *A* (74%) and *B* (9.3%); at 4358 A, $\Phi_A \cong 1.1$.

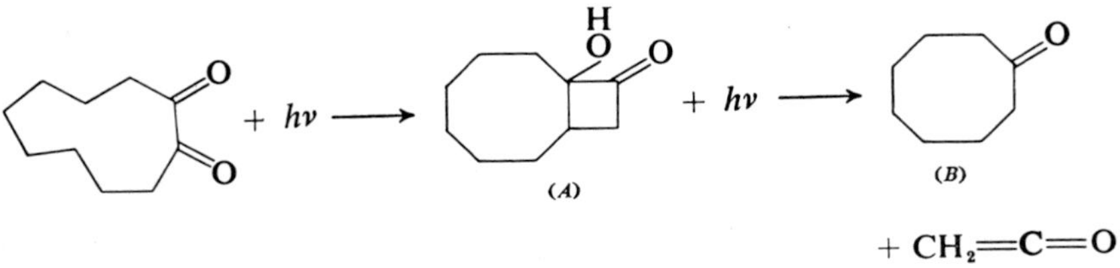

$$+ h\nu \longrightarrow \qquad + h\nu \longrightarrow$$

(A)   (B)

$$+ CH_2=C=O$$

111–117. Some steroid dienones: a few examples of the photochemical reactions of the steroid dienones are given here; for a more complete coverage reference should be made to the original papers of Barton and of Jeger and Schaffner and their colleagues,[381,384,745] and the review of Chapman.[501]

111. Prednisone acetate:[604,501] irradiation in solvents shown leads to the following reactions (p. 425); the mechanism of the rearrangements have been considered in terms of a series of alkyl shifts in polar intermediates, followed by formation of new rings.

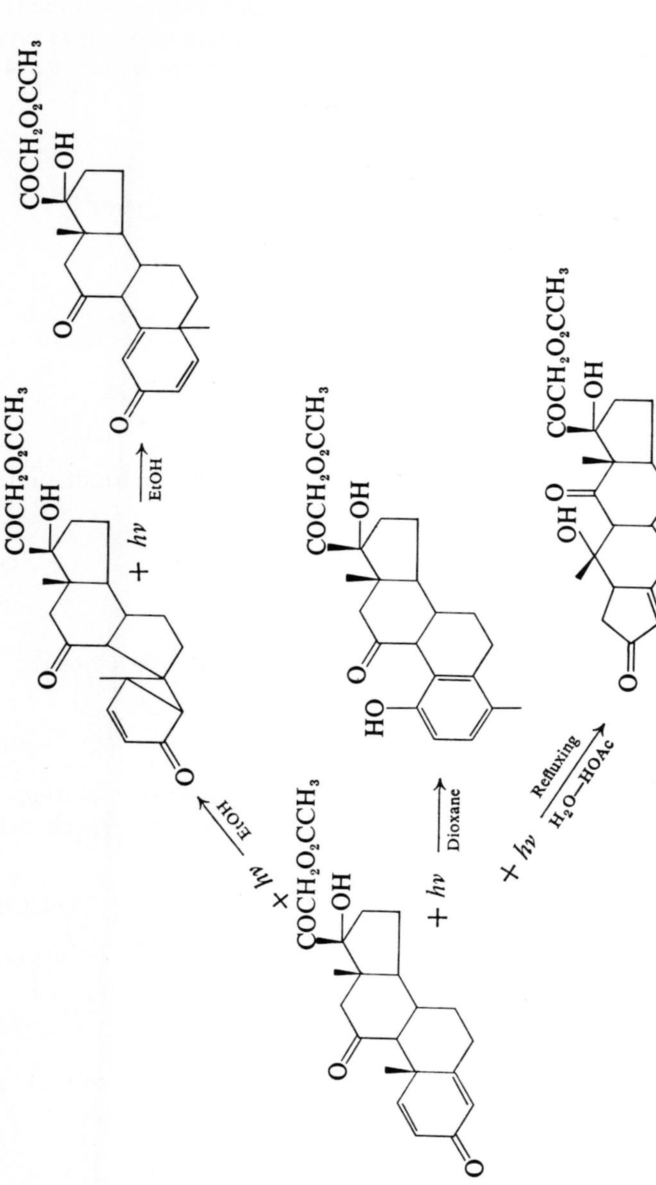
COCH2O2CCH3
OH
O
HO
+ hν
EtOH
Dioxane
Refluxing
H2O—HOAc

112. Santonin:[382,383] irradiation in the solvents shown gives the following products; the difference in the nature of the rearrangements of prednisone acetate and santonin has been attributed to the presence of a 4-methyl substituent in santonin.[501]

113. 1-Dehydro-4-methyltestosterone acetate:[606,607] on irradiation in solution, product *A* is formed cleanly in 60–70% yield.

114. 1-Dehydrotestosterone acetate:[608] irradiation in solution gives a complex mixture of ketones and phenols; *A* and *B* represent two of the products which have been identified.

115. 10β,17β-Diacetoxy-1,4-estradiene-3-one:[609] on irradiation in solution at 2537 A, the acetate group is lost and product *A* formed.

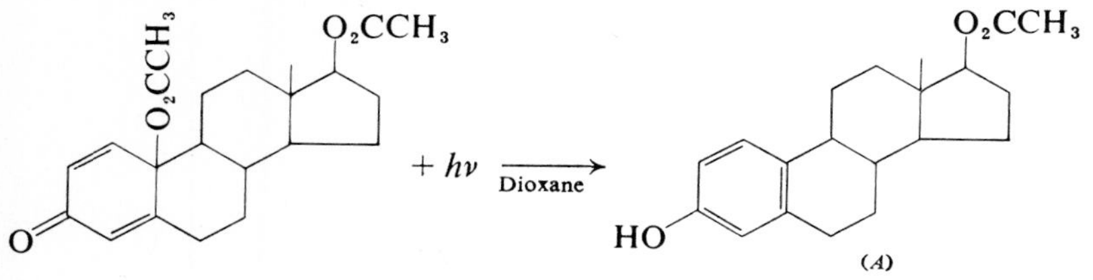

116. 3β-Acetoxypregna-5,16-dien-20-one:[610] irradiation in solution forms *A* (40–50 % yield) and *B* (30–40 % yield); the reaction forming *B* is general with both primary and secondary alcohols and provides a new method for the introduction of an oxygen-bearing 16, α-alkyl substituent into the steroid nucleus.

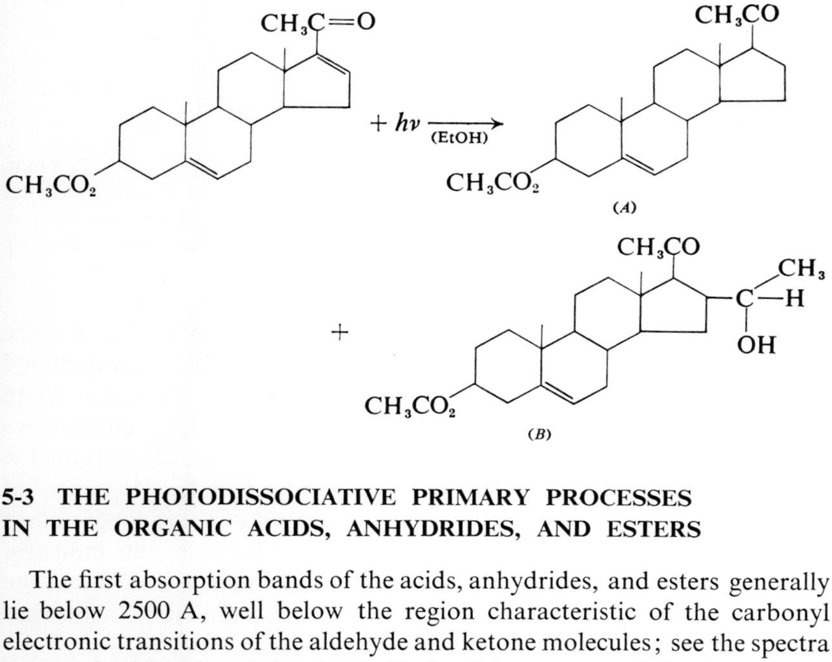

5-3 THE PHOTODISSOCIATIVE PRIMARY PROCESSES IN THE ORGANIC ACIDS, ANHYDRIDES, AND ESTERS

The first absorption bands of the acids, anhydrides, and esters generally lie below 2500 A, well below the region characteristic of the carbonyl electronic transitions of the aldehyde and ketone molecules; see the spectra summarized in Figs. 5-6 and 5-7. Each of the compounds in these classes contains the carbonyl group, and as in the case of the aldehydes, the first absorption band may be associated with an $n \rightarrow \pi^*$, singlet-singlet transition involving a non-bonding electron associated with the oxygen atom of the carbonyl linkage. The greater separation of the n and π^*

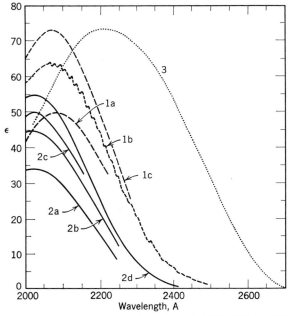

Fig. 5-6 Absorption spectra for (1) formic acid [CHO₂H(g)], 27°: (a) 2.45 mm, (b) 16.4 mm, (c) 35.2 mm; undefined amount of monomer and dimer contribute; calculated assuming monomer only; (2) acetic acid [CH₃CO₂H(g)], 26°: (a) 3.6 mm, (b) 8.3 mm, (c) 11.0 mm, (d) 12.9 mm; calculated assuming monomer only; (3) acetic anhydride [(CH₃CO)₂O(g)], 25°.[424]

energy levels for the acids, anhydrides, and esters has been attributed to the attachment of the electron-releasing group, —OH or —OR, to the carbonyl carbon atom; since the carbonyl group in its excited π^* state contains an additional electron in the π-orbital system, the effect of adding an electron-releasing group is to increase the charge density within the carbonyl π bond and thus raise the energy of the excited π^* state. A somewhat compensating energy change is expected as a result of the inductive effect of the electronegative oxygen-containing groups. However, the inductive interactions also lower the energy of the oxygen lone-pair electrons in the ground electronic state, so that inductive effects tend to cancel somewhat and affect the $n \rightarrow \pi^*$ energy separation very little.

5-3A The Organic Acids

Although little work has been done on the photochemistry of the acids, the limited information available suggests a pattern of primary processes

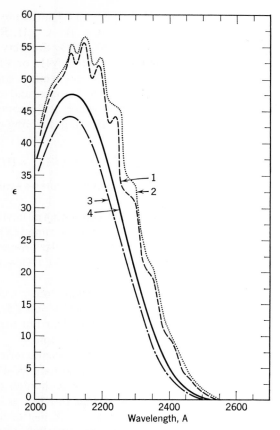

Fig. 5-7   Absorption spectra for:
   (1) methyl formate $[CH_3O_2CH(g)]$, 25°;
   (2) ethyl formate $[C_2H_5O_2CH(g)]$, 25°;
   (3) methyl acetate $[CH_3O_2CCH_3(g)]$, 25°;
   (4) ethyl acetate $[C_2H_5O_2CCH_3(g)]$, 25°.[424]

which may be accepted as tentative generalizations. The free radical
processes VII and VIII and the intramolecular process IX occur in the
simple acids and are probably important in the more complex organic
acids. ($R^{\ddagger}$ is a non-thermally equilibrated radical.)

$$RCO_2H + h\nu \rightarrow R + CO_2H^{\ddagger}(\text{or } CO_2 + H) \qquad \text{(VIIa)}$$

$$RCO_2{}^{\ddagger}(\text{or } R + CO_2) + H \qquad \text{(VIIb)}$$

$$RCO^{\ddagger}(\text{or } R + CO) + OH \qquad \text{(VIII)}$$

$$RH + CO_2 \qquad \text{(IX)}$$

The energy per quantum available at the wavelengths absorbed by the acids is more than enough to rupture any of the bonds, $R-CO_2H$, RCO_2-H, or $RCO-OH$. Since the radicals CO_2H and RCO_2 are very unstable toward decomposition, the immediate result of either VIIa or VIIb would be the same for the timing involved in most photochemical studies. By analogy with the reactions observed in aldehydes, ketones, and esters, one might expect monomeric n-butyric acid and other acids containing γ-hydrogen atoms to undergo a "Norrish Type II" split, forming olefin and smaller acid:

$$R_2CHCR_2CR_2CO_2H + h\nu \rightarrow R_2C{=}CR_2 + CR_2{=}C(OH)_2 \rightarrow HCR_2CO_2H$$

There is no experimental evidence now at hand which allows evaluation of this possibility.

In the photolysis of formic acid, the only acid containing an acyl hydrogen atom, an additional intramolecular split may occur, forming H_2O and CO; this process is completely analogous to the intramolecular primary process II observed in the photolysis of the aldehydes ($RCHO + h\nu \rightarrow RH + CO$).

Note that substitution of a halogen on the α-carbon atom can change the nature of the primary act to one of halogen atom or ion release. The nature of the primary excitation in this case is not clear but may involve promotion of a non-bonding electron in the halogen atom.

The olefinic acids exhibit photoisomerization, a characteristic of all olefinic compounds; see the maleic and fumaric acid data (p. 431).

The α-keto acids undergo photodecarboxylation with high efficiency; see the data for pyruvic acid (p. 432). The change in basic properties of the carbonyl group of acids on photoexcitation is reflected in the proton transfer reactions in aqueous solutions; note the data for o-hydroxybenzoic acid (p. 432).

1. Formic acid:[127–131,159] first absorption band shown for monomer-dimer mixtures in Fig. 5-6; full mercury arc, process 3 important, processes 1, 2, and 4 probably minor; 2540 A, 2100 A, and 1900 A, $\varphi_1 + \varphi_2 + \varphi_3 + \varphi_4 = 1.0$; $\epsilon = 2$ (2400 A), 5 (2340 A), 8.2 (2280 A). DCO_2H is similar.[131] In aqueous solution, 2537 A, 3 important, 1 unimportant.

$$HCO_2H + h\nu \rightarrow H_2O + CO \tag{1}$$

$$H_2 + CO_2 \tag{2}$$

$$HCO^{\ddagger} \text{ (or } H + CO) + OH \tag{3}$$

$$H + CO_2H^{\ddagger} \text{ (or } CO_2 + H) \tag{4}$$

2. *Acetic acid:*[132,133] first absorption band shown in Fig. 5-6 for monomer-dimer mixtures; full mercury arc, $\varphi_1 + \varphi_2 + \varphi_3 + \varphi_4 \simeq 0.5$; 2400–2500 A, $\varphi_1/(\varphi_3 + \varphi_4) \simeq 0.11$, $\varphi_2/(\varphi_3 + \varphi_4) \simeq 1.1$; the dimer $(CH_3CO_2H)_2$ apparently has the same primary processes as the monomer; CH_3CO_2D similar photochemical behavior.

$$CH_3CO_2H + h\nu \rightarrow CH_4 + CO_2 \qquad (1)$$

$$CH_3CO^{\ddagger} \text{ (or } CH_3 + CO) + OH \qquad (2)$$

$$CH_3 + CO_2H^{\ddagger} \text{ (or } CO_2 + H) \qquad (3)$$

$$CH_3CO_2{}^{\ddagger} \text{ (or } CH_3 + CO_2) + H \qquad (4)$$

3. *Monochloroacetic acid:*[134,135] in aqueous solution (0.5 M), 2537 A, $\varphi_1 = 0.32$ (25°), 0.37 (32°), 0.43 (41°), 0.62 (56°), 0.69 (69°).

$$ClCH_2CO_2H \ (aq) + h\nu \rightarrow M^*(+N) \rightarrow M(+N')$$
$$\downarrow$$
$$Cl^- \ (aq) + HOCH_2CO_2H \ (aq) + H^+ \ (aq) \qquad (1)$$

4. *Monoiodoacetic acid:*[136] in hexane solution, 2537 A, $\varphi_1 \simeq 1.0$, when O_2 not intentionally removed; 0.00, when O_2 removed well; reverse reactions of radicals with I_2 and I probably important in O_2-free solutions.

$$ICH_2CO_2H + h\nu \rightarrow I + CH_2CO_2H \qquad (1)$$

5. *Malonic acid:*[137,138] aqueous solution, $\lambda < 2500$ A, products which are radical dimers suggest 1; 2 also possible; extent of 1 and 2 uncertain.

$$HO_2CCH_2CO_2H \ (aq) + h\nu \rightarrow HO_2C(\text{or } CO_2 + H) + CH_2CO_2H \quad (1)$$

$$CO_2 + CH_3CO_2H \qquad (2)^{21}$$

6. *Maleic and fumaric acids:*[139] absorption band in ethyl alcohol below 3200 A; both maleic and fumaric acids (aqueous solutions), $\epsilon \simeq 7.5$ (3130 A), 19.4 (3020 A); full mercury arc, decomposition unimportant, isomerization occurs; for 0.01 M aqueous solutions, $\varphi_1 = 0.031$ (2070 A), 0.041 (2530 A), 0.030 (2820 A), 0.048 (3130 A); $\varphi_2 = 0.10$ (2070 A), 0.10 (2530 A), 0.13 (2820 A), 0.12 (3130 A).

$$cis\text{-}HO_2CCH{=}CHCO_2H + h\nu \rightarrow M^*(+N) \rightarrow M(+N')$$
$$\downarrow$$
$$trans\text{-}HO_2CCH{=}CHCO_2H \quad (1)$$

$$trans\text{-}HO_2CCH{=}CHCO_2H + h\nu \rightarrow M^*(+N) \rightarrow M(+N')$$
$$\downarrow$$
$$cis\text{-}HO_2CCH{=}CHCO_2H \quad (2)$$

7. o-Hydroxybenzoic acid:[140] fluorescence studies show that proton transfer to carbonyl oxygen occurs on photoactivation in aqueous solution, one of many such examples in the literature.

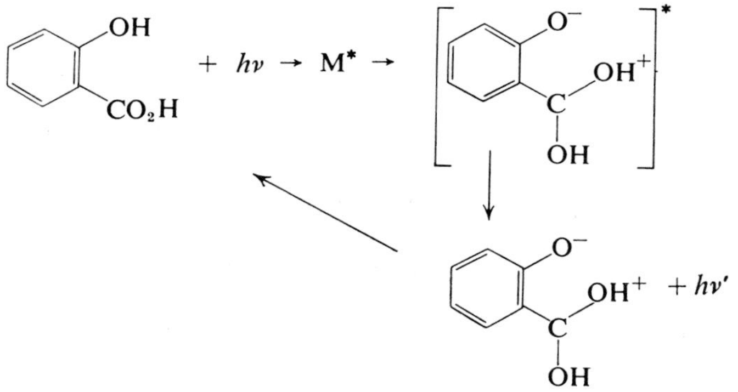

8. Pyruvic acid:[721, 722] λ_{max} and ϵ, respectively, for $n - \pi^*$ band in various solvents are as follows: 3212 A, 11.3 (H_2O); 3250 A, 4.55 (CH_3OH); 3375 A, 11.5 ($CHCl_3$); 3425 A, 14.7 (Et_2O); 3585 A, 18.9 (C_6H_6); irradiation at 3660 A in H_2O gives a quantum yield of decomposition (largely to form CO_2 and acetoin, head-to-head dimer of acetaldehyde) $\cong 0.79$; this quantum yield is near unity for gas-phase photolyses at 80°; presumably process 1 is important; in methanol solutions photoreduction to form dimethyltartaric acid occurs with nearly perfect quantum efficiency.

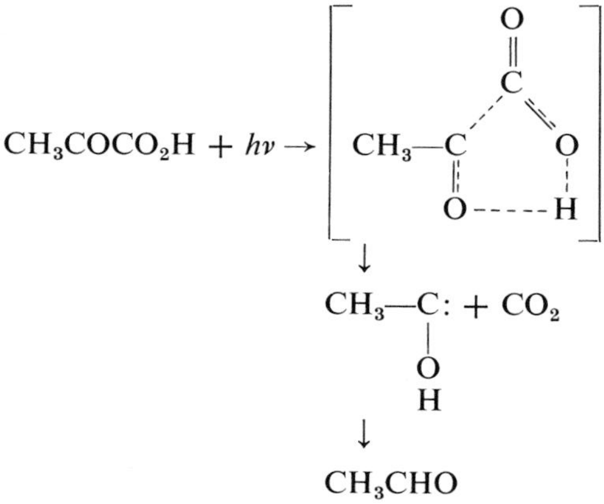

$$\text{(1)}$$

9. Benzoylformic acid ($C_6H_5COCO_2H$):[721, 723] in water, $\lambda_{max} = 3375$, $\epsilon = 48$; in C_6H_6, $\lambda_{max} = 3760$, $\epsilon = 77$; photoreduction to *s*-dihydroxydiphenylsuccinic acid occurs in isopropyl alcohol solution; in water solution, decarboxylation is dominant to form CO_2 and benzaldehyde; mechanism may be similar to that suggested for pyruvic acid.

10. Nitrophenylacetate ions:[705] photodecarboxylation occurs on irradiation in aqueous solution; at 3660 A, $\varphi_1 \leqslant 0.1$ for 2-nitrophenylacetate, $\sim$0.5 for 3-nitrophenylacetate, $\sim$0.6 for 4-nitrophenylacetate; colored transients of short lifetime (probably carbanions of the sort shown in reaction 1 for 2-nitrophenylacetate) are formed on photolyses of the phenylacetate ions substituted in the 2- and/or 4-positions by nitro groups; the undissociated nitrophenylacetic acids and the unsubstituted phenylacetate ion do not undergo photodecarboxylation efficiently for similar conditions.

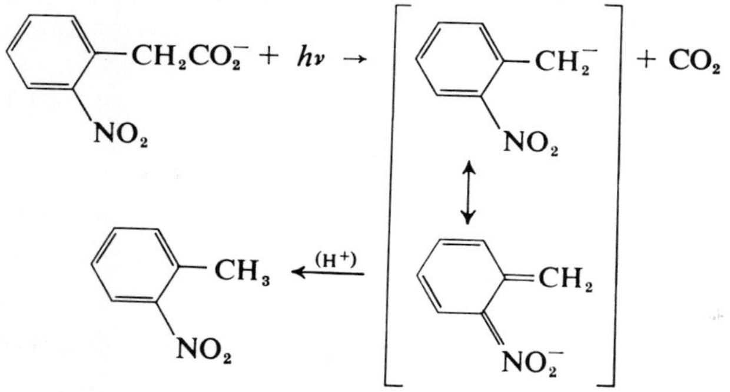

$$\text{(1)}$$

5-3B Acid Anhydrides and Acyl Halides

The primary photodissociative processes in the simple acid anhydrides show both free radical and intramolecular modes.

$$R_2CHCOCCHR_2 + h\nu \rightarrow R_2CHCO_2^{\ddagger} + R_2CHCO^{\ddagger} \quad (X)$$
$$\downarrow \qquad\qquad \downarrow$$
$$R_2CH + CO_2 \quad R_2CH + CO$$

$$R_2C{=}C{=}O + R_2CHCO_2H \quad (XI)$$

Process XI is similar to the "Norrish Type II" splits in aldehydes and ketones and undoubtedly involves a cyclic six-membered intermediate state which in this case forms the final stable products without the intermediate enol form of the product. In the one example shown for acyl halides, free radical processes are important.

1. Acetic anhydride:[141-144] first absorption band shown in Fig. 5-6; second band below 1900 A; full mercury arc, $\varphi_1 \cong \varphi_2$.

$$(CH_3CO)_2O + h\nu \rightarrow CH_3CO_2 \quad + CH_3CO \tag{1}$$

$$\downarrow \qquad\qquad \downarrow$$

$$CH_3 + CO_2 \quad CH_3 + CO$$

$$CH_2{=}C{=}O + CH_3CO_2H \tag{2}$$

2. *Propionic anhydride:*[143] full mercury arc, $\lambda < 2652$ A effective, $\varphi_1 \cong \varphi_2$.

$$(C_2H_5CO)_2O + h\nu \rightarrow C_2H_5CO_2^{\ddagger} \quad + \quad C_2H_5CO^{\ddagger} \tag{1}$$

$$\downarrow \qquad\qquad\qquad \downarrow$$

$$C_2H_5 + CO_2 \quad\quad C_2H_5 + CO$$

$$CH_3CH{=}C{=}O + C_2H_5CO_2H \tag{2}$$

3. *Oxalyl bromide:*[145,146] first absorption region 4500 to below 2600 A, some structure; $\epsilon \cong 10$ (3850 A), ~ 32 (3330 A), ~ 100 (2950 A); 4358 A, $\varphi_1 + \varphi_2 \cong 0.9$ (0.3 for CCl_4 solution), $\epsilon = 0.91$; 3660 A, $\varphi_1 + \varphi_2 \cong 0.9$ (0.4 in CCl_4 solution), $\epsilon = 18.3$; 2652 A, $\varphi_1 + \varphi_2 \cong 0.8$ (0.9 in CCl_4 solution), $\epsilon = 227$.

$$BrCOCOBr + h\nu \rightarrow Br + COCOBr \tag{1}$$

$$\searrow$$

$$2COBr \tag{2}$$

5-3C   Organic Esters

The extensive results from the esters show a regular pattern of primary processes related to the structure of the ester. Excitation of the ester molecule can be followed by any of three possible bond cleavages involving the ester linkages to form free radicals, processes XII and XIII; XIIa and XIIb would be indistinguishable for the usual experimental conditions since radical decomposition (RCO_2 and $R'OCO$) would be very rapid. R can be H or an alkyl group. The R and RO radicals, with higher activation energies for decomposition than the RCO_2, $ROCO$, or RCO radicals, can be thermally equilibrated and/or react by paths other than decomposition after the primary act.

$$\overset{O}{\overset{\|}{R C O R'}} + h\nu \rightarrow RCO_2^{\ddagger} + R' \tag{XIIa}$$

$$\downarrow$$

$$R + CO_2$$

$$R + CO_2R'^{\ddagger} \tag{XIIb}$$

$$\downarrow$$

$$CO_2 + R'$$

$$RCO^{\ddagger} + OR' \tag{XIII}$$

$$\downarrow$$

$$R + CO$$

When β-hydrogen atoms occur in the alcohol portion of the ester, or when γ-hydrogen atoms occur in the portion of the ester derived from the acid, intramolecular processes are observed which are analogs to the "Norrish Type II" splits of the aldehydes and ketones; in XIV an olefin and a smaller ester is formed; in XV an olefin and an acid are formed. Again the cyclic six-membered ring intermediate is likely, involving the inter-action of the carbonyl oxygen and a hydrogen atom attached to the carbon three atoms down-chain from the carbonyl carbon.

$$R_2CHCR_2O\overset{\overset{\textstyle O}{\|}}{C}CR_2CR_2CHR_2$$

$$+ \, h\nu \rightarrow R_2CHCR_2O\overset{\overset{\textstyle OH}{|}}{C}{=}CR_2 + CR_2{=}CR_2 \quad \text{(XIV)}$$

$$\downarrow \overset{\textstyle O}{\|}$$

$$R_2CHCR_2O\overset{\overset{\textstyle O}{\|}}{C}CR_2H$$

$$R_2C{=}CR_2 + HO_2CCR_2CR_2CHR_2 \quad \text{(XV)}$$

In formate esters an additional primary process XVI occurs which is completely analogous to the intramolecular process II forming CO and RH in the aldehyde (RCHO) photolysis.

$$RO\overset{\overset{\textstyle O}{\|}}{C}H + h\nu \rightarrow ROH + CO \qquad \text{(XVI)}$$

1. Methyl formate:[147–149] first absorption band shown in Fig. 5-7; full mercury arc, $\varphi_1 + \varphi_2 + \varphi_3 \cong 0.8$ (25°, 75 mm); 4 is also a major process; results similar in liquid phase.

$$CH_3OCHO + h\nu \rightarrow CH_3O + HCO^{\ddagger} \text{ (or } H + CO) \qquad (1)$$

$$H + CH_3OCO^{\ddagger} \text{ (or } CH_3 + CO_2) \qquad (2)$$

$$CH_3 + OCHO^{\ddagger} \text{ (or } H + CO_2) \qquad (3)$$

$$CH_3OH + CO \qquad (4)$$

2. Ethyl formate:[149,150] first asborption band shown in Fig. 5-7; full mercury arc ($\lambda < 2400$ A), 1, 2, and 3 occur but relative importance un-certain; 4 and 5 major; $\Phi_{CO}/\Phi_{C_2H_4} \cong 4.9$ (29°); solvents suppress 5, no effect on 4; probably different excited states are involved in these two processes (or decomposition from different vibrational levels of the same state).

$$C_2H_5OCHO + h\nu \rightarrow C_2H_5O + HCO^+ \text{ (or } H + CO) \tag{1}$$

$$C_2H_5OCO^+ \text{ (or } C_2H_5 + CO_2) + H \tag{2}$$

$$C_2H_5 + OCHO^+ \text{ (or } CO_2 + H) \tag{3}$$

$$C_2H_5OH + CO \tag{4}$$

$$C_2H_4 + HOCHO \tag{5}$$

3. *n-Propyl formate:*[150] full mercury arc ($\lambda < 2400$ A), results similar to those for ethyl formate; liquid phase, $\Phi_{CO}/\Phi_{C_3H_6} = 0.28$.

$$n\text{-}C_3H_7OCHO + h\nu \rightarrow n\text{-}C_3H_7O + HCO^+ \text{ (or } H + CO) \tag{1}$$

$$n\text{-}C_3H_7OCO^+ \text{ (or } n\text{-}C_3H_7 + CO_2) + H \tag{2}$$

$$n\text{-}C_3H_7 + OCHO^+ \text{ (or } CO_2 + H) \tag{3}$$

$$n\text{-}C_3H_7OH + CO \tag{4}$$

$$C_3H_6 + HOCHO \tag{5}$$

4. *n-Butyl formate:*[149] full mercury arc ($\lambda < 2400$ A) results similar to those for ethyl formate; liquid phase, $\Phi_{CO_2}/\Phi_{CO} \cong 0.9$ (45°), $\Phi_{C_3H_6}/\Phi_{CO} \cong 2.4$ (45°).

$$n\text{-}C_4H_9OCHO + h\nu \rightarrow n\text{-}C_4H_9O + HCO^+ \text{ (or } H + CO) \tag{1}$$

$$n\text{-}C_4H_9OCO^+ \text{ (or } n\text{-}C_4H_9 + CO_2) + H \tag{2}$$

$$n\text{-}C_4H_9 + OCHO^+ \text{ (or } CO_2 + H) \tag{3}$$

$$n\text{-}C_4H_9OH + CO \tag{4}$$

$$1\text{-}C_4H_8 + HOCHO \tag{5}$$

5. *Methyl acetate:*[149,151-153] first absorption band shown in Fig. 5-7; full mercury arc ($\lambda < 2400$ A), process 1 most important, both liquid and gas phase; $\lambda < 2250$ A, $\varphi_1/(\varphi_2 + \varphi_3) \cong 4.5$ (120°); about 30% of the non-thermally equilibrated CH_3CO^+ radicals decompose in an early vibration

following 1 at 30°; $CH_3CO_2CD_3$ similar photochemical behavior.[152]

$$CH_3CO_2CH_3 + h\nu \rightarrow CH_3CO^\ddagger \text{ (or } CH_3 + CO) + OCH_3 \quad (1)$$

$$CH_3 + CO_2CH_3^\ddagger \text{ (or } CO_2 + CH_3) \quad (2)$$

$$CH_3CO_2^\ddagger \text{ (or } CH_3 + CO_2) + CH_3 \quad (3)$$

6a. Ethyl acetate:[149,150,161] first absorption band is shown in Fig. 5-7; full mercury arc ($\lambda < 2400$ A), $\varphi_1/(\varphi_2 + \varphi_3) \cong 3.0$ (temperature $> 124°$), $\varphi_4/(\varphi_2 + \varphi_3) \cong 0.7$ (195°); solvent addition decreases yield of all processes but 1. Process 4 may result from an excited triplet state; biacetyl (2%) reduces liquid-phase photolysis by 80%.

$$CH_3CO_2C_2H_5 + h\nu \rightarrow CH_3CO^\ddagger \text{ (or } CH_3 + CO) + OC_2H_5 \quad (1)$$

$$CH_3 + CO_2C_2H_5^\ddagger \text{ (or } CO_2 + C_2H_5) \quad (2)$$

$$CH_3CO_2^\ddagger \text{ (or } CH_3 + CO_2) + C_2H_5 \quad (3)$$

$$CH_3CO_2H + C_2H_4 \quad (4)$$

6b. Ethyl-d_4 acetate:[161] all processes for ethyl acetate (6a) occur; process 4 involves either of the two paths 4a or 4b; at 315°K, 3.0 cm ester, $\varphi_{4a}/\varphi_{4b} = 0.67$ (full mercury arc), 0.80 (2150–2350 A), 1.06 (2250–2350 A), no effect of O_2; in liquid state, independent of λ, $\varphi_{4a}/\varphi_{4b} = 0.48e^{1000(\text{cal})/RT}$. Process 4 evidently occurs from a vibrationally equilibrated excited state. The thermal decomposition of this compound shows an almost identical isotope effect in the analogous thermal reaction.

$$CH_3CO_2CD_2CD_2H + h\nu \rightarrow CH_3CO_2H + CD_2CD_2 \quad (4a)^{21}$$

$$CH_3CO_2D + CD_2CDH \quad (4b)^{21}$$

7. n-Propyl acetate:[149] full mercury arc ($\lambda < 2400$ A), liquid phase, $\varphi_1 \cong \varphi_2 + \varphi_3$ (75°), $\varphi_4/\varphi_1 \cong 7.4$.

$$CH_3CO_2CH_2CH_2CH_3$$
$$+ h\nu \rightarrow CH_3CO^\ddagger \text{ (or } CH_3 + CO) + OCH_2CH_2CH_3 \quad (1)$$

$$CH_3 + CO_2CH_2CH_2CH_3^\ddagger \text{ (or } CO_2 + n\text{-}C_3H_7) \quad (2)$$

$$CH_3CO_2^\ddagger \text{ (or } CH_3 + CO_2) + n\text{-}C_3H_7 \quad (3)$$

$$CH_3CO_2H + C_3H_6 \quad (4)$$

8. Isopropyl acetate:[149] full mercury arc ($\lambda < 2400$ A), liquid phase, $\varphi_1 \cong \varphi_2 + \varphi_3$ (77°), $\varphi_4/\varphi_1 \cong 16$.

$$CH_3CO_2CH(CH_3)_2 + h\nu \rightarrow CH_3CO^{\ddagger} \text{ (or } CH_3 + CO) + OCH(CH_3)_2 \quad (1)$$

$$CH_3 + CO_2CH(CH_3)_2^{\ddagger} \text{ [or } CO_2 + CH(CH_3)_2] \quad (2)$$

$$CH_3CO_2^{\ddagger} \text{ (or } CH_3 + CO_2) + CH(CH_3)_2 \quad (3)$$

$$CH_3CO_2H + C_3H_6 \quad (4)$$

9. Methyl propionate:[149,150] full mercury arc ($\lambda < 2400$ A), $\varphi_1/(\varphi_2 + \varphi_3) \cong$ 4.2 (34°); solvents (e.g., C_2H_5OH) lower φ_2 and φ_3 but not φ_1; possibly different electronic levels involved (or decomposition from different vibrational levels of the same state).

$$CH_3CH_2CO_2CH_3 + h\nu \rightarrow CH_3CH_2CO^{\ddagger} \text{ (or } C_2H_5 + CO) + OCH_3 \quad (1)$$

$$C_2H_5 + CO_2CH_3^{\ddagger} \text{ (or } CO_2 + CH_3) \quad (2)$$

$$C_2H_5CO_2^{\ddagger} \text{ (or } C_2H_5 + CO_2) + CH_3 \quad (3)$$

10. Ethyl propionate:[154,155] full mercury arc ($\lambda < 2400$ A), $\varphi_1 \cong 0.68$, $\varphi_2 + \varphi_3 \cong 0.19$, $\varphi_4 \cong 0.3$ (λ dependent).

$$C_2H_5CO_2C_2H_5 + h\nu \rightarrow C_2H_5CO^{\ddagger} \text{ (or } C_2H_5 + CO) + OC_2H_5 \quad (1)$$

$$C_2H_5 + CO_2C_2H_5^{\ddagger} \text{ (or } CO_2 + C_2H_5) \quad (2)$$

$$C_2H_5CO_2^{\ddagger} \text{ (or } C_2H_5 + CO_2) + C_2H_5 \quad (3)$$

$$C_2H_5CO_2H + C_2H_4 \quad (4)$$

11. n-Propyl propionate:[156] full mercury arc ($\lambda < 2400$ A), $\varphi_1/\varphi_2 \cong 4.1$, $\varphi_3/\varphi_2 \cong 2$ (41–131°).

$$C_2H_5CO_2CH_2CH_2CH_3$$
$$+ h\nu \rightarrow CH_3CH_2CO^{\ddagger} \text{ (or } C_2H_5 + CO) + OCH_2CH_2CH_3 \quad (1)$$

$$C_2H_5CO_2^{\ddagger} \text{ (or } C_2H_5 + CO_2) + n\text{-}C_3H_7 \quad (2)$$

$$C_2H_5CO_2H + C_3H_6 \quad (3)$$

12. Isopropyl propionate:[156,157] full mercury arc ($\lambda < 2400$ A), $\varphi_1/\varphi_2 \cong 2.4$ (33–176°), $\varphi_3/\varphi_2 \cong 1.4$ (33–176°); $OCH(CH_3)_2^{\ddagger}$ is non-thermally equilibrated; fraction of these which decompose before other reactions is 0.3

(28°), 0.7 (65°).

$$CH_3CH_2CO_2CH(CH_3)_2$$
$$+ \; h\nu \rightarrow C_2H_5CO^{\ddagger} \text{ or } (C_2H_5 + CO) + OCH(CH_3)_2{}^{\ddagger} \quad (1)$$
$$\downarrow$$
$$CH_3 + CH_3CHO$$

$$C_2H_5 + CO_2 + CH(CH_3)_2 \quad (2)$$

$$C_2H_5CO_2H + C_3H_6 \quad (3)$$

13. Methyl n-butyrate:[149] full mercury arc ($\lambda < 2400$ A), $\varphi_4/\varphi_1 \cong 0.09$ (25°), $\varphi_1/(\varphi_2 + \varphi_3) \cong 3.6$ (29°); 2400–2250 A, $\varphi_4/\varphi_1 \cong 0.30$ (29°), $\varphi_1/(\varphi_2 + \varphi_3) \cong 1.0$ (29°); addition of solvent (e.g., C_2H_5OH) suppresses all processes but 1; possibly different electronic levels involved (or decomposition from different vibrational levels of the same state).

$$n\text{-}C_3H_7CO_2CH_3 + h\nu \rightarrow n\text{-}C_3H_7CO^{\ddagger} \text{ (or } n\text{-}C_3H_7 + CO) + OCH_3 \quad (1)$$

$$n\text{-}C_3H_7 + CO_2CH_3{}^{\ddagger} \text{ (or } CO_2 + CH_3) \quad (2)$$

$$n\text{-}C_3H_7CO_2{}^{\ddagger} \text{ (or } n\text{-}C_3H_7 + CO_2) + CH_3 \quad (3)$$

$$C_2H_4 + CH_3CO_2CH_3 \quad (4)^{21}$$

14. trans-Methyl crotonate:[698] 2537–2654 A, stable to decomposition at 25°; at 300° and 25 mm product quantum yields are: CO_2, 0.098; CO, 0.066; C_4H_8, 0.051; C_3H_6, 0.044; CH_4, 0.026; C_2H_4, 0.006; at 300° and 5 mm pressure product quantum yields are about double those at 25 mm; relative yields of isomeric butenes are very sensitive to temperature, 275–300°.

$$trans\text{-}CH_3CH{=}CHCO_2CH_3 + h\nu \rightarrow M^*(+N) \rightarrow M(+N')$$
$$\downarrow$$
$$C_3H_5CO + OCH_3 \quad (1)$$
$$\downarrow$$
$$C_3H_5 + CO$$

$$C_3H_5 + CO_2CH_3 \quad (2)$$
$$\downarrow$$
$$CO_2 + CH_3$$

$$C_3H_5CO_2 + CH_3 \quad (3)$$
$$\downarrow$$
$$C_3H_5 + CO_2$$

15. Methyl carbonate:[160] full mercury arc (6–80°), processes 1 and 2 important; 3 and/or 4 important.

$$(CH_3O)_2CO + h\nu \rightarrow CH_3 + CO_2 + CH_3O \qquad (1)$$

$$CH_4 + CO_2 + CH_2O \qquad (2)$$

$$2CH_3O + CO \qquad (3)$$

$$CH_3OH + CO + CH_2O \qquad (4)$$

16. β-Propiolactone:[158] absorption band below 2800 A; 2537 A, liquid phase, $\varphi_1 \cong 0.01$, $\varphi_2 \cong 0.04$ (25°); polymer formation important, which may suggest process 3; processes 1, 2, and 3 may pass through very short-lived intermediate diradical forms ($\cdot CH_2CH_2OCO\cdot$, $\cdot OCH_2CH_2\dot{C}O$).

$$\overline{OCH_2CH_2\dot{C}}{=}O + h\nu \rightarrow M^*(+N) \rightarrow M+(N')$$

$$C_2H_4 + CO_2 \qquad (1)$$

$$CO + CH_3CHO \qquad (2)$$

$$CH_2{=}C{=}O + CH_2O(?) \qquad (3)$$

17. γ-Butyrolactone:[741] absorption band below 2600 A; full arc, liquid phase, major gaseous products are CO, CO_2, cyclopropane, C_2H_4, allyl formate, cyclopropanol, propionaldehyde, and acetaldehyde; from initial slopes of product yield as a function of time, relative initial rates of formation are as follows: allyl formate, 1.0; acetaldehyde, 0.7; cyclopropanol, 0.0; propionaldehyde, 0.05; cyclopropane, 0.08; ethylene, 0.14; CO_2, 0.08; cyclopropanol may be formed in a secondary photolysis of a primary product. Cyclopropane, acetaldehyde, allylformate, and ethylene formations are quenched by olefin (*cis*-2-butene or *cis*-2-pentene) which isomerizes, and a triplet precursor for these products is probable; intermediates probably include very short-lived biradical forms (e.g., $\cdot CH_2CH_2CH_2OCO\cdot$ and $\cdot OCH_2CH_2CH_2\dot{C}O$ for processes 3 and 4).

$$\overline{OCH_2CH_2CH_2\dot{C}}{=}O + h\nu \rightarrow M^*(+N) \rightarrow M(+N')$$

$$HCO_2CH_2CH{=}CH_2 \qquad (1)$$

$$CH_3CH_2CHO + CO \qquad (2)$$

$$cyclo\text{-}C_3H_6 + CO_2 \qquad (3)$$

$$CH_3CHO + CH_2CO \qquad (4)$$

18. γ-Valerolactone:[741,742] full mercury arc, liquid phase, major product is *n*-butyraldehyde; minor products probably include acetaldehyde, acetone, methyl ethyl ketone, and methyl cyclopropane; the transfer of a methyl group is required in process 1; this is not observed in cyclic ketone photochemistry.

$$\overline{OCH(CH_3)CH_2CH_2}C{=}O + h\nu \rightarrow M^*(+N) \rightarrow M(+N')$$

$$\searrow\downarrow$$
$$CH_3CH_2CH_2CHO + CO \quad (1)$$

other processes
analogous to those for
compound 17 likely

19. α-Keto esters:[724] photolysis at 3660 A in benzene solution gave the following quantum yields for ester decomposition:

$CH_3COCO_2C_2H_5$, 0.17 $CH_3COCO_2CD(CH_3)_2$, 0.19
$CH_3COCO_2CH_3$, 0.15 $C_6H_5COCO_2C_2H_5$, 0.056
$CH_3COCO_2CH(CH_3)_2$, 0.18   ethyl α-naphthoylformate, <0.01

the overall reaction in benzene is given by 1; evidence suggests photo-decarbonylation in the primary act, leaving caged radicals which lead to the observed products through disproportionation.

$$\begin{array}{ccc} R' & O & O \\ | & \| & \| \\ RCOCO_2CH + h\nu \rightarrow CO + RCH + R'CR'' \\ | \\ R'' \end{array} \quad (1)$$

5-4 PRIMARY PHOTODISSOCIATIVE PROCESSES IN THE ALCOHOLS, ETHERS, AND PEROXIDES

The longest wavelength absorption band in the alcohols and ethers occurs. at wavelengths below 2000 A; it is of only moderate intensity ($\epsilon = 10^2$–10^3) (see Figs. 5-8 and 5-9). This band has been associated with an $n \rightarrow \sigma^*$ transition which involves the promotion of a non-bonding electron of the oxygen to an antibonding σ^* group orbital. Since the absorption in this band is not extremely intense, some forbidden character of the transition is suggested. This may arise because the σ^* level is composed largely of a

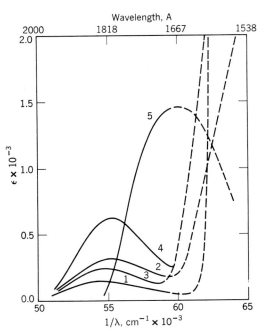

Fig. 5-8 Absorption spectra for (1) methanol [$CH_3OH(g)$]; (2) ethanol [$C_2H_5OH(g)$]; (3) 1-propanol [n-$C_3H_7OH(g)$]; (4) 2-propanol [$(CH_3)_2CHOH(g)$]; (5) water [$H_2O(g)$]. From Harrison, Cederholm, and Terwilliger.[425]

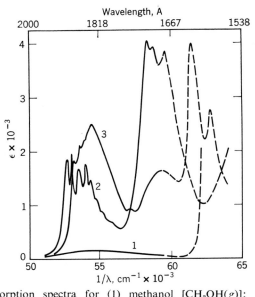

Fig. 5-9 Absorption spectra for (1) methanol [$CH_3OH(g)$]; (2) diethyl ether [$C_2H_5OC_2H_5(g)$]; (3) dimethyl ether [$CH_3OCH_3(g)$]. From Harrison and Price.[426]

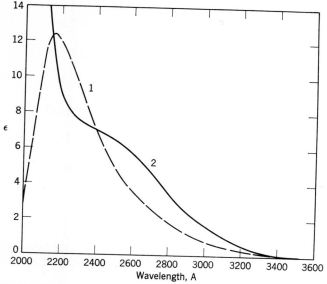

Fig. 5-10 Absorption spectra of:
(1) dimethyl peroxide $[CH_3OOCH_3(g)]$, from Takezaki, Miyazaki, and Nakahara;[173]
(2) di-*tert*-butyl peroxide $[(CH_3)_3COOC(CH_3)_3(g)]$, $25°$.[424]

p orbital in these compounds, and the $n \rightarrow \sigma^*$ transition has the character of a forbidden $p_{x,y} \rightarrow p_z$ atomic transition.

The alkyl peroxides absorb at much longer wavelengths than the ethers and alcohols. See the absorption spectrum of di-*tert*-butyl peroxide in Fig. 5-10. The peroxides contain two adjacent oxygen atoms with over-lapping lone-pair orbitals; this overlap gives rise to low-energy bonding and high-energy antibonding lone-pair molecular orbitals, both of which are filled with electrons. Thus in this class of compounds, the transitions may involve the two closer-lying levels, $\pi^*_{p_{x,y}} \rightarrow \sigma^*_{p_z}$, reflected in the absorption shift to the longer wavelengths.

5-4A Alcohols

In the higher alcohols, alternative free radical and intramolecular photodissociative processes may be used to explain the products. Either processes XVII and XVIII, followed by appropriate decompositions or disproportionation reactions of non-thermally equilibrated radicals, or processes XIX, XX, and XXI are possible. These reactions are formulated here for the normal alcohols; presumably analogous reactions are important in the branched-chain molecules.

$$RCH_2CH_2OH + h\nu \rightarrow RCH_2CH_2{}^{\ddagger} + OH^{\ddagger} \qquad (XVII)$$
$$\downarrow$$
$$R + CH_2CH_2$$

$$RCH_2CH_2O^{\ddagger} + H \qquad (XVIII)$$
$$\downarrow$$
$$RCH_2 + CH_2O$$

$$RCH{=}CH_2 + H_2O \qquad (XIX)$$

$$RCH_2CHO + H_2 \qquad (XX)$$

$$RCH_3 + CH_2O \qquad (XXI)$$

The only definitive study of primary processes in alcohols has been made with the simplest alcohol, methanol. In this case at the longer wavelengths, 1800–2000 A, process XX is dominant and XVIII probably occurs but at a lower quantum efficiency. Process XVII may become important at the shorter wavelengths, 1300–1500 A.

1. Methanol:[130,162–164] first absorption band shown in Figs. 5-8 and 5-9; $\lambda_{max} \cong 1835$ A, $\epsilon \cong 150$; second more intense band below 1600 A. In solid state at 85°K, full mercury arc gives para-H_2. 1800–2000 A, process 1 dominant, 2 occurs at lower efficiency, 3 unimportant; 1300–1500 A, excited $OH^{\ddagger}$ emission suggests importance of 3.

$$CH_3OH + h\nu \rightarrow CH_2O + H_2 \qquad (1)$$
$$CH_3O^{\ddagger} + H \qquad (2)$$
$$CH_3 + OH^{\ddagger} \qquad (3)$$

2. Ethanol:[162] first absorption band shown in Fig. 5-8; H_2-discharge lamp, $(\lambda > 1520$ A$)$, major ultraviolet absorbing products are C_2H_4, CH_3CHO, and CH_2O; not a clear choice between possible free radical, 1 and 2, and intramolecular processes, 3, 4, and 5.

$$C_2H_5OH + h\nu \rightarrow C_2H_5{}^{\ddagger} \text{ (or } C_2H_4 + H) + OH \qquad (1)$$
$$CH_3CH_2O^{\ddagger} \text{ (or } CH_3 + CH_2O) + H \qquad (2)$$
$$C_2H_4 + H_2O \qquad (3)$$
$$CH_3CHO + H_2 \qquad (4)$$
$$CH_4 + CH_2O \qquad (5)$$

3. n-Propyl alcohol:[162] first absorption band shown in Fig. 5-8; H_2-discharge lamp ($\lambda > 1520$ A), major ultraviolet absorbing products are C_2H_4, CH_3CH_2CHO, and CH_2O; importance of alternative free radical and intramolecular rearrangement processes not clear.

$$CH_3CH_2CH_2OH + h\nu \rightarrow CH_3CH_2CH_2^+ \text{ (or } C_2H_4 + CH_3) + OH \quad (1)$$

$$CH_3CH_2CH_2O^+ \text{ (or } C_2H_5 + CH_2O) + H \quad (2)$$

$$CH_2CH_2CHO + H_2 \quad (3)$$

$$C_3H_6 + H_2O \quad (4)$$

$$C_2H_6 + CH_2O \quad (5)$$

4. tert-Butyl alcohol:[162] absorption as in CH_3OH; H_2-discharge lamp ($\lambda > 1520$ A), major ultraviolet absorbing product is CH_3COCH_3; iso-C_4H_8 uncertain. Choice between 1, 2, and 3, 4 not clear.

$$(CH_3)_3COH + h\nu \rightarrow (CH_3)_3CO^+ \text{ (or } CH_3COCH_3 + CH_3) + H \quad (1)$$

$$(CH_3)_3C^+ \text{ (or iso-}C_4H_8 + H) + OH \quad (2)$$

$$CH_3COCH_3 + CH_4 \quad (3)$$

$$\text{iso-}C_4H_8 + H_2O \quad (4)$$

5. Phenol:[167–169] first absorption region shown in Fig. 5-27; $\lambda_{max} \cong 2780$, $\epsilon = 2 \times 10^3$; second band below 2380 A; in H_2O solution, decrease in basicity of the oxygen of the excited molecule is observed; similar process in related compounds; R represents a phenyl or substituted aromatic system.

$$ROH + h\nu \rightarrow ROH^*$$
$$\Updownarrow {}_{(H_2O)}$$
$$RO^{-*} + H_3O^+$$
$$\downarrow$$
$$RO^- + h\nu'$$
$$\Updownarrow {}_{(H_2O)}$$
$$ROH + OH^-$$

5-4B Ethers

The photodecomposition modes of the simple ethers cannot be resolved completely from the limited data at hand. Again both free radical and intramolecular processes can explain the product distribution. The extent of each is uncertain in most cases.

$$RCH_2CH_2OCH_2CH_2R + h\nu \rightarrow RCH_2CH_2O^{\ddagger} + CH_2CH_2R^{\ddagger} \qquad (XXII)$$

$$RCH_2 + CH_2O \qquad CH_2CH_2 + R$$

$$RCH{=}CH_2 + HOCH_2CH_2R \qquad (XXIII)$$

$$RCH_2CHO + CH_3CH_2R \qquad (XXIV)$$

The cyclic ethers show some interesting trends with increasing ring size; ethylene oxide decomposition appears to be largely a molecular rearrangement process resulting in free radical formation, while the trimethylene oxides (oxetanes) appear to rearrange in the primary process to stable molecules, although the formation of a very transient diradical precursor to final products cannot be excluded.

1. Dimethyl ether:[162] first absorption bands shown in Fig. 5-9; H_2-discharge lamp ($\lambda < 1920$ A), major product which absorbs ultraviolet light is CH_2O; both processes 1 and 2 possible.

$$CH_3OCH_3 + h\nu \rightarrow CH_3O^{\ddagger} \text{ (or } CH_2O + H) + CH_3 \qquad (1)$$

$$CH_2O + CH_4 \qquad (2)$$

2. Diethyl ether:[162] first absorption band shown in Fig. 5-9; H_2-discharge lamp ($\lambda < 1920$ A), major products absorbing in ultraviolet, C_2H_4, CH_3CHO, and CH_2O; processes 1, 2, and 3 possible; choice not clear.

$$C_2H_5OC_2H_5 + h\nu \rightarrow C_2H_5^{\ddagger} \text{ (or } C_2H_4 + H) + OC_2H_5^{\ddagger} \text{ (or } CH_3 + CH_2O)$$
$$(1)$$

$$C_2H_5OH + C_2H_4 \qquad (2)$$

$$CH_3CHO + C_2H_6 \qquad (3)$$

3. Ethyl vinyl ether:[165] full mercury arc, processes 1 and 2 major; process 2 probably involves cyclic, six-membered ring intermediate; 3 or other H_2-forming process of minor importance.

$$CH_3CH_2OCH{=}CH_2 + h\nu \rightarrow CH_2{=}CHO + C_2H_5 \qquad (1)$$

$$CH_3CHO + C_2H_4 \qquad (2)$$

$$H_2 + CH_2{=}CHOCH{=}CH_2(?) \qquad (3)$$

4. Diphenyl ether:[166] full mercury arc, isopropanol solution, 25°, *p*-hydroxydiphenyl and phenol major products; similarly phenyl benzyl ether gives *p*-benzylphenol and phenol; phenyl allyl ether gives *p*-allylphenol and phenol.

5. Ethylene oxide:[170,171] longest wavelength discontinuous absorption at 1713 A, broadens with increase in pressure so that there is an apparent continuum to 2120 A; a second band begins at 1570 A, and the third of higher extinction at 1440 A; $\lambda < 2000$ A, primary process 1 appears to be major; intermediate, highly excited CH_3CHO molecule possible, but no direct experimental evidence of this.

$$\overline{CH_2CH_2O} + h\nu \rightarrow CH_3 + CHO \text{ (or H + CO)} \tag{1}$$

6. Oxetane:[172] first absorption band below 2500 A, $\lambda_{max} \cong 1830$ A, $\epsilon = 2 \times 10^3$; shoulder in band at 2200 A, $\epsilon \cong 2$; full mercury arc, major process 1; in isooctane or H_2O solutions, same process likely.

$$\overline{CH_2CH_2CH_2O} + h\nu \rightarrow C_2H_4 + CH_2O \tag{1}$$

7. 2,2-Dimethyloxetane:[172] absorption similar to oxetane; full mercury arc, $\overline{\varphi}_1/\overline{\varphi}_2 \cong 0.85$.

$$\overline{CH_2CH_2C(CH_3)_2O} + h\nu \rightarrow CH_2O + CH_2{=}C(CH_3)_2 \tag{1}$$
$$\searrow$$
$$CH_3COCH_3 + C_2H_4 \tag{2}$$

8. 2-Phenyloxetane:[172] full mercury arc, isooctane solution, $\overline{\varphi}_1/\overline{\varphi}_2 \cong 3.5$.

$$\overline{CH_2CH_2CH(C_6H_5)O} + h\nu \rightarrow CH_2O + CH_2{=}CHC_6H_5 \tag{1}$$
$$\searrow$$
$$C_6H_5CHO + C_2H_4 \tag{2}$$

5-4C Peroxides

In the first absorption region of the alkyl and aryl peroxides (see Fig. 5-10) the primary photodissociation proceeds with rupture of the weak RO—OR' bond.

$$ROOR' + h\nu \rightarrow RO^{\ddagger} + R'O^{\ddagger} \tag{XXV}$$

Relatively large excess energies are carried off by the separating radicals: 56 kcal/mole at 3130 A, 78 kcal/mole at 2537 A. This results in significant fragmentation of the radicals before equilibration occurs in gas-phase photolyses. An alternative primary process which results in the direct formation of radical fragmentation products without the intermediate excited radicals $RO^{\ddagger}$ and $R'O^{\ddagger}$ is inconsistent with the observed collisional deactivation of the excited radicals at high moderating gas pressures and in solution. In the following summary, α represents the fraction of the radicals which decompose in an early vibration following the primary process XXV. Note the interesting difference in the radical fragmentation patterns as wavelength is changed; for example, see ethyl-*tert*-pentyl peroxide below.

At wavelengths below about 2300 A, a new primary dissociative mode appears in the alkyl peroxides, process XXVI.

$$ROOR' + h\nu \rightarrow RO_2^{\ddagger} + R' \text{ (or } R + R' + O_2) \qquad \text{(XXVI)}$$

1. Dimethyl peroxide:[173] first absorption region, 3500–2000 A, $\lambda_{max} \cong$ 2150 A; see Fig. 5-10; 2537 A, process 1 dominant; fragmentation of $CH_3O^{\ddagger}$ extensive ($\alpha \cong 1$); $\epsilon = 4.8$.

$$CH_3OOCH_3 + h\nu \rightarrow CH_3O^{\ddagger} \text{ (or } CH_2O + H) + CH_3O^{\ddagger} \qquad (1)$$

2. Diethyl peroxide:[174,187] absorption similar to dimethyl peroxide; limited information available consistent with process 1; absorption of Schumann-ultraviolet light yields an electronically excited C_2H_5O which fluoresces.

$$C_2H_5OOC_2H_5 + h\nu \rightarrow C_2H_5O^{\ddagger} \text{ (or } CH_2O + CH_3) + C_2H_5O^{\ddagger} \qquad (1)$$

3. Ethyl tert-pentyl peroxide:[175] absorption similar to dimethyl peroxide; process 1 dominant, 2537–3130 A; C_2H_5O apparently formed unexcited; a fraction of the non-thermally equilibrated radicals, $C_2H_5C(CH_3)_2O^{\ddagger}$, decompose by one of two paths in an early vibration following 1; 3130 A, $\alpha = 0.21$ (26°, 39 mm), $\alpha_a/\alpha_b = 16$ (26°); 2537 A, $\alpha = 0.60$ (26°, 39 mm), $\alpha_a/\alpha_b = 10$ (26°), 8.3 (73°).

$$C_2H_5OOC(CH_3)_2C_2H_5 + h\nu \rightarrow C_2H_5O + OC(CH_3)_2C_2H_5^{\ddagger} \qquad (1)$$
$$\text{(a)} \downarrow \qquad\qquad\qquad | \text{(b)}$$
$$C_2H_5 + CH_3COCH_3 \qquad |$$
$$\downarrow$$
$$CH_3 + C_2H_5COCH_3$$

4. Diisopropyl peroxide:[175,176] absorption similar to dimethyl peroxide; 3130 A, process 1 dominant, $\varphi_2 = 0$, $\alpha = 0.21$ (26°, 39 mm); 2537 A, $\varphi_1 \cong 1$, $\varphi_2 = 0$, $\alpha = 0.60$ (26°, 39 mm); 1900–2300 A, $\bar{\varphi}_2/\bar{\varphi}_1 \cong 0.01$–0.06.

$$(CH_3)_2CHOOCH(CH_3)_2 + h\nu \rightarrow (CH_3)_2CHO^{\ddagger} + (CH_3)_2CHO^{\ddagger} \qquad (1)$$
$$\searrow$$
$$CH_3 + CH_3CHO$$
$$\searrow$$
$$(CH_3)_2CHO_2^{\ddagger} + (CH_3)_2CH \qquad (2)$$
$$\searrow$$
$$(CH_3)_2CH + O_2$$

5. *Isopropyl tert-butyl peroxide:*[175] absorption similar to dimethyl peroxide; 2537 A, α (iso-C_3H_7O) = 0.72 (26°, 39 mm); α (*tert*-C_4H_9O) = 0.64 (26°, 39 mm).

$$(CH_3)_2CHOOC(CH_3)_3 + h\nu \rightarrow (CH_3)_2CHO^\ddagger + OC(CH_3)_3^\ddagger \qquad (1)$$

$$\downarrow \qquad\qquad \downarrow$$

$$CH_3 + CH_3CHO \quad CH_3COCH_3 + CH_3$$

6. *Di-tert-butyl peroxide:*[177–183] first absorption band shown in Fig. 5-10; values of ϵ: 0.9 (3051 A), 1.6 (3011 A), 2.5 (2894 A), 3.3 (2800 A), 4.0 (2753 A), 4.5 (2699 A), 5.4 (2625 A), 6.4 (2535 A), 7.1 (2447 A); 2537 A, $\varphi_1 = 1.0$; $\alpha = 0.62$ (26°, 22 mm), 0.56 (26°, 35 mm), 0.53 (26°, 39 mm), 0.62 (77°, 39 mm), $\varphi_2 = 0.0$; full mercury arc (3300–1900 A), $\bar{\varphi}_2/\bar{\varphi}_1 \cong 0.1$; decomposition of *tert*-C_4H_9O is unimportant in the liquid phase.

$$(CH_3)_3COOC(CH_3)_3 + h\nu \rightarrow (CH_3)_3CO^\ddagger + OC(CH_3)_3^\ddagger \qquad (1)$$

$$\searrow$$

$$CH_3COCH_3 + CH_3$$

$$(CH_3)_3CO_2{}^\ddagger + (CH_3)_3C \qquad (2)$$

$$\searrow$$

$$(CH_3)_3C + O_2$$

7. *Dicumyl peroxide:*[184] first absorption band, 3200–2400 A, $\lambda_{max} \cong$ 2570, $\epsilon \cong 415$; second band below 2400 A; in *n*-hexane or CCl_4 solvent, 20°, process 1 dominant at both 3130 and 2537 A; cumyloxy radicals formed at 3130 A fragment favoring path (a); presumably path (b) favored at 2537 A.

$$C_6H_5C(CH_3)_2OOC(CH_3)_2C_6H_5 + h\nu \rightarrow 2C_6H_5C(CH_3)_2O^\ddagger \qquad (1)$$

$$\text{(a)} \swarrow \qquad \searrow \text{(b)}$$

$$C_6H_5COCH_3 + CH_3 \quad CH_3COCH_3 + C_6H_5$$

8. *tert-Butyl hydroperoxide:*[185] first absorption band, $\lambda < 3200$ A, continuously increasing absorption to 2000 A, no maximum; $\epsilon \cong 6$ (2600 A), ~ 17 (2400 A), ~ 70 (2000 A); 3130 A, CCl_4, *n*-hexane, or dioxane solution, $\varphi_1 \cong 1$; primary process similar at 2450–2800 A.

$$(CH_3)_3COOH + h\nu \rightarrow (CH_3)_3CO^\ddagger + OH \qquad (1)$$

$$\searrow$$

$$CH_3COCH_3 + CH_3$$

9. *Cumene hydroperoxide:*[184] first absorption band, 3200–2300 A, structured, $\lambda_{max} \cong 2580$ A, $\epsilon \cong 200$; second band, $\lambda < 2300$ A; 3130 A,

in CCl_4 solution, $\varphi_1 \geqslant 0.8$ (20°).

$$C_6H_5C(CH_3)_2OOH + h\nu \rightarrow C_6H_5C(CH_3)_2O^{\ddagger} + OH \qquad (1)$$

(a) ↙   ↘ (b)

$$C_6H_5COCH_3 + CH_3 \qquad CH_3COCH_3 + C_6H_5$$

10. *Acetyl peroxide:*[186] first absorption band in cyclohexane begins $\sim$2800 A and increases continuously to below 2400 A; $\epsilon \cong 20$ (2650 A), $\sim$56 (2500 A), $\sim$89 (2400 A); full mercury arc, pure liquid, solid, or solutions in cyclohexane and ethanol, process 1 dominant; $CH_3CO_2^{\ddagger}$ very unstable and dissociates in an early vibration.

$$CH_3\overset{O}{\overset{\|}{C}}OO\overset{O}{\overset{\|}{C}}CH_3 + h\nu \rightarrow 2CH_3CO_2^{\ddagger} \rightarrow 2CH_3 + 2CO_2 \qquad (1)$$

11. *Dibenzoyl peroxide:*[188] first absorption band, 3000–2550 A, $\lambda_{max} \cong$ 2750 A, $\epsilon = 2.3 \times 10^3$; a second band below 2550 A, $\lambda_{max} = 2300$ A, $\epsilon = 2.7 \times 10^4$; full mercury arc, Pyrex filter ($\lambda \sim 3000$ A), solutions in benzene and styrene, process 1 dominant; $\alpha = 0.30$ (25–40°).

$$C_6H_5\overset{O}{\overset{\|}{C}}OO\overset{O}{\overset{\|}{C}}C_6H_5 + h\nu \rightarrow C_6H_5CO_2^{\ddagger} + C_6H_5CO_2^{\ddagger} \qquad (1)$$

↘

$$C_6H_5 + CO_2$$

12. *Anisoyl peroxide:*[188] full mercury arc, Pyrex filter ($\lambda \sim 3000$ A), process 1 important; $\alpha \cong 0.07$ (25°).

$$(p\text{-}CH_3OC_6H_4\overset{O}{\overset{\|}{C}}O\text{-})_2 + h\nu \rightarrow p\text{-}CH_3OC_6H_4CO_2^{\ddagger} + p\text{-}CH_3OC_6H_4CO_2^{\ddagger}$$

↘

$$p\text{-}CH_3OC_6H_4 + CO_2 \qquad (1)$$

5-5 NITROGEN-CONTAINING ORGANIC COMPOUNDS

The longest-wavelength absorption found in the aliphatic amines lies below 2500 A. It is of moderate intensity, $\epsilon \sim 10^2$–10^3, with the first maximum near 2200 A; see the spectra of Figs. 5-11 and 5-12. Presumably this absorption is associated with the promotion of a nitrogen-atom non-bonding electron to a σ^* group orbital, that is, an $n \rightarrow \sigma^*$ transition. The loss of this band in acid solution reflects the lowering of the energy of the lone-pair electrons as the new bond involving these electrons is made: $R_3N: + H^+ \rightarrow R_3N:H^+$. The hydrazines absorb at somewhat longer wavelengths than the amines, and the absorption character may be related to the adjacent lone-pair electron system of the nitrogen atoms in a fashion similar to that described for the peroxide system.

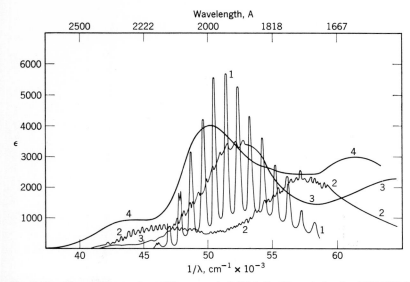

Fig. 5-11 Absorption spectra of (1) ammonia [$NH_3(g)$]; (2) methylamine [$CH_3NH_2(g)$]; (3) dimethylamine [$(CH_3)_2NH(g)$]; (4) trimethylamine [$(CH_3)_3N(g)$]. From Tannenbaum, Coffin, and Harrison.[427]

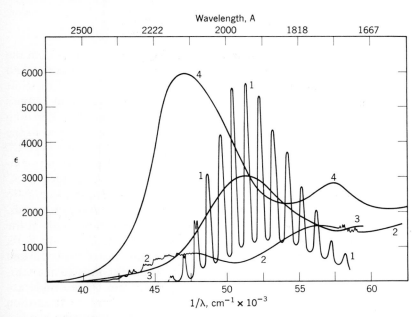

Fig. 5-12 Absorption spectra of (1) ammonia [$NH_3(g)$]; (2) ethylamine [$C_2H_5NH_2(g)$]; (3) diethylamine [$(C_2H_5)_2NH(g)$]; (4) triethylamine [$(C_2H_5)_3N(g)$]. From Tannenbaum, Coffin, and Harrison.[427]

451

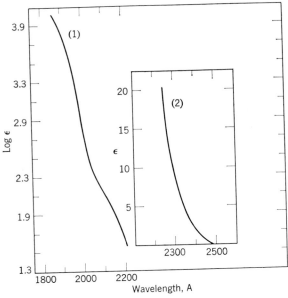

Fig. 5-13 Absorption spectrum of acetamide [CH₃CONH₂] in aqueous solution. (1) From Ley and Azends;[144] (2) from Ramart-Lucas.[429]

The amides show absorption at somewhat longer wavelengths than the amines ($\lambda < 2600$ A; see Fig. 5-13); the first band is attributed to an $n \rightarrow \pi^*$ transition involving the carbonyl group. In the amides the shift of the common carbonyl absorption band of the aldehydes and ketones occurs, as with the esters and acids, on substitution of an electron-donating group (NH₂). The $n \rightarrow \pi^*$ assignment of the first absorption band in the amides is reinforced by the fact that the intramolecular "Norrish Type II" rearrangement, found in aldehydes, ketones, and other carbonyl-containing compounds, also is present in the photolysis of the amides.

Compounds containing the double-bonded nitrogen groups, the imino (—C=N—), the azo (—N=N—), and the nitroso (—N=O) compounds, as well as the nitrites (RO—N=O), show weak absorption bands in the near-ultraviolet or the violet region of the spectrum; see Figs. 5-14, 5-16, and 5-18. In each case the longest-wavelength band appears to be related to an $n \rightarrow \pi^*$ transition of non-bonding nitrogen electrons to the antibonding π^* group orbital of the double-bond system. The visible absorption band of the nitroso group has been related to the $n \rightarrow \pi^*$ transition involving a nitrogen-atom lone-pair electron, and the ultraviolet band of this group is attributed to an $n \rightarrow \pi^*$ transition of an oxygen-atom lone-pair electron to the same antibonding π-group orbital; the higher electron

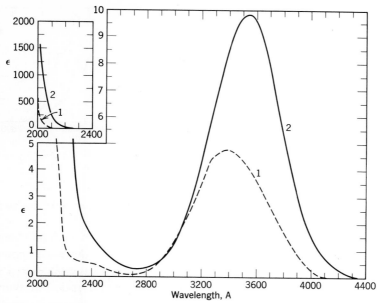

Fig. 5-14   Absorption spectra of (1) azomethane [$CH_3N{=}NCH_3(g)$], 25°; (2) azoethane [$C_2H_5N{=}NC_2H_5(g)$], 25°.[424]

affinity of the oxygen atom is reflected in the energy difference between these two transitions. This interpretation is consistent with the observed correspondence of the absorption of the nitro compounds ($R—NO_2$) and the nitrates ($R—ONO_2$) to that of the ultraviolet band of the $R—NO$ compounds; in the nitro compounds and the nitrates there are no lone-pair

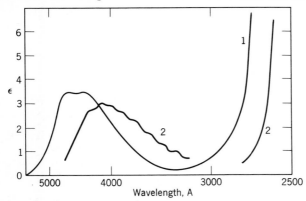

Fig. 5-15   Absorption spectra of (1) diazoethane [$CH_3CHN_2(g)$]; (2) diazomethane [$CH_2N_2(g)$], from Brinton and Volman.[239]

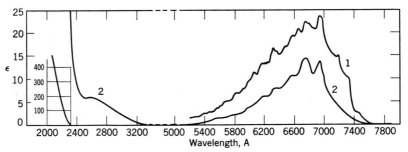

Fig. 5-16 Absorption spectra of (1) trifluoronitrosomethane [CF$_3$NO(g)], from Mason;[262] (2) 2-nitroso-2-methylpropane [(CH$_3$)$_3$CNO(g)], 25°.[424]

electrons on nitrogen and the transition is most likely an $n \to \pi^*$, involving oxygen-atom lone-pair electrons. See Figs. 5-16 and 5-17.

The nitrogen compounds which contain cumulative multiple bonds, for example, the azides (R—N=$\bar{\text{N}}$=N$^+$) and the diazo compounds (RCH=$\bar{\text{N}}$=N$^+$), show a weak absorption at longer wavelengths in the visible region ($\epsilon \sim 15$), and a somewhat stronger absorption at shorter

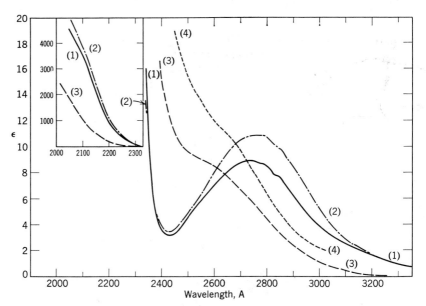

Fig. 5-17 Absorption spectra of (1) nitromethane [CH$_3$NO$_2$(g)], 25°; (2) nitroethane [C$_2$H$_5$NO$_2$(g)], 25°; (3) methyl nitrate [CH$_3$ONO$_2$(g)], 25°; (4) ethyl nitrate [C H$_5$ONO$_2$( )], 25°.[424]

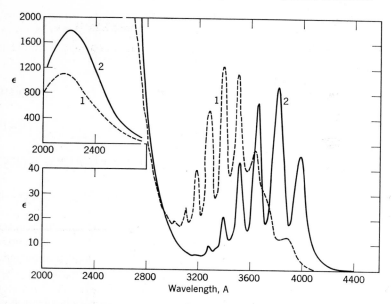

Fig. 5-18   Absorption spectra of (1) methyl nitrite [$CH_3ONO(g)$], 25°; (2) *tert*-butyl nitrite [$(CH_3)_3CONO(g)$], 25°.[424]

wavelengths; $n \rightarrow \pi^*$ transitions may be responsible for the weak absorption bands, but this is not clear. See Fig. 5-15.

The longest-wavelength absorption in the alkyl nitriles ($R—C\equiv N$) is a weak band in the vacuum ultraviolet ($\lambda_{max} \sim 1700$ A). It may originate from a $\pi \rightarrow \pi^*$ transition of the triple-bond system.

5-5A   The Amines and Hydrazines

The primary photodissociative processes of the amines are open to considerable question at this writing. Definitive studies have been made only of the simplest amine, methylamine. In this case, and apparently in the other primary aliphatic amines, photodissociation occurs largely by XXVII to form hydrogen atoms and RNH radicals.

$$RNH_2 + h\nu \rightarrow RNH + H \qquad (XXVIIa)$$

In the secondary aliphatic amines, dissociation of N—C bonds has been suggested in addition to hydrogen atom formation:

$$R_2NH + h\nu \rightarrow R_2N + H \qquad (XXVIIb)$$

$$\rightarrow R + RNH \qquad (XXVIIIa)$$

In the tertiary amines, process XXVIII dominates, but a small amount of hydrogen may be formed in a molecular rearrangement XXIX, and a down-chain cleavage of C-C bonds has been suggested as an additional minor process, XXX.

$$R_3N + h\nu \rightarrow R + R_2N \qquad\qquad \text{(XXVIIIb)}$$

$$\rightarrow H_2 + R_3N\,(-2H) \qquad\qquad \text{(XXIX)}$$

$$(RCH_2CH_2)_3N + h\nu \rightarrow RCH_2 + CH_2N(CH_2CH_2R)_2 \quad \text{(XXX)}$$

In the amine photolysis there is no analog to the "Norrish Type II" splits of the carbonyl-containing compounds.

The aromatic amines are considerably more stable photochemically than the aliphatic analogs. Fluorescence is a deactivation process encountered very commonly in these systems. However, at elevated temperatures dissociative processes XXVII and XXVIII may become important. Note in the following summary that in photolyses in rigid glasses at low temperatures, photoionization as well as photodissociation may occur in the aromatic amines.

The aryl-group-substituted hydrazines photodissociate at the weakest N—N bond:

$$R_2N\text{—}NR_2 + h\nu \rightarrow 2R_2N \qquad\qquad \text{(XXXI)}$$

Ions, rather than neutral free radicals, may form on cleavage of the bond in photolyses in rigid glasses at low temperatures.

The limited data on azines suggest the dominance of an intramolecular process XXXII, forming a nitrile and an imine in the primary step. Process XXXIII is less important at all wavelengths (3340–2380 A) but increases in significance at the shorter wavelengths.

$$RCH\text{=}N\text{—}N\text{=}CHR + h\nu \rightarrow RC\text{≡}N + HN\text{=}CHR \qquad \text{(XXXII)}$$

$$\rightarrow R + CH\text{=}N\text{—}N\text{=}CHR \qquad \text{(XXXIII)}$$

In the following summary also note the interesting photochromic behavior of certain *o*-hydroxy-substituted anils (p. 460).

1. Methylamine:[189–192] absorption spectrum shown in Fig. 5-11; 1940–2345 A, $\varphi_1 \geqslant 0.75$, $\varphi_2 \leqslant 0.07$, $\varphi_3 \leqslant 0.05$, $\varphi_4 \leqslant 0.03$, $\varphi_5 \leqslant 0.02$, $\varphi_6 \leqslant 0.05$;

$\Sigma\varphi_i \cong 0.97$; photochemistry of CD_3NH_2 and CH_3ND_2 similar.

$$CH_3NH_2 + h\nu \rightarrow CH_3NH + H \tag{1}$$

$$CH_2NH_2 + H \tag{2}$$

$$CH_3 + NH_2 \tag{3}$$

$$CH_3N + H_2 \tag{4}$$

$$CHNH_2 + H_2 \tag{5}$$

$$CH_2{=}NH + H_2 \tag{6}$$

2. Dimethylamine:[193] absorption spectrum shown in Fig. 5-11; full mercury arc, process 1 likely.

$$(CH_3)_2NH + h\nu \rightarrow (CH_3)_2N + H \tag{1}$$

3. Methylethylamine:[193,194] full mercury arc, hydrocarbon solvents, $\varphi_2/\varphi_1 \sim 0.03\text{--}0.08$.

$$CH_3NHC_2H_5 + h\nu \rightarrow H + CH_3NC_2H_5 \tag{1}$$

$$CH_3 + HNC_2H_5 \tag{2}$$

4. Trimethylamine:[193,195] first absorption region shown in Fig. 5-11; full mercury arc, process 1 important; $R_{H_2}/R_{CH_4} \cong 1.5$; nature of the H_2-forming process not clear, but conceivably analog to 5 in CH_3NH_2 photolysis is possible.

$$(CH_3)_3N + h\nu \rightarrow M^*(+N) \rightarrow M(+N')$$
$$CH_3 + N(CH_3)_2 \tag{1}$$

5. Triethylamine:[196] first absorption region shown in Fig. 5-12; full mercury arc, processes 1 and 2 major; $\varphi_2 > \varphi_1$, φ_3 small, H_2 yield independent of added NO.

$$(C_2H_5)_3N + h\nu \rightarrow C_6H_{13}N + H_2 \tag{1}$$

$$M^*(+N) \rightarrow M(+N')$$

$$(C_2H_5)_2N + C_2H_5 \tag{2}$$

$$(C_2H_5)_2NCH_2 + CH_3 \tag{3}$$

6. n-Butylamine:[193] full mercury arc:

$$n\text{-}C_4H_9NH_2 + h\nu \rightarrow H + n\text{-}C_4H_9NH \qquad (1)$$

7. n-Amylamine:[193] full mercury arc:

$$n\text{-}C_5H_{11}NH_2 + h\nu \rightarrow H + n\text{-}C_5H_{11}NH \qquad (1)$$

8. n-Hexylamine:[194] full mercury arc; hydrocarbon solvent:

$$n\text{-}C_6H_{13}NH_2 + h\nu \rightarrow H + n\text{-}C_6H_{13}NH \qquad (1)$$

9. Aniline:[197,198] first absorption region shown in Fig. 5-27; full magnesium spark, processes 1 and 2 unimportant at low temperatures but increase in significance at higher temperatures. Process 2 (and presumably a split of hydrogen from the phenyl group) becomes increasingly important at shorter wavelengths.

$$C_6H_5NH_2 + h\nu \rightarrow M^*(+N) \rightarrow M(+N')$$

$$\downarrow$$

$$M + h\nu'$$

$$H + C_6H_5NH \qquad (1)$$

$$C_6H_5 + NH_2 \qquad (2)$$

10. Diphenylamine:[202] full mercury arc, in EPA glass at 90°K:

$$(C_6H_5)_2NH + h\nu \rightarrow (C_6H_5)_2NH^+ + e^- \qquad (1)$$

$$(C_6H_5)_2NH^+ + h\nu \rightarrow (C_6H_5)_2N + H^+ \qquad (2)$$

$$(C_6H_5)_2N^-Li^+ + h\nu \rightarrow (C_6H_5)_2N + e^- + Li^+ \qquad (3)$$

11. Triphenylamine:[203,204] first band, 3450–2500 A; full mercury arc, in liquid phase or plastic film, photoionization occurs.

$$(C_6H_5)_3N + h\nu \rightarrow (C_6H_5)_3N^+ + e^- \qquad (1)$$

12. N,N,N',N'-Tetramethyl-p-phenylenediamine:[205] in 3-methylpentane glass, 77°K, process 1 occurs from a vibrationally non-equilibrated excited singlet state S_1^m, and φ_1 shows considerable variation with λ: $\varphi_1 \times 10^3 =$ 2.4 (2950 A), 5.4 (3000 A), 4.9 (3050 A), 3.2 (3100 A), 6.1 (3150 A), 1.9 (3200 A), 2.4 (3250 A), 1.8 (3300 A), 1.8 (3350 A), 0.89 (3400 A), 0.71 (3450 A). Fluorescence and phosphorescence efficiencies do not show the variation with λ evident in φ_1; presumably these emissions result from thermally equilibrated excited states.

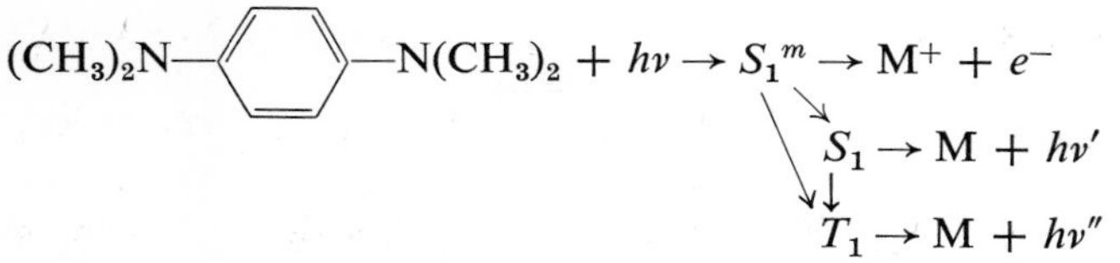

$$(CH_3)_2N\!-\!\langle\!\langle\ \rangle\!\rangle\!-\!N(CH_3)_2 + h\nu \rightarrow S_1{}^m \rightarrow M^+ + e^- \tag{1}$$

$$S_1 \rightarrow M + h\nu'$$

$$T_1 \rightarrow M + h\nu''$$

13. β-Naphthylamine:[199–201] fluorescence only observed. In aqueous solution, naphthyl ammonium ion and naphthylamine are much stronger acids in the excited state than in the ground state. α-Naphthylamine and N-methyl-β-naphthylamine show similar behavior.

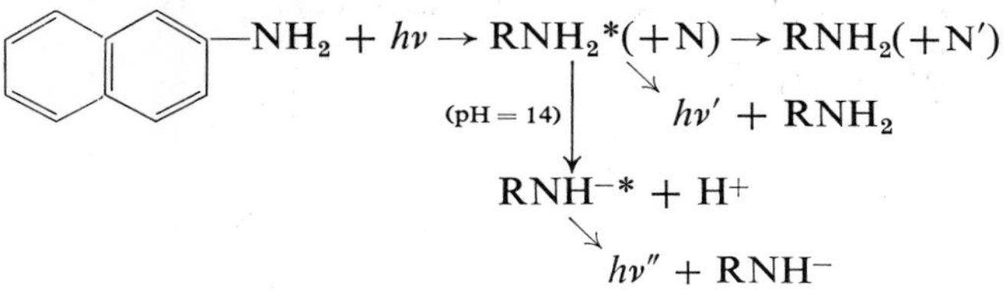

$$\text{(naphthyl)}\!-\!NH_2 + h\nu \rightarrow RNH_2{}^*(+N) \rightarrow RNH_2(+N')$$

$$\text{(pH = 14)} \qquad h\nu' + RNH_2$$

$$RNH^{-*} + H^+$$

$$h\nu'' + RNH^-$$

14. 1,1-Diphenylhydrazine:[202] full mercury arc, in EPA at 90°K:

$$(C_6H_5)_2NNH_2 + h\nu \rightarrow C_6H_5N^+ + NH_2{}^- \tag{1}$$

15. 1,2-Diphenylhydrazine:[206] 2300–2700 A, in alcohol:

$$C_6H_5NHNHC_6H_5 + h\nu \rightarrow 2C_6H_5NH \tag{2}$$

16. Tetraphenylhydrazine:[202] full mercury arc, in EPA glass at 90°K:

$$(C_6H_5)_2NN(C_6H_5)_2 + h\nu \rightarrow 2(C_6H_5)_2N \tag{1}$$

$$M^+ + e^- \tag{2}$$

$$(C_6H_5)_2N + (C_6H_5)_2N^+ \tag{3}$$

17. Acetaldazine:[207] first absorption region in hexane, 3500–2600 A, $\lambda_{max} \cong 2800$ A, $\epsilon = 86$; second band below 2600 A; process 1 dominant, 3 unimportant; $\varphi_1 = 0.45$ (3340 A), 0.50 (3130–3020 A), 0.27 (2537–2654 A), 0.18 (2380 A); $\varphi_2 \geqslant 0.005$ (3340 A), 0.04 (3020 A), 0.11 (2537 A), 0.12 (2380 A); $\varphi_3 \leqslant 0.02$ at all wavelengths.

$$CH_3CH\!=\!N\!-\!N\!=\!CHCH_3 + h\nu \rightarrow CH_3CN + CH_3CH\!=\!NH \tag{1}$$

$$CH_3 + CH\!=\!NN\!=\!CHCH_3 \tag{2}$$

$$2CHCH_3 + N_2 \tag{3}$$

18. Tetramethyltetrazene:[114] full mercury arc, rigid glass at 77°K:

$$(CH_3)_2N—N{=}N—N(CH_3)_2 + h\nu \rightarrow (CH_3)_2N—N{=}N + N(CH_3)_2 \quad (1)$$

19. Anils:[209-211,669-671,689,690] in solutions at temperatures below $-100°$, *trans* → *cis* isomerization occurs; with anils of aldehydes containing an *o*-hydroxy group (e.g., salicylaldehyde anils), photolysis involving hydrogen transfer to form deeply colored quinoid-type compounds occurs in pure solids or in matrix at low temperatures; the process is reversible on heating in the dark or on exposure to visible light; when the *o*-hydroxy group is methylated, photochromism is not observed. The isomerization occurs also in ethanol solution, but the re-formation of the anil occurs rapidly, and the process can only be observed with flash spectroscopic techniques.[720]

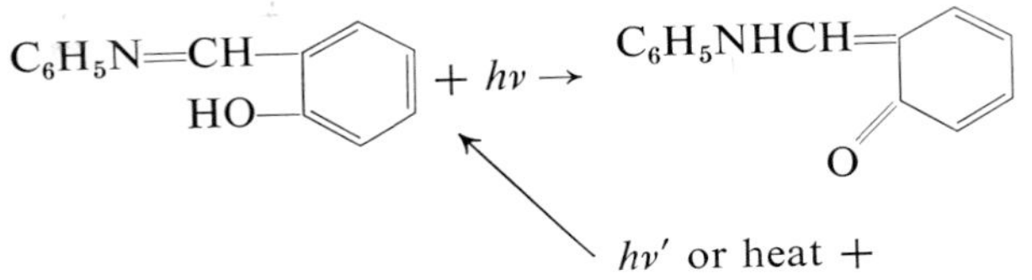

20. Pyrazine:[547] vapor-phase photolysis in the region of 1600 A apparently leads to overall process 1.

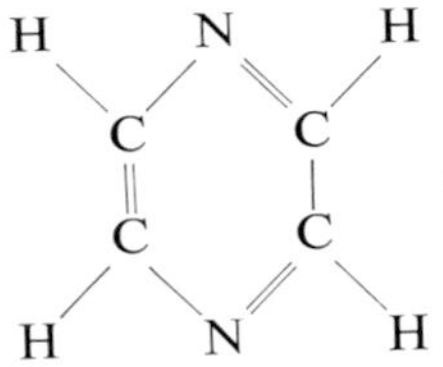

5-5B   The Amides

Although some major uncertainties remain concerning the primary processes in the photolyses of the amides, certain features of these processes are clear and may be generalized by the following reactions:

$$RCONH_2 + h\nu \rightarrow RCO^{\ddagger} \text{ (or } R + CO) + NH_2 \quad \text{(XXXIVa)}$$

$$\searrow R + CONH_2^{\ddagger} \text{ (or } CO + NH_2) \quad \text{(XXXIVb)}$$

$$RCH_2CH_2CH_2CONH_2 + h\nu \rightarrow RCH{=}CH_2 + CH_3CONH_2 \quad \text{(XXXV)}$$

Free radical formation by C-C and/or C-N bond cleavage next to the absorbing carbonyl group occurs in the photolysis of the amides, XXXIVa or b. Process XXXV is important in the higher amides and is the analog to the "Norrish Type II" split observed in other carbonyl-containing compounds; presumably it too involves the intermediate formation of the enol form of the carbonyl compound in the primary act, in this case the enol of acetamide. Intramolecular process XXXVI has been suggested as important in the photolysis of solutions of the simpler amides, but its significance in the higher amides is uncertain. Process XXXVII has been considered for photolyses in hexane or dioxane solution, but the evidence for it is not compelling; no analog exists in the other families of compounds, and it cannot be considered as established.

$$RCONH_2 + h\nu \rightarrow RCN + H_2O \qquad\qquad (XXXVI)$$
$$\searrow$$
$$RNH_2 + CO \quad (?) \qquad\qquad (XXXVII)$$

1. Acetamide:[194,212,213] absorption shown in Fig. 5-13; full mercury arc ($\lambda < 2600$ A), both processes 1 and 2 occur; process 3 is unimportant in H_2O solution and is of questionable importance in dioxane or hexane solutions.

$$CH_3CONH_2 + h\nu \rightarrow CH_3CN + H_2O \qquad\qquad (1)$$
$$\searrow$$
$$CH_3 + CONH_2 \text{ (or } CO + NH_2) \qquad (2a)$$
$$CH_3CO \text{ (or } CH_3 + CO) + NH_2 \qquad (2b)$$
$$CH_3NH_2 + CO \quad (?) \qquad\qquad (3)$$

2. Propionamide:[194] full mercury arc, dioxane solution, process 1 likely by analogy with acetamide; 2 uncertain.

$$C_2H_5CONH_2 + h\nu \rightarrow C_2H_5 + CONH_2 \text{ (or } CO + NH_2) \qquad (1)$$
$$\searrow$$
$$C_2H_5NH_2 + CO \quad (?) \qquad\qquad (2)$$

3. n-Butyramide:[194] full mercury arc, dioxane solution, processes 1 and 2 probably important, process 3 uncertain.

$$n\text{-}C_3H_7CONH_2 + h\nu \rightarrow n\text{-}C_3H_7 + CONH_2 \text{ (or } CO + NH_2) \quad (1)$$
$$\searrow$$
$$C_2H_4 + CH_3CONH_2 \qquad (2)^{21}$$
$$n\text{-}C_3H_7NH_2 + CO \quad (?) \qquad\qquad (3)$$

4. n-Valeramide:[194] as with *n*-butyramide above:

$$n\text{-}C_4H_9CONH_2 + h\nu \rightarrow n\text{-}C_4H_9 + CONH_2 \text{ (or } CO + NH_2) \quad (1)$$

$$C_3H_6 + CH_3CONH_2 \quad (2)^{21}$$

$$n\text{-}C_4H_9NH_2 + CO \quad (?) \quad (3)$$

5. n-Hexanoamide:[194] as with *n*-butyramide:

$$n\text{-}C_5H_{11}CONH_2 + h\nu \rightarrow n\text{-}C_5H_{11} + CONH_2 \text{ (or } CO + NH_2) \quad (1)$$

$$1\text{-}C_4H_8 + CH_3CONH_2 \quad (2)^{21}$$

5-5C   Azo Compounds

In the gas phase the primary processes in the alkyl azo compounds seem simple and well established. Dissociation into alkyl free radicals and nitrogen is the major dissociative process which has been observed, process XXXVIII. In most cases which have been studied, the primary efficiency of process XXXVIII approaches unity at low pressures. Collisional deactivation of the excited molecule lowers this efficiency noticeably at higher pressures, particularly in the higher alkyl azo compounds.

$$RN{=}NR + h\nu \rightarrow M^*(+N) \rightarrow M(+N')$$
$$R + N_2R \rightarrow 2R + N_2 \quad (XXXVIII)$$

The lifetime of the possible intermediate radical N_2R is so short that no evidence of its participation in reactions other than decomposition into N_2 and R has been observed, and the products of XXXVIII are usually considered to be represented well by the overall reaction, $RN{=}NR + h\nu \rightarrow 2R + N_2$. There is little evidence of non-thermalized radicals formed in XXXVIII; in fact, the disproportionation, combination, and decomposition reactions of the higher radicals formed in XXXVIII using 3660 A light appear to be those of thermal radicals at ordinary pressures of reactant. In view of these characteristics and the convenient near-ultraviolet absorption band of these compounds, they are a very common choice for the source of a desired alkyl free radical.

In the case of azomethane a primary process forming ethane and nitrogen in a concerted step seems to occur with a low quantum efficiency, 0.004–0.012, which depends in part on the wavelength of the absorbed light, pressure of reactant, etc. On the basis of this evidence, process XXXIX is suggested.

$$RN{=}NR + h\nu \rightarrow R_2 + N_2 \quad (XXXIX)$$

At this writing precise information on the importance of XXXIX with the larger azo compounds is limited; however, the almost complete suppression of R_2 product in experiments with added oxygen suggests that XXXIX is of very minor importance in azoethane and azoisobutane photolysis and, by analogy, probably with the other alkyl azo compounds.

In solution, azomethane, presumably the other alkyl azo compounds, and the aromatic azo compounds undergo *cis-trans* isomerization. The aromatic compounds show little decomposition into free radicals.

Azomethane, azoethane, and presumably other alkyl azo compounds quench the phosphorescence of triplet acetone or biacetyl with surprisingly high efficiency (higher than that of oxygen). The triplet azoalkane formed by the energy transfer either dissociates into free radicals and nitrogen (process XXXVIII) or is collisionally deactivated to the ground state.[715]

1. Azomethane:[214-219,491] first absorption band shown in Fig. 5-14; azomethane exists largely in the *trans* configuration under the usual conditions; 3660 A, $\varphi_1 = 1.0$ (0–630 mm, 25–200°); at 28°, $\varphi_2 = 0.0037$ (57 mm azo, 9.5 mm O_2), 0.0069 (222 mm azo, 25 mm O_2); Φ_{N_2} at 25° in degassed solutions of azomethane (5×10^{-3} M) in isooctane, ethanol, N,N-dimethylformamide, and water: 0.17, 0.07, 0.05, and 0.01 ± 0.01, respectively; ~3900 A, $\varphi_2 \cong 0.011$ (39°, 275 mm azo, 48 mm O_2); ~4000 A, $\varphi_2 \cong 0.012$ (41°, 243 mm azo, 45 mm O_2); *trans* ⇌ *cis* photoisomerization is the major reaction in solution and in the solid phase; *cis/trans* ratio at the photostationary state at 3660 A = 0.09 ± 0.01, independent of the temperature (−40 to +30°), in methanol; the base-catalyzed isomerization of the *cis* form occurs readily to give $CH_2{=}NNHCH_3$; the *trans* form reacts similarly but at 1/100 of the rate of the *cis* form.

$$CH_3N{=}NCH_3 + h\nu \rightarrow 2CH_3 + N_2 \qquad (1)$$
$$\searrow$$
$$C_2H_6 + N_2 \qquad (2)$$

2. Hexafluoroazomethane:[220,221] first absorption band, 4300–3050 A, $\epsilon_{max} = 1.7$; second band, 3000–2200 A, $\epsilon_{max} = 1.8$; third band, very intense below 2200 A; 2537 A, $\varphi_1 \cong 0.25$ (280–500 mm, 25°).

$$CF_3N{=}NCF_3 + h\nu \rightarrow M^*(+N) \rightarrow M(+N')$$
$$\searrow\downarrow$$
$$2CF_3 + N_2 \qquad (1)$$

3. Azoethane:[222-225] absorption shown in Fig. 5-14; 3660 A, $\varphi_1 = 0.59$ (28°, 135 mm), 0.85 (28°, 13 mm), 0.85 (152°, 165 mm), 1.0 (150°, 18 mm);

$\varphi_2 \leqslant 0.001$ (25°, 25 mm).

$$C_2H_5N{=}NC_2H_5 + h\nu \rightarrow M^*(+N) \rightarrow M(+N')$$
$$\searrow \downarrow$$
$$2C_2H_5 + N_2 \qquad (1)$$

$$C_4H_{10} + N_2 \qquad (2)$$

4. *Azo-n-propane:*[226] 3660 A, n-C_3H_7 radicals formed in process 1 react as thermally equilibrated radicals for normal pressures of reactant (11 mm).

$$CH_3CH_2CH_2N{=}NCH_2CH_2CH_3 + h\nu \rightarrow M^*(+N) \rightarrow M(+N')$$
$$\searrow \downarrow$$
$$2\ n\text{-}C_3H_7 + N_2 \qquad (1)$$

5. *Azoisopropane:*[227,228] first absorption band, 3900–2900 A, $\lambda_{max} =$ 3540 A; 3660 A, $\varphi_1 = 0.73$ (35°, 5 mm), 0.31 (35°, 43 mm), 0.56 (127°, 6 mm), 0.42 (127°, 49 mm), 1.0 (pressure $\rightarrow 0$).

$$(CH_3)_2CHN{=}NCH(CH_3)_2 + h\nu \rightarrow M^*(+N) \rightarrow M(+N')$$
$$\searrow \downarrow$$
$$2CH_3CHCH_3 + N_2 \qquad (1)$$

6. *1,1'-Azo-n-butane:*[229] 3660 A, $\varphi_1 = 0.048$ (51°, 5.7 mm), 0.060 (77°, 5.6 mm), 0.12 (108°, 8.7 mm), 0.39 (104°, 1.5 mm), 0.19 (127°, 6.4 mm), 0.35 (166°, 6.7 mm), 0.83 (202°, 7.0 mm), 0.90 (202°, 4.5 mm), 1.0 (high temperature and/or low pressure). Irradiation with a sunlamp, CCl_4 solution, forms the photoisomerization product, n-butyl-n-butylidene-hydrazine.[389] This product may arise in the base-catalyzed isomerization of the *cis* form of the azo compound produced photochemically; see the discussion of azomethane.

$$n\text{-}C_4H_9N{=}NC_4H_9 + h\nu \rightarrow M^*(+N) \rightarrow M(+N')$$
$$\searrow \downarrow$$
$$2\ n\text{-}C_4H_9 + N_2 \qquad (1)$$

7. *2,2'-Azoisobutane:*[230] 3660 A, $\varphi_1 \cong 0.63$ (25°, 20 mm); $\varphi_2 \cong 0.00$.

$$(CH_3)_3CN{=}NC(CH_3)_3 + h\nu \rightarrow M^*(+N) \rightarrow M(+N')$$
$$\searrow \downarrow$$
$$2(CH_3)_3C + N_2 \qquad (1)$$

$$(CH_3)_3CC(CH_3)_3 + N_2 \qquad (2)$$

8. 2,2′-Azoisobutyronitrile:[231,232] in benzene solution, $\epsilon = 0.85$ (4000 A), 11.9 (3600 A), 14.7 (3475 A), 11.6 (3300 A), 4.35 (3100 A); 3660 A, $\varphi_1 = 0.43$.

$$(CH_3)_2C(CN)N{=}NC(CN)(CH_3)_2 + h\nu \rightarrow M^*(+N) \rightarrow M(+N')$$
$$\searrow \downarrow$$
$$2(CH_3)_2CCN + N_2 \qquad (1)$$

9. 2,3-Diazabicyclo[2.2.1]-2-heptene:[706] the variation of the yields of products *A*, *B*, and *C* at 44° as a function of pressure (10 − 1000 μ) and wavelength (3370, 3130 A) is consistent with the decomposition of the electronically excited reactant (M*) to form the vibrationally non-equilibrated initial product $A^{\ddagger}$ which reacts by the sequence shown. $\varphi_1 \sim 1$ in solution.

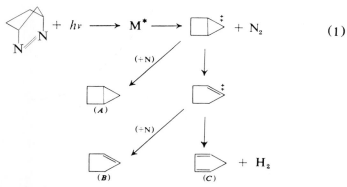

$$(1)$$

10. Azobenzene:[233,234] portion of spectrum shown in Fig. 5-29 for *trans* compound; first absorption region in ethanol, 5500–3700 A, $\lambda_{\max} = 4432$ A, $\epsilon = 510$; second region, 3700–2500 A, $\lambda_{\max} = 3196$ A, $\epsilon = 21{,}300$; *cis* compound, two absorption regions similar but $\lambda_{\max} = 4327$ A, $\epsilon = 1518$; $\lambda_{\max} = 2806$ A, $\epsilon = 5260$; in isooctane solution, 25°, at 5460, 4360, and 4050 A, $\varphi_1 = 0.48$, $\varphi_2 = 0.24$; at 2540 and 3130 A, $\varphi_1 = 0.42$, $\varphi_2 = 0.11$. M* and M** represent different electronic states of undefined nature. (Other aromatic azo compounds show similar photo-isomerization;[235–237] dissociative processes may occur at the shorter wavelengths in some compounds.)

$$cis\text{-}C_6H_5N{=}NC_6H_5 + h\nu \rightarrow M^*(+N) \rightarrow M(+N')$$
$$\searrow \downarrow$$
$$trans\text{-}C_6H_5N{=}NC_6H_5 \qquad (1)$$

$$trans\text{-}C_6H_5N{=}NC_6H_5 + h\nu \rightarrow M^{**}(+N) \rightarrow M(+N')$$
$$\searrow \downarrow$$
$$cis\text{-}C_6H_5N{=}NC_6H_5 \qquad (2)$$

11. Azoxymethane:[716] full mercury arc, N_2, N_2O, CH_4, and C_2H_6 are major products; $\Phi_{N_2}/\Phi_{N_2O} = 0.20 \pm 0.02$, independent of temperature $(27 - 121°)$; primary processes 1 and 2 are likely.

$$CH_3—N{=}N—CH_3 + h\nu \rightarrow CH_3 + N_2O + CH_3 \qquad (1)$$
$$\underset{O}{\big\downarrow} \qquad\qquad\searrow \quad CH_3 + N_2 + OCH_3 \qquad (2)$$

5-5D   Diazo Compounds

The most important primary photodissociative process of the diazo compounds, generalized as $R_2C{=}\overset{-}{N}{=}N^+$, is XL.

$$R_2C{=}\overset{-}{N}{=}N^+ + h\nu \rightarrow R_2C{:}^{\ddagger} + N_2 \qquad (XL)$$

In the simplest diazo compound, diazomethane (CH_2N_2), there is considerable evidence that the species $CH_2{:}$, formed as the primary product in XL, is predominantly in the singlet state (sometimes designated as a carbene); for example, the stereospecificity of the addition of $CH_2{:}$ to olefins and the spin conservation of the overall reaction XL support this view. The gas-phase equilibrium of $CH_2{:}$ with inert gas generates the lower-lying triplet ground-state methylene diradical, $\cdot CH_2 \cdot$. It is interesting that the triplet radical can be formed directly from diazomethane by radiationless transfer of energy from the excited triplet state of benzophenone.[119] See the discussions of diazomethane, pp. 467, 554.

With diazoethane (and probably with the higher diazo compounds) the initial vibrationally excited primary product of XL, $CH_3CH{:}^{\ddagger}$, undergoes extensive isomerization to ethylene and decomposition to acetylene and hydrogen. An unresolved alternative explanation (considered less probable) involves formation of olefin or acetylene and hydrogen in concerted intramolecular primary processes.

The quantum yields of decomposition of a variety of substituted diazomethanes have been determined in methanol solutions and are listed in the following summary.[253] The substitution of very different R groups in $RCH{=}N{=}N$ does not affect φ_{XL} strongly, although some subtle effects are present. A qualitative correlation between Hammett-σ values and the size of φ_{XL} has been suggested.[254] Since σ reflects the ground-state singlet electronic distribution and the data for φ_{XL} are from electronically excited molecules, the fact that a reasonably good correlation is seen is somewhat surprising; it has been suggested that the excited electronic state involved (presumed to be the triplet) has an electronic distribution which is very similar to that of the ground-state singlet. In any case, as the electron-donating power of the attached groups R is increased, the greater is the quantum yield of decomposition by XL.

1a. Diazomethane:[238-245] first absorption band shown in Fig. 5-15; process 1 dominant; $\Phi_{N_2} \sim 4$ (may be in error because of ϵ used).[238,239] Photolysis at the longer wavelengths forms some triplet radical ($\cdot CH_2 \cdot$) in the primary step, presumably from the dissociation of triplet diazomethane in process 2; at 4358 A, $\varphi_2/\varphi_1 \sim 0.2$.[701]

$$CH_2N_2 + h\nu \rightarrow CH_2N_2(S_1) \rightarrow CH_2: + N_2 \qquad (1)$$
$$\downarrow \qquad\qquad \downarrow_{(+N)}$$
$$CH_2N_2(T_1) \rightarrow \cdot CH_2 \cdot + N_2 \qquad (2)$$

1b. Diazarine(cyclodiazomethane):[247,743] first absorption region 3000 – 3700 A; Pyrex-filtered mercury arc ($\sim$3130 A), process 1 dominant; photoisomerization to diazomethane occurs as well.[754] $CH_3\dot{C}H$ is derived from 3-methyl-diazirine; see Frey.[743]

$$\overline{CH_2N{=}N^{\rfloor}} + h\nu \rightarrow CH_2 + N_2 \qquad (1)$$

2. Diazoethane:[239,249] first absorption band shown in Fig. 5-15; full mercury arc, 200 mm pressure, $\sim$25°, relative yield of products: N_2 1.0, C_2H_4 0.61, 2-C_4H_8 0.06, H_2 0.08, C_2H_2 0.06; $C_2H_4/C_2H_2 \cong 10$; 4358 A, process 1 important, but vibrational excitation of CH_3CH: less; at 200 mm, $\sim$25°, $C_2H_4/C_2H_2 \cong 170$. No insertion reaction, common to CH_2:, seen; addition to propylene double bond occurs (forming *cis*- and *trans*-1,2-dimethylcyclopropane) about 20 times more slowly than reaction with diazoethane (forming *cis*- and *trans*-butene-2).

$$CH_3CHN_2 + h\nu \rightarrow CH_2CH:^{\ddagger} + N_2 \qquad (1)$$
$$\downarrow$$
$$CH_2{=}CH_2^{\ddagger} + N_2$$
$$\downarrow$$
$$CH{\equiv}CH + H_2 + N_2$$

3. Diphenyldiazomethane:[242,249-251] first absorption band (in methanol), $\lambda_{max} = 5260$ A, $\epsilon = 101$; second band, $\lambda_{max} = 2880$ A, $\epsilon = 21,300$; 2880 A, in methanol, $\varphi_1 + \varphi_2 = 0.78$; electronic state of primary radicals may be either singlet or triplet, depending on the multiplicity of the state which is the precursor, but apparently transformation to triplet occurs often before chemical reactions of the radical; non-stereospecific addition to olefin is noted.

$$(C_6H_5)_2CN_2 + h\nu \rightarrow M(S_1) \rightarrow (C_6H_5)_2C: + N_2 \qquad (1)$$
$$\downarrow \qquad\qquad \downarrow$$
$$M(T_1) \rightarrow (C_6H_5)_2\dot{C} + N_2 \qquad (2)$$

4. Diazocyclopentadiene:[242,249] in N_2 matrix (20°K) or perfluoroether (77°K), fulvalene only product seen (dimer of radical formed); process 1 likely.

$$\begin{matrix} CH{=}CH & & & CH{=}CH & & \\ | & \diagdown & & | & \diagdown & \\ & C{=}N{=}N + h\nu \rightarrow & & & C: + N_2 & \quad (1)\\ | & \diagup & & | & \diagup & \\ CH{=}CH & & & CH{=}CH & & \end{matrix}$$

5–39. Miscellaneous diazo compounds:[253] The quantum yields of decomposition of diazo compound were determined in methanol solution by irradiation at the wavelength of maximum absorption indicated; the values are presumed to be equal to the primary quantum efficiency of process 1; here $R_2C:$ represents either a singlet or triplet species.

$$R_2C{=}N{=}N + h\nu \rightarrow R_2C: + N_2 \quad (1)$$

Compound	λ_{max}, A	$\epsilon \times 10^{-3}$	φ_1
(5) $C_2H_5COCH{=}N{=}N$	3600	0.021	0.66
	2690	7.11	
	2470	7.65	
(6) $C_6H_5COCH{=}N{=}N$	2940	13.5	0.46
	2500	12.3	
(7) $C_6H_5NHCOCH{=}N{=}N$	3870	0.033	
	2700	27.3	0.39
(8) $C_6H_5COCCO_2CH_3$ (with $N{=}N$ over C)	2740	10.1	0.35
	2530	10.7	
(9) $(C_6H_5CO)_2C{=}N{=}N$	2750	16.6	0.31
	2560	22.2	
(10) $CH_3{-}\langle\ \rangle{-}COCH{=}N{=}N$	2970	16.8	0.42
	2600	13.2	
(11) $CH_3O{-}\langle\ \rangle{-}COCH{=}N{=}N$	3040	24.1	0.36
(12) $Cl{-}\langle\ \rangle{-}COCH{=}N{=}N$	2990	14.5	0.41
	2570	15.2	
(13) $Br{-}\langle\ \rangle{-}COCH{=}N{=}N$	2990	15.1	0.45
	2600	16.4	
(14) $I{-}\langle\ \rangle{-}COCH{=}N{=}N$	3010	19.3	0.38
(15) $\langle\ \rangle{-}\langle\ \rangle{-}COCH{=}N{=}N$	3090	29.5	0.27

(16) C₆H₅—CO—C₆H₄—COCH=N=N

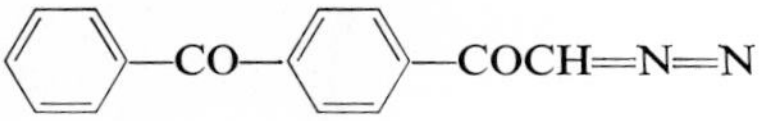

2990	16.0	0.28
2640	25.8	

(17) CH₃O₂S—C₆H₄—COCH=N=N

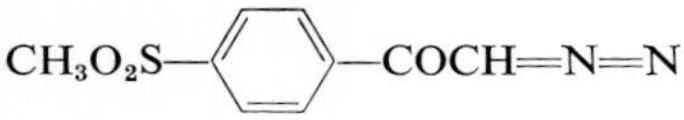

3040	12.7	0.29
2450	17.0	

(18) O₂N—C₆H₄—COCH=N=N

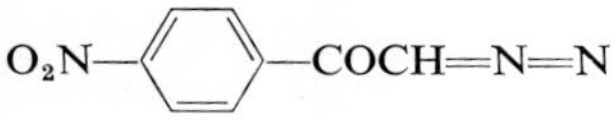

3070	13.3	0.18
2640	15.5	

(19) C₆H₅N=N—C₆H₄—COCH=N=N

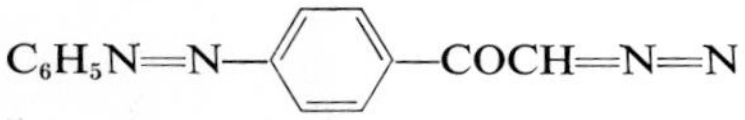

4490	0.80	
3340	35.3	0.10

(20) C₆H₄(NO₂)—COCH=N=N

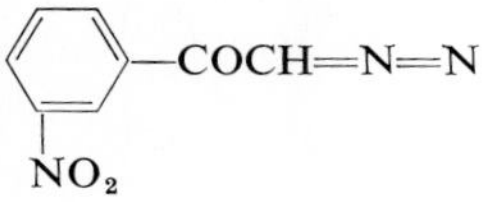

2970	14.2	0.22

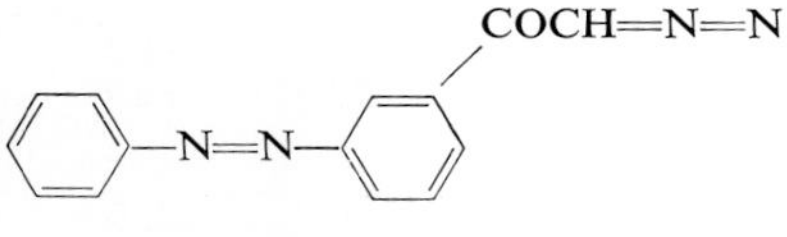

(21) C₆H₅—N=N—C₆H₄(COCH=N=N)

4410	0.55	
3070	28.8	0.18

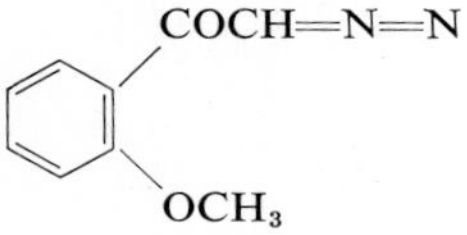

(22) C₆H₄(COCH=N=N)(OCH₃)

2880	13.0	0.49
2520	12.3	

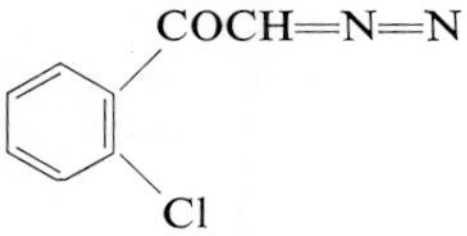

(23) C₆H₄(COCH=N=N)(Cl)

2870	12.1	0.52
2480	9.32	

(24) C₁₀H₇—COCH=N=N

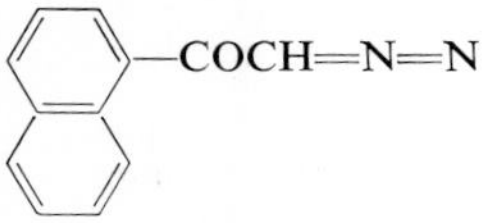

3010	11.5	0.31

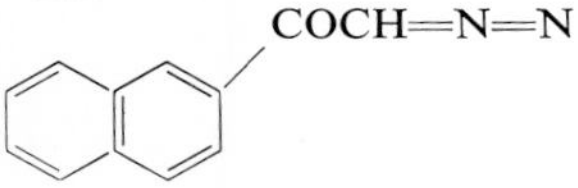

(25) C₁₀H₇—COCH=N=N

3070	18.9	0.28
2540	34.2	

(26) (thiophene)—COCH=N=N

3090	19.7	0.36
2610	9.05	

(27) (furan)—COCH=N=N

3060	23.2	0.33

(28) C₆H₄(CO)(CH₂)C=N=N

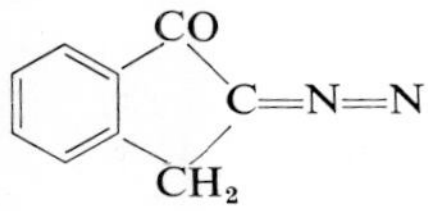

3210	12.2	0.14
2560	19.0	

(29)	3260	12.0	0.21
	2600	9.78	
(30)	3010	3.31	0.24
	2520	12.0	
(31) $N{=}N{=}CHCO(CH_2)_4COCH{=}N{=}N$	2700	17.3	0.34
	2480	19.0	
(32) $N{=}N{=}CHCOCH_2$—⟨⟩—$CH_2COCH{=}N{=}N$	2510	24.1	0.35
(33) $N{=}N{=}CHCOCOCH{=}N{=}N$	3180	11.7	0.31
	2700	15.9	
(34) $N{=}N{=}CHCO$—⟨⟩—$COCH{=}N{=}N$	3110	22.5	0.15
	2640	17.5	
(35)	5260	0.10	
	2880	21.3	0.78
(36) CH_3O—⟨⟩—	5270	0.14	
	3170	22.2	0.85
(37)	5130	0.10	0.69
	2870	20.6	
(38)	5270	0.13	
	3020	20.6	0.65
	2740	24.5	
(39)	3410	7.01	0.065
	2900	15.8	0.44

5-5E   Diazonium Salts

The products of the photodecomposition of diazonium salts, $R-N\equiv N^+X^-$, in aqueous solution seem well explained through a simple cleavage to form molecular nitrogen and carbonium ion in primary process XLI.

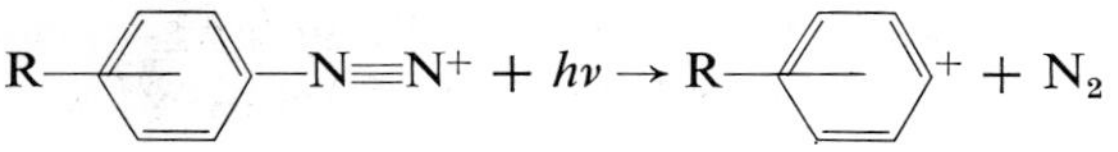

$$R-\text{⟨⟩}-N\equiv N^+ + h\nu \rightarrow R-\text{⟨⟩}^+ + N_2 \qquad \text{(XLI)}$$

The ion formed in XLI either hydrates to form the phenol as a final product,

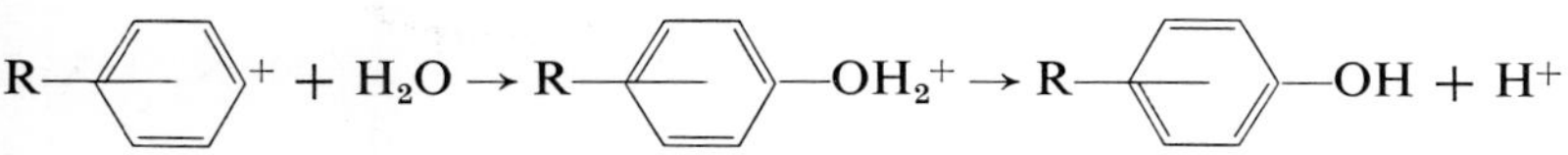

$$R-\text{⟨⟩}^+ + H_2O \rightarrow R-\text{⟨⟩}-OH_2^+ \rightarrow R-\text{⟨⟩}-OH + H^+$$

or combines with a negative ion (e.g., Cl^-) at high concentrations of added ions. Ring collapse of the primary carbonium ion product occurs in part in the *o*-hydroxy-substituted compounds in water:

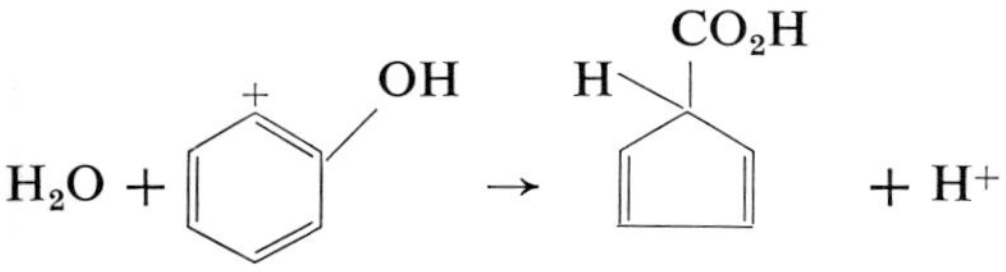

$$H_2O + \text{⟨⟩}^+ \text{OH} \rightarrow \text{⟨⟩} \overset{\text{CO}_2\text{H}}{\underset{}{\text{H}}} + H^+$$

In less polar solvents, such as ethanol solutions, the formation of free radicals by electron transfer in the primary dissociative act, process XLII, may compete favorably with the ion-forming process XLI.

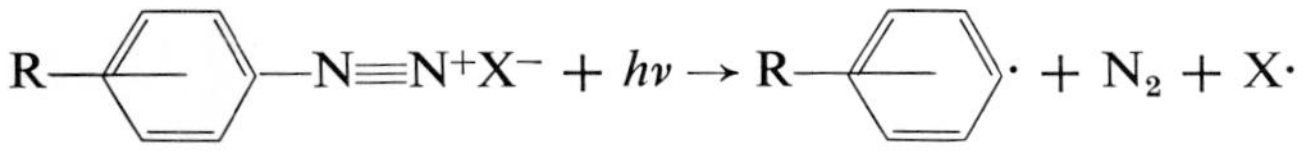

$$R-\text{⟨⟩}-N\equiv N^+X^- + h\nu \rightarrow R-\text{⟨⟩}\cdot + N_2 + X\cdot \quad \text{(XLII)}$$

Presumably X^- may be an anion, such as Cl^-, or a solvent molecule which is oxidized as the diazonium ion is reduced.

The quantum efficiency of nitrogen formation is a function of molecular structure of the diazonium salt, but no satisfactory comprehensive theory of these effects is available at this writing. There is evidence of a metastable state, possibly a triplet state or an isomer of the diazonium ion such as

$$R-\text{⟨⟩}\overset{N}{\underset{N}{\Big\langle}}{}^+$$

formed on irradiation of diazonium salt in rigid glass at $N_2(1)$ temperature. Nitrogen is not lost under these conditions, the absorption spectrum changes, and the original diazonium salt is largely re-formed as the sample is warmed.[257]

1. p-Diazo-N,N-dimethylaniline-zinc chloride complex (dihydrate):[255,256] first absorption region, 4500–3000 A, $\lambda_{max} = 3920$, $\epsilon \simeq 4.8 \times 10^3$; second band, 3000–2200 A, $\epsilon_{max} \simeq 8 \times 10^2$; 3660 A, aqueous solution, 23°, $\varphi_1 + \varphi_2 = 0.97$; solid suspended in mineral oil, $\varphi_1 + \varphi_2 \simeq 0.98$.

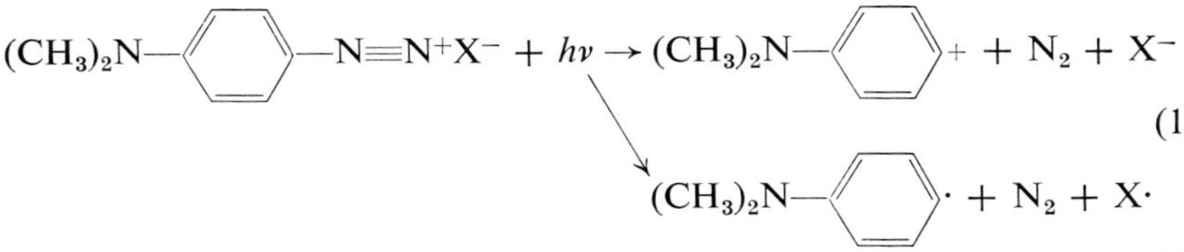

$$(CH_3)_2N-\langle\bigcirc\rangle-N{\equiv}N^+X^- + h\nu \rightarrow (CH_3)_2N-\langle\bigcirc\rangle^+ + N_2 + X^- \tag{1}$$

$$(CH_3)_2N-\langle\bigcirc\rangle\cdot + N_2 + X\cdot \tag{2}$$

2. p-Nitrobenzenediazonium chloride-stannic chloride complex:[257] 3660 A, 0°, methanol solution, $\varphi_2/\varphi_1 \simeq 21$; ethanol solution, $\varphi_2/\varphi_1 \simeq 17$; water solution, $\varphi_2/\varphi_1 = 0.0$.

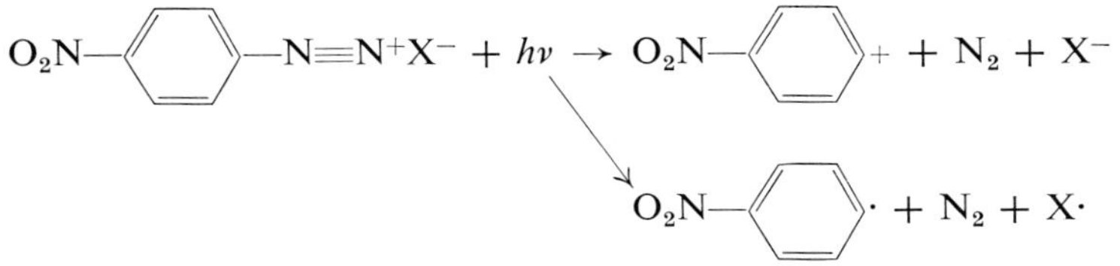

$$O_2N-\langle\bigcirc\rangle-N{\equiv}N^+X^- + h\nu \rightarrow O_2N-\langle\bigcirc\rangle^+ + N_2 + X^- \tag{1}$$

$$O_2N-\langle\bigcirc\rangle\cdot + N_2 + X\cdot \tag{2}$$

3. m-Nitrobenzenediazonium chloride-stannic chloride complex:[257] 3660 A, 0°, ethanol solution, $\varphi_2/\varphi_1 \simeq 6.6$; water solution, $\varphi_2/\varphi_1 = 0.0$.

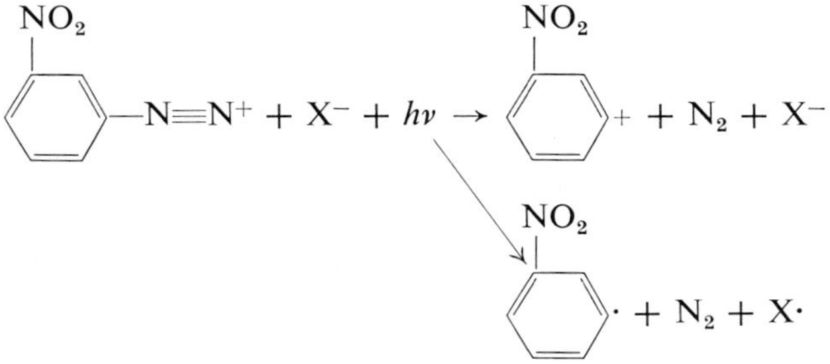

$$\overset{NO_2}{\underset{}{\langle\bigcirc\rangle}}-N{\equiv}N^+ + X^- + h\nu \rightarrow \overset{NO_2}{\underset{}{\langle\bigcirc\rangle}}^+ + N_2 + X^- \tag{1}$$

$$\overset{NO_2}{\underset{}{\langle\bigcirc\rangle}}\cdot + N_2 + X\cdot \tag{2}$$

4–12. Miscellaneous diazonium salts:[256,258] The quantum yields of nitrogen formation were determined at 3660 A in aqueous solution (4×10^{-3} M) or as indicated; these yields may be taken as estimates of $\varphi_{XLI} + \varphi_{XLII}$.

Compound	Solution or State	$\varphi_{XLI} + \varphi_{XLII}$
(4) 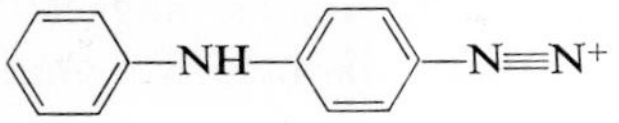	$H_2O(H_2SO_4)$	0.36
(5) 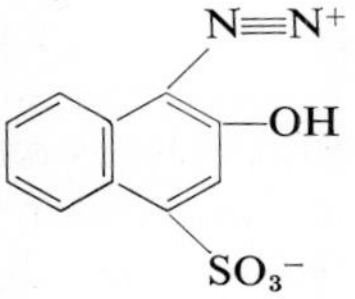	H_2O, 5% ethanol, 0.1 N H_2SO_4	0.20
(6) 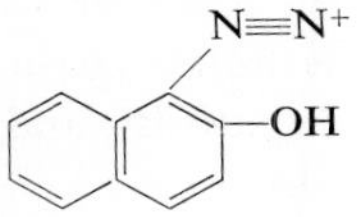	H_2O, 20% ethanol	0.22
(7) 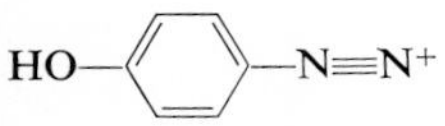	$H_2O(HSO_4^-)$	0.47
(8) 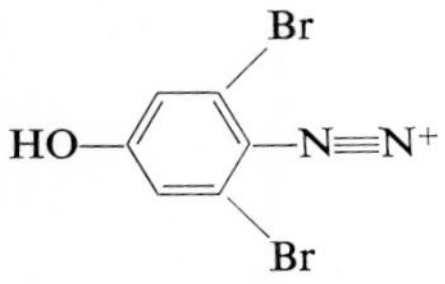	H_2O, 40% ethanol	0.74
(9) 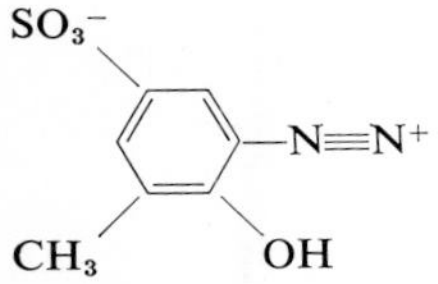	H_2O (H$^+$)	0.47
(10) 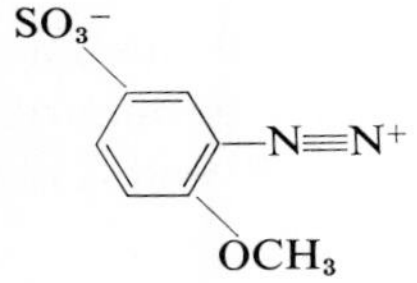	H_2O	0.25
(11) (a) 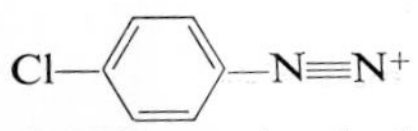 (ZnCl$_2$ complex, hydrate)	Solid suspended in mineral oil	0.64, 0.42
(b) Same as (a) but anhydrous salt	Solid suspended in mineral oil	0.70, 0.20
(12) (a) 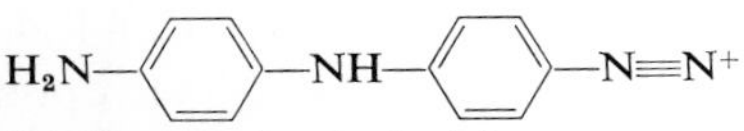 (ZnCl$_2$ complex, hydrate)	Solid suspended in isooctane	0.98, 0.65, 0.56
(b) Same as (a) but anhydrous salt	Solid suspended in mineral oil	0.96, 0.95, 0.47

5-5F   Organic Azides

Qualitative studies of the photolysis of organic azides suggest that primary process XLIII is the dominant primary dissociative mode in solution:

$$R—N{=}N{=}N + h\nu \rightarrow R—N: + N_2 \qquad \text{(XLIII)}$$

The nitrene (R—N:) formed in XLIII may be vibrationally or electronically excited or both. This species reacts largely as a diradical in solution; insertion reactions, characteristic of the carbene species (RCH:), are absent. Barton and co-workers conclude that three paths of reaction follow the nitrene formation in XLIII: isomerization to an imine (path A), H-abstraction from solvent to form ultimately an amine (path B), and 1,5-H-abstraction followed by cyclization to give pyrrolidines.

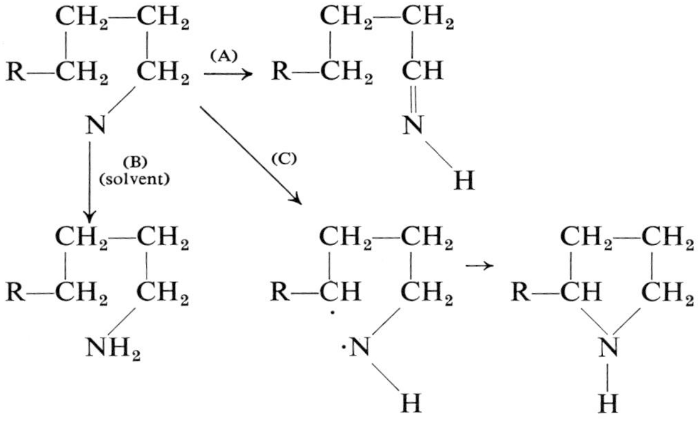

In the following summary of azide photolysis, the full mercury arc was used unless stated otherwise. Process XLIII alone is believed to be important in each case, and the relative extent of reaction by paths A, B, and C is given when known.

1. n-Propylazide:[259] in cyclohexane solution, path A important to form propionaldehyde imine.

2. n-Butylazide:[259] in benzene solution, N-*n*-butyl aniline formed, 22% path B.

3. (+)4-Methyl-n-hexylazide:[259] in cyclohexane solution, (+)4-methyl-*n*-hexylamine, 35% path B; 2-ethyl-2-methyl pyrrolidine, optically inactive, 16% path C.

4. n-Heptylazide:[259] in cyclohexane solution, 15% path C, 45% path A.

5. n-Octylazide:[259] in boiling benzene solution, N-n-octyl aniline, 31% path B; in cyclohexane, 35% path C.

6. β-Phenylethylazide:[259,260] cyclohexane solution, path A important.

7. 3-Phenylpropylazide:[259] cyclohexane solution, 21% path C.

8. o-Azidobiphenyls:[260] in tetralin or kerosene solution, parent compound or the 5-Br-, 3,5-dibromo, 5-nitro, 4'-nitro, 5,4'-dinitro, and 4,4'-dinitro derivatives decompose by process 1 and form carbazole product in 23–85% yields (path C); 3-nitro-substituted compound gives 4-phenylbenzfuroxan.

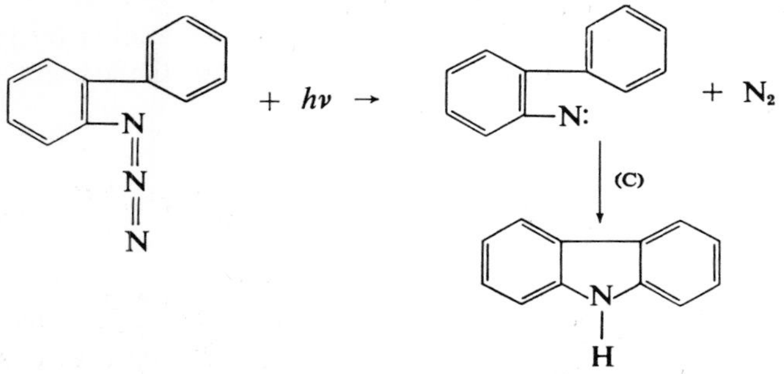

$$+ \, h\nu \rightarrow \qquad + \, N_2 \qquad (1)$$

9. Ethylazidoformate:[261] 2537 A, in cyclohexene, process XLIII important, but nitrene addition to double bond forms 7-carbethoxy-7-azabicyclo-[4.1.0]heptane (50%); in cyclohexane, $C_6H_{11}NHCO_2C_2H_5$ is a major product.

5-5G   Alkyl Nitroso Compounds

Alkyl nitroso compounds are normally unstable in monomeric form and tend to isomerize, dimerize, react with radicals, etc.; however, the perfluoronitroso compounds (CF_3NO, etc.) and other nitroso compounds without hydrogen atoms on the carbon attached to the —N═O group [$(CH_3)_3CN$═O, $RCCl(NO)R'$, etc.] are relatively stable and may be studied by conventional means. The limited data on these compounds indicate that the primary photodissociative process XLIV is important even in the long-wavelength absorption band, 7500–5000 A; see Fig. 5-16.

$$R—N═O + h\nu \rightarrow R + NO \qquad (XLIV)$$

When hydrogen atoms are present on the carbon atom adjacent to the C—N═O grouping, the occurrence of an additional intramolecular process XLV has been suggested:

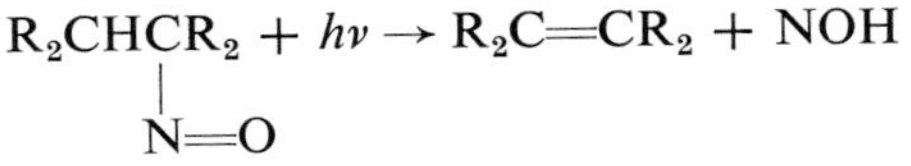

$$R_2CHCR_2 + h\nu \rightarrow R_2C{=}CR_2 + NOH \qquad (XLV)$$
$$\underset{\displaystyle N{=}O}{|}$$

The early studies of the chloronitroso compounds were interpreted in terms of an intramolecular formation of HCl in the primary act, process XLVIa.

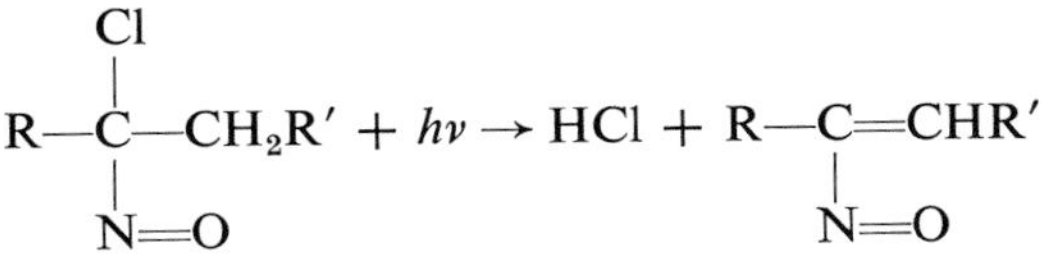

$$\underset{\displaystyle N{=}O}{\overset{\displaystyle Cl}{R{-}\overset{|}{\underset{|}{C}}{-}CH_2R'}} + h\nu \rightarrow HCl + \underset{\displaystyle N{=}O}{R{-}\overset{|}{C}{=}CHR'} \qquad (XLVIa)$$

Presumably the unsaturated nitroso compound formed in XLVIa leads to a saturated oxime final product, at least in part. An alternative primary process XLVIb involving halogen atom release fits the present experimental observations well.

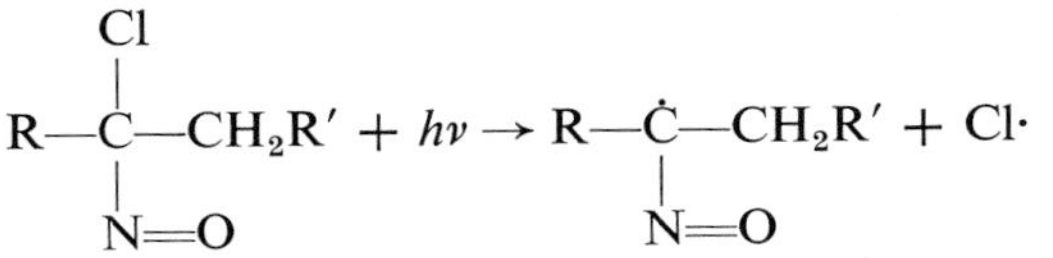

$$\underset{\displaystyle N{=}O}{\overset{\displaystyle Cl}{R{-}\overset{|}{\underset{|}{C}}{-}CH_2R'}} + h\nu \rightarrow \underset{\displaystyle N{=}O}{R{-}\overset{\displaystyle \cdot}{\underset{|}{C}}{-}CH_2R'} + Cl\cdot \qquad (XLVIb)$$

In the methanol solution used in the previous studies the radicals formed in XLVIb would abstract hydrogen atoms from the solvent to generate the observed product HCl and a nitroso compound which would quickly isomerize to the observed oxime. Primary steps alternative to XLV and XLVI involving free radical formation or ion formation in solution studies cannot be ruled out on the basis of the limited data on hand. The relative efficiencies of the alternative processes have not been clearly established in most cases, but the total primary quantum yield of decomposition is very near unity for the nitroso compounds which have been studied.

1. Trifluoronitrosomethane:[262–265] absorption spectrum shown in Fig. 5-16; in red light (5400–7800 A), $\sim$20°, $\varphi_1 \cong 1.0$; final major product of the photolysis is $(CF_3)_2NONO$.

$$CF_3N{=}O + h\nu \rightarrow CF_3 + NO \qquad (1)$$

2. 1-Nitrosoheptafluoropropane:[262] first absorption band, 7800–5000 A, $\lambda_{max} = 6840$ A, $\epsilon = 22.7$; presumably similar to CF_3NO photochemically.

3. 2-Nitroso-2-methylpropane:[266] absorption spectrum shown in Fig. 5-16; process 1 is important for absorption in the red; 2 possible.

$$(CH_3)_3CN{=}O + h\nu \rightarrow (CH_3)_3C + NO \qquad (1)$$
$$\searrow (CH_3)_2C{=}CH_2 + NOH \qquad (2)$$

4. 2-Nitroso-2-chlorobutane:[267] in methanol solution, $\lambda_{max} = 6500$ A, $\epsilon = 15.10$; ~6500 A, ~20°, $\varphi_{XLVI} \cong 1.2$; methylethylketoxime and HCl among products.

5. 2-Nitroso-2-chloro-3,3-dimethylbutane:[268] in methanol solution, ~ 6700 A, ~20°, $\varphi_{XLVI} \cong 0.62$; ~6140 A, $\varphi_{XLVI} \cong 0.93$.

6. 4-Nitroso-4-methylpentan-2-one:[270] in benzene solution, $\lambda_{max} = 6700$ A, $\epsilon = 2.6$; ~6700 A, $\varphi_1 \cong 0.96$; alternative process of free radical formation (XLIV) cannot be excluded.

$$(CH_3)_2\underset{\underset{N=O}{|}}{C}CH_2\overset{\overset{O}{\|}}{C}CH_3 + h\nu \rightarrow (CH_3)_2C{=}CH\overset{\overset{O}{\|}}{C}CH_3 + NOH \qquad (1)$$

7. 4-Nitroso-4-chloropentanoic acid:[268] in methanol solution, $\epsilon = 2.48$, 7460 A; 3.72, 7040 A; 14.89, 6590 A; 9.93, 6225 A; 2.48, 5350 A; 6550 A, ~20°, $\varphi_{XLVI} \cong 1.05$; HCl and oxime of methyl laevulate products identified.

8. 1-Nitroso-1-chlorocyclohexane:[268] in methanol solution, ~6540 A, $\varphi_{XLVI} \cong 0.96$.

9. 2-Nitroso-2,5-dimethylhexane:[270] in benzene solution, $\lambda_{max} = 6850$ A, $\epsilon = 3.0$; 6550 A, $\varphi_1 \cong 0.93$; alternative process of radical formation (XLIV) cannot be excluded.

$$(CH_3)_2\underset{\underset{N=O}{|}}{C}CH_2CH_2CH(CH_3)_2 + h\nu \rightarrow$$

$$(CH_3)_2C{=}CHCH_2CH(CH_3)_2 + NOH \qquad (1)$$

10. 2-Nitroso-2-chloro-1,4-diphenylbutane:[268,269] in methanol solution, $\epsilon =$ 1.54, 7300 A; 6.17, 7075 A; 23.12, 6500 A; 12.33, 6130 A; 1.54, 5200 A; ~6580 A, ~20°, $\varphi_{XLVI} \cong 0.78$; ~6100 A, ~20°, $\varphi_{XLVI} \cong 1.1$. Photolysis using right-handed circularly polarized red light was allowed to proceed to 90% decomposition and gave solution of optical rotation $-0.10°$; similar experiments with left-handed light gave rotation of $+0.11°$. The anisotropy factor, $(\epsilon_l - \epsilon_r)/\epsilon_0$, equals 0.04 at 6580 A.

5-5H   Nitro Compounds

The very high reactivity of the nitroalkanes and their photolysis products complicates the interpretation of the photolysis data. Most investigators agree, however, that the dominant primary photodissociative mode in the nitroalkanes is the free radical-forming process XLVII. In compounds containing hydrogen atoms on the β-carbon, intramolecular formation of olefin and nitrous acid, process XLVIII, is also important.

$$R_2CHCH_2NO_2 + h\nu \rightarrow R_2CHCH_2 + NO_2 \qquad (XLVII)$$

$$\searrow R_2C{=}CH_2 + HONO \qquad (XLVIII)$$

Intramolecular formation of aldehyde and hyponitrous acid, process XLIX, and rearrangement to the corresponding alkyl nitrite, process L, have been suggested, but more detailed recent studies show that they are relatively unimportant primary steps for the usual experimental conditions employed:

$$R_2CHCH_2NO_2 + h\nu \rightarrow R_2CH\overset{O}{\overset{\|}{C}}H + NOH \qquad (XLIX)$$

$$\searrow R_2CHCH_2ONO \qquad (L)$$

In the aromatic nitro compounds an alternative N-O bond rupture is favored in the primary act, process LI.

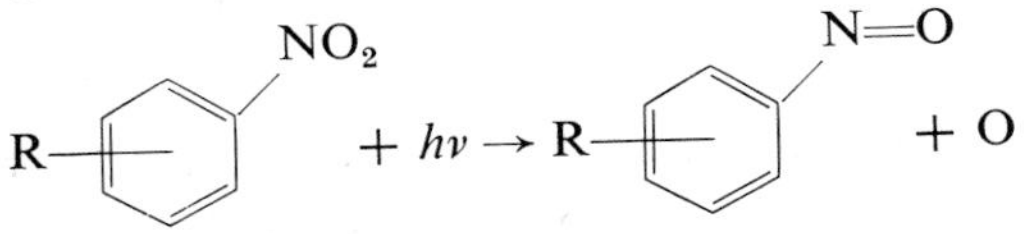

$$(LIa)$$

In the ortho-nitro-substituted aldehydes an efficient oxygen-atom transfer from the nitro group occurs with insertion in the carbonyl C-H bond:

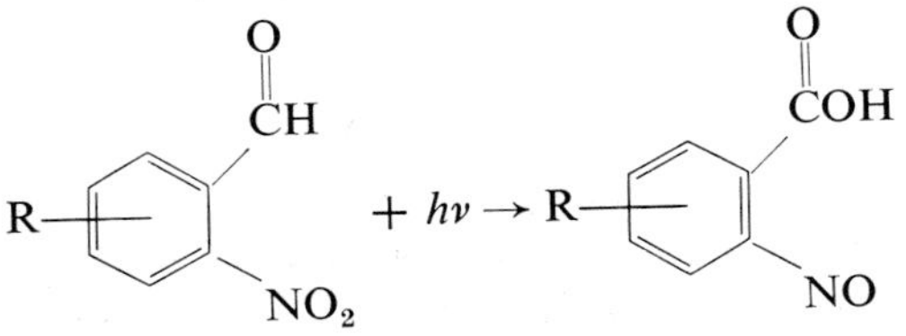

$$(LIb)$$

Conceivably processes LIa and LIb may be related; both may involve intermediate oxygen-atom formation. For the compounds with a carbonyl group ortho to the nitro group, however, exclusive insertion in the

$\overset{O}{\overset{\|}{C}}$—H bond may occur because of the proximity and high reactivity of the species. Further examples of the photolysis of nitrobenzene derivatives are reviewed by Chapman[501] and Mustafa.[494] Some interesting examples of photochromic nitro compounds have been reviewed by Dessauer and Paris;[671] see compound 9 in the following summary, p. 480.

1. Nitromethane:[271-276] absorption spectrum shown in Fig. 5-17; full mercury arc, process 1 important, 2 unimportant; $\varphi_2 \leqslant 0.04$.

$$CH_3NO_2 + h\nu \rightarrow CH_3 + NO_2 \quad (1)$$
$$\searrow$$
$$CH_2O + NOH \quad (2)$$

2. Perfluoronitromethane:[277] $\lambda_{max} = 2775$ A, $\epsilon = 11.2$; primary process forming CF_3 and NO_2 presumed important.

3. Nitroethane:[271,272,276] absorption spectrum shown in Fig. 5-17; 3130 A, processes 1 and 2 major; $\varphi_2 \cong 0.08$; liquid phase, $\varphi_2 \cong 0.002$; 2537 A, liquid phase, $\varphi_2 \cong 0.02$.

$$CH_3CH_2NO_2 + h\nu \rightarrow CH_3CH_2 + NO_2 \quad (1)$$
$$\searrow$$
$$CH_2{=}CH_2 + HONO \quad (2)$$

4. Heptafluoronitropropane:[277] $\lambda_{max} = 2795$ A, $\epsilon = 41.6$; process forming C_3F_7 and NO_2 presumed important.

5. Nitrobenzene:[278-280] absorption spectrum shown in Fig. 5-29; absorption onset at 2910 A, with four relatively weak bands to 2600 A, where strong absorption begins; full mercury arc, $\varphi_1 > \varphi_2$; major ultimate products are nitrosobenzene and *p*-nitrophenol.

$$C_6H_5NO_2 + h\nu \rightarrow C_6H_5N{=}O + O \quad (1)$$
$$\searrow$$
$$C_6H_5 + NO_2 \quad (2)$$

6. o-Nitrobenzaldehyde:[281,536,677,678,679,680,681,684] in acetone and ligroin solutions, 4040 A, $\epsilon = 35.6$, $\varphi_1 = 0.46$; 3660 A, $\epsilon = 182$, $\varphi_1 = 0.51$; solid state, $\varphi_1 = 0.50$; 3130 A, solid state, $\varphi_1 = 0.51$; KBr matrix, $\varphi_1 = 0.5$.

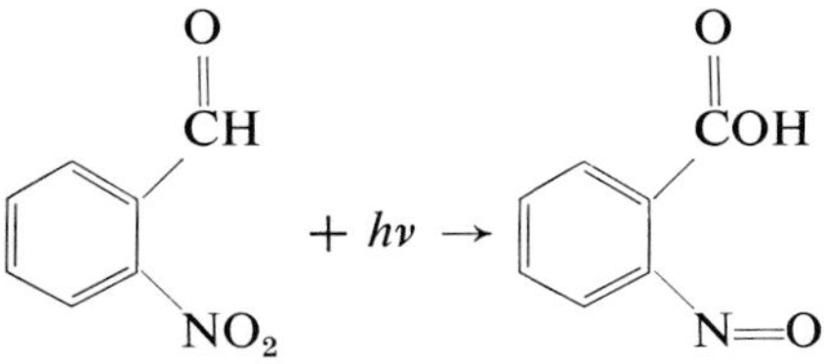

7. 2,4-Dinitrobenzaldehyde:[281] in acetone solution, 3660 A, $\epsilon = 188$, $\varphi_1 = 0.49$; solid state, $\varphi_1 = 0.51$; 3130 A, solid state, $\varphi_1 \cong 0.26$; 2654 A, solid state, $\varphi_1 \cong 0.12$.

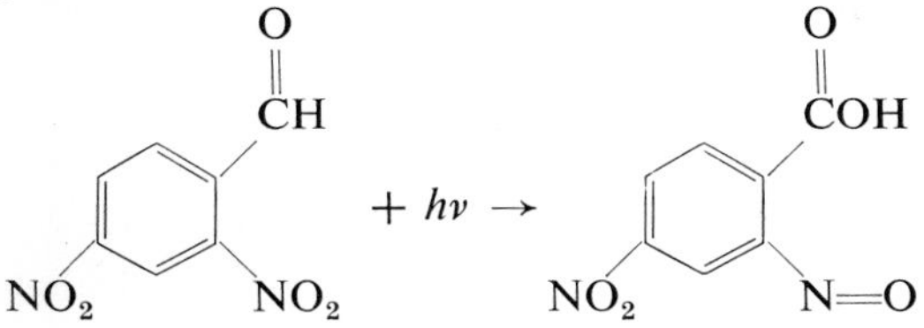

8. 2,4,6-Trinitrobenzaldehyde:[281] in acetone solution, 3660 A, $\epsilon = 192$, $\varphi_1 = 0.66$; solid state, $\varphi_1 = 0.50$; 3130 A, solid state, $\varphi_1 \cong 0.17$; 2654 A, solid state, $\varphi_1 \cong 0.06$.

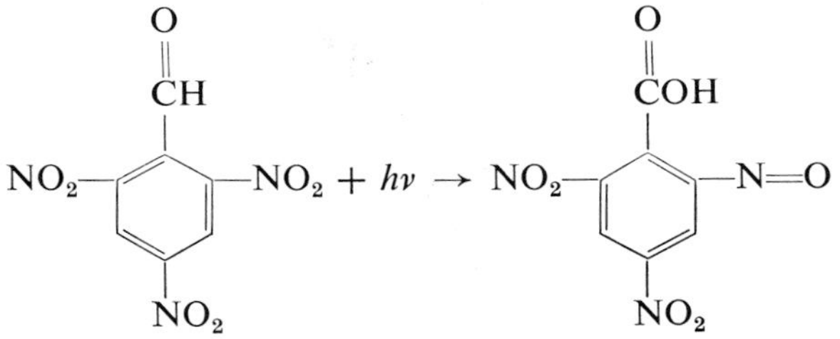

$$(1)$$

9. 2-(2'-Nitro-4'-X-benzyl)pyridines:[703,704,690] irradiation of the pure solid or solutions in ethanol, ether, or isooctane (2000–4000 A) gives a blue color which fades thermally; compounds of the general formula shown as reactant in the reaction below (with $X = NO_2$, $CONH_2$, NH_2, or CN) and many other related compounds give this behavior.[671] Hardwick and co-workers suggest the following tautomeric change to explain the photochromism:[704]

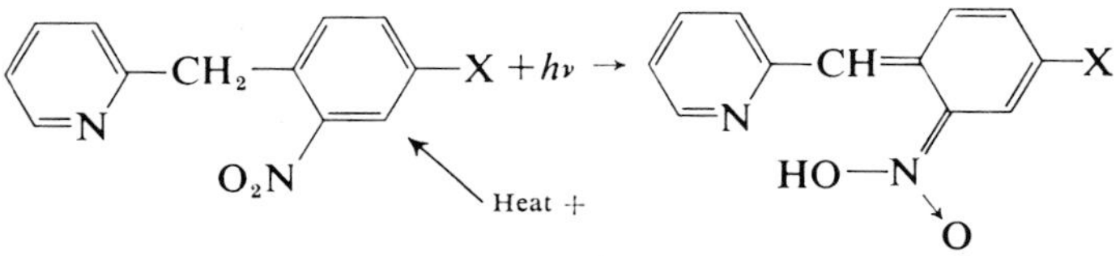

They prefer this mechanism to the alternative one involving hydrogen transfer to the pyridine nitrogen, since many aromatic nitro compounds not containing the pyridyl group are photochromic, e.g., the following compounds:

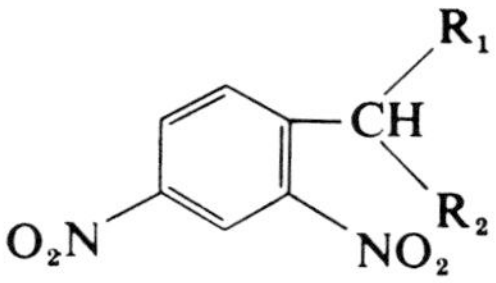

where R_1 is H, C_6H_5, CH_3, etc., and R_2 is an electron-withdrawing group which increases the acidity of the central C-H bond without screening the light absorption by the 2,4-dinitrophenyl group.

5-5I Organic Nitrites and Nitrates

The major photodissociative process in the alkyl nitrites is the homolytic cleavage of the RO-NO bond to form an alkyoxyl radical and nitric oxide, process LII.

$$RONO + h\nu \rightarrow RO + NO \qquad (LII)$$

The alkoxyl radical may be formed in a vibrationally and/or electronically excited state, and decomposition of the radical may be extensive even at room temperature for gas-phase systems, at short wavelengths, and at low pressures. The only quantitative estimates of the primary efficiency of process LII have been derived in *tert*-butyl nitrite and *tert*-pentyl nitrite photolyses; in these cases $\varphi_{LII} = 1.0$ even on photolysis in the structured long-wavelength system (see Fig. 5-18). It is likely that this high efficiency extends to the other simple nitrites, although an apparent inefficiency may be found since product formation does not always follow LII, but the rapid re-formation of the reactant from primary products can be important:

$$RO + NO \rightarrow RONO \qquad (1)$$

Photolysis of methyl nitrite in rigid matrices at low temperature has been interpreted in terms of LII together with other primary processes. Process LIIIa, involving *cis*-CH_3ONO, was suggested.

$$RCH_2ONO + h\nu \rightarrow \overset{\displaystyle O}{\overset{\displaystyle \|}{R C}} H + HNO \qquad (LIIIa)$$

An incorrect, reversed assignment of the infrared bands of the *cis*- and *trans*-methyl nitrite was assumed in the published work,[273] and the suggested mechanism must be reinterpreted in view of this error.[302] Thus the *trans*-methyl nitrite (not the *cis* form) disappears preferentially as the photolysis occurs in a rigid matrix; the simultaneous formation of formaldehyde and HNO no longer can be considered as arising from an intramolecular rearrangement of the reactant, *cis*-methyl nitrite, which is sterically favorable to process LIIIa; it seems more reasonable that these products come from the disproportionation reaction of the initial fragments CH_3O and NO, formed in process LII, and trapped in a matrix cage.

$$CH_3O + NO \rightarrow CH_2O + HNO \qquad (2)$$

$$\searrow$$

$$CH_3ONO \qquad (3)$$

Conceivably the preferential destruction of *trans*-methyl nitrite in the matrix experiments may reflect the re-formation of the more compact, matrix-acceptable *cis* form from the primary radicals by reaction 3. In view of the geometry of the transition state involved in the possible primary step LIIIa, the expected primary product would be hyponitrous acid, HON, not the observed HNO isomer; in this light, and in view of the possible occurrence of the analog in ethyl nitrate photolysis, process

LIIIb might be considered. In any case there is no conclusive evidence which allows an unambiguous evaluation of the possible importance of LIIIa or LIIIb in the matrix experiments at present.

$$RCH_2ONO + h\nu \rightarrow R\overset{\overset{\displaystyle O}{\|}}{C}H + NOH \qquad (LIIIb)$$

Recently McMillan has shown that primary processes LIIIa and LIIIb are probably unimportant in isopropyl nitrite photolysis in the gas phase at 3660 A,[287] and it is probable that they are also minor processes in the photolysis of other simple nitrites.

The previously proposed primary reaction involving the formation of nitroso and carbonyl compounds in a concerted process, for example,

$$(CH_3)_3CONO + h\nu \rightarrow CH_3COCH_3 + CH_3NO \qquad (4)$$

has been shown to be unimportant in the *tert*-butyl nitrite system; the products, among which are CH_3COCH_3 and CH_3NO, can be quantitatively explained through the occurrence of LII and conventional secondary reactions.[290]

A great variety of nitrites has been studied qualitatively in solution-phase photolyses, and there is a large interest in their photochemistry as it bears on unique synthetic methods.[295,494] In every case the dominant occurrence of the primary process LII is consistent with the data. In the solution phase the alkoxyl radicals formed in LII react by at least one of the following routes: (A) decomposition into smaller alkyl radicals and aldehyde or ketone; (B) abstraction of hydrogen atoms from solvent; or (C) internal hydrogen atom abstraction from a sterically favorable down-chain carbon atom, such that a cyclic six-membered-ring transition state is involved.

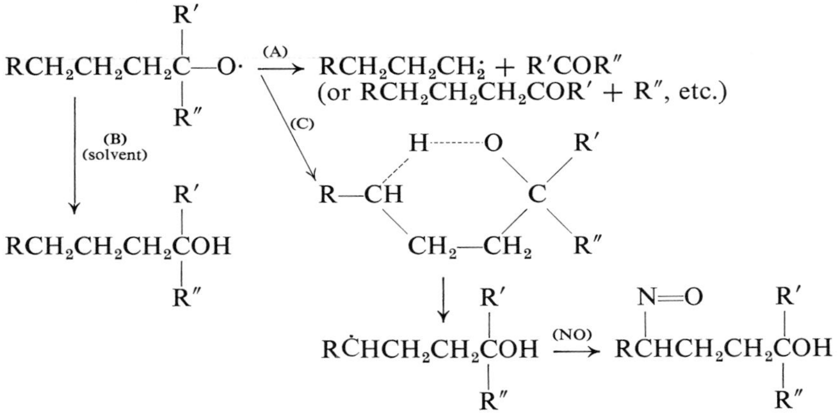

In the usual system involving nitrite photolysis, a small concentration of nitric oxide is achieved quickly; this reacts not only with the primary RO· radicals to re-form reactant or disproportionate (analogs to 2 and 3), but also with radicals $RCH_2CH_2CH_2$, R', R", and $R\dot{C}HCH_2CH_2C(R')(R")OH$ formed in paths A and C. The net result of the photolysis of a nitrite can be the formation of significant yields of nitroso compounds, or ultimately the corresponding dimer or oxime. Almost every conceivable simple nitrite has been studied in regard to the relative importance of paths A, B, and C. When the intermediate important to self-abstraction is allowed by the geometry of the molecule, path C may dominate. Excellent reviews of these studies have appeared, to which the reader is referred.[294-298]

Very little work has been reported on the alkyl nitrate photolysis, and extrapolations from these results are of limited value. However, studies of ethyl nitrate photolysis at 3130 A point to the involvement of three primary processes which have been generalized as LIV, LV, and LVI.

$$RCH_2ONO_2 + h\nu \rightarrow RCH_2O + NO_2 \qquad \text{(LIV)}$$

$$\begin{array}{c} O \\ \parallel \\ R\dot{C}H + HONO \end{array} \qquad \text{(LV)}$$

$$RCH_2ONO + O \qquad \text{(LVI)}$$

Process LIV is the analog of LII in nitrite photolysis and is the favored photodissociative mode here as well. Process LV is the analog to the disputed process LIIIb in nitrite photolysis. The relative importance of LV and LVI is difficult to assess since the products can arise from the further reactions of the products of LIV as well. However, there is some evidence that LV and LVI occur in this case, although their relative importance is less than that of process LIV; for ethyl nitrate photolysis at 3130 A, $\varphi_{LIV} > \varphi_{LVI} > \varphi_{LV}$.

1. Methyl nitrite:[273,282,283] absorption spectrum shown in Fig. 5-18; process 1 important.

$$CH_3ONO + h\nu \rightarrow CH_3O^{\ddagger} + NO \qquad (1)$$

2. Isopropyl nitrite:[287] 2537 A, 25°, 15 mm, $\varphi_1 \geqslant 0.86$; $\alpha = 0.86$ (see p. 448).

$$(CH_3)_2CHONO + h\nu \rightarrow (CH_3)_2CHO^{\ddagger} + NO \qquad (1)$$
$$\downarrow$$
$$CH_3CHO + CH_3$$

3. tert-Butyl nitrite:[288-292] absorption spectrum shown in Fig. 5-18; 2537 A, $\varphi_1 \geqslant 0.84$ (26°), $\geqslant 0.97$ (99°); $\alpha = 0.94$ (79°, pressure → 0),

0.87 (26°); 3130 A, $\alpha = 0.20$ (16 mm, 26°); 3660 A, $\varphi_1 = 1.0$ (29 mm, 25°); $\alpha \simeq 0.04$.

$$(CH_3)_3CONO + h\nu \rightarrow (CH_3)_3CO^{\ddagger} + NO \tag{1}$$

$$CH_3COCH_3 + CH_3$$

4. tert-Pentyl nitrite:[287] absorption spectrum shows band positions and relative intensities very nearly the same as those of *tert*-butyl nitrite. The individual bands are much better resolved for the *tert*-alkyl nitrites than for other simple nitrites because the former exist almost entirely in the *trans* form. The simple secondary and primary nitrites show overlapping of bands due to different absorption of *cis*- and *trans*-isomers. 2537 A, $\varphi_1 = 1.0$ (26°); $\alpha = 1.0$ (26°); $\alpha_a/\alpha_b = 6.4$ (25°).

$$
\begin{array}{c}
CH_3 \\
| \\
CH_3CH_2CONO + h\nu \rightarrow CH_3CH_2CO + NO \\
| \\
CH_3
\end{array}
\qquad
\begin{array}{c}
CH_3^{\ddagger} \\
\end{array}
\tag{1}
$$

$$C_2H_5 + CH_3COCH_3 \qquad CH_3 + CH_3COC_2H_5$$

(a) (b)

5. n-Octyl nitrite:[293] first absorption band in methanol, banded 4000–3100 A; second, more intense continuous absorption for $\lambda < 3100$ A; 3660–3340 A, in heptane solution, $\varphi_1 \geqslant 0.76$; in benzene or heptane solution, a large yield (45 and 30%, respectively) of the dimer of 4-nitroso-1-octanol product forms through route C of the discussion.

$$n\text{-}C_8H_{17}ONO + h\nu \rightarrow n\text{-}C_8H_{17}O + NO \tag{1}$$

6. Miscellaneous organic nitrites:[294–298] a very large number of simple and complex nitrites (including steroid derivatives) have been photolyzed in solution studies, and the synthetic utility of the photolyses has been assessed in excellent reviews to which the reader is referred.[294,295]

7. Methyl nitrate:[300] absorption spectrum shown in Fig. 5-17; limited data on this compound are consistent with free radical formation in primary act 1:

$$CH_3ONO_2 + h\nu \rightarrow CH_3O^{\ddagger} + NO_2 \tag{1}$$

8. Ethyl nitrate:[299–301] absorption spectrum shown in Fig. 5-17; 2537–2654 A, process 1 important; 3130 A, $\varphi_1 \geqslant 0.24$, $\varphi_2 \leqslant 0.09$, $\varphi_3 \leqslant 0.14$; full H_2 arc (through fluorite window), fluorescence (3200–4200 A) observed from electronically excited $C_2H_5O^{\ddagger}$ formed in 1 (presumed to be the analog to the electronic state observed in OH emission band, near 3064 A; this transition involves the odd electron on oxygen promoted to the C-O antibonding orbital).[187]

$$C_2H_5ONO_2 + h\nu \rightarrow C_2H_5O^{\ddagger} + NO_2 \qquad (1)$$

$$CH_3\overset{\overset{\displaystyle O}{\|}}{C}H + HONO \qquad (2)$$

$$C_2H_5ONO + O \qquad (3)$$

5-5J Organic Nitriles

Very limited data from alkyl nitrile photolysis in the Schumann ultraviolet show that at least two primary processes occur with comparable quantum efficiencies, LVII and LVIII.

$$RCH_2C{\equiv}N + h\nu \rightarrow H + RCHCN \qquad (LVII)$$

$$RCH_2 + CN^{\ddagger} \qquad (LVIII)$$

The photolysis of the leucocyanides of the triphenylmethane dyes in polar solvents (e.g., ethanol) involves a very efficient ionization to dye and cyanide ions, process LIX.

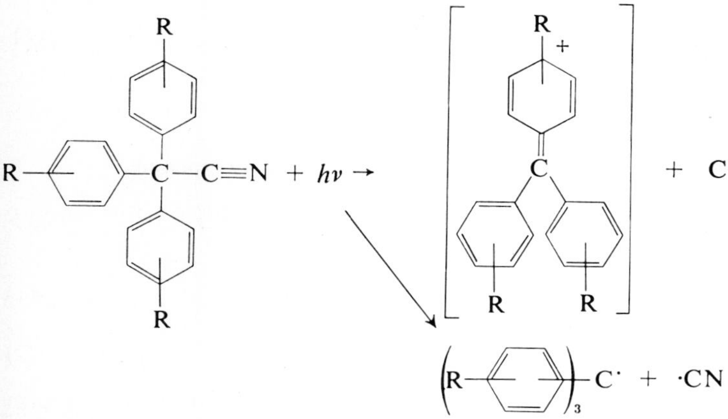

In non-polar solvents (e.g., cyclohexane) the free radical-forming process LX seems to compete favorably with LIX. In mixtures of cyclohexane, ethylene dichloride, and ethylidene dichloride with dielectric constants (ϵ) up to 4.5, $\varphi_{LIX} = 0$, and LX appears to occur; φ_{LIX} increases with increase in ϵ for solutions with $\epsilon \geqslant 4.5$.

1. Methyl cyanide:[303,304] first absorption band at $\lambda < 2160$ A; 1849 A, $\varphi_1 > \varphi_2$; unidentified solid builds up on walls of the reaction cell, complicating study; emission from electronically excited CN* (near 3883 A) is seen on irradiation of compound with spectrum of energies in Schumann ultraviolet.

$$CH_3C\equiv N + h\nu \rightarrow H + H_2CCN \tag{1}$$

$$\searrow$$

$$CH_3 + CN^* \tag{2}$$

2. Malachite green leucocyanide:[306-308] first absorption band, $\lambda < 3400$ A; in ethanol solution (10^{-3} to 10^{-5} M), 20–30°, low light intensities, $\varphi_1 = 1.00 \pm 0.03$ at 2482, 2537, 2654, 2967, 3130, and 3342 A; dye product absorbs strongly and acts as internal filter unless precautions are taken; presumably process 2 important in non-polar solvents.

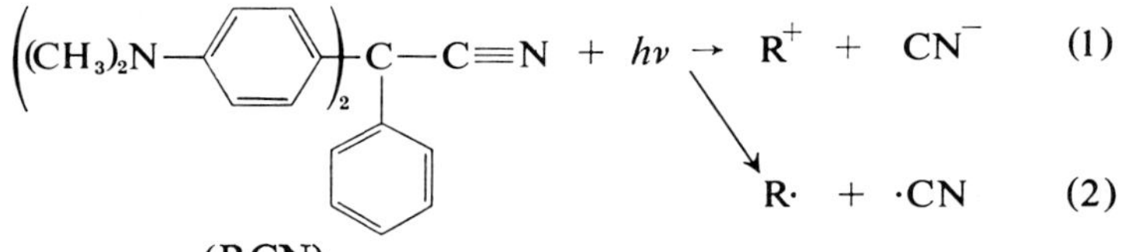

$$\left((CH_3)_2N-\!\!\!\left\langle\ \right\rangle\!\!\!\right)_2 \!\!\!\begin{array}{c} C-C\equiv N \\ | \\ \end{array} + h\nu \rightarrow \begin{array}{c} R^+ + CN^- \\ \searrow \\ R\cdot + \cdot CN \end{array} \quad \begin{array}{c}(1)\\ \\ (2)\end{array}$$

(RCN)

3. Crystal violet leucocyanide:[305,306] in ethanol solution, −6 to 36°, $\varphi_1 = 1.00 \pm 0.02$; at 2537, 2654, and 3130 A.

$$\left((CH_3)_2N-\!\!\!\left\langle\ \right\rangle\!\!\!\right)_3 \!\!\!\begin{array}{c} C-C\equiv N \\ \end{array} + h\nu \rightarrow R^+ + CN^- \tag{1}$$

(RCN)

5-5K   Miscellaneous Nitrogen-Containing Organic Compounds

1. Methyl isocyanate:[309] continuous absorption $\lambda < 2400$ A; full mercury arc, 25–150°, $\bar{\varphi}_1 \simeq \bar{\varphi}_2$; 300–420°, $\bar{\varphi}_2 > \bar{\varphi}_1$.

$$CH_3NCO + h\nu \rightarrow CH_3 + NCO \tag{1}$$

$$\searrow$$

$$CH_3N + CO \tag{2}$$

2. Spiropyrans; spiro(2-H-1-benzopyran-2,2'-indolines): the colorless form (I) photolyzes on irradiation in the ultraviolet to form (II), the colored form. The reverse reaction occurs thermally at a rate which is determined by the nature of the substituents, and it is promoted photochemically on irradiation of the colored form in the visible or ultraviolet. The quantum yield data are given for both reactions, corrected for thermal fade if it is significant. Solvents are as follows: D, dioxane; T, toluene; E, ethanol; φ_1 values in toluene are probably near zero if not shown. Color formation has been sensitized in some compounds by triplet benzophenone for certain conditions; see Sec. 5-9C-2.[428,691]

(1) [spiro-indoline-chromene structure, positions labelled 3, 4, 5, 6, 7, 8 and 4′, 5′, 6′, 7′; N—CH₃]

$$\text{(1)} \;\; \xrightarrow[\;h\nu\;(1)\;]{\;+\;h\nu\;(2)\;} \;\; \text{(II)}$$

(II) [open merocyanine form, N⁺—CH₃ / —O⁻]

Compound	Temp., °C	Solvent	λ_{max} (II), mμ	ϵ_{max} (II), ×10^{-4}	λ_{irr}, mμ	$\epsilon_{\lambda irr}$ (II), ×10^{-4}	$\epsilon_{\lambda irr}$ (I), ×10^{-3}	φ_2	φ_1	Reference
(1) 5,7-Dichloro-6-nitro-	15	D	582	5.18	366	1.20	1.19	0.58	0.015	436
					313	0.387	5.43	0.47		436
					436	0.270				436
					546	4.64				436
					579	4.93				436
(2) 6-Nitro-8-methoxy-	20	E	594	4.82	366	0.129	5.10	0.31	0.034	436
	20	T	594	4.82	313	0.849	0.964	~0.45	0.012	436
	20	T	610	3.61	366	0.976	8.71	0.55	0.010	436
	15	D	600	3.93	366	1.20	8.98	0.59	0.078	436
(3) 5-Bromo-6-nitro-8-methoxy-	15	D	581	4.35	366	0.837	4.76	0.43	0.0	436
(4) 5′-Chloro-5-bromo-6-nitro-8-methoxy-	15	D	583	4.55	366	0.733	4.68	0.44	0.0	436
								0.47		
(5) 5′-Methoxy-5-bromo-6-nitro-8-methoxy-	15	D	595	4.38	366	0.697	4.95	0.070	0.02	436
(6) 5,6-Dinitro-8-methoxy-	15	D	597	4.91	366	1.69	7.89	0.23	0.04	436
(7) 7′-Phenyl-5-bromo-6-nitro-8-methoxy-	20	T	591	3.70	366	0.643	5.11	0.72	0.0	436
(8) 6-Nitro-	26.5	E	540	~3.54	313			~0.15	~0.10	437
	26.5	E	540	~3.54	366			~0.12		437
	26.5	E			~546?					437
										437
(9) 5′-Chloro-5,7-dichloro-6-nitro-	20	T	605	5.18	366	1.96	3.93	0.76	0.0	436
(10) 5′-Chloro-6-nitro-	20	T	604	4.77	366	0.558	0.896	0.35	0.0	436
(11) 5′-Methoxy-6-nitro-	20	T	613	3.96	366	1.68	3.51	0.99	0.0	436
(12) 7′-Phenyl-6-nitro-	20	T	613	5.99	366	1.36	3.16	0.22	0.0	436
			612	5.33	366	1.82	4.39	0.66		436

3. α,N-Diphenylnitrone:[717] $\lambda_{max} = 3220$ A, $\epsilon \simeq 20,000$; 3130 A, $\varphi_1 = 0.28$ (cyclohexane solution), 0.18 (ethanol solution) independent of temperature (30–75°); reaction similar at 2537 A; no *cis-trans* isomerization is observed; the rearrangement has been interpreted as due to a significant change in the dipole moment of the N-O bond on excitation and the increase in the free valence of the carbon at the α-position in the excited state (0.53 to 0.78);[718] the oxygen atom moves rapidly to form a bond with the carbon atom before twisting of the phenyl groups about the double bond can occur.

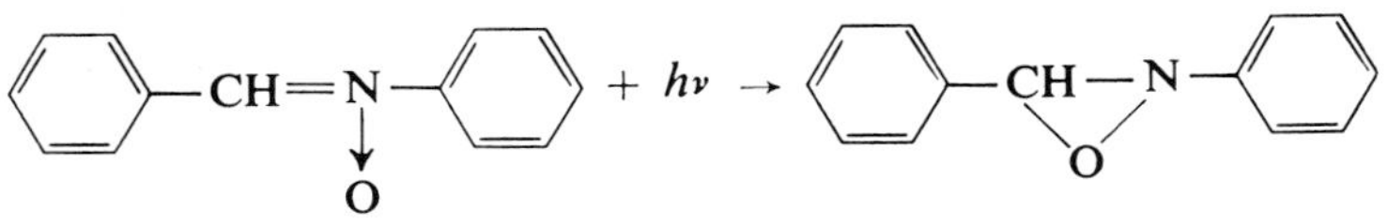

$$(1)$$

4. Alkylallenimines:[719] the photolysis at 2300–2500 A gave C_2H_2, C_2H_4, RCN, and RNC as major products, for $R = CH_3$, $\Phi_{C_2H_4} = 0.25$, $\Phi_{C_2H_2} = 0.13$ (102 mm, 24°); for similar conditions $\Phi_{C_2H_2}/\Phi_{C_2H_4} = 0.51$, 0.37, 0.26, 0.25, and 0.15 for $R = CH_3$, C_2H_5, n-C_3H_7, iso-C_3H_7, and t-C_4H_9, respectively; such a trend is consistent with the inductive effects of the groups in the weakening of the N-CH_2 ring bond and the enhancement of the C_2H_4-forming steps; the following mechanism has been suggested:

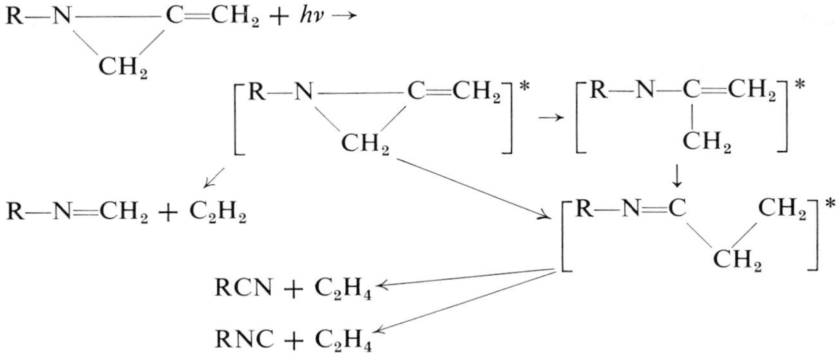

5-6 SULFUR-CONTAINING ORGANIC COMPOUNDS

The nature of the electronic transitions involved on absorption of light by sulfur compounds, mercaptans, sulfides, disulfides, thioketones, etc., follows that described previously for the oxygen-containing analogs. The lower electron affinity of the sulfur atom should lead to a higher-energy, looser-bound, non-bonding electron pair in the sulfur atom. As a consequence transitions involving these electrons, $n \rightarrow \pi^*$, $n \rightarrow \sigma^*$, etc., occur at longer wavelengths than with the oxygen-containing analogs; compare the spectra of the alcohols (Fig. 5-8), ethers (Fig. 5-9), and peroxides (Fig. 5-10), with those of the mercaptans, sulfides (Fig. 5-19), and disulfides (Fig. 5-20).

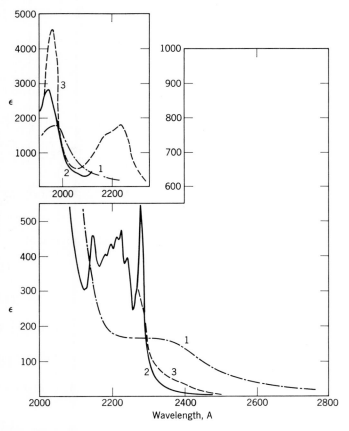

Fig. 5-19   Absorption spectra of (1) methyl mercaptan [$CH_3SH(g)$], 25°; (2) dimethyl sulfide [$CH_3SCH_3(g)$], 25°; (3) diethyl sulfide [$C_2H_5SC_2H_5(g)$], 25°.[424]

There have been few quantitative studies of the photochemistry of the sulfur-containing organic compounds.[494] The information available at this writing suggests that there are many similarities between the photodecomposition processes for the sulfur and oxygen analogs. For the

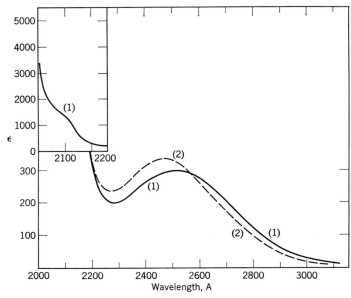

Fig. 5-20   Absorption spectra of (1) dimethyl disulfide [$CH_3SSCH_3(g)$]; 25°, (2) diethyl disulfide [$C_2H_5SSC_2H_5(g)$], 25°.[424]

mercaptans there is good evidence that process LXI is important.

$$RSH + h\nu \rightarrow RS + H \qquad\qquad\qquad (LXI)$$

$$R + SH \qquad\qquad\qquad (LXII)$$

$$R(—H) \text{ olefin} + H_2S \qquad\qquad\qquad (LXIII)$$

With the highly branched *tert*-butyl mercaptan, qualitative evidence points to the occurrence of LXII and/or LXIII.

Qualitative evidence from sulfide photolysis favors primary dissociation into free radicals:

$$RSR + h\nu \rightarrow RS^{\ddagger} + R^{\ddagger} \qquad\qquad\qquad (LXIV)$$

However, either a down-chain split of the sulfides is also important, or, more likely, there is extensive fragmentation of the $RS^{\ddagger}$ and $R^{\ddagger}$ excited primary radicals formed in LXIV.

In the disulfides rupture of the weak S-S bond is the major result of light absorption:

$$RSSR + h\nu \rightarrow 2RS \qquad\qquad\qquad (LXV)$$

Note the interesting behavior of the aryl thioketones in the following summary. The carbon skeleton is not broken by photolysis, but, depending on the environment, oxidation to the corresponding oxygen-containing aryl ketone or reduction to benzhydryl mercaptan, dibenzhydryl disulfide and tetrasulfide occurs; see p. 492.

1. Methyl mercaptan:[310,311] absorption spectrum shown in Fig. 5-19; process 1 dominant; 2537 A, $\varphi_1 \geqslant 0.9$

$$CH_3SH + h\nu \rightarrow CH_3S + H \tag{1}$$

2. Ethyl mercaptan:[312,313] process 1 favored at 2537 A; in organic matrix at 77°K, absorption at 4065 A develops on irradiation with full mercury arc; this is believed to arise from C_2H_5S formed and stabilized in the cage; disulfide is among the products on warming. Isopropyl and *n*-butyl mercaptans give similar spectra, which are attributed to the thiyl radicals formed in analogous primary processses.

$$CH_3CH_2SH + h\nu \rightarrow C_2H_5S + H \tag{1}$$

3. Miscellaneous mercaptans (thiols):[313-315] qualitative studies have been made with a variety of alkyl and aryl mercaptans. Process LXI is in accord with the analytical results in most cases. For *tert*-butyl mercaptan, LXII and/or LXIII is also likely.

4. Miscellaneous sulfides:[315] absorption spectra of dimethyl and diethyl sulfide shown in Fig. 5-19. Qualitative photochemical studies of a variety of alkyl sulfides are consistent with process LXIV. With $\overline{CH_2CH_2CH_2S}$, intramolecular formation of C_2H_4 and CH_2S seems favored as with the oxygen analog, oxetane.

5. Dimethyl disulfide:[316] absorption spectrum shown in Fig. 5-20; indirect evidence for process 1 from experiments with added ethylene and acetylene.

$$CH_3SSCH_3 + h\nu \rightarrow 2CH_3S \tag{1}$$

6. 1,2-Dithiolane:[317,318] in 95% ethanol solution, $3 \times 10^{-3} M$ HCl, 3650 A, $\varphi_1 \geqslant 0.60$; 3130 A, $\varphi_1 \geqslant 0.77$; in EPA matrix at 77°K, pink-salmon color develops and is attributed to radical formed in process 1.

$$\underset{S\text{—}S}{CH_2CH_2CH_2} + h\nu \rightarrow SCH_2CH_2CH_2S \tag{1}$$

7. 6,8-Thioctic acid:[317] in 95% ethanol solution, 3650 A, $\varphi_1 \geqslant 0.40$.

$$\underset{S\text{—}S}{CH_2CH_2CHCH_2CH_2CH_2CH_2CO_2H} + h\nu \rightarrow \underset{S}{SCH_2CH_2CH(CH_2)_4CO_2H} \tag{1}$$

8. Diphenyl disulfide:[319,202] first absorption at $\lambda < 3000$ A, $\lambda_{max} = 2450$ A; using spectrum of light below 3000 A, aqueous HCl solution, $\bar{\varphi}_1 \geqslant 0.023$;

this same quantum efficiency is found for *o*-methyl- and *p*-methyl-substituted diphenyl disulfide compounds. In EPA matrix at liquid-oxygen temperature, spectral evidence is found for C_6H_5S product and also photoionization product $[C_6H_5SSC_6H_5]^+$.

$$C_6H_5SSC_6H_5 + h\nu \rightarrow 2C_6H_5S \qquad (1)$$

9. Benzothiophenone:[320,548] first absorption band, $\lambda_{max} = 5950$ A, $\epsilon = 177$; second band, 3150 A, $\epsilon = 15,100$; 5880 A, in ethanol solution saturated with oxygen, photooxidation of reactant to benzophenone occurs with $\Phi = 0.056$; 3660 A, no net effect on reactant if oxygen present; in absence of oxygen, reduction to $(C_6H_5)_2CHSH$, $(C_6H_5)_2CHSSCH(C_6H_5)_2$ and $(C_6H_5)_2CHSSC(C_6H_5)_2SSC(C_6H_5)_2$ occurs in the ratio of 3.0:4.0:0.5; quantum yield of reduction = 0.047.

10. p,p'-Dimethoxybenzothiophenone:[320] first absorption band, $\lambda_{max} = 5700$ A, $\epsilon = 277$; second band, $\lambda_{max} = 3500$ A, $\epsilon = 26,100$; 5880 A, in ethanol solution saturated with oxygen, photooxidation to benzophenone derivative occurs with $\Phi = 0.048$.

11. p-Nitrobenzothiophenone:[320] first absorption band, $\lambda_{max} = 6100$ A, $\epsilon = 133$; second band, $\lambda_{max} = 3100$ A, $\epsilon = 12,450$; 5880 A, in ethanol solution saturated with oxygen, photooxidation to benzophenone derivative occurs with $\Phi = 0.18$.

12. Benzylic sulfones:[736] ultraviolet irradiation ($\lambda < 3200$ A) of benzene solutions of benzylic sulfones (under nitrogen at 15°) causes loss of sulfur dioxide, process 1, with high synthetic yields of products; the reaction is shown for 1,3-diphenyl-1,3-dihydronaphtho[2,3-*c*]thiophene-1,1-dioxide, one of several compounds found to undergo this reaction.

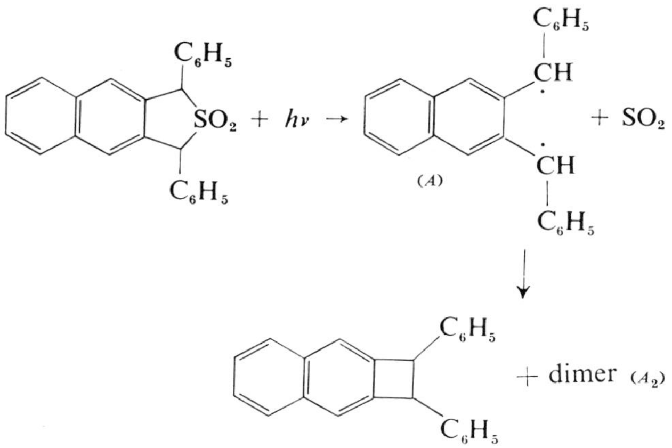

5-7 HYDROCARBONS

The first absorption band for the paraffin hydrocarbons occurs in the Schumann-ultraviolet region. Methane has its absorption onset at about 1440 A; absorption for the higher paraffins is shifted to longer wavelengths as the degree of alkyl radical substitution for hydrogen increases (see Fig. 5-21). The extinction coefficient at the maximum in the first band of the paraffins is about 10^4 and presumably corresponds to an allowed promotion of a σ-electron to a non-bonding σ^* orbital.

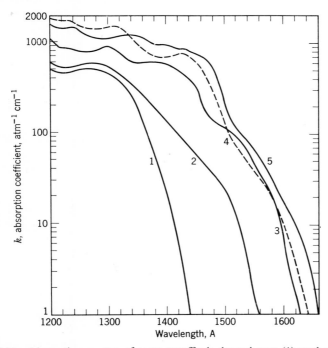

Fig. 5-21   Absorption spectra of some paraffin hydrocarbons: (1) methane [$CH_4(g)$]; (2) ethane [$C_2H_6(g)$]; (3) propane [$C_3H_8(g)$]; (4) perdeutero-*n*-butane [n-$C_4D_{10}(g)$]; (5) *n*-butane [n-$C_4H_{10}(g)$]; absorption coefficient k in equation $I = I_0 e^{-kpx}$, where p is the pressure in atmospheres at 25°, from Okabe and Becker.[430]

The first singlet-singlet absorption band of the olefins and acetylenic compounds occurs at somewhat longer wavelengths than that for the paraffins; see the spectra in Figs. 5-22 to 5-25. The maximum shifts regularly to the visible with increased number of conjugated double bonds; for example, for the compounds in the series $CH_3(CH{=}CH)_nCH_3$, λ_{max} shifts from 2260 A for $n = 2$ to 4760 A for $n = 10$. The electronic transition

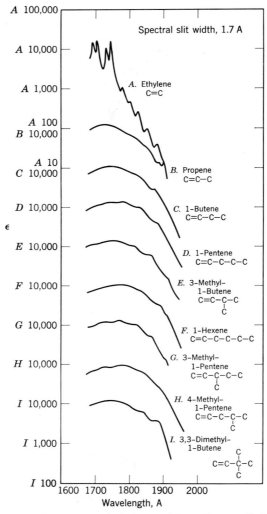

Fig. 5-22 Absorption spectra of ethylene and C_3 to C_6 monoalkylethylenes as indicated. From Jones and Taylor.[431]

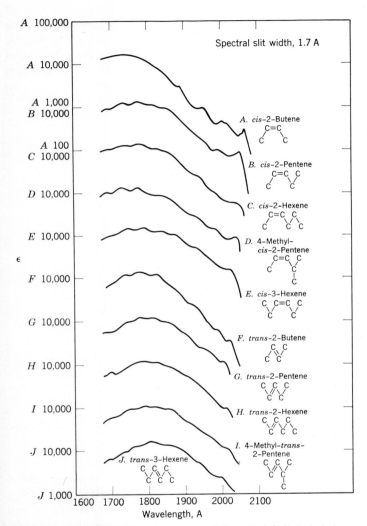

Fig. 5-23   Absorption spectra of vapors of C_4 to C_6 1,2-dialkylethylenes as indicated. From Jones and Taylor.[431]

is allowed, $\epsilon \sim 10^4$, and corresponds to the promotion of an electron in the π system to an antibonding π^* orbital.

The simple aromatic hydrocarbons show a first absorption region of moderate intensity in the ultraviolet region. For the first band in benzene $\lambda_{max} = 2560$ A with $\epsilon \simeq 160$; see Fig. 5-26. This transition is symmetry "forbidden" $(^1B_{2u} \leftarrow {}^1A_{1g})$ but is somewhat allowed by the interactions with molecular skeleton vibrations. Benzene shows vibrational structure in the first band which arises from the "breathing" vibration of the ring

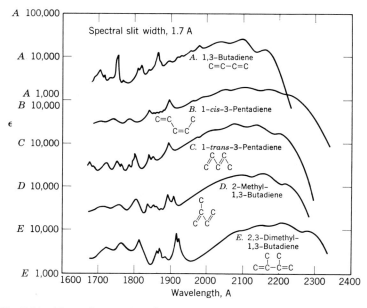

Fig. 5-24   Absorption spectra of vapors of C_4 to C_6 conjugated diolefins as indicated. From Jones and Taylor.[431]

system. A second "forbidden" band occurs in benzene at about 2000 A $(^1B_{1u} \leftarrow {}^1A_{1g})$ and an intense allowed band at about 1800 A $(^1E_{2u} \leftarrow {}^1A_{1g})$. The accumulation of conjugated aromatic rings leads to a shift in the first absorption band to longer wavelengths, the symmetry restrictions become less important, and an increase in ϵ occurs; note the spectra of Fig. 5-26.

It is interesting to note that direct singlet-triplet absorptions can be observed in the olefinic and aromatic hydrocarbons at considerably longer wavelengths than the singlet-singlet absorption when they have been intensified by the presence of high pressures of oxygen.

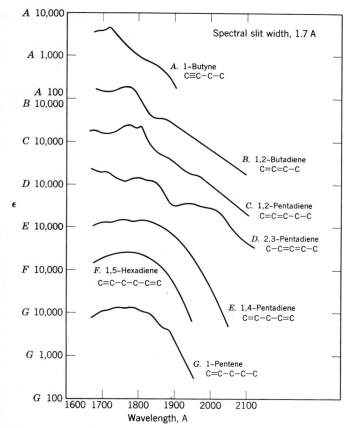

Fig. 5-25   Absorption spectra of vapors of 1-butyne and non-conjugated diolefins as indicated. From Jones and Taylor.[431]

5-7A   Paraffin Hydrocarbons

The dominant primary photodissociative mode in the 1470–1295 A photolysis of paraffins is the molecular elimination of hydrogen. The favored mechanism is the loss of two hydrogens from the same carbon atom, forming a divalent carbon species and molecular hydrogen,

$$RCH_2R' + h\nu \rightarrow R\ddot{C}R' + H_2 \qquad \text{(LXVI)}$$

Processes forming hydrogen atoms and free radicals are less important, but nearly every possible simple bond rupture and rearrangement seems to occur to some extent. For example, see the results for butane photolysis in the summary which follows. Photoionization becomes a dominant

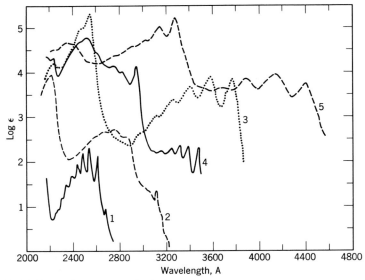

Fig. 5-26   Absorption spectra of solution of:

(1) benzene ⟨◯⟩ in cyclohexane;

(2) naphthalene ⟨◯◯⟩ in ethanol;

(3) anthracene ⟨◯◯◯⟩ in cyclohexane;

(4) phenanthrene ⟨◯◯◯⟩ in cyclhexane;

(5) 1,2-9,10-dibenznaphthacene ⟨◯◯◯◯◯◯⟩ in dioxane.

From Friedel and Orchin.[432]

primary step when the energy of the light quantum exceeds the ionization potential of the hydrocarbon; note the data for CH_4.

1. Methane:[321−326,339,418] part of the first absorption region is pictured in Fig. 5-21; one or two maxima near 900 A; 1236 A, experiments with CH_4, CH_2D_2, CHD_3, and CD_4 show process 1 to be important; $\varphi_1/\varphi_2 \cong 5.7$; $\Phi_{H_2} \cong 0.39$; Φ_{D_2} (from CD_4) $\cong 0.27$; onset of process 3 at 967 ± 10 A; $\varphi_3 = 0.19$ (932 A), 0.29 (916 A), 0.49 (883 A), 0.80 (833 A), 1.0 (796–278 A).

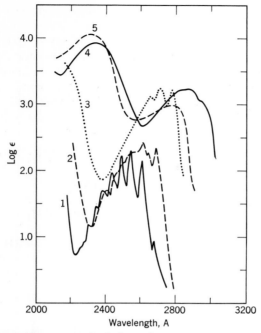

Fig. 5-27   Absorption spectra of solutions of:

(1) benzene $\left(\text{⬡}\right)$ in cyclohexane;

(2) toluene $\left(\text{⬡}-CH_3\right)$ in cyclohexane;

(3) phenol $\left(\text{⬡}-OH\right)$ in cyclohexane;

(4) aniline $\left(\text{⬡}-NH_2\right)$ in isooctane;

(5) benzoic acid $\left(\text{⬡}-CO_2H\right)$ in cyclohexane.

From Friedel and Orchin.[432]

$$CH_4 + h\nu \rightarrow CH_2 + H_2 \tag{1}$$

$$CH_3 + H \tag{2}$$

$$CH_4^+ + e^- \tag{3}$$

2. *Ethane*:[252,327–330,420,676,733] part of the first absorption region shown in Fig. 5-21; 1295 and 1470 A (largely 1470 A), experiments with C_2H_6, C_2D_6,

and CH_3CD_3 show dominant source of hydrogen is process 1; $\varphi_1 > \varphi_3$ and φ_4; at 1470 A at least 80% of the hydrogen is formed by molecular detachment; process 2 is major source of methane; $\varphi_2 \cong 0.02\varphi_1$; $\varphi_2 > \varphi_5$; $\varphi_6/\varphi_1 \cong 0.15$; in photolyses in liquid nitrogen, the decomposition of excited C_2H_4 to acetylene and hydrogen (in process 1) is almost completely suppressed; 1236 A, process 1 is dominant, but processes 2 and 6 increased in importance; $\varphi_2/\varphi_1 \cong 0.50$; $\varphi_6/\varphi_1 \cong 0.88$. 1067, 1048 A, φ_6 increased over value at 1236 A; methane is formed largely in process 2; φ_2 about the same as that at 1236 A.

$$C_2H_6 + h\nu \rightarrow H_2 + CHCH_3^{\ddagger} \rightarrow H_2 + C_2H_2 \tag{1}$$

$$\xrightarrow{M} C_2H_4$$

$$\rightarrow CH_4 + CH_2 \tag{2}$$

$$\rightarrow H_2 + CH_2{=}CH_2 \tag{3}$$

$$\rightarrow H + C_2H_5 \tag{4}$$

$$\rightarrow 2CH_3 \tag{5}$$

$$\rightarrow C_2H_4 + 2H \tag{6}$$

3. Propane:[331–334] portion of first absorption region shown in Fig. 5-21; photolyses using C_3H_8, C_3D_8, $CH_3CH_2CD_3$, and $CH_3CD_2CH_3$ show that all processes 1-5 major, 6 and 7 also occur to some extent; 1470 A (2% 1295 A), $\varphi_1 > \varphi_2$ and φ_3; $\varphi_4/\varphi_5 \cong 4$; $\varphi_4 + \varphi_5 \cong \varphi_7$; in D-substituted propane photolyses, the probablity of deuterium to hydrogen transfer in 4 and 5 $\cong$ 0.5; 1236 A (83%), 1165 A (17%), all processes occur but 7 increased in importance at this wavelength.

$$C_3H_8 + h\nu \rightarrow CH_3CCH_3 + H_2 \tag{1}$$

$$CHCH_2CH_3 + H_2 \tag{2}$$

$$CH_2{=}CHCH_3 + H_2 \tag{3}$$

$$CH_3CH + CH_4 \tag{4}$$

$$C_2H_4 + CH_4 \tag{5}$$

$$H + C_3H_7 \tag{6}$$

$$CH_3 + C_2H_5 \tag{7}$$

4. n-Butane:[335,332,430] portion of the first absorption region shown in Fig. 5-21; 1470 A, photolyses of n-C_4H_{10} and n-C_4D_{10} mixtures and $CH_3CD_2CD_2CH_3$ suggest the approximate primary quantum efficiencies of processes 1–8, respectively: 0.41, 0.12, 0.01, 0.07, 0.02, 0.06, ⩾0.24, ⩾0.07. 1236 A (75%), 1165 A (25%), estimated φ's for 1–8, respectively: 0.18, 0.20, 0.03, 0.07, 0.00, 0.15, ⩾0.27, ⩾0.10. In process 1, H_2 is preferentially expelled from the central carbon atoms, although the importance of alternative structures of C_4H_8 cannot be unambiguously assigned; by analogy with C_2H_6 and C_3H_8, $CH_3CCH_2CH_3$ may be favored.

$$n\text{-}C_4H_{10} + h\nu \rightarrow H_2 + C_4H_8 \tag{1}$$

$$2C_2H_4 + 2H \tag{2}$$

$$CH_4 + C_3H_6 \tag{3}$$

$$CH_3 + H + C_3H_6 \tag{4}$$

$$C_2H_6 + C_2H_4 \tag{5}$$

$$C_2H_6 + C_2H_2 + H_2 \tag{6}$$

$$CH_3 + C_3H_7 \tag{7}$$

$$2C_2H_5 \tag{8}$$

5. Isobutane:[336] absorption onset at about 1700 A; at 1470 A, ϵ (iso-C_4H_{10}) = 5.4 × 10³; ϵ (iso-C_4D_{10}) = 4.5 × 10³; 1470 A, photolyses of iso-C_4H_{10}, iso-C_4D_{10}, and $(CH_3)_3CD$ show processes 1–8 probably occur; $\varphi_1 + \varphi_2 \cong \varphi_3 + \varphi_4$; $\varphi_3 \cong 8\varphi_4$; $\varphi_2 > \varphi_1$; $\varphi_5 \cong \varphi_6$; 1236 A, $\varphi_1 > \varphi_2$; $\varphi_5 \cong \varphi_6$.

$$(CH_3)_3CH + h\nu \rightarrow (CH_3)_2CH\ddot{C}H + H_2 \tag{1}$$

$$(CH_3)_2C{=}CH_2 + H_2 \tag{2}$$

$$(CH_3)_2CHCH_2 + H \tag{3}$$

$$(CH_3)_3C + H \tag{4}$$

$$CH_4 + CH_3\ddot{C}CH_3 \tag{5}$$

$$CH_4 + CH_2{=}CHCH_3 \tag{6}$$

$$CH_3 + (CH_3)_2CH \tag{7}$$

$$2CH_3 + C_2H_4 \tag{8}$$

6. *Cyclopropane:*[337,338] continuous absorption with maxima at 1202, 1449, and 1594 A; 1470 A, photolyses of cyclopropane and cyclopropane-d_6 show $\varphi_1 > \varphi_2 > \varphi_3$.

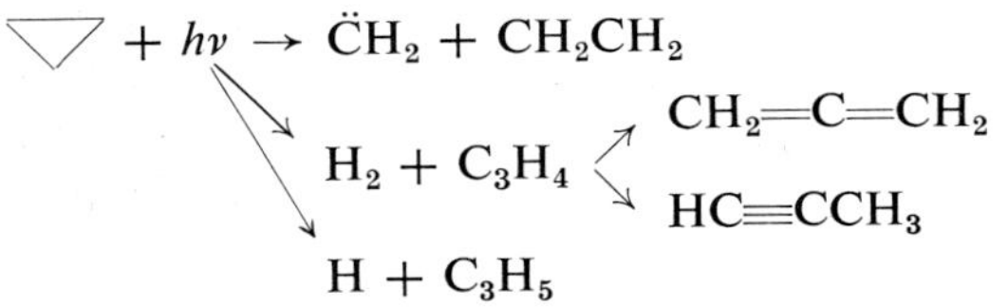

$$\triangledown + h\nu \rightarrow \ddot{C}H_2 + CH_2CH_2 \qquad (1)$$

$$H_2 + C_3H_4 \begin{cases} CH_2{=}C{=}CH_2 \\ HC{\equiv}CCH_3 \end{cases} \qquad (2)$$

$$H + C_3H_5 \qquad (3)$$

5-7B   The Olefinic and Acetylenic Hydrocarbons

The photochemistry of the olefins involves a complex interplay of several types of primary processes from several possible excited molecular states. Excitation within the first singlet-singlet absorption band may be followed by a variety of fragmentation steps involving H_2 molecule and hydrogen atom and radical formation, processes LXVII and LXVIII.

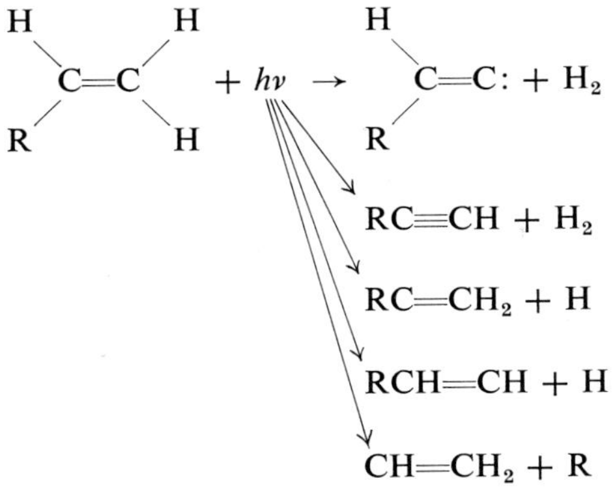

$$\begin{array}{cc} H \quad\quad H \\ \diagdown C{=}C \diagup \\ R \diagup \quad \diagdown H \end{array} + h\nu \rightarrow \begin{array}{c} H \\ \diagdown C{=}C{:} + H_2 \\ R \diagup \end{array} \qquad (LXVIIa)$$

$$RC{\equiv}CH + H_2 \qquad (LXVIIb)$$

$$RC{=}CH_2 + H \qquad (LXVIIIa)$$

$$RCH{=}CH + H \qquad (LXVIIIb)$$

$$CH{=}CH_2 + R \qquad (LXVIIIc)$$

Alternatively the major result of excitation, particularly in solution, may be the isomerization of the original olefin. Stilbene and its derivatives, dichloroethylene, etc., follow this pattern. Evidence at hand suggests that at least two alternative mechanisms of *cis-trans* isomerization may be operative. In the case of stilbene there are probably both *cis* and *trans* singlet and triplet forms, while in dichloroethylene both *cis* and *trans* compounds appear to have a common triplet intermediate state ($N* = Q*$), since the summation of the quantum yields for *trans* $\rightarrow$ *cis* and *cis* $\rightarrow$ *trans* isomerization in the triplet absorption band is near unity. (See the summary on p. 504.)

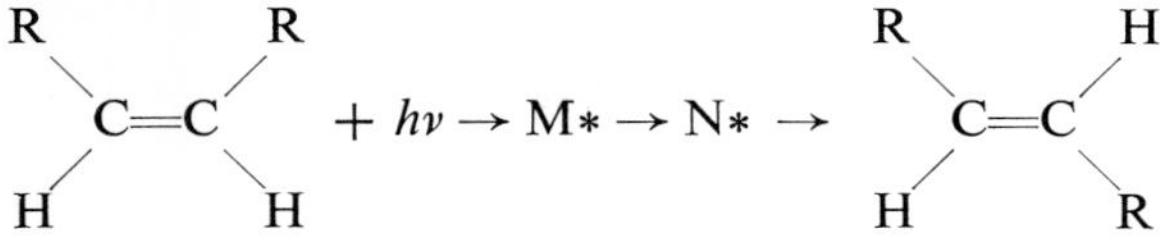

$$\underset{H}{\overset{R}{\diagdown}}C{=}C\underset{H}{\overset{R}{\diagup}} + h\nu \rightarrow M* \rightarrow N* \rightarrow \underset{H}{\overset{R}{\diagdown}}C{=}C\underset{R}{\overset{H}{\diagup}} \qquad \text{(LXIXa)}$$

$$\underset{H}{\overset{R}{\diagdown}}C{=}C\underset{R}{\overset{H}{\diagup}} + h\nu \rightarrow P* \rightarrow Q* \rightarrow \underset{H}{\overset{R}{\diagdown}}C{=}C\underset{H}{\overset{R}{\diagup}} \qquad \text{(LXIXb)}$$

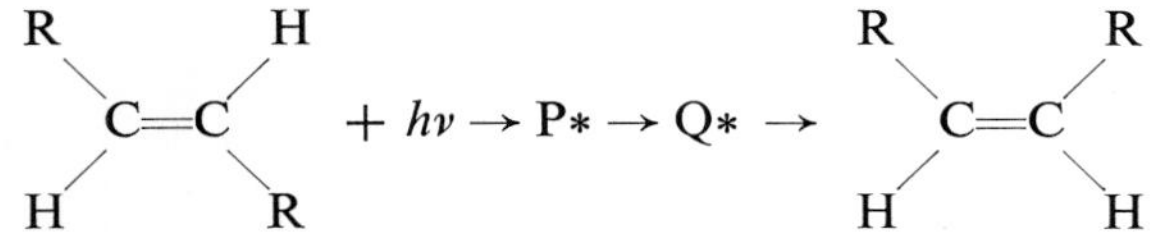

M* and P* are excited singlet and N* and Q* are excited triplet states. In most cases reactions in competition with the isomerization exist; fluorescence from the *trans* singlet, deactivation, etc.

The dienes, trienes, etc., show an interesting pattern of primary reactions. In photolyses at low pressure, radical and molecular fragmentations of the conjugated dienes are important. These processes are strongly suppressed by added gas, and this result has been interpreted as evidence of the participation of a vibrationally excited ground-state molecule formed by intersystem crossing from the excited singlet state. In solution the photolysis of the dienes results in cyclization:

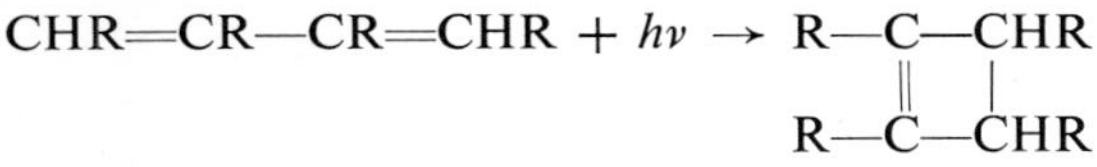

$$CHR{=}CR{-}CR{=}CHR + h\nu \rightarrow \begin{matrix} R{-}C{-}CHR \\ \| \quad | \\ R{-}C{-}CHR \end{matrix} \qquad \text{(LXXa)}$$

An analogous coupling occurs in the conjugated trienes,

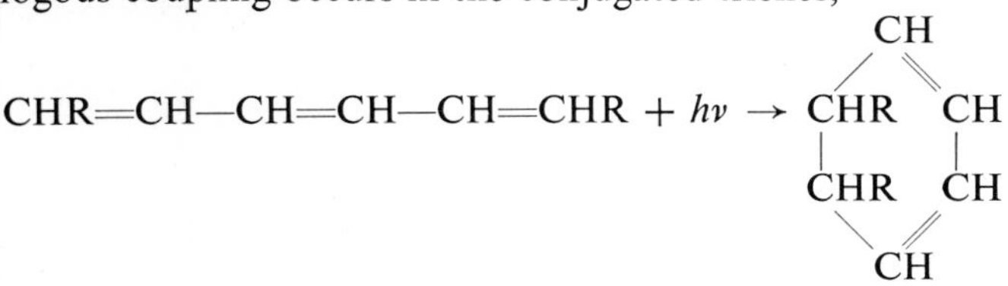

$$CHR{=}CH{-}CH{=}CH{-}CH{=}CHR + h\nu \rightarrow \begin{matrix} CH \\ \diagup \quad \diagdown \\ CHR \quad CH \\ | \qquad | \\ CHR \quad CH \\ \diagdown \quad \diagup \\ CH \end{matrix} \qquad \text{(LXXb)}$$

The cyclohexadienes react in solution to give the ring-cleavage process LXXI. In the gas phase at low pressures, various fragmentation processes

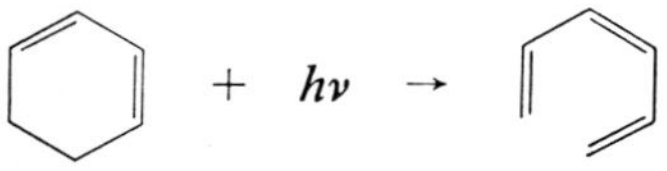

$$\bighexagon + h\nu \rightarrow \bighexagon \qquad \text{(LXXI)}$$

compete as with the trienes; these may occur from a vibrationally excited ground state.

In solution photolysis of the seven- and eight-membered-ring polyenes, bond formation occurs across the ring to give bicyclic compounds, process LXXII.

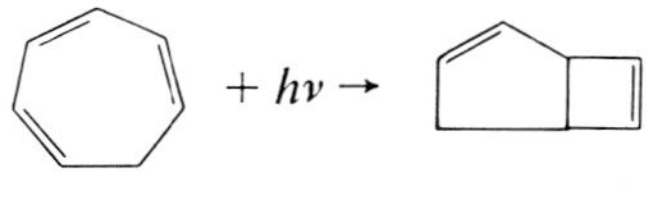

$$\text{(cycloheptatriene)} + h\nu \rightarrow \text{(bicyclic product)} \qquad \text{(LXXIIa)}$$

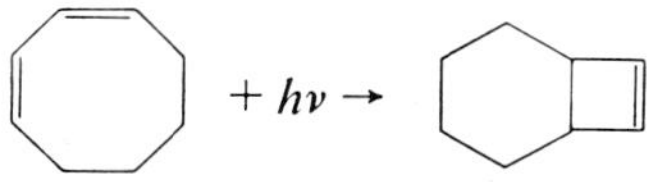

$$\text{(cyclooctatetraene)} + h\nu \rightarrow \text{(bicyclic product)} \qquad \text{(LXXIIb)}$$

$$\text{(cyclooctatetraene)} + h\nu \rightarrow \text{(bicyclic product)} \qquad \text{(LXXIIc)}$$

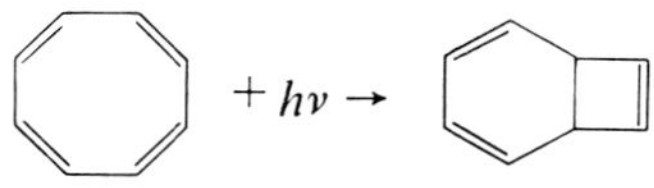

In gas-phase photolysis various other rearrangement and fragmentation products appear, conceivably from vibrationally excited, initially formed products of LXXII. Thus toluene appears at low pressures in the photolysis of 1,3,5-cycloheptatrien; benzene, acetylene, and styrene form from cyclooctatetraene. (See the recent review by Dauben and Wipke.[639])

Gas-phase photolysis of the acetylenic compounds at short wavelengths has been little studied, but the results are consistent with molecular fragmentation processes and polymer formation through excited-molecule reactions.

1. Ethylene:[335,340] absorption spectrum shown in Fig. 5-22; at 1236, 1470, and 1849 A, $\varphi_1 \cong 1.5 \; \varphi_3$; results from photolysis of *trans*-CHD=CHD suggest nearly free rotation of the molecule in its excited state; $(\varphi_2 + \varphi_4)/(\varphi_1 + \varphi_3) \cong 1.0$ at 1470 A, 1.4 at 1236 A; at 1470 A, $\varphi_5 \leqslant 0.05$.

$$CH_2{=}CH_2 + h\nu \longrightarrow CH_2C + H_2 \qquad (1)$$

$$HC{\equiv}CH$$

$$CH_2C + H + H \qquad (2)$$

$$HC{\equiv}CH + H_2 \qquad (3)$$

$$HC{\equiv}CH + H + H \qquad (4)$$

$$CH_2CH + H \qquad (5)$$

2. 1,2-Dichloroethylene:[421] pure liquid saturated with O_2, $p \leqslant 130$ atm, irradiated in singlet-triplet band (3130–3660 A), $\varphi_1 = 0.61 \pm 0.07$, $\varphi_2 = 0.45 \pm 0.06$; data favor a common triplet state for both *cis* and *trans* isomers; see also gas-phase photolysis results, p. 527.

$$\text{*trans*-CHClCHCl} + h\nu \rightarrow \text{CHClCHCl}(T_1) \rightarrow \text{*cis*-CHClCHCl} \qquad (1)$$

$$\text{*cis*-CHClCHCl} + h\nu \qquad\qquad\qquad \text{*trans*-CHClCHCl} \qquad (2)$$

3. Propylene:[208,246] photolysis of C_3H_6, C_3D_6, and $CH_3CH=CD_2$ at 1470 A gives products consistent with processes 1–6; 6 is most important; 1236 A, $\varphi_7 \cong 0.32$; other processes occur as well.

$$C_3H_6 + h\nu \longrightarrow CH_3 + H + C_2H_2 \tag{1}$$

$$CH_4 + C_2H_2 \tag{2}$$

$$H_2 + CH_2=C=CH_2 \tag{3}$$

$$H + C_3H_5 \tag{4}$$

$$CH_2 + C_2H_4 \tag{5}$$

$$CH_3 + C_2H_3^{\ddagger} \tag{6}$$

$$C_2H_2 + H$$

$$C_3H_6^+ + e^- \tag{7}$$

4. Isobutene:[341] 1990–1855 A (aluminum spark), $\varphi_1 \geqslant 0.03$, $\varphi_2 \geqslant 0.10$; large amounts of polymer formed; in view of recent detailed ethylene and propylene studies, several other primary steps are likely also.

$$(CH_3)_2C=CH_2 + h\nu \rightarrow M^*(+N) \rightarrow M(+N')$$

$$CH_2C(CH_3)=CH_2 + H \tag{1}$$

$$CH_3 + CH_3C=CH_2 \tag{2}$$

5. Free radical-forming primary processes in miscellaneous olefins:[342] full high-pressure mercury arc ($\lambda > 2500$ A); absorption in long wavelength edge of bands; EPR spectra characterized the following free radicals (believed to be primary products) on irradiation of the pure solids at 77°K: *2-butene*, 2-butenyl; *2-pentene*, 2-butenyl, 1-methyl-2-butenyl; *1-hexene*, 2-hexenyl; *2-hexene*, 2-hexenyl, 1-methyl-2-pentenyl; *2-heptene*, 2-heptenyl; *3-heptene*, 2-hexenyl, 1-methyl-2-hexenyl; *1-octene*, 2-octenyl; *2-octene*, 2-octenyl; 1-methyl-2-heptenyl; *2-methyl-2-butene*, 2- or 3-methyl-2-butenyl.

6. Styrene[356–358] ($C_6H_5CH=CH_2$): in isooctane absorption shows vibrational structure; $\lambda_{max} \cong 2905$ A ($\epsilon \cong 15$); 2820 A ($\epsilon \cong 18$); 2730 A ($\epsilon \cong 18$); 2475 A ($\epsilon \cong 68$); 2400 A ($\epsilon \cong 68$); Photopolymerization dominant reaction in solution; polystyrene (average molecular weight 50,000) in benzene depolymerizes with a quantum efficiency of the splitting process (assumed to divide into two fragments) $\cong 6.5 \times 10^{-5}$ at 2537 A.

7. *Stilbene:*[343-353] absorption bands show no vibrational structure for *cis*-stilbene in ethanol, $\lambda_{max} \cong 2800$ ($\epsilon = 1.05 \times 10^4$), 2240 A ($\epsilon = 2.46 \times 10^4$); *trans*-stilbene in heptane, first absorption band shows vibrational peaks at 2830, 2941 ($\epsilon = 2.80 \times 10^4$), 3069, and 3205 A; other bands centered at 2285 A ($\epsilon = 1.62 \times 10^4$) and 2015 A ($\epsilon = 2.38 \times 10^4$). *Cis-trans* isomerization dominant photochemical process, but dihydrophenanthrene formation also occurs from excited *cis*-singlet state, process 1; only *trans*-form shows fluorescence; isomerization can be sensitized by other excited triplet molecules (acetophenone, benzophenone, anthraquinone, etc.). Probably isomerization occurs from excited triplet states or, less likely, from vibrationally excited singlet ground states formed from triplet by intersystem crossing; 3330 ± 30 A, dilute solution in methylpentane, room temperature, $\varphi_3 = 0.67 \pm 0.2$; 3130 A, room temperature, solution in *n*-hexane $\sim 10^{-5}$ M, $\varphi_3 = 0.59^{346}$, $\sim 0.47^{355}$, in methylcyclohexane-isohexane, $0.50(25°)$, $0.46(-40°)$, $0.31(-65°)$, $0.18(-90°)$, $0.07(-123°)$, $0.006(-183°)$;[350] $\varphi_2 \cong 0.32$, in methylcyclohexane, 0.30; $\varphi_1 \cong 0.07$; in non-polar solvent at $-180°$, $\varphi_3 \cong 10^{-4}$, $\varphi_2 \cong 10^{-2}$, φ_3 decreases at concentrations $> 10^{-3}$ M; 3020 A, room temperature, solution in methylpentane, $\varphi_3 \cong 0.35$; 2650 A, room temperature, solution in methylpentane, $\varphi_3 \cong 0.35$; 2537 A, solution in *n*-hexane, $\sim 10^{-5}$ M, room temperature, $\varphi_3 \cong 0.67$, $\varphi_2 \cong 0.28$, $\varphi_1 \cong 0.07$; at $-90°$ in isooctane, $\varphi_3 \cong 0.35$, $\varphi_2 \cong 0.32$, $\varphi_f \leqslant 0.48$ (*trans* form).

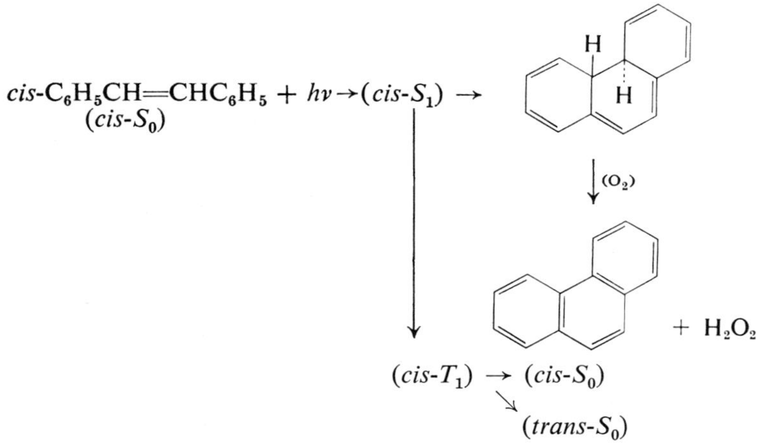

$$cis\text{-}C_6H_5CH{=}CHC_6H_5 + h\nu \rightarrow (cis\text{-}S_1) \rightarrow \qquad\qquad (1)$$
$$(cis\text{-}S_0)$$

$$(cis\text{-}T_1) \rightarrow (cis\text{-}S_0)$$
$$\searrow$$
$$(trans\text{-}S_0) \qquad (2)$$

$$trans\text{-}C_6H_5CH{=}CHC_6H_5 + h\nu \rightarrow (trans\text{-}S_1) \rightarrow (trans\text{-}S_0) + h\nu'$$
$$(trans\text{-}S_0) \qquad\qquad \downarrow$$
$$(trans\text{-}T_1) \rightarrow (trans\text{-}S_0)$$
$$\searrow$$
$$(cis\text{-}S_0) \qquad (3)$$

8–15. Miscellaneous substituted stilbenes etc.:[347] quantum yields of *cis* →
trans (φ_{c-t}) and *trans* → *cis* (φ_{t-c}) and *trans* fluorescence (φ_f) are shown for
dilute solutions in polar and non-polar solvents at room temperature
unless indicated otherwise (DMF = dimethylformamide); values are
approximate, since dihydrophenanthrene formation was not evaluated.

Compound	Solvent	λ, A	φ_{t-c}	φ_{c-t}	φ_f	Ref.
(8) 4,4′-Dinitrostilbene	C_6H_6	3660	0.27	0.34	. . .	347
	DMF	3660	0.31	0.33	. . .	347
(9) 4-Nitro-3′-	Cyclohexane	3660	0.61	0.25	. . .	347
methoxystilbene	C_6H_6	3660	0.38	0.40	. . .	347
	DMF	3660	0.20	0.38	. . .	347
(10) 4-Nitro-4′-	Benzine	3660	0.67	0.24	. . .	347
methoxystilbene	C_6H_6	3660	0.40	0.43	. . .	347
	DMF	3660	0.035	0.42	. . .	347
(11) 4-Nitro-4′-	Cyclohexane	3660	0.44	0.36	. . .	347
aminostilbene	C_6H_6	3660	0.10	0.44	. . .	347
	DMF	3660	0.00	0.20	. . .	347
(12) 4-Nitro-4′-	Cyclohexane	3660	0.20	0.40	. . .	347
dimethylamino-	C_6H_6	3660	0.016	0.40	. . .	347
stilbene	DMF	3660	0.00	0.15	. . .	347
	Cyclohexane	3130	0.14	0.45	. . .	347
	Cyclohexane	4050	0.16	0.42	. . .	347
	Cyclohexane	4360	0.16	0.37	. . .	347
	C_6H_6	3130	0.015	0.42	. . .	347
	C_6H_6	4050	0.015	0.40	. . .	347
	C_6H_6	4360	0.013	0.40	. . .	347
(13) *p*-Chlorostilbene	Methyl	3130	0.60 (25°)	0.4–0.5	. . .	350
	cyclohexane		0.45 (−40°)		. . .	350
			0.29 (−80°)		. . .	350
			0.20 (−100°)		. . .	350
			0.13 (−140°)		. . .	350
			∼0.01 (−174°)		. . .	350
(14) *p*-Bromostilbene	Methyl	3130	0.35 (25°)	0.17	0.065	350
(0.6 × 10⁻⁶ *M*)	cyclohexane		0.35 (−40°)		0.08	350
			0.35 (−115°)		0.11	350
			0.35 (−155°)		0.13	350
			0.003 (−183°)		0.17	350
(15) *p*-Dimethylamino-	C_2H_5OH	3660	0.65	0.44	. . .	347
cinnamic acid						
nitrile						

$$\text{CH}\!=\!\text{CH}$$

16. Acenaphthylene[359–362] : absorption in cyclohexane shows

vibrational structure; $\lambda_{max}(\log_{10}\epsilon)$: 4380 A (1.13); 4120 A (2.19); 3900 A
(2.34); 3390 A (3.69); 3220 A (4.01); 3100 A (3.92); 2750 A (3.46);
2650 A (3.48); 2300 A (4.72); using radiation of wavelengths 4360, 4050,
and 3660 A, average quantum yields of acenaphthalene removal (to form
dimers) in toluene solutions at temperatures and concentrations shown:
0.012 (11°, 0.163 *M*); 0.059 (11°, 1.13 *M*); 0.011 (31°, 0.158 *M*); 0.024
(31°, 0.423 *M*); 0.01 (52°, 0.163 *M*); 0.048 (52°, 1.13 *M*); quantum
yields of dimer formation higher in poorer solvent (ethanol-water) than in

good solvent (benzene); [the rate in each case is proportional to the concentration (2–12 gram/liter)]; dimer forms on irradiation of pure crystal surface as well.

17. 1,3-Butadiene:[364,369,370,419] absorption spectrum shown in Fig. 5-24; in the presence of oxygen the singlet-triplet excitation band is observed from 3500 to 5200 A (0-0 band, 4800 A); full mercury arc, 25°, 4 mm, $\overline{\varphi_2/\varphi_1} \cong 0.5$; $\overline{\varphi_3/\varphi_1} \cong 0.2$; major products are H_2, C_2H_2, C_2H_4 (amount equal to C_2H_2), C_2H_6, 1-butyne, and 1,2-butadiene; there are more than 17 minor products, but cyclobutene was not detected. Processes 1–3 decrease in efficiency as the pressure is increased; the precursor to these products may be the vibrationally excited ground state, $M^{\ddagger}$. Photolysis in solution of cyclohexane yields cyclobutene, dimer, bicyclo[1.1.0]butane, and none of the products of the gas-phase experiments; $\varphi_4 = 0.03$ (2537 A); $\varphi_4 > \varphi_5$; 2537 A irradiation of 10–15% solution of butadiene in cyclohexane until no butadiene remains gives a 50% yield of cyclobutene;[730] dimerization can be sensitized efficiently in solutions of sensitizer in liquid butadiene, using full mercury arc; relative yields of the products, *trans*-divinylcyclobutane (I), *cis*-divinylbutane (II), and 4-vinylcyclohexane (III), depend on the sensitizer employed: using benzil, 49% I, 8% II, and 43% III formed; with 2-acetonaphthone, 76% I, 17% II, and 7% III formed.

$$CH_2{=}CHCH{=}CH_2 + h\nu \rightarrow$$
$$M^* \rightarrow M^{\ddagger}(+N) \rightarrow M(+N')$$

$$CH_2{=}C{=}CHCH_3^{\ddagger} \tag{1}$$
$$\text{(N)} \quad CH_3 + C_3H_3$$
$$CH_2{=}C{=}CHCH_3(+N')$$

$$CH_2{=}CH_2 + CH{\equiv}CH \tag{2}$$

$$H_2 + C_4H_4 \tag{3}$$

$$\begin{array}{c} CH{-}CH_2 \\ \| \quad | \\ CH{-}CH_2 \end{array} \tag{4}$$

$$\begin{array}{c} HC{-}CH_2 \\ | \diagdown | \\ CH_2{-}CH \end{array} \tag{5}$$

18. 1,3-Pentadiene:[363,368] absorption shown in Fig. 5-24; 2537 A, ϵ (*trans*) = 39.5; ϵ (*cis*) = 8.4; cyclohexane solution, the *trans* form may be the only source of process 1; Φ (disappearance) = 0.04, $\varphi_1 = 0.03$ (2×10^{-4} M); *trans-cis* isomerization occurs also and some dimerization (polymerization); *cis-trans* isomerization can be sensitized by excited triplet states of certain carbonyl compounds in benzene solution, presumably through the excitation of triplet states in the 1,3-pentadiene isomers. From the 0-0 phosphorescence band positions of the sensitizer and the relative efficiencies of the sensitizers to cause isomerization, it is concluded that the $S_0 \rightarrow T_1$ transition of the *cis* form lies at slightly longer wavelengths than the *trans* form, and both lie below 5400 A.

$$CH_2{=}CHCH{=}CHCH_3 + h\nu \rightarrow \begin{array}{c} CH-CH-CH_3 \\ \| \quad | \\ CH-CH_2 \end{array} \qquad (1)$$

19. 2-Methyl-1,3-butadiene (isoprene):[363,385] absorption spectrum shown in Fig. 5-24; 2537 A, cyclohexane solution (2×10^{-4} M), $\varphi_1 = 0.09$, Φ (disappearance) $= 0.11$; dimerization of liquid isoprene is sensitized by a variety of carbonyl compounds through excitation of triplet states; seven dimers are found in amounts which vary with $S_0 \rightarrow T_1$ separation of sensitizer. However, the yields of I, II, III, IV, and V remain in the same proportion in all experiments and are formed in best yields using high-energy sensitizers ($S_0 \rightarrow T_1 > 60$ kcal/mole); these dimers are believed to arise from the *trans* triplet of isoprene ($S_0 \rightarrow T_1 \sim 60$ kcal/mole); for sensitizers with decreasing energy for $S_0 \rightarrow T_1$ (< 60 kcal/mole), products VI and VII increase in proportion and may have their origin in the *cis* triplet of isoprene ($S_0 \rightarrow T_1 \sim 53$ kcal/mole); 1-methoxy-1,3-butadiene, 2,4-dimethyl-1,3-pentadiene show no analog to process 1, but *cis-trans* isomerization is evident.

$$CH_2{=}C(CH_3)CH{=}CH_2 + h\nu \rightarrow \begin{array}{c} CH_2-C-CH_3 \\ | \quad \| \\ CH_2-CH \end{array} \qquad (1)$$

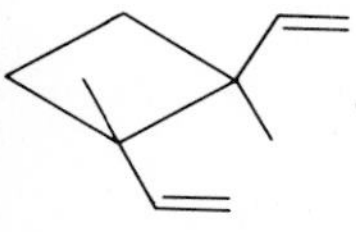

(I) 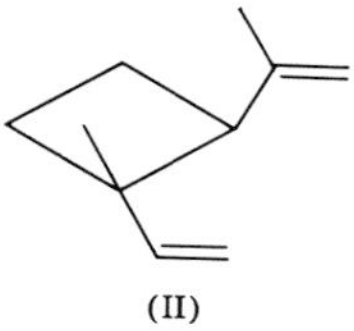   (II) 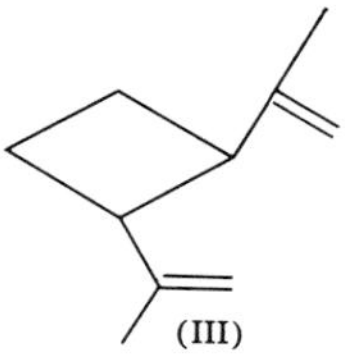   (III) 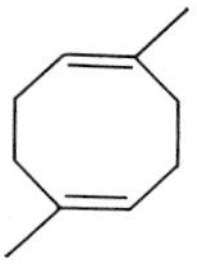   (IV)

(V) 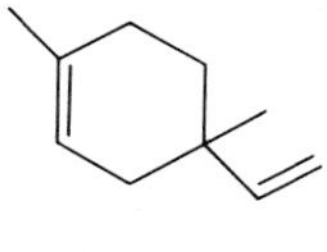   (VI) 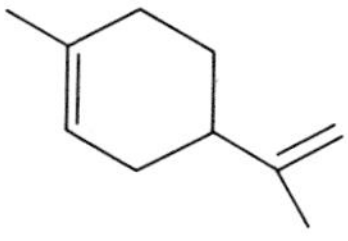   (VII)

20. 1-Phenyl-1,3-butadiene:[365] in ethanol, *cis* form $\lambda_{max} = 2650–2690$ A ($\epsilon = 1.84 \times 10^4$); *trans* form $\lambda_{max} = 2800$ A ($\epsilon = 2.98 \times 10^4$); full mercury arc, *trans-cis* isomerization dominant reaction in ethanol solution; the fluorescence of miscellaneous 1,4-diarylbutadienes has been determined and suggests highest fluorescence efficiency for *trans-trans* forms of the compounds.[366,367]

21. 2,3-Dimethyl-1,3-butadiene:[363] absorption spectrum shown in Fig. 5-24; full mercury arc, gas phase, process 1 important; φ_1 increases to limiting value as pressure of added diethyl ether increased; presumably added gas removes vibrational excitation in the original "hot" product and stabilizes it; 2537 A, diethyl ether solution (2×10^{-4} M), $\varphi_1 = 0.12$; Φ (disappearance) $= 0.12$; polymer formation becomes important at the high concentrations.

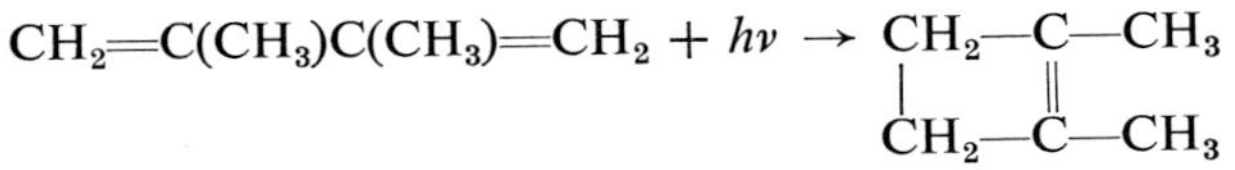

$$CH_2=C(CH_3)C(CH_3)=CH_2 + h\nu \rightarrow \begin{array}{c} CH_2-C-CH_3 \\ | \quad \| \\ CH_2-C-CH_3 \end{array} \qquad (1)$$

22. Cyclopentadiene:[368,371] full inert gas flash, spectroscopic evidence for cyclopentadienyl radical formation and process 1; the dimerization of cyclopentadiene can be sensitized by a variety of ketones dissolved in liquid diene; approximately equal amounts of I, II, and III are formed; photooxidation can be effected at $-100°$ to give endoperoxide.[372]

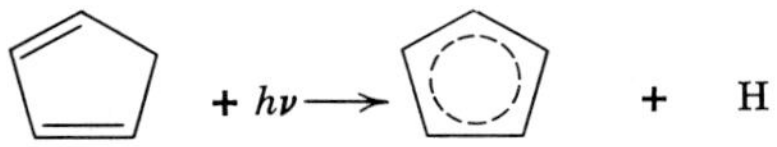

$$\text{(structure)} + h\nu \rightarrow \text{(structure)} + H \qquad (1)$$

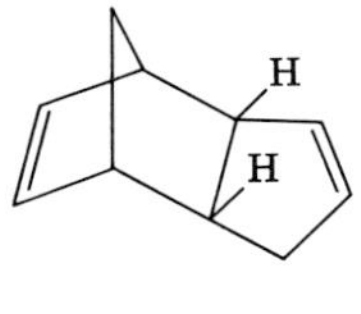

(I) 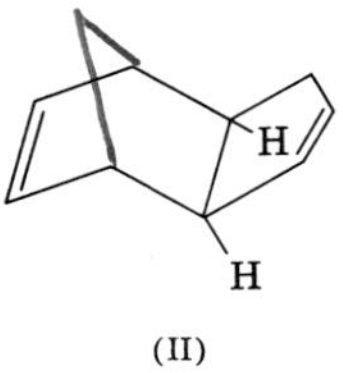   (II) 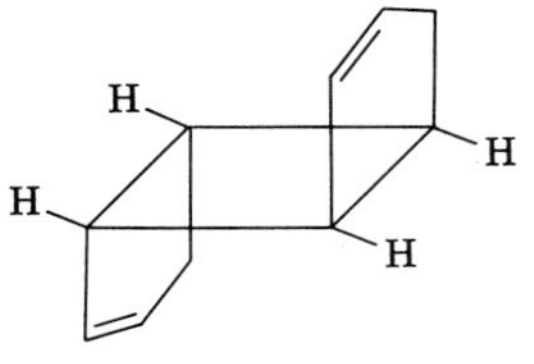   (III)

23. 1,3-Cyclohexadiene:[373,374,379,390] first absorption band, 2850–2100 A, continuous with $\lambda_{max} = 2500$ A; 2537 A, 25°, $\varphi_1 = 0.09$ (2 mm), 0.18 (0 mm); $\varphi_2 = 0.006$ (2 mm), 0.0004 (23 mm); $\varphi_3 = 0.13$ (4.8 mm); added inert gases or decrease in temperature decreases processes 1 and 2 with little effect on process 3; 1 and 2 presumed to occur from vibrationally excited ground-state molecules, $M^{\ddagger}$, formed by internal conversion of electronic energy of first excited singlet; 3 presumed to occur from excited singlet state.

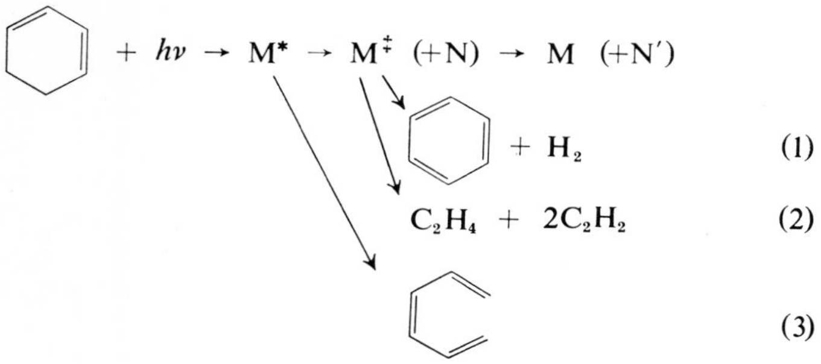

$$+ \ h\nu \ \rightarrow \ M^{*} \ \rightarrow \ M^{\ddagger} \ (+N) \ \rightarrow \ M \ (+N')$$

$$+ \ H_2 \tag{1}$$

$$C_2H_4 \ + \ 2C_2H_2 \tag{2}$$

$$\tag{3}$$

24. *α-Phellandrene:*[390] $\lambda_{max} = 2640$ A, $\epsilon = 3900$ in heptane; full mercury arc, in ether solution, process 1 dominant; only one of several *cis, trans* isomers in products is shown here; possible racemization of the originally optically active compound not clear.

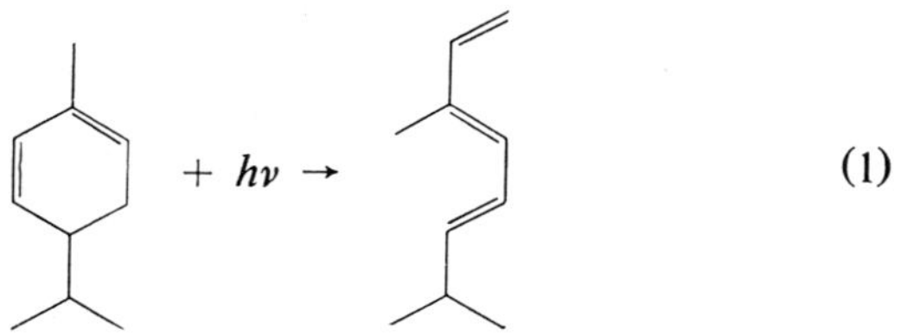

$$+ \ h\nu \ \rightarrow \tag{1}$$

25. *Δ³,⁵-Cholestadiene:*[693] on irradiation in pentane solution the saturated isomer *A* forms.

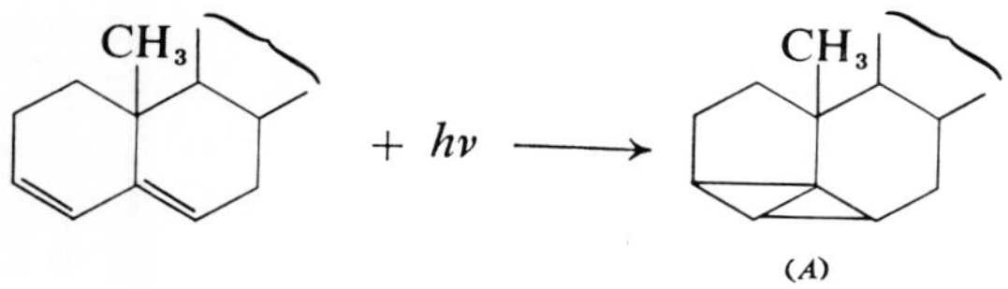

(A)

26. *Norbornadiene:*[370, 734, 735] absorption onset at about 2700 A, shoulder at 2300 A, and several bands with fine structure between 2260 and 1990 A; 2537 A, $\varphi_1 = 0.50$, $\varphi_2 = 0.06$, independent of the temperature (27–57°) and pressure (4–31 mm); in ether solution, $\varphi_1 = 0.13$, $\varphi_2 = 0.05$; process 3 occurs also on direct irradiation in solution, or the reaction can be sensitized in isopentane solution with triplet sensitizers (acetone, aceto-phenone, benzophenone).

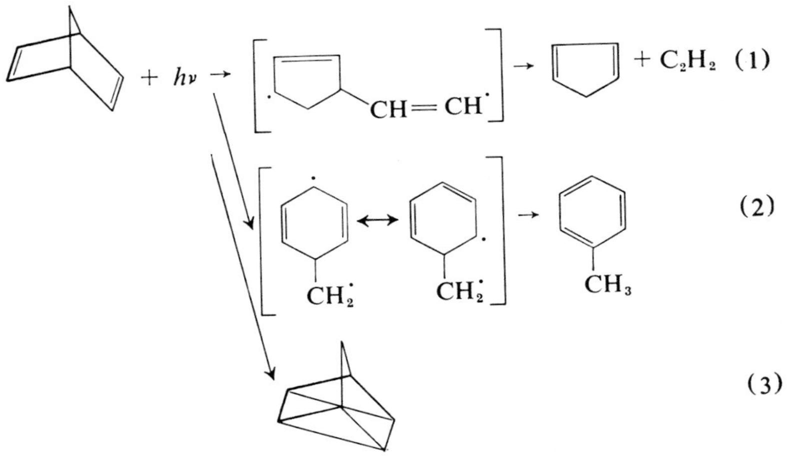

27. *1,3-Cyclooctadiene:*[363] in diethyl ether solution (2×10^{-4} M), 2537 A, $\varphi_1 = 0.14$, Φ (disappearance) $= 0.18$; some other isomerization than process 1 may occur.

28. *1,3,5-Hexatriene:*[375,376,379] absorption onset at $\sim$2800 A, banded, intense absorption for *trans* compound with absorption maxima at 2513, 2435, 2412, 2343, and 2323 A; full mercury arc, the major products are H_2, C_6H_6, 1,3-cyclohexadiene, 1,2,4-hexatriene, and polymer; *cis-trans* isomerization also occurs, and some C_2H_4 and C_2H_2 are formed. At 10 mm, 25°, $\varphi_2 \cong \varphi_4$; $\lambda > 2800$ A, $\varphi_2 \cong 0.3\ \varphi_4$; 2537 A, at 25°, $\varphi_2 = 0.03$ (16.8 mm), 0.12 (1.5 mm), 0.24 (0.30 mm); $\varphi_3 = 0.001$ (16.8 mm), 0.01 (1.5 mm); process 4 may involve an intramolecular transfer of hydrogen by way of an intermediate six-membered-ring transition state which is possible only when the groups are arranged about the central double bond in the *cis* position. The dagger marks a vibrationally non-equilibrated molecule.

$(cis, trans)$ CH_2=$CHCH$=$CHCH$=CH_2 + $h\nu$ → $(cis, trans)$ M*

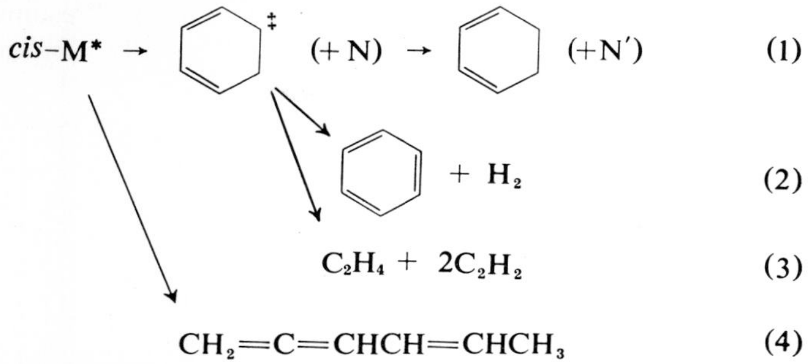

$$cis\text{-}M^* \rightarrow \quad (+N) \rightarrow \quad (+N') \qquad (1)$$

$$+ H_2 \qquad (2)$$

$$C_2H_4 + 2C_2H_2 \qquad (3)$$

$$CH_2=C=CHCH=CHCH_3 \qquad (4)$$

$trans\text{-}M^* \rightarrow cis\text{-}M$

29. Vitamin D and related compounds:[391] for solutions of compounds in ether, 2537 A, first conclusive evidence of difference in reactions between photoexcited *cis* and *trans* isomers;[391] reactions believed to involve excited singlets. Quantum yields of individual steps shown over or below arrows; R = C_9H_{17}.

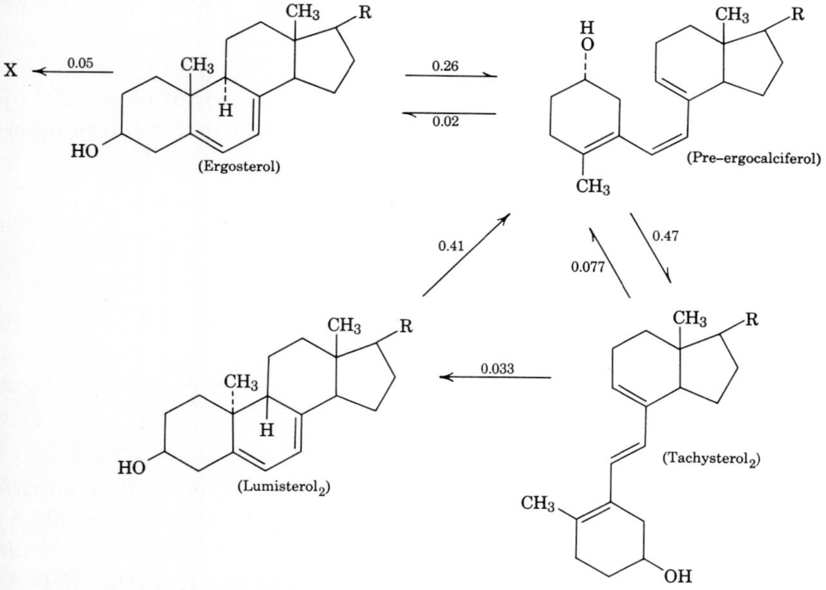

30. 1,3,5-Cycloheptatriene:[363,377,378,388] first absorption region, 3300–2250 A, $\log_{10} \epsilon_{max} = 3.62$; 2537–2654 A, 25°, 15 mm, $\varphi_1 = 0.008$, $\varphi_2 = 0.29$; φ_2 decreases with increasing pressure (helium, ether, etc.), while φ_1 increases: 0.0036 (6.2 mm), 0.010 (22.1 mm); temperature increase lowers φ_1, raises φ_2; in diethyl ether solution ($\sim 2 \times 10^{-4}$ M), $\varphi_1 = 0.03$,

Φ (disappearance) = 0.03; 3130 A, 25°, φ_1 = 0.0015 (15.1 mm), 0.0013 (2.6 mm); φ_2 = 0.016 (15.1 mm), 0.081 (2.6 mm). Presumably process 1 occurs from the first excited singlet, and initially vibrationally excited

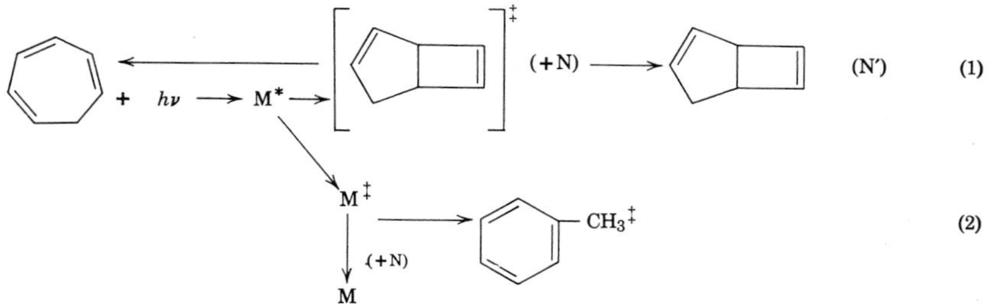

product must be deactivated or decomposition to re-form reactant occurs; process 2 is believed to involve decomposition of highly vibrationally excited ground-state singlet formed by intersystem crossing. Flash experiments show toluene formed in 2 is highly vibrationally excited at low pressure.

31. Cyclooctatetraene:[374,386,387] first absorption region, continuous, λ_{max} = 2800 A, $\log_{10} \epsilon \sim 2.5$ in cyclohexane; continuous absorption increasing in strength to 2000 A; $\sim$2537 A, φ_1 = 0.10 (6–7 mm, 28°); $\varphi_2 \cong 0.004$; in ethanol at 77°K some spectral evidence of bicyclo[4.2.0]-octatriene-2,4,7 formation; irradiation of this compound led to products of processes 1 and 2.

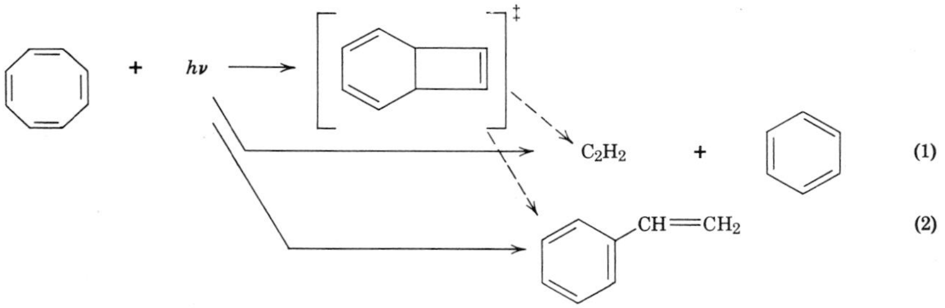

32. Acetylene:[392–397] weak absorption begins $\sim$2377 A; weak, comparitively diffuse band superimposed on a continuum from 2350–1800 A; first excited state is non-linear with H—C—C angles $\sim$120°, and molecule is in *trans* configuration with bond distances like those in C_6H_6; 1849 A, $\varphi_1 \cong 0.2$ (1.7–74 mm); polymer formation proceeds through excited-molecule formation and increases with increasing pressure; $\Phi_{C_6H_6} \cong$ 0.006 (1.7 mm), 0.170 (74 mm); Φ (disappearance) $\cong$ 2 (1.8 mm), $\sim$15 (47 mm); free spin species observable by EPR in irradiated frozen sample at 77°K[342]; process 2 onset at $\sim$1100 A, φ_2 = 0.8 at 850 A.

$$HC\equiv CH + h\nu \rightarrow M^* + M \rightarrow (CHCH)_n$$

$$\searrow\ \downarrow$$

$$HCC + H \tag{1}$$

$$\downarrow$$

$$C_2H_2^+ + e^- \tag{2}$$

33. Methylacetylene:[342] EPR signal from radical formed with full mercury-arc irradiation of sample at 77°K suggests propargyl radical and process 1.

$$CH_3C\equiv CH + h\nu \rightarrow \begin{Bmatrix} CH_2C\equiv CH \\ \updownarrow \\ CH_2{=}C{=}CH \end{Bmatrix} + H \tag{1}$$

34. Diacetylene:[398] banded absorption from 3000–2500 A, but no rotational fine structure present; predissociation indicated; full xenon flash, pressure helium/pressure diacetylene = 100, C_3 bands observed; C_2 bands absent; suggests $\varphi_1 > \varphi_2$ although unexpected conclusion; alternatively a carbon atom disproportionation reaction, e.g., $2C_2H \rightarrow C_3H + CH$ may dominate following the occurrence of process 2; 3 possible by analogy with acetylene and methyl acetylene.

$$HC\equiv C{-}C\equiv CH + h\nu \rightarrow CH + C_3H \tag{1}$$

$$\searrow$$

$$HC_2 + HC_2 \tag{2}$$

$$\downarrow$$

$$HC_4 + H \quad (?) \tag{3}$$

5-7C The Aromatic Hydrocarbons

Most of the solution-phase photochemistry of the aromatic hydrocarbons has been explained in terms of fluorescence, dimerization, photo-oxidation processes, etc.[422,423,695] (See the review by Bowen.[695]) In solution at low concentration, high fluorescence yields are common. In the higher concentration ranges, dimerization may occur; for example, anthracene and its derivatives, which are not substituted in the 9,10-positions, form dimers which are chemically bound through these positions.[695]

Photodecomposition modes of the aromatic molecules occur only with low quantum efficiencies in the first absorption bands, $\varphi \sim 0.01$–0.0001 or less. The very limited studies of these modes which have been made suggest that at least three general types of decomposition may occur in condensed media. In those compounds having alkyl groups attached to an aromatic ring system, exposure to light in the first absorption region may lead to rupture of H—C or C—C bonds to form a benzyl-type radical:[399]

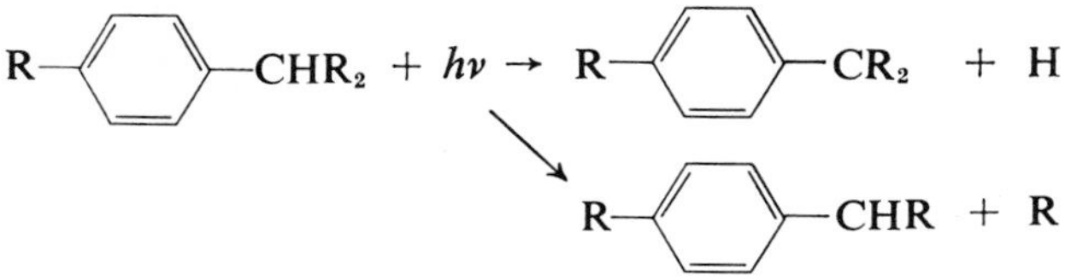

$$R\text{—}\langle\bigcirc\rangle\text{—}CHR_2 + h\nu \rightarrow R\text{—}\langle\bigcirc\rangle\text{—}CR_2 + H \qquad \text{(LXXIIIa)}$$

$$\searrow \quad R\text{—}\langle\bigcirc\rangle\text{—}CHR + R \qquad \text{(LXXIIIb)}$$

In compounds having an ethyl side chain, molecular elimination of H_2 may occur:

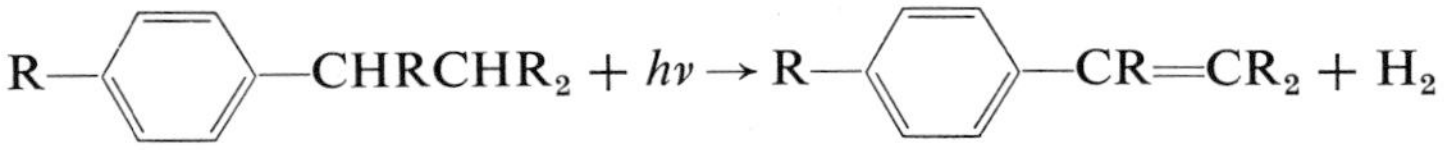

$$R\text{—}\langle\bigcirc\rangle\text{—}CHRCHR_2 + h\nu \rightarrow R\text{—}\langle\bigcirc\rangle\text{—}CR\text{=}CR_2 + H_2 \quad \text{(LXXIV)}$$

In benzene, and presumably in its alkyl-substituted derivatives, the net effect of ring rupture occurs on irradiation at 2537 A in rigid glass at 77°K. In ethanol-containing matrices a substituted triene appears to be the product, overall process LXXV:

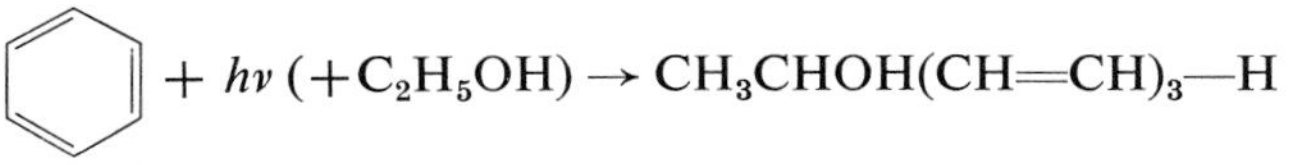

$$\langle\bigcirc\rangle + h\nu\,(+C_2H_5OH) \rightarrow CH_3CHOH(CH\text{=}CH)_3\text{—}H \quad \text{(LXXV)}$$

In the liquid phase at 50° on irradiation at 2537 A, fulvene formation has been suggested to occur by an undefined mechanism. However, the gas-phase photolysis of benzene produces some unidentified yellow solid which is definitely not fulvene or diphenyl.[589]

The 2537 A irradiation of alkyl-substituted benzenes in the gas phase or in solution induces at low efficiency an interesting 1,2-shift of an alkyl group. Isotopic labeling experiments show that the rearrangement is intramolecular; the aromatic ring carbon atom to which the alkyl group is attached migrates with the alkyl group, presumably through the intermediate formation and reaction of folded Dewar-type ring or tricyclohexene structures, shown as X in process LXXVI. The example given for o-xylene occurs with $\varphi_{LXXVI} = 0.013$ at 2500 A.

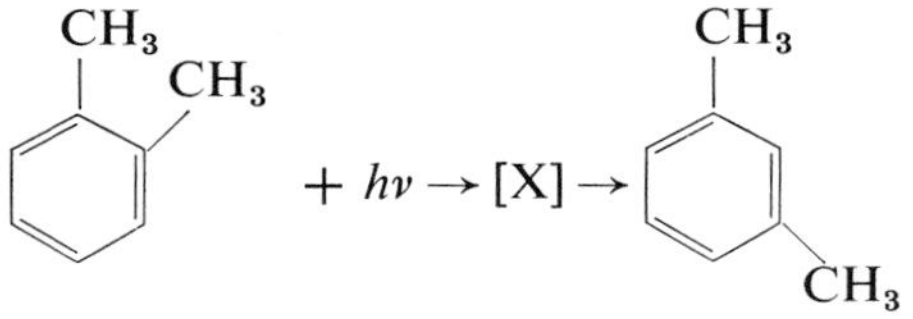

$$\underset{CH_3}{\overset{CH_3}{\langle\bigcirc\rangle}} + h\nu \rightarrow [X] \rightarrow \underset{CH_3}{\overset{CH_3}{\langle\bigcirc\rangle}}_{CH_3} \qquad \text{(LXXVI)}$$

It is interesting to note that the ultraviolet irradiation of 1,2,4-tri-t-butyl-benzene gives a Dewar-type isomer of reasonable stability; see p. 520.

The simple aromatic hydrocarbons such as benzene and toluene undergo a dramatic change in the character of their primary processes when they are irradiated in their second or third (1849 A) absorption bands, compared to their spectroscopic and photochemical behavior in their first band at 2537 A. Recently the absolute efficiencies of the radiative and non-radiative processes of benzene and some alkyl derivatives excited to their second or third singlet states have been determined.[699] There is no direct fluorescence from these states, internal conversion to the first excited state S_1 from the higher states S_2 and S_3 is highly inefficient, particularly in the vapor, and there is a very low efficiency of transfer, by any spectroscopic path, from the higher singlet states of benzene to the lower triplet state of biacetyl. (See the discussion of Noyes and Unger.[495c]) This suggests that a highly efficient photochemical reaction occurs in the vapor phase in the second and third bands;[699] this conclusion has been recently confirmed.[502] At 1849 A the quantum yield of disappearance of benzene vapor is about unity, compared to <0.000 at 2537 A (no gas-phase decomposition was observed at 2537 either, $\Phi < 0.0000$).[502] The ultimate products at 1849 A are apparently a high-energy isomer(s) of benzene which decomposes to carbon and/or polymer and traces of volatile products such as H_2, CH_4, $HC{\equiv}CH, C_2H_6$, toluene, and a C_2- or C_3-substituted benzene. The structure of the high-energy isomer(s) is not yet established. Toluene behaves photochemically and spectroscopically in much the same way.

1. Benzene:[374,399–409,416,502,589,695,699,729] first absorption region shown in Fig. 5-27; below 2200 A absorption bands become diffuse, and below 1850 A a continuum is present. 2537 A, no significant chemical change observed in the gas phase; $\varphi_1 = 0.22$, $\varphi_2 = 0.78$ at 29°, 20 mm; $\varphi_3 = 0.00$.[704] With C_6D_6 at 30°, $\varphi_f = 0.33$ (1.2 mm), 0.28 (3.0 mm), 0.26 (5.2 mm). In liquid-phase experiments at 50°, fulvene product formation has been reported but not confirmed; $\varphi_3 \sim 0.01$. At 77°K in rigid glass, fulvene not detected but presumably substituted trienes are formed with low efficiency; for an ethanol-containing glass, $\varphi_4 \cong 0.004$. The mechanism of processes 3 and 4 is not clear. Irradiation of benzene in aqueous solution yields mucondialdehyde, $\varphi < 0.001$; 1849–2000 A, vapor phase, C_2H_2, H_2, CH_4, C_2H_6, $C_6H_5CH_3$, cuprene-like polymer formed; $\Phi_{C_2H_2} \cong 0.01$; H_2 may be a secondary product; Φ (disappearance of benzene) near unity; high energy isomer possibly formed; process 5 may be important at the shorter wavelengths. $C_6H_6^*$ represents an undefined excited state.

$$C_6H_6(S_0) + h\nu \rightarrow C_6H_6(S_1) \longrightarrow C_6H_6(S_0) + h\nu' \qquad (1)$$

$$\searrow C_6H_6(T_1) \qquad (2)$$
$$\text{(+N)} \quad \downarrow \text{(+N)}$$
$$C_6H_6(S_0)$$

$$C_6H_6^* \longrightarrow CH_2{=}C\begin{smallmatrix} CH{=}CH \\ | \\ CH{=}CH \end{smallmatrix} \quad \begin{matrix}\text{(or other} \\ \text{unidentified} \\ \text{high-energy} \\ \text{isomer)}\end{matrix} \qquad (3)$$
$$\text{(}C_2H_5OH\text{)}$$

$$CH_3CHOH{-}(CH{=}CH)_3{-}H \qquad (4)$$

$$-[CH{\equiv}CH-]_3 \rightarrow 3HC{\equiv}CH \qquad (5)$$

2. *Toluene:*[410–415,502,695,699] first absorption band shown in Fig. 5-27; $\lambda \leqslant 2537$ A, process 1 proceeds with low quantum efficiency in solution and in rigid media at low temperature. Methane and ethane were reported earlier as products of the gas-phase photolysis at 2537 A, but recent work shows $\varphi < 0.0000$ with monochromatic 2537 A light. In pure liquid phase at 2537 A, $\Phi_{H_2} \sim 1 \times 10^{-4}$. Fluorescence yield for dilute toluene solutions in hexane, 0.23. At 1849 A, vapor phase, Φ_{CH_4} and $\Phi_{C_2H_6} \leqslant 0.1$, benzene also formed; Φ (disappearance $C_6H_5CH_3$) $\sim$ unity; carbon and/or polymer formed, possibly from the high-energy isomer formed in 3.

$$C_6H_5CH_3 + h\nu \rightarrow M^*(+N) \rightarrow M(+N')$$

$$M + h\nu'$$

$$C_6H_5CH_2 + H \tag{1}$$

$$C_6H_5 + CH_3 \tag{2}$$

$$[C_7H_8] \text{ (unidentified high-energy isomer)} \tag{3}$$

3. *Ethylbenzene:*[410,412,414] $\lambda \leqslant 2537$ A, both processes 1 and 2 probably occur in gaseous, liquid and rigid matrix experiments at low temperature. Methane product from gas-phase studies suggests the possibility of process 3 for certain conditions. In pure liquid phase at 2537 A, $\Phi_{H_2} \sim 3.2 \times 10^{-4}$.

$$C_6H_5C_2H_5 + h\nu \longrightarrow C_6H_5CHCH_3 + H \tag{1}$$

$$C_6H_5CH{=}CH_2 + H_2 \tag{2}$$

$$C_6H_5CH_2 + CH_3(?) \tag{3}$$

4. *Isopropylbenzene:*[410b,412] $\lambda \leqslant 2537$ A, process 1 occurs with low efficiency in all phases; decomposition by 2 appears to occur also in gas-phase experiments at 150–160°; 3 possible by analogy with ethylbenzene.

$$C_6H_5CH(CH_3)_2 + h\nu \longrightarrow C_6H_5C(CH_3)_2 + H \tag{1}$$

$$C_6H_5CHCH_3 + CH_3 \tag{2}$$

$$C_6H_5C(CH_3){=}CH_2 + H_2(?) \tag{3}$$

5. *tert-Butylbenzene:*[410b,412] $\lambda \leqslant 2537$ A, process 1 occurs with low quantum yield in all phases; Φ_{H_2} is lower than in β-hydrogen-containing compounds but seems to occur to some extent in gas phase at 150–160°. In pure liquid phase at 2537 A, $\Phi_{H_2} \sim 1.2 \times 10^{-4}$

$$C_6H_5C(CH_3)_3 + h\nu \rightarrow C_6H_5C(CH_3)_2 + CH_3 \tag{1}$$

$$\searrow$$

$$C_6H_5C(CH_3)_2CH_2 + H(?) \tag{2}$$

6. Xylenes:[412,414,727] ~2537 A, o-xylene at 35°, 6 mm, isomerizes to m-xylene; $\varphi_1 \cong 0.013$; m-xylene gives a similar rearrangement to form p-xylene and o-xylene; $\varphi_3/\varphi_2 \sim 4$; $\varphi_2 + \varphi_3 \cong 0.03$ (gas phase) and 0.006 in isohexane. A 1,2-shift in the predominant path in the photo-isomerization; the intermediate M* may be a high-energy Dewar form (or other) of benzene; see discussion of compound 8. o-Diethylbenzene also isomerizes to the m-isomer with $\varphi \cong 0.03$. Free radical splits 4 and 5 occur to a small extent, but they are less important than the rearrangements and are not responsible for the rearrangements described.

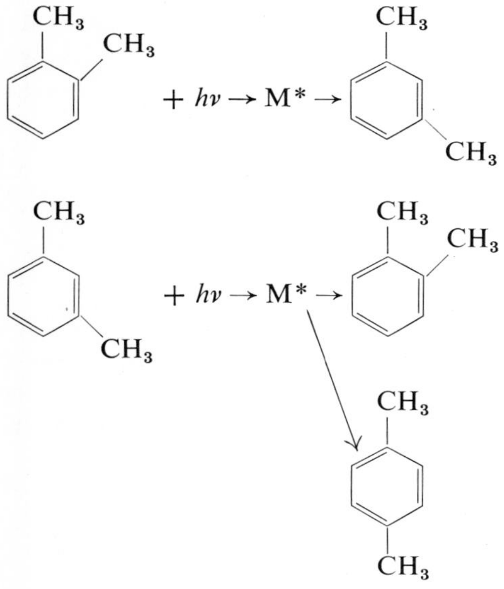

$$(CH_3)_2C_6H_4 + h\nu \rightarrow CH_3C_6H_4CH_2 + H \tag{4}$$

$$\searrow$$

$$CH_3 + C_6H_4CH_3 \tag{5}$$

7. o-Di-t-butylbenzene:[726] irradiation with full mercury arc, ether solution, gives a mixture of meta and para isomers; a mixture of the same composition is formed starting with m- or p-isomers as well. When a substituent such as nitro, acetyl, or methoxyl is present in the 4-position of the 1,2-di-t-butylbenzene, the isomerization is strongly inhibited. The

intramolecular nature of the rearrangements is clear, since irradiation of
t-butylbenzene and 1,3,5-*tert*-butylbenzene gives no di-*t*-butylbenzene.
Presumably a high-energy form of the benzene ring is involved as an
intermediate. See the discussion of compound 8.

8. Mesitylene:[410,412,725] $\lambda \leqslant 2537$ A, process 1 occurs in all phases;
Φ_{H_2} (2537 A) for pure liquid phase, $\sim 3.4 \times 10^{-4}$. The 1,3,5-$^{14}C_3$-labeled
reactant at 2537 A in isohexane solution, 30°, isomerizes to 1,2,4-tri-
methylbenzene labeled exclusively in the 1,2, and 4 ring positions; thus
the 1,2-shift of the methyl group is a consequence of ring carbon atom
interchange. Presumably a folded Dewar-type structure or tricyclohexene
may be an intermediate involved in the isomerization.

9. 1,2,4-Tri-t-butylbenzene:[728] irradiation with Vycor-filtered medium-
pressure mercury lamp, ether solution, gives a new isomer, presumably
of the Dewar structure *A*, which reforms the reactant on heating at 200°.

10. Cyclopropylbenzene:[732,744] 2537 A, $\sim 1 \times 10^{-5}$ *M*, $\varphi_2 = 0.061$ (32°),
0.079 (46°), 0.10 (83°), 0.13 (117°); $\varphi_3 = 0.080$ (32°), 0.11 (46°), 0.14 (83°),
0.17 (117°); $\varphi_1 \cong \varphi_2$; processes 1, 2, and 3 very pressure dependent;
φ_4 small in gas phase; $\varphi_f \cong 0.4$; full mercury arc photolysis in hydrocarbon solution, process 4 dominant; products of CH_2 reaction and
their ratios are identical to those obtained using CH_2N_2 photolysis as

the CH_2 source; styrene product appears as a polymer.[732]

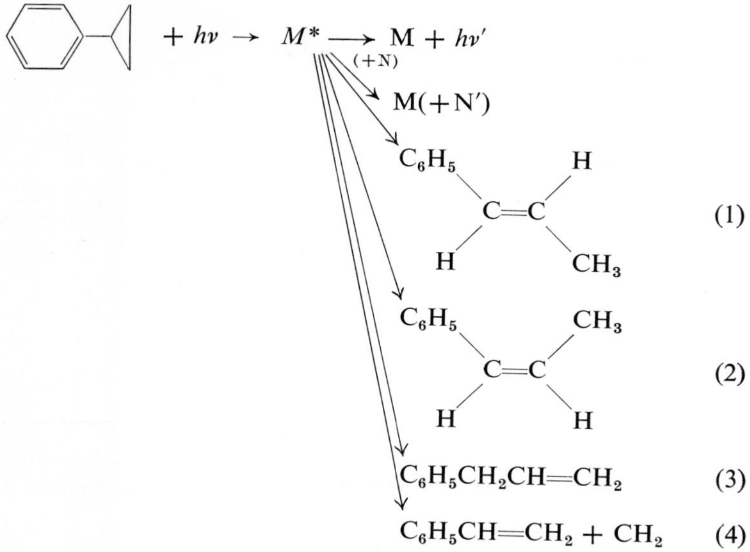

$$\text{[cyclopropyl-phenyl]} + h\nu \rightarrow M^* \xrightarrow[(+N)]{} M + h\nu'$$

$$M(+N')$$

$$\underset{H}{\overset{C_6H_5}{\diagdown}}C{=}C\underset{CH_3}{\overset{H}{\diagup}} \qquad (1)$$

$$\underset{H}{\overset{C_6H_5}{\diagdown}}C{=}C\underset{H}{\overset{CH_3}{\diagup}} \qquad (2)$$

$$C_6H_5CH_2CH{=}CH_2 \qquad (3)$$

$$C_6H_5CH{=}CH_2 + CH_2 \qquad (4)$$

11. Cyclopropylphenylmethane:[745] 2537 A, 55 and 85°, extensive fragmentation and hydrogen migration occur; no H_2 found; major products explained in terms of processes 1, 2, 3 and 4; compare with compound 10 and ketones 50 and 52 to see the analogy and effect of "insulating" CH_2 group.

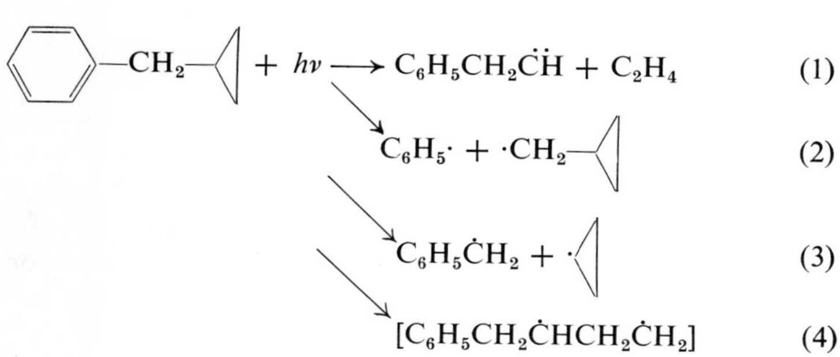

$$\text{[phenyl]}{-}CH_2{-}\text{[cyclopropyl]} + h\nu \longrightarrow C_6H_5CH_2\overset{..}{C}H + C_2H_4 \qquad (1)$$

$$C_6H_5\cdot + \cdot CH_2{-}\text{[cyclopropyl]} \qquad (2)$$

$$C_6H_5\overset{.}{C}H_2 + \cdot\text{[cyclopropyl]} \qquad (3)$$

$$[C_6H_5CH_2\overset{.}{C}HCH_2\overset{.}{C}H_2] \qquad (4)$$

12. 9,10-Dihydro-9,10-methanophenanthrene:[731] full mercury arc photolysis in hydrocarbon solution, process 1 dominant; stereospecific addition of CH_2 to olefins and the completely random insertion of CH_2 in various C-H bonds of a variety of hydrocarbons are observed; the products and their ratios are identical to those obtained using CH_2N_2 photolysis as the

CH_2 source. This hydrocarbon represents a very convenient, shelf-stable source of active methylene.

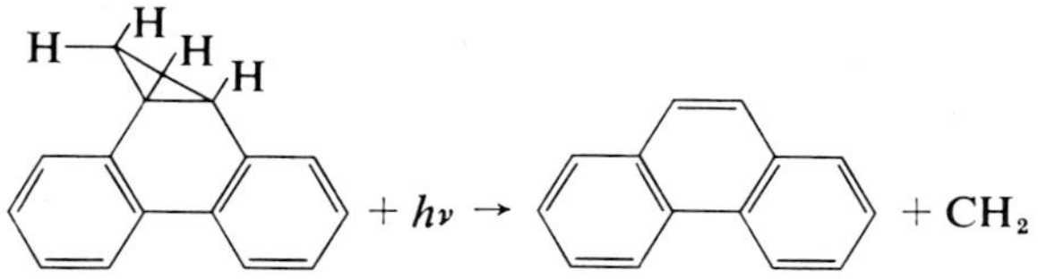

$$+ \, h\nu \; \rightarrow \qquad + \, CH_2 \qquad (1)$$

13. Triphenylmethane:[412,415] $\lambda \leqslant 2537$ A, in EPA at 77°K, $\varphi_1 = 0.011$; fluorescence yield in hexane solution, 0.23.

$$(C_6H_5)_3CH + h\nu \longrightarrow M^*(+N) \rightarrow M(+N')$$
$$\searrow M + h\nu'$$
$$\searrow (C_6H_5)_3C + H \qquad (1)$$

14–16. Miscellaneous aromatic hydrocarbons:[412,414] as determined from spectra in full mercury arc irradiated matrices or gas-phase inert-gas flash experiments.

   14. $C_6H_5CH_2C_6H_5 + h\nu \rightarrow (C_6H_5)_2CH + H$
   $$\searrow$$
   $$C_6H_5CH_2 + C_6H_5(?)$$

   15. $C_6H_5CH_2CH_2C_6H_5 + h\nu \rightarrow C_6H_5CH_2CHC_6H_5 + H$

   16. α- *or* β-*Methylnaphthalene* $+ h\nu \rightarrow$ α- or β-$CH_2C_{10}H_7 + H$

5-8   ORGANIC HALIDES AND HYPOCHLORITES

The first absorption band of the alkyl halides occurs in the ultraviolet region; it has been attributed to the promotion of a non-bonding *p* electron on the halogen atom to an antibonding σ* orbital involving largely the carbon and halogen atoms. The absorption is continuous in nature. Note the spectra in Figs. 5-28 and 5-29. The transition associated with the first absorption band is partially forbidden ($f \sim 10^{-3}$ to 10^{-2}), presumably because of the considerable *p* character to the σ* bond and the violation of the $p \nleftrightarrow p$ selection rule as in the carbonyl $n \rightarrow \pi^*$ band. The absorption maximum shifts to the longer wavelengths as the electronegativity of the halogen substituent is lowered from that of fluorine to that of iodine. For CH_3Cl, $\lambda_{max} \sim 1730$ A; for CH_3Br, $\lambda_{max} = 2030$ A, $\epsilon = 264$; and for CH_3I, $\lambda_{max} = 2576$ A, $\epsilon = 380$. The polyhaloalkanes have increasingly higher extinction coefficients with increased halogen content: CH_3Br, $\lambda_{max} = 2020$ A, $\epsilon = 264$; CH_2Br_2, $\lambda_{max} = 2200$ A, $\epsilon = 1100$; $CHBr_3$, $\lambda_{max} = 2240$ A, $\epsilon = 2130$; CH_3I, $\lambda_{max} = 2576$ A, $\epsilon = 378$; CH_2I_2, $\lambda_{max} = 2900$ A, $\epsilon = 1320$; CHI_3, $\lambda_{max} = 3490$, $\epsilon = 2170$. The spectra of the higher halogen-substituted compounds shows a broadening of the absorption region because of splitting from halogen-halogen interaction.

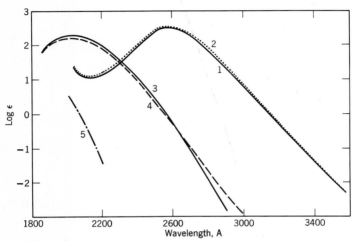

Fig. 5-28 Absorption spectra of: (1) methyl iodide [$CH_3I(g)$]; (2) ethyl iodide [$C_2H_5I(g)$]; (3) methyl bromide [$CH_3Br(g)$]; (4) ethyl bromide [$C_2H_5Br(g)$]; (5) ethyl chloride [C_2H_5Cl] in alcohol solution. (1)–(4) From Porret and Goodeve;[433] (5) from Treiber et al.[434]

Each of the alkyl iodides has a second strong absorption band within the vacuum ultraviolet (centered at 1940 A, $\epsilon \sim 7700$) which is due to the first allowed transition of a non-bonding electron on the iodine promoted to the next higher s orbital in the halogen; it is largely an excitation involving the atomic orbitals of the halogen (Rydberg transition).[435] With the halogen atom-substituted ethylenes the $\pi \to \pi^*$ absorption band of the olefin is shifted to somewhat longer wavelengths, presumably because of interaction between the lone-pair orbitals of the halogen atom and the π orbitals of the ethylene. The lowest transition is still the $\pi \to \pi^*$ type in this case, although the nature of the excited state is somewhat intermediate in character; both the C-C and C-halogen bonds have some antibonding character.

The photochemistry of the alkyl halides, RX, where X is Cl, Br, or I, is well described by dissociative primary process LXXVIII when the alkyl

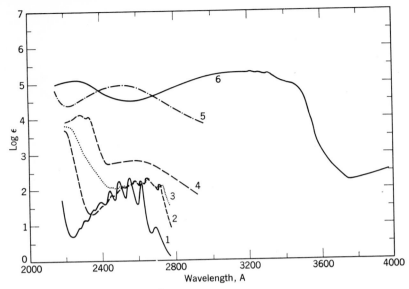

Fig. 5-29   Absorption spectra of:

(1) benzene ⟨◯⟩ in cyclohexane; from Friedel and Orchin;[432]

(2) chlorobenzene ⟨◯—Cl⟩ in isooctane;

(3) bromobenzene ⟨◯—Br⟩ in isooctane;

(4) iodobenzene ⟨◯—I⟩ in isooctane;

(5) nitrobenzene ⟨◯—NO_2⟩ in isooctane;

(6) azobenzene ⟨◯—N≡N—◯⟩ in methanol.

All but (1) from A.P.I. Project 44, National Bureau of Standards.

halide is irradiated within the first absorption band:

$$RX + h\nu \rightarrow R^{\ddagger} + X \qquad \text{(LXXVIII)}$$

The free halogen atom has been observed indirectly by its reaction with scavengers and by the appearance of ClO, BrO, and IO species after the flash photolysis of CH_3Cl,[438] CH_3Br,[439] and CH_3I.[440] The free methyl radical has been found spectroscopically in the flash photolysis of CH_3I

and CH_3Br.[442] In every case which has been quantitatively studied, $\varphi_{LXXVIII} = 1.0$ within the experimental error. Unless some excellent radical trapping agent is present, the re-formation of RX may occur efficiently in the system as X_2 builds up and $R + X_2 \rightarrow RX + X$ occurs. In solution-phase studies the primary dissociation products may recombine efficiently before escape from the solvent "cage" can occur. Also, traces of oxygen in the solution can cause an enormous variation in the yield of decomposition products. Thus Hacobian and Iredale[136] found that the quantum yield of iodine from ethyl iodide liquid-phase photolysis varied from 0.5 to 0.05 as the efficiency of degassing the solutions was improved.

A large share of the quantum energy excess after bond fission in LXXVIII remains with the alkyl radical, particularly when R is small and X is large (e.g., CH_3I); the "hot" radical may be rich in electronic, vibrational, and/or translational energy.[468]

The absorption of light within the second band of the alkyl halides may result in the molecular elimination of hydrogen halide:

$$R_2CHCH_2X + h\nu \rightarrow R_2C{=}CH_2 + HX \qquad \text{(LXXIX)}$$

Thrush[443] observed the bands of HI in the flash photolysis of C_2H_5I, $n\text{-}C_3H_7I$, and iso-C_3H_7I. Schindler and Wijnen[444] found that ethylene formation could not be suppressed completely by added oxygen in C_2H_5I photolysis in full mercury arc light; $R_{C_2H_4}/R_{C_2H_5} \sim 0.05$. Process LXXIX could be responsible for these observations.

Primary processes in the polyhalomethanes show some results of special interest. If two types of halogen atoms are present, the dominant split in the photolysis ruptures the weakest C-halogen bond; thus bromine is lost in the photolysis of $CHCl_2Br$ or CCl_2Br_2.[446]

The molecular elimination process LXXXa has been suggested through the observation of I_2 fluorescence in vacuum ultraviolet flash experiments.[445]

$$CH_2I_2 + h\nu \rightarrow CH_2 + I_2{}^* \qquad \text{(LXXXa)}$$

Process LXXXb occurs in the difluorobromomethanes (CF_2BrX) at the very short wavelengths:

$$CF_2BrX + h\nu \rightarrow CF_2 + XBr \qquad \text{(LXXXb)}$$

where X = H, F, or Br.[447]

The flash photolysis of the compounds of general formula CX_3Br, where X = H, F, Cl, or Br, gave the unexpected appearance of the carbon monohalides; the compounds which formed the specified halide species with efficiencies in the order shown are as follows: CF from $CHFBr_2 > CFBr_3$; CCl from $CHCl_2Br$, $CHClBr_2$, $CCl_2Br_2 > CH_2ClBr > CCl_3Br > CHCl_3$; CBr from $CHBr_3 > CHClBr_2 > CH_2Br_2$. The yields of these species fell with increased pressure of foreign gas, and all evidence suggests that they arise from the decomposition of a vibrationally excited halomethyl radical:

$$CHXBr_2 + h\nu \rightarrow CHXBr^{\ddagger} + Br$$

$$CHXBr^{\ddagger} \rightarrow CX + HBr \text{ (or } CBr + HX)$$

$$\underset{(+M)}{\searrow}$$

$$CHXBr$$

The disproportionately large concentration of energy in the CHXBr species may occur by one of two processes analogous to those considered for NOCl photolysis in Sec. 3-3C-2. A change in the equilibrium geometry of the polyhalomethane in passing from the ground state to the unstable excited state is expected, since one C-halogen bond must be lengthened in the $n \rightarrow \sigma^*$ transition, and through internal energy exchange within the molecule some excitation of the vibrational modes can be effected. The alternative explanation of original electronic excitation in the CHXBr species formed in the primary act, followed by internal conversion, is also possible.[449]

The hypochlorites show two absorption peaks in the ultraviolet in the ranges 2500–2600 A and 3000–3200 A. Although few quantitative data are available on the photochemistry of these systems, considerable interest has been shown in their photolysis in solution to generate alkoxyl radicals.[295] The primary photochemical process is probably as follows:

$$ROCl + h\nu \rightarrow RO + Cl \qquad (LXXXI)$$

Vibrational excitation in the RO radical may be important in some cases, as with the nitrite compounds; see Sec. 5-5I.

1. Methyl iodide:[417,450–454] first absorption band shown in Fig. 5-28; $\varphi_1 = 1$; apparent primary yield of 1 in solution-phase photolysis much less than unity; $CH_3^{\ddagger}$ is translationally and/or vibrationally excited.

$$CH_3I + h\nu \rightarrow CH_3^{\ddagger} + I \qquad (1)$$

2. Methyl bromide:[451,455,456] first absorption band shown in Fig. 5-28; $\varphi_1 = 1$; at 2537 A, $\epsilon(CH_3Br)/\epsilon(CD_3Br) = 1.38$.

$$CH_3Br + h\nu \rightarrow CH_3 + Br \qquad (1)$$

3. Polyhalomethanes:

$CHCl_3$[457,446]	CCl_4[458]	CH_2Br_2[439]
$CHBr_3$[446]	CBr_4[439]	CCl_3Br[443,439,462,446,463]
CCl_2Br_2[446]	$CHFBr_2$[449]	$CHClBr_2$[446,449]
$CHCl_2Br$[439,446]	CF_3I[460,461]	$CFBr_3$[459,446,449,460,464]

All lose the weakest bound halogen atom X on photolysis; process 1 important; the long-wavelength limit for CF_3I is 3170 A, $\lambda_{max} = 2680$ A, $\epsilon = 16.7$. The polyhalomethyl radical $R^{\ddagger}$ is vibrationally excited and decomposes unless deactivated; for example, $CHX_2^{\ddagger} \rightarrow CX + HX$. Compounds CF_2Cl_2,[446] CF_2Br_2,[464] and CF_2HBr[446,441] all give CF_2 radicals on photolysis at short wavelengths:

$$RX + h\nu \rightarrow R^{\ddagger} + X \tag{1}$$

$$CF_2X_2 + h\nu \rightarrow CF_2 + X_2 \tag{2}$$

4. Ethyl iodide:[444,450,454d,465,466,467] first absorption band given in Fig. 5-28; $\varphi_1 = 1$; full mercury arc, $\overline{\varphi_2/\varphi_1} \leqslant 0.05$; process 2 presumably important at short wavelengths; in liquid-phase values of Φ_{I_2} are very dependent on traces of O_2;[136,466] the fraction of C_2H_5 radicals which escape the solvent cage or diffusively recombine with the parent partner, using 2537 A, is 0.32 at 25°, 0.08 at $-70°$, and 5×10^{-4} in glass at $-180°$.[467]

$$C_2H_5I + h\nu \rightarrow C_2H_5^{\ddagger} + I \tag{1}$$
$$\searrow$$
$$C_2H_4 + HI \tag{2}$$

5. Ethyl bromide:[469,470] first absorption band shown in Fig. 5-28; $\varphi_1 = 1.0$; $\epsilon(^{12}CH_3{}^{12}CH_2Br)/\epsilon(^{12}CH_3{}^{13}CH_2Br) = 1.041$ at 2537 A.

$$C_2H_5Br + h\nu \rightarrow C_2H_5 + Br \tag{1}$$

6. Polyhaloethanes: $ClCH_2CH_2Cl$,[471] C_2Cl_5H,[472] $C_2H_4I_2$,[473] and CF_3CF_2I[460] all lose the weakest bound halogen atom efficiently on irradiation in the first absorption region; long-wavelength limit of C_2F_5I, 3270 A, $\lambda_{max} = 2680$ A, $\epsilon = 16.4$.

7. cis-1,2-Dichloroethylene:[474,475] photolysis with full mercury arc, $\varphi_1/\varphi_2 = 9$; light limited to $\lambda > 2200$, $\varphi_1/\varphi_2 = 3.3$; reaction 1 favored at short wavelengths; see also liquid-phase photolysis results, p. 504.

$$cis\text{-}ClCH{=}CHCl + h\nu \rightarrow [C_2H_2Cl + Cl] \tag{1a}$$
$$\searrow \qquad \downarrow$$
$$C_2H_2 + Cl + Cl \tag{1b}$$
$$\searrow$$
$$C_2HCl + HCl \tag{2}$$

8. Tetraiodoethylene:[476] 2537 A in hexane solution at 0°, Φ (decomposition) $= \sim 0.80$; $IC{\equiv}CI$ product; fractions of the process which occur by free radical and by intramolecular processes are not clear.

9. Isopropyl iodide:[450,477,478] 3130 A, $\varphi_1 \sim 0.98$; process 2 unimportant here where $\varphi_2 \leqslant 0.1$ at 3130 A; much of the C_3H_6 formed must arise in reactions other than 2.

$$(CH_3)_2CHI + h\nu \rightarrow (CH_3)_2CH + I \qquad (1)$$
$$\searrow$$
$$C_3H_6 + HI \qquad (2)$$

10. n-Propyl iodide:[477,479] liquid phase, 2537 A, reaction 1 dominant; either 2 or 1, followed by $I + n\text{-}C_3H_7 \rightarrow C_3H_6 + HI$, forms some C_3H_6.

$$n\text{-}C_3H_7I + h\nu \rightarrow n\text{-}C_3H_7 + I \qquad (1)$$
$$\searrow$$
$$C_3H_6 + HI \qquad (2)$$

11. Miscellaneous halogen-substituted hydrocarbons: quantum yields of I_2 formation in liquid phase for $n\text{-}C_3H_7I$, iso-C_3H_7I, $n\text{-}C_4H_9I$, sec-C_4H_9I, and iso-C_4H_9I similar to that for C_2H_5I at 2537 A and probably process 1 is dominant;[480] 1 is important in C_3F_7I photolysis[481] and $HC \equiv CCH_2Br$ liquid-phase photolysis at 2537 A.[482]

$$RX + h\nu \rightarrow R + X \qquad (1)$$

12. Halogen-substituted aromatic compounds: C_6H_5I, see Fig. 5-29 for absorption spectrum in hexane at 25°, $\sim$2537 A, $\phi_1 \sim 1$;[483–485] other mono-, di-, and triiodine-substituted aromatic compounds show process 1 also.[485,486]

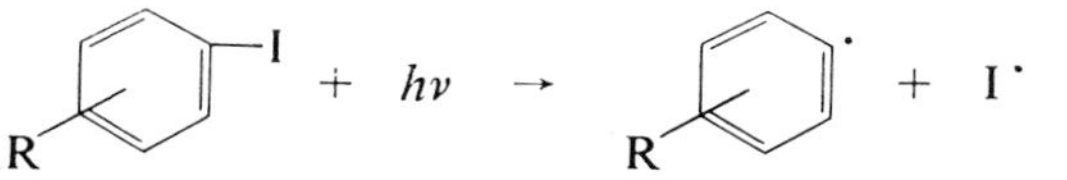

$C_6H_5CH_2Cl$ forms benzyl radical on irradiation in hydrocarbon glasses at 77°K.

5-9 THE INTERMOLECULAR REACTIONS OF ELECTRONICALLY EXCITED MOLECULES

Having considered the photochemical primary processes of a number of organic compounds with accent on their fragmentation and intramolecular rearrangement modes, we shall now classify types of photochemical reactions with emphasis on their important liquid-phase non-dissociative processes. These include the intermolecular reactions of photodimerization, photoreduction, and photosensitization; they are of great mechanistic and synthetic interest, especially to the "organic photochemist."

We saw in Chapter 4 that photophysical processes of molecules with n, π^* first excited states generally differ significantly from those whose lowest states are π, π^*. In particular, the natural lifetimes and the degree of localization of excitation are greater and the $S_1 \rightarrow T_1$ energy gaps are less for n, π^* states. Pronounced differences in photochemical reactivity, due in part to these factors, also exist. Thus, for example, the first absorption bands of anthracene and benzophenone fall in the same region [$\Delta E(S_0 \rightarrow S_1) = 26{,}200$ and $26{,}000$ cm^{-1}, respectively], but irradiation of degassed solutions in a solvent such as isopropyl alcohol yields dianthracene in one case, an example of photodimerization, and benzopinacol and acetone in the other, a typical photoreduction. With anthracene the excitation is delocalized in the π-electron system and dimerization occurs across the ring at the 9,10-positions. Apparently the reactive state is the first excited singlet, and the solvent participates only to the extent that it affects the relative probabilities of the several photophysical processes involved.

In contrast, $n \rightarrow \pi^*$ transitions involving carbonyl groups are believed to lower the ground-state dipole moment and reduce the negative charge localized on or near the oxygen atom. Furthermore, the primary photochemically reactive state of benzophenone in solution is the triplet which is formed with virtually unit efficiency by intersystem crossing from the excited singlet $^1(n, \pi^*) \rightsquigarrow {}^3(n, \pi^*)$. The triplet species, $\phi_2CO(T_1)$, effectively abstracts hydrogen atoms from the solvent, giving ketyl ($\phi_2\dot{C}OH$) and solvent radicals; these subsequently undergo a variety of secondary reactions including combination of two ketyls to give benzopinacol. The simplified sequence of events can be written thus:

Excitation:

$$\begin{array}{c}\diagdown \\ \diagup \end{array}C{=}O + h\nu \;\rightarrow\; \overset{*}{\underset{n}{\begin{array}{c}\diagdown \\ \diagup\end{array}C{-}\overset{**}{O}{:}}} \;\leftrightarrow\; \underset{n}{\begin{array}{c}\diagdown \\ \diagup\end{array}\overset{**^-}{C}{-}\overset{*^+}{O}{:}}$$

or in MO terminology

$$\rightarrow\; \underset{n}{\begin{array}{c}\diagdown \\ \diagup\end{array}\overset{\delta^-}{C}\overset{\pi^*}{=}\overset{\delta^+}{O}{:}}$$

Intersystem crossing:

$$\phi_2CO\;{}^1(n, \pi^*) \rightsquigarrow \phi_2CO\;{}^3(n, \pi^*)$$

H atom abstraction:

$$\phi_2CO\;{}^3(n, \pi^*) + RH \rightarrow \phi_2\dot{C}OH + R$$

Combination:

$$2\phi_2\dot{C}OH \;\rightarrow\; \begin{array}{c}\phi \quad OH \quad OH \quad \phi \\ \diagdown \;|\quad\;\; |\; \diagup \\ C{-}{-}C \\ \diagup \qquad\quad \diagdown \\ \phi \qquad\qquad \phi\end{array}$$

---

* In fact, the system is more complex, but space limitations prevent a more detailed discussion of the mechanism here. See Sec. 5-9B for references.

These fundamental differences in the photochemistry of the two spectroscopic classes of compounds should be considered when evaluating various photochemical systems. However, one point should be kept in mind; $\pi \rightarrow \pi^*$ excitation does not necessarily mean that delocalization of excitation in the (π, π^*) state will be an important factor in determining the photochemistry of the system. Thus irradiation of benzophenone-alcohol solutions at 2537 A results initially in a $^1(\pi, \pi^*)$ state of benzophenone, but the products of irradiation and their quantum yields are virtually the same for experiments at 3660 A, where the absorption is $n \rightarrow \pi^*$. This is reasonable if one assumes that $\pi \rightarrow \pi^*$ absorption to the S_2 state is followed by rapid internal conversion to the S_1 state, $^1(n, \pi^*)$, which then undergoes a radiationless intersystem crossing to give T_1, $^3(n, \pi^*)$, the identical reactive triplet formed at 3660 A.

We have stressed this point because of the growing tendency to speak of "(π, π^*) photochemistry" and "(n, π^*) photochemistry," and to cite their differences, without properly emphasizing that entirely different classes of compounds are being considered. Significant differences in the (n, π^*) and (π, π^*) photochemistry of a given compound *may* occur, for example, possibly in the vapor-phase photolysis of ketones. But one must guard against citing differences in products and their yields as one goes from one absorption band to another as being due simply to differences in the electronic structures of the two initially formed excited states. The results *may* be due to different light intensities or other experimental conditions, or simply an *energy* effect which changes the yields of products but does not drastically alter the character of the photochemistry of the system.

Ketones and aromatic hydrocarbons and olefins are prime examples of n, π^* and π, π^* systems, and most of the quantitative, definitive work to date on solution-phase systems has been done on these molecules. We shall consider ketones and aldehydes here, since their photochemistry includes most types of solution-phase primary photochemical processes usually encountered. Aromatic hydrocarbons are discussed in Sec. 5-7C and in the review by Bowen;[695] olefins are treated in Sec. 5-7B and in the reviews by Chapman[501] and Dauben and Wipke.[639]

The organic photochemistry of sulfur and nitrogen heteroatomic organic compounds recently has been reviewed by Mustafa,[494] the unsaturated nitro compounds by Chapman and co-workers,[747] while organic nitrites and hypohalites have been treated by Akhtar.[295] Their established primary dissociative processes have been summarized in Secs. 5-5 and 5-6; space limitations preclude further considerations here.

In addition to articles on specific subjects appearing in the series *Advances in Photochemistry*, the following general references review important aspects of "organic photochemistry" with particular attention to the chemistry involved: 120, 295, 493–495, 501, 523–535, 540, 613, 695, 743–753. References emphasizing the spectroscopic and photophysical energy transfer aspects are given in Chapter 4.

In this section we will consider the classes of reactions summarized in Table 5-4; (1) the intermolecular photoreduction of ketones in solution;

TABLE 5-4 Some Examples of the Intermolecular Reactions of Electronically Excited Molecules

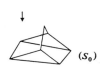

1. Intermolecular photoreduction $(C_6H_5)_2C{=}O + h\nu \xrightarrow{(RH)} (C_6H_5)_2\dot{C}OH + R\cdot$

2. Photodimerizations
   (a) Photocyclodimerization

(b) Carbonyl photocycloaddition to olefin $(C_6H_5)_2C{=}O + h\nu \xrightarrow{(C_2H_4)} (C_6H_5)_2C{-}O$ with $CH_2{-}CH_2$

(c) Olefin addition across C=C bonds in α,β-unsaturated ketones

3. Molecular photosensitized reactions; isomerization is the example given
   $(C_6H_5)_2C{=}O(S_0) + h\nu \to (C_6H_5)_2C{=}O(S_1)$
   $(C_6H_5)_2C{=}O(S_1) \rightsquigarrow (C_6H_5)_2CO(T_1)$

   $(C_6H_5)_2CO(T_1) +$ [norbornadiene] $\to$

   $[\text{bicyclic diradical} (T_1)] + (C_6H_5)_2CO(S_0)$

   $\downarrow$

   [quadricyclane] (S_0)

(2) the photodimerization reactions, including photocyclodimerization, carbonyl cycloaddition to olefins, and olefin addition across C=C bonds in α,β-unsaturated ketones; and (3) molecular photosensitized reactions, including *cis-trans* isomerization, isomerizations involving ring closure and ring opening, addition reactions, molecular decompositions, and oxidations.

5-9A   The Intermolecular Photoreduction
of Ketones in Solution

Photochemical reductions of aromatic ketones in solution have been the subject of many investigations since the original discovery of Ciamician and Silber[536] that the action of sunlight on a solution of benzophenone in ethanol gave a good yield of benzopinacol. Up to 1950 most of the work was directed towards synthetic applications of photoreductions, since the yields in many cases are good and the products more readily prepared than by the usual non-photochemical routes. This is well illustrated in an important early review article by Schönberg and Mustafa,[533] who did much of the pioneer synthetic photochemistry of the carbonyl compounds. The mechanistic aspects of these systems were first examined critically by Bäckström[537] and by Weizmann, Bergmann, and Hirshberg[112] in the 1930's. Since then benzophenone in particular has been studied extensively in the laboratories of Bäckström, Cohen, Franzen, Hammond, Linschitz, Moore, Pitts, Porter, and Schenck. Key references to the more "chemical mechanistic" aspects of the problem include 118, 119, 533, 539–544; spectroscopic considerations, including energy transfer, are considered in detail in Chapter 4. Space limitations preclude a detailed discussion of the mechanism of photoreduction of benzophenone and related non-enolizable ketones, but the overall aspects can be summarized as follows.

Irradiation of benzophenone in thoroughly deoxygenated hydrogen-donor solvents, such as isopropyl alcohol, gives a quantitative yield of benzopinacol and acetone:[118]

$$2\phi_2CO + CH_3CHOHCH_3 + h\nu \rightarrow \underset{\phi}{\underset{|}{\phi—C}}\overset{OH}{\overset{|}{—}}\overset{OH}{\overset{|}{—}}\underset{\phi}{\underset{|}{C—\phi}} + CH_3COCH_3$$

The quantum yield of benzophenone disappearance depends on the solvent, intensity of light absorbed,[543] etc., as seen in Table 5-5.

It has now been well established by a variety of techniques, such as physical quenching, flash spectroscopic detection of intermediates, and emission spectra, that the hydrogen-atom abstracting state of benzophenone is the lowest n, π^* triplet formed by intersystem crossing from the original excited singlet state (see Chapter 4 and references therein). A variety of secondary reactions of the ketyl, $\phi_2\dot{C}OH$, and solvent radicals formed in the abstraction process lead to the observed products. While the photopinacolization of benzophenone can be quenched by energy transfer to naphthalene,[539,545] it can also be suppressed by chemical scavenging of the ketyl radicals with mercaptans or disulfides.[544]

The possible formation of mixed pinacols has been studied by Johnson and co-workers, who irradiated vacuum-degassed binary mixtures of benzophenone, 4,4'-dichlorobenzophenone, and 4,4'-dimethoxybenzophenone under equimolar and equiabsorbance conditions.[546] Only one system, the mixture of benzophenone and 4,4'-dichlorobenzophenone, gave about 15–20% of cross pinacols. The failure of cross-pinacol

TABLE 5-5 Photoreduction of Benzophenone in Various Solvents[a]

Solvent	Concentration of Benzophenone	$\Phi_{(\text{Disappearance of } \phi_2\text{CO})}$
Water	$10^{-4}M$	0.02
Benzene	$10^{-2}M$	0.05
Toluene	$10^{-2}M$	0.45
Hexane	10^{-2} to $10^{-4}M$	1.0
Ethanol	10^{-4} to $10^{-1}M$	1.0
Isopropanol	10^{-5} to $10^{-1}M$	0.80 to 2[b]

[a] From Porter and Beckett.[543]
[b] This variation is due to a light intensity effect.[543]

formation in the other two systems may be due to a triplet-triplet energy transfer, or it could result from an intermolecular hydrogen-atom transfer from a ketyl radical to a ketone molecule.[546]

In contrast to the large amount of work on the Type II split involving intramolecular hydrogen abstraction, the photochemical reduction of aliphatic aldehydes and ketones has not been extensively studied. A few reports indicate that photoexcited acetone molecules are, to a small extent, reduced either by self-quenching or by abstraction from the solvent. With aliphatic ketones containing γ-hydrogen atoms, few if any intermolecular photoreductions occur. Similarly when butyrophenone is irradiated in hydroxylic solvents the Type II split is far more probable than intermolecular hydrogen atom abstraction.[498,499] It is not yet established whether or not the intra- and intermolecular hydrogen abstraction involves the same excited state.

Finally, intermolecular photoreduction of cyclic ketones has not been systematically investigated, but it is believed that in hydrocarbon or aqueous solutions the reaction between the photoexcited cyclic ketone and the solvent becomes important:

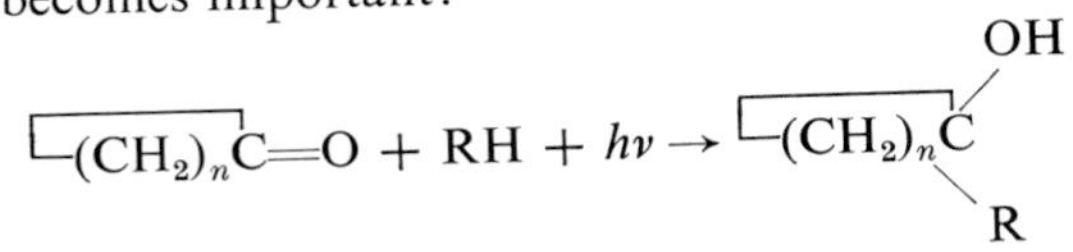

$$\text{—(CH}_2)_n\text{C=O} + \text{RH} + h\nu \rightarrow \text{—(CH}_2)_n\text{C}\begin{matrix}\text{OH}\\ \diagup \\ \diagdown \\ \text{R}\end{matrix}$$

For example, photolysis of cyclohexanone in cyclohexanol solution leads to the formation of cyclohexyl pinacol,[538] and irradiation of 2-fluorocyclohexanone in methanol gives a very low yield of methyl-6-fluorohexanoates.[557]

The efficiency of both intermolecular and intramolecular photoreduction depends not only on the reactivity of the hydrogen donor but also on the structure of the abstracting ketone. As we noted in Chapter 4, substituted benzophenones show dramatic differences in their reactivity. Thus, *ortho* substitution of a hydroxy group with a hydrogen atom which can participate in a six-membered ring with the carbonyl oxygen* completely quenches the intermolecular hydrogen-atom abstraction process, and $\Phi_{\text{pinacol}} = 0.00$.[549] The six-membered ring is important for stabilization since both *o*-methoxy- and *o*-carboxybenzophenone photopinacolize;[549] *o*-methylbenzophenone, however, does not.[550]

The process by which this quenching occurs has been termed "photoenolization" by Yang and Rivas,[550] who, as part of their definitive work, demonstrated the effect by irradiating A in CH_3OD and showing that deuterium was introduced into the alkyl side chain:

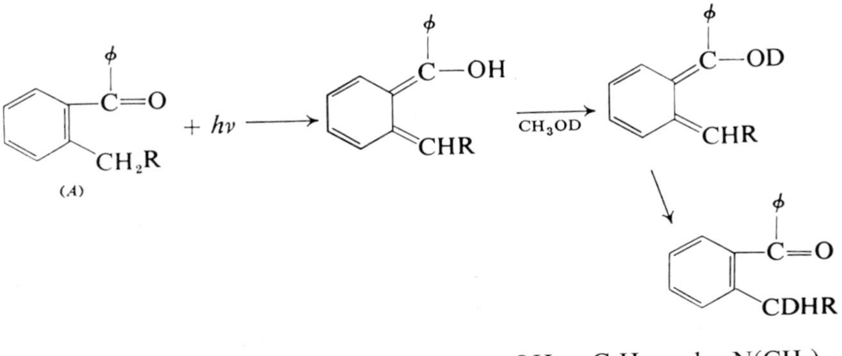

Certain *para* substituents, such as $-NH_2$, $-OH$, $-C_6H_5$, and $-N(CH_3)_2$, greatly reduce the tendency for intermolecular photoreduction of the carbonyl chromophore by hydrogen-atom abstraction from the solvent. Thus, for example, Pitts, Sharp, and co-workers[517,551,552] found that the quantum yield of photopinacolization of *p*-NH_2-benzophenone was zero. They proposed that the mechanism does not involve photoenolization but was

---

* Ketones of this type are widely used commercially as "sun-screening" agents.

related to a *decrease in chemical* reactivity of the lowest triplet state, which, through an intermolecular energy transfer, was $^3(\pi, \pi^*)$ rather than $^3(n, \pi^*)$ as with normal aromatic ketones. Phosphorescence and ESR spectra were cited in support of this idea. (See Sec. 4-11 for spectroscopic details.) Concurrently and independently, Hammond and Leermakers cited the same concept to explain the absence of photoreduction of 2-acetyl-naphthone and 1-naphthaldehyde in normal hydrogen-atom-donating solvents.[39]

Subsequently Porter and coworkers[543,553] confirmed and extended the evidence for the *para*-substituent effect and recently suggested that the lowest excited state in certain abnormal benzophenones was not $^3(\pi, \pi^*)$ but an "intramolecular charge-transfer state."[553] We prefer to consider such lowest states to be $^3(\pi, \pi^*)$ with some charge-transfer character, but in any case there seems to be general agreement that the lack of reactivity is explained by both delocalization of $^3(\pi,\pi^*)$ excitation and increased negative charge on the excited carbonyl oxygen,[543,551-553] as with the substituted butyrophenones.[497-499]*

Further dependence of chemical behavior on the nature of the excited states is illustrated by the photochemical reactions of the aromatic diketones *cis*-dibenzoylethylene *B* and *trans*-dibenzoylcyclopropene *D*, p. 536. Thus Griffin and O'Connell[554] showed that direct irradiation of *B* involves an excited singlet state which mainly undergoes rearrangement involving a 1,5-phenyl migration followed by addition of alcohol to give the ester *C*. On the other hand, sensitization by triplet benzophenone produces *B* in its triplet state. This is subsequently photoreduced via intermolecular hydrogen-atom transfer from the solvent.

---

* As evidence for an "intramolecular charge transfer state," Porter and Suppan[758] report that 4,4'-N,N-dimethylaminobenzophenone, which is known to be virtually non-reactive in isopropyl alcohol solvent, is reactive in cyclohexane with a quantum yield of disappearance of 0.6. However, Walling and Gibian[759] have reported that this "abnormal" benzophenone is non-reactive in both isopropyl alcohol and cyclohexane.

Direct irradiation of *D* leads only to *cis-trans* conversion. However, in hydrogen-atom-donating solvents containing an efficient triplet sensitizer such as benzophenone, the reaction follows a different course, giving 1,3-dibenzoylpropane *E*.[555]

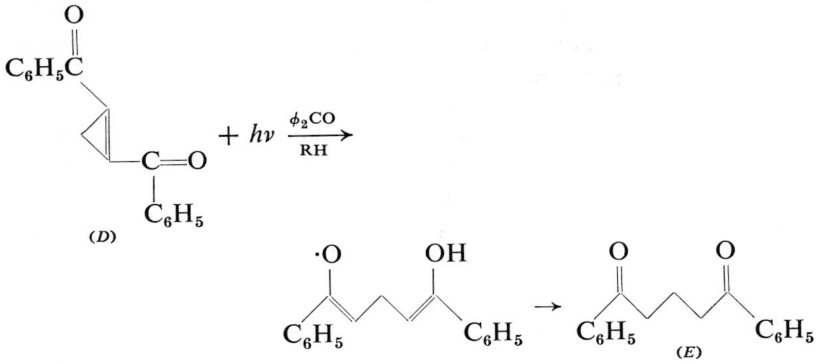

5-9B   Photodimerization Reactions

In this section a few examples are given of intermolecular interactions of excited molecules which result in photocyclodimerization (Sec. 5-9B-1), carbonyl cycloaddition to olefins (Sec. 5-9B-2), and olefin addition across C=C bonds in α,β-unsaturated ketones (Sec. 5-9B-3).

5-9B-1   Photocyclodimerization

Photocyclodimerization to give cyclobutane derivatives is an important reaction of α,β-unsaturated aromatic carbonyl compounds.[532] Although the reaction has been studied extensively in the condensed phase, the analogous reaction is not known in the vapor phase.

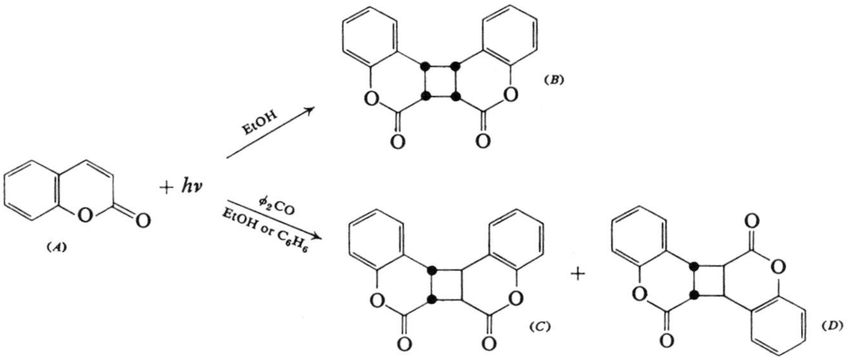

Solvent effects on the course of dimerization are illustrated in the reactions of coumarin *A*.[558,559,560] Thus Schenk and coworkers[559] found that irradiation of coumarin in ethanol gives a *cis* head-to-head dimer *B*, but no reaction occurs in benzene. However, dimerization of coumarin can be phosensitized by benzophenone in either solvent, giving the *trans* dimer *C* and a trace of the *trans* head-to-tail dimer *D*.

In their studies Hammond, Stout, and Lamola showed that direct photolysis of coumarin produces an excited singlet state which leads only to self-quenching in a non-polar solvent such as benzene and to the formation of *B* in very low yields in a polar solvent such as ethanol.[560] In the benzophenone sensitized reactions, triplet coumarin gives *C* and *D* with relatively high quantum yields. At high dilution and in the absence of benzophenone, direct photolysis of coumarin also presumably produces triplet coumarin via intersystem crossing, and *C* is formed. When benzophenone is present in small amounts and most of the light is absorbed by coumarin, they suggest that singlet excitation is transferred from coumarin to benzophenone, and intersystem crossing takes place efficiently in the excited benzophenone. The triplet excitation is then transferred back to coumarin, which, as the triplet species, gives the dimers *C* and *D*. They also suggest that the absence of dimer *B* in the sensitized reaction indicates that transfer of singlet excitation from benzophenone to coumarin is not as efficient as the reverse process.[560]

Another interesting example is the photodimerization of cyclopentenone in the pure liquid or in various solvents; Eaton showed this gave *trans* head-to-tail and head-to-head dimers in equal yield.[561] This non-stereo-specific behavior suggests that the cyclodimerization may involve highly reactive excited singlet states. In the presence of a large excess of cyclo-

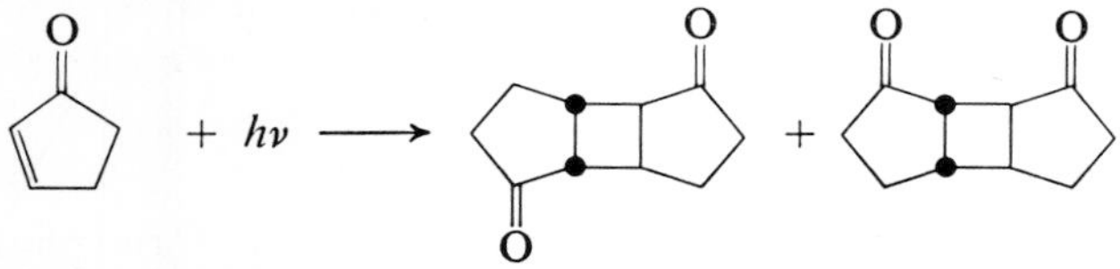

pentene, cross addition occurs in preference to self-dimerization, yielding exclusively the *trans* dimer.[562]

Irradiation of *E* in either the solid state or aqueous solution leads to dimerization in good yields.[598,600]

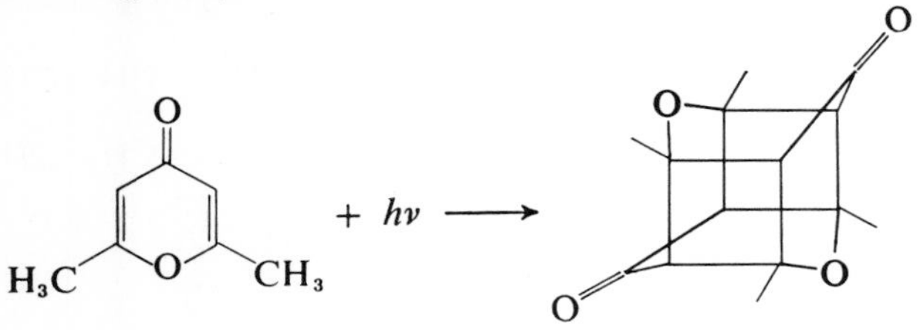

Irradiation of α-pyridones *F* in aqueous solution with an unfiltered high-pressure mercury arc results in dimerization.[601-603]

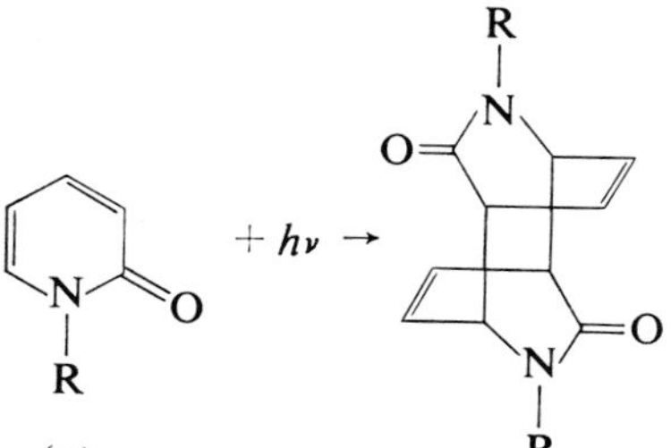

(*F*)

Irradiation of solid chalcone, $C_6H_5CH{=}CHCOC_6H_5$, yields both head-to-tail and head-to-head dimers.[681] While *m*-nitrochalcone undergoes similar photodimerization in the solid state, solid *p*-nitrochalcone yields only a small quantity of photodimers.[682] The photochemistry of the organic solid state has been reviewed by Cohen.[746]

A few α,β-unsaturated ketones have also been found to dimerize when irradiated as solids. Thus, coumarin yields a head-to-head photodimer.[683] Uracil *G* and thymine[685] *H* and their derivatives apparently photodimerize, giving cyclobutane derivatives *I* or the analogous head-to-head dimers.

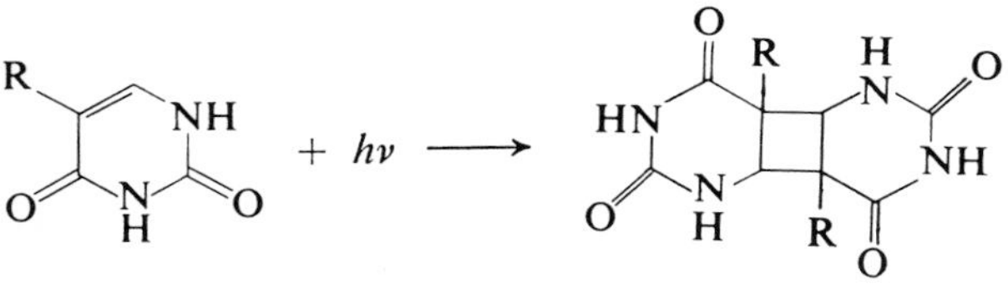

(*G*) R = H

(*H*) R = CH$_3$

(*I*)

Some unsaturated ketones such as solid 4-pyrone form photodimers involving two pairs of olefinic bonds; this is sometimes referred to as double dimerization. A cyclic structure is not required for a double

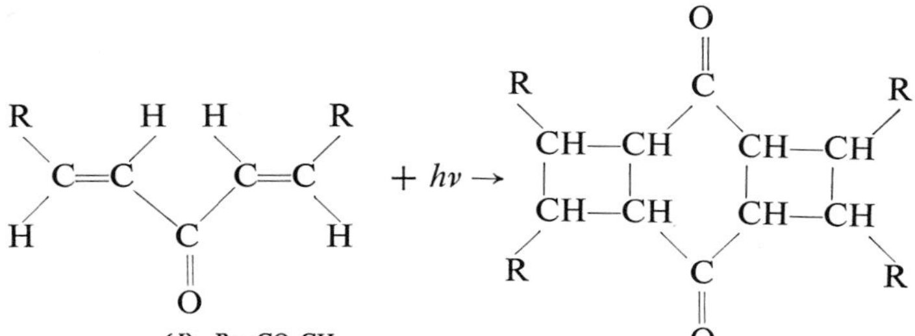

(*J*) R=CO$_2$CH$_3$

(*K*)

dimerization. Thus, the solid cyclic ketone, 2,5-disubstituted thymoquin-one, yields open dimers[686] when irradiated, whereas solid dimethyl-3-oxo-1,4-pentadiene-1,5-dicarboxylate J with an open-chain structure gives tetramethyl tricyclo[6.2.0.0^{3,6}]-2,7-dioxodecane-4,5,9,10-tetracarboxalate K[687,688] (see p. 538).

5-9B-2   Carbonyl Cycloaddition to Olefins

The cycloaddition of olefins to photoexcited carbonyl groups to form oxetanes was shown by Büchi and co-workers to be a general reaction.[567] The yield of oxetanes from the photocycloaddition of benzophenone and derivatives to olefins depends markedly on the structure of the olefin as well as the structure of the benzophenone.[563,568] Thus, substituted benzo-phenones which do not photoreduce do not undergo this addition, and Arnold et al. suggest that the addition reaction requires the lowest excited state to be $^3(n, \pi^*)$ in character. Yang suggests that other factors may be involved.[568]

The effect of olefin structure is illustrated by the addition of benzo-phenone to propylene and isobutylene. These reactions gave the corre-sponding oxetanes, A and B, in 5% and 93% yield, respectively. The results are explained by assuming that the triplet energy level of the

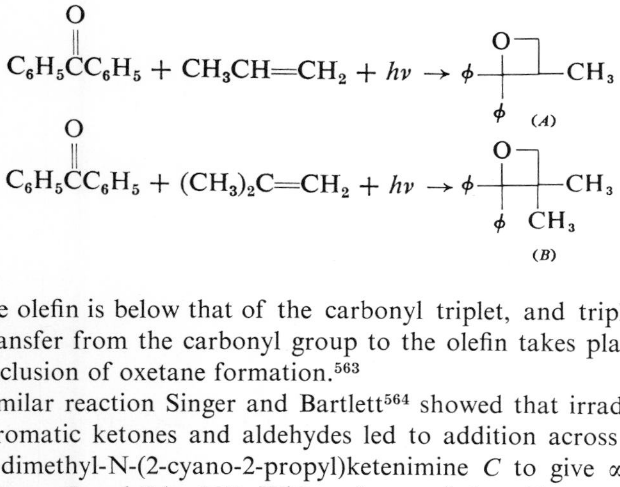

$$C_6H_5\overset{\overset{O}{\|}}{C}C_6H_5 + CH_3CH{=}CH_2 + h\nu \rightarrow \phi\underset{\phi}{\overset{O}{\rule{0pt}{12pt}}}{-}CH_3 \quad (A)$$

$$C_6H_5\overset{\overset{O}{\|}}{C}C_6H_5 + (CH_3)_2C{=}CH_2 + h\nu \rightarrow \phi\underset{\phi\;\;CH_3}{\overset{O}{\rule{0pt}{12pt}}}{-}CH_3 \quad (B)$$

unreactive olefin is below that of the carbonyl triplet, and triplet-triplet energy transfer from the carbonyl group to the olefin takes place to the virtual exclusion of oxetane formation.[563]

In a similar reaction Singer and Bartlett[564] showed that irradiation of several aromatic ketones and aldehydes led to addition across the C-C bond of dimethyl-N-(2-cyano-2-propyl)ketenimine C to give α- and β-iminooxetanes D and E (p. 540). With cyclopropyl phenyl ketone as donor, transfer of triplet energy to ketenimine was so efficient that the formation of oxetane was suppressed completely and tetramethyl succinonitrile F was formed exclusively. The ratio of oxetane formation to that of F was

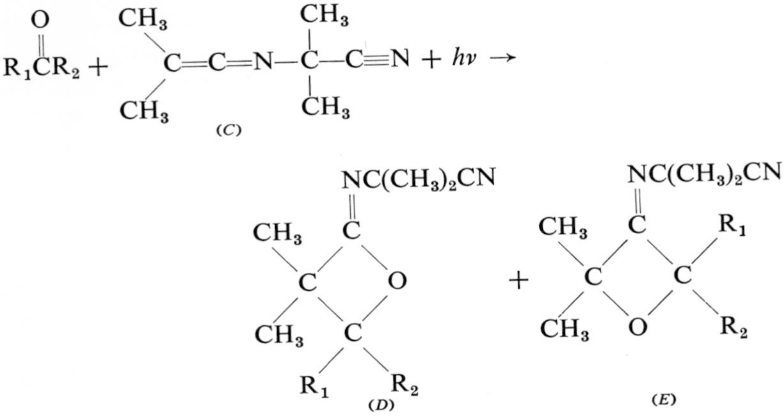

$$R_1\overset{O}{\overset{\|}{C}}R_2 + \underset{CH_3}{\overset{CH_3}{C}}\!\!=\!\!C\!\!=\!\!N\!\!-\!\!\underset{CH_3}{\overset{CH_3}{C}}\!\!-\!\!C\!\!\equiv\!\!N + h\nu \rightarrow$$

(C)

Structures (D) and (E):

(D): $NC(CH_3)_2CN$ / C ring with CH_3, CH_3, C, O, C, R_1, R_2

$+$

(E): $NC(CH_3)_2CN$ / C ring with CH_3, CH_3, C, C, O, R_1, R_2

found to vary from one carbonyl compound to the other, and the carbonyl compounds with higher triplet energy gave a higher yield of F. 2-Aceto-

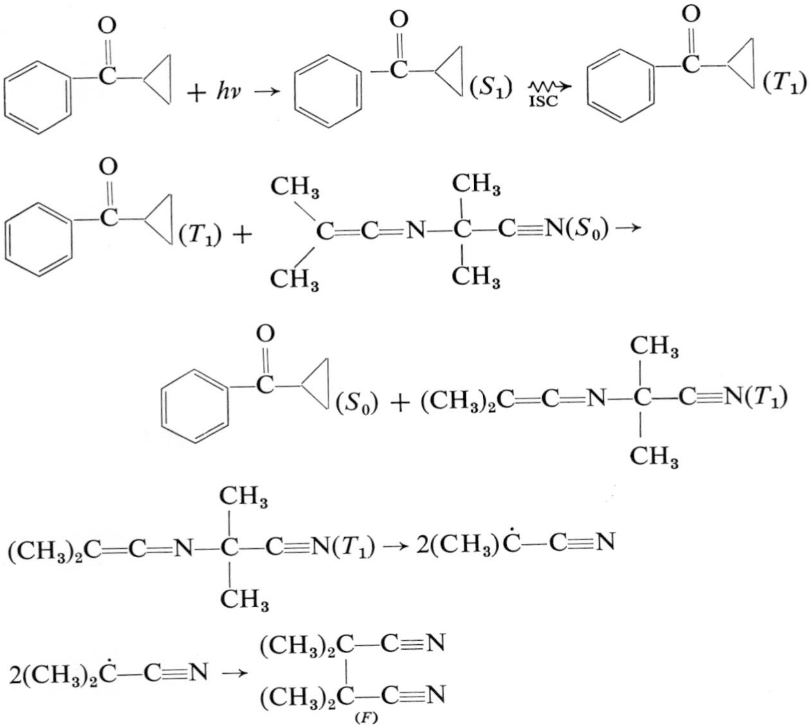

$$\underset{}{\overset{O}{\overset{\|}{Ph\,C}}}\!\!-\!\!\triangleleft + h\nu \rightarrow \overset{O}{\overset{\|}{Ph\,C}}\!\!-\!\!\triangleleft(S_1) \underset{ISC}{\leadsto} \overset{O}{\overset{\|}{Ph\,C}}\!\!-\!\!\triangleleft(T_1)$$

$$\overset{O}{\overset{\|}{Ph\,C}}\!\!-\!\!\triangleleft(T_1) + \underset{CH_3}{\overset{CH_3}{C}}\!\!=\!\!C\!\!=\!\!N\!\!-\!\!\underset{CH_3}{\overset{CH_3}{C}}\!\!-\!\!C\!\!\equiv\!\!N(S_0) \rightarrow$$

$$\overset{O}{\overset{\|}{Ph\,C}}\!\!-\!\!\triangleleft(S_0) + (CH_3)_2C\!\!=\!\!C\!\!=\!\!N\!\!-\!\!\underset{CH_3}{\overset{CH_3}{C}}\!\!-\!\!C\!\!\equiv\!\!N(T_1)$$

$$(CH_3)_2C\!\!=\!\!C\!\!=\!\!N\!\!-\!\!\underset{CH_3}{\overset{CH_3}{C}}\!\!-\!\!C\!\!\equiv\!\!N(T_1) \rightarrow 2(CH_3)\dot{C}\!\!-\!\!C\!\!\equiv\!\!N$$

$$2(CH_3)_2\dot{C}\!\!-\!\!C\!\!\equiv\!\!N \rightarrow \underset{(CH_3)_2C-C\equiv N}{\overset{(CH_3)_2C-C\equiv N}{\mid}}$$

(F)

naphthone and 1-naphthaldehyde do not undergo photoreduction,[39] and the yields of oxetane and of F are zero.[564]

Additions to cyclic olefinic systems have been reported by Hammond and Turro:[523]

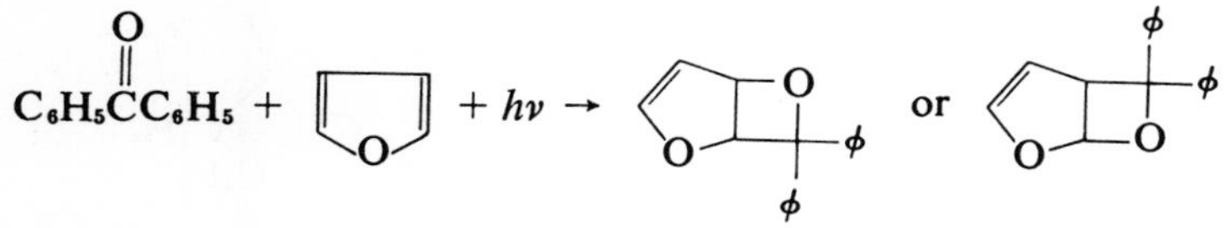

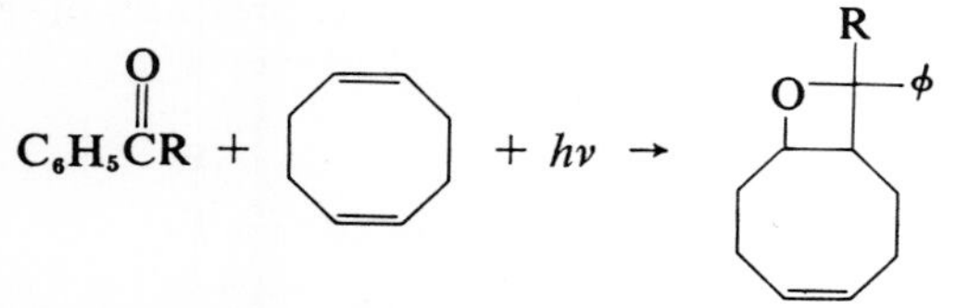

$$C_6H_5\overset{O}{\underset{\|}{C}}C_6H_5 + \quad + hv \rightarrow \quad \text{or}$$

and by Yang and coworkers:[568]

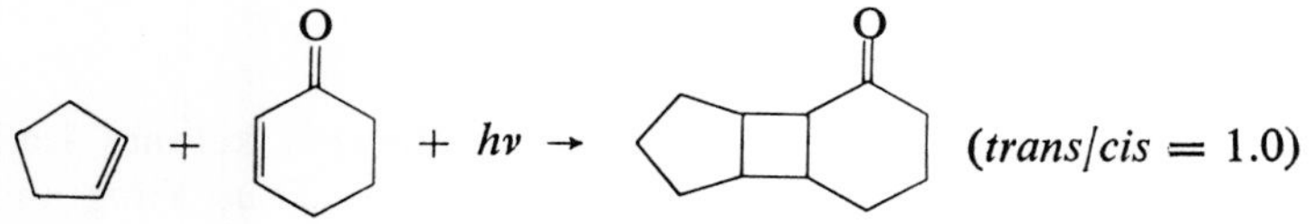

$$+ \quad + hv \rightarrow \quad (trans/cis = 1.0)$$

Photoaddition involving aliphatic carbonyl compounds also has been reported. For example, n-butyraldehyde adds to trimethyl ethylene to give an oxetane.[523]

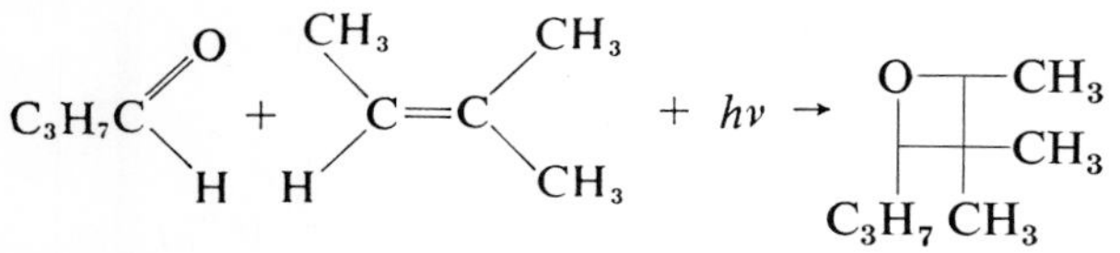

$$C_3H_7C\overset{O}{\underset{H}{\diagdown}}_H + \overset{CH_3}{\underset{H}{\diagup}}C=C\overset{CH_3}{\underset{CH_3}{\diagdown}} + hv \rightarrow$$

Fluoroaldehydes, fluoroketones, and fluoroacyl fluoride also add photochemically across the olefinic bonds of vinylidene fluorides to give fluoroxetanes in good yield.[565]

In the vapor phase acetaldehyde undergoes photocyloaddition with fluoro- and other halogen-substituted ethylenes to give oxetane in about 1.3 to 2.6% synthetic yield.[566]

Examples of carbonyl photocycloaddition to acetylenic bonds are the addition of benzaldehyde and of acetophenone to 5-decyne to give α,β-unsaturated ketones.[567] Büchi et al. suggest that an oxetane is an intermediate:

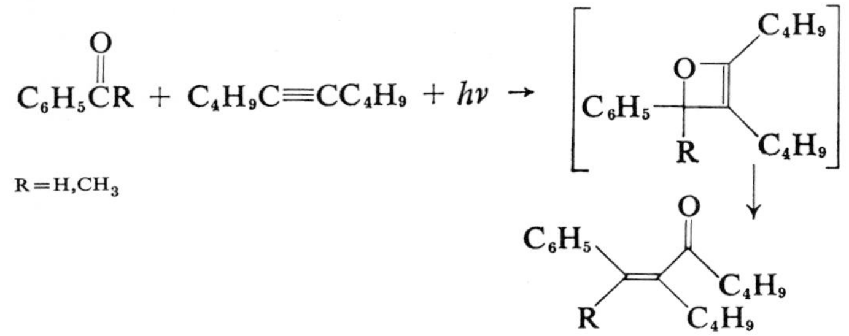

$$\text{C}_6\text{H}_5\overset{\overset{\text{O}}{\|}}{\text{C}}\text{R} + \text{C}_4\text{H}_9\text{C}{\equiv}\text{CC}_4\text{H}_9 + h\nu \ \rightarrow$$

R=H,CH₃

In one case, photoaddition of a cyclic fluoroketone to a fluoroolefin gives an oxetane as the final product. Thus, Harris and Coffman report that irradiation of hexafluorocyclobutanone in the presence of hexafluoropropylene gives a bicyclic oxetane in 33 % yield:[565]

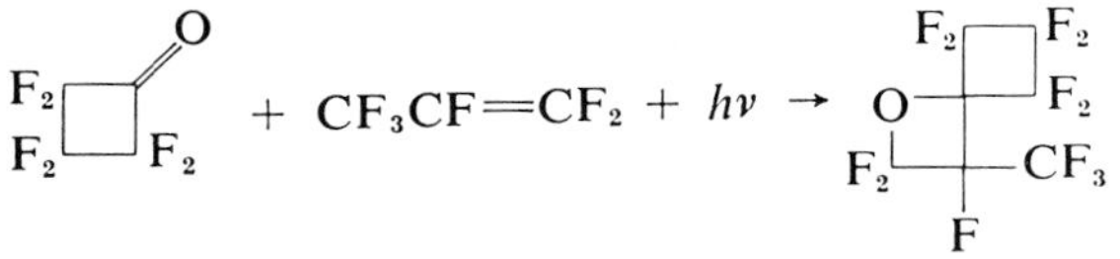

$$\text{F}_2\text{—}\overset{\text{O}}{\text{C}}\text{—F}_2 + \text{CF}_3\text{CF}{=}\text{CF}_2 + h\nu \ \rightarrow$$

5-9B-3   Olefin Addition across C=C
Bonds in α,β-Unsaturated Ketones

Addition of olefins across certain α,β-unsaturated ketones leads to derivatives of cyclobutane rather than of oxetane. Thus Yang and co-workers have studied the photoaddition of isobutylene to cyclohexenone and found the following products and synthetic yields:[568]

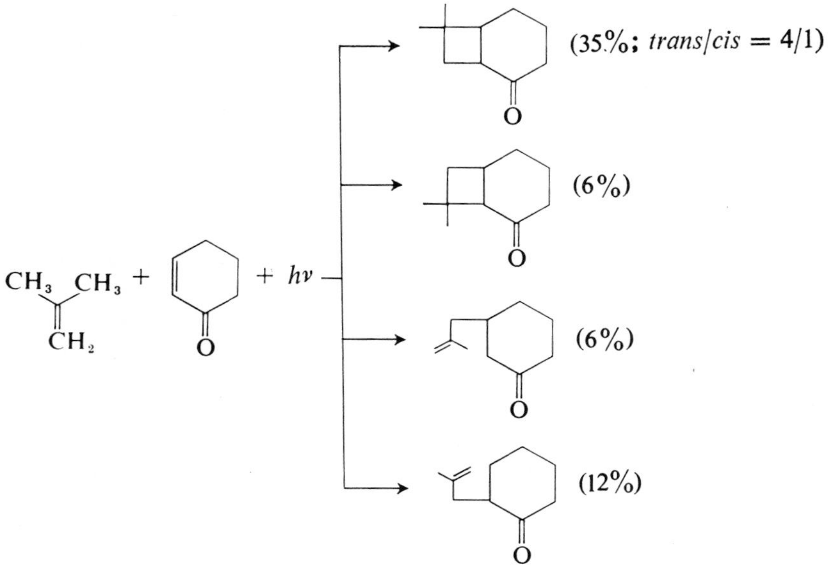

(35%; *trans/cis* = 4/1)

(6%)

(6%)

$$\text{CH}_3 \ \text{CH}_3 + \ \ + \ h\nu$$
$$\overset{|}{\text{CH}_2}$$

(12%)

Addition also occurred with cyclopentene:

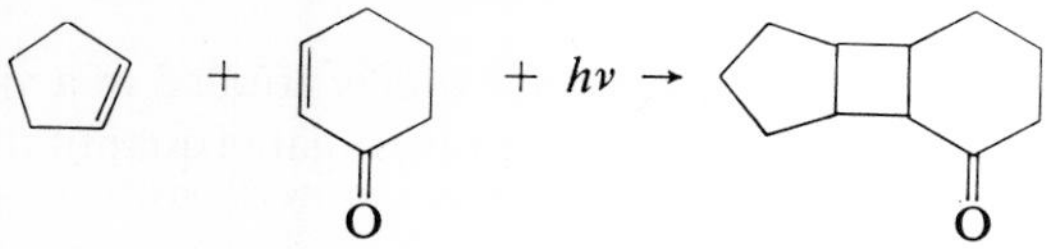

$(trans/cis = 1)$

The order of reactivity of olefinic adduct was as follows:

$$(MeO)_2C = CH_2, 30;$$

, 5; $CH_2 = C$, 1.3;   and $CH_2 = C = CH_2$, 1.

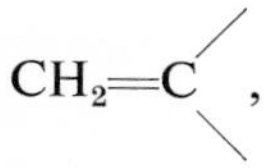

A type of photoaddition in which cyclization is not involved in the final product has been reported by de Mayo *et al.* Irradiation of acetylacetone in cyclohexene gives *B* in 78% yield, presumably through the intermediate *A*. Similar reactions have also been observed in good yields with 1-octene and other olefins.[597]

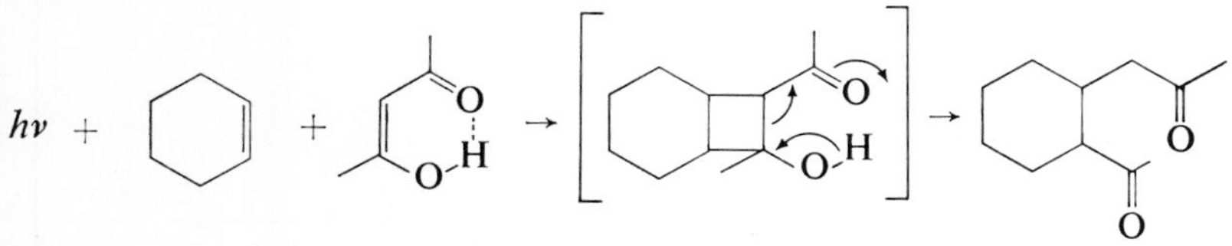

(A)   (B)

5-9C   Molecular Photosensitized Reactions

The field of sensitized photochemical reactions is much too large to consider in detail here. Thus, we shall confine our attention primarily to systems in which benzophenone and similar aromatic ketones act as donors, since they are becoming well understood (e.g. their triplet energies are known) and since they include the *types* of photosensitized reactions of general interest in mechanistic and synthetic organic chemistry.* A number of examples of such photosensitized reactions already have been cited in Chapter 4 and in the summary in Chapter 5, particularly Sec. 5-7B on olefins.

Several types of photosensitized isomerization are recognized, including *cis-trans* processes[350,351,614—617] and reactions involving energy transfer with consequent breaking of simple bonds in the acceptor.[617] We shall illustrate each of these.

---

* Dye-photosensitized processes and dye photochemistry in general are most important subjects but generally cannot be dealt with in this book; the papers of the Osters,[611] Lindqvist,[612] Gollnick and Schenk,[613] and Terenin[628,647,694] should be consulted for recent discussions and references to the original literature.

5-9C-1   Photosensitized *cis-trans* Isomerization

Direct *cis-trans* photoisomerization has been widely studied in a variety of systems. In particular the stilbenes have been investigated quantitatively, and several mechanisms have been proposed.[345–347,350,352,353,614,615,618,619,696] Recently Hammond and co-workers have considered the mechanism of the sensitized process in terms of extensive quantitative spectroscopic, chemical, and kinetic evidence on four pairs of isomers; the stilbenes, the

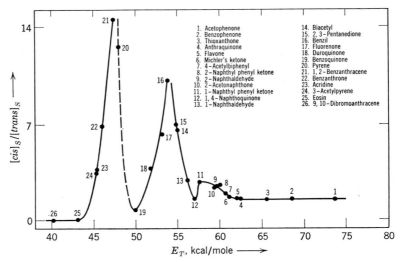

Fig. 5-30   *Cis/trans* ratio at the photostationary state of the stilbenes as a function of the triplet energy of the sensitizer. From Hammond *et al.*[615]

1,2-diphenylpropenes, the piperylenes (1,3-pentadienes), and ethyl maleate-ethyl fumarate.[615] The results with sensitizers are correlated with those obtained by direct excitation of the stilbenes and 1,2-dephenyl-propenes, and their mechanistic arguments are cogent.

In sensitized systems they find that the composition of the mixtures in the photostationary states is a complicated function of the nature of the photosensitizers. This is evident in Fig. 5-30, where the *cis/trans* ratio in the photostationary state of the stilbenes is plotted against the triplet energy of the sensitizer. However, all results for both direct and sensitized *cis-trans* isomerizations can be rationalized on the assumption that transfer of triplet excitation may involve excitation of acceptors to non-spectroscopic ("phantom" triplets) as well as spectroscopic states. Thus, they infer that the stilbene triplets exist in two interconvertible states, one transoid (spectroscopic) and one twisted (non-spectroscopic), as seen in

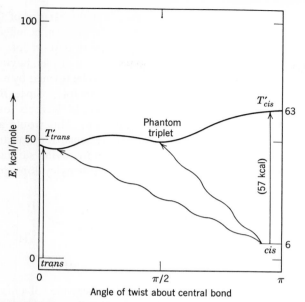

Fig. 5-31   Potential function for stilbene triplet states. From Hammond *et al.*[615]

Fig. 5-31. Self-quenching of stilbene triplets by ground-state *trans*-stilbene is significant. Hammond *et al.* note that sensitizers having low excitation energies function as true "photocatalysts;" that is, in the presence of excited states of the sensitizers the composition of the photostationary mixture approaches that at thermal equilibrium.[615]

5-9C-2   Photosensitized Isomerization Involving Ring Closure and Ring Opening

The ring-closure process, reaction 1, is an example of valence isomerization:

$$\text{(A)} + h\nu \xrightarrow[\text{Sensitized}]{\text{Direct or}} \text{(B)} \tag{1}$$

It occurs on direct irradiation[378] or sensitization by benzophenone or acetophenone.[370] The reaction may be explained in terms of interaction between the double bonds in *A* giving rise to "spectroscopic" triplet states lying lower than those of the sensitizers.[370]

Of more theoretical interest is the fact that the *reverse* of (1), that is, photoisomerization involving a saturated center, can be effected in the presence of certain photosensitizers.[617] Hammond *et al.* propose a mechanism involving direct excitation of *B* to a triplet having approximately the same nuclear configuration as would be formed by excitation of *A* in accordance with the Franck-Condon principle. Since *B* is a high-energy isomer of *A*, the $B \rightarrow A^*$ process would have a lower energy requirement than would the $A \rightarrow A^*$ excitation. This would account for the relatively high reactivity of the *low-energy* sensitizers towards *B*.

Another interesting sensitized isomerization involving saturated centers is the interconversion of *cis*- and *trans*-1,2-diphenylcyclopropane *C* and *D*.[617]

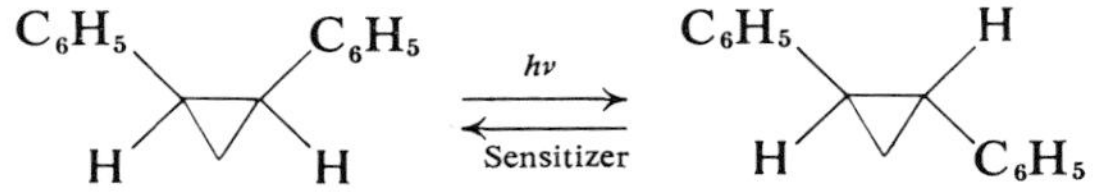

(C)   (D)

Conversion in either direction is observed in benzene solvents containing benzophenone, fluorenone, 9,10-dibromoanthracene, or 2-acetonaphthone as sensitizer. Presumably the mechanism involves triplet energy transfer to the hydrocarbon with breaking and subsequent re-forming of the weak C-C bond connecting the two ring members which bear the phenyl substituents.[617]

Bercovici and Fischer[691] and Becker and Roy[428] have investigated the benzophenone-photosensitized colorations of some spiropyrans. For example, at temperatures below $-100°C$ with light at 3650 A the photosensitized reaction of ring cleavage of *E* proceeds with a unit quantum

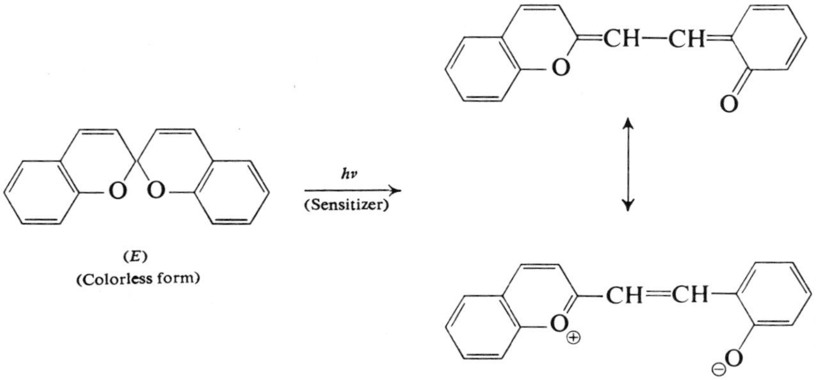

(E)
(Colorless form)

(Colored form)

yield as compared to a yield of only about 0.10 on direct irradiation at 3130 A;[691] see also the data for direct photolysis of spiropyrans in Sec. 5-5K, p. 486.

5-9C-3   Photosensitized Addition Reactions

Sensitized photodimerization of conjugated olefins is a common process, and we have already seen many examples, e.g., butadiene and cyclopentadiene (Sec. 5-7B). One important difference is noted; utilization

of different sensitizers leads to variation in the relative yields of the three products from butadiene but not the three products from cyclopentadiene. This has been explained by Hammond and Turro in terms of the existence of non-interconvertible, stereoisomeric triplet states of open-chain dienes.[523]

Schenck and coworkers have photosensitized the cyclodimerization of activated monoolefins including coumarin and maleic anhydride.[559]

They also found that maleic anhydride added to benzene and toluene[540,620,621] through sensitization with benzophenone. Schenk's mechanism differs from that of Hammond et al. in that it involves biradicals in a radical-addition-elimination process* that can be written as

Sensitizer + $h\nu$ → Sens (radical)

Sens (radical) + Acceptor (A) → [Sens – – – A] radical

[Sens – – – A] radical + A → Dimer A—A + Sensitizer

Another type of addition is the benzophenone-sensitized addition of the solvent, isopropyl alcohol, to maleic acid to give terebic acid.[118,622] In this type the sensitizer abstracts a hydrogen atom from the solvent, and the $(CH_3)_2\dot{C}OH$ radical formed adds to the double bond of maleic acid giving

---

* See Ref. 613 for citations to the original literature on Schenck's theories.

a monoradical; after this radical abstracts another hydrogen atom and water is lost, the lactone, terebic acid (A), is formed. Schenck refers to this example as a "Type 1" process involving monoradicals in the propagation and termination steps in contrast to sensitized cycloaddition, which he suggests is a "Type 2" mechanism involving only biradicals.[613]

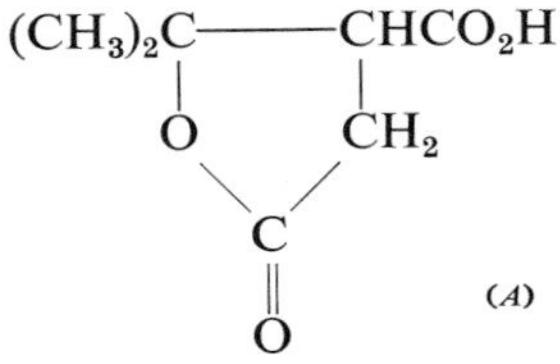

$$(CH_3)_2C\text{———}CHCO_2H$$

with

$$\begin{array}{ccc} & O & CH_2 \\ & \diagdown & \diagup \\ & & C \\ & & \parallel \\ & & O \end{array} \quad (A)$$

5-9C-4   Photosensitized Molecular Decomposition

Ethyl pyruvate is an interesting case in which the sensitized decomposition is more efficient than direct photolysis. Thus at 3130 A in a benzene solvent the quantum yield of direct decomposition, reaction 1, is 0.17, but it is 0.32 in the benzophenone-sensitized reaction (2):[368]

$$CH_3COCO_2Et \begin{cases} \xrightarrow[C_6H_6]{3130\ A} 2CH_3CHO + CO & (1) \\ \xrightarrow[\text{Sensitized, } \phi_2CO]{3130\ A} 2CH_3CHO + CO & (2) \end{cases}$$

The triplet energy of ethyl pyruvate is about 65 kcal/mole, and while benzophenone ($E_T = 69$ kcal/mole) is effective as a sensitizer for decomposition, 2-acetonaphthone ($E_T = 59$ kcal/mole) is not.[368] Other examples of sensitized decomposition are found in the summary of reactions.

5-9C-5   Photosensitized Oxidations

The area of photosensitized oxidations is most important from practical as well as theoretical considerations. Unfortunately we cannot do more here than outline the subject and cite several key articles which provide extensive references to the original literature. The more recent of these are the reviews by Gollnick and Schenck[613] and the articles by Kasche and Lindqvist[612] and Foote and Wexler;[623] the latter deals with olefin oxidations with excited singlet molecular oxygen.

Two general classes of photosensitized oxidation are recognized. One type is illustrated by the benzophenone-sensitized oxidation of isopropyl alcohol in the presence of air, first reported by Bäckström.[537] The products of this reaction include isopropanol hydroperoxide,[613,624,625] hydrogen peroxide, and acetone.[118] Gollnick and Schenck[613] suggest that the reaction sequence forming the hydroperoxide is a "primary dehydro-genation photosensitized reaction with oxygen," involving monoradicals in the propagation and terminating steps. Their mechanism is as follows:

$$\text{Sens} + h\nu \rightarrow \cdot S \cdot \xrightarrow{\text{AH}} \cdot SH + \cdot A$$

$$\cdot A + O_2 \rightarrow \cdot AOO \xrightarrow{\text{AH}} AOOH + \cdot A$$

$$\cdot AOO + \cdot SH \rightarrow AOOH + \text{Sens}$$

A second, and photochemically more interesting, type is the dye-photo-sensitized autoxidation of acceptors such as the acenes, cyclohexadiene derivatives, olefins with isolated double bonds and allylic hydrogen atoms, furans, sulfides, and sulfoxides. The products are endoperoxides, allylic hydroperoxides, alkoxyhydroperoxides (when run in alcohol as a solvent), sulfoxides, and sulfones, respectively.[613] Examples from the review of Gollnick and Schenck are shown below (see Ref. 613a and b for original literature):

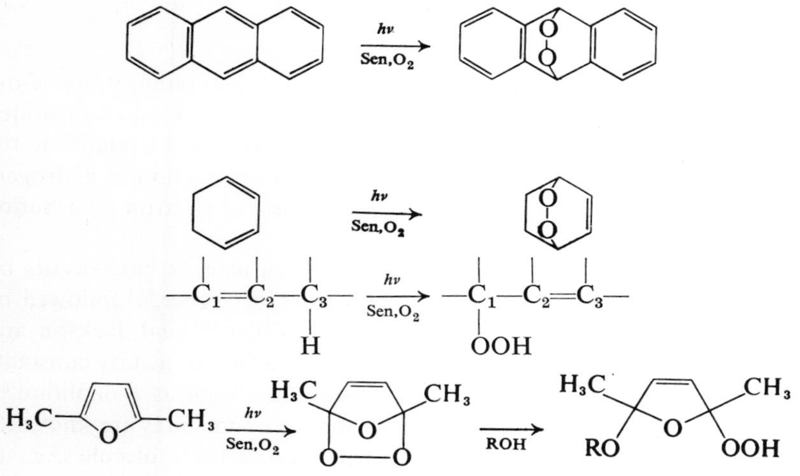

$$-\overset{|}{\underset{|}{C_1}}=\overset{|}{\underset{|}{C_2}}-\overset{|}{\underset{\underset{H}{|}}{C_3}}- \xrightarrow[\text{Sen,O}_2]{h\nu} -\overset{|}{\underset{\underset{OOH}{|}}{C_1}}-\overset{|}{\underset{|}{C_2}}=\overset{|}{\underset{|}{C_3}}-$$

$$2R-S-R \xrightarrow[\text{Sen,O}_2]{h\nu} 2R-SO-R$$

$$2R-SO-R \xrightarrow[\text{Sen,O}_2]{h\nu} 2R-SO_2-R$$

Several mechanisms have been proposed;[613] one involves a short-lived excited sensitizer-oxygen adduct (complex), a species proposed independently by Schenck,[626] Terenin,[627,628] and Schönberg,[629,630] and the other, excited singlet molecular oxygen as proposed by Kautsky and co-workers[631] and recently by Foote and Wexler[623] (see also Ref. 612).

In the Schenck mechanism the photoexcited sensitizer acts as a biradical, ·S·, which adds oxygen to give the short-lived excited sensitizer-oxygen adduct ·SOO·. This species then transfers the oxygen to the unsaturated substrate A, giving the product AO_2 and the sensitizer in its ground state. A variety of kinetic, spectroscopic, and chemical data is advanced to support this idea.

On the other hand, Foote and Wexler have developed a novel and useful synthetic method for the oxidation of olefins and dienoid compounds which gives products identical to those found in the dye-photosensitized autoxidations cited above. The reactive species appears to be molecular oxygen in an excited singlet state, formed *in situ* by the reaction between sodium hypochlorite and hydrogen peroxide.[623] The significance of "singlet oxygen" relative to the mechanism of photosensitized autoxidations has been considered by both Foote and Wexler[623] and Gollnick and Schenck.[613]

5-9D Electron Distribution and Reactivity of Excited States

We have already considered the important chemical implications of the nature of the electron distribution in the excited states of *para*-substituted butyrophenones (Sec. 5-2B) and benzophenones (Sec. 5-9A), relative to the efficiencies of intramolecular and intermolecular abstraction of hydrogen. We shall now consider other aspects of alteration of electron distribution by excitation.

The idea that a large change in acidity of an acid or base occurs on electronic excitation arose from the early work of Weber,[632] followed by the more quantitative studies of Förster,[633] Weller,[634] and Jackson and Porter.[635] A good example is furnished by comparing the acidity constants of the S_0, S_1, and T_1 states of a very weak acid such as β-naphthol.[634] Acid strengths of aromatic molecules in their ground states are known to be highly sensitive to the electron distribution of the molecule (i.e., to substituent effects). However, even more striking than acid-strengthening effects of substituents is the enhanced acidity observed on exciting 2-naphthol to its first singlet state, S_1; the $pK_{S_1} = 3.1$ compared to $pK_{S_0} = 9.5$. Thus absorption of a quantum changes 2-naphthol from a weak acid to one as strong as citric acid ($pK = 3.1$), the equilibrium being

$$\text{ROH}(S_0) + \text{H}_2\text{O} \rightleftharpoons \text{RO}^-(S_0) + \text{H}_3\text{O}^+; \ pK_{S_0} = 9.5$$

$$\text{ROH}(S_1) + \text{H}_2\text{O} \underset{k_r}{\overset{k_f}{\rightleftharpoons}} \text{RO}^-(S_1) + \text{H}_3\text{O}^+; \ pK_{S_1} = 3.1$$

The method employed by Förster and Weller for estimation of the acidity of excited singlets depends on the rate of gain or loss of a proton by the molecule in its excited state being *fast* relative to the rate of fluorescence. This is indeed the case for β-naphthol, where absorption by the ground-singlet state of the molecule is followed by fluorescence emission from the electronically excited molecule, $ROH(S_1)$, or ion, $RO^-(S_1)$, or both, depending on the pH of the solution. By studying the relative fluorescence yields of these two excited species as functions of pH and temperature, Weller obtained values of the rate constant $(25°)$ $k_f = 4.1 \times 10^7$ sec^{-1} and $k_r = 5.1 \times 10^{10}$ l mole^{-1} sec^{-1} (see equation, p. 550), from which $pK_{S_1} = 3.1$, natural radiative lifetimes of 1.1×10^{-8} and 8.1×10^{-9} sec, respectively, of the S_1 states of β-naphthol and β-naphtholate ion. Values for ΔH and ΔS for the ionization of the excited species also were estimated from the temperature dependence of the equilibrium constant, k_f/k_r.[634]

This treatment was similar to the earlier definitive work by Förster on the weak base β-naphthylamine,[633] which gave values of $pK_{S_0} = 4.1$ and $pK_{S_1} = -2$, respectively, for the equilibria

$$RNH_3^+ + H_2O \rightleftharpoons RNH_2 + H_3O^+; \quad pK_{S_0} = 4.1$$

and

$$RNH_3^+(S_1) + H_2O \rightleftharpoons RNH_2(S_1) + H_3O^+; \quad pK_{S_1} = -2$$

Jackson and Porter, using flash spectroscopic techniques in liquid solutions and determinations of phosphorescence spectra in solid solutions, have obtained acidity constants for the triplet states of seven aromatic molecules, including β-naphthol and β-naphthylamine.[635] They found that in each case the acidity constants of the ground and lowest triplet states are comparable, but that of the excited singlet differs by a factor of about 10^6. For example, with β-naphthylamine, RNH_2, the values for the dissociation of the conjugate acid RNH_3^+ are $pK_{S_0} = 4.1$, $pK_{S_1} = -2$, and $pK_{T_1} = 3.3$ and 3.1 by flash photolysis and phosphorescence spectra, respectively. On the basis of acidity differences between the excited singlet and triplet states of quinoline, acridine, and the naphthoic acids, Jackson and Porter suggest that they may have $n \rightarrow \pi^*$ absorptions but that the lowest triplet states are $^3(\pi, \pi^*)$ in character.[635]

Reid has noted that the coiled chains of proteins are known to uncurl because of ionic repulsions when ionization occurs. He then makes the interesting speculation that some biological processes "triggered" by an impulse may involve excitation by the impulse followed by dissociation of the molecule in its excited state.[530]

Photoexcitation by $\pi \rightarrow \pi^*$ processes produces more subtle effects on the electronic structure of an aromatic molecule, since the electron is promoted from a delocalized bonding π-orbital to a delocalized non-bonding π^* orbital. However, a significant effect is noted by Reid,[530] who pointed out that photoexcitation produces an effect rarely achieved thermally in that "not only the ease of reaction but the path of reaction is often altered by irradiation" (as we have seen above for acidity constants of excited species). For example, it is well known that the path of substitution reactions of, say, toluene can be correlated with the different electron distributions in the *ortho, meta,* and *para* positions. "*Excitation alters this electron distribution, so that if we carry out a reaction under conditions of intense irradiation, we expect to vary the ratio of o-, m-, and p-products* [italics are the authors']. The stationary-state concentration of excited molecules may be only a small fraction of the total, but their greater reactivity should enhance the effect."

One of the first examples of the effect of altered electron distribution on excitation of aromatic compounds is that of Havinga and coworkers, who studied the photochemical hydrolysis of *m-* and *p-*nitrophenyl dihydrogen phosphates. They observed, contrary to what might be expected on the basis of ground-state electronic distributions estimated by simple valence bond theory, that the effect of irradiation on the hydrolysis rate was greatest for the *meta* isomer;[636] the *para* isomer shows little or no photodissociation.

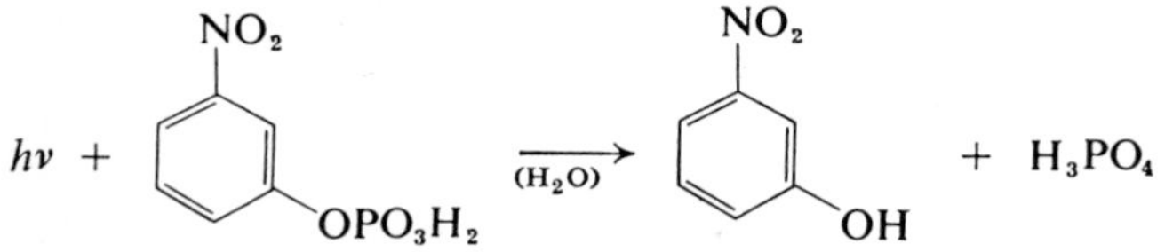

Subsequently studies by Zimmerman and his co-workers showed the same effect of photoactivation of ionization of a substituent *meta* to a nitro group.[637] They studied the rate of hydrolysis of *m-*nitrophenyl and *p-*nitrophenyl trityl ether in 90% aqueous dioxane in the dark and under irradiation. In the dark the *para* isomer solvolyzes smoothly, while the *meta* isomer is almost completely unreactive. This is in accord with ground-state substituent effects, since p-nitrophenylate is a better departing anion than *m-*nitrophenolate. On irradiation the *meta* isomer hydrolyzes rapidly to *m-*nitrophenol and triphenyl carbinol as major products, but the rate of solvolysis of the *para* isomer is virtually unaffected. The effect was attributed to selective withdrawal of electrons from positions *meta* to the nitro groups in the excited states, and MO calculations are in agreement with this idea.[638] The implications of the MO calculations may be expressed by the statement that resonance structures such as those shown below make substantial contributions to the excited states.

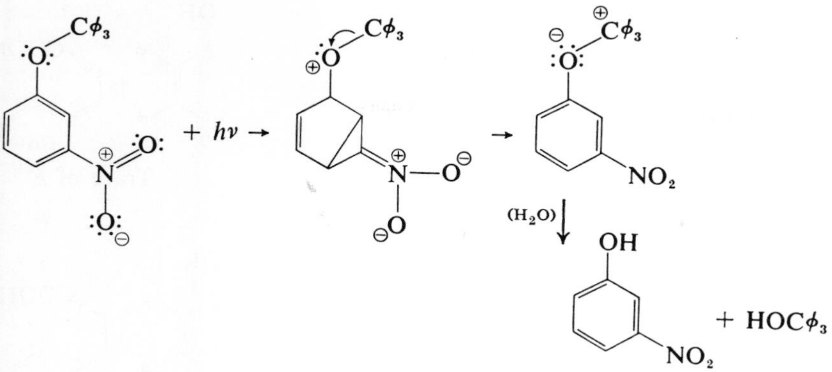

$+ h\nu \rightarrow$ $\rightarrow$

(H_2O)

$+ HOC\phi_3$

Letsinger, Ramsay, and McCain[739] report that the irradiation ($\lambda >$ 2890 A) of p-nitrophenylphosphate and p-nitroanisole in dilute aqueous solution at 3° gives 1-acylpyridinium nitrites. m-Nitroanisole, nitrobenzene, and p-dinitrobenzene fail to react. They suggest that p-phosphoryl and p-methoxyl may function as "activating" substituents in nucleophilic displacement of a nitro group from an aromatic compound in the excited state; this is in marked contrast to the chemistry of the ground-state molecules. Quenching processes, both dependent on and independent of the added nucleophile, are competitive with substitution.

The chemical implications of altered electronic structures in photo-excited states have been extended to a variety of other types of systems. Thus, Havinga has pointed out that a study of the photoinduced and the thermal isomerization reactions of the hexatriene-cyclohexadiene system in the pro- and previtamins D reveals that there is a pronounced configurational difference between photo and thermal products[636b] even in cases where the two classes of reaction lead to products of the same structure (e.g., ring closure of hexatriene to cyclohexadiene derivatives). He proposes describing these selectivities in terms of steric factors and electronic structures in the excited species analogous to the current pedagogy for the ground state.

Dauben has clearly shown the photochemical consequences of an anti-bonding MO in the ground state of a diolefin becoming a bonding MO in the excited state. Furthermore, he has pointed out the possibility that olefin reactions also may occur in a variety of possible vibrationally excited ground states.[639]

An interesting case of "mechanistic photochemistry" involves the photorearrangements of dienones. Thus, in a careful study, Zimmerman and co-workers[380,521,692] have photolyzed 4,4-diphenylcyclohexadienone and isolated the following products; the yield of E was equal to that of C.

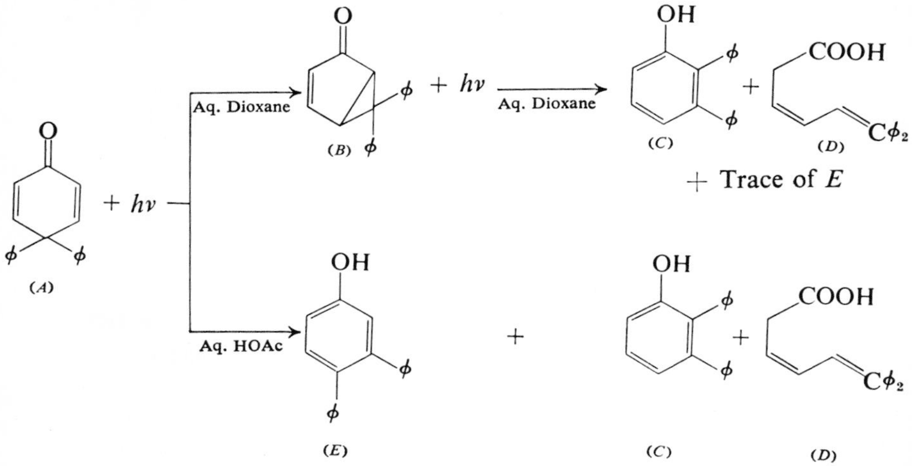

Zimmerman rationalizes the processes in terms of a path involving gradual reduction of electronically excited states through stages involving "rebonding," "demotion of a π^* electron," and rearrangement. (See details in Ref. 637.) Chapman, on the other hand, suggests that all rearrangements of α,β-unsaturated ketones can be considered to involve electron-deficient π systems without specifying the precise sequence of formation of the electron deficiency.[501] He further suggests the interesting possibility that some excited states may be protonated before rearrangement, thus offering an explanation for certain product differences in protic and aprotic solvents.

An important and widely studied example of the effect of electronic structure on chemical reactivity involves the simplest carbene, methylene.* Singlet methylene is formed virtually exclusively by direct photolysis of ketene vapor in the region 2700–2900 A, but Noyes and coworkers find that from 3400–3800 A at least half the methylene radicals formed are triplet, the fraction apparently being temperature dependent.[644] See the discussion of ketene in Sec. 5-2. In solution methylene can be generated either in the singlet state by direct photolysis of diazomethane at the short wavelengths (however, it may decay to the triplet species before reacting) or in the triplet state ($\cdot CH_2 \cdot$) by the benzophenone-sensitized photodecomposition of diazomethane,[119]

$$\phi_2CO(S_0) + h\nu \longrightarrow \phi_2CO(S_1) \rightsquigarrow \phi_2CO(T_1)$$
$$\phi_2CO(T_1) + CH_2N_2 \longrightarrow \cdot CH_2 \cdot + \phi_2CO(S_0) + N_2$$

or in the Hg($^3P_1$) photosensitized decomposition of ketene.[737]

---

* For discussions and original literature see the reviews by Frey,[640] de More and Benson,[641] Bell,[642] Gaspar and Hammond,[643] and Hine.[740]

The important chemical distinction between the two CH_2 species is that singlet methylene adds stereospecifically to double bonds and inserts in C-H bonds. Triplet methylene adds to alkenes in a non-stereospecific manner.[645,646] However, caution must be exercised in relating the spin state of the singlet or triplet reactant with the configuration of the olefin addition product for the heavier atoms of the oxygen family.*

5-10   EXCITATION TO HIGHER ENERGY STATES

Light sources and materials and techniques for photochemical studies in the vacuum ultraviolet have become more available in recent years, and the photochemistry of this "Schumann region" has experienced a rapid transition from the pioneering studies of Groth[323,333,334] on simple molecules (see Chapter 3) to current investigations of "complex" organic molecules. Concurrently, studies of the radiation chemistry and electron impact processes of "organic" molecules have achieved widespread attention. The three areas have in common the population of energy states higher than those usually achieved on irradiation in the visible and ultraviolet region, and it seems useful to comment briefly on several aspects of photo-chemical reactions involving these higher states of organic molecules. No attempt is made to offer a complete literature survey; this is available from the following books and reviews: Refs. 647–651, and compounds cited in the summary in this chapter.

5-10A   Photoionization

Several dyes undergo photoionization to charged species on absorption of visible light. Particularly notable are the leucocyanides of the tri-phenylmethane dyes in polar solvents, e.g., malachite green leucocy-anide.[306–308]

"Self-ionization" describes a process with occurs in frozen rigid solutions of dyes such as fluorescein at 77°K. An electron is detached from an excited singlet dye molecule, is trapped by the medium, and ultimately recombines with the positive ion to give an excited molecule which then radiates. This sequence leads to the very long-lived fluorescence observed

---

* Sulfur atoms in *either the singlet or the triplet state* add to the olefin double bond to form episulfides with high retention of configuration (H. E. Gunning, International Conference on Photochemistry, Tokyo, Japan, August, 1965). Apparently the spin conservation rule is much less stringent for the intermediate involving the heavier sulfur atom than that with the oxygen atom; inversion of the spin of the original triplet product of the $S(^3P)$ addition to the double bond with subsequent rapid closure of the episulfide ring competes successfully with the rotation of the groups about the C-C bond.

in these systems[202] (see Ref. 650 for survey of original literature). Recently it has been shown that the phenomenon is a biphotonic process in that, while one photon is adequate to photoionize the molecule, absorption of a second photon is necessary to promote the electron from the vicinity of the parent molecule into the trap.[652]

In these two cases the light causing ionization is in the visible or ultraviolet region, and the lowest excited states are involved. Recently Terenin and co-workers reported on their detailed mass spectrometric studies of the vapor-phase dissociation and ionization of organic molecules by vacuum ultraviolet radiation.[647,650] Photolysis of aromatic amines, the amino acids, and the nitrogenous bases under these conditions resulted in three main types of photoprocesses:

(1) Electron abstraction at a threshold $h\nu_1$, without dissociation of the parent molecule:

$$R_1 \!\!-\!\! R_2 + h\nu_1 \rightarrow R_1 \!\!-\!\! R_2^+ + e^- \tag{1}$$

(2) Dissociation into an ionized fragment and a neutral hydrogen atom, or a radical, which has its onset at a higher photon energy, $h\nu_2$:

$$R_1 \!\!-\!\! R_2 + h\nu_2 \rightarrow R_1^+ + R_2 \text{ (or H)} + e^- \tag{2}$$

(3) Decomposition of cyclics at still higher energies, $h\nu_3$:

$$R_1 \!\!-\!\! R_2 + h\nu_3 \rightarrow R_1^+ + R_2 + e^- \tag{3}$$

As an example, glycine photodissociates according to the following reaction:

$$H_2N \!\!-\!\! CH_2 \!\!-\!\! COOH + h\nu \ (\geqslant 9.6 \text{ ev}) \rightarrow H_2N \!\!-\!\! CH_2^+ + COOH + e^-$$

Terenin points out the interesting fact that the excess energy utilized to dissociate the glycine, beyond that required for photoionization, is only a fraction of the bond strength of the same bond in the unionized neutral molecule. Thus after photoionization, process 1, the presence of only 0.6 ev more energy in the photon absorbed leads to process 2, disruption of the C—C bond, a process requiring 3.7 ev in the neutral molecule. This suggests an extensive redistribution of the electron density in the ion formed and results in a significant lowering of the bond strength at specific linkages.[650]

Another useful example of dissociative photoionization is that of N-methyl aniline which has been deuterated specifically to identify the site of hydrogen-atom elimination:[650]

$$C_6H_5 \!\!-\!\! N \begin{matrix} {}^{\displaystyle D} \\ {}^{\diagup} \\ {}_{\diagdown} \\ {}_{\displaystyle CH_3} \end{matrix} + h\nu \ (\geqslant 11.0 \text{ ev}) \rightarrow \left[C_6H_5 \!\!-\!\! N \begin{matrix} {}^{\displaystyle D} \\ {}^{\diagup} \\ {}_{\diagdown} \\ {}_{\displaystyle CH_2} \end{matrix} \right] + H^+ + e^-$$

The only bond broken is the C—H of the methyl group; rupture of the C_6H_5—N or N—CH_3 bonds did not occur.

5-10B Sensitized Decomposition Involving Biphotonic Processes

An interesting type of alkyl benzene-sensitized decomposition of hydrocarbon solvents has been reported.[650,653] The necessary energy is supplied as a result of biphotonic absorption (successive) by the sensitizer followed by energy transfer to the solvent (e.g., 3-methylpentane = RH):

$$\phi CD_3 + h\nu_1 \longrightarrow \phi CD_3(S_1) \rightsquigarrow \phi CD_3(T_1)$$

$$\phi CD_3(T_1) + h\nu_2 \longrightarrow \phi CD_3(T_x) \overset{RH}{\longrightarrow} \phi CD_3 + H + R$$

$$H + RH \rightarrow H_2 + R \ (94\%)$$

$$H + \phi CD_3 \rightarrow HD + \phi \dot{C}D_2 \ (6\%)$$

Hydrogen atoms can be split from alcoholic solvents by a similar biphotonic process in which aromatic amines (e.g., diphenylamine) or N-heterocycles (e.g., carbazole) act as the photosensitizer.[650,654]

5-10C Comparative Effects of Non-ionizing Ultraviolet Radiation, Gamma Rays, and Electron Impact

The comparative effects of radiation are a subject of great interest and current activity.[653] We cannot consider the matter in detail here, but we would like to make this observation: for some classes of organic compounds useful correlations exist between certain rearrangements induced by electron impact, non-ionizing ultraviolet, and ionizing radiation.[502] For example, Nicholson,[74] and independently Martin and Pitts,[85] first noted that the mass spectra of those methyl ketones which have a γ-hydrogen atom and dissociate photochemically to give acetone and an olefin (Sec. 5-2B) also have significant peaks at $m/e = 58$. They proposed that this "peak" was due to the acetone molecule-ion formed in an electron induced mass spectrometric "Type II" ionic cycloelimination process which involved γ-hydrogen atom transfer via a six-membered cyclic intermediate.

Subsequent research established the validity of this idea[657–661] and the fact that a "Type II" cycloelimination is a major process in the radiolysis of aliphatic ketones with γ-hydrogen atoms.[657,662,663] Thus, we have a well-documented example of an important intramolecular reaction that is induced by ultraviolet, electron impact, and ionizing radiation.[657]

It is significant that the "Type II" cycloelimination process is not restricted to aliphatic ketones. Thus, for example, analogous rearrangement peaks are important in the mass spectra of those aldehydes, esters, amides, carboxylic acids, nitriles, alkyl benzenes, and alkyl quinolines which can form cyclic six-membered transition states by transfer of γ-hydrogen atoms. The photochemistry and radiation chemistry of most of these compounds are not well established, yet one would predict on the basis of their mass spectra that in the structurally suited cases cycloelimination of an olefin will be one of the primary reactions.[502,657,664] It will be interesting to see whether similar correlations can be developed for other types of process as our knowledge of mass spectrometry, photochemistry, and radiation chemistry increases.

In this regard, Table 5-6 compares the effects of mercury $6(^3P_1)$ sensitization, gamma rays, and far-ultraviolet radiation on the relative yields of

TABLE 5-6   Relative Yields of D_2, HD, and H_2 Formed in the Decomposition of Dideuteroethylene by Mercury Photosensitization, γ-Ray Radiolysis, and Far-Ultraviolet Photolysis[a]

Ethylene	Pressure, cm	Technique	Per Cent of Total Hydrogen			H_2/D_2	Ref.
			D_2	HD	H_2		
cis-CHDCHD	1.1	$Hg6(^3P_1)$	11.0	66.5	22.5	2.05	666
cis-CHDCHD	30^b	$Hg6(^3P_1)$	11.5	66.1	22.2	1.93	666
cis- and trans-CHDCHD	25	$Hg6(^3P_1)$	11.0	66.8	22.2	2.02	667
cis- and trans-CHDCHD	3.0	$Hg6(^3P_1)$	11.4	65.5	23.1	2.03	667
CH_2CD_2	3.0	$Hg6(^3P_1)$	14.1	60.1	25.8	1.83	667
cis- and trans-CHDCHD	3.0	γ-Rays	12.6	68.75	18.85	1.48	667
CH_2CD_2	3.0	γ-Rays	17.8	50.8	31.4	1.76	667
trans-CHDCHD	1.5	1236 A	9.4	73.3	17.4	1.85	340
trans-CHDCHD	1.9	1470 A	9.6	73.2	17.2	1.79	340
trans-CHDCHD	1.5	1849 A	10.3	74.5	15.2	1.48	340
CH_2CD_2	3.5	1236 A	17.6	40.7	41.7	2.37	340
CH_2CD_2	2.2	1470 A	19.7	40.0	40.3	2.05	340
CH_2CD_2	1.6	1470 A	18.4	42.8	38.8	2.11	340
CH_2CD_2	2.5	1849 A	20.0	40.0	40.0	2.00	340

[a] From Cvetanovic.[665]
[b] 1 cm C_2H_4 + 29 cm CO_2.

D_2, HD, and H_2 from several dideuteroethylenes.[340,665-667] Cvetanovic notes that the isotopic distribution of the hydrogens is virtually independent of wavelength in the far ultraviolet but differs significantly between the 1,1-isomer and *trans*-1,2-isomer. Both of these distributions differ significantly from the corresponding values obtained by mercury photosensitization and radiolysis, and he suggests that three different excited states are involved in the three types of processes.[665]

PROBLEMS

1. (a) From the spectral data for azoethane in Fig. 5-14, estimate the *f*-number of the first absorption band in the 3400 A region.

(b) Draw a simplified picture of the occupied molecular orbitals and atom positions for azoethane in its ground electronic state.

(c) In view of (a) and (b) what do you predict will be the nature of the transition in azoethane when light absorption occurs in the first band?

(d) Draw a simplified picture of the occupied molecular orbitals and atom positions in the probable excited state formed on absorption of 3600 A light.

(e) Describe two experiments that you might perform to test your hypothesis in the above answers.

2. Describe in qualitative terms (a) the general absorption regions for the following compounds; (b) the nature of the electronic transition involved; (c) the approximate ϵ in each region; (d) the approximate radiative lifetime of the excited state formed; (e) the nature of the photochemical changes which you expect on irradiation of the compounds in the first absorption region.

(i) $CH_3CHCH_2CH_3$ (gas at 25°, 1 mm).
      |
     ONO
(ii) $CH_3COCH_2CH_2CH_2N\!=\!NC_2H_5$ (solution in cyclohexane at 25°).
(iii) $CH_3CH_2CH_2COCH(CH_3)_2$ (solution in cyclohexane at 25°).
(iv) $CH_3COCH_2CH\!-\!CH_2$ (in argon matrix at liquid-nitrogen temperature).
            | |
          CH$\!=\!$CH
(v) $CH_2\!=\!C(CH_3)C(CH_3)\!=\!CHCH_3$ (in cyclohexane at 25°).
(vi) $(CH_3)_2CHNO_2$ (gas at 25°, low pressure).
(vii) $CH_3CHBrCl$ (gas at 25°, low pressure).

REFERENCES TO CHAPTER 5

1. (a) M. A. Khan, R. G. W. Norrish, and G. Porter, *Proc. Roy. Soc. (London)*, **A219**, 312 (1953); (b) G. Wettermark, *Arkiv Kemi*, **18**, 1 (1961).
2. C. S. Parmenter and W. A. Noyes, Jr., *J. Am. Chem. Soc.*, **85**, 416 (1963).
3. R. P. Borkowski and P. Ausloos, *J. Am. Chem. Soc.*, **84**, 4044 (1962).
4. P. Borrell and R. G. W. Norrish, *Proc. Roy. Soc. (London)*, **A262**, 19 (1961).
5. R. G. W. Norrish and F. W. Kirkbride, *J. Chem. Soc.*, **1932**, 1518.

6. R. Klein and L. J. Schoen, *J. Chem. Phys.*, **24**, 1094 (1956).
7. J. G. Calvert and E. W. R. Steacie, *J. Chem. Phys.*, **19**, 176 (1951).
8. J. G. Calvert, *J. Phys. Chem.*, **61**, 1206 (1957).
9. (a) P. J. Dyne, *J. Chem. Phys.*, **20**, 811 (1952); (b) G. W. Robinson and V. E. DiGiorgio, *Can. J. Chem.*, **36**, 31 (1958).
10. F. E. Blacet and D. E. Loeffler, *J. Am. Chem. Soc.*, **64**, 893 (1942).
11. F. E. Blacet and J. D. Heldman, *J. Am. Chem. Soc.*, **64**, 889 (1942).
12. J. G. Calvert, J. N. Pitts, Jr., and D. D. Thompson, *J. Am. Chem. Soc.*, **78**, 4239 (1956).
13. F. E. Blacet and R. K. Brinton, *J. Am. Chem. Soc.*, **72**, 4715 (1950).
14. E. Murad, *J. Phys. Chem.*, **64**, 942 (1960).
15. R. E. Dodd and J. W. Smith, *J. Chem. Soc.*, **1957**, 1465.
16. F. E. Blacet and J. N. Pitts, Jr., *J. Am. Chem. Soc.*, **74**, 3382 (1952).
17. F. E. Blacet and R. A. Crane, *J. Am. Chem. Soc.*, **76**, 5337 (1954).
18. G. O. Pritchard, G. H. Miller and J. K. Foote, *Can. J. Chem.*, **40**, 1830 (1962).
19. F. E. Blacet and J. G. Calvert, *J. Am. Chem. Soc.*, **73**, 667 (1951).
20. F. E. Blacet and J. G. Calvert, *J. Am. Chem. Soc.*, **73**, 661 (1951).
21. By analogy with the results for methyl-*n*-propyl ketone and methyl-*n*-butyl ketone photolyses, it is likely that one of the products of this process is first formed in the enol form of the carbonyl compound, and a cyclic, six-membered ring transition state is involved.
22. R. N. Birrell and A. F. Trotman-Dickenson, *J. Chem. Soc.*, **1960**, 4218.
23. J. G. Calvert, *Chem. Revs.*, **59**, 569 (1959).
24. J. T. Gruver and J. G. Calvert, *J. Am. Chem. Soc.*, **78**, 5208 (1956).
25. J. T. Gruver and J. G. Calvert, *J. Am. Chem. Soc.*, **80**, 3524 (1958).
26. J. A. Kerr and A. F. Trotman-Dickenson, *J. Chem. Soc.*, **1960**, 1602.
27. C. H. Bamford and R. G. W. Norrish, *J. Chem. Soc.*, **1935**, 1504.
28. H. W. Thompson and J. W. Linnett, *J. Chem. Soc.*, **1935**, 1452.
29. F. E. Blacet, G. H. Fielding, and J. G. Roof, *J. Am. Chem. Soc.*, **59**, 2375 (1937).
30. F. E. Blacet and J. G. Roof, *J. Am. Chem. Soc.*, **58**, 73 (1936).
31. F. E. Blacet and J. E. LuValle, *J. Am. Chem. Soc.*, **61**, 273 (1939).
32. J. N. Pitts, Jr., D. D. Thompson, and R. W. Woolfolk, *J. Am. Chem. Soc.*, **80**, 66 (1958).
33. C. A. McDowell and S. Sifniades, *J. Am. Chem. Soc.*, **84**, 4606 (1962).
34. F. E. Blacet and R. W. Moulton, *J. Am. Chem. Soc.*, **63**, 868 (1941).
35. J. G. Calvert and G. S. Layne, *J. Am. Chem. Soc.*, **75**, 856 (1953).
36. G. Herzberg and D. A. Ramsay, *Proc. Roy. Soc. (London)*, **A233**, 34 (1955).
37. F. E. Blacet and R. D. Vanselow, *Abstracts*, Div. Phys. Chem., 131st American Chemical Society Meeting, Miami, Fla., April, 1957.
38. G. Ciamician and P. Silber, *Ber.*, **34**, 1530 (1901).
39. G. S. Hammond and P. A. Leermakers, *J. Am. Chem. Soc.*, **84**, 207 (1962).
40. W. Davis, Jr., and W. A. Noyes, Jr., *J. Am. Chem. Soc.*, **69**, 2153 (1947).
41. P. P. Manning, *J. Am. Chem. Soc.*, **79**, 5151 (1957).
42. P. Ausloos and R. E. Rebbert, *J. Am. Chem. Soc.*, **83**, 4897 (1961).
43. G. B. Porter, *J. Am. Chem. Soc.*, **79**, 827 (1957).
44. B. T. Connelly and G. B. Porter, *Can. J. Chem.*, **36**, 1640 (1958).
45. A. N. Strachan and W. A. Noyes, Jr., *J. Am. Chem. Soc.*, **76**, 3258 (1954).
46. W. G. Paterson and H. Gesser, *Can. J. Chem.*, **35**, 1137 (1957).
47. G. B. Kistiakowsky and B. H. Mahan, *J. Am. Chem. Soc.*, **79**, 2412 (1957).
48. R. A. Holroyd and F. E. Blacet, *J. Am. Chem. Soc.*, **79**, 4830 (1957).
49. W. A. Noyes, Jr., G. B. Porter, and J. E. Jolley, *Chem. Revs.*, **56**, 49 (1956).

50. A. J. Harrison, private communication; 5th Report on Research, Petroleum Research Fund, 1960, p. 115.
51. P. Ausloos and E. Murad, *J. Phys. Chem.*, **65**, 1519 (1961).
52. (a) J. Heicklen, *J. Am. Chem. Soc.*, **81**, 3863 (1959). (b) J. Heicklen and W. A. Noyes, Jr., *J. Am. Chem. Soc.*, **81**, 3858 (1959).
53. R. D. Doepker and G. J. Mains, *J. Am. Chem. Soc.*, **83**, 294 (1961).
54. R. A. Sieger and J. G. Calvert, *J. Am. Chem. Soc.*, **76**, 5197 (1954).
55. A. N. Strachan and F. E. Blacet, *J. Am. Chem. Soc.*, **77**, 5254 (1955).
56. R. Bowles, H. Derbyshire, J. R. Majer, and C. R. Patrick, *Nature*, **185**, 683 (1960).
57. R. Bowles, J. R. Majer, and J. C. Robb, *Trans. Faraday Soc.*, **58**, 1541 (1962).
58. R. Bowles, J. R. Majer, and J. C. Robb, *Trans. Faraday Soc.*, **58**, 2394 (1962).
59. S. Hautecloque, *Compt. Rend.*, **250**, 3992 (1960); *ibid.*, **254**, 3671 (1962).
60. R. Srinivasan, *J. Am. Chem. Soc.*, **84**, 2475 (1962).
61. V. R. Ells and W. A. Noyes, Jr., *J. Am. Chem. Soc.*, **60**, 2031 (1938).
62. J. N. Pitts, Jr., and F. E. Blacet, *J. Am. Chem. Soc.*, **72**, 2810 (1950).
63. G. R. Martin and H. C. Sutton, *Trans. Faraday Soc.*, **48**, 823 (1952).
64. R. P. Taylor and F. E. Blacet, *J. Am. Chem. Soc.*, **78**, 706 (1956).
65. W. Davis, Jr., *J. Am. Chem. Soc.*, **70**, 1868 (1948).
66. L. M. Dorfman and Z. D. Sheldon, *J. Chem. Phys.*, **17**, 511 (1949).
67. K. O. Kutschke, M. H. J. Wijnen, and E. W. R. Steacie, *J. Am. Chem. Soc.*, **74**, 714 (1952).
68. J. E. Jolley, *J. Am. Chem. Soc.*, **79**, 1537 (1957).
69. P. Ausloos, *Can. J. Chem.*, **36**, 400 (1958).
70. M. H. J. Wijnen and E. W. R. Steacie, *Can. J. Chem.*, **29**, 1092 (1951).
71. D. S. Weir, *J. Am. Chem. Soc.*, **83**, 2629 (1961).
72. R. D. Doepker and G. J. Mains, *J. Phys. Chem.*, **66**, 690 (1962).
73. G. Giacometti, H. Okabe, S. J. Price, and E. W. R. Steacie, *Can. J. Chem.*, **38**, 104 (1960).
74. A. J. C. Nicholson, *Trans. Faraday Soc.*, **50**, 1067 (1954).
75. J. R. McNesby and A. S. Gordon, *J. Am. Chem. Soc.*, **80**, 261 (1958).
76. N. C. Yang and D.-D. H. Yang, *J. Am. Chem. Soc.*, **80**, 2913 (1958).
77. J. L. Michael and W. A. Noyes, Jr., *J. Am. Chem. Soc.*, **85**, 1027 (1963); J. L. Michael, Ph.D. Thesis, University of Rochester, 1962.
78. R. P. Borkowski and P. Ausloos, *J. Phys. Chem.*, **65**, 2257 (1961).
79. R. S. Tolberg and J. N. Pitts, Jr., *J. Am. Chem. Soc.*, **80**, 1304 (1958).
80. A. Padwa, "Photochemical Transformation of Small Ring Carbonyl Compounds," chapter to appear in Ref. 120.
81. J. E. Wilson and W. A. Noyes, Jr., *J. Am. Chem. Soc.*, **65**, 1547 (1943).
82. R. Srinivasan, *J. Am. Chem. Soc.*, **81**, 5061 (1959).
83. V. Brunet and W. A. Noyes, Jr., *Bull. Soc. Chim. France*, **1958**, 121.
84. R. Srinivasan, *J. Am. Chem. Soc.*, **82**, 775 (1960).
85. T. W. Martin and J. N. Pitts, Jr., *J. Am. Chem. Soc.*, **77**, 5465 (1955); presented at Conference on Photochemistry and Free Radicals, Univ. of Rochester, September 1964.
86. P. Ausloos, *J. Phys. Chem.*, **65**, 1616 (1961).
87. C. R. Masson, *J. Am. Chem. Soc.*, **74**, 4731 (1952).
88. S. G. Whiteway and C. R. Masson, *J. Am. Chem. Soc.*, **77**, 1508 (1955).
89. C. A. Heller and A. S. Gordon, *J. Phys. Chem.*, **62**, 709 (1958).
90. G. H. Miller, G. O. Pritchard, and E. W. R. Steacie, *Z. Physik. Chem.* (*Frankfurt*), **15**, 262 (1958).
91. J. W. Kraus and J. G. Calvert, *J. Am. Chem. Soc.*, **79**, 5921 (1957).

92. J. E. Guillet and R. G. W. Norrish, *Nature*, **173**, 625 (1954).
93. J. E. Guillet and R. G.W. Norrish, *Proc. Roy. Soc. (London)*, **A233**, 153, 172 (1955).
94. K. F. Wissbrun, *J. Am. Chem. Soc.*, **81**, 58 (1959).
95. J. N. Pitts, Jr., and I. Norman, *J. Am. Chem. Soc.*, **76**, 4815 (1954).
96. I. Norman and J. N. Pitts, Jr., *J. Am. Chem. Soc.*, **77**, 6104 (1955).
97. S. W. Benson and G. B. Kistiakowsky, *J. Am. Chem. Soc.*, **64**, 80 (1942).
98. F. E. Blacet and A. Miller, *J. Am. Chem. Soc.*, **79**, 4327 (1957).
99. R. Srinivasan, *J. Am. Chem. Soc.*, **81**, 5541 (1959).
100. R. Srinivasan, "Photochemistry of Cyclic Ketones," *Advances in Photochemistry*, Vol. I, ed. by W. A. Noyes, Jr., G. S. Hammond, and J. N. Pitts, Jr., Interscience Publishers, a division of John Wiley & Sons, New York, 1963, p. 83.
101. R. Srinivasan, *J. Am. Chem. Soc.*, **81**, 1546 (1959).
102. R. Srinivasan, *J. Am. Chem. Soc.*, **83**, 4344 (1961).
103. H. M. Frey, *Chem. & Ind. (London)*, **1961**, 1367.
104. J. R. Dunn and K. O. Kutschke, *Can. J. Chem.*, **32**, 725 (1954).
105. M. Bernard and N. C. Yang, *Proc. Chem. Soc. (London)*, **1958**, 302.
106. R. Srinivasan, *J. Am. Chem. Soc.*, **81**, 2601 (1959).
107. S. M. E. Kellner and W. D. Walters, quoted in Ref. 100; p. 102.
108. (a) C. H. Bamford and R. G. W. Norrish, *J. Chem. Soc.*, **1938**, 1521. (b) *ibid.*, 1544.
109. S. Cremer and R. Srinivasan, *Tetrahedron Letters*, No. 21, 24 (1960).
110. R. Srinivasan, *J. Am. Chem. Soc.*, **83**, 2590 (1961).
111. M. C. Flowers and H. M. Frey, *J. Chem. Soc.*, **1960**, 2758.
112. C. Weizmann, E. Bergmann, and Y. Hirschberg, *J. Am. Chem. Soc.*, **60**, 1530 (1938).
113. H. H. Glazebrook and T. G. Pearson, *J. Chem. Soc.*, **1939**, 589.
114. R. G. Sowden and N. Davidson, *J. Am. Chem. Soc.*, **78**, 1291 (1956).
115. F. J. Duncan and A. F. Trotman-Dickenson, *J. Chem. Soc.*, **1962**, 4672.
116. R. M. Smith and J. G. Calvert, *J. Am. Chem. Soc.*, **78**, 2345 (1956).
117. W. Fielding and H. O. Pritchard, *J. Phys. Chem.*, **66**, 821 (1962).
118. J. N. Pitts, Jr., R. L. Letsinger, R. P. Taylor, J. M. Patterson, G. Recktenwald, and R. B. Martin, *J. Am. Chem. Soc.*, **81**, 1068 (1959).
119. K. R. Kopecky, G. S. Hammond, and P. A. Leermakers, *J. Am. Chem. Soc.*, **84**, 1015 (1962).
120. O. L. Chapman, Ed., *Some Aspects of Organic Photochemistry*, M. Dekker Book Co., New York, to appear in 1966.
121. J. Heicklen, *J. Am. Chem. Soc.*, **81**, 3863 (1959).
122. W. A. Noyes, Jr., W. A. Mulac, and M. S. Matheson, *J. Chem. Phys.*, **36**, 880 (1962).
123. H. L. J. Bäckström and K. Sandros, *Acta Chem. Scand.*, **14**, 48 (1960).
124. G. B. Porter, *J. Chem. Phys.*, **32**, 1587 (1960).
125. W. H. Urry and D. J. Trecker, *J. Am. Chem. Soc.*, **84**, 118 (1962).
126. W. E. Bell and F. E. Blacet, *J. Am. Chem. Soc.*, **76**, 5332 (1954).
127. E. Gorin and H. S. Taylor, *J. Am. Chem. Soc.*, **56**, 2042 (1934).
128. M. Burton, *J. Am. Chem. Soc.*, **58**, 1655 (1936).
129. H. C. Ramsperger and C. W. Porter, *J. Am. Chem. Soc.*, **48**, 1267 (1926).
130. A. Terenin and H. Neujmin, *J. Chem. Phys.*, **3**, 436 (1935).
131. R. Gorden, Jr., and P. Ausloos, *J. Phys. Chem.*, **65**, 1033 (1961).
132. K. Clusius and W. Schanzer, *Ber.*, **75B**, 1795 (1942).
133. P. Ausloos and E. W. R. Steacie, *Can. J. Chem.*, **33**, 1530 (1955).
134. R. N. Smith, P. A. Leighton, and W. G. Leighton, *J. Am. Chem. Soc.*, **61**, 2299 (1939).
135. L. B. Thomas, *J. Am. Chem. Soc.*, **62**, 1879 (1940).

136. S. Hacobian and T. Iredale, *Nature*, **166**, 156 (1950).
137. I. D. S. Rao, *J. Univ. Bombay*, **9**, Pt. 3, 94 (1940); *C.A.*, **35**, 6868[6].
138. A. Miolati and G. Semerano, *Atti Ist. Veneto Sci.*, Pt. II, **100**, 187 (1941); *C.A.*, **37**, 6247[6].
139. A. R. Olson and F. L. Hudson, *J. Am. Chem. Soc.*, **55**, 1410 (1933).
140. A. Weller, *Z. Elektrochem.*, **60**, 1144 (1956).
141. R. J. Kandel and H. A. Taylor, *J. Chem. Phys.*, **19**, 1250 (1951).
142. H. Burwasser and H. A. Taylor, *J. Chem. Phys.*, **23**, 2295 (1955).
143. P. Ausloos, *Can. J. Chem.*, **34**, 1709 (1956).
144. H. Ley and B. Arends, *Z. Physik. Chem.*, **B17**, 177 (1932).
145. J. E. Tuttle and G. K. Rollefson, *J. Am. Chem. Soc.*, **63**, 1525 (1941).
146. K. Atwood and G. K. Rollefson, *J. Chem. Phys.*, **9**, 506 (1941).
147. J. K. Royal and G. K. Rollefson, *J. Am. Chem. Soc.*, **63**, 1521 (1941).
148. D. H. Volman, *J. Am. Chem. Soc.*, **64**, 1820 (1942).
149. P. Ausloos, *Can. J. Chem.*, **36**, 383 (1958).
150. P. Ausloos, *J. Am. Chem. Soc.*, **80**, 1310 (1958).
151. M. H. J. Wijnen, *J. Chem. Phys.*, **27**, 710 (1957).
152. M. H. J. Wijnen, *J. Chem. Phys.*, **28**, 271 (1958).
153. M. H. J. Wijnen, *J. Chem. Phys.*, **28**, 939 (1958).
154. M. H. J. Wijnen, *J. Am. Chem. Soc.*, **80**, 2394 (1958).
155. M. H. J. Wijnen, *J. Am. Chem. Soc.*, **82**, 3034 (1960).
156. M. H. J. Wijnen, *Can. J. Chem.*, **36**, 691 (1958).
157. M. H. J. Wijnen, *J. Am. Chem. Soc.*, **82**, 1847 (1960).
158. R. H. Linnell and W. A. Noyes, Jr., *J. Am. Chem. Soc.*, **72**, 3863 (1950).
159. G. E. Adams and E. J. Hart, *J. Am. Chem. Soc.*, **84**, 3994 (1962).
160. M. H. J. Wijnen, *J. Phys. Chem.*, **65**, 2105 (1961).
161. P. Ausloos and R. E. Rebbert, *J. Phys. Chem.*, **67**, 163 (1963).
162. A. J. Harrison and J. S. Lake, *J. Phys. Chem.*, **63**, 1489 (1959).
163. L. Farkas, Y. Hirshberg, and L. Sandler, *J. Am. Chem. Soc.*, **61**, 3393 (1939).
164. R. P. Porter and W. A. Noyes, Jr., *J. Am. Chem. Soc.*, **81**, 2307 (1959).
165. E. Murad, *J. Am. Chem. Soc.*, **83**, 1327 (1961).
166. M. S. Kharasch, G. Stampa, and W. Nudenberg, *Science*, **116**, 309 (1952).
167. K. Breitschwerdt, T. Förster, and A. Weller, *Naturwiss.*, **43**, 443 (1956).
168. L. I. Grossweiner and E. F. Zwicker, *J. Chem. Phys.*, **32**, 305 (1960).
169. C. Sandorfy, *Compt. Rend.*, **232**, 841 (1951).
170. R. Gomer and W. A. Noyes, Jr., *J. Am. Chem. Soc.*, **72**, 101 (1950).
171. T.-K. Liu and A. B. F. Duncan, *J. Chem. Phys.*, **17**, 241 (1949).
172. J. D. Margerum, J. N. Pitts, Jr., J. G. Rutgers, and S. Searles, *J. Am. Chem. Soc.*, **81**, 1549 (1959).
173. Y. Takezaki, T. Miyazaki, and N. Nakahara, *J. Chem. Phys.*, **25**, 536 (1956).
174. M. Barak and D. W. G. Style, *Nature*, **135**, 307 (1935).
175. G. R. McMillan, *J. Am. Chem. Soc.*, **84**, 2514 (1962).
176. G. R. McMillan, *J. Am. Chem. Soc.*, **83**, 3018 (1961).
177. E. R. Bell, F. F. Rust, and W. E. Vaughan, *J. Am. Chem. Soc.*, **72**, 337 (1950).
178. D. H. Volman and W. M. Graven, *J. Am. Chem. Soc.*, **75**, 3111 (1953).
179. L. M. Dorfman and Z. W. Salsburg, *J. Am. Chem. Soc.*, **73**, 255 (1951).
180. G. R. McMillan and M. H. J. Wijnen, *Can. J. Chem.*, **36**, 1227 (1958).
181. H. M. Frey, *Proc. Chem. Soc. (London)*, **1959**, 385.
182. H. B. Henbest, J. A. W. Reid, and C. J. M. Stirling, *J. Chem. Soc.*, **1961**, 5239.
183. G. R. McMillan, *J. Am. Chem. Soc.*, **82**, 2422 (1960).
184. R. G. W. Norrish and M. H. Searby, *Proc. Roy. Soc. (London)*, **A237**, 464 (1956).

185. J. T. Martin and R. G. W. Norrish, *Proc. Roy. Soc. (London)*, **A220**, 322 (1953).
186. O. J. Walker and G. L. E. Wild, *J. Chem. Soc.*, **1937**, 1132.
187. D. W. G. Style and J. C. Ward, *Trans. Faraday Soc.*, **49**, 999 (1953).
188. J. C. Bevington and T. D. Lewis, *Trans. Faraday Soc.*, **54**, 1340 (1958).
189. O. C. Wetmore and H. A. Taylor, *J. Chem. Phys.*, **12**, 61 (1944).
190. C. I. Johnson and H. A. Taylor, *J. Chem. Phys.*, **19**, 613 (1951).
191. J. S. Watson and B. deB. Darwent, *J. Chem. Phys.*, **20**, 1041 (1952).
192. J. V. Michael and W. A. Noyes, Jr., *J. Am. Chem. Soc.*, **85**, 1228 (1963); J. V. Michael, Ph.D. Thesis, University of Rochester, 1962.
193. C. H. Bamford, *J. Chem. Soc.*, **1939**, 17.
194. G. H. Booth and R. G. W. Norrish, *J. Chem. Soc.*, **1952**, 188.
195. H. Gesser, J. T. Mullhaupt, and J. E. Griffiths, *J. Am. Chem. Soc.*, **79**, 4834 (1957).
196. P. J. Kozak and H. Gesser, *J. Chem. Soc.*, **1960**, 448.
197. D. Bertrand, *Bull. Soc. Chim. France*, **12**, 1010 (1945).
198. A. T. Vartanjan, *Compt. Rend. Acad. Sci., U.R.S.S.*, **30**, 635 (1941); *C.A.*, **37**, 314[4].
199. H. G. Curme and G. K. Rollefson, *J. Am. Chem. Soc.*, **74**, 28 (1952).
200. T. Förster, "Elementary Processes in Solution" in *Photochemistry in the Liquid and Solid State*, ed. by L. J. Heidt, R. S. Livingston, E. Rabinowitch, and F. Daniels, John Wiley & Sons, New York, 1960, p. 10.
201. H. Boaz and G. K. Rollefson, *J. Am. Chem. Soc.*, **72**, 3435 (1950).
202. G. N. Lewis and D. Lipkin, *J. Am. Chem. Soc.*, **64**, 2801 (1942).
203. G. O. Schenck, W. Meder, and M. Pape, *Proceedings Second U. N. International Conference on Peaceful Uses of Atomic Energy*, Geneva, 1958, **29**, 352; published in 1959.
204. H. Rüppel and H. T. Wilt, *Z. Physik. Chem. (Frankfurt)*, **15**, 321 (1958).
205. W. C. Meyer and A. C. Albrecht, *J. Phys. Chem.*, **66**, 1168 (1962).
206. J. Weiss, *Trans. Faraday Soc.*, **36**, 856 (1940); P. F. Holt and B. P. Hughes, *J. Chem. Soc.*, **1955**, 98.
207. R. K. Brinton, *J. Am. Chem. Soc.*, **77**, 842 (1955).
208. D. A. Becker, H. Okabe, and J. R. McNesby, *J. Phys. Chem.*, **69**, 538 (1965).
209. G. Lindemann, *Z. Wiss. Phot.*, **50**, 347 (1955).
210. M. D. Cohen, Y. Hirshberg, and G. M. J. Schmidt, H-Bonding Symposium at Ljubljana, 1957; papers published in 1959, p. 293.
211. E. Fischer and Y. Frei, *J. Chem. Phys.*, **27**, 808 (1957).
212. D. H. Volman, *J. Am. Chem. Soc.*, **63**, 2000 (1941).
213. B. C. Spall and E. W. R. Steacie, *Proc. Roy. Soc. (London)*, **A239**, 1 (1957).
214. T. W. Davis, F. P. Jahn, and M. Burton, *J. Am. Chem. Soc.*, **60**, 10 (1938).
215. C. V. Cannon and O. K. Rice, *J. Am. Chem. Soc.*, **63**, 2900 (1941).
216. M. H. Jones and E. W. R. Steacie, *J. Chem. Phys.*, **21**, 1018 (1953).
217. G. R. Hoey and K. O. Kutschke, *Can. J. Chem.*, **33**, 496 (1955).
218. W. C. Sleppy and J. G. Calvert, *J. Am. Chem. Soc.*, **81**, 769 (1959).
219. R. E. Rebbert and P. Ausloos, *J. Phys. Chem.*, **66**, 2253 (1962).
220. J. R. Dacey and D. M. Young, *J. Chem. Phys.*, **23**, 1302 (1955).
221. G. O. Pritchard, H. O. Pritchard, H. I. Schiff, and A. F. Trotman-Dickenson, *Trans. Faraday Soc.*, **52**, 849 (1956).
222. P. Ausloos and E. W. R. Steacie, *Bull. Soc. Chim. Belges*, **63**, 87 (1954).
223. H. Cerfontain and K. O. Kutschke, *Can. J. Chem.*, **36**, 344 (1958).
224. B. C. Roquitte and J. H. Futrell, *J. Chem. Phys.*, **37**, 378 (1962).
225. D. P. Dingledy and J. G. Calvert, *J. Am. Chem. Soc.*, **85**, 856 (1963).
226. J. A. Kerr and J. G. Calvert, *J. Am. Chem. Soc.*, **83**, 3391 (1961).
227. R. W. Durham and E. W. R. Steacie, *Can. J. Chem.*, **31**, 377 (1953).

228. R. H. Riem and K. O. Kutschke, *Can. J. Chem.*, **38**, 2332 (1960).
229. W. E. Morganroth and J. G. Calvert, Abstracts, Division of Phys. Chem., 148th Meeting American Chemical Society, Chicago, September, 1964, p. 17V.
230. S. S. Thomas and J. G. Calvert, *J. Am. Chem. Soc.*, **84**, 4207 (1962).
231. R. Back and C. Sivertz, *Can. J. Chem.*, **32**, 1061 (1954).
232. J. C. Roy, J. R. Nash, R. R. Williams, Jr., and W. H. Hamill, *J. Am. Chem. Soc.*, **78**, 519 (1956).
233. G. Zimmerman, L.-Y. Chow, U.-J. Paik, *J. Am. Chem. Soc.*, **80**, 3528 (1958).
234. I. Hausser, *Z. Naturforsch.*, **5a**, 56 (1950).
235. W. H. Martin, H. D. Bett, R. G. Romans, and W. Tidridge, *Trans. Roy. Soc. Can.*, Sec. III, **34**, 35 (1940).
236. P. P. Birnbaum and D. W. G. Style, *Trans. Faraday. Soc.*, **50**, 1192 (1954).
237. E. Fischer, M. Frankel, and R. Wolovsky, *J. Chem. Phys.*, **23**, 1367 (1955).
238. F. W. Kirkbride and R. G. W. Norrish, *J. Chem. Soc.*, **1933**, 119.
239. R. K. Brinton and D. H. Volman, *J. Chem. Phys.*, **19**, 1394 (1951).
240. G. B. Kistiakowsky and K. Sauer, *J. Am. Chem. Soc.*, **78**, 5699 (1956).
241. H. M. Frey and G. B. Kistiakowsky, *J. Am. Chem. Soc.*, **79**, 6373 (1957).
242. W. B. DeMore, H. O. Pritchard, and N. Davidson, *J. Am. Chem. Soc.*, **81**, 5874 (1959).
243. G. W. Robinson and M. McCarty, Jr., *J. Am. Chem. Soc.*, **82**, 1859 (1960).
244. T. D. Goldfarb and G. C. Pimentel, *J. Am. Chem. Soc.*, **82**, 1865 (1960).
245. F. A. L. Anet, R. F. W. Bader, and A. M. Van der Auwera, *J. Am. Chem. Soc.*, **82**, 3217 (1960).
246. J. A. R. Samson, F. F. Marmo, and K. Watanabe, *J. Chem. Phys.*, **36**, 783 (1962).
247. H. M. Frey and I. D. R. Stevens, *Proc. Chem. Soc. (London)*, **1962**, 79.
248. H. M. Frey, *J. Chem. Soc.*, **1962**, 2293.
249. W. Kirmse, L. Horner, and H. Hoffmann, *Ann.*, **614**, 19 (1958).
250. R. M. Etter, H. S. Skovronek, and P. S. Skell, *J. Am. Chem. Soc.*, **81**, 1008 (1959).
251. W. Fielding and H. O. Pritchard, *J. Phys. Chem.*, **64**, 278 (1960).
252. R. F. Hampson, Jr., J. R. McNesby, H. Akimoto, and I. Tanaka, *J. Chem. Phys.*, **40**, 1099 (1964).
253. W. Kirmse and L. Horner, *Ann.*, **625**, 34 (1959).
254. H. Ziffer and N. E. Sharpless, *J. Org. Chem.*, **27**, 1944 (1962).
255. A. Baril, Jr., *J. Chem. Phys.*, **22**, 1275 (1954).
256. G. Gavlin, Armour Research Foundation Final Report, "Increased Light Sensitivity for Diazo-type Substance," Project no. 90-595 C, April 15, 1950.
257. W. E. Lee, J. G. Calvert, and E. W. Malmberg, *J. Am. Chem. Soc.*, **83**, 1928 (1961).
258. J. de Jonge, R. Dijkstra, and G. L. Wiggerink, *Rec. Trav. Chim.*, **71**, 846 (1952).
259. D. H. R. Barton and L. R. Morgan, Jr., *J. Chem. Soc.*, **1962**, 622.
260. P. A. S. Smith and B. B. Brown, *J. Am. Chem. Soc.*, **73**, 2435 (1951).
261. W. Lwowski and T. W. Mattingly, *Tetrahedron Letters*, **1962**, No. 7, 277.
262. J. Mason, *J. Chem. Soc.*, **1963**, 4537.
263. J. Jander and R. N. Haszeldine, *Naturwiss.*, **40**, 579 (1953).
264. R. N. Haszeldine and B. J. H. Mattinson, *J. Chem. Soc.*, **1957**, 1741.
265. A. Y. Yakubovich, S. P. Makarov, V. A. Ginsburg, N. F. Privezentseva, and L. L. Martynova, *Doklady Akad. Nauk S.S.S.R.*, **141**, 125 (1961).
266. J. G. Calvert and S. S. Thomas, unpublished work.
267. S. Mitchell and J. Cameron, *J. Chem. Soc.*, **1938**, 1965.
268. S. Mitchell, K. Schwarzwald, and G. K. Simpson, *J. Chem. Soc.*, **1941**, 602.
269. S. Mitchell and I. M. Dawson, *J. Chem. Soc.*, **1944**, 452.
270. K. D. Anderson, C. J. Crumpler, and D. L. Hammick, *J. Chem. Soc.*, **1935**, 1679.

271. E. Hirschlaff and R. G. W. Norrish, *J. Chem. Soc.*, **1936**, 1580.
272. P. Gray, A. D. Yoffe, and L. Roselaar, *Trans. Faraday Soc.*, **51**, 1489 (1955).
273. H. W. Brown and G. C. Pimentel, *J. Chem. Phys.*, **29**, 883 (1958).
274. G. C. Pimentel and G. K. Rollefson, unpublished work quoted in *Formation and Trapping of Free Radicals*, ed. by A. M. Bass and H. P. Broida, Academic Press, New York, 1960, p. 97.
275. A. J. C. Nicholson, *Nature*, **190**, 143 (1961).
276. R. E. Rebbert and N. Slagg, *Bull. Soc. Chim. Belges*, **71**, 709 (1962).
277. J. Mason, *J. Chem. Soc.*, **1957**, 3904.
278. O. N. Shelegova, *J. Exptl. Theoret. Phys. (USSR)*, **9**, 1527 (1939); *C.A.*, **35**, 1700⁵.
279. H. Schüler and A. Woeldike, *Physik. Z.*, **45**, 171 (1944).
280. S. H. Hastings and F. A. Matsen, *J. Am. Chem. Soc.*, **70**, 3514 (1948).
281. (a) P. A. Leighton and F. A. Lucy, *J. Chem. Phys.*, **2**, 756 (1934); (b) F. A. Lucy and P. A. Leighton, *J. Chem. Phys.*, **2**, 760 (1934).
282. J. A. Gray and D. W. G. Style, *Trans. Faraday Soc.*, **48**, 1137 (1952).
283. P. L. Hanst and J. G. Calvert, *J. Phys. Chem.*, **63**, 2071 (1959).
284. L. H. Piette, J. D. Ray, and R. A. Ogg, Jr., *J. Chem. Phys.*, **26**, 1341 (1957).
285. P. Gray and M. W. T. Pratt, *J. Chem. Soc.*, **1958**, 3403.
286. R. F. Grant, D. W. Davidson, and P. Gray, *J. Chem. Phys.*, **33**, 1713 (1960).
287. G. R. McMillan, private communication to the authors.
288. G. R. McMillan, *J. Am. Chem. Soc.*, **84**, 4007 (1962).
289. G. R. McMillan, *J. Phys. Chem.*, **67**, 931 (1963).
290. G. R. McMillan, J. G. Calvert, and S. S. Thomas, *J. Phys. Chem.*, **68**, 116 (1964).
291. C. S. Coe and T. F. Doumani, *J. Am. Chem. Soc.*, **70**, 1516 (1948).
292. P. Tarte, *Bull. Soc. Roy. Liége*, **22**, 226 (1953).
293. P. Kabasakalian and E. R. Townley, *J. Am. Chem. Soc.*, **84**, 2711 (1962).
294. A. L. Nussbaum and C. H. Robinson, *Tetrahedron*, **17**, 35 (1962).
295. M. Akhtar, "Some Recent Developments in the Photochemistry of Organic Nitrites and Hypohalites," *Advances in Photochemistry*, Vol. 2, ed. by W. A. Noyes, Jr., G. S. Hammond, and J. N. Pitts, Jr., Interscience Publishers, a division of John Wiley & Sons, 1964, p. 263.
296. P. Kabasakalian, E. R. Townley, and M. D. Yudis, *J. Am. Chem. Soc.*, **84**, 2716, 2718 (1962).
297. P. Kabasakalian and E. R. Townley, *J. Am. Chem. Soc.*, **84**, 2723, 2724 (1962).
298. (a) D. H. R. Barton, J. M. Beaton, L. E. Geller, and M. M. Pechet, *J. Am. Chem. Soc.*, **82**, 2640 (1960); (b) *ibid.*, **83**, 4076 (1961).
299. J. A. Gray and D. W. G. Style, *Trans. Faraday Soc.*, **49**, 52 (1953).
300. P. Gray and G. T. Rogers, *Trans. Faraday Soc.*, **50**, 28 (1954).
301. R. E. Rebbert, *J. Phys. Chem.*, **67**, 1923 (1963).
302. The authors are indebted to G. R. McMillen for pointing out their error; see the assignments of Piette *et al.*, Ref. 284, Gray and Pratt, Ref. 285, and Grant *et al.*, Ref. 286.
303. A. Terenin and H. Neujmin, *Nature*, **134**, 255 (1934).
304. D. E. McElcheran, M. H. J. Wijnen, and E. W. R. Steacie, *Can. J. Chem.*, **36**, 321 (1958).
305. E. Weyde and W. Frankenburger, *Trans. Faraday Soc.*, **27**, 561 (1931).
306. L. Harris and J. Kaminsky, *J. Am. Chem. Soc.*, **57**, 1154 (1935).
307. J. G. Calvert and H. J. L. Rechen, *J. Am. Chem. Soc.*, **74**, 2101 (1952).
308. E. O. Holmes, Jr., *J. Phys. Chem.*, **61**, 434 (1957).
309. D. A. Bamford and C. H. Bamford, *J. Chem. Soc.*, **1941**, 30.
310. N. P. Skerrett and H. W. Thompson, *Trans. Faraday Soc.*, **37**, 81 (1941).

311. T. Inabe and B. deB. Darwent, *J. Phys. Chem.*, **64**, 1431 (1960).
312. M. Meissner and H. W. Thompson, *Trans. Faraday Soc.*, **34**, 1238 (1938).
313. K. Rosengren, *Acta Chem. Scand.*, **16**, 1418 (1962).
314. R. H. Pallen and C. Sivertz, *Can. J. Chem.*, **35**, 723 (1957).
315. W. E. Haines, G. L. Clark, and J. S. Ball, *J. Am. Chem. Soc.*, **78**, 5213 (1956).
316. T. Ueno and Y. Takezaki, *Bull. Inst. Chem. Research, Kyoto Univ.*, **36**, 19 (1958).
317. R. B. Whitney and M. Calvin, *J. Chem. Phys.*, **23**, 1750 (1955).
318. J. A. Barltrop, P. M. Hayes, and M. Calvin, *J. Am. Chem. Soc.*, **76**, 4348 (1954).
319. W. E. Lyons, *Nature*, **162**, 1004 (1948).
320. G. Oster, L. Citarel, and M. Goodman, *J. Am. Chem. Soc.*, **84**, 703 (1962).
321. B. H. Mahan and R. Mandal, *J. Chem. Phys.*, **37**, 207 (1962).
322. P. J. Ausloos and S. G. Lias, *J. Chem. Phys.*, **38**, 2207 (1963).
323. W. Groth, *Z. Physik. Chem. (Leipzig)*, **B38**, 366 (1937).
324. P. A. Leighton and A. B. Steiner, *J. Am. Chem. Soc.*, **58**, 1823 (1936).
325. R. W. Ditchburn, *Proc. Roy. Soc. (London)*, **A229**, 44 (1955).
326. N. Wainfan, W. C. Walker, and G. L. Weissler, *Phys. Rev.*, **99**, 542 (1955).
327. H. Okabe and J. R. McNesby, *J. Chem. Phys.*, **34**, 668 (1961).
328. M. H. J. Wijnen, *J. Chem. Phys.*, **24**, 851 (1956).
329. K. Faltings, *Ber.*, **72**, 1207 (1939).
330. M. D. Scheer, J. R. McNesby, and R. Klein, *J. Chem. Phys.*, **36**, 3504 (1962).
331. H. Okabe and J. R. McNesby, *J. Chem. Phys.*, **37**, 1340 (1962).
332. W. Kemula and A. Dyduszynski, *Roczniki Chem.*, **17**, 423 (1937).
333. W. E. Groth and G. Scharfe, *Z. Physik. Chem. (Frankfurt)*, **2**, 142 (1954).
334. W. Groth, *Z. Elektrochem.*, **58**, 752 (1954).
335. M. C. Sauer, Jr., and L. M. Dorfman, *J. Chem. Phys.*, **35**, 497 (1961).
336. H. Okabe and D. A. Becker, *J. Am. Chem. Soc.*, **84**, 4004 (1962).
337. C. L. Currie, H. Okabe, and J. R. McNesby, *J. Phys. Chem.*, **67**, 1494 (1963).
338. P. Wagner and A. B. F. Duncan, *J. Chem. Phys.*, **21**, 516 (1953).
339. P. Ausloos, R. E. Rebbert, and S. G. Lias, *J. Chem. Phys.*, **42**, 540 (1965).
340. H. Okabe and J. R. McNesby, *J. Chem. Phys.*, **36**, 601 (1962).
341. W. F. Kieffer and J. P. Howe, *J. Am. Chem. Soc.*, **64**, 1 (1942).
342. C. P. Poole, Jr., and R. S. Anderson, *J. Chem. Phys.*, **31**, 346 (1959).
343. G. N. Lewis, T. T. Magel, and D. Lipkin, *J. Am. Chem. Soc.*, **62**, 2973 (1940).
344. R. E. Buckles, *J. Am. Chem. Soc.*, **77**, 1040 (1955).
345. R. H. Dyck and D. S. McClure, *J. Chem. Phys.*, **36**, 2326 (1962).
346. H. Stegemeyer, *J. Phys. Chem.*, **66**, 2555 (1962).
347. D. Schulte-Frohlinde, H. Blume, and H. Güsten, *J. Phys. Chem.*, **66**, 2486 (1962).
348. (a) F. B. Mallory, J. T. Gordon, and C. S. Wood, *J. Am. Chem. Soc.*, **85**, 828 (1963); (b) F. B. Mallory, C. S. Wood, and J. T. Gordon, *J. Am. Chem. Soc.*, **86**, 3094 (1964).
349. W. M. Moore, D. D. Morgan, and F. R. Stermitz, *J. Am. Chem. Soc.*, **85**, 829 (1963).
350. S. Malkin and E. Fischer, *J. Phys. Chem.*, **68**, 1153 (1964).
351. G. S. Hammond and J. Saltiel, *J. Am. Chem. Soc.*, **84**, 4983 (1962).
352. S. Malkin and E. Fischer, *J. Phys. Chem.*, **66**, 2482 (1962).
353. T. Förster, *Z. Elektrochem.*, **56**, 716 (1952).
354. E. Lippert and W. Lüder, *J. Phys. Chem.*, **66**, 2430 (1962).
355. A. Smakula, *Z. Physik. Chem.*, **B25**, 90 (1934).
356. G. M. Burnett, *Trans. Faraday Soc.*, **46**, 772 (1950).
357. S.-W. Chen, *J. Phys. & Colloid Chem.*, **53**, 486 (1949).
358. G. Goldfinger and C. Heffelfinger, *J. Polymer Sci.*, **13**, 123 (1954).

359. A. Pullman, B. Pullman, E. D. Bergmann, G. Berthier, E. Fischer, Y. Hirshberg, and J. Pontis, *J. Chim. Phys.*, **48**, 359 (1951).
360. E. J. Bowen and J. D. F. Marsh, *J. Chem. Soc.*, **1947**, 109.
361. V. A. Crawford and C. A. Coulson, *J. Chem. Soc.*, **1948**, 1990.
362. K. Ueberreiter and K. Jander, *Makromol. Chem.*, **40**, 95 (1960).
363. R. Srinivasan, *J. Am. Chem. Soc.*, **84**, 4141 (1962).
364. R. Srinivasan, *J. Am. Chem. Soc.*, **82**, 5063 (1960).
365. O. Grummitt and F. J. Christoph, *J. Am. Chem. Soc.*, **71**, 4157 (1949).
366. Y. Hirshberg, E. Bergmann, and F. Bergmann, *J. Am. Chem. Soc.*, **72**, 5117 (1950).
367. M. Barbaron and P. Pesteil, *Compt. Rend.*, **236**, 1763 (1953).
368. G. S. Hammond, P. A. Leermakers, and N. J. Turro, *J. Am. Chem. Soc.*, **83**, 2396 (1961).
369. D. F. Evans, *J. Chem. Soc.*, **1960**, 1735.
370. G. S. Hammond, N. J. Turro, and A. Fischer, *J. Am. Chem. Soc.*, **83**, 4674 (1961).
371. N. J. Turro and G. S. Hammond, *J. Am. Chem. Soc.*, **84**, 2841 (1962).
372. G. O. Schenck and D. E. Dunlap, *Angew. Chem.*, **68**, 248 (1956).
373. R. Srinivasan, *J. Chem. Phys.*, **38**, 1039 (1963).
374. E. Migirdicyan and S. Leach, *Bull. Soc. Chim. Belges*, **71**, 845 (1962).
375. R. Srinivasan, *J. Am. Chem. Soc.*, **83**, 2806 (1961).
376. G. F. Woods and L. H. Schwartzman, *J. Am. Chem. Soc.*, **70**, 3394 (1948).
377. R. Srinivasan, *J. Am. Chem. Soc.*, **84**, 3432 (1962).
378. W. G. Dauben and R. L. Cargill, *Tetrahedron*, **12**, 186 (1961).
379. H. Schüler, E. Lutz, and G. Arnold, *Spectrochim. Acta*, **17**, 1043 (1961).
380. H. E. Zimmerman and D. I. Schuster, *J. Am. Chem. Soc.*, **83**, 4486 (1961).
381. D. H. R. Barton and P. T. Gilham, *J. Chem. Soc.*, **1960**, 4596.
382. D. Arigoni, H. Bosshard, H. Bruderer, G. Büchi, O. Jeger, and L. J. Krebaum, *Helv. Chim. Acta*, **40**, 1732 (1957).
383. D. H. R. Barton, P. de Mayo, and M. Shafiq, *Proc. Chem. Soc. (London)*, **1957**, 205; *J. Chem. Soc.*, **1958**, 140.
384. D. H. R. Barton, J. F. McGhie, and M. Rosenberger, *J. Chem. Soc.*, **1961**, 1215.
385. G. S. Hammond and R. S. H. Liu, *J. Am. Chem. Soc.*, **85**, 477 (1963).
386. I. Tanaka, S. Miyakawa, and S. Shida, *Bull. Chem. Soc. Japan*, **24**, 119 (1951).
387. I. Tanaka and M. Okuda, *J. Chem. Phys.*, **22**, 1780 (1954).
388. B. A. Thrush and J. J. Zwolenik, *Bull. Soc. Chim. Belges*, **71**, 642 (1962).
389. L. Kaplan, private communication to the authors.
390. R. J. de Kock, N. G. Minnaard, and E. Havinga, *Rec. Trav. Chim.*, **79**, 922 (1960).
391. E. Havinga, R. J. de Kock, and H. P. Rappoldt, *Tetrahedron*, **11**, 276 (1960).
392. M. Zelikoff and L. M. Aschenbrand, *J. Chem. Phys.*, **24**, 1034 (1956).
393. G. B. Kistiakowsky, *Phys. Rev.*, **37**, 276 (1931).
394. H. W. Melville, *Trans. Faraday Soc.*, **32**, 258 (1936).
395. R. Cherton, *Bull. Soc. Roy. Sci. Liége*, **11**, 203 (1942).
396. C. K. Ingold, *J. Chim. Phys.*, **53**, 472 (1956).
397. W. C. Walker and G. L. Weissler, *J. Chem. Phys.*, **23**, 1547 (1955).
398. J. H. Callomon and D. A. Ramsay, *Can. J. Phys.*, **35**, 129 (1957).
399. E. J. Anderton, H. T. J. Chilton, and G. Porter, *Proc. Chem. Soc. (London)*, **1960**, 352.
400. H. J. F. Angus, J. M. Blair, and D. Bryce-Smith, *J. Chem. Soc.*, **1960**, 2003.
401. G. E. Gibson, N. Blake, and M. Kalm, *J. Chem. Phys.*, **21**, 1000 (1953).
402. I. Norman and G. Porter, *Proc. Roy. Soc. (London)*, **A230**, 399 (1955).
403. D. J. E. Ingram, W. G. Hodgson, C. A. Parker, and W. T. Rees, *Nature*, **176**, 1227 (1955).

404. S. Leach, *J. Chim. Phys.*, **51**, 556 (1954).
405. J. E. Wilson and W. A. Noyes, Jr., *J. Am. Chem. Soc.*, **63**, 3025 (1941).
406. C. E. Lane, Jr., and W. A. Noyes, Jr., *J. Am. Chem. Soc.*, **54**, 161 (1932).
407. W. West, *J. Am. Chem. Soc.*, **57**, 1931 (1935).
408. H. Ishikawa and W. A. Noyes, Jr., *J. Chem. Phys.*, **37**, 583 (1962).
409. M. R. Wright, R. P. Frosch, and G. W. Robinson, *J. Chem. Phys.*, **34**, 934 (1960).
410. (a) R. R. Hentz and M. Burton, *J. Am. Chem. Soc.*, **73**, 532 (1951); (b) T. J. Sworski, R. R. Hentz, and M. Burton, *J. Am. Chem. Soc.*, **73**, 1998 (1951).
411. G. Porter, *Chem. Soc. (London), Spec. Publ.* No. 9, 139 (1957).
412. G. Porter and E. Strachan, *Trans. Faraday Soc.*, **54**, 1595 (1958).
413. G. Porter and E. Strachan, *Spectrochim. Acta*, **12**, 299 (1958).
414. G. Porter and F. J. Wright, *Trans. Faraday Soc.*, **51**, 1469 (1955).
415. E. J. Bowen and A. H. Williams, *Trans. Faraday Soc.*, **35**, 765 (1939).
416. I. Loeff and G. Stein, *J. Chem. Soc.*, **1963**, 2623.
417. R. D. Doepker and P. Ausloos, *J. Chem. Phys.*, **41**, 1865 (1964).
418. P. Ausloos, R. Gorden, Jr., and S. G. Lias, *J. Chem. Phys.*, **40**, 1854 (1964).
419. I. Haller and R. Srinivasan, *J. Chem. Phys.*, **40**, 1992 (1964).
420. A. H. Laufer and J. E. Sturm, *J. Chem. Phys.*, **40**, 612 (1964).
421. Z. R. Grabowski and A. Bylina, *Trans. Faraday Soc.*, **60**, 1131 (1964).
422. (a) E. J. Bowen, *Trans. Faraday Soc.*, **50**, 97 (1954); (b) E. J. Bowen and D. W. Tanner, *Trans. Faraday Soc.*, **51**, 475 (1955).
423. R. Livingston and V. S. Rao, *J. Phys. Chem.*, **63**, 794 (1959).
424. Spectra were determined by Mrs. Veronique McMillan, using a 10 cm cell and Bausch and Lomb model 505 spectrometer. Spectra at temperatures above 25° were determined using a water-jacketed cell at the desired temperature; the cell was equipped with an all glass valve which could be closed to avoid contact of the vapors with stopcock grease during measurement. Extinction coefficients were calculated from measurements at several pressures.
425. A. J. Harrison, B. J. Cederholm, and M. A. Terwilliger, *J. Chem. Phys.*, **30**, 355 (1959).
426. A. J. Harrison and D. R. W. Price, *J. Chem. Phys.*, **30**, 357 (1959).
427. E. Tannenbaum, E. M. Coffin, and A. J. Harrison, *J. Chem. Phys.*, **21**, 311 (1953).
428. R. S. Becker and J. K. Roy, *J. Phys. Chem.*, **69**, 1435 (1965).
429. P. Ramart-Lucas, *Bull. Soc. Chim. France*, **9**, 850 (1942).
430. H. Okabe and D. A. Becker, *J. Chem. Phys.*, **39**, 2549 (1963).
431. L. C. Jones, Jr., and L. W. Taylor, *Anal. Chem.*, **27**, 228 (1955).
432. R. A. Friedel and M. Orchin, *Ultraviolet Spectra of Aromatic Compounds*, John Wiley & Sons, New York, 1951.
433. D. Porret and C. F. Goodeve, *Proc. Roy. Soc. (London)*, **A165**, 31 (1938).
434. E. Treiber, W. Berndt, and H. Toplak, *Angew. Chem.*, **67**, 69 (1955).
435. K. Kimura and S. Nagakura, *Spectrochim. Acta*, **17**, 166 (1961).
436. H. Schwab, Fundamental Research Division, National Cash Register Co., Dayton, Ohio, private communication.
437. C. A. Heller, D. A. Fine, and R. A. Henry, *J. Phys. Chem.*, **65**, 1908 (1961).
438. J. P. Simons and A. J. Yarwood, unpublished work, quoted in Ref. 441.
439. A. P. Zeelenberg, *Nature*, **181**, 42 (1958).
440. J. F. McKeller and R. G. W. Norrish, *Proc. Roy. Soc. (London)*, **A263**, 51 (1961).
441. J. R. Majer and J. P. Simons, "Photochemical Processes in Halogenated Compounds," *Advances in Photochemistry*, Vol. II, ed. by W. A. Noyes, Jr., G. S. Hammond, and J. N. Pitts, Jr., Interscience Publishers, a division of John Wiley & Sons, New York, 1964, p. 137.

442. G. Herzberg, *Proc. Chem. Soc. (London)*, **1959**, 116.
443. B. A. Thrush, *Proc. Roy. Soc. (London)*, **A243**, 555 (1958).
444. R. Schindler and M. H. J. Wijnen, *Z. Physik. Chem. (Frankfurt)*, **34**, 109 (1962).
445. D. W. G. Style and J. C. Ward, *J. Chem. Soc.*, **1952**, 2125.
446. J. P. Simons and A. J. Yarwood, *Trans. Faraday Soc.*, **57**, 2167 (1961).
447. J. R. Majer and C. R. Patrick, *Nature*, **192**, 866 (1961).
448. J. P. Simons and A. J. Yarwood, *Trans. Faraday Soc.*, **59**, 90 (1963).
449. A. J. Yarwood and J. P. Simons, *Proc. Chem. Soc. (London)*, **1962**, 62.
450. W. West and L. Schlessinger, *J. Am. Chem. Soc.*, **60**, 961 (1938).
451. P. T. McTigue and A. S. Buchanan, *Trans. Faraday Soc.*, **55**, 1153 (1959).
452. T. Iredale and E. R. McCartney, *J. Am. Chem. Soc.*, **68**, 144 (1946).
453. R. D. Schultz and H. A. Taylor, *J. Chem. Phys.*, **18**, 194 (1950).
454. (a) F. P. Hudson, R. R. Williams, Jr., and W. H. Hamill, *J. Chem. Phys.*, **21**, 1894 (1953); (b) R. D. Souffie, R. R. Williams, Jr., and W. H. Hamill, *J. Am. Chem. Soc.*, **78**, 917 (1956); (c) R. F. Pottie, W. H. Hamill, and R. R. Williams, Jr., *J. Am. Chem. Soc.*, **80**, 4224 (1958); (d) W. H. Hamill and R. H. Schuler, *J. Am. Chem. Soc.*, **73**, 3466 (1951).
455. A. Gordon and H. A. Taylor, *J. Am. Chem. Soc.*, **63**, 3435 (1941).
456. A. A. Gordus and R. B. Bernstein, *J. Chem. Phys.*, **30**, 973 (1959).
457. J. Horiuchi and M. Katayama, *J. Research Inst. Catalysis, Hokkaido Univ.*, **6**, 44 (1958); *C.A.*, **53**, 10997*g*.
458. K. Pfordte, *J. Prakt. Chem.* [4], **5**, 196 (1957).
459. J. P. Simons and A. J. Yarwood, *Nature*, **187**, 316 (1960).
460. J. Banus, H. J. Emeléus, and R. N. Haszeldine, *J. Chem. Soc.*, **1950**, 3041.
461. J. R. Dacey, *Discussions Faraday Soc.*, **1953**, No. 14, 84.
462. S. Hautecloque, *Compt. Rend.*, **256**, 2601 (1963).
463. B. P. McGrath and J. M. Tedder, *Bull. Soc. Chim. Belges*, **71**, 772 (1962).
464. D. E. Mann and B. A. Thrush, *J. Chem. Phys.*, **33**, 1732 (1960).
465. B. M. Norton, *J. Am. Chem. Soc.*, **56**, 2294 (1934).
466. M. C. L. Gerry and G. B. Porter, *Nature*, **189**, 655 (1961).
467. R. H. Luebbe, Jr., and J. E. Willard, *J. Am. Chem. Soc.*, **81**, 761 (1959).
468. D. L. Bunberry, R. R. Williams, Jr., and W. H. Hamill, *J. Am. Chem. Soc.*, **78**, 6228 (1956).
469. H. L. Friedman, R. B. Bernstein, and H. E. Gunning, *J. Chem. Phys.*, **26**, 528 (1957).
470. R. Barker and A. Maccoll, *J. Chem. Soc.*, **1963**, 2839.
471. W. F. Yates and L. J. Hughes, *J. Phys. Chem.*, **64**, 672 (1960).
472. G. A. Razuvaev and N. A. Osanova, *Zhur. Obshcheĭ Khim.*, **24**, 1771 (1954).
473. (a) W. H. Janneck and E. O. Wiig, *J. Am. Chem. Soc.*, **62**, 1877 (1940); (b) R. J. Grabenstetter and E. O. Wiig, *J. Am. Chem. Soc.*, **69**, 1027 (1947).
474. H. E. Mahncke and W. A. Noyes, Jr., *J. Am. Chem. Soc.*, **58**, 932 (1936).
475. M. H. J. Wijnen, *J. Am. Chem. Soc.*, **83**, 4109 (1961).
476. J. W. Tamblyn and G. S. Forbes, *J. Am. Chem. Soc.*, **62**, 99 (1940).
477. C. E. McCauley, W. H. Hamill, and R. R. Williams, Jr., *J. Am. Chem. Soc.*, **76**, 6263 (1954).
478. G. R. McMillan and W. A. Noyes, Jr., *J. Am. Chem. Soc.*, **80**, 2108 (1958).
479. C. E. McCauley and G. J. Hilsdorf, *J. Am. Chem. Soc.*, **80**, 5101 (1958).
480. E. L. Cochran, W. H. Hamill, and R. R. Williams, Jr., *J. Am. Chem. Soc.*, **76**, 2145 (1954).
481. D. A. Barr, W. C. Francis, and R. N. Haszeldine, *Nature*, **177**, 785 (1956).
482. M. Trachtman, *J. Phys. Chem.*, **68**, 1415 (1964).

483. R. A. Durie, T. Iredale, and A. H. Kingsbury, *Nature*, **164**, 786 (1949).
484. J. M. Blair and D. Bryce-Smith, *J. Chem. Soc.*, **1960**, 1788.
485. (a) W. Wolf and N. Kharasch, *J. Org. Chem.*, **26**, 283 (1961); (b) N. Kharasch, W. Wolf, T. J. Erpelding, P. G. Naylor, and L. Tokes, *Chem. & Ind. (London)*, **1962**, 1720.
486. J. A. Kampmeier and E. Hoffmeister, *J. Am. Chem. Soc.*, **84**, 3787 (1962).
487. G. R. McMillan, J. G. Calvert, and J. N. Pitts, Jr., *J. Am. Chem. Soc.*, **86**, 3602 (1964).
488. R. D. McQuigg and J. G. Calvert, Symposium on Structure and Photochemistry of Excited States, American Chemical Society, 149th Meeting, Detroit, April, 1965.
489. R. E. Rebbert and P. Ausloos, *J. Am. Chem. Soc.*, **86**, 4803 (1964).
490. E. A. Davidowicz and C. R. Patrick, *J. Chem. Soc.*, **1964**, 4250.
491. R. F. Hutton and C. Steel, *J. Am. Chem. Soc.*, **86**, 745 (1964).
492. A. Zahra and W. A. Noyes, Jr., *J. Phys. Chem.*, **69**, 943 (1965).
493. J. N. Pitts, Jr., and J. K. S. Wan, "The Photochemistry of Ketones and Aldehydes," in *The Carbonyl Group*, ed. by S. Patai, John Wiley & Sons, New York, in press.
494. A. Mustafa, "Photochemical Reactions of Sulphur and Nitrogen Heteroatomic Organic Compounds," *Advances in Photochemistry*, Vol. II, ed. by W. A. Noyes, Jr., G. S. Hammond, and J. N. Pitts, Jr., Interscience Publishers, a division of John Wiley & Sons, New York, 1964, p. 63.
495. (a) W. A. Noyes, Jr., *Festschrift Arthur Stoll*, Birkhauser A. G., Basel, 1958, p. 64; (b) Academia Das Ciencias de Lisboa, May, 1964; (c) W. A. Noyes, Jr., and I. Unger, "Some Aspects of Transitions Between Electronic Levels," in *Organic Photochemistry*, I.U.P.A.C., Butterworths, London, 1965, p. 461. See also Ref. 49.
496. D. H. Volman and L. W. Swanson, *J. Am. Chem. Soc.*, **82**, 4141 (1960).
497. J. N. Pitts, Jr., L. D. Hess, E. J. Baum, E. A. Schuck, J. K. S. Wan, P. A. Leermakers, and G. F. Vesley, IV International Congress of Photobiology, Oxford, July, 1964 (proceedings published as *Recent Progress in Photobiology*, ed. by E. J. Bowen, Blackwells, Oxford, 1965); *J. Photochem. and Photobiol.*, in press.
498. E. J. Baum, J. K. S. Wan, and J. N. Pitts, Jr., Symposium on Structure and Reactivity of Excited Molecules, *Abstracts*, 149th National Meeting, American Chemical Society, Detroit, April, 1965, 7S; *Abstracts*, Div. Phys. Chem., Detroit, April, 1965 30S.
499. E. J. Baum, Doctoral Dissertation, University of California, Riverside, 1965.
500. P. Ausloos and R. E. Rebbert, *J. Am. Chem. Soc.*, **86**, 4512 (1964).
501. O. L. Chapman, "Photochemical Rearrangements of Organic Molecules," *Advances in Photochemistry*, Vol. 1, ed. by W. A. Noyes, G. S. Hammond, and J. N. Pitts, Jr., Interscience Publishers, a division of John Wiley & Sons, New York, 1963, p. 323.
502. J. N. Pitts, Jr., J. K. Foote, and J. K. S. Wan, *J. Photochem. and Photobiol.*, in press; presented at Symposium on Photochemistry and Photobiology in Space Research, IV, International Congress on Photobiology, Oxford, 1964; published as *Recent Progress in Photobiology*, ed. by E. J. Bowen, Blackwells, Oxford, 1965, p. 357.
503. W. A. Noyes, Jr., private communication; A. Zahra, Doctoral Dissertation, University of Rochester, June, 1964.
504. L. D. Hess and J. N. Pitts, Jr., unpublished results.
505. D. J. Coyle, R. V. Peterson, and J. Heicklen, *J. Am. Chem. Soc.*, **86**, 3850 (1964).

506. G. O. Schenck and R. Steinmetz, *Ber.*, **96**, 520 (1963).
507. D. I. Schuster, M. Axelrod, and J. Auerbach, *Tetrahedron Letters*, **1963**, 1911.
508. G. Quinkert, B. Wegemund, and E. Blanke, *Tetrahedron Letters*, **1962**, 221.
509. N. C. Yang, A. Morduchowitz, and D-D. H. Yang, *J. Am. Chem. Soc.*, **85**, 1017 (1963).
510. K. H. Schulte-Elte and G. Ohloff, *Tetrahedron Letters*, **1964**, 1143.
511. J. W. Wheeler, Jr., and R. H. Eastman, *J. Am. Chem. Soc.*, **81**, 236 (1959).
512. M. J. Jorgenson and N. C. Yang, *J. Am. Chem. Soc.*, **85**, 1698 (1963).
513. N. C. Yang and M. J. Jorgenson, *Tetrahedron Letters*, **1964**, 1203.
514. L. D. Hess, Ph.D. Dissertation, University of California, Riverside, 1965.
515. J. N. Pitts, Jr., and R. W. Woolfolk, *Abstracts*, 133rd National Meeting, American Chemical Society, San Francisco, April, 1958, p. 42.
516. S. Cremer and R. Srinivasan, *J. Am. Chem. Soc.*, **86**, 4197 (1964).
517. J. H. Sharp, Ph.D. Dissertation, University of California, Riverside, 1963.
518. S. Cremer and R. Srinivasan, *J. Am. Chem. Soc.*, in press.
519. E. R. Altwicker and C. D. Cook, *J. Org. Chem.*, **29**, 3087 (1964).
520. G. Büchi and E. M. Burgess, *J. Am. Chem. Soc.*, **84**, 3104 (1962).
521. H. E. Zimmerman and J. S. Swenton, *J. Am. Chem. Soc.*, **86**, 1436 (1964).
522. C. K. Johnson, B. Dominy and W. Reusch, *J. Am. Chem. Soc.*, **85**, 3894 (1963).
523. G. S. Hammond and N. J. Turro, *Science*, **142**, 1541 (1963).
524. N. J. Turro, *Organic Photochemistry*, W. J. Benjamin and Co., in press.
525. J. N. Pitts, Jr., *J. Chem. Educ.*, **34**, 112 (1957).
526. R. M. Hochstrasser and G. B. Porter, *Quart Revs.*, **14**, 146 (1960).
527. J. P. Simons, *Quart. Revs.*, **13**, 1 (1959).
528. (a) P. de Mayo and S. T. Reid, *Quart. Revs.*, **15**, 393 (1961); (b) P. de Mayo in *Advances in Organic Chemistry*, Vol. II, ed. by R. A. Raphael, E. C. Taylor, and H. Wynberg, Interscience Publishers, New York, 1960, p. 367.
529. P. A. Leermakers and G. F. Vesley, *J. Chem. Educ.*, **41**, 535 (1964).
530. (a) C. Reid, *Excited States in Chemistry and Biology*, Butterworths, London, 1957; (b) C. Reid, *Quart. Revs.*, **12**, 205 (1958).
531. C. R. Masson, V. Boekelheide, and W. A. Noyes, Jr., "Photochemical Reactions," *Techniques of Organic Chemistry*, Vol. II, 2nd Ed., ed. by A. Weissberger, Interscience Publishers, New York, 1956, p. 257.
532. A. Mustafa, *Chem. Revs.*, **51**, 1 (1952).
533. A. Schönberg and A. Mustafa, *Chem. Revs.*, **40**, 181 (1947).
534. E. J. Bowen, *The Chemical Aspects of Light*, 2nd Ed., Clarendon Press, Oxford, 1946.
535. A. Schönberg, *Präparative Organische Photochemie*, Springer, Berlin, 1958.
536. (a) G. Ciamician and P. Silber, *Ber.*, **33**, 2911 (1900); (b) *Ibid.*, **34**, 1530 (1901).
537. (a) H. L. J. Bäckström, *Z. Physik. Chem.*, **B25**, 99 (1934): (b) H. L. J. Bäckström, *The Svedberg* (Memorial Volume), ed. by A. Tiselius and K. O. Pedersen, Almqvist and Wiksells, Uppsala, 1944, p. 45.
538. R. Srinivasan and S. E. Cremer, *J. Am. Chem. Soc.*, **87**, 1647 (1965).
539. W. M. Moore, G. S. Hammond, and R. P. Foss, *J. Am. Chem. Soc.*, **83**, 2789 (1961).
540. G. O. Schenck and R. Steinmetz, *Bull. Soc. Chim. Belg.*, **71**, 781 (1962).
541. V. Franzen, *Ann.*, **633**, 1 (1960).
542. W. M. Moore and M. Ketchum, *J. Am. Chem. Soc.*, **84**, 1368 (1962).
543. A. Beckett and G. Porter, *Trans. Faraday Soc.*, **59**, 2038, 2051 (1963).
544. S. G. Cohen, D. A. Laufer, and W. V. Sherman, *J. Am. Chem. Soc.*, **86**, 3060 (1964).
545. (a) G. Porter and F. Wilkinson, *Trans. Faraday Soc.*, **57**, 1686 (1961); (b) *Ibid.*, *Proc. Roy. Soc. (London)*, **A264**, 1 (1961).

546. H. W. Johnson, Jr., J. N. Pitts, Jr., and M. Burleigh, *Chem. & Ind. (London)*, **1964**, 1493.

547. K. K. Innes, *Abstracts*, 149th National Meeting American Chemical Society, Detroit, Mich., April, 1965; private communication to the authors.

548. E. T. Kaiser and T. F. Wulfers, *J. Am. Chem. Soc.*, **86**, 1897 (1964).

549. J. N. Pitts, Jr., and R. M. Martin, *Abstract* 27B, Report to the American Chemical Society, Petroleum Research Fund, 1959.

550. N. C. Yang and C. Rivas, *J. Am. Chem. Soc.*, **83**, 2213 (1961).

551. L. H. Piette, J. H. Sharp, T. Kuwana, and J. N. Pitts, Jr., *J. Chem. Phys.*, **36**, 3094 (1962).

552. J. N. Pitts, Jr., H. W. Johnson, Jr., and T. Kuwana, *J. Phys. Chem.*, **66**, 2456 (1962); *Proceedings of the Symposium on Reversible Photochemical Processes*, Duke University, April, 1962.

553. G. Porter and P. Suppan, *Abstracts Intern. Conf. on Org. Photochemistry*, University of Strasbourg, Strasbourg, July 1964, published as *Organic Photochemistry*, I.U.P.A.C., Butterworths, London, 1965, p. 499; (b) *Proc. Chem. Soc.*, **1964**, 191.

554. G. W. Griffin and E. J. O'Connell, *J. Am. Chem. Soc.*, **84**, 4148 (1962).

555. G. W. Griffin, E. J. O'Connell, and H. A. Hammond, *J. Am. Chem. Soc.*, **85**, 1001 (1963).

556. E. Heine and J. N. Pitts, Jr., unpublished results, presented at International Conference on Photochemistry, Tokyo, August 1965.

557. H. G. Ferguson, P. de Mayo, F. L. M. Pattison, and T. Tabata, *Can. J. Chem.*, **41**, 2099 (1963).

558. R. Anet, *Can. J. Chem.*, **40**, 1249 (1962).

559. (a) G. O. Schenck, I. von Wilucki, and C. H. Krauch, *Ber.*, **95**, 1409 (1962); (b) G. O. Schenck, W. Hartmann, S.-P. Mannsfeld, W. Metzner, and C. H. Krauch, *Ber.*, **95**, 1642 (1962).

560. G. S. Hammond, C. A. Stout, and A. A. Lamola, *J. Am. Chem. Soc.*, **86**, 3103 (1964).

561. P. E. Eaton, *J. Am. Chem. Soc.*, **84**, 2344 (1962).

562. P. E. Eaton, *J. Am. Chem. Soc.*, **84**, 2454 (1962).

563. D. R. Arnold, R. L. Hinman, and A. H. Glick, *Tetrahedron Letters*, **1964**, 1425.

564. L. A. Singer and P. D. Bartlett, *Tetrahedron Letters*, **1964**, 1887.

565. J. F. Harris, Jr., and D. D. Coffman, *J. Am. Chem. Soc.*, **84**, 1553 (1962).

566. E. R. Bissell and D. B. Fields, *J. Org. Chem.*, **29**, 249 (1964).

567. G. Büchi, J. T. Kofron, E. Koller, and D. Rosenthal, *J. Am. Chem. Soc.*, **78**, 876 (1956).

568. N. C. Yang and coworkers recently have reported at several conferences detailed studies on such systems, specifically at Columbia University, April, 1964, and Strasbourg, July, 1964, the latter is in *Organic Photochemistry*, Butterworths, London, 1965, p. 539.

569. J. J. I. Overwater, H. J. Hofman, and H. Cerfontain, *Rec. Trav. Chim.*, **83**, 637 (1964).

570. F. C. Goodspeed and F. E. Blacet, *J. Phys. Chem.*, **67**, 2501 (1963).

571. O. L. Chapman and G. W. Borden, *J. Org. Chem.*, **26**, 4185 (1961).

572. O. L. Chapman, D. J. Pasto, G. W. Borden, and A. A. Griswold, *J. Am. Chem. Soc.*, **84**, 1220 (1962).

573. G. Quinkert, K. Opitz, W. W. Wiersdorff, and J. Weinlich, *Tetrahedron Letters*, **1963**, 1863.

574. W. H. Urry, D. J. Trecker, and D. A. Winey, *Tetrahedron Letters*, **1962**, 609.

575. N. J. Turro, G. W. Byers and P. A. Leermakers, *J. Am. Chem. Soc.*, **86**, 955 (1964).

576. H. G. Richey, Jr., J. M. Richey, and D. C. Clagett, *J. Am. Chem. Soc.*, **86**, 3906 (1964).

577. P. A. Leermakers, G. F. Vesley, N. J. Turro, and D. C. Neckers, *J. Am. Chem. Soc.*, **86**, 4213 (1964).

578. R. H. Eastman, J. E. Starr, R. St. Martin, and M. K. Sakata, *J. Org. Chem.*, **28**, 2162 (1963).

579. G. Ciamician and P. Silber, *Ber.*, **43**, 1340 (1910).

580. R. Srinivasan, *J. Am. Chem. Soc.*, **81**, 2604 (1959).

581. P. Yates and L. Kilmurry, *Tetrahedron Letters*, **1964**, 1739.

582. C. D. Gutsche and C. W. Armbruster, *Tetrahedron Letters*, **1962**, 1297.

583. G. Quinkert, K. Opitz and J. Weinlich, *Angew. Chem.*, **74**, 507 (1962).

584. C. Lehmann, K. Schaffner and O. Jeger, *Helv. Chim. Acta*, **45**, 1031 (1962).

585. E. F. Ullman and W. A. Henderson, Jr., *J. Am. Chem. Soc.*, **86**, 5050 (1964).

586. J. J. Hurst and G. H. Whitham, *J. Chem. Soc.*, **1960**, 2864.

587. P. J. Kropp, *J. Am. Chem. Soc.*, **86**, 4053 (1964).

588. P. J. Kropp and W. F. Erman, *J. Am. Chem. Soc.*, **85**, 2456 (1963).

589. T. M. Dunn, *Abstracts*, 149th Meeting, American Chemical Society, Detroit, Mich., April, 1965, p. 48S.

590. D. H. R. Barton and G. Quinkert, *J. Chem. Soc.*, **1960**, 1.

591. R. Y. Levina, V. N. Kostin and P. A. Gembitskii, *J. Gen. Chem. USSR*, **29**, 2421 (1959).

592. R. Simonitis and J. N. Pitts, Jr., unpublished results.

593. M. Mousseron-Canet, M. Mousseron, and P. Legendre, *Bull. Soc. Chim. France*, **1961**, 1509.

594. R. E. Lutz, P. S. Bailey, C-K. Dien, and J. W. Rinker, *J. Am. Chem. Soc.*, **75**, 5039 (1953).

595. G. Büchi and I. M. Goldman, *J. Am. Chem. Soc.*, **79**, 4741 (1957).

596. P. E. Eaton and T. W. Cole, Jr., *J. Am. Chem. Soc.*, **86**, 3157 (1964).

597. P. de Mayo, H. Takeshita, and A. B. M. A. Sattar, *Proc. Chem. Soc.*, **1962**, 119.

598. P. Yates and I. W. J. Still, *J. Am. Chem. Soc.*, **85**, 1208 (1963).

599. P. de Mayo in *Advances in Organic Chemistry*, Vol. II, ed. by R. A. Raphael, E. C. Taylor, and H. Wynberg, Interscience Publishers, New York, 1960, p. 394.

600. P. Yates and M. J. Jorgenson, *J. Am. Chem. Soc.*, **80**, 6150 (1958).

601. G. Slomp, F. A. MacKellar, and L. A. Paquette, *J. Am. Chem. Soc.*, **83**, 4472 (1961).

602. E. C. Taylor and W. W. Paudler, *Tetrahedron Letters*, No. 25, 1 (1960).

603. W. A. Ayer, R. Hayatsu, P. de Mayo, S. T. Reid, and J. B. Stothers, *Tetrahedron Letters*, **1961**, 648.

604. (a) D. H. R. Barton and W. C. Taylor, *Proc. Chem. Soc.*, **1957**, 96; (b) D. H. R. Barton and W. C. Taylor, *J. Chem. Soc.*, **1958**, 2500.

605. C. S. Parmenter, *J. Chem. Phys.*, **41**, 658 (1964).

606. H. Dutler, H. Bosshard, and O. Jeger, *Helv. Chim. Acta*, **40**, 494 (1957).

607. E. Utzinger, H. Dutler, K. Weinberg, D. Arigoni, and O. Jeger, *Angew. Chem.*, **71**, 80 (1959).

608. K. Weinberg, E. C. Utzinger, D. Arigoni, and O. Jeger, *Helv. Chim. Acta*, **43**, 236 (1960).

609. R. Warszawski, K. Schaffner, and O. Jeger, *Helv. Chim. Acta*, **43**, 500 (1960).

610. I. A. Williams and P. Bladon, *Tetrahedron Letters*, **1964**, 257.

611. (a) G. K. Oster, G. Oster, and C. Dobin, *J. Phys. Chem.*, **66**, 2511 (1962); (b) G. Oster, G. K. Oster, and G. Karg, *ibid.*, **66**, 2514 (1962).

612. V. Kasche and L. Lindqvist, *J. Phys. Chem.*, **68**, 817 (1964).

613. (a) K. Gollnick and G. O. Schenck, *Pure and Appl. Chem.*, **9**, 507 (1964); (b) K. Gollnick and G. O. Schenck in *Organic Photochemistry*, I.U.P.A.C., Butterworths, London, 1965, p. 507.
614. J. Saltiel and G. S. Hammond, *J. Am. Chem. Soc.*, **85**, 2515 (1963); also Ref. 351.
615. G. S. Hammond, J. Saltiel, A. A. Lamola, N. J. Turro, J. S. Bradshaw, D. O. Cowan, R. C., Counsell, V. Vogt, and C. Dalton, *J. Am. Chem. Soc.*, **86**, 3197 (1964).
616. G. S. Hammond, N. J. Turro, and P. A. Leermakers, *J. Phys. Chem.*, **66**, 1144 (1962); see also Ref. 368.
617. G. S. Hammond, P. Wyatt, C. D. de Boer, and N. J. Turro, *J. Am. Chem. Soc.*, **86**, 2532 (1964).
618. G. N. Lewis, T. T. Magel, and D. Lipkin, *J. Am. Chem. Soc.*, **62**, 2973 (1940).
619. S. Yamashita, *Bull. Chem. Soc. Japan*, **34**, 490 (1961).
620. G. O. Schenck, *Z. Electrochem.*, **64**, 997 (1960).
621. G. O. Schenck and R. Steinmetz, *Tetrahedron Letters*, No. 21, 1 (1960).
622. G. O. Schenck, G. Koltzenburg, and H. Grossmann, *Angew. Chem.*, **69**, 177 (1957).
623. C. S. Foote and S. Wexler, *J. Am. Chem. Soc.*, **86**, 3879, 3880 (1964).
624. G. O. Schenck and H.-D. Becker, *Angew. Chem.*, **70**, 504 (1958).
625. G. O. Schenck, H.-D. Becker, K. H. Schulte-Elte, and C. H. Krauch, *Ber.*, **96**, 509 (1963).
626. G. O. Schenck, *Naturwiss.*, **35**, 28 (1948).
627. A. N. Terenin, *Acta Physicochim. URSS*, **18**, 210 (1943).
628. A. N. Terenin, *Photochemistry of Dyes and Related Organic Compounds*, Chapter 7 (translated by "Kresge-Hooker Scientific Library"), Academy of Sciences Press, Moscow and Leningrad, 1947.
629. A. Schönberg, *Ber.*, **67**, 633 (1934).
630. A. Schönberg, *Ann.*, **518**, 299 (1935).
631. H. Kautsky, A. Hirsch, and W. Flesch, *Ber.*, **68**, 152 (1935); see this for earlier references.
632. K. Weber, *Z. Phys. Chem.*, **B15**, 18 (1931).
633. (a) T. Förster, *Z. Electrochem.*, **54**, 42 (1950); (b) *ibid.*, **54**, 531 (1950).
634. (a) A. Weller, *Z. Phys. Chem. (Frankfurt)*, **3**, 238 (1955); (b) A. Weller, *Discussions Faraday Soc.*, **27**, 28 (1959); see for earlier references.
635. (a) G. Jackson and G. Porter, *Discussions Faraday Soc.*, **27**, 103 (1958); (b) G. Jackson and G. Porter, *Proc. Roy. Soc. (London)*, **A260**, 13 (1961).
636. (a) E. Havinga, R. O. de Jongh, and W. Dorst, *Rec. Trav. Chim.*, **75**, 378 (1956); (b) *Abstracts*, Photochemistry Conference University of Rochester, March 1963; see other papers by Havinga *et al.* for details.
637. H. E. Zimmerman, "A New Approach to Mechanistic Organic Photochemistry," *Advances in Photochemistry*, Vol. I, ed. by W. A. Noyes, Jr., G. S. Hammond, and J. N. Pitts, Jr., Interscience Publishers, a division of John Wiley & Sons, New York, 1963, p. 183.
638. H. E. Zimmerman and S. Somasekhara, *J. Am. Chem. Soc.*, **85**, 922 (1963).
639. W. G. Dauben and W. T. Wipke, International Symposium on Organic Photochemistry, Strasbourg, July, 1964, published as *Organic Photochemistry*, I.U.P.A.C., Butterworths, London, 1965, p. 539.
640. H. M. Frey, "The Reactions of Methylene and some Simple Carbenes," *Progress in Reaction Kinetics*, Vol. II, ed. by G. Porter, Pergamon Press, Oxford, 1964, p. 131.

641. W. B. deMore and S. W. Benson, "Preparation, Properties, and Reactivity of Methylene," *Advances in Photochemistry*, Vol. II, ed. by W. A. Noyes, Jr., G. S. Hammond, and J. N. Pitts, Jr., Interscience Publishers, a division of John Wiley & Sons, New York, 1964, p. 219.

642. J. A. Bell, "The Properties and Reactivity of Methylene: Derived Principally from its Gas Phase Reactions," in *Progress in Physical Organic Chemistry*, Vol. II, ed. by S. Cohen, A. Streitwieser, and R. W. Taft, Jr., Interscience Publishers, a division of John Wiley & Sons, New York, 1964.

643. P. Gaspar and G. S. Hammond, in *Carbene Chemistry*, ed. by W. Kirmal, Academic Press, 1964.

644. S.-Y. Ho, I. Unger, and W. A. Noyes, Jr., *J. Am. Chem. Soc.*, **87**, 2297 (1965).

645. W. V. E. Doering, R. G. Buttery, R. G. Laughlin, and N. Chaudhuri, *J. Am. Chem. Soc.*, **78**, 3224 (1956).

646. P. S. Skell and R. C. Woodworth, *J. Am. Chem. Soc.*, **78**, 4496 (1956).

647. A. Terenin and F. Vilessov, "Photoionization and Photodissociation of Aromatic Molecules by Vacuum Ultraviolet Radiation," *Advances in Photochemistry*, Vol. II, ed. by W. A. Noyes, Jr., G. S. Hammond, and J. N. Pitts, Jr., Interscience Publishers, a division of John Wiley & Sons, 1964, p. 385.

648. L. Kevan and W. F. Libby, "The Chemistry of Ionic States in Solid Saturated Hydrocarbons," *Advances in Photochemistry*, Vol. II, p. 183.

649. J. R. McNesby and H. Okabe, "Vacuum Ultra-Violet Photochemistry," *Advances in Photochemistry*, Vol. III, 1964, p. 157.

650. A. Terenin, Introductory Lecture, Symposium on Basic Photochemistry in Relation to Photobiology, IVth International Congress of Photobiology, Oxford, July 1964 (published in *Recent Progress in Photobiology*, ed. by E. J. Bowen, Blackwells, Oxford, 1965, p. 3).

651. J. W. T. Spinks and R. J. Woods, *An Introduction to Radiation Chemistry*, John Wiley & Sons, New York, 1964.

652. A. H. Kalantar and A. C. Albrecht, *J. Phys. Chem.*, **66**, 2279 (1962).

653. V. G. Vinogradova, B. N. Shelimov, N. V. Fok, and V. V. Voevodskii, *Doklady Akad. Nauk. SSSR*, **154**, 188 (1964).

654. V. E. Kholmogorov, E. V. Baranov, and A. N. Terenin, *Doklady Akad. Nauk SSSR*, **149**, 142 (1963); **152**, 1399 (1963).

655. *Comparative Effects of Radiation*, ed. by M. Burton, J. S. Kirby-Smith, and J. L. Magee, John Wiley & Sons, New York, 1960.

656. E. R. Allen and J. N. Pitts, Jr., *Abstracts*, 144th National Meeting, American Chemical Society, Los Angeles, Calif., April, 1963, p. 44P; to be published in *J. Am. Chem. Soc.*

657. J. N. Pitts, Jr., and A. D. Osborne, in *Chemical Reactions in the Upper and Lower Atmosphere*, John Wiley & Sons, New York, 1961, p. 129.

658. (a) F. W. McLafferty, *Anal. Chem.*, **31**, 82 (1959); (b) F. W. McLafferty, *Appl. Spectroscopy*, **11**, 148 (1957).

659. F. W. McLafferty, *Mass Spectrometry of Organic Ions*, ed. by F. W. McLafferty, Academic Press, New York, 1963.

660. S. Meyerson and J. D. McCollum, *Advan. Anal. Chem. Instr.*, **2**, 179 (1963); see references herein.

661. S. Meyerson, *J. Phys. Chem.*, **68**, 968 (1964).

662. P. Ausloos and J. F. Paulson, *J. Am. Chem. Soc.*, **80**, 5117 (1958).

663. J. N. Pitts, Jr., and A. D. Osborne, *J. Am. Chem. Soc.*, **83**, 3011 (1961).

664. E. R. Bell and J. N. Pitts, Jr., unpublished data.

665. R. J. Cvetanovic, "Mercury Photosensitized Reactions," in *Progress in Reaction Kinetics*, Vol. II, ed. by G. Porter, Pergamon Press, 1964, p. 39.

666. A. B. Callear and R. J. Cvetanovic, *J. Chem. Phys.*, **24**, 873 (1956).

667. P. Ausloos and R. Gorden, Jr., *J. Chem. Phys.*, **36**, 5 (1962).

668. H. S. A. Gilmour, in *Physics and Chemistry of the Organic Solid State*, Vol. I, ed. by D. Fox, M. M. Labes, and A. Weissberger, Interscience Publishers, a division of John Wiley & Sons, New York, 1963, p. 329.

669. M. D. Cohen and G. M. J. Schmidt, in *Reactivity of Solids*, ed. by J. H. deBoer, Elsevier, Amsterdam, 1961, p. 556.

670. M. D. Cohen, Y. Hirshberg, and G. M. J. Schmidt, *J. Chem. Soc.*, **1964**, 2051, 2060.

671. R. Dessauer and J. P. Paris, "Photochromism," in *Advances in Photochemistry*, Vol. I, ed. by W. A. Noyes, G. S. Hammond, J. N. Pitts, Jr., Interscience Publishers, a division of John Wiley & Sons, New York, 1963, p. 275.

672. S. N. Foner, E. L. Cochran, V. A. Bowers, and C. K. Jen, *J. Chem. Phys.*, **32**, 963 (1960).

673. E. L. Cochran and F. J. Adrian, *5th International Symposium on Free Radicals*, Uppsala, July, 1961; published in *Preprints of Papers*, Almqvist and Wiksell, Stockholm, 1961, paper No. 12.

674. R. A. Varbanskaya, B. N. Shelimov, and N. V. Fok, *Doklady Akad. Nauk S.S.S.R.*, **140**, 818 (1961).

675. L. H. Piette, in *NMR and EPR Spectroscopy* (Papers presented at Varian's 3rd Annual Workshop, Palo Alto), Pergamon Press, 1960, p. 221.

676. R. F. Hampson, Jr., and J. R. McNesby, *J. Chem. Phys.*, **42**, 2200 (1965).

677. E. J. Bowen, H. Hartley, W. D. Scott, and H. G. Watts, *J. Chem. Soc.*, **1924**, 1218.

678. A. J. Tench and P. Coppens, *J. Phys. Chem.*, **67**, 1378 (1963).

679. P. Coppens and G. M. J. Schmidt, *Acta Cryst.*, **17**, 222 (1964).

680. J. N. Pitts, Jr., J. K. S. Wan, and E. A. Schuck, *J. Am. Chem. Soc.*, **86**, 3606 (1964).

681. H. Stobbe and K. Bremer, *J. Prakt. Chem.*, **123**, 1 (1929).

682. I. Tanasescu and F. Hodosan, *Chem. Abstr.*, **50**, 14628 (1956).

683. K. T. Ström, *Ber.*, **37**, 1383 (1904).

684. E. C. Taylor and W. W. Paudler, *Tetrahedron Letters*, No. 25, 1 (1960).

685. S. Y. Wang, *Nature*, **190**, 690 (1961).

686. E. Zavarin, *J. Org. Chem.*, **23**, 47 (1958).

687. H. Stobbe and E. Färber, *Ber.*, **58**, 1548 (1925).

688. J. Corse, B. J. Finkle and R. E. Lundin, *Tetrahedron Letters*, **1961**, 1.

689. V. de Gaouck and R. J. W. Le Fèvre, *J. Chem. Soc.*, **1939**, 1457.

690. J. D. Margerum, L. J. Miller, E. Saito, M. S. Brown, H. S. Mosher, and R. Hardwick, *J. Phys. Chem.*, **66**, 2934 (1962).

691. T. Bercovici and E. Fischer, *J. Am. Chem. Soc.*, **86**, 5687 (1964).

692. H. E. Zimmerman and D. I. Schuster, *J. Am. Chem. Soc.*, **84**, 4527 (1962).

693. W. G. Dauben and F. G. Willey, *Tetrahedron Letters*, **1962**, 893.

694. (a) A. Terenin, *Proc. Chem. Soc. (London)*, **1961**, 321; (b) A. Terenin, *Electrical Conductivity in Organic Solids*, Interscience Publishers, New York, 1961, p. 39.

695. E. J. Bowen, "The Photochemistry of Aromatic Hydrocarbon Solutions," *Advances in Photochemistry*, Vol. 1, ed. by W. A. Noyes, Jr., G. S. Hammond, and J. N. Pitts, Jr., Interscience Publishers, a division of John Wiley & Sons, New York, 1963, p. 23.

696. R. B. Cundall, "The Kinetics of *Cis-Trans* Isomerizations," in *Progress in Reaction Kinetics*, Vol. 2, ed. by G. Porter, Pergamon Press, 1964, p. 167.

697. N. C. Yang, private communication.

698. J. N. Pitts, Jr., J. Quinlan, and L. D. Hess, *Abstracts*, American Chemical Society—Petroleum Research Fund, 1960; unpublished data, J. Quinlan, L. D. Hess, F. C. Goodspeed, and J. N. Pitts, Jr.

699. C. L. Braun, S. Kato, and S. Lipsky, *J. Chem. Phys.*, **39**, 1645 (1963).

700. B. Rickborn, R. L. Alumbaugh, and G. O. Pritchard, *Chem. & Ind. (London)*, **1964**, 1951; more detailed report submitted to *J. Phys. Chem.*, May, 1965.

701. H. M. Frey and C. S. Elliot, personal communication.

702. R. W. Carr, Jr., and G. B. Kistiakowsky, submitted to *J. Phys. Chem.*, June, 1965, private communication.

703. J. Weinstein, Gordon Conference on Organic Photochemistry, Tilton School, N. H., July, 1965.

704. (a) H. S. Mosher, C. Souers, and R. Hardwick, *J. Chem. Phys.*, **32**, 1888 (1960); (b) R. Hardwick and H. S. Mosher, *J. Chem. Phys.*, **36**, 1402 (1962).

705. J. D. Margerum, Gordon Conference on Organic Photochemistry, Tilton School, N. H., July, 1965; *J. Am. Chem. Soc.*, in press.

706. T. F. Thomas and C. Steel, submitted to *J. Am. Chem. Soc.*, June 14, 1965.

707. D. P. Chong and G. B. Kistiakowsky, *J. Phys. Chem.*, **68**, 1793 (1964).

708. G. O. Pritchard, M. Venugopalan, and T. F. Graham, *J. Phys. Chem.*, **68**, 1786 (1964).

709. P. G. Bowers and G. B. Porter, *J. Phys. Chem.*, **68**, 2982 (1964).

710. L. C. Fischer and G. J. Mains, *J. Phys. Chem.*, **68**, 188 (1964).

711. G. O. Pritchard and R. T. Thommarson, *J. Phys. Chem.*, **69**, 1001 (1965).

712. E. F. Ullman and J. E. Milks, *J. Am. Chem. Soc.*, **86**, 3814 (1964); *ibid.*, **84**, 1315 (1962).

713. N. Padnos and W. A. Noyes, Jr., *J. Phys. Chem.*, **68**, 464 (1964).

714. N. J. Turro, P. A. Leermakers, H. R. Wilson, D. C. Neckers, G. W. Byers, and G. F. Vesley, *J. Am. Chem. Soc.*, **87**, 2613 (1965).

715. R. E. Rebbert and P. Ausloos, *J. Am. Chem. Soc.*, **87**, 1847 (1965).

716. B. G. Gowenlock, *Can. J. Chem.*, **42**, 1936 (1964).

717. K. Shinzawa and I. Tanaka, *J. Phys. Chem.*, **68**, 1205 (1964).

718. T. Kubota and M. Yamakawa, *Bull. Chem. Soc. Japan*, **36**, 1564 (1963).

719. R. K. Brinton, *J. Phys. Chem.*, **68**, 2652 (1964).

720. D. G. Anderson and G. Wettermark, *J. Am. Chem. Soc.*, **87**, 1433 (1965).

721. P. A. Leermakers and G. F. Vesley, *J. Am. Chem. Soc.*, **85**, 3776 (1963).

722. G. F. Vesley and P. A. Leermakers, *J. Phys. Chem.*, **68**, 2364 (1964).

723. A. Schönberg, N. Latif, R. Moubasher, and A. Sina, *J. Chem. Soc.*, **1951**, 1364.

724. P. A. Leermakers, P. C. Warren, and G. F. Vesley, *J. Am. Chem. Soc.*, **86**, 1768 (1964).

725. L. Kaplan, K. E. Wilzbach, W. G. Brown, and S. S. Yang, *J. Am. Chem. Soc.*, **87**, 675 (1965).

726. A. W. Burgstahler and P.-L. Chien, *J. Am. Chem. Soc.*, **86**, 2940 (1964).

727. K. E. Wilzbach and L. Kaplan, *J. Am. Chem. Soc.*, **86**, 2307 (1964).

728. E. E. van Tamelen and S. P. Pappas, *J. Am. Chem. Soc.*, **84**, 3789 (1962).

729. J. A. Poole, *J. Phys. Chem.*, **69**, 1343 (1965).

730. R. Srinivasan, Gordon Conference on Hydrocarbon Chemistry, Colby College, N.H., June, 1965.

731. D. B. Richardson, L. R. Durrett, J. M. Martin, Jr., W. E. Putnam, S. C. Slaymaker, and I. Dvoretzky, *J. Am. Chem. Soc.*, **87**, 2763 (1965).

732. I. Dvoretzky, Gordon Conference on Hydrocarbon Chemistry, Colby College, N.H., June, 1965.

733. A. H. Laufer and J. R. McNesby, *J. Chem. Phys.*, **42**, 3329 (1965).

734. B. C. Roquitte, *J. Phys. Chem.*, **69**, 2475 (1965).
735. W. G. Dauben and R. L. Cargill, *Tetrahedron*, **15**, 197 (1961).
736. M. P. Cava, R. H. Schlessinger, and J. P. Van Meter, *J. Am. Chem. Soc.*, **86**, 3173 (1964).
737. F. J. Duncan and R. J. Cvetanovic, *J. Am. Chem. Soc.*, **84**, 3593 (1962).
738. C. H. Nichol and J. G. Calvert, to be published.
739. R. L. Letsinger, O. B. Ramsay, and J. H. McCain, *J. Am. Chem. Soc.*, **87**, 2945 (1965).
740. J. Hine, *Divalent Carbon*, Ronald Press Co., New York (1964).
741. J. N. Pitts, Jr., R. Simonaitis, and J. M. Vernon, *Tetrahedron Letters*, in press; *Abstracts*, Conference on Photochemistry, Tokyo, August, 1965.
742. R. Simonaitis, J. M. Vernon, and J. N. Pitts, Jr., unpublished results.
743. H. M. Frey, "Photolysis of the Diazirines," in *Organic Photochemistry*, I.U.P.A.C., Butterworths, London, 1965, p. 572.
744. J. K. Foote and J. N. Pitts, Jr., presented at the Photochemistry Conference, Tokyo, August, 1965; J. K. Foote, Doctoral Dissertation, University of California, Riverside, 1965.
745. O. Jeger, K. Schaffner, and H. Wehrli, "Photochemical Transformation of α,β-Epoxyketones and Related Carbonyl Systems," in *Organic Photochemistry*, I.U.P.A.C., Butterworths, London, 1965, p. 555.
746. M. D. Cohen, "Photochemistry of the Organic Solid State," in *Organic Photochemistry*, I.U.P.A.C., Butterworths, London, 1965, p. 567.
747. O. L. Chapman, A. A. Griswold, E. Hoganson, G. Lanz, and J. Reasoner, "Photochemistry of Unsaturated Nitrocompounds," in *Organic Photochemistry*, I.U.P.A.C., Butterworths, London, 1965, p. 585.
748. H. E. Zimmerman, "Report on Recent Photochemical Investigations," in *Organic Photochemistry*, I.U.P.A.C., Butterworths, London, 1965, p. 493.
749. R. C. Cookson, "Stereospecificity in Photochemical Reactions of Ketones," in *Organic Photochemistry*, I.U.P.A.C., Butterworths, London, 1965, p. 575.
750. P. de Mayo, "Photochemical Reactions of Dicarbonyl Compounds," in *Organic Photochemistry*, I.U.P.A.C., Butterworths, London, 1965, p. 597.
751. G. Quinkert, "Photochemistry of Non-conjugated Ketones in Solution," in *Organic Photochemistry*, I.U.P.A.C., Butterworths, London, 1965, p. 607.
752. J. Saltiel, "The Mechanisms of Some Photochemical Reactions of Organic Molecules," in *Survey of Progress in Chemistry*, ed. by A. F. Scott, Academic Press, New York, 1965.
753. M. Mousseron, "Isomerization Photochimique de Systemes Polyeniques," in *Organic Photochemistry*, I.U.P.A.C., Butterworths, London, 1965, p. 481.
754. M. J. Amrich and J. A. Bell, *J. Am. Chem. Soc.*, **86**, 292 (1964).
755. B. A DeGraff and J. G. Calvert, unpublished results, suggest that processes 1 and 2 are reactions of the $^3A_2$ and $^1A_2$ states, respectively, and that φ_2/φ_1 increases with decrease in wavelength.
756. F. O. Rice and E. Teller, *J. Chem. Phys.*, **6**, 489 (1938).
757. P. J. Wagner and G. S. Hammond, *J. Am. Chem. Soc.*, **87**, 4009 (1965).
758. G. Porter and P. Suppan, *Trans. Faraday Soc.*, **61**, 1664 (1965).
759. C. Walling and M. Gibian, *J. Am. Chem. Soc.*, **87**, 3361 (1965).

6

Determination of the Mechanism of a Photochemical Reaction

The formulation of a mechanism for a photochemical reaction should follow detailed experimentation which has been carefully designed to yield the maximum information for a given expenditure of effort. Usually one starts with a logical evaluation of the possible effects of varying the experimental parameters characteristic of the type of system to be studied (e.g., solid, liquid, or gas, direct or sensitized photolysis, etc.). Having set up a priority schedule for the program in terms of the degree to which each of the various experiments will yield significant results, one then carries out the key preliminary experiments.

Many useful techniques and methods have been developed which often may be applied successfully in such experiments; the first portion of this chapter is devoted to a discussion of some of those which have proven generally useful. Obviously these methods often will vary, depending on whether the reaction is run in the vapor, liquid, or solid phase and depending on the specific feature of the overall reaction that the investigator is attempting to establish (e.g., free radical reaction rate data, energy transfer, kinetics of intersystem crossing in the excited states, possible participation of a vibrationally excited ground state, etc.). In this chapter, as elsewhere in the book, we have selected methods which have been applied to both "physical" and "organic" photochemistry, if indeed there is any valid distinction.

Obviously one should not limit experimentation to the application of existing conventional methods of research. The testing of a mechanism suggested on the basis of preliminary experiments assumes a varied pattern which is planned particularly for the reaction under study, and the ingenuity of the investigator is reflected in the choice of definitive experiments. It is the thoughtful design of the unique experiment, its meticulous execution, and the realization of the unambiguous result which provide the fascination and intellectual stimulation associated with research and which lead to a significant advance in science.

One of the fundamental aims of the photochemist is to establish the nature and efficiency of the primary spectroscopic and photochemical processes. It is through such information that useful relations can be obtained between spectroscopic properties, molecular structure, and photodecomposition modes. Because of major difficulties encountered in many of these determinations there is a scarcity of quantitative information of this kind today. If a stable product is formed directly in the primary process, the quantum yield of the product is a direct measure of the efficiency of this step. The difficulties arise in proving a given product to be a primary product, in establishing the nature of the excited state from which it originated, and in estimating the primary quantum efficiencies of free radical or excited molecule formation. Thus to establish the exact fate of all the light-absorbing molecules and of all the free radicals formed in a photochemical system is an analytical task which to date has been nearly impossible to perform. Even an exact product analysis and a thorough knowledge of all product quantum yields may be insufficient to establish with certainty the nature and efficiency of the primary processes. Ambiguities are encountered in trying to relate final product yields to primary process yields, since often one of the many reaction paths of the primary free radicals re-forms the original reactant; other reactions may generate products which are the same as those which could have been formed concurrently by direct primary intramolecular rearrangement of the reactant molecule. Several successful approaches to solving such problems have been developed and will be reviewed in this chapter (e.g., flash photolysis, photolysis in rigid matrices, isotopic labeling, free radical trapping techniques, and emission spectra and lifetimes).

Another major aim of the photochemist is to determine the nature of the secondary reactions of the free radicals and other intermediates formed in the primary processes. Thus, a large part of the useful information which we now have on the mechanisms and rate constants for elementary reactions has been derived from photochemical studies. For this reason the second portion of this chapter is devoted to a consideration of the important conventional methods of reaction kinetics and to some special kinetic techniques useful in photochemistry (e.g., the rotating sector method, emission spectra and lifetimes, etc., which are important in determining photochemical reaction mechanisms).

6-1 THE NATURE OF THE REACTANTS AND THE PRODUCTS

It is axiomatic that the nature and the yields of the products of a photochemical reaction must be known if the overall chemical changes and the reaction mechanism are to be well established. In most photochemical experiments designed to develop or test mechanisms today, one restricts the amount of substrate reacted to a few per cent or less (often to 0.05%) to avoid complications which might arise from subsequent thermal or photochemical reactions of the primary products of the photodecomposition. Such a procedure presumes use of chromatographic separation and identification techniques supplemented by the most modern micro methods of mass spectrometry, infrared and ultraviolet spectroscopy, etc. The reason for this presumption is clear if we consider a typical gas-phase photolysis. Under the usual conditions employed the total starting material would correspond to about 100 μl of liquid. If the reaction is carried out only 0.1% to completion and one finds the usual number of products, say 10 to 15, the total volume of which is 0.1 μl, the analytical problem is self-evident. It is also clear why much of the literature on kinetics and mechanisms in photochemistry is simply not reliable if published before the development and widespread use of modern instrumentation and microanalytical techniques, particularly separation by chromatographic methods (VPC). However, in cases where the noncondensable gases were simple mixtures analyzable by accurate microchemical techniques (e.g., the Blacet-Leighton micro gas analysis apparatus) the results can be as reliable as the best of the results today.

Having cited the virtues of VPC techniques, we feel compelled to add a word of caution. One must be absolutely certain that the chromatographic peaks observed are really due to only one component; furthermore, one must not put blind faith in retention times as being absolute proof of structure. These points seem self-evident but often they are overlooked or ignored. Also sometimes one can simply run into bad luck, such as situations where two homologs have very nearly the same boiling points and retention times on the columns generally employed and where even mass spectrometric, infrared, and ultraviolet spectrometric techniques cannot establish the presence of a relatively small amount of one component in the presence of a large excess of the other. A specific example, which to our knowledge has plagued at least four laboratories (including each of ours, independently), is that of diethyl ketone as an impurity in methyl n-propyl ketone. After an expensive and frustrating experience it was learned that the "high-quality" methyl n-propyl ketone sold by a major chemical company contained up to 25% of diethyl ketone; this contaminant did not show up on the usual columns employed for ketone separation.

Another area where reactant purity is essential is in condensed-phase spectroscopic and photochemical studies of highly oxygen-sensitive systems. Dissolved oxygen has a relatively large solubility in many organic solvents (e.g., alcohols), and heroic efforts must be made if one wants to remove the last traces of oxygen from solution (actually, of course, this is never achieved). Thus only recently has it been generally recognized how tenaciously oxygen remains in solution despite flushing with N_2 or argon, freezing and pumping, etc. A good example of this problem is seen in the case of the first-order rate constants which have been determined for the non-radiative decay of triplet anthracene. Reported values have dropped from several thousand per second to about zero in the past few years as the solvent purification and oxygen degassing techniques have improved. See Sec. 4-9B. Generally six bulb-to-bulb distillations, with magnetic stirring of the solution while it warms after freezing and pumping, will reduce the dissolved oxygen to a level where its effect on many photochemical reactions is negligible. However, further purification may be necessary, particularly when spectroscopic properties (ESR, ultraviolet spectra, triplet lifetimes, etc.) are involved.

Because of the analytical difficulties it has not been uncommon in photochemical studies to follow the rate of reaction by measuring the accompanying pressure change. This has been the procedure in some cases where there was only a limited knowledge of the products. Certain "expected" products were assumed, or the composition of the products found under a limited set of conditions was considered invariant and then extrapolated to many completely different conditions. Mechanisms based on such data obtained from the photolysis of compounds of even limited complexity are generally unreliable, and the neglect of unknown variations in the composition of products can lead to a completely erroneous choice of mechanism. Confidence can be placed in mechanisms only on the basis of a thorough knowledge of the products formed.

6-2 THE ABSORPTION AND EMISSION SPECTRA OF THE REACTANT

Important information concerning the mechanism of photolysis often can be gained from a careful study of the absorption spectrum of the compound under investigation. If an interpretation of the vibrational-rotational structure is to be attempted, the gas-phase absorption spectrum of the compound should be obtained by using an instrument of high resolution. Some qualitative observations may be made readily from the spectrum. For example, if the spectrum is banded or has significant fine structure in the wavelength region used in the photodecomposition study, a relatively long-lived excited state is indicated. For example, the lifetime τ must be greater than about 10^{-11} sec, because the structured spectrum indicates that the molecule does not dissociate within its first few vibrations. With this type of spectrum the quantum yield of total primary decomposition may be less than unity, since collisional deactivation or fluorescence may be important; this is true particularly if τ is greater than 10^{-8} sec (in the gas phase a molecule makes about 100 collisions during this time at standard conditions) and the temperature is moderate.

If a simple compound exhibits continuous absorption in a particular wavelength region, this is usually indicative of a short-lived excited state ($\tau < 10^{-12}$ sec) and a high primary photochemical decomposition efficiency. The blurring of rotational-vibrational lines in a given region of the spectrum may suggest a high probability of intersystem crossing to a dissociative state at this level (predissociation; see Sec. 3-1D-3). However, for complex molecules the number of vibrational and rotational modes is so great that overlap of the energy levels occurs, and often little fine structure is discernible even though a long-lived excited state may be formed. Actually the sharpness of rotational lines in absorption is a very insensitive measure of the occurrence of predissociation in a molecule. If a molecule has a radiative lifetime of τ_0 and undergoes a radiationless transition with mean lifetime τ_t, the natural band width of the absorption line is given by an extension of Eq. 2-27:

$$\Delta\omega = \frac{1}{2\pi c}\left(\frac{1}{\tau_0} + \frac{1}{\tau_t}\right) \text{cm}^{-1} \qquad (2\text{-}27a)$$

For the common case of $\tau_0 \cong 10^{-8}$ sec, and with $\tau_t = \infty$, $\Delta\omega \cong 0.001$ cm^{-1}; for $\tau_0 = 10\tau_t$, $\Delta\omega \cong 0.01$ cm^{-1}; for $\tau_0 = 100\tau_t$, $\Delta\omega \cong 0.1$ cm^{-1}. Because of Doppler broadening in the usual system, the observed bandwidths of lines are of the order of ~ 0.1 cm^{-1}, so that τ_t must be equal to or less than $0.01\tau_0$ before it is possible to detect significant blurring of the absorption line due to predissociation. Emission, on the other hand, is a very sensitive indicator of predissociation since the diminution of intensity of emission from a given level is directly related to the shortening of the lifetime of the state by predissociation or other radiationless transitions. For example, if $\tau_0 = 10\tau_t$, then the intensity of the emission will be about one-tenth of that with $\tau_t = \infty$. These principles are illustrated well in the spectroscopic studies of formaldehyde vapor. All the rotational-vibrational lines in the long wavelength absorption spectrum of formaldehyde show the usual Doppler width, $\Delta\omega \cong 0.1$ cm^{-1}; however, in the fluorescence emission of formaldehyde the 1 $\pm$ inversion doublet near 28,728 cm^{-1} is of vanishingly small intensity, and the observation suggests convincingly that predissociation occurs from this energy level.[152]

In some compounds excitation may occur to one of several possible states. For example, this appears to be the case for the acetaldehyde absorption in its near-ultraviolet band.[1] Some of these states may result in immediate dissociation, whereas others may have relatively long lifetimes. The observed spectrum in this case is a superposition of the different lines, bands, and continua characteristic of each transition. Thus it is possible that on excitation of a molecule by a given wavelength a very short-lived excited state may be formed a given fraction of the time even though much fine structure is apparent in the spectrum at this region; the continuum corresponding to this state may be masked by the overlying fine structure of some long-lived states. These and other complications may make the interpretations of mechanisms largely from absorption spectra of limited value, particularly for polyatomic molecules.

The intensity of the absorption band may be helpful in establishing the nature of the original excitation process. If the radiative lifetime is to be estimated from the absorption band, a relatively low-resolution spectrum is desirable, since the plotting and integration processes are simplified. Consider the absorption spectra of the simple aldehydes shown in Figs. 5-1 and 5-2. The f-numbers calculated for these bands (by integration of ϵ versus ω plots and application of Eq. 3-41) are small (about 2.6×10^{-4} for CH_2O) and the radiative lifetimes long (about 5×10^{-6} sec for CH_2O). These facts suggest a "forbidden" character to the electronic transition. Thus, as we saw in Chapters 4 and 5, in theory the excitation of a non-bonding electron in the oxygen atom to an antibonding π^* molecular orbital in the carbonyl group has the required "forbidden" character and is favored as the description of the excitation process[2] (See Sec. 4-2C).

The vibrational structure involved in the spectra of the simple aldehydes (Figs. 5-1 and 5-2) gives further insight into the excitation process. The near constancy of the magnitude of the energy separation between vibrational bands in acetaldehyde, propionaldehyde, and n-butyraldehyde (~ 1100 cm^{-1}) suggests a common origin for these bands which involves the carbonyl group.* Presumably the normal carbonyl stretching frequency (~ 1746 cm^{-1} for CH_2O) has been decreased (~ 1182 cm^{-1} in CH_2O) by the excitation of the molecule because of the bond weakening associated with the promotion of the non-bonding electron on its oxygen atom to the antibonding π^* MO of the carbonyl group (see Sec. 4-2C). Thus, since the equilibrium carbonyl bond distance is substantially greater in the excited state than in the ground state and since from the Franck-Condon principle the C-O bond distance does not change in the electronic transition, we can

---

* The highly structured formaldehyde spectrum involves the participation of out-of-plane H_2C-wagging frequency (124 cm^{-1}) and other vibrational modes which add to complicate the casual interpretation of the low resolution spectrum and mask the C—O stretching mode readily apparent in the spectra of the higher aldehydes.

infer that immediately after excitation the C=O group is in a compressed state and vibrational excitation within the carbonyl group must be present.

As we saw in Chapter 4, not only is the magnitude of ϵ_{max} important diagnostic evidence, but also the displacement of λ_{max} in various types of solvents can give important information as to the nature of the electronic transition. A small value of ϵ_{max} (e.g., about 13 for the aliphatic ketones) and a displacement of λ_{max} to the blue in polar solvents are characteristic of $n \rightarrow \pi^*$ transitions. Large values of ϵ_{max} (about 5000–10,000 for nonsymmetry-forbidden transitions) and a red shift in polar solvents suggest a $\pi \rightarrow \pi^*$ transition (see details in Sec. 4-2C).

Perturbing a system with a high pressure of oxygen or the use of long-path spectroscopy in certain cases allows one to obtain directly the singlet-triplet absorption spectrum of a compound, and hence the energy of the lowest triplet state (see Sec. 4-9B). We have noted how the techniques of triplet-triplet absorption in both flash photolysis in solution and high-intensity crossed-beam irradiation in rigid glasses will, in many cases, give the energy levels of the second triplet state. We have discussed certain important techniques of spectrofluorophosphorimetry with which the emission spectra and lifetimes of excited states can be obtained. From this information the relative rates of intersystem crossing from the triplet to the vibrationally excited ground state, and the rates of bimolecular reactions of the electronically excited species, may be estimated. This information, much of which is also available from flash photolysis studies, is crucial in evaluating the efficiencies of the primary physical radiative and non-radiative processes. Particularly interesting is the technique of comparing the spectroscopic properties of normal versus perdeuterated molecules, and thereby estimating true natural radiative lifetimes. Finally, the technique of utilizing sensitizers of different triplet energies to establish triplet levels of acceptor molecules in solution has proven to be highly useful. The theory and application of these techniques are considered in Chapter 4 and in Sec. 6-7D, where references to original literature are found.

Obviously a knowledgeable molecular spectroscopist can deduce far more from detailed spectroscopic studies of a system than the average photochemist. For example, from a good banded vapor-phase spectrum he can derive the complete vibrational-rotational analysis of the excited state and calculate the structural parameters of the excited state.[3] However, one does not have to be a spectroscopist to obtain important information about the energies, lifetimes, and reactivities of excited states, and an attempt to make these determinations with the aid and counsel of the spectroscopist is certainly useful and often profitable to both parties.

6-3 QUANTUM YIELDS

The quantum yield is one of the most useful and fundamental quantities in the study of photochemical reaction mechanisms. Its size and the influence of the experimental variables upon it give important information as to the nature of the reaction. As we have seen, several types of quantum yields are used in photochemistry: primary quantum yields (usually symbolized by φ), product quantum yields (Φ), quantum yields of fluorescence, decomposition, rearrangement, etc. To avoid confusion one should always indicate the type of quantum yield which is given, and not merely state "The quantum yield of the reaction is . . . ." In a more precise definition of these quantities than we have given before it will be convenient to consider the general reaction of a molecule M which undergoes photodecomposition by primary processes 6-1 and 6-2:

$$M + h\nu \rightarrow A + B \qquad (6\text{-}1)$$
$$\searrow$$
$$C + D \qquad (6\text{-}2)$$

A, B, C, and D are stable molecules or reactive molecular fragments formed as the immediate effect of light absorption by M. The primary quantum yield of process 6-1 is defined by 6-3:

$$\varphi_1 = \frac{d[A]/dt}{I_a} = \frac{\text{No. of molecules, radicals, or ions of A formed/cm}^3\text{-sec}}{\text{No. of quanta absorbed by M/cm}^3\text{-sec}}$$

$$(6\text{-}3)$$

φ_2 is similarly defined by 6-4.

$$\varphi_2 = \frac{d[C]/dt}{I_a} = \frac{\text{No. of molecules, radicals, or ions of C formed/cm}^3\text{-sec}}{\text{No. of quanta absorbed by M/cm}^3\text{-sec}}$$

$$(6\text{-}4)$$

The primary quantum yield φ_i of the ith mode of primary photodecomposition may be thought of as the fraction of molecules absorbing light which undergo decomposition by the ith process. From the second law of photochemistry it follows that the sum of all n of the primary quantum yields of the n different primary processes cannot exceed unity.

$$\sum_{i=1}^{n} \varphi_i \leqslant 1 \qquad (6\text{-}5)$$

When collisional deactivation, fluorescence, radiationless transitions, and other similar photophysical primary processes are unimportant or are included in the summation, then the equality applies in 6-5.

Primary quantum yields are of great theoretical importance, but they are difficult to estimate in the common case where A, B, C, and D are free radicals or atoms. The total number of quanta absorbed by M/cm³-sec, I_a, can be estimated readily from a measurement of the total energy incident on the system/sec, E_t, the fraction of this energy absorbed by the molecules M ($Q_m = 1 - 10^{-\epsilon cl}$), the energy per quantum of radiation of wavelength λ used ($E = hc/\lambda$), and the volume V of the irradiated system:

$$I_a = \frac{E_t Q_m \lambda}{Vhc} \tag{6-6}$$

The major difficulty lies in the determination of the primary yield of free radicals or atoms formed, $d[A]/dt/I_a$. Indirect methods of some value have been developed and are considered later.

Usually one measures overall quantum yields of products. At times reasonable estimates of primary quantum yields can be derived from these overall yields; in any case, the magnitude of the overall quantum yield of a product always provides information concerning the mechanism. Thus, the rate of formation of some stable product can be measured irrespective of whether it is formed directly in a primary process or in a secondary thermal reaction involving free radicals or atoms. Then the quantum yield of any stable product X from the photodecomposition of M may be defined by

$$\Phi_X = \frac{d[X]/dt}{I_a} = \frac{\text{No. of molecules or ions of X formed/cm}^3\text{-sec}}{\text{No. of quanta absorbed by M/cm}^3\text{-sec}} \tag{6-7}$$

The quantum yields of fluorescence, decomposition, isomerization, etc., are defined in an analogous fashion. The *sensitized* quantum yield of product formation is defined as the number of molecules formed from energy acceptors divided by the number of quanta absorbed by energy donors for a given time interval and volume of system; see Sec. 4-10A.

When there are several competing modes of photodecomposition and decomposition occurs from a non-vibrationally equilibrated excited state, the efficiency of a given mode may vary with the energy supplied by the absorbed quantum. Hence it is necessary to use monochromatic light in the determination of quantum yields.

Small quantum yields of all decomposition products (Φ's $\ll$ 1) indicate important deactivation, fluorescence, or other processes that lead to no net chemical change. A highly stable compound of this sort in solution is

o-hydroxybenzophenone:

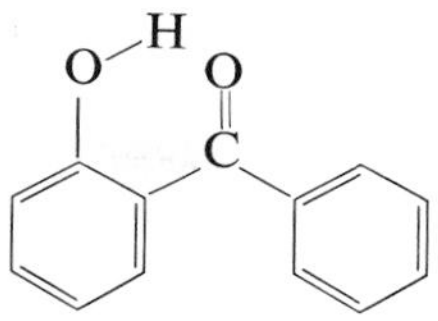

The 2-hydroxy-4-methoxybenzophenone is the ingredient in many commercial preparations added to increase stability to ultraviolet light exposure. (See the discussion of Sec. 5-9A.)

Large product quantum yields (Φ's $\gg$ 1) indicate the importance of a chain reaction forming these products. Quantum yields of hydrogen chloride formation from the photolysis of highly purified chlorine and hydrogen mixtures in visible light can be as high as 10^6–10^7 at room temperature. In explanation, a mechanism must be suggested in which over a million molecules of HCl will be formed for every one quantum of light absorbed by chlorine. Such a scheme is the following:[4]

$$Cl_2 + h\nu \rightarrow 2Cl \qquad (6\text{-}8)$$

$$Cl + H_2 \rightarrow HCl + H \qquad (6\text{-}9)$$

$$H + Cl_2 \rightarrow HCl + Cl \qquad (6\text{-}10)$$

For each atom of chlorine formed by the action of light in 6-8, reactions 6-9 and 6-10 may occur a million times. A chlorine atom is destroyed in 6-9, but one is regenerated in 6-10. A cycle of reactions which continues to form product and regenerate reactant is called a *chain reaction*. Presumably this cycle may be stopped eventually by chain-terminating reactions which remove the reactive species. Reaction 6-11,

$$2Cl + M \rightarrow Cl_2 + M \qquad (6\text{-}11)$$

or a combination of two hydrogen atoms, or a hydrogen and a chlorine atom in the gas phase or at a wall, may be chain-terminating steps in this case. It is interesting to note that the chain reaction between H_2 and Cl_2 is so exothermic, so very fast, and has such a high quantum yield that a violent explosion results if a highly purified equimolar mixture of the two gases in the dark is suddenly irradiated with a bright light.

If the quantum yield of a product is finite and invariant with changes in experimental conditions, the formation of this product in a primary rate-determining process is indicated. From the photolysis of di-n-propyl ketone at 3130 A $\Phi_{C_2H_4}$ is about 0.21 and is relatively insensitive to temperature (up to 161°C) and other experimental variables.[5] This suggests C_2H_4 formation in the primary process:

$$(CH_3CH_2CH_2)_2CO + h\nu \rightarrow C_2H_4 + CH_3COCH_2CH_2CH_3 \qquad (6\text{-}12)$$

The invariance of a finite product quantum yield may also reflect product formation in a non-chain step, which always follows a rate-determining primary process. For example, Φ_{CO} from diisopropyl ketone photolysis increases with temperature up to about 60°C, where it remains near unity with further increase in temperature (studied to 150°C).[6] There is extensive evidence for the intermediate formation of free radicals in this system. These facts are consistent with the following reaction sequence:

$$(CH_3)_2CHCOCH(CH_3)_2 + h\nu \rightarrow (CH_3)_2CHCO + (CH_3)_2CH \quad (6\text{-}13)$$

At temperatures above 60° isobutyryl radicals formed in 6-13 must participate almost exclusively in reaction 6-14:

$$(CH_3)_2CHCO \rightarrow (CH_3)_2CH + CO \quad (6\text{-}14)$$

Evidently no chain of events leading to CO formation is initiated by reactions of the isopropyl radicals with the ketone substrate at temperatures up to 150°C and above 60; Φ_{CO} is controlled by, and is possibly a measure of, φ_{13}.

Quantum yields of products are critical to the proper evaluation of a photochemical reaction mechanism, and their determination is strongly recommended for every fundamental mechanistic photochemical study. The experimental details of quantum yield determinations are given in Secs. 7-4 and 7-5.

6-4   DIRECT SPECTROSCOPIC IDENTIFICATION OF PRIMARY PROCESSES

6-4A   Flash Photolysis

There are at present several spectroscopic techniques which can offer direct evidence concerning the nature of the primary processes. Norrish and Porter[7] (1949), Davidson and co-workers[8] (1951), and Herzberg and Ramsay[9] (1952) developed the so-called "flash photolysis" technique; see Fig. 7-14. A pulse of extremely high-intensity light (about 1 einstein in a millisecond) is passed into an absorbing system. Under these conditions large concentrations of intermediates are formed, so that conventional spectroscopic means (absorption of light from a second flash shortly after the first) can be used to identify them and to follow their reactions. By using these systems, the absorption spectra of many free radicals (NH_2, HCO, CS, etc.) and triplet excited molecules have been observed for the first time (see Chapter 7 for recent references and discussions).

In Fig. 6-1 are given portions of the high-resolution absorption spectra taken by Herzberg and Ramsay[10] immediately after the flash photolysis of acetaldehyde and deuteroacetaldehyde at 50–100 mm pressure. Flashes (containing considerable short-wavelength ultraviolet) in glyoxal, formaldehyde, propionaldehyde, acrolein, methylformate, and ethylformate also give the identical band systems. A detailed analysis of the rotational and vibrational structure of the bands shows their origin to be a simple triatomic species, the formyl radical (HCO and DCO). The treatment of Herzberg and Ramsay shows that the HCO radical is bent in its lowest observed state ($^2A''$) with an HCO angle of 119°30′ ± 1°30′ and these

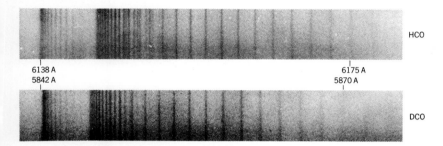

Fig. 6-1   Absorption spectrum of the formyl radical formed in the flash photolysis of acetaldehyde; fine structure of the strongest HCO and DCO absorption bands; spectrogram obtained in the second order of a 21 ft grating spectrograph with a dispersion of 1.2 A/mm. From Herzberg and Ramsay.[10]

bond distances: C—H, 1.08 ± 0.02 A; C—O, 1.20 ± 0.01 A. In its excited state ($^2\Sigma^+$) it is linear with bond distances of C—H, 1.07 ± 0.01 A; C—O, 1.183 ± 0.003 A.

The absorption of the tremendous energies of the flash in a short period of time may raise the temperature of the absorbing system as much as a thousand degrees and may result in serious thermal decomposition of products and reactant unless some means of temperature moderation is used. The addition of a large quantity of non-light-absorbing gas or use of a liquid solvent moderates the temperature rise of such a system. The very high intensities to which these systems owe their uniqueness are obtained only if the full flash of the polychromatic radiation is used, so that it is impossible to estimate meaningful quantum efficiencies. With the extremely high-intensity spark system of Claesson and co-workers[11] some filtering of the flash can be done and still retain very high intensities, so that in these systems approximate estimates of quantum yields have been made.

Many of the usual disadvantages of the flash-photolysis system seem to have been eliminated by Ramsay[12] in a spectroscopic technique which uses continuous illumination and an unusually long optical path for absorption spectra measurements of intermediates at their low steady-state concentrations. In this manner absorption bands of NH_2 and CN radicals were observed from photolyses of NH_3 and $(CN)_2$, respectively. In Sec. 7-1F the experimental details of the methods of flash photolysis are given.

6-4B   Photolysis in Rigid Media

G. N. Lewis and his co-workers[13] originated in 1941 an interesting and important technique for the study of intermediate species in photochemical systems. They formed solid solutions of fluorescein dye in boric acid glass. The phosphorescence phenomena associated with the activation of the dye were studied, and the absorption spectrum of the transient triplet state of the dye was observed (Sec. 4-7A). In 1951 Rice and Freamo[14] renewed the interest of the scientific world in the technique of trapping unstable intermediates. They passed a stream of HN_3 in a rapid-flow system through a tube heated to $1000°C$ and then allowed the output hot stream of gases to impinge on a cold finger maintained at liquid-nitrogen temperatures. They observed that a blue deposit [possibly NH or a polymeric form $(NH)_n$] formed on the cold finger. The blue solid formed white ammonium azide, NH_4N_3, on warming to $-125°C$.

Linschitz and Rennert[15] (1952), Mador and Williams (1954),[16] and Norman and Porter (1954)[17] have reported studies of unstable intermediates formed photochemically in glasses at liquid-nitrogen temperature. In these experiments the light-sensitive compound to be investigated was dissolved in a suitable solvent (e.g., ether, isopentane, ethanol: 3:3:5, termed EPA) and cooled to liquid-nitrogen temperature, where a glass formed. Photodecomposition occurred upon irradiation of the glass, and presumably some of the radicals had sufficient escaping energies to melt the glass in their vicinity and to separate some distance, where they too were frozen into position. Abstraction and other chemical reactions which have significant activation energies are extremely slow at these temperatures, so that usually reactive free radicals and other intermediate species can be kept for some time without change; hence the usual spectroscopic and other techniques of analysis can be applied "leisurely" to identify fragments and establish the nature of primary processes.

One of the most successful and promising of the developments in this area have been made by Pimentel and his co-workers.[18] They prepare a suitable light-sensitive compound in a solid xenon, nitrogen, or argon matrix at $20°K$; the ratio of matrix to compound is usually kept in the range from $100:1$ to $500:1$. The photolysis of the compound in the matrix is effected, and the products, which may include normally unstable species, are observed, using infrared absorption spectrometry. In the inert-gas matrices the vibrational frequencies of the molecules and the stabilized fragments are nearly the same as those observed in the gas phase. Hence, the identification of a molecular fragment or unstable intermediate in the photolysis of some compound in matrix experiments at low temperatures suggests its formation also in the usual photochemical experiments involving this compound at higher temperatures. However, it appears that some species (e.g., p-nitrobenzenediazonium salts) which decompose readily at ordinary temperatures are stable to light when in glasses at very low temperatures.[19] Thus, the failure to see some expected intermediate in the matrix photolyses at low temperatures does not necessarily exclude its contribution to the reaction mechanism at ordinary temperatures. An excellent review of photolysis in rigid media has been given by Pimentel.[18d]

Recently a technique of irradiating compounds dispersed in a potassium bromide matrix and simultaneously quantitatively determining the products and their rate of formation has been reported by Pitts, Wan, and Schuck.[15l] The conversion of o-nitrobenzaldehyde to o-nitrobenzoic acid is employed as an actinometer. Both unimolecular and bimolecular photochemical reactions can be studied in the solid phase at room temperature by this technique, but as in the case of p-nitrobenzenediazonium salts cited above, some photochemical reactions which occur readily in liquid solution at room temperature do not occur in the KBr matrix.

6-4C Mass Spectrometric Methods

The direct identification of the primary products of photodecomposition by means of mass spectrometry has been a goal of photochemists for years. Many investigations, particularly the detailed studies of Lossing and co-workers, have shown that thermally produced free radicals can be detected quantitatively in a mass spectrometer.[20] With the photochemical formation of radicals the need for high light absorption to provide a sufficient concentration of free radicals for detection must be compromised with the relatively low pressures which will enable rapid diffusion into the ionization chamber of the spectrometer.

Several attempts to detect primary free radical products in specially designed mass spectrometers have met with little success,[21] but Farmer, Lossing, Marsden, and Steacie[22] found one type of solution to the problem. They took advantage of the large absorption coefficient of mercury to carry out mercury-sensitized reactions at 2537 A at low pressure in a flow cell located next to (actually containing) the "leak" into the ionization chamber of a mass spectrometer. The sensitized decomposition of the substrate occurs at a sufficient rate to make possible the detection of primary radical fragments and stable products formed in intramolecular processes. In many experiments they added $(CD_3)_2Hg$ to the system so that CD_3 radicals are generated simultaneously by reaction with the excited mercury atoms; these CD_3 radicals added to primary radicals formed from the substrate to trap and label them before entering the ionization chamber of the spectrometer. The primary modes of reaction of $Hg(^3P_1)$ atoms with a variety of compounds have been determined in this way.[23] (See Sec. 2-13A-1 for discussion and references.)

The first successful mass spectrometric detection of a radical formed by direct photolysis was reported by Beckey and Groth[24] who obtained the parent peak of the acetyl radical, 43 mass/charge units, from the direct photolysis of acetone vapor in a field emission-ion source mass spectrometer. The practical instrument for the direct mass spectrometric observation of primary photochemical products appears to be forthcoming.

6-4D   Other Spectroscopic Methods

The use of long-path infrared equipment offers promise for the identification of intermediates of moderate stability. Stephens, Hanst, Doerr, and Scott[25] have used a 432-meter-path infrared spectrometer to identify some interesting transient species formed in various photochemical and thermal reactions important in Los Angeles "smog." McMillan, Calvert, and Pitts[26] have identified the enol-acetone intermediate through cross-beam, long-path infrared analysis during methyl-*n*-propyl ketone photolysis. See Fig. 7-47.

The method of electron spin resonance (ESR) is widely used to monitor free radicals generated by a variety of techniques and trapped in solid or viscous media.[27] An early example of the use of ESR in the study of photochemical systems is that by Piette and Landgraf[28] who followed directly the butoxyl radical concentration in the photolysis of the pure liquid butyl hydroperoxides at temperatures from -40 to $22°$. The radical concentrations were about at the limit of detection in the experiments at $22°$. The current literature contains many examples of this technique. Radical concentrations in the typical gas-phase photochemical experiment are below the detection limits of the instruments available today, but studies of vapor-phase atom reactions are in progress, and the field is promising.

The first ESR observations of the triplet state were of naphthalene oriented in crystalline durene by Hutchison and Mangum.[29] Van der Waals and de Groot[30] found "low-field" ESR absorption for triplet states in randomly oriented polynuclear hydrocarbons in glycerol. A study with direct photochemical implications is that of Piette, Sharp, Kuwana, and Pitts,[31] who observed the triplet states of several para-substituted benzophenones through ESR signals at 1500 gauss when the compounds were irradiated at 77°K in a rigid solvent. Phosphorescence decay lifetimes were measured and agreed with ESR signal decay. Those para-substituted benzophenones which gave ESR signals were shown to have low photochemical reactivity in the pinacolization reaction; see Table 5-3 and the discussion of Sec. 5-2B. For example, p-aminobenzophenone gives a strong triplet ESR signal and does not significantly photopinacolize.

6-5 ISOTOPIC STUDIES

All fields of science have benefited by the development of tracer techniques and the availability of high-purity stable and radioactive isotopes, and photochemistry is no exception. For example, Gunning and co-workers[32] have gained unique information about the mechanism of $Hg(^3P_1)$-sensitized reactions through selective excitation of the ^{202}Hg isotope in natural mercury vapor. Thus Wan and Gunning used a ^{202}Hg-filled low-pressure resonance lamp to irradiate mixtures of natural mercury with hydrogen chloride or the alkyl chlorides. With HCl at 28°, low pressures, and added butadiene (as a radical scavenger), irradiation in a fast-flow system gave an Hg_2Cl_2 product which was highly enriched in ^{202}Hg (35%). The quantum yield of the total calomel formation was near unity, so one can conclude that on the interaction of $Hg(^3P_1)$ atoms with HCl primary reactions 6-15 and 6-16 occur to the extent of 35% and 65%, respectively (see Sec. 2-15G).

$$Hg(^3P_1) + HCl \rightarrow HgCl + H \qquad (6\text{-}15)$$
$$\searrow$$
$$HgH \text{ (or } Hg + H) + Cl \qquad (6\text{-}16)$$

Some unexpected primary photochemical processes in hydrocarbon photolysis have been discovered largely through isotopic labeling techniques. For example, the H_2, D_2, and HD yields from the photolysis of CH_4-CD_4 mixtures, CH_2D_2, and CHD_3 at 1236 A prove the dominance of the molecular hydrogen elimination reaction 6-17 compared to hydrogen-atom formation in 6-18.[33a-c]

$$CH_4 + h\nu \rightarrow CH_2 + H_2 \qquad (6\text{-}17)$$
$$\searrow$$
$$CH_3 + H \qquad (6\text{-}18)$$

A similar procedure in which a mixture of C_2H_4 and C_2D_4 was employed was used to demonstrate that the mercury-photosensitized decomposition of ethylene goes virtually exclusively by intramolecular elimination of molecular hydrogen in the primary act, rather than direct dissociation into $C_2H_3 + H$.[33d]

6-6 THE USE OF FREE RADICAL TRAPS IN THE DETERMINATION OF PRIMARY PHOTODECOMPOSITION MODES

A successful quantitative scheme which has been used to elucidate the primary reactions involves the rapid removal of free radicals in fast secondary reactions. A variety of different chemicals which are very reactive toward free radicals has been used as free radical "traps" or scavengers which stop completely or inhibit the usual secondary reactions of these species. The usefulness and limitations of some of these techniques are described in the following sections.

6-6A   Photolyses in Medicinal Paraffin Solution

One of the first important contributions to the problem of primary process determination was provided by Norrish and co-workers (1934).[34] Many significant qualitative results were obtained from a comparison of the photolysis of aldehydes and ketones in the pure vapor state and in medicinal paraffin solutions. It was suggested for the solution photolyses that if free radicals, R, were formed in a primary process they would react with the large excess of paraffin (typical formula $C_{15}H_{32}$) to abstract hydrogen atoms:

$$R + C_{15}H_{32} \rightarrow RH + C_{15}H_{31} \qquad (6\text{-}19)$$

The resulting paraffin radicals would presumably disproportionate,

$$2C_{15}H_{31} \rightarrow C_{15}H_{30} + C_{15}H_{32} \qquad (6\text{-}20)$$

and produce unsaturation ($C_{15}H_{30}$) in the paraffin solution, and the amount of unsaturation formed was taken as a measure of the free radical type of photodecomposition which had occurred.

If, at a constant intensity of absorbed light, the rate of formation of a given product, e.g., propylene from methyl n-butyl ketone photolysis, was the same in photolyses in the gas phase as in the paraffin solution, Norrish et $al.$ proposed that these products were formed directly by an intramolecular primary process. It is interesting to note that the designation of the free radical and the intramolecular primary processes in aldehydes and ketones as the Norrish Type I and Type II splits came from these early studies.

Much information about primary processes was gathered in these pioneering experiments, but the complexity of the systems is actually greater than the simple mechanism would indicate, and the interpretations are difficult and often in error. In many cases evidence for radical formation was negative in these experiments, but later more sensitive means showed conclusively that radical formation was important. Some of the difficulty probably arises from the fact that reaction 6-19 is not particularly fast, and it is undoubtedly only one of many reactions of the R radicals in these solutions. Also it is unlikely that an unsaturated molecule would be formed on each interaction between two paraffin radicals. In the gas phase, combination of alkyl free radicals is usually more important than disproportionation, and it is probable that 6-21 is a dominant reaction in the paraffin solution.

$$2C_{15}H_{31} \rightarrow C_{30}H_{62} \qquad (6\text{-}21)$$

Furthermore, the appearance of unsaturation in the paraffin solution is not unambiguous evidence for radical formation, since in the photodecomposition of the higher ketones, aldehydes, esters, acids, amides, etc., olefin products are formed in a primary non-free-radical step.

6-6B Metallic Mirror Removal

Paneth and Hofeditz[35] developed one of the first techniques to demonstrate the presence of free radicals in systems undergoing thermal decomposition. It is based on the removal of thin layers of metal, called mirrors, by the reactive radicals or atoms. The free radicals are transported from the generating oven to the mirror site in a carrier gas pumped by a fast-flow system. The technique was first applied to photochemical systems by Pearson and Purcell.[36] In a series of definitive experiments they identified ethyl and propyl radicals from the photolysis of diethyl ketone and the dipropyl ketones, respectively. This was established by the analysis of the products which these radicals formed on interaction with arsenic mirrors.

Mirror experiments have provided much good evidence to help in the choice of mechanism[37] (e.g., the experiments of F. O. Rice and co-workers). However, in the hands of research men who are unpracticed in this method, mirror experiments can give results of a semiqualitative nature only (sometimes completely misleading), since the reaction is heterogeneous and the form and reactivity of the mirrors are difficult to reproduce.

6-6C Nitric Oxide Inhibition

Nitric oxide has been a popular inhibitor to demonstrate the occurrence of chain reactions and of free radicals in the thermal and photochemical decompositions of organic compounds. The molecule contains an odd number of electrons and thus may be expected to combine with odd electron atoms and free radicals. Mitchell and Hinshelwood[38] made the first NO-inhibited photochemical studies with acetaldehyde and propionaldehyde. Chain decomposition of both aldehydes could be inhibited strongly with relatively small pressures of NO. Nitric oxide has been used repeatedly since this work to prove or disprove the presence of radicals.

It is likely that the first step in the reaction of nitric oxide with a free radical R is the following:

$$R + NO \rightarrow RNO \qquad (6\text{-}22)$$

However, there has been some uncertainty in the nature of the final products of the reactions between nitric oxide and the free radicals. Raley, Rust, and Vaughan[39] have studied the thermal decomposition of di-*tert*-butyl peroxide and have identified formaldoxime as a definite product of the reaction between methyl radicals and nitric oxide at temperatures above 220°C. Bryce and Ingold[40] have successfully followed the methyl-nitric oxide reaction through mass spectrometric studies of the thermal decomposition of dimethylmercury in nitric oxide. In short reaction times at high temperatures (480–900°C) the major product of the methyl-nitric oxide interaction was a compound of parent mass 45, presumed to be CH_3NO. With long reaction times, NH_3, H_2O, HCN, CO, N_2, CO_2, and CH_3CN were also detected; neither $(CH_3NO)_2$ nor $(CH_2{=}NOH)_3$ was formed in detectable amounts under these conditions. Calvert, Thomas, and Hanst[41] have shown that the major product of the reaction between methyl radicals and nitric oxide at 25° is nitrosomethane, CH_3NO. At relatively high concentrations of the CH_3NO, the dimer, $(CH_3NO)_2$, forms in a rapid gas-phase reaction and settles out on the cell walls as a solid material. The various other products which have been observed for the R + NO reactions are explicable in terms of the rearrangements and reactions of the dimeric forms of RNO reported by Chilton, Gowenlock, and Trotman,[42] or radical and nitric oxide addition to the initial monomer product.[43]

The extremely complex mixture of products from the reactions which follow 6-22 in the usual photochemical systems offers an undesirable complication in kinetic studies. Further nitric oxide is capable of oxidizing and catalyzing the thermal decomposition of certain compounds. There is some question as to whether the minimum in the inhibited rates found with increased nitric oxide pressure corresponds to complete inhibition or to the stopping and starting of chains with equal efficiency. The latter seems the most probable at high temperatures.[44]

6-6D Inhibition by Oxygen

Important information regarding oxidation mechanisms has been obtained in oxygen-inhibited photolyses. However, oxygen has been used intentionally only rarely as a free radical trap in photochemical studies which are designed to establish primary processes. There is little doubt that the primary reaction between a free radical R and oxygen at ordinary temperatures is described by

$$R + O_2 (+ M) \rightarrow RO_2 (+ M) \qquad (6\text{-}23)$$

but the secondary reactions of the peroxyl radicals lead to a multitude of oxidation products, some of them short lived, which complicate the interpretations of the results. The rate constant for 6-23 is large ($k_{23} \cong$ 4.2 $\times$ 10^9 liters/mole-sec at 22° for R = C_2H_5),[62] so that even a few microns pressure of oxygen is sufficient to complete seriously with other usual reactants of free radicals in photochemical systems. Consequently the experimenter must take great precautions to eliminate oxygen in a usual system in which radicals are to be produced and reactions other than photooxidations studied.

The interaction of oxygen with electronically excited molecules can be important and can lead to complications. The quenching of singlet and triplet excited molecules by oxygen in the vapor and solution phase has been recognized for years.[45] In fact, the bimolecular rate constants for the quenching reactions of the excited triplet-state molecule by oxygen are near the collision number; for acetone triplet with oxygen, $k = 8.2 \times 10^9$ liters/mole-sec (30–75°).[46] The rate constants for quenching by oxygen of the excited singlet and triplet states do not appear to be greatly different in cases where measurements are available.[47] However, because of the much shorter lifetime of the excited singlet states, their steady-state concentration is well below that of triplets and their reactions with oxygen are usually of little importance in experiments at low oxygen pressures.

Many diverse explanations have been offered for the very high facility of oxygen to quench electronically excited states:[48] one must invoke some mechanism other than simple collisional deactivation of the excited states by oxygen, since such rates are slower by many orders of magnitude. The various mechanisms which have been suggested include transfer of electronic energy, leading to the excitation of oxygen from its ground state ($^3\Sigma_g^-$) to one of its low-lying singlet states ($^1\Sigma_g^+$, $^1\Delta_g$),[49] paramagnetism of oxygen, which presumably enhances spin-orbit interactions in the excited molecule and allows restrictions attending singlet-triplet transitions to be relaxed,[50,51] and oxygen involvement in the formation of a charge-transfer complex with the molecule in its excited state, with subsequent catalysis of internal conversion processes within the excited molecule.[52,53,54]

The interactions of excited states with oxygen can lead directly to chemical changes in the excited molecules, as is observed in biacetyl photolysis[55] and in the reactions of polynuclear aromatics.[47] The interaction can be much more subtle, as in the case of the alkyl ketone photooxidations.[55c] Srinivasan and Noyes[56] report that an unexpected type of oxygen-atom exchange occurs between $^{18}O_2$ and the carbonyl oxygen of acetone or diethyl ketone during photooxidation of these compounds. An unusual chemical intermediate, of structure as yet unproved, forms presumably through the triplet excited state of the ketone.[57,58] The extent of the exchange depends on the conditioning of the cell wall; some heterogeneous character of the reaction is evident.[158]

Obviously it is naive to assume that the only function of oxygen added to a photochemical system will be to react with free radicals formed in the primary photochemical processes. However, there are types of photochemical systems in which the use of oxygen can help define the primary decomposition modes. The intramolecular primary photodecomposition processes which do not involve free radical intermediates or triplet excited states are not disturbed greatly by the presence of oxygen. If the quantum yield of a given product is found to be relatively insensitive to variation in oxygen pressure, this is rather compelling evidence that it is formed in the primary act, probably from the decomposition of an excited singlet state, although a short-lived triplet state is also possible. For example, Brunet and Noyes[59] have found that the rates of propylene and acetone formation are equal in the photolysis of 2-hexanone and relatively independent of the pressure of added oxygen gas. Thus it is reasonably certain that these products are formed in a primary act which probably involves a singlet excited state (or a very short-lived triplet), and free radical intermediates certainly cannot play any part. The use of oxygen has served as a diagnostic test for the participation of the triplet-state molecules in certain photochemical systems.[72]

6-6E   Inhibition of Photolyses by Ethylene, Propylene, Etc.

The olefins exhibit chain-inhibiting properties which are often attributed to free-radical additions to the C=C bond. The photodecomposition of aldehydes in ethylene, propylene, and butylene was studied by Danby and Hinshelwood.[60] They found that at large olefin pressures the inhibition was marked. The efficiency of inhibition decreased in the order butylene > propylene > ethylene. Although olefin inhibition has often been used to detect (or suppress) the presence of free radicals, its use in quantitative experiments is not always straightforward. The products may be many and complex, and in some systems large amounts of olefin are required to approach complete inhibition of chains. However, in other systems olefin addition has proven a useful diagnostic tool in quantitative experiments.[61] An example is the mercury-sensitized reaction of an alkane in which traces of olefins deliberately have been added to test the efficiency of hydrogen-atom self-scavenging by olefins formed in the reaction (see Sec. 2-13A). Butadiene is a useful "trap" in systems where monoisotopic photosensitization is being studied[32] (see Sec. 2-15G).

In the use of olefins as radical trapping agents one should be aware of the fact that the lowest triplet state for ethylene lies about 82 kcal/mole above the ground state;[156] for the alkyl- and aryl-substituted ethylenes the triplet lies at somewhat lower energies. Thus quenching of the triplet excited molecules by added olefin can be important for certain conditions. Rebbert and Ausloos[157] have found that the triplet of acetone (formed in photolyses at 3130 A) is quenched effectively by olefins although the singlet state of acetone is unaffected, as would be expected in view of the very high energy of the excited singlet states of the olefins. They estimate that the probability that triplet-triplet energy transfer will occur upon collision between electronically excited acetone and an olefin molecule is as follows: styrene, 0.5; 1,3-butadiene, 1.5×10^{-2}; 2,3-dimethyl-2-butene, 1.5×10^{-4}; 2-pentene, 2.1×10^{-5}; 1-pentene, 6.5×10^{-6}; ethylene, 2.6×10^{-6}. It is concluded that, when the energy transfer process is endothermic, the quenching efficiency increases with diminishing ΔH of the reaction; when it is exothermic no correlation is seen between the quenching efficiencies and the ΔH of the reaction.

Triplet energy transfer from biacetyl to mono-olefins occurs with very low efficiency, presumably because of the relatively small energy difference of the 0—0 band of the $S_0 \rightarrow T_1$ transition in biacetyl ($\sim$56 kcal/mole). The probability that triplet energy will be transferred from biacetyl to olefin upon collision is as follows: 1,3-butadiene, 1.6×10^{-4}; styrene, 2.5×10^{-5}; 2,3-dimethyl-2-butene, 1.6×10^{-7}.

6-6F   Iodine-Inhibited Photolyses

Many of the usual difficulties in the determination of the nature and extent of primary photodecomposition modes are eliminated in iodine-inhibited photolyses. The techniques were first proposed and utilized by Gorin[63] and later extended and improved, primarily by Blacet and co-workers.[64] The method involves the photodecomposition of a gaseous reactant in the presence of iodine vapor. Iodine is transparent over the range 4000–2500 A (see Fig. 3-30), and it reacts very rapidly with most atoms and free radicals. In fact, evidence indicates that almost every iodine-organic radical (R) collision results in reaction.[65]

$$R + I_2 \rightarrow RI + I \qquad (6\text{-}24)$$

Thus only a few millimeters pressure of iodine inhibits the occurrence of most of the other reactions of these species even when 80 mm or more of the reactant molecule is present. The great variety of reaction products which ordinarily result from secondary free radical reactions is usually eliminated, and iodides appear as the only products of the radicals.* The methods of analysis are quite straightforward and quantitative.

Primary reaction modes which produce stable products without intermediate radical formation appear to be affected little by the presence of iodine, and the quantum yields are assumed to be measures of the primary process efficiency; that is, the quantum yield of a given iodide, RI, is used as an indication of the efficiency of the primary process in which the radical R is formed.

Radioactive iodine has been utilized in the identification of radicals formed in primary processes.[67] It is added to the reaction mixture before irradiation; then known quantities of alkyl iodides, believed to be the same as those formed in the photolysis, are added as carriers after irradiation.[67] By determination of the specific activity by a standard technique, the products from the photoproduced radicals can be identified (isotopic dilution analysis).

Iodine inhibition is an important technique in photochemistry, but it too has limitations that may be serious in certain systems. The extent of excited molecule deactivation by iodine (as well as by other scavengers) is not known in the case of simple aldehydes and ketones and may be large. Thus there is good evidence at 3130 A that excited acetone[64c,66] and acetaldehyde[68] molecules are deactivated by iodine through some undefined energy-transfer mechanism. For these systems the quantum yields of methyl iodide are not a measure of the primary efficiency of the Type I radical split in the photolysis of pure acetone or acetaldehyde vapor. In the case of acetone-iodine mixtures the product yields are temperature dependent, and other evidence of deactivation is apparent. In the acetaldehyde case the yields of methyl iodide, methane, and carbon monoxide are not temperature dependent (60–150°) when iodine is present at a few millimeters pressure.[64b] Presumably one electronic state (possibly a triplet) in acetaldehyde is readily deactivated, whereas another (perhaps singlet) is not, so that one cannot generalize that deactivation will be evident from the experimental results of iodine-inhibited experiments if it is important in a reactant-iodine mixture.

In addition to the possible deactivation of long-lived excited molecules

---

* The formyl radical reaction with iodine forms carbon monoxide and hydrogen iodide (HCO + $I_2 \rightarrow$ HI + CO + I), conceivably by way of the unstable intermediate product formyl iodide, HCOI.

by iodine, other problems in the use of iodine inhibition frustrate the worker. Iodine-inhibition experiments are limited to a fairly narrow range of temperatures from about 50 to 175°C, since a significant thermal reaction between iodine and many compounds occurs at higher temperatures, and the vapor pressure of iodine (2 mm at 50°C) is not sufficient at the lower temperatures to ensure radical trapping throughout the experiment. In the photolysis of aldehyde-iodine mixtures extreme care must be exercised to remove traces of water, polymer, or other contaminant from the reaction system; otherwise, a rapid thermal reaction between iodine and aldehyde occurs on the walls of the system. Obviously all mercury liquid and vapor must be eliminated from the reaction system.

6-6G Other Trapping Agents

O'Neal and Benson[69] report that gaseous hydrogen iodide is a promising free radical trap. They irradiated acetone-hydrogen iodide mixtures at 3130 A and found no observable decomposition of the acetyl free radical ($CH_3CO \rightarrow CH_3 + CO$) at temperatures up to 165°. With a mole ratio of $HI/CH_3COCH_3 = 0.023$, all the acetyl and other free radicals (R) were scavenged effectively by the rapid reaction

$$R + HI \rightarrow RH + I \qquad (6\text{-}25)$$

The formation of iodine in the mixture as the reaction proceeds may cause some complications if it is allowed to accumulate in runs of significant conversion, since it is a somewhat better trapping agent for free radicals than hydrogen iodide; for $R = CH_3$, $\log(k_{25}/k_{24}) = -0.38 - 1300/4.755T$.

The common free radical trap in thermal solution studies, 2,2-diphenyl-1-picrylhydrazyl (DPPH), is not well suited for photochemical use. It is highly colored (λ_{max} at 520 and 330 mμ) and undergoes rapid photolysis when irradiated in the short-wavelength band.[70] Galvinoxyl [2,6-di-*tert*-butyl-α-(3,5-di-*tert*-butyl-4-oxo-2,5-cyclohexadiene-1-ylidine)-*p*-tolyloxy], although ten times more reactive than iodine (toward 2-cyano-2-propyl radicals) at the same concentration, absorbs light strongly in most of the useful photochemical range (visible maxima at 407, 431, and 772 mμ).[71]

Nitrous oxide has proved to be a useful electron trap in solution-phase photolyses of iodide ion and should be of great value in many other systems.[73]

Various interesting chemical techniques have been suggested to detect the role of triplet excited molecules in solution-phase reactions and to determine triplet energy levels.[72,149] These are discussed in Chapter 4 and Sec. 6-7C of this chapter.

6-7   THE TECHNIQUES OF KINETICS IN PHOTOCHEMICAL MECHANISM DETERMINATIONS

Chemical kinetics and reaction rate theory are among the most important tools which the photochemist has at his disposal in the elucidation of reaction mechanism and the determination of the roles of electronically excited molecules and free radicals formed in photodissociative processes. Thus a brief review of the fundamentals of reaction kinetics and the applications of kinetic techniques to the study of photochemical mechanisms is given in the following sections of this chapter.

6-7A   Elementary Chemical Kinetics

The rate of an elementary or one-step reaction between a molecules of type A, b molecules of type B, etc.,

$$aA + bB + \cdots \rightarrow \text{Products} \tag{6-26}$$

is described by

$$\frac{-d[A]}{dt} = k[A]^a[B]^b \cdots \tag{6-27}$$

where k, the reaction rate constant, is a constant for a given temperature, and its magnitude is characteristic of the particular reaction. The brackets indicate concentration. The form of Eq. 6-27 is consistent with reaction rate theory and is anticipated in terms of the probability of collisions.

The experimental dependence of the rate on the concentration of the reactants, that is, the size of a and b, defines the reaction order. If $a = 0, 1, 2,$ or 3, respectively, then the reaction is said to be zero, first, second, or third order with respect to reactant A. The total order of a reaction is the sum of the orders of all the reactants; the total order $= a + b + \cdots$. The molecularity of a reaction is the actual number of molecules involved in the intermediate species (activated complex) which leads to the reaction products.

The order of a reaction is established readily by using one of the many common experimental methods.[74] For example, a plot of the logarithm of the initial rate versus the logarithm of the initial concentration of one of the reactants (the others held constant) has a slope equal to the order with respect to that reactant. The molecularity is usually equal to the total order of an elementary reaction (except for first-order reactions in the high-pressure region). It is difficult to establish the molecularity for complex chain reactions, etc., and this must be inferred from both the total order of the reaction and other evidence of the mechanism.

The reaction rate constant may be evaluated from 6-27 or one of its integrated forms by using the measured rates and the concentrations of the reactants or products.[74] The units of k depend on the choice of concentration and time units and the order of the reaction.

The temperature dependence of experimental rate data usually can be represented well by the Arrhenius equation,

$$k = Ae^{-E_a/RT} \qquad (6\text{-}28)$$

Here k is the reaction rate constant, A is the pre-exponential factor or frequency factor, E_a is the experimental activation energy, T is the absolute temperature in $°K$, and R is the gas constant. Reaction rate theories have been developed which give theoretical significance to the various terms in this equation. Two such theories are in common use today, the collision theory and the transition state theory. Extensive use of the collision theory has been stimulated by the simplicity of its application, although in its older forms (as given here) it is recognized to be at best a very incomplete and inaccurate picture of the true nature of chemical reactions. However, it provides a basis for the discussion and comparison of reactions. Certainly a working knowledge of the collision theory is important in reaction studies, if for no other reason than to be able to evaluate properly the vast quantity of rate data which have been presented in terms of this theory.

Many of the limitations of the older collision picture are overcome by the transition state theory. For example, it is theoretically possible to calculate the rate constant of a chemical reaction from only a knowledge of the energy states of the reacting species and their complex. In actual practice the calculation is difficult and often impossible because of the inaccessibility of the needed information.

6-7A-1   The Collision Theory
for Bimolecular Reactions

By far the most common type of reaction encountered in all rate studies is that which occurs on collision between two species. This is a consequence of the improbability of simultaneous collisions between many molecules. The collision theory for bimolecular reactions grew out of the works of van't Hoff (1884),[75] Arrhenius (1889),[76] and Lewis (1918).[77] It describes the rate constant k_{II} of a bimolecular reaction,

$$A + B \rightarrow \text{Products} \qquad (6\text{-}29)$$

in terms of Eq. 6-28, but the pre-exponential factor A is separated into the product of two terms, the collision number Z and the steric factor P.

Equation 6-30 is derived by considering the number of collisions between molecules A and B and the effectiveness of these collisions.

$$k_{II} = PZe^{-E_a/RT} \qquad (6\text{-}30)$$

A and B are assumed to be rigid spheres with diameters σ_A and σ_B, respectively. A collision is defined as the contact between these spheres. In terms of this concept, the kinetic molecular theory, and Maxwell's molecular velocity distribution law, the number of collisions per cubic centimeter per second (z_{AB}) between two unlike molecules A and B, as given in 6-31, may be calculated. The similar relation for the number of collisions between like molecules (z_{AA}) is given in 6-32.

$$z_{AB} = \left[\frac{8\pi RT}{\mu}\right]^{1/2} \sigma_{AB}^2 [A][B] \qquad (6\text{-}31)$$

$$z_{AA} = 2\left[\frac{\pi RT}{M_A}\right]^{1/2} \sigma_A^2 [A][A] \qquad (6\text{-}32)$$

Here $\mu = M_A M_B/(M_A + M_B)$, M_A and M_B being the respective gram molecular weights of A and B; R is the gas constant (8.314×10^7 ergs/mole-deg); T is the absolute temperature in $^\circ$K; $\sigma_{AB} = (\sigma_A + \sigma_B)/2$ in centimeters; and the concentrations of A and B are in molecules/cubic centimeter. In the description of k_{II} by 6-30 it is convenient to separate the concentration terms in 6-31 and 6-32 and to define collision numbers, Z_{AB} and Z_{AA}:

$$Z_{AB} = \frac{z_{AB}}{[A][B]} \qquad (6\text{-}33)$$

$$Z_{AA} = \frac{z_{AA}}{[A][A]} \qquad (6\text{-}34)$$

For most bimolecular reactions at a given temperature and concentration of reactants, z_{AB} is much larger than the measured rate of reaction. If 0.5 atm pressure each of A and B is present in a system at 25°C, $z_{AB} = 3.8 \times 10^{28}$ collisions/cm³-sec, for the reasonable case of $\sigma_{AB} = 4 \times 10^{-8}$ cm and $M_A = M_B = 50$ grams/mole. This is to be compared to the rates of chemical reactions which are often less than about 10^{12} molecules/cm³-sec.

To explain this discrepancy it is proposed that only a certain few collisions are effective in producing reaction, namely, those for which the orientation and the energy requirements for the reaction are met. The theory suggests that molecules must have a minimum energy E_a to promote the reorganization of the atoms and their electrons on collision and to provide reaction. This energy is usually assumed to be the kinetic energy associated with the motion of the molecules parallel to the line of nuclear centers at the moment of collision. The fraction of bimolecular collisions which have such kinetic energies greater than E_a can be shown to be equal to $e^{-E_a/RT}$. On this basis the main temperature dependence of reaction rate constants is described well. The units of E_a are determined by those chosen for R; kilocalories/mole or calories/mole are most commonly used.

The magnitude of the effect of E_a on the rate constant can be seen from the data of Table 6-1. The factor $e^{-E_a/RT}$ is shown for various E_a values

TABLE 6-1   Values of $e^{-E_a/RT}$ for Various E_a and Temperature Values

E_a, kcal/ mole	Temperature, °K					
	300	400	500	600	700	800
0	1.0	1.0	1.0	1.0	1.0	1.0
2	3.5×10^{-2}	8.1×10^{-2}	1.3×10^{-1}	1.9×10^{-1}	2.4×10^{-1}	2.8×10^{-1}
5	2.2×10^{-4}	1.9×10^{-3}	6.5×10^{-3}	1.5×10^{-2}	2.8×10^{-2}	4.3×10^{-2}
10	5.2×10^{-8}	3.4×10^{-6}	4.3×10^{-5}	2.3×10^{-4}	7.6×10^{-4}	1.8×10^{-3}
15	1.2×10^{-11}	6.4×10^{-9}	2.8×10^{-7}	3.4×10^{-6}	2.1×10^{-5}	8.0×10^{-5}
20	2.7×10^{-15}	8.5×10^{-11}	1.8×10^{-9}	5.2×10^{-8}	5.8×10^{-7}	3.5×10^{-6}
25	6.2×10^{-19}	2.2×10^{-14}	1.2×10^{-11}	7.9×10^{-10}	1.6×10^{-8}	1.5×10^{-7}
30	1.4×10^{-22}	4.1×10^{-17}	7.7×10^{-14}	1.2×10^{-11}	4.3×10^{-10}	6.5×10^{-9}
35	3.2×10^{-26}	7.6×10^{-20}	5.1×10^{-16}	1.8×10^{-13}	1.2×10^{-11}	2.8×10^{-10}
40	7.2×10^{-30}	1.4×10^{-22}	3.3×10^{-18}	2.7×10^{-15}	3.3×10^{-13}	1.2×10^{-11}
45	1.7×10^{-33}	2.6×10^{-25}	2.2×10^{-20}	4.1×10^{-17}	9.0×10^{-15}	5.1×10^{-13}
50	3.8×10^{-37}	4.8×10^{-28}	1.4×10^{-22}	6.2×10^{-19}	2.5×10^{-16}	2.2×10^{-14}

and absolute temperatures. For a given E_a the fraction of collisions which have energies greater than E_a increases as the temperature rises, reflecting the usual increase in rate with temperature. For a given temperature, this fraction decreases with increasing E_a. Furthermore, it can be seen that for a given temperature, the higher the E_a the greater the rate of increase of $e^{-E_a/RT}$ (and the reaction rate) with temperature. Thus a reaction with $E_a = 10$ kcal/mole will increase in rate by a factor of about 4.4×10^3 for a temperature rise from 300 to 500°K, while a reaction with $E_a = 50$ kcal/mole increases by about 1.6×10^{18} for the same temperature change (neglecting the temperature dependence of the A factors).

The additional empirical term P, the steric factor in Eq. 6-30, is simply considered in the older theory as the fraction of collisions which have the proper orientation for reaction. In reality P involves many factors, including the orientation; it serves to hide a multitude of difficulties inherent in the older forms of the collision theory. For simple reactions (e.g., $Na + I_2 \rightarrow NaI + I$) P is near unity, while for reactions of complex species it may be as small as 10^{-5}. There is no foolproof way of estimating its size from the older collision theory; reasonable guesses can be made by means of the transition state theory or more elegant collision theory, but it is usually calculated from 6-30, 6-31, and 6-32, using experimental rate data.

6-7A-2 The Transition State or Absolute Reaction Rate Theory of Bimolecular Reactions

The need for a quantitative theory of reaction rates was long appreciated in the field of chemical kinetics. It was recognized that serious limitations exist on any interpretations of reactivity and molecular structure based on the collision theory, since the reactant molecules are regarded unrealistically as solid inflexible spheres of matter. The calculation of the rates of chemical reactions from this theory is possible for only a very few reactions between atoms and simple molecules where P is near unity and E_a near zero. Little can be predicted concerning most reactions, even those between molecules of limited complexity. Chemical thermodynamics offered no solution in the development of rate theory because it applies only to the prediction of final equilibrium concentrations of the reactants and products; it can indicate nothing about the rate of a reaction.* The rate may be very slow although the tendency to react, as measured by the free energy change, is very great. For example, the reaction $2H_2(g) + O_2(g) \rightarrow 2H_2O(g)$ has a free energy change at 298.2°K of -54.64 kcal/mole of H_2O formed, reflecting a large tendency for hydrogen and oxygen gases to form water vapor at room temperature. However, in the absence of a catalyst the reaction at 25°C is immeasurably slow.

With the development of the transition state theory a radically different approach has been made toward the *a priori* prediction of rates from only a detailed knowledge of the energy states of the molecules involved. In principle, this theory considers all the internal motions of vibration and rotation as well as the translation of the reacting species.

Eyring, Polanyi, and many other scientists contributed significantly to the development of the transition state theory.[78] In the early quantitative applications of this theory, the nature of the potential energy of the interacting molecules was calculated as a function of the relative positions of the different nuclei. This represents a formidable task for even the simplest

---

* There is an important exception to this generalization, which is considered in Sec. 6-7A-7c. If the thermodynamic functions are available for a given overall reaction, then the equilibrium constant for the reaction can be calculated as a function of temperature. Now, if the rate constant for the given elementary reaction in the forward direction (k_1) is known, we can calculate the rate constant for the reverse elementary reaction (k_2) from the relation, $K_{eq} = k_1/k_2$.

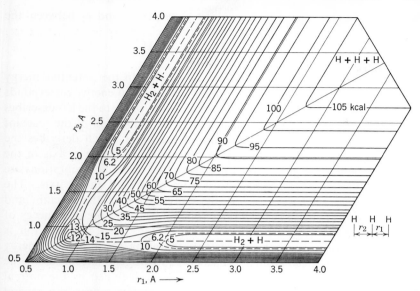

Fig. 6-2   Potential energy diagram for the reaction $H + H_2 \rightarrow H_2 + H$. From Eyring, Gershinowitz, and Sun.[78c]

of systems. Figure 6-2 reproduces one of the few theoretical potential energy surfaces which have been calculated.* Eyring and co-workers[78c] derived it in consideration of the theoretical rate of the conversion of ortho- to parahydrogen:

$$H + H_2(ortho) \rightarrow H_2(para) + H \qquad (6-35)$$

The configurations of the three hydrogen nuclei of lowest potential energy, and hence the most important configurations as far as reaction rates are concerned, are those in which the three nuclei lie along a straight line. These are the only configurations considered in the derivation of the surface shown in Fig. 6-2. The coordinates of any point on the potential

---

* The axes in Fig. 6-2 are tilted from the usual angle of 90° in order to show the inter-conversion of vibrational and translation energy; we will not be concerned with this subtle feature here. Also the potential well which occurs in the surface at $r_1 = r_2 = 0.86$ A may be not real but only a consequence of approximations made in the derivation of the potential energy surface. However, even recently some calculations of this potential energy surface still predict a potential well and an H_3 species of small stability.[79] We normally consider the activated molecule to be the configuration at a saddle point which looks directly down to both the potential energy valley for the reactants and the valley for products.

energy surface of the figure give the distances r_1 and r_2 between the hydrogen nuclei:

$$H \ldots \ldots H \ldots \ldots \ldots H$$
$$r_2 \qquad\qquad r_1$$

Paralleling each of the axes a valley can be seen in the potential energy surface. At the right of the lower valley the potential energy corresponds to that of the reactants. The upper portion of the valley to the left describes the potential energy of the product molecules. Vibration of the reactant molecule can be pictured as a motion of the point which describes the positions of the nuclei in a direction perpendicular to the r_1 axis in the valley to the lower right. Similarly the product molecule's vibrations are shown as motion of the point away from or toward the r_2 axis. The potential energy function used in the construction of the reactant and product valleys is the familiar Morse function for the potential energy of the diatomic vibrator, shown previously in Fig. 3-7. The reaction is visualized to proceed over the surface, following the potential energy valleys. As a hydrogen atom approaches the hydrogen molecule along the line of its nuclei (or at such small angles as are included by the normal bending vibrations of the activated state), the system moves in a general westerly direction in the valley parallel to the r_1 axis, as shown by the dotted line, called the reaction coordinate. Superimposed on this motion along the reaction coordinate will be motion lateral to this line which represents the periodic vibrations of the nuclei. As the hydrogen atom moves to within a few angstrom units of the molecule, the repulsive forces between the two systems become significant, the speeds of the approaching atom and molecule gradually decrease, and the potential energy of the system gradually increases. If the colliding atoms have sufficient translational energy they continue to approach, and the point which describes the configuration of the system climbs to the top of the hill at the western end of the valley, where $r_1 = 1.25$ and $r_2 = 0.78$ A.

The transient species which exists at the crest of this hill or the saddle point in the potential energy surface (at 14 kcal energy in Fig. 6-2) is called the *transition state* or *activated complex*. If the original kinetic energy of the reactants is sufficient, greater than 14 kcal in the present case, then the system may pass over the saddle point, move along the dotted line into the valley which parallels the r_2 axis, and eventually proceed to products represented at the upper left of the potential energy valley. The minimum energy necessary for the reactants to climb to the top of the saddle point and reach the configuration of the activated complex is related to E_a, the activation energy of the reaction in the old collision theory; it is the minimum potential energy which the reactant molecules must have to form products.

For reactions between molecules composed of many atoms, a large number of coordinates are necessary to describe the potential energy as a function of the different atom positions. Because of the complexity of the calculations, the potential energy surfaces for only a few relatively simple reaction systems have been derived, and in these various approximate methods were employed. Fortunately much of the usefulness of the absolute reaction rate theory can be derived without the complete construction of the potential energy surface which describes the reaction. It is a helpful concept to visualize reactants gradually blending into an activated complex which dissociates smoothly into products through reference to the movements of a point on a potential energy surface; this concept of the nature of an elementary chemical reaction should be retained even though for most practical systems the quantitative construction of the potential energy surfaces cannot be realized today.

The basic assumption which is made in the derivation of the rate equation in the absolute reaction rate theory is that the reactant molecules are in equilibrium with the transition state or activated complex. With this assumption an equilibrium constant $K^{\ddagger}$ can be formulated for the bimolecular reaction between molecules A and B, $A + B \rightleftharpoons AB^{\ddagger} \rightarrow$ Products:

$$K^{\ddagger} = \frac{[AB^{\ddagger}]}{[A][B]} \qquad (6\text{-}36)$$

where $[AB^{\ddagger}]$ is the concentration of the activated complex. From statistical thermodynamics the equilibrium constant $K^{\ddagger}$ can be evaluated in terms of the partition function Q' of the molecular species involved.

$$K^{\ddagger} = \frac{Q'_{AB^{\ddagger}}}{Q_A' Q_B'} e^{-E_0/RT} \qquad (6\text{-}37)$$

$Q' = Q/N$, where N is the number of molecules, and Q, the molecular partition function, is related to the probability that a molecule will exist in any one or another of its possible energy states E_i of degeneracy g_i; it is defined by

$$Q = \sum g_i e^{-E_i/kT} \qquad (6\text{-}38)$$

All the different translational, vibrational, rotational, and electronic energy states are included in the summation of 6-38. In Eq. 6-37 the zero-point energy difference E_0 has been separated from the total partition functions.

From a consideration of the rate of passage of activated complexes over the potential energy barrier and the concentration of activated complexes derived from 6-36 and 6-37, the rate constant of the general bimolecular reaction can be calculated:

$$k_{II} = \frac{kT\kappa K^{\ddagger}}{h} = \frac{kT\kappa}{h} \frac{Q'_{AB^{\ddagger}}}{Q_A' Q_B'} e^{-E_0/RT} \qquad (6\text{-}39)$$

where **k** is Boltzmann's constant, h is Planck's constant, and κ is the transmission coefficient, defined as the fraction of activated complexes which, after reaching the saddle point, continue on their paths on the potential energy surface and form products

By the use of 6-39 a calculation of the bimolecular rate constant of any reaction is theoretically possible. In actuality the calculation poses several problems of large magnitude. The partition functions Q_A and Q_B for the stable molecules A and B, respectively, can be evaluated usually for the simple molecules from the known molecular configuration and the energy states by using well established methods of statistical thermodynamics. However, since the configuration and the vibrational and rotational states of the activated complex are not known and are not subject to experimental determination, they must be estimated by some indirect means. Several useful approximate methods of estimating these values will be considered in Sec. 6-7A-7. E_0 can be obtained from the depths of the passes ony if the potential energy surface is well defined; we have seen that this is usually not the case. κ, the transmission coefficient, may appear at first sight to function in a way analogous to the P factor of the collision theory, that is, a correction factor to make the theory and experiment match. However, these quantities are not actually related, and there is reasonably sound theoretical justification for the κ of the transition state theory. Its value appears to be near unity for most reactions, but for the bimolecular association reactions of atoms κ is zero.

In the treatment of actual rate data by the transition state theory it is convenient to define some thermodynamic quantities related to the reactants and the activated state. The free energy of activation $\Delta F^{\ddagger}$, the enthalpy of activation $\Delta H^{\ddagger}$, and the entropy of activation $\Delta S^{\ddagger}$ are defined by equations analogous to those of thermodynamics:

$$\Delta F^{\ddagger} = -RT \ln K^{\ddagger} \qquad (6\text{-}40)$$

$$\Delta H^{\ddagger} = RT^2 \frac{d(\ln K^{\ddagger})}{dT} - (n-1)RT \qquad (6\text{-}41)$$

$$\Delta S^{\ddagger} = \frac{\Delta H^{\ddagger} - \Delta F^{\ddagger}}{T} \qquad (6\text{-}42)$$

Here n is the molecularity of the gas-phase reaction. $K^{\ddagger}$ is given in concentration units which correspond to those used for the rate constants. The terms $\Delta F^{\ddagger}$, $\Delta H^{\ddagger}$, and $\Delta S^{\ddagger}$ are the differences in free energy, enthalpy, and entropy, respectively, between those of the activated complex and those of the reactants with each in its standard state. The standard state is determined by the choice of units for concentration in evaluating k_{II}.

For example, if concentrations are given in molecules/cubic centimeter, then the standard states are 1 molecule/cm^3.

From 6-39, 6-40, 6-41, and 6-42 it follows that the reaction rate constant may be defined as

$$k_{II} = \frac{\mathbf{k}T\kappa}{h} e^{\Delta S^{\ddagger}/R} e^{-\Delta H^{\ddagger}/RT} \tag{6-43}$$

In terms of the transition state theory the rate of a reaction may be considered to be determined from the enthalpy and entropy changes involved in the formation of the activated complex. $\Delta H^{\ddagger}$ is related to the potential energy barrier for the reaction, and of course the larger this term the slower the rate. In the interpretation of the pre-exponential factor, $A \cong (\mathbf{k}T/h)\kappa e^{\Delta S^{\ddagger}/R}$, by the transition state theory, a small factor indicates an improbable complex ($\Delta S^{\ddagger}$ is negative), while a large factor is indicative of a very probable or "loose" complex ($\Delta S^{\ddagger}$ is positive).

For gas-phase bimolecular reactions, the pre-exponential factor A usually lies in the range from about 10^4 liters/mole-sec for certain complex dimerizations to about 10^{10} liters/mole-sec for reactions between free radicals, atoms, or very simple molecules.

6-7A-3 The Relations Between the Two Reaction Rate Theories

Some instructive and interesting comparisons between the two reaction rate theories can be made from the various equations for bimolecular rate constant k_{II}: 6-30, 6-39, and 6-43.

For the case of the reaction between two atoms A and B which react bimolecularly to form products, the internuclear distance between A and B in the activated complex will be equivalent to σ_{AB} of the collision theory. Calculation of k_{II} from 6-39, using this value and no vibrational degrees of freedom, leads directly to the collision theory equation, Eq. 6-30, with Z_{AB} given by Eq. 6-31, $P = 1$, and $E_a = E_0$. This is the only case where complete correspondence between the two theories is found; in all others vibrational and rotational states contribute to k_{II}, and only in the transition state theory are these considered.[*]

The relation between the different energy terms, E_a, and E_0 and $\Delta H^{\ddagger}$ of the theories may be examined. In calculating an experimental activation

---

[*] The agreement between the two theories in the case cited is not found if one considers the actual rate of the reaction of two simple atoms in the reaction of combination; unless some third body removes some of the energy released as the bond is formed, the molecule will always dissociate (unless energy is emitted as radiation), and the rate of combination will be zero.

energy in the usual manner one concentrates the temperature dependence in the exponential function; that is, the pre-exponential function A is assumed to be temperature independent. When Eq. 6-28 is solved for E_a, Eq. 6-44 results.

$$E_a = -R\left[\frac{d \ln k}{d(1/T)}\right] = RT^2\left[\frac{d \ln k}{dT}\right] \tag{6-44}$$

If the rate constant is expressed in concentration units, as in the usual case, then in terms of the transition state theory

$$k = \frac{\mathbf{k}T}{h}\kappa K_c^{\ddagger} \tag{6-45}$$

where $K_c^{\ddagger}$ is expressed in concentration units. From 6-44, 6-45, and the usual thermodynamic relations, the equations relating the energy quantities can be derived. For gas-phase reactions of molecularity n, and cases where the temperature dependence of the partition function ratio is given by $Q_{ABC\ddagger}/Q_A Q_B Q_C = BT^m$, the relations are:

$$E_0 = E_a - (m + 1)RT \tag{6-46}$$

$$\Delta H^{\ddagger} = E_0 + (m - n + 1)RT \tag{6-47}$$

$$\Delta H^{\ddagger} = E_a - nRT \tag{6-48}$$

For solution-phase reactions, relation 6-49 holds, independent of n:

$$\Delta H^{\ddagger} = E_a - RT \tag{6-49}$$

In Eqs. 6-30 and 6-43 the two exponential terms are approximately equal, and it can be shown that $\kappa \mathbf{k}T/h$ is of the order of magnitude of Z. It follows that $P \cong e^{\Delta S^{\ddagger}/R}$ (for the reference states of 1 mole/cm³). Thus the so-called steric factor of the collision theory can be thought of as a function primarily of the entropy change associated with the formation of the activated complex, which is, of course, related to the molecular orientation on collision, as well as many other factors (degree of rotation of the parts of the complex, etc.).

The collision theory demands that the temperature dependence of the pre-exponential factor be proportional to $T^{1/2}$. The exponent of the temperature in the pre-exponential factor of the transition-state theory, $A \cong (\mathbf{k}T/h)e^{\Delta S^{\ddagger}/R}$, is usually in the range from 2 to -2, depending on the nature of the reaction and the temperature dependence of $\Delta S^{\ddagger}$. Since the influence of these temperature terms on the rate constant is usually slight compared to the exponential term, the method of treatment of the data to obtain $\Delta H^{\ddagger}$ or E_a is fairly insensitive to the power of T chosen for the A factor. In fact it is most common to assume that the A factor is temperature independent in the treatment of experimental data. See Sec. 6-7A-8.

6-7A-4   Rate Theories for Termolecular Reactions

In the gas phase, where the molecularity of a reaction is best defined, there appears to be a limited number of true termolecular reactions. The rate of the termolecular reaction

$$A + B + C \rightleftharpoons ABC^{\ddagger} \rightarrow Products \tag{6-50}$$

is given by

$$-\frac{d[A]}{dt} = k_{III}[A][B][C] \tag{6-51}$$

where k_{III} may be expressed in terms of the old collision theory, $k_{III} = PZ_{III}e^{-E_a/RT}$. The collision number Z_{III} may be calculated from Tolman's[80] equation:

$$Z_{III} = 8\sqrt{2}\pi^{3/2}\sigma_{AB}^2\sigma_{BC}^2 \; \delta\sqrt{RT}\left(\frac{1}{\sqrt{\mu_{AB}}} + \frac{1}{\sqrt{\mu_{BC}}}\right) \tag{6-52}$$

A collision between the three molecules is defined as the approach of two molecules A and C to within the distance δ from B. The size of δ is unknown, but it is assumed to be of the order of magnitude of molecular dimensions (1×10^{-8} cm.) The other symbols in 6-52 have their usual significance.

Gershinowitz and Eyring[81] have shown the transition state theory to be successful in accounting for the termolecular reactions between NO and O_2, H_2, D_2, and the halogens ($2NO + X_2 \rightarrow 2NOX$). In general for reaction 6-50, k_{III} is calculated from

$$k_{III} = \frac{kT\kappa}{h}\frac{Q'_{ABC^{\ddagger}}}{Q_A'Q_B'Q_C'} e^{-E_0/RT} \tag{6-53}$$

It may be represented in form 6-54 also,

$$k_{III} = \frac{kT\kappa}{h} e^{\Delta S^{\ddagger}/R} e^{-\Delta H^{\ddagger}/RT} \tag{6-54}$$

where the terms have their usual significance.

In the interpretation of many gas-phase photochemical experiments, association reactions of atoms (H, Cl, Br, I, etc.) are suggested to be termolecular. A simple diatomic molecule cannot form from its component atoms unless some of the energy released on bond formation is removed by some mechanism, for example, by collision with a third body (a third molecule or a wall); otherwise the molecule will dissociate again with its first vibration. It is interesting to note that small negative activation energies are found for the association of halogen atoms where the third body is a rare-gas molecule or halogen. Several markedly different theories have been suggested to account for this phenomenon.[82]

The rate of association of methyl radicals to form ethane is second order in $[CH_3]$ in the usual pressure region but begins to depend on the concentration of the third body at pressures below 10 mm.[83] The radicals composed of many atoms seem to have a sufficiently large number of vibrational and rotational modes so that the energy released on combination has a high probability of being transferred to other modes within the molecule; in this case the lifetime of the active molecule (formed by radical association) may be sufficiently great compared to the time between collisions that stabilization by collision may occur even at relatively low pressures. A molecule formed by the association of two given radicals has a finite probability of dissociation into fragments other than the original radicals, providing that the energies of the bonds involved are comparable and collisional deactivation is not dominant. Both experiment and theory support the conclusion that dissociation processes of this kind decrease in importance with increasing number of degress of freedom of the decomposing molecule. The general theoretical problem of the rates of termolecular reactions and the consideration of the distribution of energy in molecules have been treated by Marcus and Rice in terms of the transition state theory.[84]

6-7A-5 The Theories of Pseudo-Unimolecular Reactions

The various primary photodecomposition modes of photoactivated molecules in the dilute gas phase follow rapidly after the absorption of radiation. These are examples of a type of unimolecular reaction, although in the strictest sense they might be considered bimolecular reactions between a molecule and a quantum of light. Radioactive decay is a familiar example of a unimolecular decomposition. Many thermal reactions of gaseous molecules have been observed to be first order; they follow the rate law

$$- \frac{d[A]}{dt} = k_I[A] \qquad (6\text{-}55)$$

Presumably the thermal decompositions of many alkyl and alkoxy radicals are of this type over a large pressure range.

A satisfactory explanation of these apparent unimolecular reactions in terms of the collision theory was a major problem in the field of reaction kinetics. This theory necessitates excitation by collision preceding reaction, and such a mechanism was thought to require second-order kinetics. Lindemann[85] in 1922 first suggested a reasonable scheme in terms of the collision theory. The molecules A are activated by collision with other molecules of A to an excited state A* (vibrational or other excitation).

$$A + A \rightarrow A^* + A \text{ (rate constant } k_2) \qquad (6\text{-}56)$$

Reaction to form products can occur only by passing through the state A*, which part of the time undergoes a true unimolecular decomposition.

$$A^* \rightarrow \text{Products (rate constant } k_1) \qquad (6\text{-}57)$$

Presumably the majority of the time A* is deactivated by a bimolecular collision.

$$A^* + A \rightarrow 2A \text{ (rate constant } k_{-2}) \qquad (6\text{-}58)$$

If 6-56 and 6-58 are fast compared to 6-57, then the rate will be determined by

$$-\frac{d[A]}{dt} = k_1[A^*] \qquad (6\text{-}59)$$

[A*] is derived from the reaction sequence, assuming that the rate of formation of A* is equal to its rate of destruction; that is, $d[A^*]/dt = 0$.[†] The resultant rate of reaction of A is

$$-\frac{d[A]}{dt} = \frac{k_1 k_2 [A]^2}{k_1 + k_{-2}[A]} \qquad (6\text{-}60)$$

At high [A], where $k_{-2}[A] \gg k_1$, Eq. 6-60 reduces to

$$-\frac{d[A]}{dt} = \frac{k_1 k_2 [A]}{k_{-2}} \qquad (6\text{-}61)$$

and the reaction is first order. At low [A], $k_{-2}[A] \ll k_1$ and 6-60 becomes

$$-\frac{d[A]}{dt} = k_2[A]^2 \qquad (6\text{-}62)$$

and the reaction now appears to be second order. The rate constant evaluated experimentally, assuming the reaction to be first order, is given by

$$k_{\mathrm{I}} = \frac{k_2 k_1 [A]}{k_1 + k_{-2}[A]} \qquad (6\text{-}63)$$

The Lindemann theory is in qualitative accord with experiment. Several pseudo-unimolecular reactions have been found to shift toward the second-order kinetics required by 6-60 at low pressures. Furthermore, the

---

[†] Note that this mechanism choice is equivalent to the postulate of the transition state theory that the activated complex is in equilibrium with the reactants.

addition of a sufficiently large quantity of inert gas to the system at low [A] causes a return to the same first-order rate obtained at high [A].[86]

Major corrections and improvements in the Lindemann theory are necessary to explain some of the details of the experimental first-order reaction rate data. For example, it was noted that activation in 6-56 could not be fast enough in terms of the bimolecular collision theory to maintain the first-order kinetics to the very low [A] range observed experimentally. Hinshelwood[87] showed from classical mechanics that the fraction of molecules having energies greater than E distributed at random between s vibrational degrees of freedom (s can equal up to a maximum of $3n - 6$ in a non-linear molecule, where n is the number of atoms in the molecule) was not the factor $e^{-E/RT}$ derived by the consideration of translational energies only, but rather was given by Y of Eq. 6-64:

$$Y = \frac{(E/RT)^{s-1}e^{-E/RT}}{(s-1)!}$$ (6-64)

A possible explanation of the apparent rapid rate of 6-56 is evident if $E \gg RT$; s is large for complex molecules and Eq. 6-64 is significantly greater than the $e^{-E/RT}$ of the simple theory. The size of s required to make the rate of activation, $Z_{AB} Y[A][B]$, in accord with experiment in actual cases, is usually consistent with the total number of degrees of freedom for the molecule. On the basis of this theory it is expected that the decomposition of complex molecules (like di-*tert*-butyl peroxide) or large radicals might follow first-order kinetics to much lower pressures than the small uncomplicated species like HCO. Indeed such is the case.

It is seen from a rearrangement of 6-63,

$$\frac{1}{k_I} = \frac{1}{k_2[A]} + \frac{k_{-2}}{k_1 k_2}$$ (6-65)

that the Lindemann theory predicts a linear relation between $1/k_I$ and $1/[A]$. Pseudo-unimolecular reaction rate data fit this form qualitatively, but they deviate from this relation at high [A]. In explanation Rice, Ramsperger, and Kassel[88] have suggested that there are many excited states above the minimum energy E from which decomposition can take place, and that the probability of molecule decomposition is greater, the greater the activation above E. For a molecule which has s weakly coupled internal degrees of freedom ($s = 3n - 6$) and an energy E^* shared between them, where $E^* \geqslant E$, the probability that the minimum energy E necessary for the reaction to occur will accumulate in the particular vibrational mode which leads to bond breakage or other reaction is given by $(1 - E/E^*)^{s-1}$. The rate constant for the decomposition of the excited molecule will be proportional to this probability factor and to a proportionality factor ν, related to the rate of internal energy transfer. Then the particular rate constant for a given excited molecule of energy E^* is given by

$$k_{E^*} = \nu\left(1 - \frac{E}{E^*}\right)^{s-1} \tag{6-66}$$

Equations of the same form are derived from more sophisticated models, and the significance of ν and s varies somewhat with the assumptions made in the derivations.[84,88–91] In terms of these theories the various rate constants of 6-63 are weighted averages of the many different k's which correspond to the different excited molecules.

According to these theories, the value of the low-pressure second-order rate constant k_2 for the activation process 6-56 should be given approximately by

$$k_2 = \frac{Z}{(s-1)!}\left(\frac{E}{RT}\right)^{s-1} e^{-E/RT} \tag{6-67}$$

where Z is the collision number calculated from 6-31 and 6-33 (or 6-32 and 6-34), and the other terms have their usual significance. k_{-2} can be no larger than the collision number Z.

The notions expressed in the unimolecular reaction rate theories of Hinshelwood, Kassel, Rice, and Ramsberger have been considerably refined in the later works of Marcus and Rice.[84] The basic feature of this "amalgamated" theory (designated herein as the HKRRM theory) is an assumption of free exchange of energy between the various molecular modes of excitation. According to this theory, decomposition of the molecule results when, at a rate determined by the laws of statistics, a sufficient energy or number of quanta of vibration accumulates in the bond which is to be broken.

A rather different approach to the theory of unimolecular reactions was conceived by Polanyi and Wigner[92] and developed quantitatively by Slater.[89] The Slater theory assumes no energy exchange between the normal modes of vibration within the molecule. Reaction occurs, not when some critical energy gets into a particular mode, but when the normal mode vibrations come suitably into phase and some critical coordinate becomes sufficiently extended. Slater's theory is more difficult to apply in practice than the HKRRM theory, but its usefulness may grow as approximate methods for its application are developed.

According to the Slater theory, the rate constant k_2 for the rate of the activation process 6-56 is given approximately by

$$k_2 = Z\left(\frac{4\pi E}{RT}\right)^{(n-1)/2} \prod_{k=1}^{n} \mu_k \, e^{-E/RT} \tag{6-68}$$

Here the number of modes $= n$. The values of μ_k, the amplitude factors, involved in the product term are fractions related to the amplitudes of the atoms along the critical coordinate in the various normal modes of vibration; they are obtained from a detailed vibrational analysis of the molecule. The various μ's are normalized to satisfy the relation $\mu_1^2 + \mu_2^2 + \mu_3^2 + \cdots \mu_n^2 = 1$, so that the maximum product of the μ's is $n^{-n/2}$. The actual product has a much smaller value than $n^{-n/2}$ since some of the μ's are very small; that is, there is little stretching of the critical coordinate when certain normal vibrational modes are excited. The rate equations of Slater for the high-pressure limit reduce approximately to

$$k_1 = \bar{\nu} e^{-E/RT} \tag{6-69}$$

$\bar{\nu}$ is the square root of the weighted averages of the squares of the normal vibration frequencies which describe the decomposition, and E is the minimum energy for dissociation.

Tests of the different theories of unimolecular reactions have shown somewhat varied results. For example, "Monte Carlo" calculations were made by Bunker[93] to determine the distribution of lifetimes with respect to the high-pressure dissociation as a function of energy for a variety of rotating anharmonic triatomic molecular modes; he found adequate agreement with the HKRRM theory. On the other hand, the attempts of Steiner, Giese, and Inghram[94] to fit quantitatively the simple statistical theory of energy exchange to the low-pressure first order kinetic processes involved after photoionization of a series of alkanes have failed in large part.

Many tests of the HKRRM and Slater theories have been made to determine which describes better the actual fall-off of the first-order rate constants with decrease in pressure for a series of different molecules. Gill and Laidler[95] have made several tests of this type which suggest that each theory seems to apply under certain conditions. They propose in modification of the unimolecular reaction rate theory a compromise between the assumptions of the HKRRM and Slater theories. They allow a definite probability of energy flow between normal modes of a molecule energized in the HKRRM sense (but not having the right distribution of energy to be energized according to the Slater picture) and the Slater energized molecule. From their considerations they conclude that Slater's expression for the high-pressure rate (6-69) will always apply in experiments at high pressures. At low pressures the HKRRM formula (6-67) for the rate of energization should hold. This compromise of theories is somewhat attractive, but it must be accepted with caution. Note that Slater's approximate expression for the limiting high-pressure rate is restricted by the frequency of the normal mode vibrations; it cannot be larger than the maximum fundamental vibration frequency. Thus with Slater's picture it is difficult to explain experimental A factors for first-order rate constants which are larger than 10^{13}–10^{14} sec^{-1} (the normal vibration frequency of molecules) although it is possible to rationalize A-factors of 10^{18} in terms of the HKRRM theories.[84] It should be apparent to the reader that there is not unanimous acceptance of either the HKRRM or the Slater theory of unimolecular reactions, although most rate data are not sufficiently accurate to provide a critical test of the theories.

When a reaction is in the first-order region of kinetics and the rate of passage over the energy barrier and not the rate of activation by collision is the rate-determining step, the rate data may be handled in the usual way by the transition state theory Eqs. 6-70 and 6-71:

$$k_{\mathrm{I}} = \frac{\mathbf{k}T}{h} \frac{Q_{\mathrm{A}}^{\ddagger}}{Q_{\mathrm{A}}} e^{-E_0/RT} \tag{6-70}$$

$$k_{\mathrm{I}} = \frac{\mathbf{k}T}{h} e^{\Delta S^{\ddagger}/R} e^{-\Delta H^{\ddagger}/RT} \tag{6-71}$$

In the presentation of experimental first-order rate data it is customary to derive the pre-exponential factor A and the activation energy E_a for the equation

$$k_{\mathrm{I}} = A e^{-E_a/RT} \tag{6-72}$$

Measured A values for first-order gas-phase reactions vary from 10^5 sec^{-1} for certain *cis-trans* isomerization (presumably slow because of a quantum multiplicity restriction) to about 10^{18} sec^{-1}.

Most of the discussions in this section have been aimed toward the treatment of rates of thermally equilibrated free radicals and molecules in the photochemical systems. However, reaction rate theory is of major interest in the description of the reactions of the electronically excited molecules formed in photochemical systems. There are significant differences between the photochemically activated and thermally activated systems. A major difference is in the distribution of vibrational energy states in the reactant. In a thermal reaction the Maxwell-Boltzmann equilibrium distribution is approximated at high pressures; that small fraction of the molecules which possess sufficient energy for the reaction have a chance of undergoing decomposition. At low pressures the high-energy molecules decompose before they can be deactivated, and the rate is limited by the rate of activation; that is, the reaction becomes second order.

In many photodissociative processes in the gas phase, dissociation occurs only from vibrational levels of the excited state significantly above that level corresponding to thermal equilibrium of the excited state (e.g., $v' = 0$ at room temperature). These high vibrational states are reached in the act of absorption, the level attained being a function of the wavelength of the quantum and the temperature of the system. At low pressures there is little deactivation of the vibrational energy, and the molecule has a high probability of dissociating in a unimolecular process. At high pressures the reverse is true; rapid degradation toward an equilibrium distribution of vibrational states can occur, and the rate of decomposition falls off. This behavior is just the opposite of that which we saw in thermal decomposition, where the rate is second order at low pressures and first order at high pressures.

In the solution phase (equivalent to very high pressures of gas) vibrational equilibration of the excited states is most common as evidenced by the fact that fluorescence is from the $v' = 0$ level, independent of the wavelength of excitation (Sec. 4-6). However, it is important to note that photodissociation from high vibrational levels can occur in solution. For example, Φ_{N_2} from the decomposition of benzenediazonium salts shows a marked wavelength dependence. Obviously the lifetime of the excited state undergoing the particular primary process is the critical factor in determining the order of the kinetics of the elementary process.

The use of reaction rate theory for excited molecules is in a rather primitive state, but significant studies have been made by a few workers.[96] If an electronically excited molecule has two paths of reaction in competition, for example, decomposition and collisional deactivation or two different decomposition modes, then equations of the form of 6-66 can be employed in the treatment of the data. Let us consider a simplified case which may be illustrative. A molecule M is excited by absorption of a quantum and then reacts by dissociation to form products A and B, reaction 6-74, or by collisional deactivation in 6-75:

$$M + h\nu \rightarrow M^* \qquad (\varphi I_a) \qquad (6\text{-}73)$$

$$M^* \rightarrow A + B \qquad (k_1) \qquad (6\text{-}74)$$

$$M^* + M \rightarrow 2M' \qquad (k_2) \qquad (6\text{-}75)$$

If only these reactions occur, then Eq. 6-76 applies:

$$\frac{1}{\Phi_A} = 1 + \frac{k_2}{k_1}[M] \qquad (6\text{-}76)$$

Values of k_2/k_1 can be obtained from the slopes of the plots of $1/\Phi_A$ versus [M] from runs at a given temperature and wavelength; k_2 may be assumed equal to Z_2, and values of k_1 calculated. A satisfactory fit of the ketene photolyses data obtained in this fashion from experiments at

3660, 3340, and 3130 A has been obtained by Porter and Connelly,[96b] using relation 6-66 to describe the variation of k_1 with the energy of the absorbed quantum. The agreement is somewhat fortuitous, however, since most of the parameters in 6-66 had to be chosen rather arbitrarily. The actual dissociation of an excited molecule must involve a much more complicated kinetic scheme, and Porter and Connelly consider some of the probable complications of the real case. These include contributions to dissociation from lower vibrational levels than that reached on excitation because of cascade collisional deactivation, contribution from triplet dissociation, internal conversion to the ground state, and fluorescence. Photochemical data on competing primary processes are not sufficiently accurate at this writing to justify more quantitative tests of unimolecular reaction rate theory, although this important problem must receive a significant effort in the years ahead.

As we have seen in Sec. 4-8B-2, the highly vibrationally excited ground-state molecules can be formed in photochemical experiments through the mechanism of internal conversion of electronic excitation. Among the other evidence for this phenomenon is the observation that for a great number of molecules the summation of the primary quantum yields of all measurable processes involving the excited state (that is, decomposition, fluorescence, phosphorescence, etc.) is much less than unity. The unambiguous determination of the importance of this process and the subsequent reactions of the vibrationally excited molecule is most difficult at present.

In competition with the decomposition modes of the vibrationally excited molecule is the process of vibrational relaxation through energy transfer by collisions with other molecules. In dense gaseous media or the solution phase, vibrational equilibration occurs in a period shorter than 10^{-8} sec in the solution phase, since fluorescence emission which occurs with this timing originates from molecules in the lowest vibrational levels of the electronically excited state and is independent of the wavelength of the exciting light.

However, in the photochemistry of relatively simple molecules in the dilute gas phase, the decomposition of the vibrationally excited ground-state molecules formed may compete with collisional relaxation processes. For example, Srinivasan[159] in his study of the 3130 A photolysis of 1,3,5-cycloheptatriene at low pressures and Parmenter[153] in the 4358 A glyoxal photolysis at low pressures have suggested that certain photolysis products arise from highly vibrationally excited ground-state species. In these cases the decomposition of the vibrationally excited species is almost completely quenched at moderate gas pressures. Thus Parmenter reported that the ratio of rate constants for dissociation of vibrationally excited ground-state glyoxal $[(CHO)_2^{\ddagger} \rightarrow H_2 + 2CO]$ to that for the vibrational relaxation $[(CHO)_2^{\ddagger} + (CHO)_2 \rightarrow 2(CHO)_2]$ was equal to 12.5 mm; thus at only 100 mm pressure about nine-tenths of the vibrationally excited glyoxal molecules are deactivated before decomposition can occur.

Srinivasan found that the quantum yield of toluene from the photolysis of cycloheptatriene at 3130 A and 83° was near unity at very low pressures but decreased very rapidly with increase in pressure: $\Phi_{C_6H_5CH_3} = 1.0$ at 0.0 mm, 0.081 at 2.6 mm, 0.016 at 15 mm. The data followed well a Stern-Volmer type plot (Sec. 6-7C); that is, the reciprocal of the toluene quantum yield was a linear function of the pressure. The toluene product from photolyses at 2600 A was quenched much less effectively: $\Phi_{C_6H_5CH_3} = 1.0$ at 0.0 mm, 0.29 at 15 mm.

The reactions of the vibrationally excited ground-state molecules have been invoked by various workers to explain the data from the photolysis of even complex molecules in the solution-phase experiments. In this regard the considerations of Ullman and Henderson[154] have been discussed in Sec. 4-8B-2. It seems improbable to us that molecular decomposition from vibrationally excited ground-state molecules is generally important for photochemical experiments in the solution phase or at high gas pressures. For polyatomic molecules of reasonable complexity the probability is low that a sufficient number of quanta of vibration will accumulate in the particular vibrational mode which will lead to reaction before vibrational relaxation can occur. The rate constant for unimolecular decay of the vibrationally excited species, described at least qualitatively by Eq. 6-66, decreases rapidly as the complexity of the molecule and the number of internal degrees of freedom (and the exponent s) grow. It seems likely that only in the simplest molecules and for low-pressure photolyses can decomposition of ground-state vibrationally excited molecules compete favorably with vibrational relaxation. Correlation between observed modes of photochemical processes and purely thermal modes of reaction for molecules in solution is not compelling evidence for the participation of vibrationally excited ground-state molecules in the photochemical system. One must certainly exercise great caution in invoking such a mechanism in dense media.

Vibrational relaxation of diatomic molecules has been studied extensively. Millikan and White[155] have found that the logarithm of the product of the pressure and the vibrational relaxation time is a linear function of the reciprocal of the one-third power of the absolute temperature for a variety of simple gaseous molecules. The decrease in vibrational relaxation time with increase in temperature has been used as a diagnostic tool in the consideration of the participation of ground-state vibrationally excited molecules in glyoxal photolysis.

6-7A-6 Kinetics of Reactions in Condensed Phases

Several similarities and several striking differences are encountered in comparing the reactions in the gas and liquid phases.[97] The rate constant for a given reaction between neutral free radicals and molecules is usually not greatly different in the two phases. However, certain thermal reactions of ions and photochemical primary processes involving ion formation and electron transfer, unknown to the gas phase, become energetically favorable and are important in solutions of high dielectric constant. If homogeneous light absorption is maintained, then liquid-phase systems are usually less complicated by wall reactions than the gas-phase counterparts because of the much lower diffusion rates for liquid systems. On the other hand, it is often said by the "sophisticated" gas-phase kineticist that solution-phase reactions and mechanisms are more complicated than the gas-phase systems to interpret since effects of solvent-molecule interactions are difficult to treat quantitatively.

In the theoretical treatment of solution kinetics the equations of the transition state theory may be modified to account for deviations from perfect solution behavior. For the equilibrium between reactants and transition state, $A + B + C + \cdots \rightleftharpoons (ABC)^{\ddagger}$, an equilibrium expression must be formulated in terms of activities:

$$K^{\ddagger} = \frac{[(ABC)^{\ddagger}]}{[A][B][C]\ldots}\left[\frac{\gamma_{ABC^{\ddagger}}}{\gamma_A\gamma_B\gamma_C}\right] \qquad (6\text{-}77)$$

The rate constant expression assumes the form 6-78, taking $\kappa = 1$:

$$k = \frac{kT}{h}K^{\ddagger}\frac{\gamma_A\gamma_B\gamma_C}{\gamma_{ABC^{\ddagger}}} = \frac{kT}{h}e^{\Delta S^{\ddagger}/R}e^{-\Delta H^{\ddagger}/RT}\frac{\gamma_A\gamma_B\gamma_C}{\gamma_{ABC^{\ddagger}}} \qquad (6\text{-}78)$$

In the treatment of ionic reactions the refinement of including the activity coefficient term is most important. Commonly for dilute solutions the limiting form of the Debye-Hückel law can be employed to approximate the γ terms.[74d]. There is an impressive mass of mechanistic detail which can be gleamed from a study of the magnitudes of $\Delta S^{\ddagger}$ and $\Delta H^{\ddagger}$ in a related series of reactants or on change in solvent; a number of excellent discussions of this subject have appeared.[97,98]

Perhaps the most striking of the effects encountered in solution-phase photochemistry which are not observed in the dilute gas phase is the so-called "cage effect" first delineated by Franck and Rabinowitch (1934).[99] Free radical partners formed on homolytic bond rupture in solution are encircled or "caged" by solvent molecules. There is a high probability that two such original radical partners will recombine before diffusion to the average distance between "free" radicals in solution can occur. As a result of this phenomenon (as well as deactivation of excited molecules by solvent, etc.), the quantum yields of product derived from free radical formation are often significantly lower than in the analogous gas-phase experiments.

Lampe and Noyes[100] estimated that the fraction of iodine atoms (formed by the photodissociation of molecular iodine) which could escape a solvent cage and react with scavenger (allyl iodide and oxygen) varied markedly with the solvent employed and the temperature: for hexane, 0.50 (50°), 0.66 (25°); for carbon tetrachloride, 0.11 (17.5°), 0.14 (25°), 0.21 (38°); for hexachloro-1,3-butadiene, 0.042 (15°), 0.075 (25°), 0.15 (31°). The observed difference in escape facility has been related to the differences in mass and viscosity of the solvent molecules. Although differences in the viscosity are expected to influence the escape efficiency, the small differences between the viscosities of the solvents used here cannot explain the major effect seen. Barring differences in iodine molecule dissociation efficiency in the different solvents, Lampe and Noyes reasoned that the heavier the molecules in the cage walls, the more critical is the orientation of the iodine atoms that can escape. One would anticipate from "billiard ball" mechanics that the lowest escape efficiency would occur when the mass of the solvent molecule and that of the iodine atoms are about the same. This is consistent with the trend observed.

R. M. Noyes[100,101] and others[102] have developed rather detailed theories of the "cage" effect, and although there may be some question of their quantitative nature,[103] the treatment of solution-phase photochemical data dealing with geminate radical association has been facilitated greatly through their use. It is interesting to note that a "cage" effect has been demonstrated in *gas-phase* photolysis of azomethane in propane gas at several atmospheres pressure.[104] This is not surprising when one realizes that the diffusion coefficient for methyl radicals at these pressures of propane is not much larger than in the solution phase.

The rates of reactions which occur on practically every collision in the gas phase [i.e., radical-radical combination and disproportionation, fluorescence quenching, "allowed" electronic energy-transfer reactions, $D(T_1) + A(S_0) \rightarrow D(S_0) + A(T_1)$, and some reactions between ions in solution] are limited in the solution phase by the rate of diffusion of the reactants. In this case of *diffusion-controlled rates* the rate constant for the reaction is often estimated from the modified Debye equation:[105]

$$k_{\text{diff}} = \frac{1}{4}\left(2 + \frac{d_1}{d_2} + \frac{d_2}{d_1}\right) \frac{8RT}{3 \times 10^3 \eta} \tag{6-79}$$

where k_{diff} is in the units of liters/mole-second when η, the viscosity of the solvent, is in grams/second-centimeter or poise units, $R = 8.31 \times 10^7$

ergs/mole-deg K, and d_1 and d_2 are the diameters of the reacting species, which are assumed spherical.

Observed rate constants for the diffusion-controlled reactions show, at least qualitatively, the expected relation to the change in viscosity of the solvent with temperature. Apparent activation energies of about 2-3 kcal/mole are observed for the usual diffusion-controlled reactions in solvents such as CCl_4, hexane, benzene, and methyl methacrylate.

TABLE 6-2 Viscosity[a] and Diffusion-Controlled Rate Constants[b] for Various Solvents

Compound	Viscosity, $\eta \times 10^3$, poise, at a Temperature, °C, of					$k_{diff} \times 10^{-10}$, liters/mole-sec, at 20°
	0°	10°	20°	30°	40°	
Isopentane	2.78	2.49	2.25	2.05	...	2.9
n-Pentane	2.79	2.55	2.35	2.16	...	2.8
n-Hexane	3.81	3.62	3.13	2.85	2.62	2.1
n-Heptane	5.26	4.67	4.18	3.77	3.43	1.6
n-Octane	7.13	6.20	5.47	4.87	4.37	1.2
Chloroform	6.99	6.25	5.63	5.10	4.64	1.2
Toluene	7.73	6.70	5.87	5.20	4.65	1.1
Methanol	8.08	6.90	5.93	5.15	4.49	1.1
Benzene	...	7.60	6.49	5.62	4.92	1.0
Carbon tetrachloride	14.03	11.35	9.69	8.42	7.38	0.67
Cyclohexane	...	11.80	9.80	8.26	7.04	0.66
Water	17.93	13.10	10.09	8.00	6.54	0.64
Ethanol	...	...	11.92	...	...	0.55
n-Propyl alcohol	38.6	29.2	22.6	17.7	14.0	0.29
Isopropyl alcohol	45.6	32.5	23.7	17.7	12.9	0.27
Ethylene glycol	...	...	173	...	...	0.038
Glycerol	...	...	10700	3800	...	0.00061

[a] Data from *International Critical Tables*, McGraw-Hill Book Co., New York, 1933; "Selected Values of Physical and Thermodynamic Properties of Hydrocarbons and Related Compounds," *API Project* 44, Carnegie Press, Pittsburgh, 1953.
[b] Calculated, assuming $d_1 = d_2$ in Eq. 6-79.

Diffusion-controlled rate constants can be varied over a wide range through the proper choice of solvent: for example at 20°C, $k_{diff} = 2.9 \times 10^{10}$, 2.9×10^9, and 6×10^6 for isopentane, n-propyl alcohol, and glycerol, respectively, calculated from Eq. 6-79 and the viscosities in Table 6-2. Table 6-2 also contains values of the viscosity at 0, 10, 20, 30, and 40° and diffusion-controlled rate constants at 20° for a variety of common solvents.

The direct measurement of the diffusion coefficient of radical intermediates in solution can be accomplished through an ingenious technique of photochemical space intermittency developed by R. M. Noyes.[107] The technique is based on the facts that if photochemically produced radicals are destroyed by a second-order process, and if a cell is illuminated with a pattern of light and dark areas (leopard- or zebra-like patterns), the average concentration of radicals in space is dependent on the size of the light areas at a given total absorbed light energy. The effect is very similar in origin to that of the rotating sector technique described in Sec. 6-7B-4b.

Much effort has been expended in the study of a few solid-phase photochemical reactions. The kinetics and photochemistry of the photographic process which depends on the photochemical liberation of silver from silver bromide have been the object of intensive study for years.[108] Even now the process is not fully understood in all its details; however, the general features have been clarified greatly through works such as those of Mitchell and Mott.[109] Research on photoconductors and photosensitized reactions on solids has been active also in recent years. In general, however, solid-phase photochemistry has not received the amount of quantitative effort afforded the liquid and gaseous systems.

Many difficulties peculiar to the solid-phase photochemical system have helped to maintain its unpopularity. For example, profound differences in photochemical behavior appear as a result of crystal defects such as cracks, lattice imperfections, trace impurities in the lattice, and ion vacancies. The absorption of light by many solids is so great in their photoactive regions that only the diffuse reflectance spectrum is obtainable. The very high extinction coefficients of many solids in the near ultraviolet results in extremely non-homogeneous light absorption. Kitchener[110] estimates that about 98% of the light, of wavelengths less than the absorption threshold, which enters a typical crystal may be absorbed within a distance of 10^{-6} cm, of about 100 atomic layers. There is always an uncertainty in the physical state of the reactants adsorbed on solids.

In the consideration of solid photosensitized reactions one must be concerned with the possible changes in the absorption spectrum of the adsorbed molecules and the solid surface. There is evidence that the decomposition of adsorbed molecules is effected at wavelengths below and above the usual gas-phase absorption bands.[111] For example, ammonia adsorbed on NH_4Cl aerosols shows an absorption between 3100 and 2400 A, in which region also lies the maximum of its photodecomposition on various adsorbents ($CuSO_4$, CdI_2, MgO, Cu, and glass).[111e] It is not clear whether the possibility of solid photosensitized reactions was considered by the investigators in some of these cases. In any event, the possibility of an altered absorption spectrum of the absorbed reactant cannot be overlooked.

A further complication to the study of reactions on photosensitive solids arises in the change of adsorption of reactants upon irradiation of the solid. Photosensitive CdS has a much lower affinity for phenolphthalein and other dyes when irradiated in aqueous ethanol solution than in the dark.[112] The red form of HgS, which is also the most highly photosensitive form, adsorbs up to six times more phenolphthalein when illuminated than it does in the dark. The black form of HgS shows little difference between powers of adsorption in the dark and in the light.[112c] Often the encaging of primary products within solid crystals occurs and may be followed by a reversal of the primary steps. Because of these and other difficulties, the results of studies of a given system by different investigators often are in direct disagreement, and true progress in this field is slow.

Radiation absorbed by inorganic solids may result in color change, decomposition, certain photosensitized reactions at the surface of the solid, or re-emission of light. These changes usually have a common origin in conduction electrons and valence band "holes" formed by light absorption. The ultimate course of the reaction is determined by many factors; among them are the nature and number of lattice imperfections, the ease of reduction of component ions, the stability of lattice photolysis products, the mobilities of "holes" and electrons, and the nature and number of adsorbed molecules on the surface of the solid.

The mechanistic studies of the photochemistry of solids involve several measurements unique to the solid-state area: photoconductivity, photo-adsorption, ion and electron mobilities, crystal imperfections, etc. Each has its highly specialized techniques.[113]

The definitive, fundamental research necessary to develop adequate theories of solid-state reactions appears to be forthcoming. Eyring and co-workers have given theoretical consideration to the solid-phase reactions in terms of the transition state theory.[114] They conclude that because of space requirements the rate of almost any change in the solid will be negligibly slow except at interfaces or at imperfections in the crystal lattice. Interest is growing in the study of the solid-phase systems, and perhaps some detailed discussion of methods of this interesting area can be justified in the future.

6-7A-7 The Calculation of Rate Constants from Theory

The accurate determination of A and E_a in the expression for the rate constant, $k = Ae^{-E_a/RT}$, requires an experimental measurement of the temperature dependence of the rate constant. However, sometimes experimental difficulties preclude the obtainment of this information. Then recourse to some approximate methods of estimation must be made. Obviously to obtain an estimate of the rate constant for a given reaction from theory alone requires the determination of both A and E_a. The complete description of the potential energy of the reactants and transition state must be known before an accurate theoretical evaluation of E_a is possible. Some semiempirical rules have been formulated to aid in this process for the simplest of activated complexes.[78c] The procedures become impossibly complicated for the usual activated complexes of four or more atoms, and in most cases it is necessary to surrender the hope of calculation of E_a from theoretical potential energy surfaces. A few useful approximate methods have been suggested for the estimation of E_a for certain reactions, but on the whole little progress in the theoretical estimation of E_a has been made. Fortunately the theoretical calculation of the A factors is not dependent on a detailed knowledge of the potential energy surfaces for the reactions, and some excellent methods exist for their estimation for certain reactions. A few of these methods will be considered briefly at this point.

6-7A-7a The Theoretical Estimation of the Pre-exponential Factor A. Using Eq. 6-39 and taking the temperature dependence of the Q function as T^m, it can be shown that the pre-exponential factor A in the relation $k = Ae^{-E_a/RT}$ for a reaction of any molecularity is related to the partition functions and other parameters by

$$A = e^{m+1} \frac{kT}{h} \kappa \frac{Q'_{AB}{}^{\ddagger} \cdots}{Q_A' Q_B' \cdots} \tag{6-80}$$

Here $e = 2.7183$, the base of the natural logarithms, and the other symbols have their usual significance. If, as is usually done, one assumes $\kappa = 1$, then the theoretical evaluation of the A factor reduces to an estimation of the partition functions for the reactants and the activated complex.

In the evaluation of the partition function of a molecule as defined by 6-38, it is assumed that the total energy E of the molecule is separable into translational E_t, rotational E_r, vibrational E_v, and electronic E_e energies: $E = E_t + E_r + E_v + E_e$. With this simplifying assumption the total partition functions of a molecule Q may also be separated into partition functions involving only transitional Q_t, rotational Q_r, vibrational Q_v, and electronic Q_e, energies. Since Q involves the energy in an exponential function 6-38, relation 6-81 follows:

$$Q = Q_t Q_r Q_v Q_e \tag{6-81}$$

The calculation of the separated partition functions for each type of energy is usually handled through the appropriate equations of statistical and quantum mechanics.

The translational partition function per molecule is defined by

$$Q_t = \left(\frac{2\pi m k T}{h^2}\right)^{3/2} V \tag{6-82}$$

Here V represents the volume (cm³) in which the molecules are confined, and the other symbols have their usual significance.* It is evident that the only molecular parameter on which Q_t depends is the mass of the molecule, m; Q_t can be evaluated with high precision for any molecule or transition state.

The rotational partition function for a diatomic molecule is given by 6-83.

$$Q_r = \frac{8\pi^2 IkT}{\sigma h^2} \qquad (6\text{-}83)$$

where I is the moment of inertia of the molecule and is equal to $r^2 m_1 m_2/(m_1 + m_2)$, m_1 and m_2 are the masses of the atoms in the molecule, and r is the internuclear separation; σ, the symmetry number, is the number of equivalent ways of orienting the molecule in space, taking identical atoms as indistinguishable; for heteronuclear diatomic molecules $\sigma = 1$; for homonuclear molecules $\sigma = 2$. For a polyatomic molecule the rotational partition function is derived by using

$$Q_r = \frac{8\pi^2(8\pi^3 ABC)^{1/2}(kT)^{3/2}}{\sigma h^3} \qquad (6\text{-}84)$$

Here A, B, and C are the three principal moments of inertia of the molecule,† and the other terms are as before.

In the calculation of the vibrational partition function each vibrational mode is usually considered harmonic in nature, and function 6-85 is derived for each of the vibrational modes in the molecule

$$Q_{v_i} = (1 - e^{-h\nu_i/kT})^{-1} \qquad (6\text{-}85)$$

where ν_i is the fundamental vibration frequency of the ith mode. For a non-linear molecule of n atoms there are $3n - 6 - i$ vibrational modes, where i is the number of internal rotational modes; for a linear molecule there are $3n - 5 - i$ modes. A value of Q_{v_i} is calculated for each of the fundamental vibrational modes, and the total vibrational partition function Q_v is then given by the product of the individual functions:

$$Q_v = Q_{v_1} Q_{v_2} Q_{v_3} \cdots Q_{v_i} \qquad (6\text{-}86)$$

---

* The various Q values are dimensionless quantities as required by the defining equation 6-38; in the evaluation of the rate constant, V from 6-82 and N in the terms $Q' = Q/N$ of Eq. 6-80 are set equal to unity; if the usual units are employed in the other quantities, the dimensions on the rate constants will be in cubic centimeters, molecules, and seconds. For example, the bimolecular rate constant will be given in the units cubic centimeters/molecule-second. Setting V and N equal to unity is equivalent to taking the reference state of the molecule as 1 molecule/cm³.

† See Ref. 74d, p. 205.

The Q_{v_i} values are not significantly different from unity near room temperature for most of the fundamental frequencies of ordinary molecules; thus they do not affect greatly the magnitude of the pre-exponential factor A. The only significant contributions to Q_v come from the low-frequency bending modes. This is apparent in the following data for Q_{v_i} at some selected fundamental frequencies (ω) of the hydrocarbons at 298, 500, and 700°K: 2936 cm^{-1}, 1.000 (298°), 1.000 (500°), 1.002 (700°); 1471 cm^{-1}, 1.001 (298°), 1.015 (500°), 1.051 (700°); 950 cm^{-1}, 1.010 (298°), 1.069 (500°), 1.164 (700°); 380 cm^{-1}, 1.189 (298°), 1.506 (500°), 1.845 (700°); 270 cm^{-1}, 1.372 (298°), 1.845 (500°), 2.331 (700°).

Since the lowest excited state of the normal molecule is usually of the order of 100 kcal/mole above the ground electronic energy state, terms involving the energies of the upper electronic levels of molecules usually do not contribute significantly to the electronic partition function at ordinary temperatures, and Q_e is found from

$$Q_e = \sum g_i e^{-E_i/kT} \cong g_i \qquad (6\text{-}87)$$

Here g_i is the degeneracy of the ith electronic energy level and is given by $2j + 1$, where j is the total spin of the molecule. For most even-electron molecules $j = 0$ and $Q_e = g_i = 1$, but for molecules, atoms, and free radicals which have unpaired electrons $j \neq 0$. For simple free radicals and odd-electron transition states involving a normal molecule and a free radical it is commonly assumed that $j = \frac{1}{2}$ and thus $g_i = 2$.

For molecules which possess internal modes of rotation suitable approximate methods of estimation of the Q for internal rotation can be employed.[115]

The procedure given briefly above can be used to evaluate Q's for the reactant molecules. The difficulties arise in the estimation of the partition function for the activated molecule. Johnston and Pitzer and their co-workers have suggested several approximate solutions to this problem.[116] The activated complex is considered to be like an ordinary molecule with translational, rotational, and vibrational energies; it is different in one important respect—one of its vibrational modes is removed; vibration along the bonds which constitute the reaction coordinate is missing; motion of the nuclei along the reaction coordinate leads to products or reactants. If a reasonable model of the transition state can be developed, the partition functions can be calculated readily for this transient species, assuming the usual translation, rotation, and vibration in $3n - 7 - i$ different modes for a non-linear complex. The selection of molecular parameters for the activated complex may seem rather arbitrary at first sight, and the selection of a realistic model is critical, since an assumed variation in bond distances in the complex through several angstrom units or the variation of the vibration frequencies through several hundred wave numbers (particularly for the low-frequency bending modes) results in a great range of possible theoretical A factors. However, the situation is not impossible, for there are certain reasonable rules which can be followed in the selection of a model. You will recall that the equilibrium constant of an elementary reaction equals the ratio of the rate constant for the forward and the reverse reactions: furthermore the activated complex must be the same for both the forward and the reverse reactions, since all reference to the complex must cancel out in the equilibrium expression. Thus the activated complex should be regarded as equally well made up of reactants and products. A suitable hybrid species must be chosen which is properly related geometrically to both the reactant and the product molecules.

Bond distances around the site of chemical change may be evaluated by Pauling's rules for fractional bonds.[117] Consideration must be made of the bonding differences between atoms of different elements. Thus, in the $Cl + RH \rightarrow HCl + R$ reaction, the transition state will probably involve a very unequal bonding between the atoms undergoing change,[150] $Cl\text{------}H\text{------}R$ (bond order ~ 0.10 for $Cl\text{---}H$ and ~ 0.90 for $H\text{---}R$ positions), while a reaction such as $CH_3 + C_2H_6 \rightarrow CH_4 + C_2H_5$ will probably involve equal bonding between the hydrogen atoms and the two carbon atoms at the seat of the reaction, $CH_3\text{------}H\text{------}CH_2CH_3$ (bond orders for both $C\text{---}H$ positions ~ 0.50). The methods of Johnston and co-workers give a rational scheme for the estimation of such transition state structures, to which the interested reader is referred.[118] The assignment of stretching force constants may be made by Badger's rule,[119] and reduced moments of inertia for internal rotations can be estimated by the approximate methods of Pitzer.[115,116a]

Admittedly the calculations suggested can only lead to an approximation of the real transition state, but it is gratifying to find reasonable agreement between the theoretical and the reliable experimental A factors for several dozen reactions for which the calculations have been made; usually the agreement is within a factor of 2. Pitzer has presented some major simplifications in the theoretical calculations of A factors through the use of classical partition functions.[116d,e]

Another approximate method suggested by Johnston and Pitzer and co-workers[116a] for the theoretical estimation of A factors is attractive and readily used for a variety of reactions. Equation 6-88 follows from relations 6-28, 6-48, and 6-43, the thermodynamic formulation of the rate constant of a reaction of molecularity n.

$$A = e^n \frac{kT}{h} \kappa e^{\Delta S^{\ddagger}/R} \qquad (6\text{-}88)$$

If we make the usual assumption that $\kappa = 1$, and the entropies of the reactants are known, we need only to estimate the entropy of the activated complex to evaluate A. It has been observed that entropy is not sensitive to exact atomic locations if the general pattern of the masses is fixed. Thus for reactions involving simple compounds of nitrogen, oxygen, carbon, and fluorine the entropy should not differ much from that of the hydrocarbon with the analogous skeleton structure. For example, the transition state for the reaction $2NO_2 \rightarrow 2NO + O_2$ might be expected to have the bonding

$$O \qquad O \qquad N$$
$$\diagdown \diagup \diagdown \diagup \diagdown$$
$$N \qquad O \qquad O$$

so the choice of hydrocarbon analog could be n-hexane in this case. The entropies of a great many hydrocarbons have been determined from heat capacity data. Of course a hydrocarbon may have many C—H vibrations and CH_3-group internal rotations which do not exist in the analog to the activated complex. Formulas and tables are available for calculating the thermodynamic properties of hydrocarbons as the sum of contributions from stretching and bending vibrations, etc.[120] These data may be used to secure terms due to vibrations and CH_3-group internal rotations as corrections to be subtracted from the experimental entropies of the hydrocarbon analog to the transition state.

It is necessary to make one additional correction if there is an unpaired electron in the activated complex; in this case the correction, $R \ln g$, is added to the entropy of the hydrocarbon analog; if there is one unpaired electron, as in a simple free radical, then $g = 2$. Care must be taken in the application of this method to use a reference state for the reactant and transition state molecules which is in accord with the units desired for the A factor.* In spite of the approximations involved, this method leads to theoretical A factors which are in fair agreement with reliable experimental values, providing that a suitable choice of hydrocarbon analog to the activated complex has been made.

---

* Data for $S°$ of gaseous compounds are usually given for the molecules in the standard state of 1 atm pressure. Thus these must be corrected for the entropy increase in expanding the gas from 1 atm pressure to the actual pressure, which corresponds to the standard state fixed by the choice of units for A; thus if A is desired in units of molecules, cubic centimeters, and seconds, then the entropy of each reactant and the complex must be raised by the quantity

$$\Delta S = R \ln \frac{p_1}{p_2} = R \ln \frac{6.02 \times 10^{23}}{82.05 T} \text{ eu}$$

before calculation of $\Delta S^{\ddagger}$.

For unimolecular reactions, in theory the formulations of HKRRM and Slater may be used for the calculation of A factors. However, in practice the theories have been used only to check the experimental results, and few scientists have been bold enough to predict *a priori* rate constant data for a reaction which has not been studied experimentally. Steacie[121] has suggested that in the absence of other data the assumption of $A = 10^{13}$ sec^{-1} for unimolecular reactions is a reasonable guess but that it may be in error by several powers of 10 and in the extreme case by as much as 10^8.

6-7A-7b   **Approximate Methods for the Estimation of E_a.** For a pseudo-unimolecular decomposition reaction involving the homolytic fission of one chemical bond in a molecule, it is usually a fair approximation to assign E_a equal to the estimated energy of the bond broken. For example, the E_a for the reaction

$$CH_3CH_3 \rightarrow CH_3 + CH_3 \tag{6-89}$$

would be approximately equal to the CH_3—CH_3 bond dissociation energy, or about 84 kcal/mole. We assume that the E_a for the reverse reaction

$$CH_3 + CH_3 \rightarrow CH_3CH_3 \tag{6-90}$$

is near zero. For all such atom and ordinary free radical combination and disproportionation reactions this assumption appears justified.

Radical decomposition reactions like

$$CH_3CH_2 \rightarrow CH_2{=}CH_2 + H \tag{6-91}$$

involve the formation of molecules of greatly different bond type, and a different method of E_a estimation must be used. The approximate E_a for temperatures near 25°C may be calculated from the appropriate thermal data (heats of formation and bond dissociation energies; see Tables A-1 to A-5 in the Appendix) for 298°K for the related reactions:

$$CH_3CH_2 + H \rightarrow CH_3CH_3, \qquad \Delta H^\circ = -99 \text{ kcal/mole} \tag{6-92}$$

$$CH_3CH_3 \rightarrow CH_2{=}CH_2 + H_2, \qquad \Delta H^\circ = 33 \text{ kcal/mole} \tag{6-93}$$

$$H_2 \rightarrow 2H, \qquad \Delta H^\circ = 104 \text{ kcal/mole} \tag{6-94}$$

The net chemical change of these three reactions is equivalent to 6-91, and from the enthalpy changes involved we estimate that $\Delta H^\circ_{91} = -99 + 33 + 104 = 38$ kcal/mole. E_a for 6-91 can be estimated from these data and a consideration of the E_a for the reverse reactions:

$$H + CH_2{=}CH_2 \rightarrow CH_3CH_2 \tag{6-95}$$

The approximate energy relations between these reactions can be seen by reference to Fig. 6-3. The activation energies E_{91} and E_{95} correspond approximately to $\Delta H^{\ddagger}$ values of the transition state theory. The x-axis in Fig. 6-3 represents distance along the reaction coordinate (analogous to the dotted line in Fig. 6-2). The maximum in the energy diagram is analogous to the saddle point and represents the minimum energy of the activated complex which is common to both reactions 6-91 and 6-95. ΔH_{91} is the enthalpy difference between products and reactants. From the diagram it is seen that the desired activation energy $E_{91} \cong \Delta H_{91} + E_{95}$. Rate data for 6-95 show that $E_{95} \leqslant 4$ kcal/mole, so we estimate that

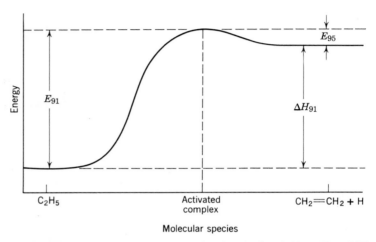

Fig. 6-3   Simplified potential energy diagram for the reaction $C_2H_5 \rightarrow H + C_2H_4$.

$E_{91} \leqslant 42$ kcal/mole. Where direct experimental estimates of the E_a of such radical decompositions have been possible, reasonable agreement is found with approximate thermochemical calculations of this kind. Thus in the example given E_{91} was found experimentally to be about 40 kcal/mole.[122]

It was first observed by Evans and Polyanyi[123] that there is a qualitative relationship between the exothermicities for a series of reactions of a given type and the activation energy of the reactions. Various relations have been suggested to help in estimation of E_a's for new reactions of the same class. Semenov[124] suggested the modified Evans-Polanyi relation 6-96 from a consideration of data from a variety of hydrogen-atom and halogen-atom abstraction reactions of H, Na, CH_3, and OH. For exothermic reactions of these classes which evolve q kcal/mole, E_a can be estimated from

$$E_a = 11.5 - 0.25q \text{ kcal/mole} \qquad (6\text{-}96)$$

For endothermic reactions of the same classes the following relation holds approximately:

$$E_a = 11.5 + 0.75q \text{ kcal/mole} \qquad (6\text{-}97)$$

In 6-97 q is the heat absorbed in kilocalories/mole. Of course in the application of any such equation one should use the same source of thermal data which was chosen in establishing the relationships. The use of these approximate methods for estimation of E_a can only lead to conclusions of a qualitative nature. In dealing with reaction rates and activation energies in particular, there is no good substitute for experiment.

Johnston and Parr[118] have achieved what appears to be a significant breakthrough in the problem of activation energy estimation for H-abstraction reactions, $X + RH \rightarrow HX + R$, where X and R are F, OH, H, CF_3, Cl, CH_3, C_2H_5, $(CH_3)_2CH$, $(CH_3)_3C$, Br, I, etc. Their method yields potential energies of activation which differ only slightly (usually a little larger) from E_a because of zero-point energy and thermal energy differences between reactant and complex. The technique is based on the application of simple valence bond theory to derive the minimum potential energy of the complex through considerations of the bonding and anti-bonding contributions at the reaction site in the transition state. Excellent agreement is obtained between experimental and "theoretical" energies of activation. Even the energies for the halogen-atom reactions are in accord with experiment, although the modified Evans and Polanyi relations fail to some extent in these cases. Reference to this important method should be made by all who deal with theoretical calculations of rate constants.

6-7A-7c Theoretical Checks on the Consistency of Rate Data and Thermal Data. If the rate constants for both the forward and the reverse of a given chemical reaction can be obtained, the data can be checked for consistency with thermal data. In illustration consider the reactions as follows:

$$A + B \underset{k_2}{\overset{k_1}{\rightleftharpoons}} C + D \qquad (6\text{-}98)$$

Assume that we have determined the experimental values of $k_1 = A_1 e^{-E_1/RT}$ and $k_2 = A_2 e^{-E_2/RT}$. At equilibrium $k_1[A][B] = k_2[C][D]$, so that $K_{eq} = k_1/k_2$; from thermodynamics we know that $K_{eq} = e^{-\Delta H^\circ/RT} e^{\Delta S^\circ/R}$, where ΔH° and ΔS° refer to the overall reaction 6-98 with reactants and products in their standard states. There is a high probability that the same transition state will be involved for both the forward and the reverse reactions, and the κ's must be equal in this case regardless of their size. The application of the absolute reaction rate theory equations for this situation gives

$$\Delta S^\circ = R \ln \frac{A_1}{A_2} \tag{6-99}$$

$$\Delta H^\circ = E_1 - E_2 \tag{6-100}$$

The overall entropy change of the reaction ΔS° and the enthalpy change ΔH° can be estimated easily for many reactions from available data for the reactants and products (see Tables A-1 to A-4 in the Appendix). Obviously the calculation in this case is independent of the actual configuration and of the entropy of the activated complex, which were the uncertain quantities in the theoretical estimation of the individual pre-exponential factors A_1 and A_2. The experimental ratio of pre-exponential factors A_1/A_2 and ΔS° for the overall reaction 6-98 should satisfy the equality given by 6-99, or errors in one or both of these factors are indicated.* Also the difference between the activation energies for the forward and the reverse reactions should equal within the experimental error the enthalpy change for the reaction as required by 6-100, or an inconsistency is indicated.† Equations 6-99 and 6-100 seem to hold well for many elementary reactions which have been studied; in several other cases errors in rate data have become evident through the application of these relations.

6-7A-8   The Evaluation of E_a, A, P, $\Delta H^\ddagger$, and $\Delta S^\ddagger$ from Experimental Rate Data

The experimental activation energy E_a is usually defined by 6-44. As the definition implies, it is customary to neglect the temperature dependence of the A factor in determining E_a. A graphical solution for E_a may be obtained from a plot of $\log_{10} k$ (or $\log_{10}$ of some other function directly proportional to k) as ordinate versus $1/T$ (temperature in °K) as abscissa. Obviously the slope of the best straight line through these points ($\Delta y/\Delta x$) is related to E_a by

$$E_a = -(2.303)(0.001987)(\text{slope}) = -(0.00458)(\text{slope}) \text{ kcal/mole} \tag{6-101}$$

If the actual k's are used in the plot, then the intercept on the y-axis ($1/T = 0$) is an estimate of $\log_{10} A$.

The presentation of kinetic data in terms of the older collision theory is uncommon today and is not recommended. In the older literature where

---

* In applying relation 6-99 the standard state taken for reactants and products must be consistent with the units employed in the A_1 and A_2 factors. See the footnote on p. 634.

† Note that 6-100 applies to an elementary reaction involving no net change in number of molecules. For elementary gaseous reactions with a reactant and b product molecules the appropriate relation which replaces 6-100 is

$$\Delta H^\circ = E_1 - E_2 - (a - b)RT$$

it does appear, the following calculation techniques were generally employed. The determination of the P factor for bimolecular reactions was accomplished by using the logarithmic form of Eq. 6-30:

$$\log_{10} k_{\mathrm{II}} = \log_{10} \left[\left(\frac{8\pi R}{\mu}\right)^{\!\frac{1}{2}} \sigma_{\mathrm{AB}}{}^2 P \right] + \tfrac{1}{2} \log_{10} T - \frac{E_a{}'}{2.303 \, RT} \qquad (6\text{-}102)$$

The actual rate constants were used in this case and care was taken to employ consistent dimensions throughout. A plot of $\log_{10} k_{\mathrm{II}} - \tfrac{1}{2}\log_{10} T$ versus $1/T$ gave the intercept at $1/T = 0$, $\log_{10}[(8\pi R/\mu)^{\frac{1}{2}}\sigma_{\mathrm{AB}}{}^2 P]$, from which P was calculated. Estimates of σ_{A} and σ_{B} were taken from diffusion, heat conductivity, or viscosity data, or from the approximate molecular dimensions. The slope of the plot determines $E_a{}'$, using 6-101. For reactions of low $E_a{}'$ this value is slightly less than that found by neglecting the temperature dependence of Z.

Kinetic data from many systems, especially those involving free radicals, are often of low precision, and it is difficult to decide by eye which line is the best one to draw through the plot of the log k versus $1/T$ experimental points. The experimenter and those who later deal with his data gain much greater confidence in the result when E_a and A values are obtained from the experimental data by using an impartial statistical method of computation. The most common method employed today in kinetics is the method of least squares; it is to be recommended because of the relative ease of the computations and the impartial character of the fitting of the best line to the data. In the application of the least squares method it is customary to assume that there are no systematic errors in the determinations and that all of the random error is in the rate data (no error in the temperature determination); this is usually a fair approximation in rate studies. To evaluate A and E_a of 6-28 we represent the equation in the form $y = a + bx$, where $y = \log_{10} k$ and $x = 1/T$ (°K). The intercept $a = \log_{10} A$ and the slope $b = -E_a/2.303 \, R$ are calculated from the usual least squares equations for a straight line:

$$a = \frac{\sum x^2 \sum y - \sum x \sum xy}{n \sum x^2 - (\sum x)^2} \qquad (6\text{-}103)$$

$$b = \frac{n \sum xy - \sum x \sum y}{n \sum x^2 - (\sum x)^2} \qquad (6\text{-}104)$$

where n is the number of x-y pairs measured experimentally. $\Delta H^{\ddagger}$ may be calculated from E_a by using Eq. 6-48 or 6-49. $\Delta S^{\ddagger}$ for a given temperature can be calculated from 6-43, assuming $\kappa = 1$. If you have access to a computor facility, you will find that there is available a variety of least-squares programs which can be applied conveniently in treating kinetic data.

6-7B   Kinetic Studies and Rate Law Determination

Reaction kinetics studies which are properly applied to a photochemical system can lead to important evidence concerning the mechanism. However, there is an inherent difficulty which is peculiar to photochemical reaction kinetics and which should be appreciated. Significant differences between measured rates of reaction and the theoretically important local rates of reaction can exist unless certain precautions are taken.

6-7B-1   Measured Total Rates and Local Rates of Reaction

When a beam of quanta passes through an absorbing medium, the number of quanta absorbed in each volume increment is proportional to the product of the concentrations of the quanta and the absorbing molecules present in this volume. As long as any appreciable absorption occurs, the number of quanta absorbed (or the absorbed light intensity) will vary from a certain value at the front of the reaction cell to a lower value at the back of the cell. Thus the rates of generation of radicals and other products, their concentrations, and the rates of their reactions will not be homogeneous over the entire cell volume. Hence in photochemical systems the measured total or average rates of reactions are not always truly representative of the individual local rates to which the usual theories apply. The equality of the two rates exists for only certain special cases:

1. The absorption of light is entirely uniform in the reaction volume.
2. The lifetimes of radicals and other reactive species are sufficiently long so that uniform concentrations throughout the reaction volume result from diffusion.
3. The rates of product formation are directly proportional to the first power of the absorbed light intensity.

In all other cases the local and measured total rates will not be identical.

By following the treatment of Noyes and Leighton,[125] the relation between measured and local rates can be seen for a simple case where the above conditions are not met. Let us assume that the theoretical or the local rate law* has the form,

$$\left(\frac{d[A]}{dt}\right)_{\text{local}} = \beta I_a^{\,n} \tag{6-105}$$

---

* The theoretical or local rate law is that which applies to a small volume increment where the first two conditions stated in the text exist.

where A is the product of the reaction, and β is a function which includes all reactant concentrations and temperature-dependent terms; then actually the measured total rate will be given by 6-106, where l is the distance from the front of the cell.

$$\left(\frac{d[A]}{dt}\right)_{measured} = \frac{1}{l}\int_0^l \left(\frac{d[A]}{dt}\right)_{local} dl = \frac{1}{l}\int_0^l \beta I_a{}^n \, dl \qquad (6\text{-}106)$$

This integral can be evaluated readily for certain ideal cases. For a system employing a parallel light beam uniform in intensity over the cross section and filling the cell completely and where diffusion of radicals from a given small volume increment to another is unimportant, β is independent of l, and I_a can be calculated as a function of l, assuming the Beer-Lambert law:

$$I_a = -\frac{dI}{dl} = \frac{d[I_0(1 - e^{-\alpha cl})]}{dl} = \alpha c I_0 \, e^{-\alpha cl} \qquad (6\text{-}107)$$

Here I_0 represents the total quanta incident per second per square centimeter of area perpendicular to the cell axis. Substitution of 6-107 in 6-106 and integration gives the relation between the measured total rate and the variables for this special case:

$$\left(\frac{d[A]}{dt}\right)_{measured} = \frac{\beta I_0{}^n(1 - e^{-n\alpha cl})}{nl(\alpha c)^{1-n}} \qquad (6\text{-}108)$$

The ratio of measured to local or theoretical rates is given by

$$\frac{(d[A]/dt)_{measured}}{(d[A]/dt)_{local}} = \frac{(\alpha cl)^{n-1}(1 - e^{-\alpha cln})}{n(1 - e^{-\alpha cl})^n} \qquad (6\text{-}109)$$

It can be shown that the ratio of rates in 6-109 approaches unity, that is, the measured and the local rates become equal, only for special conditions: $c \to 0$, $l \to 0$, $\alpha \to 0$, or $n = 1$.

The magnitude of the ratio of the two rates can be estimated from 6-109 for a common case of $n = \frac{1}{2}$ at several different fractions of the incident light absorbed. When 5, 10, 15, 20, and 50% of the incident light is absorbed in passing through the cell, the ratios of the measured to local rates are 1.01, 1.05, 1.62, 2.23, and 6.90, respectively. Thus, if less than 10% of the incident light is absorbed, then the two rates are not seriously different, but for 50% of the incident light absorbed we expect in theory a serious discrepancy between the measured and the local rates of product formation. However, the use of 6-109 actually overcorrects for non-homogeneity in the usual photochemical system, since there is some diffusion of radicals from one volume element to another. The actual extent of diffusion in a system is difficult to access quantitatively, and a better description of the variation of local rates with distance along the cell length is difficult and is rarely attempted. For several systems it has been learned through experience that there is no large difference between the total measured rates and the local rates as long as the percentage of incident light absorbed in the reaction vessel is kept below about 50%. However, where highly reactive molecular fragments are involved (e.g., chlorine atoms), the diffusion from one volume element to another may be unimportant, and the theoretical estimates of the ratio of measured to local rates will more nearly apply, so that the absorption of a high fraction of the incident light cannot be tolerated. Since there may be large differences in the rates and the equality of the measured and local rates is assumed, there is no alternative but to test the rate law for the given system at a number of different fractions of absorbed light (different concentrations of reactant) and restrict the quantitative measurements to those conditions which minimize this source of error.

It is common practice to express the rate of a reaction as a function of measured variables in an empirical rate law like 6-105, which is derived from kinetic experiments. Then possible mechanisms are suggested which give a theoretical rate law of the same form as the experimental law. In the derivation of the theoretical rate laws the steady state assumption is encountered. We will consider this in the next section.

6-7B-2   The Steady State Assumption in the Treatment of Photochemical Reaction Rates

A serious complication is encountered in the evaluation of rate constants for the reaction of free radicals and other very reactive species formed in most photochemical systems. The concentration of the free radicals is very small in the usual system (about 10^{-10} M) as a consequence of the very high reactivity of these species and the relatively low intensities of absorbed light normally used. In the treatment of kinetic data from such systems special techniques are required to eliminate the unknown radical concentrations and make possible the evaluation of rate constants and rate laws.

When a photochemical system at a given temperature is irradiated with a constant intensity of light under conditions of approximate equality of measured and local rates, it is a reasonable assumption that the very active intermediates, like free radicals and atoms which do not appear as final products, build up in concentration quickly to some constant, relatively low value. At this time the rate of reaction of these species equals the rate of their formation. Thus use of this picture in treating kinetic data is referred to as the *steady state* assumption.[126] In Fig. 6-4 a plot is made of the time variation of the theoretical methyl radical concentration in the thermal decomposition of acetaldehyde vapor at a concentration of 1×10^{-3} M at temperatures of 400, 450, and 500°. Note that the concentration of the methyl radical rises quickly as the reaction starts and reaches a limiting value which for the thermal reaction is largest at the highest temperature. [CH$_3$] has reached its limiting value in a few seconds at 500°, while it is only about 95% of its limiting value in 60 sec in the run at 400°. It is obvious that the steady state approximation can yield realistic rate data

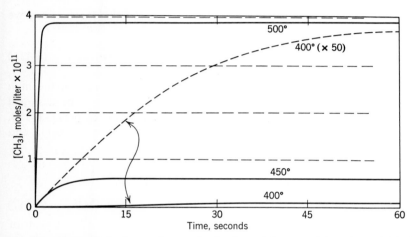

Fig. 6-4   Approach to the steady state in the thermal decomposition of acetaldehyde; the time dependence of the [CH$_3$] calculated for three temperatures; the dotted curve represents a 50-fold expansion of the 400° data; calculations of W. J. Pobst.

only if the time of product formation in the rate study is long compared to the period of attainment of the steady state. Fortunately this is the common situation which is encountered, although one should be aware of the possible complication.

The application of the steady state assumption can be illustrated in the derivation of the theoretical rate law, using the photochemical reaction between bromine and hydrogen. The experimentally observed rate law for the photochemical formation of hydrogen bromide in Br$_2$-H$_2$ mixtures is given

$$\frac{d[\text{HBr}]}{dt} = \frac{aI_a^{\frac{1}{2}}[\text{H}_2]}{1 + b\dfrac{[\text{HBr}]}{[\text{Br}_2]}} \tag{6-110}$$

where a and b are constants at a given temperature, and I_a is the intensity of the absorbed light. (Bromine is the absorbing species in this system.)

The following reaction mechanism was suggested by Bodenstein and Lütkemeyer[127] in explanation of these results:

$$Br_2 + h\nu \rightarrow 2Br \qquad (\text{Rate} = 2\varphi I_a) \qquad (6\text{-}111)$$

$$Br + H_2 \rightarrow HBr + H \qquad (k_1) \qquad (6\text{-}112)$$

$$H + Br_2 \rightarrow HBr + Br \qquad (k_2) \qquad (6\text{-}113)$$

$$H + HBr \rightarrow H_2 + Br \qquad (k_3) \qquad (6\text{-}114)$$

$$(+M) \; Br + Br \rightarrow Br_2 \; (+M) \qquad (k_4) \qquad (6\text{-}115)$$

Expressing the rate of formation of HBr in terms of this mechanism, we have

$$\frac{d[HBr]}{dt} = [Br][H_2]k_1 + [H][Br_2]k_2 - [H][HBr]k_3 \qquad (6\text{-}116)$$

[Br] and [H] are immeasurably small in the system because of the high reactivity of these atoms. A steady state concentration can be assumed for them. That is, the rate of bromine atom formation in 6-111, 6-113, and 6-114 is assumed to be equal to the rate of its removal in 6-112 and 6-115:

$$\frac{d[Br]}{dt} = 0 = 2I_a\varphi + [H][Br_2]k_2 + [H][HBr]k_3$$
$$- [Br][H_2]k_1 - 2[Br]^2[M]k_4 \qquad (6\text{-}117)$$

I_a is the absorbed light intensity, and φ is the primary quantum yield of process 6-111.

A similar steady state assumption for [H] gives

$$\frac{d[H]}{dt} = 0 = [Br][H_2]k_1 - [H][Br_2]k_2 - [H][HBr]k_3 \qquad (6\text{-}118)$$

In 6-117 and 6-118 we have two equations which involve only two unknown concentrations, [H] and [Br]; thus a solution for these in terms of measurable concentrations and reaction rate constants is possible. In more complex systems involving a given large number of reactive fragments, an equally large number of independent equations can be written to relate these, and a solution is always theoretically possible. Often the actual solution is quite complex, and there is no general method of solution which is always unique. In the present example the solution for [Br] is obtained readily by taking the sum of 6-117 and 6-118:

$$2I_a\varphi = 2[Br]^2[M]k_4 \qquad (6\text{-}119)$$

from which

$$[Br] = \left(\frac{I_a\varphi}{k_4[M]}\right)^{1/2} \qquad (6\text{-}120)$$

By substitution of 6-120 in 6-118 we have:

$$[H] = \frac{[H_2]k_1(I_a\varphi/k_4[M])^{\frac{1}{2}}}{[Br_2]k_2 + [HBr]k_3} \tag{6-121}$$

From 6-116, 6-120, and 6-121 the theoretical expression for the rate is derived:

$$\frac{d[HBr]}{dt} = \left(\frac{I_a\varphi}{k_4[M]}\right)^{\frac{1}{2}} \frac{2[H_2]k_1}{1 + (k_3[HBr]/k_2[Br_2])} \tag{6-122}$$

This is the form of the experimentally observed rate law, provided the effective concentration of the third body M (H_2, Br_2, or other added substance) is constant in the series of runs; the constants a and b in the theoretical rate law are presumed to be $2k_1(\varphi/k_4[M])^{\frac{1}{2}}$ and k_3/k_2, respectively, in terms of the proposed mechanism.

It is gratifying to find that a proposed reaction scheme will predict an observed rate law. A mechanism cannot be considered unless this is the case. However, a given mechanism is not necessarily correct just because it leads to the form of the experimentally observed rate law. Actually in many cases several entirely different mechanisms will be consistent with the same rate law, and then the final choice cannot be made until new experiments are devised to differentiate between the possible mechanisms. Although one can attempt to go too far with conclusions based on kinetic data, the fact remains that much important information is gained from the study of the effect of each experimental variable on the rate or the quantum yield of the reaction.

In the kinetic study of photochemical systems it is advisable to keep constant all but one of the variables, such as light intensity, wavelength, reactant concentration, temperature, or inert-gas concentration, while the effect of that variable is determined. In the following sections a review is given of some of the common effects of the variables on the rate and the possible interpretations of these in terms of reaction mechanisms.

6-7B-3   The Effect of Temperature on the Rate of a Photochemical Reaction

From the effect of temperature on the rate of the reaction many critical decisions concerning the nature of the primary and secondary reactions can be made. The investigation should be restricted to temperatures for which negligible thermal reaction occurs in the dark during the time necessary for the photochemical run. Thermal corrections to measured total rates of reaction to obtain photochemical rates usually are not justified unless the photochemical and the thermal reactions occur by independent reaction steps, a situation which is uncommon.*

The temperature independence of the rate of formation or the quantum yield of some product is often used as a criterion for the formation of the product in a primary process. All the evidence now at hand indicates that most primary dissociative processes are relatively insensitive to temperature changes. In contrast to thermal reactions, where only high-energy molecules react, molecules which absorb light and undergo photo-decomposition, rearrangement, etc., have the usual distribution of thermal energies in their ground state. The increase in average thermal energies encountered in the temperature range of the usual photochemical study is small compared to the magnitude of the electronic excitation induced by the absorbed quantum. For example, a rise in temperature of acetaldehyde from 20 to 220°C causes an increase in average thermal energy of about 3 kcal/mole, while the usual electronic excitations are near 100 kcal/mole. Thus in most cases thermal energies are unimportant in determining the mode and the efficiency of photodecomposition. Temperature dependence of a primary process may be significant in certain cases, for example, where insufficient energy for bond rupture is available from the absorbed quantum, or there is an activation energy for the dissociation of the light-activated molecule. Furthermore, temperature independence of a product rate does not always indicate that the product is formed in a primary process. It can often be explained in terms of "hot" radical or low activation energy secondary reactions as well. These possibilities must be evaluated before definite conclusions can be made.

The excess of the energy of an absorbed quantum remaining after scission of a molecular bond must be carried away by the separating fragments. If the energy is large compared to the normal thermal energies of the fragments, then the radicals formed in the light may be abnormally reactive. In this case they are often termed "hot" radicals or atoms. Consider in this regard the molecule AB, which dissociates photochemically according to the reaction

$$AB + h\nu \rightarrow A + B \tag{6-123}$$

For the simplest possible case let us assume that the excess energy is removed as kinetic energy only (no extra vibrational, rotational, or electronic excitations of the radicals A and B are involved). Energy and momentum must be conserved as 6-123 occurs. Let D_{A-B} be the bond dissociation energy of the molecule AB, and M_A and M_B the respective masses of the primary fragments A and B. The total excess kinetic energy

---

* See Ref. 125, pp. 198–200.

of A and B in reaction 6-123 will be:

$$E = \frac{hc}{\lambda} - D_{A-B} \tag{6-124}$$

The energy taken by A is

$$E_A = \left(\frac{hc}{\lambda} - D_{A-B}\right)\left(\frac{M_B}{M_A + M_B}\right) \tag{6-125}$$

and that by B is

$$E_B = \left(\frac{hc}{\lambda} - D_{A-B}\right)\left(\frac{M_A}{M_A + M_B}\right) \tag{6-126}$$

It is seen from 6-125 and 6-126 that for the case of light and heavy fragments formed photochemically most of the kinetic energy must be carried by the light fragment. It is in these cases that "hot" radical reactions are most likely. For example, in CH_3I photolysis at 2537 A,[128] the primary process has been demonstrated to be

$$CH_3I + h\nu \rightarrow CH_3 + I \tag{6-127}$$

The observed activation energy for CH_4 formation is near zero,[129] although its formation arises in the reaction

$$CH_3 + CH_3I \rightarrow CH_4 + CH_2I \tag{6-128}$$

which is considered to have an appreciable activation energy (about 9 kcal/mole). If the iodine atom is formed in the ground electronic state $(^2P_{3/2})$, the CH_3 radicals formed in reaction 6-127 in photolysis of CH_3I at wavelength 2537 A would have about 53 of the 59 kcal/mole total excess energy, neglecting any additional energy which might be partitioned to methyl radical as electronic, vibrational, or rotational energy. The heavy iodine atom would carry the other 6 kcal/mole. If iodine is formed in its $^2P_{1/2}$ state, then CH_3 radicals would have an excess energy of about 32 kcal/mole. Hence it is not surprising that the methane yield from CH_3I photolysis at 2537 A is relatively insensitive to variations in experimental conditions, for the very "hot" CH_3 species might be expected to react with CH_3I molecules in an early collision.

There is a good chance that the photodecomposition of methyl iodide leads to a vibrationally or electronically excited methyl radical (and subsequently to a vibrationally excited radical) as well as translational enrichment of the methyl radical compared to the halogen atom as considered above. The NO molecule formed in NOCl photolysis,[130] SO from SO_3 photolysis,[131] CO from CH_2CO photolysis,[132] and CHX_2 (X = halogen atom) from CHX_2Br photolysis,[133] all give evidence of very high vibrational excitation immediately after their formation. (See Sec. 3-3C-2.)

Direct products of primary processes and the products of "hot" radical reactions can usually be differentiated by the addition of a huge excess of inert gas or an inert solvent which serves to thermally equilibrate the "hot" species as a result of collisions. The average fraction of kinetic energy $\Delta E/E$ transferred per billiard ball collision between a moving particle of mass M_1 and a stationary particle of mass M_2 is:

$$\frac{\Delta E}{E} = \frac{M_1 M_2}{(M_1 + M_2)^2} \tag{6-129}$$

The fraction transferred is a maximum for $M_1 = M_2$; that is, a moderating gas of molecular weight nearly equal to that of the non-thermally equilibrated species is best for the moderation of translational energy excess. For the case of CH_3 radicals with 53 kcal/mole kinetic energy in a medium of neon (considered motionless) only about 14 collisions are theoretically necessary to reduce the kinetic energy of the "hot" CH_3 radical to below 1 kcal/mole.

Vibrational and rotational excitations are also likely for separating fragments composed of a large number of atoms, as was indicated above. Rotational energy can be transferred rather easily to translational energy on collision, but there is a much less efficient transfer of vibrational energy. Zener[134] has calculated that the probability that a nitrogen molecule in its first vibrational state will transfer its energy in a head-on collision with helium is 6×10^{-8}, and that for transfer to another nitrogen molecule is 4×10^{-5}. Experimental evidence from gas-phase experiments also favors the interpretation of inefficiency of transfer of vibrational excitation to translational energy. Because of this, a very large ratio of the concentration of inert gas to that of the reactant must be used to ensure thermal equilibration of high-energy particles and to test conclusively for "hot" radical reactions. "Hot" atom reactions should be evident at much lower ratios of inert gas to reactant.

It is apparent that temperature independence of a product rate will also be observed if reactive species formed in the primary process undergo only reactions of low activation energy. In the photolysis of isobutyraldehyde at 3130 A and in the temperature range near room temperature, the rate of CO formation is fairly insensitive to temperature change (up to 100°C).[135] It has been established that only a small fraction of these products is formed in the primary process.[64f] Presumably the major primary process at 3130 A is

$$(CH_3)_2CHCO + h\nu \rightarrow (CH_3)_2CH + HCO \tag{6-130}$$

A possible explanation of the temperature independence is that 6-130 is followed usually by reactions of low activation energy at the low temperatures:

$$(CH_3)_2CH + HCO \rightarrow C_3H_8 + CO \qquad (6\text{-}131)$$

$$\searrow$$

$$(CH_3)_2CHCHO \qquad (6\text{-}132)$$

$$2HCO \rightarrow CH_2O + CO \qquad (6\text{-}133)$$

$$2(CH_3)_2CH \rightarrow (CH_3)_2CHCH(CH_3)_2, \text{ etc.} \qquad (6\text{-}134)$$

At the higher temperatures the rates are temperature dependent. Reactions 6-135 and 6-136 have finite activation energies and may become important compared to 6-131, 6-132, 6-133, and 6-134 under these conditions.

$$(CH_3)_2CH + (CH_3)_2CHCHO \rightarrow C_3H_8 + (CH_3)_2CHCO \qquad (6\text{-}135)$$

$$(CH_3)_2CHCO \rightarrow (CH_3)_2CH + CO \qquad (6\text{-}136)$$

Frequently the extension of the temperature range of the rate experiments will be sufficient to distinguish this case of temperature independence from the others.

Usually the temperature dependence of rates may be assigned either to specific reaction rate constants or to a function of several constants in terms of an assumed mechanism which fits the rate law. For example in the theoretical rate law for HBr formation, Eq. 6-122, the temperature dependence at low HBr concentrations is assigned to $k_1/k_4^{1/2}$; under these conditions the observed activation energy of the reaction would be $E_1 - E_4/2$, and the pre-exponential factor, $2A_1(\varphi/A_4[M])^{1/2}$. A comparison of such estimates with other independent values for the same constants is useful in deciding on the reliability of the proposed mechanism.

In the usual photochemical system which employs steady illumination with an absorbed intensity of about 10^{13} quanta/cm^3-sec, the individual rate constants for free radical reactions cannot be derived; the steady-state concentration of free radicals (about 10^{-10} M) is below the detection limits of present analytical equipment. With these systems one is restricted to the determination of relative rate constants for free radical reactions. The great majority of published free radical rate constant data have been determined from such relative rate measurements. In illustration of the application of this technique commonly employed, let us suppose that we desire to measure the rate constant for the H-atom abstraction reaction involving the free radical R:

$$R + BH \rightarrow RH + B \ (k_a) \qquad (6\text{-}137)$$

The desired free radical R may be formed by the photodecomposition of the appropriate light-sensitive compound; for example, R_2CO or $R—N{=}N—R$ may be used. The source of radicals will be present together with the transparent reactant BH. The rate of hydrogen abstraction reaction 6-137 will be followed by RH formation.*

The radical concentration is monitored from the rate of formation of the radical dimer R_2:

$$2R \rightarrow R_2 \ (k_c) \tag{6-138}$$

If 6-137 and 6-138 are the only sources of RH and R_2, then the rate laws are

$$\frac{d[RH]}{dt} = [R][BH]k_a \tag{6-139}$$

$$\frac{d[R_2]}{dt} = [R]^2 k_c \tag{6-140}$$

Since [R] is indeterminable, the individual rate constants k_a and k_c are as well. A function of the product rates can be derived to eliminate the unknown [R]. In the present case relation 6-141 is seen to be independent of [R]:

$$\frac{(d[RH]/dt)}{(d[R_2]/dt)^{1/2}} = \frac{[R][BH]k_a}{[R](k_c)^{1/2}} = \frac{[BH]k_a}{k_c^{1/2}} \tag{6-141}$$

In terms of the suggested mechanism a plot of $(d[RH]/dt)/(d[R_2]/dt)^{1/2}$ versus [BH] is linear in theory with a slope $k_a/k_c^{1/2}$. Trotman-Dickenson and Steacie demonstrated well the great utility of this technique of free radical studies; they photolyzed acetone in gaseous hydrocarbon mixtures and derived relative rate constant ratios for a variety of H-abstraction reactions of the methyl radical. The accuracy and simplicity of the method have stimulated its extensive use for the study of a great variety of free radical reactions.

6-7B-4 Effects of Light Intensity on the Rate

The variables of absorbed light intensity and wavelength or energy input are unique to the study of photochemical reactions. The effects of continuous and intermittent illumination on the rates of reaction give important information concerning the reaction mechanism.

---

* When RH is also formed in the disproportionation reaction, $2R \rightarrow RH + R(—H)$, where $R(—H)$ represents an olefin molecule, then the measure of the rate of 6-137 will be given by the function $(d[RH]/dt) - (d[R(—H)]/dt)$, provided that the disproportionation reaction is the only source of olefin.

6-7B-4a   Effect of Steady Illumination of Varied Intensity. The intensity dependence of a product rate can help to establish whether a product is formed in a primary act or from a secondary reaction. Since only one quantum is absorbed to initiate the primary process, the rates of primary processes are directly proportional to the absorbed light intensity (I_a). The quantum yields of primary products are independent of I_a, since $\Phi_A = (d[A]/dt)/I_a$. Rates of products formed in secondary reactions usually show some other than first-power dependence on I_a. In general, bimolecular termination by a reaction involving active chain-carrying species results in rates proportional to $I_a^{1/2}$. Termination which occurs from a first-order reaction removing a carrier at the wall leads to a rate which is dependent on the first power of I_a. To observe this effect for a given case let us consider reaction sequence 6-111 to 6-115, which was proposed to describe the photochemical formation of HBr from Br_2 and H_2. If instead of chain termination by 6-115 a wall termination occurs,

$$Br(\text{wall}) \rightarrow \tfrac{1}{2}Br_2(\text{wall}) \qquad (k_5) \qquad\qquad (6\text{-}142)$$

then the usual steady-state treatment leads to the theoretical rate law 6-143 (neglecting the influence of total concentration on diffusion of bromine to the wall).

$$\frac{d[HBr]}{dt} = \frac{4I_a\varphi[H_2]k_1}{k_5\left(1 + \dfrac{[HBr]k_3}{[Br_2]k_2}\right)} \qquad\qquad (6\text{-}143)$$

Eq. 6-143 differs from 6-122 primarily in the expected dependency of the rate on I_a. The assumed first-order termination reaction leads to a rate proportional to I_a, while the second-order termination gives a dependency on $I_a^{1/2}$. Second-order termination is favored by high radical concentrations or high I_a. First-order wall termination may dominate at low I_a and at low concentrations where diffusion is rapid. Thus, if very wide ranges of I_a and concentrations are studied in a given chain reaction, a change over from $I_a^{1/2}$ to I_a dependence in the rate law might be observed as the mechanism of chain termination changes.

6-7B-4b   Effect of Intermittent Illumination: the Rotating Sector Technique. If the rate of formation of some product A in steady illumination, $(d[A]/dt)_s$, is given by

$$\left(\frac{d[A]}{dt}\right)_s = \beta I_a^{\,n} \qquad\qquad (6\text{-}144)$$

where n is neither unity nor zero, then the interesting technique of intermittent illumination devised by Chapman and Briers[136] can be applied successfully to the system to derive lifetimes of active intermediates and individual absolute rate constants.[137] In the application of this technique the light is chopped into pulses of any selected frequency through the use of a slotted wheel which rotates between the light source and the cell. Let the ratio of the dark to light periods be r; then the fraction of the time that the light is on will be given by $1/(r + 1)$. If the time between light periods is long compared to the lifetime of the active intermediates (radicals) formed, the measured rate of formation of A in intermittent light with slow sector speed is merely the time average of the rate under steady state illumination, $(d[A]/dt)_s = \beta I_a{}^n$, and the zero rate for the dark periods:

$$\left(\frac{d[A]}{dt}\right)_{\text{slow sector}} = \frac{\beta I_a{}^n}{r + 1} \tag{6-144a}$$

For fast sector speeds, where the time between flashes is short compared to the lifetimes of intermediates, the effective light intensity is $I_a/(r + 1)$, and the measured rate becomes

$$\left(\frac{d[A]}{dt}\right)_{\text{fast sector}} = \beta\left(\frac{I_a}{r + 1}\right)^n \tag{6-145}$$

The ratio of the rate with intermittent illumination to that under steady illumination changes from 6-146 at slow sector speeds,

$$\frac{(d[A]/dt)_{\text{slow sector}}}{(d[A]/dt)_s} = \frac{1}{r + 1} \tag{6-146}$$

to 6-147 at fast sector speeds,

$$\frac{(d[A]/dt)_{\text{fast sector}}}{(d[A]/dt)_s} = \frac{1}{(r + 1)^n} \tag{6-147}$$

Providing that n is not unity, 6-146 and 6-147 are different; for example, for $n = \frac{1}{2}$ and $r = 3$ the ratio of rates in 6-146 is 0.25, while in 6-147 it is 0.50. The transition between these two values occurs when the period of time between light flashes is of the order of magnitude of the lifetime of the intermediates. Hence it is apparent that information concerning lifetimes of radicals can be obtained from these experiments.

Consider in some detail the application of the rotating sector technique to the obtainment of radical lifetimes and rate constants in the chain photo-decomposition of the molecule A for the special case where termination is bimolecular. R_1, R_2, and R_3 are free radicals, and B, C, and D are stable product molecules.*

Initiation: $A + h\nu \rightarrow R_1 + R_2$ (Rate of R_1 formation $= I_a\varphi_i$)   (6-148)

Chain propagation: $\begin{cases} R_1 + A \rightarrow B + R_3 & \text{(Rate} = [R_1][A]k_p) & \text{(6-149)} \\ R_3 \rightarrow R_1 + C & \text{(Fast compared to 6-149) (6-150)} \end{cases}$

Chain termination: $R_1 + R_1 \rightarrow D$ (Rate $= [R_1]^2k_t$)   (6-151)

Let us assume that A is stable toward thermal decomposition at the temperatures used and that 6-148 to 6-151 describe the only important reactions of the photodecomposition. Aldehyde photolysis at moderate temperatures,* many photopolymerizations, etc., follow this general reaction scheme. From the usual steady state treatment of this mechanism one can show that for experiments with continuous illumination the concentration of R_1 at the steady state, $[R_1]_s$, will be:

$$[R_1]_s = \left(\frac{I_a\varphi_i}{k_t}\right)^{1/2} \qquad (6\text{-}152)$$

and the rate law under steady state conditions is

$$-\left(\frac{d[A]}{dt}\right)_s = \left(\frac{I_a\varphi_i}{k_t}\right)^{1/2}[A]k_p \qquad (6\text{-}153)$$

During the light period of intermittent illumination the steady state is not established, but $[R_1]$ increases according to the equation

$$\frac{d[R_1]}{dt} = \varphi_i I_a - [R_1]^2 k_t \qquad (6\text{-}154)$$

During the dark periods $[R_1]$ decreases according to 6-155:

$$-\frac{d[R_1]}{dt} = [R_1]^2 k_t \qquad (6\text{-}155)$$

If 6-154 is integrated from $[R_1]_1$, the concentration of R_1 at the time t_1 at

---

* For the case of A $=$ acetaldehyde, $R_1 =$ CH$_3$, $R_2 =$ HCO, $R_3 =$ CH$_3$CO, B $=$ CH$_4$, C $=$ CO, D $=$ C$_2$H$_6$; at high temperature the decomposition of R_2 occurs for the case where A is an aldehyde, and subsequently another R_1 radical is generated: CHO $\rightarrow$ H $+$ CO; H $+$ CH$_3$CHO $\rightarrow$ H$_2$ $+$ CH$_3$CO; CH$_2$CO $\rightarrow$ CH$_3$ $+$ CO. Then the rate of R_1 radical generation at high temperatures becomes $2\varphi I_a$ instead of φI_a as assumed in the general treatment given here. In any case where R_1 and R_2 both start chains, the rate of initiation of chains will be given by $2\varphi I_a$, and this quantity should replace φI_a in all the functions derived herein.

the start of the flash, to $[R_1]_t$, the concentration at a later time t during the flash,

$$\int_{[R_1]_1}^{[R_1]_t} \frac{d[R_1]}{\varphi_i I_a - [R_1]^2 k_t} = \int_{t_1}^{t} dt \qquad (6\text{-}156)$$

Eq. 6-157 is obtained. This equation describes the variation of $[R_1]_t$ during the flash:

$$\tanh^{-1} [R_1]_t \left(\frac{k_t}{\varphi_i I_a}\right)^{\frac{1}{2}} - \tanh^{-1} [R_1]_1 \left(\frac{k_t}{\varphi_i I_a}\right)^{\frac{1}{2}} = (\varphi_i I_a k_t)^{\frac{1}{2}}(t - t_1) \qquad (6\text{-}157)$$

In a similar fashion the variation of $[R_1]$ during the dark period is given by 6-158, which is obtained by integration of 6-155:

$$\frac{1}{[R_1]_t} - \frac{1}{[R_1]_1} = k_t(t - t_1) \qquad (6\text{-}158)$$

The time dependence of the radical concentration may be calculated from 6-157 and 6-158 for light and dark periods involved in a rotating sector experiment. Figure 6-5, derived from calculations of this sort, shows the variation in $[R_1]$ with time for a hypothetical system, using two different speeds of a sector having a 3 to 1 dark to light ratio ($r = 3$). The durations of the light flashes are arbitrarily taken as 0.05 and 0.4 sec, respectively, for the fast and slow sector speeds. In the calculation k_t is assumed to be 1×10^{13} cm^3/mole-sec, $I_a = 10^{-11}$ einstein/cm^3-sec, and $\varphi_i = 1$. It is noticed from Fig. 6-5 that toward the end of the light period at the slower sector speed $[R_1]$ effectively reaches the steady state value characteristic of constant illumination of intensity I_a (the dotted line at $R_1 = 10 \times 10^{-13}$ mole/cm^3), and it falls almost to zero during the dark period. For the faster sector speed $[R_1]$ increases but never reaches the steady-state concentration during the light flash, and it decreases but never reaches zero during the dark period. After only a few cycles the concentration of R_1 oscillates between essentially constant maximum and minimum values; that is, the increase in $[R_1]$ in the light is just equal to its decrease in the dark. For this situation the rate of the reaction will depend on the average concentration of the radical R_1 over both the dark and the light periods, $\overline{[R_1]}$; the rate with rotating sector $= \overline{[R_1]}[A]k_p$. From equations 6-153, 6-154, and 6-155 an expression can be derived[137b] for the ratio of the average concentrations of R_1 in an experiment with intermittent light (intensity I_a when the light is on) to the concentration of R_1 in an experiment with steady illumination of intensity I_a, $[R_1]_s$:

$$\frac{\overline{[R_1]}}{[R_1]_s} = \left[\frac{1}{r + 1}\right]\left\{1 + m^{-1} \ln \left(\frac{rm}{1 + [R_1]_s/[R_1]_2} + 1\right)\right\} \qquad (6\text{-}159)$$

$$m = k_t \lambda_1 [R_1]_s = (\varphi_i I_a k_t)^{\frac{1}{2}} \lambda_1 \qquad (6\text{-}160)$$

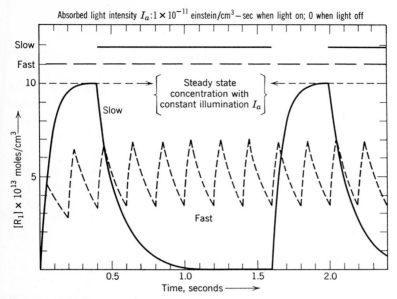

Fig. 6-5   Time dependence of the radical concentration in the rotating sector experiment, calculated for the conditions outlined in the text. The dark lines opposite "Fast" and "Slow" at the top of the figure represent periods of darkness; open spaces are periods of irradiation.

Here λ_1 is the duration of the light flash, and $[R_1]_2$ is the concentration of radical R_1 at the end of the light flash. The ratio $[R_1]_s/[R_1]_2$ which appears in 6-159 can be described by 6-161.

$$\frac{[R_1]_s}{[R_1]_2} = \frac{2(rm + \tanh m)}{rm \tanh m + [r^2m^2 \tanh^2 m + 4(rm + \tanh m) \tanh m]^{1/2}}$$

$$(6\text{-}161)$$

From 6-159, 6-160, and 6-161 the ratio of $[\overline{R_1}]/[R_1]_s$ can be expressed solely as a function of the parameters r and m. It is seen that the ratio $[\overline{R_1}]/[R_1]_s$ is also equal to the ratio of the measured rates of reaction with intermittent and steady illumination. The average lifetime of R_1 under steady state conditions, τ_s, is defined as the average number of seconds which the R_1 radicals exist at the steady state:

$$\tau_s = \frac{[R_1]_s}{-d[R_1]/dt} = \frac{[R_1]_s}{k_t[R_1]_s^2} = \frac{1}{k_t[R_1]_s} = \frac{\lambda_1}{m} \qquad (6\text{-}162)$$

From 6-152 and 6-162 it follows that

$$\tau_s = \left(\frac{1}{k_t \varphi_i I_a}\right)^{1/2} \tag{6-163}$$

Now, using the equations which have been presented, let us trace the necessary steps for the evaluation of the averge lifetime τ_s of the radical R_1 in the steady state, and the individual rate constants for the termination (k_t) and the propagation (k_p) reactions, by means of the rotating sector method.

1. The ratio of the rate under intermittent illumination to that under steady illumination is equal to the concentration ratio $[\overline{R_1}]/[R_1]_s$. This ratio should be found for a fast sector speed, for a slow sector speed, at several critical intermediate speeds where the transition in $[\overline{R_1}]/[R_1]_s$ occurs, and at several values of I_a. Keep the total fraction of the incident light absorbed below 50%.

2. The theoretical curve for $[\overline{R_1}]/[R_1]_s$ as a function of m and r values can be calculated from 6-159, 6-160, and 6-161. Burnette and Melville[137b] have made some of these calculations, which are summarized in Table 6-3. The pertinent data of this table may be used to construct a curve of $[\overline{R_1}]/[R_1]_s$ as a function of m for the r value used in the given experiments. Values of m corresponding to measured $[\overline{R_1}]/[R_1]_s$ can then be read from the curve.

3. Then the average lifetimes τ_s may be calculated from 6-162 ($\tau_s = \lambda_1/m$) for the various m and λ_1 values which correspond to the different conditions used.

4. A knowledge of I_a, the intensity of absorbed light, can be obtained by using conventional procedures described in Sec. 7-4. A reliable estimate of φ_i, the primary quantum yield of the photochemical initiating step, is difficult to obtain but can be made by means of one of the several techniques described in Sec. 6-6. A plot of τ_s versus $(1/\varphi_i I_a)^{1/2}$ should pass through the origin and have a slope $(1/k_t)^{1/2}$, from which k_t can be calculated. See relation 6-163.

5. The rate of the reaction under steady illumination of intensity I_a is given by 6-153. All the factors can be estimated experimentally so that the ratio of $k_p/k_t^{1/2}$ can be calculated. Since k_t has been found in step 4, k_p can now be obtained.

The technique described was first developed and applied by Chapman and Briers[136] (1928); they discussed the results of their photobromination experiments in intermittent light in terms of a bimolecular interaction involving an "active catalyst" which we would now identify as bromine

TABLE 6-3 Values of $[\overline{R_1}]/[R_1]_s$ as a Function of m for Various Values of r[a]

m	$r = 1$	$r = 2$	$r = 3$	$r = 4$	$r = 5$
Small	0.707	0.577	0.500	0.447	0.408
0.10	0.707	0.577	0.499	0.446	0.407
0.20	0.707	0.576	0.498	0.445	0.406
0.30	0.706	0.574	0.496	0.442	0.403
0.40	0.705	0.572	0.493	0.438	0.399
0.50	0.704	0.569	0.489	0.433	0.393
0.60	0.702	0.566	0.484	0.429	0.387
0.70	0.701	0.562	0.480	0.423	0.381
0.80	0.699	0.558	0.476	0.418	0.375
0.90	0.697	0.555	0.471	0.412	0.369
1.00	0.695	0.552	0.467	0.407	0.363
1.50	0.684	0.533	0.443	0.381	0.336
2.00	0.672	0.515	0.422	0.360	0.315
2.50	0.662	0.500	0.406	0.343	0.298
3.00	0.653	0.487	0.392	0.330	0.286
3.50	0.645	0.477	0.381	0.319	0.278
4.00	0.637	0.467	0.372	0.310	0.267
4.50	0.631	0.460	0.364	0.302	0.259
5.00	0.625	0.453	0.357	0.296	0.253
5.50	0.620	0.447	0.351	0.290	0.248
6.00	0.616	0.442	0.346	0.286	0.244
6.50	0.611	0.437	0.341	0.281	0.240
7.00	0.607	0.432	0.337	0.277	0.236
7.50	0.604	0.429	0.334	0.274	0.233
8.00	0.601	0.425	0.330	0.271	0.230
8.50	0.598	0.422	0.327	0.268	0.228
9.00	0.595	0.419	0.324	0.265	0.225
9.50	0.592	0.416	0.322	0.263	0.223
10.00	0.590	0.413	0.319	0.261	0.221
15.00	0.571	0.395	0.303	0.246	0.207
20.00	0.560	0.384	0.293	0.237	0.199
25.00	0.552	0.377	0.287	0.232	0.194
30.00	0.546	0.372	0.282	0.227	0.191
35.00	0.542	0.368	0.278	0.224	0.188
40.00	0.538	0.364	0.276	0.222	0.186
45.00	0.535	0.362	0.274	0.220	0.184
50.00	0.533	0.360	0.272	0.218	0.183
60.00	0.529	0.356	0.269	0.216	0.181
70.00	0.526	0.354	0.267	0.214	0.179
80.00	0.523	0.352	0.265	0.213	0.178
90.00	0.521	0.350	0.264	0.212	0.177
100.00	0.520	0.349	0.263	0.211	0.176
200.00	0.512	0.342	0.257	0.206	0.172
300.00	0.508	0.340	0.255	0.204	0.170
400.00	0.507	0.338	0.254	0.2033	0.1695
500.00	0.5065	0.3375	0.2533	0.2028	0.1690
600.00	0.5048	0.3369	0.2528	0.2024	0.1687
700.00	0.5042	0.3364	0.2525	0.2021	0.1684
800.00	0.5037	0.3361	0.2522	0.2018	0.1682
900.00	0.5034	0.3358	0.2520	0.2016	0.1680
1000.00	0.5031	0.3356	0.2518	0.2015	0.1679
High	0.5000	0.3333	0.2500	0.2000	0.1667

From Burnett and Melville.[137b]

atoms. Haden and Rice[138] (1942) first successfully estimated the rate constant for the reaction $2CH_3 \rightarrow C_2H_6$ from rotating sector experiments with acetaldehyde; since that time many rate constants have been determined by using these methods.

The more complex treatments of rotating sector data, involving the effects of constant dark reaction, non-uniformity of light absorption, a trapezoidal light flash rather than the ideal square wave, and the more general reaction sequence including both first- and second-order termination of chains, are summarized by Burnett and Melville.[137b]

The great utility of the rotating sector procedures is not restricted to the study of chain processes alone; with the proper choice of conditions individual rate constants can be determined in non-chain systems. In illustration consider the work of Shepp.[139] He photolyzed acetone in experiments at high light intensity and at temperatures above 100°C. Under these conditions the following mechanism is likely:

$$CH_3COCH_3 + h\nu \rightarrow CH_3CO + CH_3 \qquad (\varphi I_a) \qquad (6\text{-}164)$$

$$CH_3CO \rightarrow CH_3 + CO \qquad (k_1) \qquad (6\text{-}165)$$

$$CH_3 + CH_3COCH_3 \rightarrow CH_4 + CH_2COCH_3 \qquad (k_2) \qquad (6\text{-}166)$$

$$CH_3 + CH_2COCH_3 \rightarrow C_2H_5COCH_3 \qquad (k_3) \qquad (6\text{-}167)$$

$$2CH_3 \rightarrow C_2H_6 \qquad (k_4) \qquad (6\text{-}168)$$

Assuming this mechanism, at the steady-state $d[CH_3]/dt$ will be given by

$$\frac{d[CH_3]}{dt} = 0 = 2I_a\varphi - 2[CH_3][CH_3COCH_3]k_2 - 2[CH_3]^2k_4 \quad (6\text{-}169)$$

In Shepp's experiments the light intensity was kept high so that the inequality $2[CH_3]^2k_4 \gg 2[CH_3][CH_3COCH_3]k_2$ was maintained, but the rate of methane formation was measurable, although small. For these conditions 6-169 reduces to

$$2I_a\varphi \cong 2[CH_3]^2k_4 \qquad (6\text{-}170)$$

From 6-170 and the usual rate equations for ethane and methane formation, 6-171 can be obtained:

$$[CH_3COCH_3]\frac{d[C_2H_6]}{dt} \Big/ \frac{d[CH_4]}{dt} = \frac{(I_a\varphi k_4)^{1/2}}{k_2} \qquad (6\text{-}171)$$

The rate function 6-171 is proportional to $I_a^{1/2}$ and will show variation with sector speed as in the chain case. Values of m for different λ_1's may be found, τ_s calculated from 6-162, and k_4 determined from 6-163 as before. A great many radical association constants have been measured with these interesting techniques.

6-7B-5 Effect of Wavelength of the Absorbed Light on the Reaction Mechanism

The wavelength of the absorbed light is an important variable unique to photochemical systems. One can alter the energy of the reacting molecule by precisely known amounts and study the effect on primary and secondary processes. One of the critical precautions in any such study is to keep the intensity of light *absorbed* as nearly as possible the same at all wavelengths studied, particularly if one is examining the products of secondary reactions. Studies should be made with monochromatic light of known wavelength distribution, and the fraction of this incident light absorbed by the reactant should be known accurately, or reasonably so. This is true because, as we have seen earlier, the quantum yields of products of certain secondary relations in photochemical systems are a function of light intensity (e.g., products of alkyl radical combination and disproportionation versus abstraction), while others are not (e.g., complete molecules formed in an intramolecular primary process). In dealing with the former type of system, either exclusively or as one of several primary processes (e.g., an alkyl ketone with both a Type I and a Type II split), if one does not keep I_a constant, a variation in product ratio may be misinterpreted as a "wavelength effect."

Perhaps we would not be as specific about this obvious point if we had not recently encountered a study in which a pronounced "wavelength effect" on the reactivity of the excited molecule was claimed by the author, yet he had not used reasonably monochromatic light and had not compensated for the greatly different extinction coefficients of the compound at the wavelengths studied. Consequently his values for I_a may have varied by as much as a factor of 10^3 over the experimental wavelength range. Since at least some of the products appeared to be formed by intensity-dependent reactions, his "wavelength effect" may or *may not* be as he interpreted it.

The implications from wavelength effects can be varied and significant in character. If within a given absorption band a wavelength dependence of the primary quantum yields is observed, then vibrational equilibration has not been achieved in the electronically excited state; the reaction probably proceeds from a short-lived ($\tau < 10^{-11}$ sec) vibrationally and electronically excited singlet state (S_1^v).

Several other possibilities exist; however, they are less likely:

Internal conversion ($S_1^v \rightarrow S_0^{v'}$) occurs quickly after absorption (before vibrational cascade, $v' \rightarrow v = 0$), and the primary process occurs from a vibrationally excited ground state $S_0^{v'}$. A wavelength dependency would be observed if:

(a) The probability of internal conversion depended on the vibrational level v of the excited state S_1^v.

(b) The primary process yield depended on the vibrational level v' of the ground state $S_0^{v'}$.

A similar argument could be made if one assumed that intersystem crossing from S_1 to $T_1^{v'}$ is faster than vibrational equilibration of S_1 and dissociation occurs from the vibrationally excited triplet state T_1^v before it is vibrationally equilibrated.

If the wavelength variation has no effect on the quantum yield of a given photochemical primary process, one of two reaction mechanisms seems likely: (1) the excited state or states produced are very short-lived and completely rearrange, dissociate, fluoresce, or react by some other single path at all wavelengths of absorbed light; or (2) the initially formed species S_1^v is vibrationally equilibrated to S_1^0 from this state it decomposes or undergoes radiational or non-radiational transitions to lower excited states from which it reacts. The latter situation is often encountered in solution-phase photochemistry.

Generally over a given absorption band photochemical systems do not seem to show abrupt changes in photodecomposition mechanisms at some critical wavelength region in the band. If changes do occur, there is a gradual shift in mechanism of photolysis as the absorbed energy is varied regularly. A shift toward the shorter wavelengths or higher energies usually results in a higher efficiency of primary photodecompositions, assuming that the molecule does not already decompose efficiently at the longer wavelengths. The shorter the wavelength of the light absorbed by a molecule the higher is the vibrational level to which the molecule is carried in the primary act; thus the lifetime is shorter, since the rate constant for unimolecular decomposition or other reactions is larger; recall relation 6-66. Accordingly, fluorescence efficiencies are commonly lower in these systems, and molecular fragmentation is much more extensive at the short wavelengths. Also, "hot" radical reactions in gas-phase experiments become more likely in the short-wavelength region, since greater energies are carried off by the products of the dissociation.

6-7B-6   Effect of Concentration of Reactant and Inert Gases on Rates of Photolysis

The reaction mechanism can be elucidated from determinations of order and molecularity of a reaction. The effect of the variation of the concentration of the reactant molecules on the rate of a photochemical reaction is difficult to determine directly. For a constant incident light intensity the absorbed light intensity changes as the reactant concentration is varied. This tends to mask a possible concentration effect. One can adjust the incident intensity for each experiment through the use of different arc currents and/or filters so that I_a is maintained constant; this procedure is tedious and often impractical. Usually the incident intensity is maintained constant as the concentration is varied, and the rates are corrected to a constant absorbed light intensity from the known variation of rates with I_a. If this plan is used, the influence of I_a on the rate must be established over the range of concentration used. Otherwise a change in mechanism may occur with concentration change (e.g., a wall reaction may become important in the low concentration range), and the effect of I_a may change. This would lead to the application of a faulty correction and hence an incorrect order for the reactants.

When rates are changed by the addition of inert gas or by varying the size or the surface to volume ratio of the reaction cell, a contribution from diffusion-controlled wall reactions is suggested. Atoms and radicals may diffuse to a wall, and there combine or react in some fashion with adsorbed species. Since the rate of diffusion of a given species through a gaseous medium is lowered by an increase in the concentration of the molecules in the medium, the rate of product formation can be influenced by the concentration of all molecules in the medium when wall reactions are important.

Several detailed theoretical considerations have been made of diffusion equations applicable to photochemical systems.[140] However, all quantitative treatments are dependent on a knowledge of the probability of reflection or reaction of a radical on collision with a wall, and this information is usually unobtainable without a very detailed study of the particular system of interest.[141] Furthermore, it is probable that any one such determination would be of little value in later experiments. The reflection efficiency of a wall must be extremely sensitive to the nature of its surface, and the surface must vary continuously as products and reactants are sorbed and desorbed upon it during the runs. It is generally concluded that in gas-phase studies the elimination of surface reactions is usually much easier than any attempt to treat them quantitatively.

R. M. Noyes[140c] has suggested a qualitative theoretical test of the possible importance of wall reactions in a system undergoing chain decomposition. When the quantity d,

$$d = 0.9\left(\frac{D^2}{\varphi I_a k}\right)^{1/4} \tag{6-172}$$

is small compared to the linear dimensions of the reaction cell, wall termination of chains should be unimportant; d is the approximate thickness of a shell in which the atom or radical concentration is near zero. (It is assumed that every collision with the wall removes the active species.) D is the diffusion coefficient of the radical, φI_a is the rate of production of chains, and k is the rate constant for homogeneous second-order termination. For the usual conditions of gas-phase chain photochemical reactions $d = 0.1$ cm. For liquid systems $d = 0.01$ cm. Noyes concludes that chain termination at the wall in most liquid systems is very unlikely, but it may be important in gas systems unless relatively high intensities and high pressures are used. This view appears to be in general agreement with experiment. Hill[140b] has suggested that the root-mean-square distance which a radical diffuses in its lifetime be used as a criterion of the importance of wall reactions. Nicholson[140d] feels that direct experimental evaluation of the importance of wall reactions is usually much easier than any attempt to treat them quantitatively. If one works with low total absorption, varies the length and volume of the cell over a wide range, varies the nature of the surface of the cell (NaCl, etc.), and looks for an effect of these variables without necessarily interpreting it quantitatively, he will be in a good position to evaluate the importance of wall reactions in his system.

Very high values of I_a and strongly exothermic reactions can lead to convection currents within a system. The actual importance of radical transport by this process is difficult to access. R. M. Noyes[140c] wisely suggests that it is preferable to avoid serious thermal gradients by proper design of equipment rather than to attempt to correct for them mathematically.

The recombination of atoms and very simple radicals in the gas phase often requires a third body, and an increase in reactant or inert-gas concentration will cause a rise in rate. Collisional activation leading to the decomposition of very simple radicals such as OH, ClO, and HCO may appear to be second order even at commonly used pressures. In these cases an increase in gas concentration will be attended by an increase in rate of the decompositions. Molecules which absorb light to form relatively stable, long-lived excited states may often suffer collisional deactivation and lowered efficiency of photodecomposition, and hence a slower rate of product formation is expected in these cases as the concentration of added gas is increased. Mention has been made previously of the effect of "hot" atom and radical moderation by added gas.

It is seen that the effects of added inert gas in the gas-phase systems are many, and a complete interpretation of them is often difficult. Nevertheless the effects of added gases frequently provide a crucial test of possible reaction mechanisms. CO_2, N_2, helium, neon, and argon are commonly used as "inert" gases. They are often poor choices, since they contain few degrees of freedom and cannot be highly effective as third bodies or as deactivators. Perfluorohydrocarbons are to be preferred in theory, for they not only are "inert" gases but also have a large number of degrees of freedom; however, in the limited work in which they have been used their efficiency has not been as high as one would anticipate.

6-7C Fluorescence, Phosphorescence, Intersystem Crossing Studies

From quantitative fluorescence and phosphorescence studies a multitude of important information sometimes can be obtained: lifetimes of the excited molecules, rates of intersystem crossing, the number and nature of excited states, the nature of the fluorescence quenching mechanism, the effective quenching cross sections of molecules, the efficiency of electronic energy transfer, estimates of the total primary quantum yield of decomposition, etc. It is somewhat surprising in view of the usefulness of fluorescence studies to find that relatively few quantitative experiments of this kind have been made until recent years. As in the usual case, it seems that experimental complications of the research method discourage its use.

One of the simplest and yet most common types of fluorescence quenching mechanisms, called the *Stern-Volmer mechanism*,[142] may be considered to illustrate the treatment of fluorescence experiments. Consider a case in which M^* represent the only electronic excited state of the molecule M:

$$M + h\nu \rightarrow M^* \qquad (\varphi_i I_a) \qquad (6\text{-}173)$$

Assume that fluorescence, 6-174, collisional deactivation by M or some other molecule A, 6-175, and photodecomposition, 6-176, are the only processes which can follow 6-173.

$$M^* \rightarrow h\nu' + M \qquad (k_2) \qquad (6\text{-}174)$$

$$M^* + M \text{ (or A)} \rightarrow M + M' \text{ (or A')} \qquad (k_3) \qquad (6\text{-}175)$$

$$M^* \rightarrow B + C \qquad (k_4) \qquad (6\text{-}176)$$

The mean lifetime τ of the excited state may be defined as the time required after termination of the exciting radiation for $[M^*]$ to decrease to $1/e$th of its previous value. In terms of the simple mechanism presented and under conditions where collisional deactivation, 6-175, is unimportant, it can be shown that $\tau = 1/(k_2 + k_4)$. The lifetime can be determined directly by a measure of the decay of fluorescence intensity following an exposure of the reactant (see Sec. 7-5C-2). If the results are obtained at concentrations where 6-175 is unimportant or extrapolations can be made to these conditions, then

$$\tau = \frac{1}{k_2 + k_4} = \frac{t' - t}{\ln (I_f/I_f')} \tag{6-177}$$

where I_f/I_f' is the relative intensity of the fluorescence at times t and t', respectively, after the exposure.

Define I_a and I_f as the intensity of absorbed light and the intensity of fluorescence (quanta/cm^3-sec), respectively, in a given small volume of the reaction system in which I_a and I_f can be considered as uniform. If it is assumed that a steady state is reached between M* formation in 6-173 and its destruction in 6-174, 6-175, and 6-176, it can be shown that

$$\frac{I_a}{I_f} = 1 + \frac{k_4}{k_2} + \frac{k_3[M]}{k_2} \tag{6-178}$$

If this simple mechanism is operative, a straight line is expected when I_a/I_f (called the "quenching") is plotted versus [M]. The slope defines k_3/k_2, and the intercept is $1 + k_4/k_2$. Since $k_2 + k_4$ can be determined independently as described, k_4 and k_3 can be calculated.

The primary quantum yield of decomposition of M by 6-176 (φ_4) is defined by

$$\varphi_4 = \frac{d[B]/dt}{I_a}. \tag{6-179}$$

In terms of the above mechanism and the steady state assumption for M* it can be shown that

$$\frac{d[B]}{dt} = [M^*]k_4 = \frac{k_4 I_a}{k_2 + k_4 + k_3[M]} \tag{6-180}$$

and hence

$$\varphi_4 = \frac{k_4}{k_2 + k_4 + k_3[M]} \tag{6-181}$$

Since the various constants and [M] are known, φ_4 can be calculated for this simple system. In actual practice the assumption of I_a and I_f uniformity may not be justified over the volume element from which observation is made. Correction for this leads to more exact expressions which apply to the usual measured quantities. (See Noyes and Leighton.[125])

It is often desirable to have some measure of the effectiveness of the interaction of M* with various quencher molecules A in reaction 6-175. Such information is helpful in mechanism considerations involving activated molecules. For this purpose the effective quenching cross section for fluorescence is defined in terms of the collision theory as $\sigma_Q{}^2$. For the Stern-Volmer mechanism given by reactions 6-173 to 6-176, k_3 can be evaluated from quenching and fluorescence decay experiments as described. Then $\sigma_Q{}^2$ is calculated from the collision theory equation, Eq. 6-31, assuming that $k_3 = Z_{M^*-A}$, that is, that every collision is effective in deactivation. (See Sec. 2-9B.)

When the absorbing species has a very large molar extinction coefficient and the frequency of the fluorescence ν' is the same as that of the exciting radiation ν, as with mercury atoms excited by 2537 or 1849 A radiation, the effective imprisonment of the radiation can occur. Then complications not anticipated in this simple treatment are introduced in the evaluation of the various constants from the measured data.[143] Further complications enter when more than one excited state is observed in the fluorescence decay experiments.[144]

Sensitized fluorescence and phosphorescence studies have become important diagnostic tools in establishing the details of photochemical mechanisms. Consider one of the definitive studies of this sort carried out by Heicklen and Noyes,[145] using acetone at 3130 A. They observed that Φ_{CO} from acetone photolysis at 3130 A, 40°, and an acetone pressure of 52 mm, decreased significantly as the percentage of conversion was increased. Biacetyl is known to be a product of the reaction, and since it had been observed that emission from biacetyl is sensitized when acetone is irradiated in its presence,[146] they surmised that biacetyl might build up during a run and act as a quencher. Indeed this seemed to be the case, for the addition of small amounts of biacetyl decreased the quantum efficiency of product formation from acetone; at about 0.1 mm of added biacetyl a limiting suppression was found.

Biacetyl does not absorb light strongly at 3130 A (see Fig. 5-5), and its emission characteristics are well known;[147] see Sec. 4-10A. Biacetyl excited with 4358–3650 A light exhibits both fluorescence from a singlet state ($\tau \sim 8 \times 10^{-6}$ sec) in a band at 4500–5000 A and phosphorescence from a triplet state ($\tau \sim 2 \times 10^{-3}$ sec) in a band at 5000–6100 A. Acetone excited at 3130 A has a weak blue emission ($\varphi_f = 2 \times 10^{-3}$) from 3800–4700 A; this involves two states: an excited singlet emitting at the shorter wavelengths ($\tau \sim 8 \times 10^{-6}$ sec) and a longer-lived triplet ($\tau \sim 2 \times 10^{-4}$ sec) emitting at the longer wavelengths. Heicklen and Noyes monitored the emission at 4000 and 4313 A from acetone-biacetyl mixtures which were irradiated at 3130 A. These data are presented in Fig. 6-6.

The emission at these wavelengths has a contribution from both the singlet and triplet states of acetone but essentially none from biacetyl emission. Note that the emission from acetone approaches a constant value at added biacetyl pressures above about 0.1 mm. The emission is the same as that observed with acetone with added oxygen (a known quencher of triplet acetone). The fall-off of the triplet emission parallels

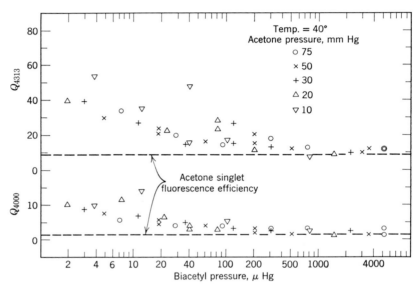

Fig. 6-6 Emission efficiency of acetone versus biacetyl pressure; acetone-biacetyl photolysis at 3130 A. The Q values on the ordinate are proportional to $\varphi_p + \varphi_f$ for acetone at the wavelengths indicated by the subscript. From Heicklen and Noyes.[145]

the decrease in the product quantum yields from acetone, as mentioned earlier. Furthermore, accompanying these changes with biacetyl addition is the appearance of the triplet emission from biacetyl as measured at 5000 A. One is urged to conclude from all these facts that triplet acetone is present to a certain extent in acetone photolysis at 3130 A and is deactivated to the ground state by energy transfer to form triplet biacetyl. The results show that the singlet is present also but is apparently unaffected by biacetyl addition under these conditions.

Heicklen and Noyes further studied the relative quantum efficiency of the sensitized phosphorescence emission from biacetyl (φ_p^s) as a function of acetone concentration [A] and added biacetyl [B]. A linear plot was obtained when $[B]/\varphi_p^s$ was plotted versus [B]; see Fig. 6-7. The explanation of this relation requires a consideration of the detailed mechanism. One

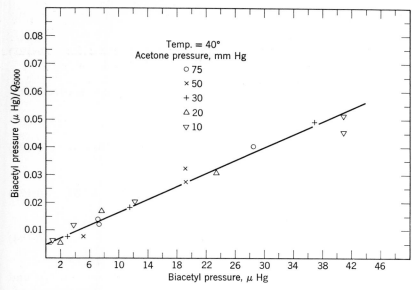

Fig. 6-7 Biacetyl pressure/phosphorescence efficiency (at 5000 A) versus biacetyl pressure; acetone-biacetyl photolysis at 3130 A; Q_{5000} is proportional to φ_p^s of biacetyl at 5000 A. From Heicklen and Noyes.[145]

might suggest on the basis of the earlier results that the mechanism of acetone photolysis at 3130 A with added biacetyl should include the following steps:

$$A + h\nu \rightarrow A(S_1) \qquad (I_a\varphi_1) \qquad \qquad (6\text{-}182)$$

$$A(S_1) \rightarrow A + h\nu' \qquad (k_2) \qquad \qquad (6\text{-}183)$$

$$A(S_1) \rightarrow A(T_1) \qquad (k_3) \qquad \qquad (6\text{-}184)$$

$$A(T_1) \rightarrow A + h\nu'' \qquad (k_4) \qquad \qquad (6\text{-}185)$$

$$A(S_1) \rightarrow CH_3CO + CH_3 \qquad (k_5) \qquad \qquad (6\text{-}186)$$

$$A(T_1) \rightarrow CH_3CO + CH_3 \qquad (k_6) \qquad \qquad (6\text{-}187)$$

$$A(T_1) + B \rightarrow A + B(T_1) \qquad (k_7) \qquad \qquad (6\text{-}188)$$

$$B(T_1) \rightarrow B + h\nu''' \qquad (k_8) \qquad \qquad (6\text{-}189)$$

$$B(T_1) \rightarrow \text{Products} \qquad (k_9) \qquad \qquad (6\text{-}190)$$

In terms of this mechanism the quantum yield of sensitized emission of phosphorescence from biacetyl will be given by

$$\varphi_p{}^s = \frac{[B(T_1)]k_8}{I_a} \tag{6-191}$$

Assuming the steady state condition for the intermediate excited states $A(S_1)$, $A(T_1)$, and $B(T_1)$, we obtain

$$\frac{d[B(T_1)]}{dt} = 0 = -[B(T_1)](k_8 + k_9) + [A(T_1)][B]k_7 \tag{6-192}$$

$$\frac{d[A(T_1)]}{dt} = 0 = [A(S_1)]k_3 - [A(T_1)]\{k_4 + k_6 + k_7[B]\} \tag{6-193}$$

$$\frac{d[A(S_1)]}{dt} = 0 = I_a\varphi_1 - [A(S_1)](k_2 + k_3 + k_5) \tag{6-194}$$

Solving 6-192, 6-193, and 6-194 for $[A(S_1)]$, $[A(T_1)]$, and $[B(T_1)]$ and substituting the results in 6-191 gives the relation

$$\frac{[B]}{\varphi_p{}^s} = \frac{(k_8 + k_9)(k_2 + k_3 + k_5)(k_4 + k_6 + k_7[B])}{k_8 k_7 k_3 \varphi_1} \tag{6-195}$$

From 6-195 the linear plot observed in Fig. 6-7 is rationalized, and the mechanism is seen to be consistent with all of the observations. The kinetics of the fluorescence, sensitized phosphorescence, and the product quantum yields all point to the nature of the electronic states involved in acetone photolysis at 3130 A and the mechanism choice to be made.

Bäckström and Sandros[148] have designed a very interesting kinetic method to determine triplet lifetimes in solution through sensitized phosphorescence, using benzophenone as the sensitizer.

Recently, triplet energy transfer in fluid solution has been utilized by Lamola and Hammond to measure *directly* a very important quantity that to date has not been accessible by optical spectroscopy, the quantum yield of intersystem crossing, φ_{ISC} (see Sec. 4-8B and Table 4-17).* In this simple chemical-kinetic method the substance to be studied is used as a sensitizer in some well characterized reaction. Several *cis-trans* isomerization reactions have been used with concordant results. The

---

* We are indebted to Professor G. S. Hammond and Dr. A. A. Lamola for these unpublished observations.

following equations illustrate the principles:

$$S + h\nu \rightarrow S^{*(1)} \tag{6-196}$$

$$S^{*(1)} \rightarrow S \quad \text{Fluorescence or radiationless decay} \quad (k_1) \tag{6-197}$$

$$S^{*(1)} \rightarrow S^{*(3)} \quad \text{Intersystem crossing} \quad (k_2) \tag{6-198}$$

$$S^{*(3)} + \underset{H}{\overset{R}{\diagdown}}C=C\underset{H}{\overset{R}{\diagup}} \rightarrow S + RCH=CHR^{*(3)} \quad (k_3) \tag{6-199}$$

$$RCH=CHR^{*(3)} \rightarrow \underset{H}{\overset{R}{\diagdown}}C=C\underset{H}{\overset{R}{\diagup}} \quad (k_4) \tag{6-200}$$

$$RCH=CHR^{*(3)} \rightarrow \underset{H}{\overset{R}{\diagdown}}C=C\underset{R}{\overset{H}{\diagup}} \quad (k_5) \tag{6-201}$$

Lamola and Hammond designate S as the sensitizer molecule, and the superscripts $*(1)$ and $*(3)$ refer to the first excited singlet and triplet states, respectively. If the excitation energy of $S^{*(3)}$ is sufficiently higher than that required to promote the unsaturated substrate to its lowest triplet state, energy transfer, reaction 6-199, becomes a diffusion-controlled process. Consequently, at moderate concentrations of the substrate, all the triplet excitation that arrives in S is transferred, that is, the quantum yield for isomerization becomes independent of the substrate concentration. Under these conditions the quantum yield of isomerization becomes a direct measure of the quantum yield for intersystem crossing in S.

$$\Phi_{c \rightarrow t} = \frac{k_1}{k_1 + k_2} \frac{k_5}{k_4 + k_5} = \varphi_{\text{ISC}} \frac{k_4}{k_4 + k_5} \tag{6-202}$$

The value of the decay ratio $k_4/(k_4 + k_5)$, can be measured independently. In order for the method to be reliable one must choose a system in which the sum of the quantum yields for the two isomerization reactions is unity, that is, $\Phi_{c \rightarrow t} + \Phi_{t \rightarrow c} = 1$. In order to avoid possible complication from transfer of singlet excitation from $S^{*(1)}$ to the unsaturated substrate, the latter must be chosen so that its lowest excited singlet lies above that of S. Table 4-17 in Chapter 4 shows representative results.

It is hoped that this brief discussion of methods of studying photochemical mechanisms will indicate the common "tools" available and the types of information that can be derived from their use. The application of these methods is best implemented by a consideration of the practical aspects of the laboratory measurements involved; these are dealt with in Chapter 7.

PROBLEMS

1. The thermal decomposition of di-*tert*-butyl peroxide gives primarily acetone and ethane as products; methane and methyl ethyl ketone are formed in smaller amounts. The rate of the gas-phase decomposition of this peroxide was measured at a temperature of 154.7°C, and the following data obtained [Raley, Rust, and Vaughan, *J. Am. Chem. Soc.*, **70**, 88 (1948)]:

Time, min	Pressure of di-*tert*-Butyl Peroxide, mm
0	169.3
2	162.4
3	159.3
5	153.4
6	150.4
8	144.6
9	141.7
11	136.1
12	133.8
14	128.8
15	126.4
17	121.7
18	119.1
20	115.0
21	117.6

(a) Determine the order of the reaction with respect to di-*tert*-butyl peroxide concentration.

(b) Calculate the reaction rate constant from the data. (Use units of moles, liters, and seconds.)

2. Consider the following reaction rate data for the H_2 and I_2 reaction, $H_2 + I_2 \rightarrow 2HI$ [Lewis, *J. Chem. Soc.*, **113**, 471 (1918)]:

Rate Constant, k_{II}, liters/mole-sec	Temperature, °K
4.44×10^{-5}	556
2.25×10^{-3}	629
1.42×10^{-2}	666
6.42×10^{-2}	700

Calculate the activation energy of this reaction by the graphical or the method of least squares.

3. From the data of Problem 2 calculate the "steric factor" P in the collision theory equation. Assume that the collision diameters of I_2 and H_2 are 4.6 and 2.74 A, respectively.

4. (a) From the data and your solutions in the preceding problems calculate $\Delta H^{\ddagger}$, $\Delta S^{\ddagger}$, and $\Delta F^{\ddagger}$ as used in transition state theory. Take the standard state as 1 mole/liter. Assume that the transmission coefficient $\kappa = 1$.

(b) Describe in detail the exact chemical change to which these changes in enthalpy, etc., refer.

(c) Calculate $\Delta S^{\ddagger}$ for the standard state of 1 mole/cm³. Using this value, calculate $e^{\Delta S^{\ddagger}/R}$ and compare the size of this term with the steric factor P from Problem 3.

5. Consider the two hypothetical gaseous molecules A and B both of which undergo pseudo-unimolecular decomposition at high pressures. The activation energy is 40 kcal/mole in each case, and the A factors for the high-pressure rate constants $= 10^{13}$ sec^{-1}. A and B have 3 and 30 atoms/molecule, respectively.

(a) Compare the magnitude of the maximum possible Hinshelwood factor, Y in equation 6-64, with the term $e^{-E_a/RT}$ for A and B at 300°K.

(b) Calculate the approximate pressure region (in millimeters of Hg) at which the decomposition of pure A and pure B will undergo transition to second-order kinetics ($k_1 \cong k_{-2}[A]$ in Eq. 6-60); take the gram molecular weights of A and B as 30 and 180 grams/mole, respectively; $\sigma_A = 2$ A; $\sigma_B = 8$ A.

6. Estimate the order of magnitude of the rate constants (from the activation energy and the pre-exponential factor estimates) for the reactions:

(a) $CH_3 + HI \rightarrow CH_4 + I$

(b) $CH_3 + C_2H_6 \rightarrow CH_4 + C_2H_5$

(c) $H + C_3H_8 \rightarrow H_2 + iso\text{-}C_3H_7$

(d) $CH_3CH_2CH_3 \rightarrow CH_3CH_2 + CH_3$

(e) $n\text{-}C_3H_7 + CH_3 \rightarrow n\text{-}C_4H_{10}$

(f) $CH_3CH_2CH_2CH_2 \rightarrow CH_3CH_2 + CH_2{=}CH_2$

7. The two possible transition states I and II may be considered for the reaction $2NO_2 \rightarrow O_2 + 2NO$.

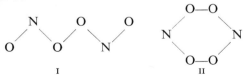

(a) Using the hydrocarbon analog method for the estimation of $\Delta S^{\ddagger}$, estimate the theoretical A factors for the two types of complexes.

(b) The experimental A factor is 1.8×10^{12} cm³/mole-sec. Which is the more reasonable transition state?

(c) Are there other possible transition states which should be considered?

8. In the photolysis of azomethane-nitric oxide mixtures the transient species CH_3NO has been observed by infrared spectrophotometry. The following data were obtained by absorption measurements in the characteristic band of CH_3NO at 6.32 μ in experiments at 25°C [Calvert, Thomas, and Hanst, *J. Am. Chem. Soc.*, **82**, 1 (1960)]:

$d(\log I_0/I)/dt \times 10^4$ at time t, sec^{-1}	$\log I_0/I$ at time t
0.60	0.023_2
1.54	0.036_2
2.52	0.048_7
3.25	0.051_9
4.36	0.059_4
0.0056_6	0.0024_1

(a) What is the order of the reaction by which CH_3NO disappears?

(b) If the molar extinction coefficient $\epsilon = 77$ (liters/mole-cm) for CH_3NO at 6.32 μ and the path length used above is 10 cm, estimate the rate constant for the CH_3NO decay reaction.

9. Trotman-Dickenson and Steacie [*J. Chem. Phys.*, **18**, 1097 (1950)] have measured rates of CH_4 and C_2H_6 formation in the photolysis of acetone vapor. They have calculated the function of the rates,

$$F = (d[CH_4]/dt)/\{(d[C_2H_6]/dt)^{1/2}[CH_3COCH_3]\}$$

at various temperatures. The value of F is independent of variation in I_a and $[CH_3COCH_3]$ over a wide range. The data suggest that the methane and ethane are formed only in reactions 1 and 2, respectively:

$$CH_3 + CH_3COCH_3 \rightarrow CH_4 + CH_2COCH_3 \tag{1}$$

$$2CH_3 \rightarrow C_2H_6 \tag{2}$$

(a) From the following data estimate the activation energy difference, $E_1 - E_2/2$, and the ratio of pre-exponential factors, $A_1/A_2^{1/2}$; use the method of least squares (Sec. 6-7A-8):

Temperature, °K	F, (cm^3/sec-molecule)$^{1/2}$, $\times 10^{13}$
394	3.52
404	4.88
423	7.89
440	13.2
449	16.0
471	25.8
507	54.6
536	92.0
544	108.0
573	158

(b) Taking $k_2 = 2.2 \times 10^{10}$ liters/mole-sec (independent of temperature), calculate k_1 as a function of temperature.

(c) Calculate $\Delta S^{\ddagger}$ and $\Delta H^{\ddagger}$ for reaction 1.

10. An increase in pressure occurs when pure Cl_2 gas in a sealed bulb is irradiated with blue light. This phenomenon is called the Budde effect. How may this effect be explained qualitatively? (Note that the effect is not explained in terms of the fraction of the chlorine present as atoms, for at any instant during irradiation this is negligibly small compared to that present as molecules.)

11. The following sequence of reactions is suggested to explain the photobromination of ethane to form C_2H_5Br during the initial stage of the reaction:

$$Br_2 + h\nu \rightarrow 2Br \tag{1}$$

$$Br + C_2H_6 \rightarrow HBr + C_2H_5 \tag{2}$$

$$C_2H_5 + Br_2 \rightarrow C_2H_5Br + Br \tag{3}$$

$$M + Br + Br \rightarrow M + Br_2 \tag{4}$$

$$(\text{Wall}) \; Br \rightarrow \tfrac{1}{2}Br_2 \; (\text{Wall}) \tag{5}$$

(a) Derive an expression for $d(C_2H_5Br)/dt$ (in terms of rate constants, etc.), assuming that reaction 4 is the only chain-terminating step (no reaction 5).

(b) Derive a similar expression, assuming that reaction 5 is the only chain-terminating step (no reaction 4).

(c) The rate with which ethyl bromide is formed at low pressure of reactants and low light intensities is proportional to I_a, while at high pressures and high light intensities the rate is proportional to $I_a^{1/2}$. Are these facts consistent with the rate laws from (a) and (b) and the assumptions made in their derivation?

12. A molecule of ^{127}I—^{35}Cl absorbs a quantum of light of wavelength 4000 A.

(a) Calculate the total kinetic energy in ergs which the two atoms will have as they separate if dissociation into $I(^2P_{1/2})$ and $Cl(^2P_{3/2})$ atoms occurs. The bond strength in ICl is about 44.0 kcal/mole. When a mole of iodine atoms undergoes the change, $I(^2P_{3/2}) \rightarrow I(^2P_{1/2})$, 21.6 kcal/mole is absorbed.

(b) What fraction of this kinetic energy will each of the two atoms take?

(c) What moderating gas would you choose to best equilibrate the atoms?

13. A cylindrical photolysis cell, 15.0 cm in length, contains glyoxal gas at a pressure of 132 mm and at a temperature of 155°C. A collimated beam of 3130 A light is passed through the length of the cell. The incident light intensity just inside the front window of the cell is 7.14×10^{14} quanta/sec. The molar extinction coefficient of glyoxal at 155°C and 3130 A is 9.79 liters/mole-cm. After 90 min exposure, an analysis of the products shows that 0.144 ml of CO gas (STP) was formed. Calculate Φ_{CO}.

14. It has been suggested that the glyoxal photolysis at 3130 A is described by a simple mechanism which involves two primary processes (both intramolecular rearrangements to form stable products).

$$(HCO)_2 + h\nu \rightarrow H_2 + 2CO \tag{1}$$

$$\searrow \qquad\qquad\qquad$$

$$CH_2O + CO \tag{2}$$

Show that the following rate equation is consistent with this mechanism:

$$\frac{d[CO]}{dt} = I_0(1 - 10^{-\epsilon cl})(\varphi_2 + 2\varphi_1)$$

Here I_0 is the incident light intensity; ϵ, the molar extinction coefficient; c, the molar concentration of $(CHO)_2$; and l, the path length (cm); φ_2 and φ_1 are the primary quantum yields of processes 2 and 1, respectively.

15. The ratio of Φ_{H_2}/Φ_{CO} in the products of glyoxal photolysis at 3130 A was found to be 0.13. Assuming that the mechanism suggested in Problem 14 is correct (and that no deactivation, etc., occurs), calculate the expected absolute values of Φ_{CO} and Φ_{H_2}. Compare this "theoretical" Φ_{CO} value with the value of Φ_{CO} found experimentally in Problem 13.

16. It has been shown experimentally that the rate of phosgene formation in an irradiated mixture of Cl_2 and CO is described by the rate equation

$$\frac{d[COCl_2]}{dt} = k'[Cl_2]\{-1 + \sqrt{k''[CO]I_a + 1}\}$$

where k' and k'' are constants at a given temperature, and I_a is the intensity of absorbed light. It has been postulated that the following steps describe the reactions:

$$Cl_2 + h\nu \rightarrow 2Cl \qquad (\varphi_1 I_a) \qquad (1)$$

$$Cl + CO + M \rightleftharpoons COCl + M \qquad (K_2) \qquad (2)$$

$$COCl + Cl_2 \rightarrow COCl_2 + Cl \qquad (k_3) \qquad (3)$$

$$COCl + Cl \rightarrow CO + Cl_2 \qquad (k_4) \qquad (4)$$

$$Cl + Wall \rightarrow \tfrac{1}{2}Cl_2 + Wall \qquad (k_5) \qquad (5)$$

M is a molecule of any gas. Note that reaction 2 is assumed to be in equilibrium.

(a) Show how the observed rate law is consistent with the mechanism suggested. Evaluate k' and k'' in terms of the constants in the suggested mechanism.

(b) It has been shown that Φ_{COCl_2} is about 10^4 at 25°C. Explain this result in terms of the suggested mechanism.

17. Nitrosyl chloride is decomposed by visible light according to the overall equation:

$$2NOCl \rightarrow 2NO + Cl_2$$

The absorption spectrum in this region consists of well-defined bands. NOCl gas at 0.5 atm pressure and temperature 27°C in a reaction cell 8 cm long was exposed to parallel light of 4350 A, and the following data were collected:

Incident energy = 48,200 ergs sec^{-1}
Absorption coefficient, α = 0.25 atm^{-1}cm^{-1} ($I/I_0 = 10^{-\alpha l p}$)
Time of exposure = 6 hours
Chlorine produced = 0.0243 gram

(a) Assuming no change in absorption with time and no absorption by the reaction products, calculate the "quantum yield" of NOCl consumption.

(b) Suggest a reaction mechanism which is in accord with the above facts.

(c) Further experimentation disclosed that the quantum yield of NOCl consumption decreased rapidly with decrease in pressure in the range below 0.1 atm. How may this be explained?

(d) The temperature coefficient of this reaction when carried out at 0.5 atm was found to be 1.00 over the range 0–78°C. How may this be explained?

(e) Suggest a further definitive experiment which might be made to differentiate between alternative mechanisms.

18. The following reaction mechanism has been suggested to explain the form of the hydrogen production rate law in CH_2O vapor photolysis at 3130 A and low light intensities:

$$CH_2O + h\nu \rightarrow CO + H_2 \tag{I}$$
$$\searrow CHO + H \tag{II}$$
$$H + CH_2O \rightarrow H_2 + CHO \tag{1}$$
$$CHO + M \rightarrow CO + H + M \tag{2}$$
$$CHO + Wall \rightarrow \tfrac{1}{2}CO + \tfrac{1}{2}CH_2O + Wall \tag{3}$$

(a) Derive the theoretically expected rate law for hydrogen molecule formation in formaldehyde photolysis at 3130 A.

(b) Suggest experiments which you might perform to test for the occurrence of both (I) and (II) in formaldehyde vapor photolysis at 3130 A.

(c) Could rotating sector techniques be applied to the determination of individual rate constants in this system? Explain.

19. Di-n-propyl ketone photolysis at 3130 A (gas phase) gave the following results:

C_2H_4, C_3H_8, CO, n-C_6H_{14}, and C_3H_6 are major gaseous products at temperatures below 250°. At high temperatures (above 250°) CH_4 becomes a major product. (Liquid ketone products were not analyzed.)

$\Phi_{C_2H_4}$ is constant at 0.21 independent of temperature (up to 160°), light intensity, and ketone concentration. Above 160° $\Phi_{C_2H_4}$ increases rapidly with temperature concurrently with the appearance of CH_4 in the product; Φ_{CH_4} and $\Phi_{C_2H_4}$ show a similar increase with temperature.

The rate expression $\dfrac{d(C_3H_6)/dt}{d(C_6H_{14})/dt}$ is a constant independent of temperature (at temperatures below 250°), light intensity, and ketone concentration.

(a) Explain each of these results qualitatively in terms of a reaction mechanism which you propose.

(b) What quantitative experiments would you propose to carry out in order to test your mechanism?

20. A flash photolysis study is made, using Cl_2 gas at 25° and 50 mm pressure. The gas is contained in a cell of 0.25 liter volume. A flash lasting 0.001 sec

provides 1×10^{21} quanta. Ten per cent of this radiation is absorbed by the Cl_2, and the average wavelength of the absorbed flash is 3000 A.

(a) Calculate the average temperature of the Cl_2 gas a few seconds after the flash. For $Cl_2(g)$, $c_v = 0.115$ cal/gram-deg. (Assume that the process is completely adiabatic, and that no heat is lost to the flask in the first few seconds after the flash.)

(b) Calculate the average temperature of a gaseous mixture a few seconds after the flash if the mixture contains the same amount of Cl_2 as above, together with 10 atm of helium gas at 25°. (c_v for helium gas $= 0.75$ cal/gram-deg.)

(c) In view of the results of (a) and (b) what suggestions can you make regarding the best conditions for the study of flash photolysis (so that there will be as little complicating thermal reaction as possible)?

21. Rotating sector experiments with the hypothetical aldehyde RCHO were made at a temperature of 200°C. The sector was divided so that the ratio of dark to light periods was 3 to 1. The steady state rate law at 200° was found to be

$$- \frac{d[\text{RCHO}]}{dt} = 3.90 \times 10^{-12}[\text{RCHO}]I_a^{\frac{1}{2}} \text{ molecules/cm}^3\text{-sec}$$

The ratio of the rate with intermittent illumination to that with steady illumination ($[\overline{R_1}]/[R_1]_s$) was determined with several sector speeds and at several absorbed light intensities. These data are summarized in the following table.

$[\overline{R_1}]/[R_1]_s$	λ_1, sec	I_a, quanta/cm^3-sec
0.502	Small	1.50×10^{13}
0.424	0.0500	1.50×10^{13}
0.371	0.1000	1.50×10^{13}
0.294	0.5000	1.50×10^{13}
0.248	Large	1.50×10^{13}
0.496	Small	6.00×10^{13}
0.421	0.0250	6.00×10^{13}
0.373	0.0500	6.00×10^{13}
0.292	0.250	6.00×10^{13}
0.254	Large	6.00×10^{13}
0.501	Small	13.5×10^{13}
0.422	0.0167	13.5×10^{13}
0.370	0.0333	13.5×10^{13}
0.295	0.167	13.5×10^{13}
0.245	Large	13.5×10^{13}

(a) Calculate the absolute value of the termination rate constant for the reaction $2R \rightarrow R_2$ at 200°C. Assume the primary efficiency of radical formation, $\varphi = 1$.

(b) Calculate the absolute value of the propagation rate constant for the reaction $R + RCHO \rightarrow RH + RCO$ at 200°C.

22. Calculate the time required to reach a methyl radical concentration which is 99 % of its steady state value in the thermal decomposition of CH_3CHO at 500°C and 50 mm pressure. Assume the following values for the rate constants involved:

$$CH_3CHO \rightarrow CH_3 + CHO; \quad k_1 = 10^{15.34}e^{-80.8(\text{kcal/mole})/RT} \text{ sec}^{-1}$$

$$2CH_3 \rightarrow C_2H_6; \quad k_2 = 2.2 \times 10^{13} \text{ cm}^3/\text{mole-sec}$$

The apparent rate constant k' in the relation $d[CH_3CHO]/dt = k'[CH_3CHO]^{3/2}$ equals $7.5 \times 10^{10}e^{-46(\text{kcal/mole})/RT}$ (moles/liter)$^{-1/2}$ sec^{-1}.

23. Fifty microliters (STP) of products are necessary for the accurate analysis of the data in a given experiment as described in Problem 22 (thermal decomposition of CH_3CHO at 500°C, etc.). If the reaction vessel is 250 ml in volume, how long should your run be allowed to proceed to obtain this amount of products (CO + CH$_4$ largely)?

24. In view of your answers to Problems 22 and 23 what is the magnitude of the error which you introduce in calculated rate constant k' by assuming the steady state concentration for CH_3 radicals to be present throughout the experiment?

25. Assume that the following mechanism is operative in the photolysis of CH_3CHO at 3130 A at temperatures above 100°. Derive the function relating the observed experimental rate constant k in the relation $-d[CH_3CHO]/dt = k[CH_3CHO]I_a^{1/2}$ to the rate constants, etc., and relate the apparent experimental activation energy to the individual E's, etc., of the mechanism for the following conditions:

(a) Reaction 6 is the only termination step; 7 and 8 are unimportant.
(b) Reaction 7 is the only termination step; 6 and 8 are unimportant.
(c) Reaction 8 is the only termination step; 6 and 7 are unimportant.
(d) Termination occurs by all three reactions; 6, 7, and 8 are important.
Note that, when chains are long, the approximation $[CH_3][CH_3CHO]k_4 \cong [CH_3CO][M]k_5$ may be used in the last stages of your solution.

$$CH_3CHO + h\nu \rightarrow CH_3 + HCO \tag{1}$$
$$HCO + M \rightarrow CO + H + M \tag{2}$$
$$H + CH_3CHO \rightarrow H_2 + CH_3CO \tag{3}$$
$$CH_3 + CH_3CHO \rightarrow CH_4 + CH_3CO \tag{4}$$
$$CH_3CO + M \rightarrow CH_3 + CO + M \tag{5}$$
$$CH_3 + CH_3 \rightarrow C_2H_6 \tag{6}$$
$$CH_3 + COCH_3 \rightarrow CH_3COCH_3 \tag{7}$$
$$CH_3CO + CH_3CO \rightarrow (CH_3CO)_2 \tag{8}$$

26. Describe briefly the spectroscopic or other experiments which you would perform, the data you would obtain, and the method of treating the data to calculate the following:

(a) The rate constant of the gaseous unimolecular reaction,

$$CH_3CHO(T_1) \rightarrow CH_3CHO(S_0) + h\nu$$

(b) The dissociation energy of the gaseous ClO radical.

(c) The molar absorbancy index (ϵ) of gaseous NO_2 at 3130 A and 25 °C.

(d) The rate constant of the bimolecular reaction,

$$(CH_3)_3C + (CH_3)_3C \rightarrow (CH_3)_3CC(CH_3)_3$$

27. (a) Calculate the ratio of the concentration of *cis*-azobenzene to that of *trans*-azobenzene ($C_6H_5—N{=}N—C_6H_5$) which is to be expected at 25 °C after an extended exposure of the pure *cis*-azobenzene in CCl_4 solution to 4327 A light; assume that decomposition is negligible at this wavelength. $\varphi_{cis \rightarrow trans} = 0.48$, $\epsilon_{cis} = 1518$; $\varphi_{trans \rightarrow cis} = 0.24$, $\epsilon_{trans} = 460$ cm³/mole-cm.

(b) At this temperature the thermodynamic equilibrium ratio of isomers is approximately 0.04; how do you explain the magnitude of the photochemically expected ratio in view of this?

28. Professor L. J. Heidt has studied the use of a mixture of $Ce(ClO_4)_3$ and $Ce(ClO_4)_4$ in $HClO_4$-containing aqueous solution for the conversion of light energy to chemical energy through the sensitized decomposition of water ($H_2O \rightarrow H_2 + \frac{1}{2}O_2$). In aqueous solutions of weakly complexing anions, such as ClO_4^-, the Ce^{3+} ion absorbs strongly below 2600 A, while Ce^{4+} absorbs strongly below 3200 A. Discuss the possible detailed mechanism which might apply in this system. Is it practical for solar energy conversion? Explain.

29. The decomposition of formaldehyde may occur from an excited triplet, an excited singlet state, or a vibrationally excited ground-state singlet, on excitation with 3340 A light. Describe several definitive experiments you would perform to determine accurately the nature of the excited state from which the decomposition occurs.

30. In the photolysis of a fixed pressure of biacetyl ($CH_3COCOCH_3$) at 4358 A and at absorbed light intensities of 1×10^{12} quanta/sec-cm³, the rate of CO formation is proportional to $I_a{}^2$; $\Phi_{CO} = 0.03$ at 25 °C and 1×10^{12} quanta/sec-cm³. Luminescence is very evident. At 3660 A the rate of CO formation is proportional to I_a, and $\Phi_{CO} = 0.25$ at 25 °C and 1×10^{12} quanta/sec-cm³ ($\Delta H^\circ_{298} \cong 70$ kcal/mole for the reaction $CH_3COCOCH_3 \rightarrow 2CH_3CO$). Suggest a photolysis mechanism in accord with these results.

31. Explain the fact that the decay of fluorescence in anthracene is exponential in character, while the decay of phosphorescence in most inorganic solids (doped slightly with impurities) is hyperbolic in character.

32. You propose to study the gas-phase reactions of the radical

$$\cdot CH_2CH_2CH_2\overset{\cdot}{C}HCH_3 \text{ (triplet)}.$$

(a) Suggest a reactant and experimental conditions you would choose to generate these radicals so that your system will be as free as possible from complicating reactions of other radicals. (b) How would you minimize any complications which are inherent with your system?

REFERENCES TO CHAPTER 6

1. A. D. Walsh, *J. Chem. Soc.*, **1953**, 2318.
2. (a) H. L. McMurry and R. S. Mulliken, *Proc. Natl. Acad. Sci. U.S.*, **26**, 312 (1940); (b) H. L. McMurry, *J. Chem. Phys.*, **9**, 231, 241 (1941).
3. (a) E. B. Wilson, Jr., J. C. Desius, and P. C. Cross, *Molecular Vibrations*, McGraw-Hill Book Co., New York, 1955; (b) G. Herzberg, *Spectra of Diatomic Molecules, Molecular Spectra and Molecular Structure*, Vol. 1, 2nd Edition, D. Van Nostrand Co., Princeton, N.J., 1950; (c) G. Herzberg, *Infrared and Raman Spectra of Polyatomic Molecules, Molecular Spectra and Molecular Structure*, Vol. II, D. Van Nostrand Co., Princeton, N.J., 1945.
4. W. Nernst, *Z. Elektrochem.*, **24**, 335 (1918).
5. C. R. Masson, *J. Am. Chem. Soc.*, **74**, 4731 (1952).
6. S. G. Whiteway and C. R. Masson, *J. Am. Chem. Soc.*, **77**, 1508 (1955).
7. (a) R. G. W. Norrish and G. Porter, *Nature*, **164**, 658 (1949); (b) G. Porter, *Proc. Roy. Soc. (London)*, **A200**, 284 (1950).
8. N. Davidson, R. Marshall, A. E. Larsh, Jr., and T. Carrington, *J. Chem. Phys.*, **19**, 1311 (1951).
9. (a) G. Herzberg and D. A. Ramsay, *J. Chem. Phys.*, **20**, 347 (1952); (b) D. A. Ramsay, *J. Chem. Phys.*, **21**, 960 (1953).
10. G. Herzberg and D. A. Ramsay, *Proc. Roy. Soc. (London)*, **A233**, 34 (1955).
11. (a) S. Claesson, B. Nyman, and G. Wettermark, to be published; (b) equipment described by G. Wettermark, *Arkiv Kemi*, **18**, 1 (1961).
12. D. A. Ramsay, *J. Chem. Phys.*, **21**, 165 (1953).
13. (a) G. N. Lewis, D. Lipkin, and T. T. Magel, *J. Am. Chem. Soc.*, **63**, 3005 (1941); (b) G. N. Lewis and D. Lipkin, *J. Am. Chem. Soc.*, **64**, 2801 (1942).
14. F. O. Rice and M. Freamo, *J. Am. Chem. Soc.*, **73**, 5529 (1951).
15. H. Linschitz and J. Rennert, *Nature*, **169**, 193 (1952).
16. (a) I. L. Mador, *J. Chem. Phys.*, **22**, 1617 (1954); (b) I. L. Mador and M. C. Williams, *J. Chem. Phys.*, **22**, 1627 (1954).
17. (a) I. Norman and G. Porter, *Nature*, **174**, 508 (1954); (b) I. Norman and G. Porter, *Proc. Roy. Soc. (London)*, **A230**, 399 (1955).
18. (a) E. Whittle, D. A. Dows, and G. C. Pimentel, *J. Chem. Phys.*, **22**, 1943 (1954); (b) E. D. Becker and G. C. Pimentel, *J. Chem. Phys.*, **25**, 224 (1956); (c) H. W. Brown and G. C. Pimentel, *J. Chem. Phys.*, **29**, 883 (1958); (d) G. C. Pimentel, Chapter 4 in *Formation and Trapping of Free Radicals*, ed. by A. M. Bass and H. P. Broida, Academic Press, New York, 1960, pp. 69–116.
19. W. E. Lee, J. G. Calvert, and E. W. Malmberg, *J. Am. Chem. Soc.*, **83**, 1928 (1961).
20. F. P. Lossing and A. W. Tickner, *J. Chem. Phys.*, **20**, 907 (1952).
21. (a) T. Rubin and R. O. Leach, *J. Am. Chem. Soc.*, **76**, 4674 (1954); (b) G. B. Kistiakowsky and P. H. Kydd, *J. Am. Chem. Soc.*, **79**, 4825 (1957).
22. (a) J. B. Farmer, F. P. Lossing, D. G. H. Marsden, and E. W. R. Steacie, *J. Chem. Phys.*, **23**, 1169 (1955); (b) F. P. Lossing, D. G. H. Marsden, and J. B. Farmer, *Can. J. Chem.*, **34**, 701 (1956).
23. (a) P. Kebarle and F. P. Lossing, *Can. J. Chem.*, **37**, 389 (1959); (b) A. G. Harrison and F. P. Lossing, *Can. J. Chem.*, **37**, 1478 (1959); (c) *ibid.*, **37**, 1696 (1959).
24. H. D. Beckey and W. Groth, *Z. Physik. Chem. (Frankfurt)*, **20**, 307 (1959).
25. (a) E. R. Stephens, P. L. Hanst, R. C. Doerr, and W. E. Scott, *Ind. Eng. Chem.*, **48**, 1498 (1956); (b) E. R. Stephens, W. E. Scott, P. L. Hanst, and R. C. Doerr, *Proc. Am. Petrol. Inst.*, Sec. III, 36, 288 (1956).

26. G. R. McMillan, J. G. Calvert, and J. N. Pitts, Jr., *J. Am. Chem. Soc.*, **86**, 3602 (1964).

27. For a good discussion of the ESR method see D. J. E. Ingram, *Free Radicals as Studied by Electron Spin Resonance*, Butterworths Scientific Publications, London, 1958, pp. 170–181.

28. L. H. Piette and W. C. Landgraf, *J. Chem. Phys.*, **32**, 1107 (1960).

29. (a) C. A. Hutchison, Jr. and B. W. Mangum, *J. Chem. Phys.*, **29**, 952 (1958); (b) *ibid.*, **34**, 908 (1961).

30. (a) J. H. van der Waals and M. S. de Groot, *Mol. Phys.*, **2**, 333 (1959); (b) M. S. de Groot and J. H. van der Waals, *Mol. Phys.*, **3**, 190 (1960):

31. L. H. Piette, J. H. Sharp, T. Kuwana, and J. N. Pitts, Jr., *J. Chem. Phys.*, **36**, 3094 (1962); (b) J. N. Pitts, Jr., H. W. Johnson, Jr., and T. Kuwana, *Proceedings Symposium on Reversible Photochemical Processes*, Duke University, 1962; *J. Phys. Chem.*, **66**, 2456 (1962).

32. (a) H. E. Gunning, *Can. J. Chem.*, **36**, 89 (1958); (b) C. C. McDonald, J. R. McDowell, and H. E. Gunning, *Can. J. Chem.*, **37**, 930 (1959); (c) K. R. Osborn and H. E. Gunning, *Can. J. Chem.*, **37**, 1315 (1959); (d) J. R. McDowell, C. C. McDonald, and H. E. Gunning, *Can. J. Chem.*, **37**, 1432 (1959); (e) H. E. Gunning and O. P. Strausz, *Advances in Photochemistry*, Vol. I, ed. by W. A. Noyes, Jr., G. S. Hammond, and J. N. Pitts, Jr., Interscience Publishers, a division of John Wiley & Sons, New York, 1963, p. 209; (f) J. K. S. Wan, O. P. Strausz, W. F. Allen, and H. E. Gunning, *Can. J. Chem.*, **42**, 2056 (1964); *ibid.*, **43**, 318 (1965).

33. (a) B. H. Mahan and R. Mandal, *J. Chem. Phys.*, **37**, 207 (1962); (b) P. Ausloos, R. Gorden, Jr., and S. G. Lias, *J. Chem. Phys.*, **40**, 1854 (1964); (c) J. R. McNesby and H. Okabe, *Advances in Photochemistry*, Vol. III, ed. by W. A. Noyes, Jr., G. S. Hammond, and J. N. Pitts, Jr., Interscience Publishers, a division of John Wiley & Sons, New York, 1964, p. 157; (d) R. J. Cvetanovic and A. B. Callear, *J. Chem. Phys.*, **23**, 1182 (1955).

34. R. G. W. Norrish, *Trans. Faraday Soc.*, **30**, 103 (1934); R. G. W. Norrish and M. E. S. Appleyard, *J. Chem. Soc.*, **1934**, 874; C. H. Bamford and R. G. W. Norrish, *J. Chem. Soc.*, **1935**, 1504; **1938**, 1521, 1531, 1544.

35. F. Paneth and W. Hofeditz, *Ber.*, **62**, 1335 (1929).

36. (a) T. G. Pearson and R. H. Purcell, *Nature*, **136**, 221 (1935); (b) T. G. Pearson and R. H. Purcell, *J. Chem. Soc.*, **1936**, 253; (c) H. H. Glazebrook and T. G. Pearson, *J. Chem. Soc.*, **1936**, 1777.

37. For an excellent review of the mirror techniques for the detection of radicals see E. W. R. Steacie, *Atomic and Free Radical Reactions*, 2nd Edition, Reinhold Publishing Corp., New York, 1954, pp. 37–53.

38. J. W. Mitchell and C. N. Hinshelwood, *Proc. Roy. Soc.* (*London*), **A159**, 32 (1937).

39. J. H. Raley, F. F. Rust, and W. E. Vaughan, *J. Am. Chem. Soc.*, **70**, 88 (1948).

40. W. A. Bryce and K. U. Ingold, *J. Chem. Phys.*, **23**, 1968 (1955).

41. J. G. Calvert, S. S. Thomas, and P. L. Hanst, *J. Am. Chem. Soc.*, **82**, 1 (1960).

42. (a) H. T. J. Chilton, B. G. Gowenlock, and J. Trotman, *Chem. & Ind.*, **1955**, 538; (b) B. G. Gowenlock and J. Trotman, *J. Chem. Soc.*, **1955**, 4190.

43. (a) M. I. Christie, *Proc. Roy. Soc.* (*London*), **A249**, 258 (1959); (b) L. Batt and B. G. Gowenlock, *Trans. Faraday Soc.*, **56**, 682 (1960); (c) A. Y. Yakubovich, S. P. Makarov, V. A. Ginsburg, N. F. Privezentseva, and L. L. Martynova, *Doklady Akad. Nauk S.S.S.R.*, **141**, 125 (1961); (d) B. G. Gowenlock and K. A. Redish, *Z. Physik. Chem.* (*Frankfurt*), **31**, 169 (1962); (e) D. E. Hoare, *Can. J. Chem.*, **40**, 2012 (1962); (f) O. P. Strausz and H. E. Gunning, *Trans. Faraday*

Soc., **60**, 347, (1964); (g) A. Maschke, B. S. Shapiro, and F. W. Lampe, *J. Am. Chem. Soc.*, **86**, 1929 (1964).

44. Ref. 37, pp. 117–128.
45. For examples see (a) P. Pringsheim, *Fluorescence and Phosphorescence*, Interscience Publishers, New York, 1949; (b) T. Förster, *Fluoreszenz organischen Verbindungen*, Vandenhoeck u. Ruprecht, Göttingen, 1951; (c) G. Porter and M. W. Windsor, *Discussions Faraday Soc.*, **17**, 178 (1954).
46. H. J. Groh, Jr., G. W. Luckey, and W. A. Noyes, Jr., *J. Chem. Phys.*, **21**, 115 (1953).
47. R. Livingston and V. S. Rao, *J. Phys. Chem.*, **63**, 794 (1959).
48. See the reviews: (a) B. Stevens, *Chem. Revs.*, **57**, 439 (1957); C. Reid, *Quart. Revs. (London)*, **12**, 205 (1958).
49. H. Kautsky, *Trans. Faraday Soc.*, **35**, 216 (1939).
50. A. Terenin, *Acta Physicochim. U.R.S.S.*, **18**, 210 (1943); *C.A.*, **38**, 5149[8] (1944).
51. (a) G. Porter and M. R. Wright, *J. Chim. Phys.*, **55**, 705 (1958); (b) D. F. Evans, *Proc. Roy. Soc. (London)*, **A255**, 55 (1960).
52. H. Linschitz and L. Pekkarinen, *J. Am. Chem. Soc.*, **82**, 2411 (1960).
53. J. Weiss, *Trans. Faraday Soc.*, **35**, 48 (1939); *ibid.*, **42**, 133 (1946).
54. H. Tsubomura and R. S. Mulliken, *J. Am. Chem. Soc.*, **82**, 5966 (1960).
55. (a) G. B. Porter, *J. Chem. Phys.*, **32**, 1587 (1960); (b) R. M. Hochstrasser and G. B. Porter, *Quart. Revs. (London)*, **14**, 146 (1960); (c) D. E. Hoare and G. S. Pearson, *Advances in Photochemistry*, Vol. III, ed. by W. A. Noyes, Jr., G. S. Hammond, and J. N. Pitts, Jr., Interscience Publishers, a division of John Wiley & Sons, New York, 1964, p. 83.
56. R. Srinivasan and W. A. Noyes, Jr., *J. Am. Chem. Soc.*, **82**, 5591 (1960).
57. G. S. Pearson, *J. Phys. Chem.*, **67**, 1686 (1963).
58. D. Gàl and K. O. Kutschke, *Abstracts*, 145th American Chemical Society Meeting, New York, 1963, p. 12w.
59. V. Brunet and W. A. Noyes, Jr., *Bull. Soc. Chim. France*, **121**, (1958).
60. C. J. Danby and C. N. Hinshelwood, *Proc. Roy. Soc. (London)*, **A179**, 169 (1942).
61. F. F. Rust, F. Seubold, and W. E. Vaughan, *J. Am. Chem. Soc.*, **70**, 95 (1948).
62. D. P. Dingledy and J. G. Calvert, *J. Am. Chem. Soc.*, **85**, 856 (1963).
63. E. Gorin, *J. Chem. Phys.*, **7**, 256 (1939).
64. (a) F. E. Blacet and J. D. Heldman, *J. Am. Chem. Soc.*, **64**, 889 (1942); (b) F. E. Blacet and D. E. Loeffler, *J. Am. Chem. Soc.*, **64**, 893 (1942); (c) J. N. Pitts, Jr., and F. E. Blacet, *J. Am. Chem. Soc.*, **74**, 455 (1952); (d) F. E. Blacet and J. N. Pitts, Jr., *J. Am. Chem. Soc.*, **74**, 3382 (1952); (e) J. N. Pitts, Jr., and F. E. Blacet, *J. Am. Chem. Soc.*, **72**, 2810 (1950); (f) F. E. Blacet and J. G. Calvert, *J. Am. Chem. Soc.*, **73**, 667 (1951).
65. (a) E. Horn, M. Polanyi, and D. W. G. Style, *Trans. Faraday Soc.*, **30**, 189 (1934); (b) E. Horn and M. Polanyi, *Z. Physik. Chem.*, **B25**, 151 (1934).
66. W. A. Noyes, Jr., *J. Phys. & Colloid Chem.*, **55**, 925 (1951).
67. (a) R. W. Durham, G. R. Martin, and H. C. Sutton, *Nature*, **164**, 1052 (1949); (b) R. R. Williams, Jr., and W. H. Hamill, *J. Am. Chem. Soc.*, **72**, 1857 (1950).
68. J. G. Calvert, J. N. Pitts, Jr., and D. D. Thompson, *J. Am. Chem. Soc.*, **78**, 4239 (1956).
69. E. O'Neal and S. W. Benson, *J. Chem. Phys.*, **36**, 2196 (1962).
70. J. N. Pitts, Jr., E. A. Schuck, and J. K. S. Wan, *J. Am. Chem. Soc.*, **86**, 296 (1964).
71. P. D. Bartlett and T. Funahashi, *J. Am. Chem. Soc.*, **84**, 2596 (1962).
72. G. S. Hammond, P. A. Leermakers, and N. J. Turro, *J. Am. Chem. Soc.*, **83**, 2395 (1961).

73. J. Jortner, M. Ottolenghi, and G. Stein, *J. Phys. Chem.*, **66**, 2037 (1962).
74. There are many useful textbooks of reaction kinetics available; for example, see (a) K. J. Laidler, *Chemical Kinetics*, McGraw-Hill Book Co., New York, 1950; (b) A. A. Frost and R. G. Pearson, *Kinetics and Mechanism*, 2nd Edition, John Wiley & Sons, New York, 1961; (c) *Technique of Organic Chemistry*, Vol. VIII, Parts I and II, 2nd Edition, *Investigation of Rates and Mechanisms of Reactions*, ed. by S. L. Friess, E. S. Lewis, and A. Weissberger, Interscience Publishers, a division of John Wiley & Sons, New York, 1961 and 1963; (d) S. W. Benson, *The Foundations of Chemical Kinetics*, McGraw-Hill Book Co., New York, 1960; (e) V. N. Kondratiev, *Chemical Kinetics of Gas Reactions*, Pergamon Press, Oxford, 1964.
75. J. H. van't Hoff, *Etudes de Dynamique Chimique*, F. Muller and Co., Amsterdam, 1884.
76. S. Arrhenius, *Z. Physik. Chem.*, **4**, 226 (1889).
77. W. C. McC. Lewis, *J. Chem. Soc.*, **1918**, 471.
78. (a) H. Eyring and M. Polanyi, *Z. Physik. Chem.*, **B12**, 279 (1931); (b) H. Eyring, *Chem. Revs.*, **10**, 103 (1932); (c) H. Eyring, H. Gershinowitz, and C. E. Sun, *J. Chem. Phys.*, **3**, 786 (1935); (d) for a good comprehensive treatise on the development of the transition state theory see S. Glasstone, K. J. Laidler, and H. Eyring, *The Theory of Rate Processes*, McGraw-Hill Book Co., New York, 1941.
79. (a) E. R. Lippincott and A. Leifer, *J. Chem. Phys.*, **28**, 769 (1958); (b) see, as an example of another detailed calculation of the $H + H_2 \rightarrow H_2 + H$ reaction, E. M. Mortensen and K. S. Pitzer, Symposium on the Transition State, University of Sheffield, 1962, *The Chemical Society (London)*, *Spec. Publ.* No. 16, 1962, p. 57.
80. R. C. Tolman, *Statistical Mechanics*, Chemical Catalog Co., New York, 1927.
81. H. Gershinowitz and H. Eyring, *J. Am. Chem. Soc.*, **57**, 985 (1935).
82. (a) K. E. Russell and J. Simons, *Proc. Roy. Soc. (London)*, **A217**, 271 (1953); (b) M. I. Christie, R. G. W. Norrish, and G. Porter, *Discussions Faraday Soc.*, **17**, 107 (1954); (c) D. L. Bunker and N. Davidson, *J. Am. Chem. Soc.*, **80**, 5085, 5090 (1958); (d) D. Husain and H. O. Pritchard, *J. Chem. Phys.*, **30**, 1101 (1959); (e) G. Porter and J. A. Smith, *Nature*, **184**, 446 (1959).
83. (a) A. F. Trotman-Dickenson and E. W. R. Steacie, *J. Chem. Phys.*, **18**, 1097 (1950); (b) R. H. Linnell and W. A. Noyes, Jr., *J. Am. Chem. Soc.*, **73**, 3986 (1951); (c) K. U. Ingold, I. H. S. Henderson, and F. P. Lossing, *J. Chem. Phys.*, **21**, 2239 (1953).
84. (a) R. A. Marcus and O. K. Rice, *J. Phys. & Colloid Chem.*, **55**, 894 (1951); (b) R. A. Marcus, *J. Chem. Phys.*, **20**, 352, 355, 359 (1952); (c) G. M. Wieder and R. A. Marcus, *J. Chem. Phys.*, **37**, 1835 (1962).
85. F. A. Lindemann, *Trans. Faraday Soc.*, **17**, 598 (1922).
86. (a) L. A. K. Staveley and C. N. Hinshelwood, *J. Chem. Soc.*, **1936**, 812; (b) J. Franck and A. Eucken, *Z. Physik. Chem.*, **B20**, 460 (1933); (c) M. Volmer *et al.*, *Z. Physik. Chem.*, **B19**, 85 (1932), **B21**, 257 (1933), **B25**, 81 (1934); (d) D. V. Sickman and O. K. Rice, *J. Chem. Phys.*, **4**, 608 (1936).
87. C. N. Hinshelwood, *Proc. Roy. Soc. (London)*, **A113**, 230 (1927).
88. (a) O. K. Rice and H. C. Ramsperger, *J. Am. Chem. Soc.*, **49**, 1617 (1927), **50**, 617 (1928); (b) L. S. Kassel, *J. Phys. Chem.*, **32**, 225 (1928).
89. For references to the earlier papers and an excellent summary of the Slater and other theories of unimolecular reaction rates see N. B. Slater, *Theory of Unimolecular Reactions*, Cornell University Press, Ithaca, N.Y., 1959.
90. H. M. Rosenstock, A. L. Wahrhaftig, and H. Eyring, *J. Chem. Phys.*, **23**, 2200 (1955).

91. A. Kropf, E. M. Eyring, A. L. Wahrhaftig, and H. Eyring, *J. Chem. Phys.*, **32**, 149 (1960).
92. M. Polanyi and E. Wigner, *Z. Physik. Chem.*, **A139**, 439 (1928).
93. D. L. Bunker, *J. Chem. Phys.*, **40**, 1946 (1964).
94. B. Steiner, C. F. Giese, and M. G. Inghram, *J. Chem. Phys.*, **34**, 189 (1961).
95. E. K. Gill and K. J. Laidler, *Proc. Roy. Soc. (London)*, **A250**, 121 (1959).
96. (a) M. Boudart and J. T. Dubois, *J. Chem. Phys.*, **23**, 223 (1955); (b) G. B. Porter and B. T. Connelly, *J. Chem. Phys.*, **33**, 81 (1960).
97. An excellent review of the area of free radical reactions in solution is given by C. Walling, *Free Radicals in Solution*, John Wiley & Sons, New York, 1957.
98. (a) B. K. Morse, "Homogeneous Solution Reactions," Chapter XI, *Technique of Organic Chemistry*, Vol. VIII, Part I, *Investigation of Rates and Mechanisms of Reactions*, ed. by S. L. Friess, E. S. Lewis, and A. Weissberger, Interscience Publishers, a division of John Wiley & Sons, New York, 1961; (b) L. L. Schaleger and F. A. Long, "Entropies of Activation and Mechanisms of Reactions in Solution," *Advances in Physical Organic Chemistry*, Vol. I, ed. by V. Gold, Academic Press, New York, 1963, pp. 1–33.
99. J. Franck and E. Rabinowitsch, *Trans. Faraday Soc.*, **30**, 120 (1934).
100. F. W. Lampe and R. M. Noyes, *J. Am. Chem. Soc.*, **76**, 2140 (1954).
101. (a) R. M. Noyes, *J. Chem. Phys.*, **22**, 1349 (1954); (b) R. M. Noyes, *J. Am. Chem. Soc.*, **77**, 2042 (1955); (c) R. M. Noyes, *J. Am. Chem. Soc.*, **78**, 5486 (1956); (d) R. M. Noyes, *J. Phys. Chem.*, **65**, 763 (1961); (e) R. M. Noyes, *Progress in Reaction Kinetics*, Vol. 1, ed. by G. Porter, Pergamon Press, London, 1961, p. 129.
102. (a) J. C. Roy, R. R. Williams, Jr., and W. H. Hamill, *J. Am. Chem. Soc.*, **76**, 3274 (1954); (b) L. Monchick, *J. Chem. Phys.*, **24**, 381 (1956).
103. (a) H. P. Waits and G. S. Hammond, *J. Am. Chem. Soc.*, **86**, 1911 (1964); (b) G. S. Hammond and J. R. Fox, *J. Am. Chem. Soc.*, **86**, 1918 (1964).
104. R. K. Lyon, *J. Am. Chem. Soc.*, **86**, 1907 (1964).
105. (a) P. Debye, *Trans. Electrochem. Soc.*, **82**, 265 (1942); (b) H. L. J. Bäckström and K. Sandros, *Acta Chem. Scand.*, **14**, 48 (1960).
106. R. Marshall and N. Davidson, *J. Chem. Phys.*, **21**, 2086 (1953).
107. (a) R. M. Noyes, *J. Am. Chem. Soc.*, **81**, 566 (1959); (b) G. A. Salmon and R. M. Noyes, *J. Am. Chem. Soc.*, **84**, 672 (1962).
108. For a good discussion and review of work up to 1954 see C. E. K. Mees, *The Theory of the Photographic Process*, Rev. Edition, Macmillan Co., New York, 1954.
109. J. W. Mitchell and N. F. Mott, *Phil. Mag.*, **2**, 1149 (1957).
110. J. A. Kitchener, *Sci. J. Roy. Coll. Sci.*, **16**, 1 (1946).
111. (a) A. N. Terenin, *Uchenye Zapiski Leningrad. Gosudarst. Univ., Ser. Fiz. Nauk*, **1939**, No. 5 (No. 38), 26; *C. A.*, **36**, 2193[6]; (b) V. Bellelovskii, *Zhur, Fiz. Khim.*, **13**, 586 (1939); (c) K. Y. Kasparov and A. Terenin, *Acta Physicochim. U.R.S.S.*, **15**, 343 (1941); (d) V. I. Danilova, *Zhur, Fiz. Khim.*, **18**, 315 (1944); (e) N. A. Prilezhaeva, *Bull. Acad. Sci. U.R.S.S., Ser. phys.*, **9**, 211 (1945).
112. (a) J. A. Hedvall, G. Borgstrom, and G. Cohn, *Kolloid-Z.*, **94**, 57 (1941); (b) J. A. Hedvall and S. Nord, *Arkiv Kemi, Mineral. Geol.*, **17A**, No. 11 (1943); (c) V. Kohlschütter and A. d'Almendra, *Ber.*, **54B**, 1961 (1921).
113. A good review of many aspects of solid-state chemistry is given in *Chemistry of the Solid State*, ed. by W. E. Garner, Butterworths Scientific Publications, London, 1955.
114. H. Eyring, C. J. Christensen, and F. W. Cagle, Jr., *Abstracts*, 127th National Meeting, American Chemical Society, Cincinnati, Ohio, March, 1955, p. 16Q.

115. K. S. Pitzer and L. Brewer, *Thermodynamics*, 2nd Edition, McGraw-Hill Book Co., New York, 1961, p. 438.
116. (a) D. R. Herschbach, H. S. Johnston, K. S. Pitzer, and R. E. Powell, *J. Chem. Phys.*, **25**, 736 (1956); (b) D. J. Wilson and H. S. Johnston, *J. Am. Chem. Soc.*, **79**, 29 (1957); (c) H. S. Johnston, W. A. Bonner, and D. J. Wilson, *J. Chem. Phys.*, **26**, 1002 (1957); (d) K. S. Pitzer, *J. Am. Chem. Soc.*, **79**, 1804 (1957); (e) O. Sinanoglu and K. S. Pitzer, *J. Chem. Phys.*, **30**, 422 (1959).
117. (a) L. Pauling, *Nature of the Chemical Bond*, Cornell University Press, Ithaca, N.Y., 1940; (b) L. Pauling, *J. Am. Chem. Soc.*, **69**, 542 (1947).
118. H. S. Johnston and C. Parr, *J. Am. Chem. Soc.*, **85**, 2544 (1963).
119. (a) R. M. Badger, *J. Chem. Phys.*, **2**, 128 (1934); (b) *ibid.*, **3**, 710 (1935).
120. (a) K. S. Pitzer, *J. Chem. Phys.*, **8**, 711 (1940); (b) W. B. Person and G. C. Pimentel, *J. Am. Chem. Soc.*, **75**, 532 (1953).
121. E. W. R. Steacie, *Atomic and Free Radical Reactions*, 2nd Edition, Reinhold Publishing Corp., New York, 1954.
122. S. Bywater and E. W. R. Steacie, *J. Chem. Phys.*, **19**, 326 (1951).
123. M. G. Evans and M. Polanyi, *Trans. Faraday Soc.*, **34**, 11 (1938).
124. N. N. Semenov, *Some Problems of Chemical Kinetics and Reactivity*, Vol. 1 (translated by J. E. S. Bradley), Pergamon Press, London, 1958, p. 27.
125. W. A. Noyes, Jr., and P. A. Leighton, *The Photochemistry of Gases*, Reinhold Publishing Corp., New York, 1941, pp. 200–202.
126. (a) M. Bodenstein, *Z. Physik. Chem.*, **85**, 329 (1913); (b) O. K. Rice, *J. Phys. Chem.*, **64**, 1851 (1960).
127. M. Bodenstein and H. Lütkemeyer, *Z. Physik. Chem.*, **114**, 208 (1925).
128. For a detailed study of this photolysis see (a) G. M. Harris and J. E. Willard, *J. Am. Chem. Soc.*, **76**, 4678 (1954); (b) see also the discussion and review, J. R. Majer and J. P. Simons, *Advances in Photochemistry*, Vol. II, ed. by W. A. Noyes, Jr., G. S. Hammond, and J. N. Pitts, Jr., Interscience Publishers, a division of John Wiley & Sons, New York, 1964, p. 137.
129. (a) R. D. Schultz and H. A. Taylor, *J. Chem. Phys.*, **18**, 194 (1950); (b) F. P. Hudson, R. R. Williams, Jr., and W. H. Hamill, *J. Chem. Phys.*, **21**, 1894 (1953).
130. (a) N. Basco and R. G. W. Norrish, *Nature*, **189**, 455 (1961); (b) N. Basco and R. G. W. Norrish, *Proc. Roy. Soc. (London)*, **A268**, 291 (1962).
131. R. G. W. Norrish and G. A. Oldershaw, *Proc. Roy. Soc. (London)*, **A249**, 498 (1959).
132. G. Herzberg, *Proc. Chem. Soc. (London)*, **1959**, 116.
133. (a) J. P. Simons and A. J. Yarwood, *Trans. Faraday Soc.*, **57**, 2167 (1961); (b) A. J. Yarwood and J. P. Simons, *Proc. Chem. Soc. (London)*, **1962**, 62.
134. C. Zener, *Phys. Rev.*, **37**, 556 (1931).
135. F. E. Blacet and J. G. Calvert, *J. Am. Chem. Soc.*, **73**, 661 (1951).
136. D. L. Chapman and F. Briers, *J. Chem. Soc.*, **1928**, 1802.
137. Excellent detailed discussions of the rotating-sector techniques are given by (a) R. G. Dickinson in Ref. 125, pp. 202–209; (b) G. M. Burnett and H. W. Melville, Chapter XX, "Determination of Active Intermediates in Reactions," *Technique of Organic Chemistry*, Vol. VIII, 2nd Edition, Part II, *Investigations of Rates and Mechanisms of Reactions*, ed. by S. L. Friess, E. S. Lewis, and A. Weissberger, Interscience Publishers, a division of John Wiley & Sons, New York, 1963, pp. 1107–1137; much of the symbolism of Burnett and Melville has been adopted in this book.
138. W. L. Haden, Jr., and O. K. Rice, *J. Chem. Phys.*, **10**, 445 (1942).
139. A. Shepp, *J. Chem. Phys.*, **24**, 939 (1956).

140. (a) See Ref. 125, pp. 182–187; (b) T. L. Hill, *J. Chem. Phys.*, 17, 1125 (1949); (c) R. M. Noyes, *J. Am. Chem. Soc.*, 73, 3039 (1951); (d) A. J. C. Nicholson, *J. Am. Chem. Soc.*, 73, 3981 (1951); (e) R. Gomer, *J. Chem. Phys.*, 19, 284 (1951).
141. R. M. Noyes and L. Fowler, *J. Am. Chem. Soc.*, 73, 3043 (1951).
142. O. Stern and M. Volmer, *Physik. Z.*, 20, 183 (1919).
143. (a) M. W. Zemansky, *Phys. Rev.*, 36, 919 (1930); (b) E. W. Samson, *Phys. Rev.*, 40, 940 (1932); (c) T. Holstein, *Phys. Rev.*, 72, 1212 (1947); 83, 1159 (1951); (d) P. J. Walsh, *Phys. Rev.*, 116, 511 (1959); (e) T. Tako, *J. Phys. Soc. Japan*, 16, 2016 (1961).
144. W. E. Kaskan and A. B. F. Duncan, *J. Chem. Phys.*, 16, 223 (1948).
145. J. Heicklen and W. A. Noyes, Jr., *J. Am. Chem. Soc.*, 81, 3858 (1959).
146. (a) M. S. Matheson and J. W. Zabor, *J. Chem. Phys.*, 7, 536 (1939); (b) H. Okabe and W. A. Noyes, Jr., *J. Am. Chem. Soc.*, 79, 801 (1957).
147. For a review of this information see W. A. Noyes, Jr., G. B. Porter, and J. E. Jolley, *Chem. Revs.*, 56, 49 (1956).
148. H. L. J. Bäckström and K. Sandros, *Acta Chem. Scand.*, 14, 48 (1960).
149. R. B. Cundall and D. G. Milne, *J. Am. Chem. Soc.*, 83, 3902 (1961).
150. See the discussion and review of the earlier literature on this subject by M. Szwarc, *Chem. Soc. (London), Spec. Publ.*, No. 16, 1962, p. 91.
151. J. N. Pitts, Jr., J. K. S. Wan, and E. A. Schuck, *J. Am. Chem. Soc.*, 86, 3606 (1964).
152. (a) J. C. D. Brand and F. I. Reed, *J. Chem. Soc.*, 1957, 2386; (b) G. W. Robinson and V. E. DiGiorgio, *Can. J. Chem.*, 36, 31 (1958).
153. C. S. Parmenter, *J. Chem. Phys.*, 41, 658 (1964).
154. E. F. Ullman and W. A. Henderson, Jr. *J. Am. Chem. Soc.*, 86, 5050 (1964).
155. R. C. Millikan and D. R. White, *J. Chem. Phys.*, 39, 3209 (1963).
156. D. F. Evans, *J. Chem. Soc.*, 1957, 1351; 1960, 1735.
157. R. E. Rebbert and P. Ausloos, private communication to the authors; to be published.
158. R. Srinivasan, *J. Phys. Chem.*, 68, 1997 (1964).
159. R. Srinivasan, *J. Am. Chem. Soc.*, 84, 3982 (1962).

7

Experimental Methods in Photochemistry

Two major groups are active in photochemical research today. One, composed largely of physical and physical-organic chemists, is concerned with the elucidation of detailed mechanisms of photochemical reactions and the chemistry of the excited state through the determination of spectroscopic properties, quantum yields, rate data, etc. The other group, primarily synthetic organic chemists, seeks new and unique synthetic routes through the action of light on molecules. The experimental methods and equipment employed by the two groups differ in many respects. In this chapter an introduction to both these areas of experimental photochemistry will be given.

Rather elaborate equipment is needed to make quantitative measurements of quantum yields required in basic physical and physical-organic photochemical studies. Such determinations entail the use of a controlled source of monochromatic light, a suitable optical train and photolysis cell through which a collimated beam of the light is passed, a means of measuring both the absolute intensity of the incident light and the fraction of this light which is absorbed by the reactant, and a quantitative determination of the number of molecules of product formed or the number of quanta of light emitted as fluorescence or phosphorescence. We will consider the experimental methods and equipment in common use for accomplishing these basic quantum yield measurements. The special techniques of the rotating sector, flash photolysis, low-temperature photochemical matrix experiments, and fluorescence lifetime measurements also will be outlined.

The synthetic photochemist's foremost need is a high-intensity light source, rich in the wavelengths of light absorbed by the reactant and suitably located within a reaction chamber. We will consider these and other practical factors of special interest to the synthetic photochemist. No attempt will be made to cover the extensive literature in all these areas, but representative modern equipment and methods which either the authors

686

or their colleagues have found satisfactory will be described. References to the more extensive literature surveys of each area will be given.

7-1 LIGHT SOURCES

Since light must be absorbed to effect a photochemical change, the choice of light source is dictated by the absorption spectrum of the reactant to be studied. Thus the first step in any photochemical study should be the determination of the ultraviolet and visible absorption spectra of the reactant, preferably in the same physical state in which its photochemical properties are to be studied.

By far the most widely used sources of ultraviolet and visible light for conventional photochemical experiments using steady illumination are the mercury arcs. There are three basic types: the low-pressure or "resonance" lamp, the medium-pressure arc, and the high-pressure mercury arcs. Each offers features which makes it particularly well suited for certain experimental needs. The emission spectra of these three basic mercury arcs are compared in Fig. 7-1; theoretical aspects were treated, in part, in Sec. 2-7. The low-pressure mercury arc is rich in 2537 A radiation; if Suprasil quartz is used it is rich also in 1849 A radiation. Note in Fig. 7-1 that the photographic plate has been greatly overexposed in the 2537 A region of the 10 micron lamp in order to show the weaker lines of the spectrum; however, about 90% of the total energy of the radiation with $\lambda < 7600$ A is in a narrow band at 2537 A. No attempt was made to photograph the 1849 A line.

The low-pressure arcs are required for the study of mercury-sensitized reactions and are often useful where direct photolysis at 2537 A is desired in mercury-free systems in which a lamp of low intrinsic brilliance (small number of quanta emitted/second-unit area of arc) can be tolerated. A large number of "lines" of near equal intensities are evident in the spectrum of the medium-pressure arc; such a lamp in combination with a monochromator or suitable filter system provides the best intense source of a variety of near monochromatic frequencies which are desired in many photochemical studies. The spectrum of the high-pressure mercury arcs shows extensive pressure-broadened mercury "lines" superimposed on a continuous background of radiation (see the 100 atm arc distribution of Fig. 7-1). Arcs of this type have a high intrinsic brilliancy and are most useful for applications which demand a very high-intensity, near-point source of radiation and in which some sacrifice of the monochromatic character of the radiation from the lower-pressure arcs is not critical.

A few details on the operation of these arcs may be of value to the inexperienced person and will be considered here. In the use of all types

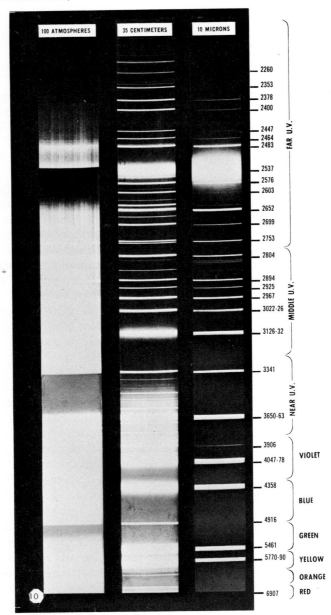

Fig. 7-1   The emission spectrum of the low-pressure (10 μ), medium-pressure (35 cm), and high-pressure (100 atm) mercury arcs. Photograph courtesy of Westinghouse Electric Corporation, Bloomfield, N.J.

of ultraviolet lamps *one should never look directly at an unshielded, operating lamp unless protective glasses are worn.* Prolonged exposure of the skin to intense ultraviolet should be avoided as well. Painful injury to the eyes and skin may result from seemingly short exposures. The authors speak from some considerable and unhappy experience in this regard.

7-1A   Low-Pressure Mercury Arcs

A mercury arc which is operated at or near room temperature, where the vapor pressure of mercury is about 10^{-3} mm, emits primarily two bands of radiation centered at 2536.5 and 1849 A. These correspond to the transitions $Hg(^3P_1) \rightarrow Hg(^1S_0) + h\nu$ and $Hg(^1P_1) \rightarrow Hg(^1S_0) + h\nu'$, respectively. Only with these low-pressure lamps is it possible to obtain the "pure" 2537 and 1849 A resonance lines required to initiate mercury-photosensitized reactions. As we saw in Sec. 2-7, self absorption in medium- and high-pressure arcs results in their "lines" at 2537 and 1849 A being *reversed*; hence they are incapable of being reabsorbed by mercury in the reaction cell.

One should recognize also that, if such a low-pressure lamp is used for *direct photolysis* in a system containing any mercury in manometers, valves, diffusion pumps, McLeod gauges, etc., *an undesired mercury-photosensitized reaction may result.* Thus the absorption coefficients of mercury at 2537 and 1849 A are so large that the major fraction of the resonance radiation from the lamp will be absorbed by mercury atoms even though they may represent an extremely small fraction of the species present in the system. Actually it is very difficult to remove mercury completely from a system in which it was once present, even if gold foil or other trapping methods are used. Thus, if one wants to study a direct photochemical reaction at 2357 A (or 1849 A) without fear of a complicating photosensitized reaction, he should use either the reversed 2537 A radiation from a medium-pressure arc or a 2537 A resonance lamp with a completely new mercury-free system (oil diffusion pumps, manometers, etc.) that has never been exposed to mercury.

Three basic types of low-pressure mercury lamps are in use today: the heated-cathode lamp, which operates on a relatively low voltage (e.g., General Electric's 30 w Germicidal lamp, 103 v, 0.34 amp; see Fig. 7-2); the cold-cathode lamp, which requires considerably higher voltages to induce electron emission at the unheated cathode [e.g., Westinghouse's 17 w Sterilamp (782 L-30), 750 v to start, 410 v in operation at 0.050 amp]; and the electrodeless discharge excited by microwave frequencies. Cold-cathode lamps have the advantage of longer useful lifetime (see Table 7-1) but require a high-voltage transformer for operation. Excitation of low-pressure mercury in the electrodeless discharge tubes by means of a microwave generator (e.g., 2450 Mc oscillator) may provide extremely narrow-line resonance radiation. The "resonance" radiation from a cooled electrodeless lamp containing isotopically enriched ^{198}Hg or ^{202}Hg

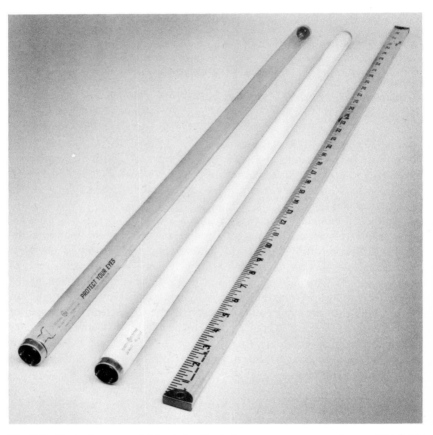

Fig. 7-2   Typical commercial heated-cathode low-pressure mercury lamp. The lamp with the clear envelope is General Electric's 30 w Germicidal lamp, the output of which is rich in 2537 A. The white tube is the phosphor-covered, Black-Light, 30 w lamp of the General Electric Co.; its output is rich in near ultraviolet light.

is of such narrow band width that it selectively excites ^{198}Hg or ^{202}Hg, respectively, in mercury vapor containing the natural abundance of its many isotopes.[1,2]   (See Sec. 2-7D.)

If one has reasonably proficient quartz-working ability, cold-cathode low-pressure mercury lamps can be constructed readily from neon sign electrodes, quartz-Pyrex graded seals, and conventional quartz and Pyrex

TABLE 7-1 Comparison of Ultraviolet Output and Operating Conditions for Several Commercial High-, Medium-, and Low-Pressure Mercury Arcs

Lamp Designation	Manufacturer	Arc Operating Conditions			Useful Arc Length, inches	Total UV Output, watts, $\lambda < 3800$ A	UV Energy per Inch of Arc Length	Efficiency of UV Generation, %	Approx. Useful Lifetime of Arc, hr
		Volts	Amperes	Input Energy, watts					
(a) Low-Pressure Mercury Lamps									
G15T8 (heated cathode)	a,b	55	0.30	16.5	14	3.0	0.21	18	2500
G30T8 (heated cathode)	a,b	100	0.34	34.0	32	7.5	0.23	22	2500
2852Q (cold cathode)	c	450	0.030	13.5	24	3.3	0.14	24	12000
WL-782-20 (cold cathode)	d	325	0.055	17.9	20	2.0	0.10	11	4500
WL-782L-30 (cold cathode)	d	410	0.050	20.5	30	5.2	0.17	25	12000
ST46A22 (cold cathode)	b	200	0.120	24.0	11	3.4	0.31	14	12000
ST30A32 (cold cathode)	b	300	0.120	36.0	25	7.0	0.28	19	12000
(b) Medium-Pressure Mercury Lamps									
SH(616A)	c	100	1.2	120	1.7(U)	6.3	3.7	5	1000[f]
UA-2	a	92	3.1	285	3	30.6	10.2	20	1000
UA-3	a	135	3.1	419	6	38.8	6.5	9	1000
A (673A)	c	145	4.5	653	4.5	95	21.1	15	1000
LL (189A)	c	285	4.7	1340	12	339	28.3	25	1000
UA-11	a	450	3.1	1395	17.7	240	13.6	17	1000
UA-15	a	2000	1.58	3160	48	810	16.9	26	1000
PIS (57A)	c	1260	4.5	5670	46.5	1066	22.9	19	1000
(c) High-Pressure Mercury Lamps									
AH6 (quartz jacket)	a	840	1.4	1176	1	195	195	17	75
(d) Compact Mercury or Mercury-Xenon Point Source Lamps									
537B9	c	~65	~18	1000	0.26	87	335	9	200
PEK 107	e	~20	~5	100	0.12				100
PEK 200	e	~58	~3.5	200	0.10				200

[a] General Electric Company, Lamp Division, Cleveland, Ohio.
[b] Sylvania Electric Products, Inc., Salem, Mass.
[c] Hanovia Lamp Division, Engelhard Industries, Newark, N.J.
[d] Westinghouse Electric Corporation, Lamp Division, Bloomfield, N.J.
[e] PEK, Inc., Palo Alto, Calif.
[f] The lifetimes shown are approximate lower limits; when the medium-pressure mercury arcs are operated in proper ventilated housings, and with fairly continuous operation, this rating may be increased by several thousand hours.

tubing. In addition to a small drop of mercury, usually about 6 mm of neon or other inert gas is added to the low-pressure lamps to facilitate starting. The details of construction are well described by Noyes and Leighton[3] and Masson, Boekelheide, and Noyes.[4]

Typical cold-cathode low-pressure mercury arcs, one designed to encircle a photolysis cell and the other for immersion in a reaction vessel, are shown in Fig. 7-3. The electrode chambers may be water-jacketed (as in

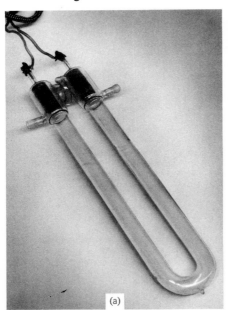
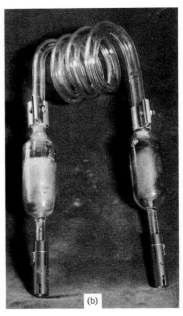

(a)   (b)

Fig. 7-3 (a) A mercury low-pressure resonance lamp with water-jacketed electrode regions, designed for immersion in a reaction vessel. (b) A commercial mercury low-pressure resonance lamp (Hanovia, SC 2537) designed to encircle a reaction vessel.

Fig. 7-3a) to aid in achieving a constant light output; see comments 2 and 3 below. With the proper design of "home-made" resonance lamps very large intensities are possible. For example, Lossing[5] and co-workers have achieved absorbed intensities of 2537 A which are greater than 10^{18} quanta/sec in an ultralow-pressure reactor attached to the ionization chamber of a mass spectrometer; this intensity was sufficient to create mass spectrometrically observable radical concentrations during the mercury-photosensitized decomposition of compounds at low pressure.

Commercial manufacturers, such as Hanovia Lamp Division, Engelhard Industries, Newark, N.J., will fabricate low-pressure resonance lamps in a variety of forms—straight tube, looped (see Fig. 7-3b) tube, helical grids, etc.—from regular quartz and from Suprasil quartz, which has a high transmission at 1849 A.

A few specific comments on the operation of low-pressure arcs may be of value.

1. There is an important and unusual characteristic of *all* arcs, including low-pressure mercury arcs, which complicates their use. They do not follow Ohm's law but possess a negative volt-ampere characteristic; that is, the voltage drop across the lamp decreases as the current through the lamp increases. As a result, a voltage taken directly from a conventional regulator or low-impedance power source cannot be used; the arc will either destroy or extinguish itself. To achieve stability of operation it is necessary to place in series with the arc a sufficiently large resistance, or reactance (inductance and/or capacitance) in the case of an a-c operated arc, so that the series combination achieves the stable condition of a voltage increase resulting in a current increase, and vice versa. Commercial a-c arcs are provided with a ballast reactance, often as part of the transformer circuit.

2. The intensity of light emitted by low-pressure mercury lamps is sensitive to the temperature of the arc wall and the current through the lamp. Heidt and Boyles[6] studied the effect of several experimental variables on the 2537 A output of a conventional low-pressure resonance lamp constructed of 10 mm tubing (see Fig. 7-4). They report that a sharp maximum occurs in the intensity of 2537 A radiation at a lamp wall temperature of 45°. At 25° and low values of arc current ($i \sim 15$ ma), the intensity I of 2537 A radiation emitted by the arc was directly proportional to the arc current; at higher current values ($i \sim 130$ ma) in a new lamp, I/i increased rapidly with i. The aging of the lamp was most serious for high current values. They report that if a control of the light intensity is required to $\pm 1\%$, the current through the lamp must be controlled to $\pm 0.6\%$ at 120–130 ma and to $\pm 0.8\%$ at 15–30 ma, while the temperature of the lamp must be controlled to $\pm 0.1°$ at 130 ma and $\pm 0.05°$ at 15 ma operation. It is evident that some means of current regulation and temperature control are imperative for quantitative work with the low-pressure resonance lamp.

3. Since the low-pressure arcs are of rather low specific brilliancy, they are often mounted parallel to or coiled about the reaction cell as in Fig. 7-4. If the temperature of the electrode chambers is held constant, for example, by circulating water from a thermostated bath through the water jackets on the electrode chambers (using a lamp constructed as in Fig. 7-3a), the main light-emitting tube may be included in the furnace for the reaction cell and be heated along with it without serious change in light intensity with temperatures up to 600°.[7]

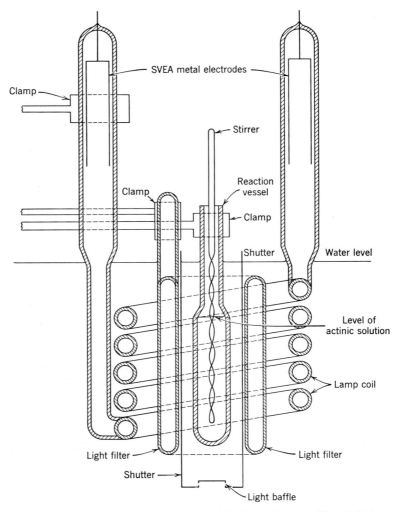

Fig. 7-4 The mercury low-pressure lamp and photolysis assembly of Heidt and Boyles;[6] see the text.

4. It is good practice to include an ammeter and voltmeter in the circuits used for all light sources in quantitative work and to note regularly the voltage and amperage during operation. Not only is the fine adjustment of the amperage facilitated, but also variation in the line voltage or changes which may occur in the lamp (electrode and tube degassing, air leaks, etc.) are quickly noted.

5. In special cases, such as in the study of photopolymerizations, it is undesirable to operate the light source from an a-c supply (see Sec. 6-7B-4b). With the low-pressure lamp the intensity of the lamp follows closely the variations in the current, and it drops to nearly zero 120 times a second for a 60-cycle a-c source. In these cases d-c operation is possible but with some loss in lifetime of the arc; of course, a resistance (preferably variable) must be included in series with the lamp to achieve stable operation.

The commercial low-pressure mercury arcs are usually constructed of an envelope material which absorbs most of the 1849 A line. However, resonance lamps of highly transmitting quartz (e.g., Suprasil from Hanovia), which are rich in 1849 A output, can be made or purchased. Several useful studies of the factors which govern production of 1849 A radiation from these lamps have appeared.[8,9,10]

7-1B   Medium-Pressure Mercury Arcs

We saw in Sec. 2-7 that in lamps operating at 1 atm or more pressure the center of the 2537 A line is missing because of self-absorption in the sheath of relatively cool atoms near the inside of the walls of the arcs (see Fig. 2-15). Such 2537 A *reversed radiation* will not be useful for initiating mercury-photosensitized reactions, but it is a satisfactory source for direct photolyses.

Another striking change occurs in the emission spectrum as one passes from the low-pressure to medium-pressure arcs; a profusion of lines of high intensity appears (see Figs. 7-1 and 2-15). These reflect the increased population of excited states other than $^3P_1$. The $^3P_1$ atoms which would normally radiate at the lower pressures of the resonance lamp are now in part excited to higher states by the more frequent collisions with electrons, ions, and molecules and radiate from these states; in part they are deactivated to the metastable $^3P_0$ state. From this state they are reactivated to the $^3P_1$ level, or in time radiate 2654 A light. The latter is sufficiently probable that a photochemically useful line is generated at that wavelength.

It is interesting to compare in Table 7-2 the relative energy distributions in the low-and medium-pressure mercury arcs. By means of the medium-pressure mercury arc, together with a monochromator or suitable filter combinations, usable intensities of near monochromatic radiation are available for many wavelengths in the visible and ultraviolet range: 5770–5790 (yellow lines), 5461 (green line), 4358 (blue line), 4045–4078 (violet lines), 3650–3663, 3341, 3126–3132, 3022–2967, 2804, 2652–2655, 2537 (reversed radiation), and the "2380 A" group of lines. Some of these

TABLE 7-2   Energy Distribution in Low- and Medium-Pressure Mercury Arcs

Wavelength, A	Relative Energy	
	Low-Pressure Mercury Arc[a]	Medium-Pressure Mercury Arc[b]
13,673	...	15.3
11,287	...	12.6
10,140	...	40.6
5770–5790	10.14	76.5
5461	0.88	93.0
4358	1.00	77.5
4045–4078	0.39	42.2
3650–3663	0.54	100.0
3341	0.03	9.3
3126–3132	0.60	49.9
3022–3028	0.06	23.9
2967	0.20	16.6
2894	0.04	6.0
2804	0.02	9.3
2753	0.03	2.7
2700	...	4.0
2652–2655	0.05	15.3
2571	...	6.0
2537	100.00	16.6[c]
2482	0.01	8.6
2400	...	7.3
2380	...	8.6
2360	...	6.0
2320	...	8.0
2224	...	14.0

[a] Hanovia Lamp Division, Engelhard Industries, Newark, N.J., SC-2537 lamp.
[b] Hanovia's Type A, 673 A, 550 w lamp.
[c] Reversed radiation.

"lines" consist of several closely spaced lines which are ordinarily taken together since complete separation is impossible with the usual photochemical equipment.

Table 7-1 has an interesting comparison of the total ultraviolet ($\lambda <$ 3800 A) energy radiated by some of the low-pressure, medium-pressure, and high-pressure mercury arcs available commercially. The percentage of the actual power dissipated in the arcs which is converted to ultraviolet light with $\lambda <$ 3800 A does not vary greatly for the different types of arcs, but the ultraviolet energy emitted per unit length of the arc is as much as 50–100 times greater for the medium-pressure arcs than with the "resonance" lamps. The relatively high intrinsic brilliancy of the medium-pressure arcs and the near-line character of the emission spectra make these lamps particularly well suited for photochemical use with monochromator and filter systems. The medium-pressure 550 w lamp (673 A) of Hanovia, used extensively in photochemical work, is shown in Fig. 7-5a. Connections suitable for suspension in an arc or immersion in a light well are shown.

The operation of the medium-pressure lamps is straightforward, but there are a few suggestions which may be helpful and may not be obvious.

1. If the lamp is to be used in an optical train where a unidirectional beam is desired, it should be mounted in a protective housing which will prevent the escape of light in directions other than that of the optical system and will help maintain a constant temperature during operation of the lamp by preventing variable drafts, etc., from striking the arc. A shutter should be attached to the housing to provide access to the beam as desired. A typical lamp housing for a Hanovia Type A, 673 A, 550 w medium-pressure lamp is shown in Figs. 7-5b and c. Since these lamps are usually constructed for use in unconfined areas which have some circulation of air, the housing must be equipped with a means of temperature control; otherwise the lamp will overheat and deteriorate quickly. On the other hand, if the lamp is cooled too effectively it will never warm up sufficiently to obtain its proper power dissipation. The satisfactory cooling system for the lamp housing shown in Fig. 7-5b involves the use of water cooling through copper coils soldered to the cylindrical brass housing. The rate of flow of water through the coils need not be fast, but once a satisfactory rate is found, it should be reproduced fairly closely each time the arc is started if highly reproducible incident light intensities are sought. The variation in the temperature of tap water is usually so small that it introduces no problem.

2. As with all arcs, a resistance must be included in series with the lamp unless it is to be used with a commercial power supply of proper reactance provided by the manufacturer. A typical simple circuit for use with the medium-pressure arcs (such as Hanovia's 673 A, 550 w lamp) operated on a-c power is shown in Fig. 7-6. If good control of the intensity of the lamp is required, the input voltage to the commercial transformer should be controlled by means of a voltage regulator (such as the Sorenson, 1000S, or other). The secondary of the transformer T may be connected in series with a large variable resistance R (such as an Ohmite, 500 w, 50Ω) and an ammeter A. The voltmeter V is of value in following the warm-up period

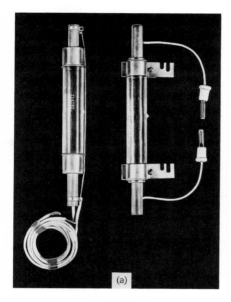

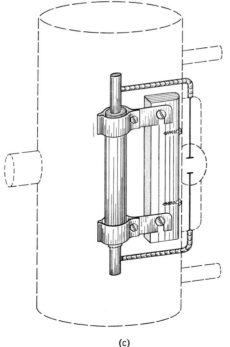

Fig. 7-5 (a) A typical commercial mercury medium-pressure arc; Hanovia Chemical and Manufacturing Company, #673A, 500 w; the electrode connections are made for suspension in a light well (left) and arc housing (right). (b) A typical water-cooled housing for the medium-pressure mercury arc. (c) Inner construction of the medium-pressure mercury-arc mounting.

of the lamp and in measuring its aging with use. For d-c operation a 220 v d-c regulated source (such as Nobitron E-200-4) is connected to points *a* and *b* and replaces the combination transformer and a-c regulator.

3. When the proper a-c voltage is applied to a medium-pressure arc it usually starts immediately; however, if the arc does not start on application of an a-c voltage, or whenever a d-c voltage is applied, it may be necessary to initiate the discharge by bringing the spark from a Tesla coil near the lamp.

4. The lifetime of the arcs can be extended appreciably if the series resistance is adjusted to its maximum value before the arc is started. When an arc is first started its resistance is low, and the current through the

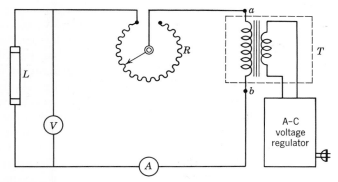

Fig. 7-6   Simple circuit for the operation of the medium-pressure mercury arc.

lamp will be high unless it is restricted through the use of the series resistance. As the lamp warms up (usually after 5 min or so) its resistance grows, the voltage drop across the lamp increases, and the current starts to fall. At this time the variable resistance should be adjusted to a lower value so that the current is raised again to the desired operating level. This process must be continued for a few minutes until the lamp has achieved full power (about 165 v at 4.0 amp for Hanovia's 763 A, 550 w lamp). An increase in intensity can be gained by operation at higher amperages, but the lifetime of the arc is shortened significantly. An arc of this type will last several thousand hours with very little reduction in intensity at most wavelengths.

5. When a new arc is installed it should be "aged" for several hours before it is used. Many arcs suffer the most dramatic changes in intensity (particularly at the shorter wavelengths) in the first few hours of operation; hence it is well to allow this aging to occur before using the lamp in quantitative work. Ozone is very noticeable near many of the mercury

arcs when new because of the generation of some very short wavelength radiation below 2000 A and its absorption by oxygen in the air (O_2 + $hv \rightarrow 2O$; $O + O_2 + M \rightarrow O_3 + M$); see Sec. 3-3B. As the quartz envelope of the arc ages it becomes more and more opaque to these shorter wavelengths, and in many cases ozone is not detectable near an arc after a few days. However, if ozone formation continues after a reasonable aging period, and the arc is to be used in quantitative work in the ultraviolet region at or below 3130 A, certain precautions should be taken. In addition to the health hazard which ozone presents in the laboratory (0.1 ppm is considered the threshold limit), its presence may lead to an undesirable variation in the ultraviolet intensity because of its strong ultraviolet absorption (see Fig. 3-41). A low steady state concentration of ozone may be established in a completely stagnant arc atmosphere and optical path, but random drafts may cause considerable variation in the ozone concentration in the light beam and hence large fluctuations in the ultraviolet intensity reaching the cell. The problem may be solved in several ways. Some experimenters merely vent the ozone to the hood, using a slow, controlled current of air through the arc housing. As an alternative solution the air atmosphere around the arc may be replaced by a slow flush of nitrogen gas, and the short-wavelength radiation absorbed by a suitable quartz plate filter mounted at the window in the arc housing.

6. The quartz envelope of the arc, or indeed any part of an optical train where light is to be transmitted, should not be handled. The finger marks generated will "burn" into the quartz and reduce its transmission. If the quartz envelope becomes dirty, it should be cleaned with CCl_4 or alcohol and dried with solt lens paper. Cleanliness in handling all parts of an optical path pays off in longer lifetime and better transmission.

7-1C   High-Pressure Mercury Arcs

The most intense sources of ultraviolet radiation are the high-pressure arcs. The pressure and temperature broadening of the spectral lines increase as the pressure and operating temperature are raised, and at very high pressures (several hundred atmospheres) the emission is almost continuous in nature. This is seen in Fig. 7-1 and by comparing the ultraviolet output for $\lambda < 3800$ A of General Electric's high-pressure (110 atm) mercury AH6 lamp with that of the medium- and low-pressure arcs in Table 7-1. The output is about 10 times that for the medium-pressure arcs and about 1000 times that for the low-pressure arcs, per unit length of arc. The high-pressure mercury arc is also very rich in visible light; it has about twice the visible energy of a 1000 w tungsten bulb. Since the AH6 emission is derived from a small capillary quartz envelope while the other two basic types of arcs are made of 10-20 mm diameter tubing, the energy emitted per unit area of arc surface is even many times greater than our comparison of energy per unit arc length suggests. In fact the brightness of the AH6 central core is almost one-fifth the brightness of the sun.[11]

High-pressure arcs of the AH6 type operate at very high temperatures, and water or forced-air cooling is required to avoid melting the quartz envelope. A high rate of water circulation (3 qt/min) is used on AH6 lamps. This leads to difficulties in quantitative work, since impurities in the tap water may absorb some of the desired radiation at the shorter wavelengths and may allow some conductivity between the electrodes, leading to instability.

The high-pressure lamp is excellent for qualitative and semiquantitative photochemical work and for synthetic photochemistry which does not demand very high stability and reproducibility of intensity. However, the medium-pressure lamps and the high-pressure point-source lamps (to be described) are less subject to violent intensity changes; they have considerably longer lifetimes than the very high-pressure lamps and are to be preferred for quantitative work. Both Pyrex and quartz water-jacketed lamps are available commercially (e.g., General Electric, PEK, etc.). Figure 7-7 shows a high-pressure lamp element and its water-jacket mounting.

Schulz[12] and Baum and Dunkelman[13] described several years ago the construction and operation of an intense point-source arc using xenon at about 20 atm pressure. In recent years several companies (e.g., Osram, Hanovia, PEK) have placed on the market excellent near-point sources of intense ultraviolet and visible light similar to the original arc design of Schulz. These consist of a high-powered discharge in xenon, mercury, or a mercury-xenon mixture compressed into a very small space and having a bulb-like design that does not require water cooling of the arc. See Fig. 7-8. Both two- and three-electrode models are available; the third electrode serves as a starting electrode to which a high-voltage pulse can be applied as the arc is first started. With the two electrode models a special power supply is used to provide a high-voltage starting pulse through the main conducting electrodes. The spatial distribution of the intensity of the light emitted from the Hanovia xenon-mercury 1000 w point-source a-c lamp is pictured in Fig. 7-9. Since the pressures in some of these lamps are not extremely high (near 20 atm), much line structure is superimposed on the continuum in the mercury-containing lamps and they are particularly attractive photochemical sources (see Fig. 7-10). The xenon point sources are excellent for a high-intensity continuum (see the emission spectrum shown in Fig. 7-10). Both d-c and a-c operation of most of these lamps is possible.

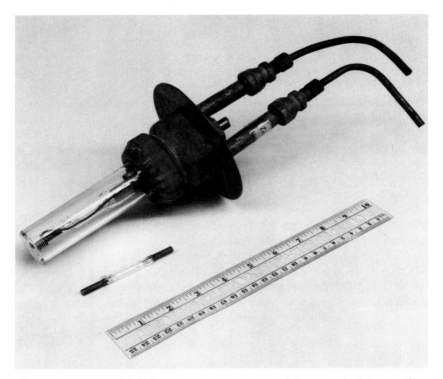

Fig. 7-7 A commercial high-pressure mercury arc and its water-jacket mounting; General Electric Co., AH6, 1000 w.

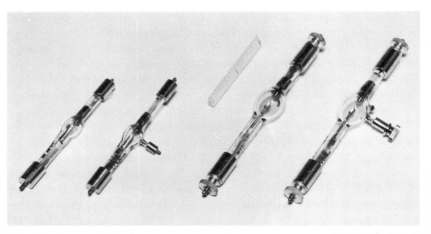

Fig. 7-8 Commercial point-source mercury lamps; PEK, Inc., #109, 107, 200 (2 electrode), and 200 (3 electrode) models are shown; the 109 and 107 are for d-c operation only, while the 200 can be operated on a-c or d-c current.

702

The point-source lamps are not water- or air-cooled. However, a special lamp enclosure is necessary to protect the operator against the strong ultraviolet radiation and possible injury in case of a violent lamp failure, and to regulate the ambient air temperature for optimum performance of

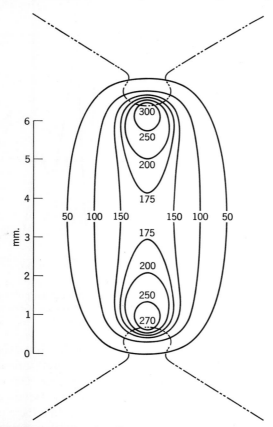

Fig. 7-9 The brightness distribution in candles per square millimeter for a commercial 1000 w xenon-mercury point-source lamp with a-c operation (Hanovia Chemical and Manufacturing Co., #537B).

the lamp. Unfortunately at present most of the companies which make lamps do not have the photochemist in mind and do not provide either suitable housings for quantitative photochemical use or the detailed data for their construction. Some guesswork is required, and a few expensive lamps are sacrificed by most researchers before the proper design of housing is found. The Osram Company gives a few useful recommendations. They say that the surface of the housing should cover an area of

4 cm²/lamp watt and should be painted black inside to aid in heat dissipation. Openings at the top and bottom may provide controlled ventilation. The design is rather critical, for too small an enclosure leads to overheating of the lamp and shortened life, whereas too big an enclosure or forced air cooling may prevent the lamp from heating and acquiring the necessary

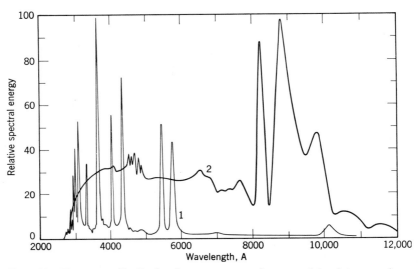

Fig. 7-10 The energy distribution from two types of commercial point-source lamps. Curve 1 was obtained from the mercury HBO 200 lamp of Osram (Germany); curve 2, from the xenon X-75 lamp of PEK, Inc.

pressure. Figure 7-11 (pp. 706 and 707) gives a picture and a scale drawing of a housing constructed and tested in the authors' laboratories for a 200 w, two electrode, point-source lamp. For 100, 500, and 1000 w lamps the dimensions of Fig. 7-11b should be multiplied by the factors of 0.71, 1.6, and 2.2, respectively. It seems likely to the authors that these point-source lamps will receive increasing use in photochemical research. For this reason some suggestions as to the optimum operating conditions for these lamps are given here.[14]

1. The lamp should be operated vertically, and in any event not more than 45° from the vertical, with the cathode at the top.

2. The ventilation of the lamphouse should be so restricted that with a lamp dissipation of 100 watts a chromel-alumel thermocouple (0.004 diameter wire) attached to the outside of the quartz bulb shows a temperature of 800 ± 25°C. With the arrangement shown in Fig. 7-11 a completely closed housing is used with satisfactory operation.

3. It is necessary that these lamps be permitted to warm up to operating temperature as fast as possible, because on each occasion the operation goes through a sputtering phase which is destructive to the electrodes and to the inside of the quartz envelope. It is essential to minimize the time spent in the sputtering phase if a reasonable lamp life is to be attained.

4. Provision should be made so that the current through the lamp may be adjusted for a dissipation of the rated wattage within 5%. Too high a dissipation may cause failure because of either an excessive pressure rise inside the envelope or heating of a ribbon in one of the seals. Too low a dissipation, particularly if combined with excessive ventilation, will cause electrode damage and sharply reduced lamp life.

5. The electrical connection which carries the starting high-voltage pulses to the lamp should be insulated for at least 12 kv. Failure of lamps to start, particularly when hot, has frequently been traceable to a flashover at some point in the wiring where the insulation has been weak.

6. A lamp should be left burning if the period for which it must stand idle does not exceed 30 min. The sputtering phase on start-up is likely to be as damaging as the extra time spent running. A point-source lamp on standby should *not* be run at reduced wattage.

7. Power supplies for the point-source high-pressure lamps are available from the manufacturers. It may be easier for most researchers to buy these than to construct their own, since there are some unusual requirements in the circuit components of the supplies.

7-1D   Resonance Lamps Using Metals Other than Mercury

Sodium vapor resonance lamps are available commercially, and lamps using the other alkali metals can be either purchased or constructed easily. They usually offer little interest for photochemical use since the electronic transitions involved are of such small energy. Cadmium[15] and zinc[16] resonance lamps have been built and used successfully. Inert-gas resonance lamps are described in the following section.

7-1E   Lamps for Photochemical Studies in the Far-Ultraviolet Region

Various ingenious designs of discharge lamps for short-wavelength ultraviolet are described in the current literature. Since this area of photochemistry is expanding rapidly today, it is likely that new and improved lamps will appear regularly; therefore the current literature should be consulted. A windowless source from a low-pressure discharge in hydrogen has been found to be very rich in the 800–2000 A region.[17] High-intensity noble-gas discharges have been described using low pressures

(a)

of krypton (1165, 1236 A) and xenon (1296, 1470 A).[18] Hot-cathode low-pressure discharges using H_2, helium, argon, or N_2 provide radiation in the 500–1650 A region.[19] Very high-intensity Schumann-ultraviolet continuum and line spectra have been observed from electrodeless microwave-excited discharges in low pressures of inert gases (xenon, krypton, and neon).[20,21,22] Romand and Vodar[23a] and McNesby and Okabe[23b,23c] have given excellent reviews of the methods of generation and detection of radiation from 2000 A to the X-ray region. Commercial arcs are also available for use in the vacuum ultraviolet.

The rare-gas, microwave-excited resonance lamps have been utilized most successfully by many research groups in the generation of photochemically useful intensities of far-ultraviolet light, and it will be of some value to have a few details of their operation given here. The simplicity of construction (see Fig. 7-12), their high intensity (greater than 10^{14} quanta/sec), and the relatively monochromatic nature of the emission all

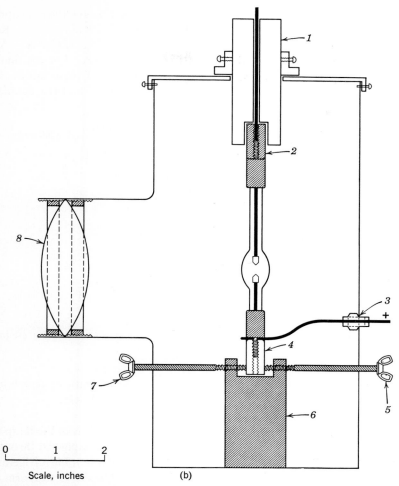

Scale, inches   (b)

Fig. 7-11 (a) View of housing for 200 w, point-source, high-pressure mercury arc. (b) Schematic diagram of housing for 200 w point-source, high-pressure mercury arc pictured in (a); shaded parts made of brass construction; clear parts are insulating material. *1*, Machined Steotite (lava) rod which can be raised from the housing with the arc and connecting wires to facilitate change of arc and adjustment of its vertical position; *2*, brass threaded connector to which the external power lead to the cathode is silver-soldered and into which the arc cathode connector screws; *3*, Teflon insulator which pushes into the housing with connecting wire when arc is to be replaced; *4*, Steotite, threaded connector which screws tight against the anode connector and the lamp base; *6*, brass support column; *5* and *7* two of the three wing nut adjustment screws to position lamp at anode end; *8*, 4″ focal length lens with position adjustable away and toward the arc to achieve best focus.

favor their use. A variety of wavelengths is available through the appropriate choice of the filling gas: Xe, 1469.6 A (98%), 1295.6 A (2%); Kr, 1235.8 A (78%), 1164.9 A (22%); H_2, 1215.7 A; D_2, 1215.3 A; Ar, 1066.7 A, 1048.2 A; Ne, 743.7 A, 735.9 A; He, 584.4 A. For the many important details in the construction and operation of these lamps the reader is referred to the McNesby and Okabe review[23b] and the detailed

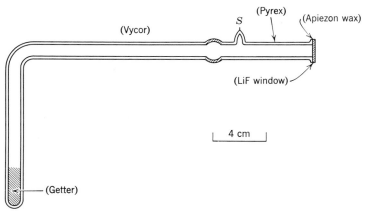

Fig. 7-12   Construction of a simple electrodeless rare-gas resonance lamp for use in a microwave field. From McNesby and Okabe;[23b] see text.

paper of Okabe.[23c] There are, however, some unusual features associated with the use of these lamps which should be mentioned here.

1. It is important to note that water must be removed from the lamp to achieve the desired purity of emission; this can be accomplished through the use of a chemical "getter" (e.g., Ba-Al-Ni alloy) or a suitable refrigerant (e.g., with the krypton lamp, liquid nitrogen applied to the vertical arm in Fig. 7-12), or by extensive baking under vacuum. Compare in Fig. 7-13 the emission spectra of the krypton microwave-excited resonance lamp used without "getter," refrigerant, or baking to remove water (dotted curve) and that from a similar lamp with which a chemical "getter" was employed.[23b,23c] The details of the different possible water-removing operations need not be reviewed here, but a brief description of the "getter" technique will be instructive. The lamp as pictured in Fig. 7-12 with "getter" material in the side arm is attached to a vacuum line by a T-tube seal at point S; it is pumped to 10^{-5} mm, the tube is heated repeatedly with a hand torch, and the "getter" is prepared by degassing, warming, and then heating the "getter" tube to a dull red glow. The desired pressure

of the gas is introduced (see point 2 below), and the tube is sealed off from the vacuum line by collapsing the T-tube side arm with a torch flame at a prepared constriction at S.

2. The intensity of the resonance line emission from xenon- and krypton-filled lamps maximizes at about 0.7 and 1 mm pressures of the

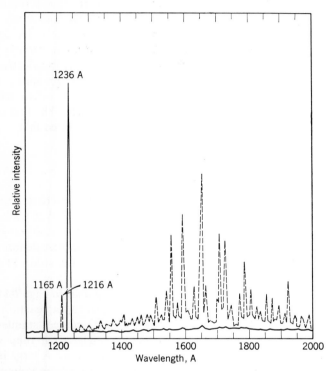

Fig. 7-13 Emission from a krypton-filled, microwave-excited, resonance lamp used without "getter," refrigerant, or baking to remove water (dotted curve), and emission from a similar lamp with which a chemical "getter" was employed (solid trace). From McNesby and Okabe.[23b, c]

gas, respectively, although the pressure used is not critical. An increase in intensity of the krypton line can be obtained by using a mixture of 10% krypton and 90% helium at a total of 1 mm pressure.[23b]

3. The tube is placed in the cavity of a suitable microwave generator of the type produced in the United States by Raytheon Corporation [model KV-104 (NB), 125 w full power, 2450 Mc/sec]; at low power it may be necessary to initiate the lamp operation by sparking it with a Tesla coil.

7-1F   Sources of High-Intensity Flashes of
Light for Flash Photolysis Studies

When a sudden flash of high-intensity light is absorbed by a reactant, a relatively large concentration of free radicals or other transient species is formed, and these transients can be detected spectroscopically and characterized. Flash photolysis is a powerful tool for the study of the primary processes in photochemical systems (see Sec. 6-4A and the excellent review of Porter[26b] for a discussion and literature survey). There are three basic types of flash systems in use today: (1) the electrical discharge between inert metal electrodes in a gas at low pressure; (2) the high-energy spark discharge between magnesium or other relatively volatile metal electrodes; (3) the "exploding wire" flash. The first of these methods has been most widely used and will be considered first.

7-1F-1   Flash Lamps Employing Discharges
in Gases at Low Pressures

As early as 1932 high-intensity flash discharge lamps were described for use in high-speed photography.[24] Norrish and Porter[25,26] at Cambridge, Davidson and co-workers[27] at California Institute of Technology, and Ramsay[28] at the National Research Council in Ottawa first demonstrated the great utility of the gas discharge flash lamp for the study of photochemical systems.

Consider the operation of the basic flash unit shown in Fig. 7-14. The "initiating" flash tube F_1 is usually mounted parallel to the reaction cell R, and both tubes are enclosed in an aluminum, MgO-coated, stainless steel or other highly reflecting cylindrical shield S. The flash tube usually contains about 6–15 cm of some inert gas such as xenon. A large bank of condensers B of capacitance C farads is charged to a high voltage of V volts which is applied to the large tungsten electrodes E_1 and E_2 located in opposite ends of the quartz flash tube. When the high alternating voltage from a spark coil is sent to the small trigger electrode E_3, ionization of the gas is induced and the energy stored by the condensers, $CV^2/2$ joules, discharges suddenly between electrodes E_1 and E_2. In the very short time interval of the flash a part of the electrical energy stored in the condensers (about 5–10%) appears as an intense burst of light accompanied by a sharp audio report.

The intensity of the flash as a function of time is shown in Fig. 7-15 for a typical Porter-type flash tube. The duration of the flash is most commonly considered as the time after flash initiation at which the intensity reaches $1/e$th (1/2.718) of the intensity at the maximum. For example, in

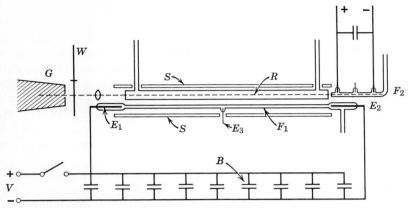

Fig. 7-14   Diagram of the basic flash photolysis unit of Norrish and Porter;[25,26] see text.

Fig. 7-15 the flash duration would be about 0.9 msec. The duration of the flash may be as long as several milliseconds or as short as a few microseconds, depending on the inductance of the lamp-capacitor bank combination, the initial voltage applied, the dimensions of the flash tube, and the nature and pressure of the gas it contains. The gaseous discharge flash lamps emit a near continuum which extends from the far ultraviolet to the near infrared.

An appreciable fraction of a reactant contained in a photolysis cell R which parallels the flash tube is photolyzed during the light flash, which

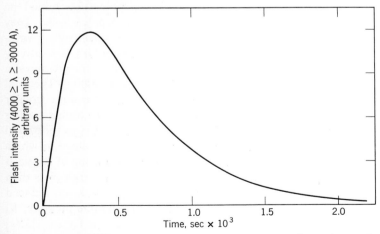

Fig. 7-15   The relative intensity of the Norrish and Porter-type flash tube[25,26] as a function of time; radiation reaching the phototube was filtered so that only 3000–4000 A was seen by the tube; flash energy 4800 j.

may contain as many as 10^{20} quanta/flash. A spectroscopic examination of the primary products formed in the burst of light is made possible by the flash of light from a smaller second "spectroscopic" flash tube F_2 of Fig. 7-14; this flash, which follows the initiating flash after some selected delay time, sends a beam of nearly continuous radiation down the length of the photolysis cell and into the spectrograph G, where the absorption due to initial products can be detected. A slotted wheel W, rotated by a synchronous motor, can be used to isolate the spectrograph G from the light of the initiating flash, and through contacts attached to the shaft of the wheel the desired delay in the firing of the spectroscopic flash can be controlled.

The flash lamps of the original design used by Porter have flash durations in the millisecond range; this is too long a flash duration to allow spectroscopic observation of most short-lived transients. These flash lamps are of greatest value today for the study of the final products formed by radical-radical interactions at high radical concentrations.[29] The construction of the lamps is relatively simple. Most continuous discharge lamps may be modified for flash work for flashes of energy up to 100 j. Above this range it is necessary to construct the lamps of fused quartz and use large electrodes of tungsten or other high current capacity material. The lamps described by Porter are useful up to flash energies of 10,000 j. In his work, electrodes E_1 and E_2 of Fig. 7-14 were made of ⅜ in diameter tungsten rod which was sealed by means of tungsten-molybdenum-quartz seals into the ends of the quartz flash tube; the tube itself was 1 meter in length and about 1 cm in diameter, with the small tungsten trigger electrode placed at the center of the tube. Christie and Porter[30] have determined the effect of several variables on the emission from this type of flash. They report that the intensity in the continuum is rather independent of wavelength in the range 2600–4400 A, and that the distribution is relatively insensitive to the nature and pressure of the inert-gas filling for pressures in the range 4-15 cm and the flash energy for the range 800–4000 j. The total ultraviolet output is independent of gas pressure for pressures greater than 5 cm but falls off for lower pressures. For energy inputs greater than 800 j the flash output of radiation in the ultraviolet is proportional to $C(V^2 - V_0^2)$, where C is the capacitance and V the voltage to which the condensers are charges, V_0 is a constant for any one filling of the flash tube, and the output per flash is highly reproducible for energies less than 2500 j. After 1000 flashes at this energy, the output per flash was reduced only 5%. With different fillings of the same gas at the same pressure, V_0 varied considerably; a $\pm 10\%$ variation in the output for a flash of 2500 j was observed. The addition of mercury to the rare-gas filling increases the energy in the ultraviolet region, but this practice is undesirable for most work since the output is very irreproducible, particularly at the higher energy flashes. At very high energy values the discharge decomposes the material of the tube and the electrodes and liberates any occluded gas not removed before filling. Although a small amount of oxygen or other impurity gas has little effect on the output of the flash, it may prevent firing

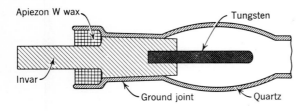

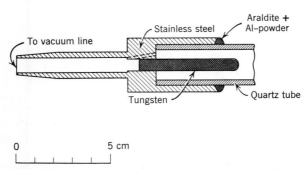

0   5 cm

Fig. 7-16   Construction of tungsten electrode seals for operation of flash lamps up to 33,600 j, used by Claesson and Lindqvist.[31]

when the trigger pulse is applied; it may delay the initiation of the flash (about 1 millisec) following the trigger pulse.

Claesson and Lindqvist[31] have developed an improved design of gaseous discharge flash lamps for use at very high energies up to 33,600 j (1370 μf at 7000 v). At flash energies above 10,000 j the tungsten electrode seals of the Porter-type lamps usually break. Two seal designs used successfully by Claesson and Lindqvist at energies up to 33,600 j are shown in Fig. 7-16. These workers use two identical flash lamps in series with the high voltage and mounted on opposite sides of the photolysis cell as shown in Fig. 7-17. The electrically common electrode is maintained at ground potential, and the voltage is supplied to one of the other ends by one-half of the condenser bank charged to $V/2$ volts positive with respect to ground.

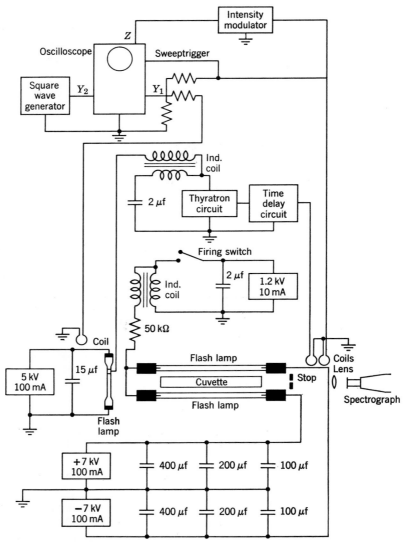

Fig. 7-17   One arrangement of a high-energy flash photolysis system designed by Claesson and Lindqvist.[31]

The other end is charged to $-V/2$ volts by the other half of the condenser bank. The trigger voltage which fires both lamps is applied at the common electrode which is normally at ground potential. Since oxygen evolution from the flash tube is most serious with high-energy flashes, Claesson and Lindqvist have chosen oxygen (2–5 mm)-argon (about 20 mm) mixtures for the filling gas. Then small increases in the oxygen pressure during use cause little change in the firing characteristics. The flash duration using twin tubes in series is no longer than that of a single flash tube. For a 5 kv charging voltage the flash duration in the 3600–3800 A region is approximately proportional to the capacitance used: about 60 μsec at 500 μf; about 150 μsec for 1400 μf. For a fixed capacitance the flash duration increases with charging voltage: for $C = 800 \mu$f, the flash duration was about 110 μsec for $V = 6000$ v; about 80 μsec for 3800 v.

Flash tubes with very short flash duration are desirable for use in spectral studies of highly reactive intermediates. If one lowers the inductance of the lamp-condenser bank combination, and for a given power flash raises the charging voltage and lowers the total capacitance, the flash duration is shortened. Claesson and Lindqvist[31b] describe a high-energy flash system which has a very short flash duration. Specially designed low-inductance capacitors of the single-pole type are employed, with all connections and mounting arranged to minimize the inductance. The lamp, shown in Fig. 7-18, is about 10 cm long and is equipped with a tungsten ring electrode (labeled *18* in Fig. 7-18); the discharge occurs uniformly distributed in the cylindrical shell between two concentric quartz tubes. The cylindrical reaction cell was mounted in the center of the lamp. With this arrangement a flash of 7500 j (5000 v at 275 μf) had a flash duration of only 17 μsec; about 7×10^{18} quanta/ml of the cell are obtained per flash for the wavelength range absorbed by the uranyl oxalate actinometer. Charlson, Harrison, and Hardwick[32] describe a Pyrex flash tube of similar design but of somewhat simpler construction, which should be very useful for studies within the Pyrex-transparent region.

Commercial flash lamps of various designs and outputs are made by several manufacturers; some of the types available from PEK, Inc., are shown in Fig. 7-19.

For the direct determination of fluorescence lifetimes of very short duration (10^{-8} to 10^{-9} sec) from the time dependence of measured fluorescence intensities, flash lamps with flash duration in the millimicrosecond range (nanosecond, 10^{-9} sec) are necessary. Malmberg[33] has considered in detail the design of low-intensity, short-flash-duration lamps suitable for such measurements. When very short pulses of light are desired, one is concerned not only with the inductance and capacitance of the flash circuit and the length of the current pulse, but also with the timing of the processes which occur in the gas after the current pulse ends. Thus, immediately after the discharge, the flash tube contains an electron gas at very high temperature as well as neutral and ionized molecules which are near room temperature. The electron-gas cools by collisions with molecules, and some of these collisions may excite molecules which then emit. To have a very short flash duration the electron gas must be cooled quickly. The rate of cooling is proportional to the number of collisions/second or the pressure of the gas present in the tube and the mean energy transfered per collision, which is inversely proportional to the mass of the molecules (see Eq.

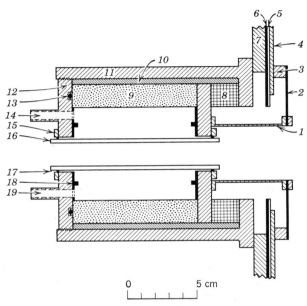

0   5 cm

Fig. 7-18 Section through a cylindrical flash lamp of Claesson and Lindqvist.[31b] *1*, Copper tube; *2*, copper foil; *3*, flange; *4*, copper plate serving as a high-voltage lead; *5*, polyethylene sheet; *6*, Bakelite sheet; *7*, grounded copper plate; *8*, Bakelite ring; *9*, opaque quartz tube; *10*, cable-filling wax; *11*, brass tube; *12*, brass plate; *13*, rubber gasket; *14*, tube for evacuation; *15*, flange; *16*, transparent quartz tube; *17*, rubber gasket; *18*, ring-shaped tungsten electrode and tungsten foil protection for the brass plate; *19*, tube for gas admission.

6-129). Energy loss due to inelastic collisions with a molecule depends in a complicated fashion on the number of internal modes of energy available in the molecule and the energy separation of these modes; of course it is greater for a diatomic molecule than for a monatomic gas.

With these facts in mind Malmberg reasoned that the use of a relatively high pressure of hydrogen gas in the flash tube might provide most rapid electron gas cooling. This was borne out by his experiments. He prepared small flash lamps for visible work from General Electric NE-2 bulbs. The bulb was opened, the $\frac{1}{32}''$ cylindrical electrodes, about $\frac{5}{16}''$ in length, were bent so that they were parallel and had a spacing of about $\frac{1}{64}''$, the tube was resealed, evacuated, flamed, and filled with hydrogen at about 10 cm pressure. A voltage of about 4000 v was applied across a series combination of the flash lamp and a thyratron tube which was biased to make it non-conducting. The initiation of the flash was controlled by a square wave positive voltage pulse applied to the control grid of the thyratron

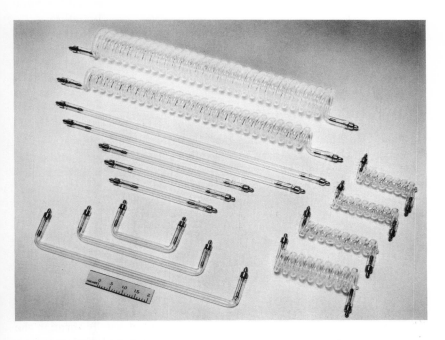

Fig. 7-19   Some commercially available flash lamps manufactured by PEK, Inc.; the spiral lamps to the right and top of the figure are the XE5 series (largest power, 12,000 j); the capillary flash lamps are of the XE1 series (largest power, 1,200 j).

tube which allowed the energy to discharge through it and the flash tube. A very small capacitance, either that inherent in the leads and circuit components or about 200 $\mu\mu$f, was employed in series with the tubes, so that the energy per flash was only about 0.0016 j. However, because of the very high sensitivity of the photomultiplier detector system used, this flash intensity was sufficient to create easily measurable fluorescence intensities. The duration of the flash was of the order of 1 nanosecond (10^{-9} sec). Lamps of this basic design have been used successfully by Brody[34] and Bennett[35] in the determination of fluorescence lifetimes in the nanosecond range. Nanosecond light sources of very low intensity are now produced commercially (e.g., PEK Inc.).

Considerable electronic circuitry is employed with flash lamps for spectral work. Circuits are necessary to control the firing of the initiating flash tube and the spectral flash tube after a suitable delay, and to measure the interval between flashes and the time dependence of the flash energy. The circuits given by Porter are suitable for use with tubes of millisecond flash duration.[26] Several useful circuits designed for microsecond[31,32,36] and millimicrosecond[34,35] flash work are also described in the literature.

A high-intensity, low-energy flash lamp for use down to the short-wavelength region (1500 A) has been described by Golden and Myerson.[37a] More recently Black and Porter have reported flash photolysis studies in the vacuum ultraviolet.[37b]

7-1F-2   High-Intensity Light Flash from Spark Discharges

Mains, Roebbler, and Rollefson[38] describe a high-intensity spark discharge which has been used successfully in flash photolysis studies. A 10 μf condenser bank charged to 20,000 v was discharged between magnesium metal rod electrodes located about the reaction cell in a low-pressure chamber. A major advantage gained in this type of flash system is the near monochromatic nature of the energy emission; 2795.5 and 2802.7 A lines characteristic of magnesium predominate, and the next most intense line present is well removed at 3830 A. Thus, for experiments with compounds which absorb below 3700 A, the flash energy is practically monochromatic. Ten magnesium electrode spark gaps and series condensers were used in a parallel combination. The cylindrical spark chamber (constructed of Plexiglas) housed the ten pairs of $\frac{1}{4}''$ magnesium rod electrodes uniformly spaced around a 32 mm quartz tube which extended axially through the cylinder. The cylindrical shell housing the electrodes was evacuated to a pressure of about 5 mm. The photolysis cell was a 22 mm diameter quartz tube, 30 cm in length, located on the axis of the flash housing. The flash duration varied with conditions as follows: for $C = 1$ μf, 4 μsec at 10,000 v and 9 μsec at 25,000 v; with $C = 10$ μf, 200 μsec at 25,000 v and 130 μsec at 15,000 v. A maximum intensity of 10^{21} quanta/sec in a 100 cc reaction vessel could be obtained. Although this intensity is about 100 times less than that possible with the gas discharge flash of Porter, the advantage of the nearly monochromatic character of the radiation makes the system of Mains and co-workers well suited for quantitative photochemical work. Conceivably cadmium, zinc, or other electrode materials could be chosen to alter the wavelength region of the flash. A disadvantage of the magnesium spark system of this design is the deposit of MgO which forms on the inner quartz tube housing the spark electrodes. Periodic cleaning of the flash tube is necessary to avoid serious changes in the output.

A spark discharge useful at energies up to 400,000 j has been developed by Claesson, Nyman, and Wettermark.[39] In their system a condenser bank of 1000 μf total capacitance can be charged to a maximum voltage of 30,000 v. In an investigation described by Wettermark[39b] the condensers were discharged between two conical brass electrodes in air. The discharge region between the electrodes was almost spherical with a diameter of about 30 mm. The electrodes were kept sufficiently far apart (about 22 mm) so that spontaneous firing did not occur as the condensers were charged. The discharge was started by blowing a stream of argon axially through the spark gap. The time dependence of the intensity of the emission shows a damped oscillation of a duration dependent on the wavelength range considered: for energies of 100,000 j the flash duration was less than 100 μsec at 2110 A; about 300 μsec at 2500 A; about 500 μsec at 3500 A; and about 600 μsec at 5100 A. About 10^{22} quanta [absorbed by $K_3Fe(C_2O_4)_3$ actinometer solution] are emitted in a single flash. The very small volume element from which the bulk of the light is emitted makes possible flash experiments with fairly parallel light.

7-1F-3 The High-Intensity Light Flash from Exploding Wires

The exploding wire technique of producing short flashes of intense light[40] has been used somewhat in high-speed photography.[41] Oster and Marcus[42] have developed the exploding wire flash techniques for use in photochemical experiments. In their work a bank of condensers (33 μf) was charged to 8000 v. The energy was discharged through a thin high-resistance Nichrome wire (30 cm long, B.S. 40). The wire exploded with a loud noise and a strong burst of light. At least 34 j of energy are necessary to produce the flash; about 33 j are required to vaporize the metal wire. The flash duration is about 0.3 msec when 1056 j are used. The emission contains all the visible and ultraviolet lines of nickel and chromium. About 10% of the input power appears as radiation in the 2000–3300 A range. Of course, the wire is destroyed in each flash and must be replaced. Oster and Marcus recommended exploding wire flash photolysis as a source of considerable brilliance and excellent reproducibility. Since the exploding wire acts as a line source, the beam can be rendered nearly parallel by suitable reflectors or lenses. The spectral output can be varied at will by choosing appropriate metals (e.g., copper wires emit an intense green light). Since no jacket is employed, this technique may be useful in the far ultraviolet. The duration of the flash can be decreased by choosing a wire of lower resistance or using higher voltages and lower capacitance.

7-1F-4   Experimental Problems Associated with Flash Photolysis

The investigator who plans to use flash photolysis for the first time should be cognizant of several problems which are common to this area of research (see also Porter[26b]).

1. The very high voltages and large energies stored in the condenser bank of the flash system are a dangerous hazard which must be treated with great respect. It is desirable to arrange the apparatus so that charging and discharging cycles are controlled from some point well removed from the high voltage. In many laboratories elaborate safety devices are employed; all controls and instrumentation may be in an adjacent room, and the condenser bank may be automatically discharged through suitable high-wattage resistances by a safety relay which is actuated as the door is opened to the room housing the flash equipment.

2. The time dependence of the flash intensity varies considerably with the wavelength range selected.[39b,43] For quantitative work which demands an accurate knowledge of the time dependence of the flash intensity, it is important to determine the timing for the particular wavelength region which is most strongly absorbed by the compound of interest.

3. The degassing of a gaseous discharge flash tube through use and the resulting change in the firing characteristics of the tube can be minimized by intense heating of the tube during evacuation; the tube should be filled, then discharged at high energy, and evacuated again. This process should be repeated several times. Tubes prepared in this fashion may be fired as many as a thousand times without degassing problems. However, Porter notes that in discharge flash tubes containing inert gases flashed at very high energies (10,000 j) it was still necessary to refill the lamps frequently.

4. The reaction temperature may be uncertain in flash photolysis systems because of the absorption of such large energies by the reactant in the very short flash time. The amount of the temperature rise can be reduced by increasing the heat capacity of the system by the addition of large amount of inert gas. However, Marcus[44] has pointed out that this procedure may result in a misleading effect when relatively long-lived excited states are involved. He suggests a simple alternative test to detect the importance of thermal effects; this is to investigate the effect of altering the intensity of the flash on the product yields. If the intensity is reduced, the temperature rise of the system will drop accordingly. At these high intensities, it is unlikely that the quantum yields of the products will vary with light intensity if no temperature change occurs, so that the volume of products formed should be directly proportional to the intensity

of the flash. If this is the case, it is likely that thermal effects are unimportant; either temperature changes do not occur, or if they do, their effect on the reaction products is negligible.

7-1G   Production of Intermittent Square Wave Light Pulses for "Rotating Sector" Experiments

Stroboscopic flashes from suitable flash lamps, steady illumination coupled with a Kerr cell (see Sec. 7-5C-2), or other electronically controlled sources of pulsed light have a sophistication which is unnecessary to achieve the rather limited range of light intervals required for most radical lifetime studies (0.5–0.001 sec). In fact, in this application there are serious disadvantages associated with intermittent flash lamps and Kerr cells; most flash lamps have the undesirable features of wide energy distribution and do not generate ideal square wave light pulses, while the use of the Kerr cell is restricted to studies within the limited range of wavelengths for which the Kerr cell compound is transparent. The most generally applicable and the simplest square light wave generator has been the rotating slotted disc used in conjunction with a conventional continuous light source, monochromator, and filter system. The wheel is placed in the light path so that light is transmitted to the cell only when the slots in the rotating wheel are in line with the light beam. For experiments in the near-ultraviolet and visible regions the wheel may be made of solid transparent plastic with the desired segments blackened with paint. A high stability of the wheel is obtained with this construction, and there are no serious problems of wheel balancing. For wavelength regions including the ultraviolet a metal disc is usually employed, and segments of the disc are cut away to achieve the desired ratio r of dark to light time period; $r = 3$ is a common choice. This wheel must be balanced for high speeds of rotation by fastening weights around the hub. A symmetrical pattern of openings on the wheel makes the balancing job easier.

The disc so prepared is attached either directly or through a reduction gear box to a synchronous motor. The motor speed may be controlled accurately by a relatively simple electronic regulator such as that described by Kwart, Broadbent, and Bartlett.[45] The speed of rotation can be determined for a given setting of the resistance and the gear box by direct timing at the slower speeds and by means of a stroboscopic unit or a phototube electronic-counter combination, etc., at higher speeds. The circuit of Kwart et al.[45] can be used to regulate sector speeds to $\pm 3\%$ for speeds of 300 rpm and $\pm 1\%$ for lower speeds.

The reader is referred to the excellent review of the rotating sector by Burnett and Melville[46] for further discussion of the techniques involved.

7-1H   Other Useful Continuous Sources of
Light for Photochemical Experiments

The carbon arcs and continuous metallic sparks, popular years ago in photochemical research, are little used today. They have few if an advantages over other arcs available, and they have many serious disadvantages.

Various commercial incandescent bulbs (photofloods, automobile headlights, etc.) and fluorescent tubes are useful for photochemical work in the visible and near-ultraviolet region. It should be remembered in choosing a visible source that the total visible energy emitted by a 1000 w photoflood bulb amounts to only about 185 w, whereas the 1000 w high-pressure mercury arc (General Electric's AH-6) gives 290 w of visible light.

For many synthetic purposes the sun can be used as an effective source of radiation. The radiation from the sun which we receive at the surface of the earth extends about from 3000 A to the far infrared. About 4 % of the total energy lies in the ultraviolet below 4000 A; however, this fraction is sensitive to changes in latitude, elevation, clarity of the atmosphere, time of the day, and season of the year. From the data of Forsythe and Christison[47a] we may estimate that for a typical clear day in midsummer in Cleveland, Ohio (latitude 41.5°N), the total number of quanta incident per second per square centimeter of horizontal surface will be about 3×10^{13} for $\lambda < 3100$ A; 2×10^{15} for $\lambda < 3500$ A; 7×10^{15} for $\lambda < 4000$ A; and 1×10^{17} for $\lambda < 7000$ A (see the excellent chapter on solar radiation by Leighton[47b]). About one-half of the sun's energy is in the infrared region, so some provision for sample temperature control or infrared filtering may be necessary when using sunlight as a photochemical light source.

Probably the most common source of a continuous spectrum of ultraviolet for spectral determinations is the hydrogen discharge tube. The xenon point sources described above should find considerable use also as a broad structureless continuum for spectrographic work; see Fig. 7-10. However, some wandering of the discharge between the electrodes occurs in many of the point-source arcs of the type in manufacture at this printing, and this makes it difficult to keep the image directly on the spectrographic slit. It is claimed that this problem has been minimized by some manufacturers.

Plasma jets have been suggested as a convenient high-intensity source for photochemistry.[48a] A commercial vortex stabilized plasma jet with an input of 24.8 kw has an output of 2.6 kw of ultraviolet light (2000–4000 A) from a 1 cm × 0.3 cm area.

Some spectacular photochemical applications of lasers can be expected because the laser produces a high-intensity, well-collimated, coherent, monochromatic beam of light.[48b,c] Development in this field is proceeding rapidly, and several companies manufacture lasers which provide far-visible and near-infrared, highly collimated, monochromatic radiation. At this writing no lasers are available commercially for most of the visible and the ultraviolet ranges; such lasers are possible in theory, research in this area is active, and ultraviolet lasers should be available in time.

7-2 THE ISOLATION OF "MONOCHROMATIC" RADIATION FOR PHOTOCHEMICAL USE

Although the full arc spectrum is often employed in synthetic photochemical work or in the study of free radical reactions, quantitative determinations of the nature and efficiency of primary photochemical processes normally require irradiation with isolated wavelengths or regions of light; this is necessary particularly for the gas-phase systems, since the importance of the different competing primary photochemical processes is often a function of the energy or wavelength of the absorbed quantum. For many liquid- and solid-phase systems the initial energy of the excited molecule may be quite unimportant in determining the reaction mode, since deactivation of all excited molecules to the same lower vibrational levels of the excited states occurs quickly. However, even for these systems experiments using monochromatic light in different wavelength regions of the absorption spectrum of the reactant are necessary to establish the independence or dependence of the quantum yield on wavelength.

There are many advantages in the use of monochromatic light in the study of photochemical reactions. It is possible to determine directly and accurately the data required for quantum yield determination, the intensity of the incident light, and the fraction of the light which is absorbed. In addition one may often make a choice of wavelengths for a given experiment which minimizes the "hot" radical effects and the undesirable photochemical transformation of certain products. It is possible to estimate approximate "average" quantum yields of products in experiments using the full spectrum of an arc from a knowledge of the arc energy distribution, the absorption spectrum and absorption coefficients of the reactant, and from studies using a suitable actinometer system, but such quantum yield information is qualitative in nature and is often of questionable value in the interpretation of the photochemical mechanism. For these and other reasons it is important for us to consider the current methods of isolating monochromatic light and bands of radiation from the full arc spectrum.

7-2A   Monochromators for the Production
of Monochromatic Light

Both refraction (prism type) monochromators and diffraction (grating) instruments are used by photochemists today. These monochromators, employed in conjunction with a medium-pressure mercury arc (or other high-intensity line source), are excellent sources of high-intensity monochromatic light for photochemical use. They offer the best means of isolation of certain wavelength regions for which the available chemical or glass filter systems are inadequate today, that is, the lines at 2537, 2652, 2804, and 3025–2967 A.

In order to cause observable chemical change in a reasonable period of time at least 10^{14} quanta/sec should be absorbed by the reactant. At this rate of light absorption and with a quantum yield of a specific product equal to unity, a relatively long 15 hour exposure will be required to form 200 μl (STP) of the specific gaseous product (about 10^{-5} mole). The demands for high-intensity monochromatic light in photochemistry cannot be met by the usual equipment designed for spectrographic use. Fortunately the needs of the photochemist are rather easily satisfied with special monochromators having large slits, small f-numbers,* and large optics. Although the resolution of fine-line structure is imperative for the spectroscopist and intensity is of little concern, a high intensity is desired by the photochemist, who need not resolve the closely spaced lines of a given group; he need only isolate the closely spaced group of lines from its relatively widely spaced neighbors in most of his work. Thus, the resolution of the 3126–3132 A group is unimportant to the photochemist, since the energy of the quanta at the extremes of this "3130 A" band varies insignificantly (91.46 to 91.22 kcal/mole), but it is desirable that this "line" should be resolved from its 3341 and 3025 A neighbors.

In many long-established photochemical laboratories, crystal-quartz prism monochromators, constructed by the experimentalist to satisfy his special demands, are still in use.[49] The design of a monochromator which has been of great utility in the laboratories of G. S. Forbes, P. A. Leighton, and F. E. Blacet[50] is shown in Fig. 7-20. The prism P in the monochromator unit (9.5 cm base, 6.4 cm high) is composed of two mirror-image prisms of equal size, one each of d- and l-quartz; this avoids the double-image difficulties inherent in birefringent optical components. The fused

---

* The f-number of a lens is equal to the ratio of the effective diameter to the focal length of the lens; it is a measure of the light-gathering power of the system. When one considers a point source of light with a lens placed at its focal length away from the light, then the number of quanta which the lens can gather and transmit in a parallel beam is inversely proportional to the square of the f-number.

quartz lenses are of focal length 21 cm (yellow light) and are 7.5 cm in diameter. Lens L_1 is placed 20 cm from the slit S_1. The design fixes the direction of the emergent beam to that of the photolysis cell axis. The operator selects the desired wavelength by rotating the monochromator about the pivot located under the lens L_2. This point is attached to a rectangular bar which rides in a slotted track; it serves to fix the direction of the beam relative to the reaction cell and allows movement of the monochromator toward or away from the slit S_2 to focus the slit image of the desired wavelength upon it. (Methods of focusing the invisible ultraviolet lines are described in Sec. 7-3D.)

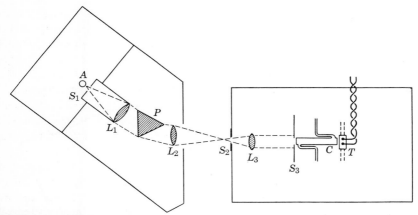

Fig. 7-20   A crystal quartz monochromator for photochemical use; design of Forbes, Leighton, and Blacet;[50] see text.

The medium-pressure arc A is placed as close as is practicable to the entrance slit S_1; this slit is adjusted to a width of about 1.5 mm and is in the shape of an arc of 30 mm length to provide a rectilinear image at S_2. With the width of the slit S_2 set at about 1 mm, reasonably clean separations of the mercury arc "lines" are possible.

Several designs of reflection grating monochromators suitable for photochemical work have been described.[51] In recent years excellent low-cost replica gratings have become available from optical companies, and there has been renewed interest in the use of grating monochromators in photochemical work. The grating instruments have an advantage of higher resolution in the visible range, where the refraction of light at an air-quartz interface is low. The prism monochromators concentrate the energy within a single spectrum, and the losses of light encountered are from surface reflections and absorption in the optical material of the

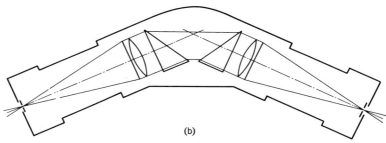

Fig. 7-21   (a) A commercial quartz prism monochromator useful in photochemical work; Farand Optical Co., model 300 UV.   (b) Diagram of the optical system for the Farand model 300 UV monochromator.

prism and lenses. With the diffraction grating monochromator, however, the light entering the instrument is dispersed into several spectra which correspond to the different orders. Although modern gratings are made with a carefully controlled groove shape which causes a high percentage of the total energy to appear in a single order, the grating instruments are subject to overlapping of orders, and care must be exercised to recognize this undesirable characteristic and correct it by using a suitable filter to separate the interfering orders of impurity light. Impurities in the emergent beam due to scattered radiation may be a little less serious with expensive grating instruments than with those having prism optics, but stray light is a problem with moderate- and low-priced grating mono-chromators. The replica grating instruments are considerably less ex-pensive to construct than crystal-quartz prism equipment with the same optical "speed" (f-number). However, the advantages of the grating instruments are somewhat offset by their less rigid, less permanent character. Thus, the reflection of the replica gratings may be seriously altered in the usual polluted atmosphere of the chemical laboratory, and the gratings are easily scratched and broken.

The absorption of light by quartz at wavelengths less than 2000 A (Schumann region) demands LiF, CaF_2, or other transparent optical components for prism instruments used in the isolation of the short-wavelength ultraviolet. (See the discussion in Sec. 7-3A of the transmission of various optical materials employed in systems.) Thus the vacuum reflection grating monochromator seems best suited for use in the Schumann region.

Commercial models of both prism and grating monochromators are available (e.g., see Figs. 7-21 and 7-22).

(a)

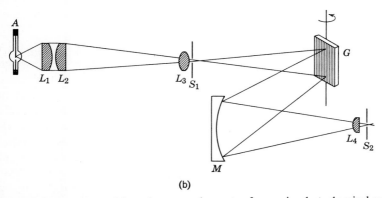

(b)

Fig. 7-22   (a) A commercial grating monochromator for use in photochemical work; Bausch and Lomb, Inc., model 33-86-25-05 monochromator and 33-86-36-01 mercury-arc source and power supply. (b) Design of the optical system for the Bausch and Lomb monochromator; A, point-source mercury arc; L_1 and L_2, condenser system; L_3, slit collective lens; S_1, entrance slit; G, diffraction grating; M, concave mirror; L_4, aberration corrector lens; S_2, exit slit.

There is a major disadvantage in the use of both prism and grating monochromators in photochemical work; the rectangularly shaped image of the slit leads to a light beam within a photolysis cell which is not compatible with the usual cell shape and is far from homogeneous in intensity in the horizontal direction across the beam. This is a far cry from the ideal distribution of intensity for kinetic studies; here a homogeneous, circular-cross-section light beam which fills the entire cell volume is desired. Point-focusing monochromators would be of some interest for use with the new point-source lamps. A more nearly ideal geometry of the beam would be obtainable for photochemical experiments, but the loss of light purity by use of the partial-continuum emitting point source would have to be tolerated.

Plane polarized monochromatic light is easily generated by reflection of an incident monochromatic beam from a stack of thin quartz plates (or glass plates for visible work), arranged so that the light is taken off at the calculated polarizing angle for the wavelength and optical material employed (see Sec. 1-3C). Linear polarizers constructed of quartz or other optical materials are available from commerical sources.

Techniques have been described in the literature for the production of high intensities of circularly or elliptically polarized light for the study of the photochemistry of asymmetric molecules.[52,53] (See Sec. 1-3C.) Quarter-wave plates made from crystal quartz for designated wavelengths can be purchased from optical companies.

7-2B The Production of Monochromatic Radiation Using Chemical and Glass Filters

There is an increasing use of chemical and glass filter systems for the isolation of monochromatic light by photochemists. This trend, which is evident even within the strongholds of classical quantitative photochemistry, is not surprising, however, since chemical and glass filter systems now available, when used with a medium-pressure mercury arc, provide a purity and an intensity of monochromatic light which are often higher than those obtainable from conventional photochemical monochromator systems. For example, Hunt and Davis[54] describe a good band pass chemical filter for isolation of the 3130 A band of the medium-pressure mercury arc (components shown in Table 7-5). It transmits about 19% of the incident 3126–3132 A radiation with less than a few tenths of a per cent of extraneous ultraviolet radiation; see Fig. 7-25. This is probably a little better filtering action than that obtained by isolating the 3130 A band of equal intensity with the conventional photochemical monochromator systems.

A multitude of chemical filters for isolating regions of the visible and ultraviolet have been proposed through the years.[55] In Tables 7-3 to 7-11 and in Figs. 7-23 to 7-30 we have summarized the properties of the chemical

TABLE 7-3   Filter Solution for Isolation of the 2537 A Region from the Medium-Pressure Hg-Arc Spectrum

Components:	(1)	(2)	(3)	(4)
	$NiSO_4 \cdot 6H_2O$, 27.6 gram/100 cc aqueous solution	$CoSO_4 \cdot 7H_2O$, 8.4 grams/100 cc aqueous solution	I_2, 0.108 gram plus KI, 0.155 gram/1000 cc water	Cl_2 gas, 1 atm at 25°
Path length:	5 cm	5 cm	1 cm	5 cm
Testing time:	95 hr	95 hr	25 hr	25 hr

Light stability: (T represents per cent transmission; $+\Delta T/T$ represents an increase in transparency.)

$\Delta T/T = +4.2\%$/hr at 2537 A during first 4 hr; $+0.02\%$/hr at 2537 A during subsequent time	$\Delta T/T =$ $+1.5\%$/hr at 2537 A during first 4 hr; $+0.05\%$/hr at 2537 A during subsequent time.	$\Delta T/T =$ $+0.4\%$/hr at 2537 A; linear with time.	T constant

Impurity light: approximate relative intensity of the medium-pressure Hg-arc lines after transmission through the "2537 A" filter: 2482 A (13); *2537 A (100)*; 2571 A (28); 2652–2655 A (11).

Remarks:

1. A 4 hr preirradiation of $NiSO_4$ and $CoSO_4$ raises the transmittance to a value which is then fairly constant with continued irradiation. This high transmittance value is maintained when the light is cut off, even for several days. In some cases, when the preirradiated solutions were allowed to stand in the cells in the dark for 10 days or more, the transmittance of $NiSO_4$ was observed to have dropped somewhat. A 30 min irradiation then restored the former high transmittance. These observations are real but remain unexplained. *For use of the $NiSO_4$ and $CoSO_4$ solutions in quantitative work it is apparent that a preirradiation of the solutions is essential.* This fact does not seem to be widely appreciated.

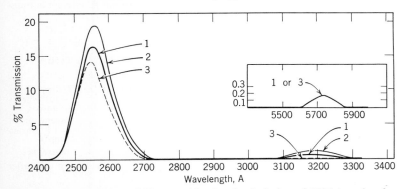

Fig. 7-23 Transmission of filter combination for isolation of 2537 A region from the medium-pressure mercury-arc spectrum. Curve 3, filter as described in Table 7-3 after preirradiation of $NiSO_4$ and $CoSO_4$ solutions; curve 1, same as 3 but Cl_2 cell removed; curve 2, same as 1 after 25 hr irradiation.

2. Attempts were made to replace the $NiSO_4$ and $CoSO_4$ compartments by a single compartment containing both $NiSO_4$ and $CoSO_4$ at the same concentrations as above. If this solution was kept in the dark, its transmittance remained constant, but during the first 4 hr of irradiation its transmittance at 2537 A dropped from 62% to 45%. Continued irradiation slowly increased the transmittance; however, after 45 hr, no plateau was reached, and the solution was still less transparent than the combination $NiSO_4$-$CoSO_4$ in separate compartments after 4 hr of irradiation.

3. The KI_3 solution should be made accurately to the given concentrations to ensure the best monochromaticity. Iodine should be put into solution by adding I_2 and KI to 305 ml of water with stirring before diluting to 1 liter.

4. The KI_3 solution loses I_2 by volatilization comparatively easily, particularly in a small 1 cm cell. Using a well-stoppered cell with ground-glass stopper reduces the loss but does not eliminate it. The loss of iodine is accompanied by an increase in transparency observed in the dark or upon irradiation; the rate of increase in transparency seemed somewhat higher during irradiation. Sealing the glass stopper with paraffin had no noticeable effect on the rate of increase of transparency. No attempt was made in this study to provide the cell with a permanent glass seal, although this would be recommended.

5. *trans-trans*-1,4-Diphenyl-1,3-butadiene (4.24 mg/100 cc ether or spectro-quality cyclohexane, 1 cm) transmits light between 2600 and 2500 A with a maximum transmission of 46% at 2560 A. The solution was tested for light stability in combination with $NiSO_4$ and $CoSO_4$. It rapidly became more opaque in the 2600 A region and then gradually lost its monochromaticity; $\Delta T/T = -20$ to -25%/hr. This change may be due partly to photoisomerization of the compound [see J. H. Pinckard, B. Willie, and H. Zechmeister, *J. Am. Chem. Soc.*, **70**, 1938 (1948)]. Addition of traces of iodine improved the light stability and helped in retaining the monochromaticity, but the solution was still judged very poor for filter use.

6. The transmission of the combined recommended filter for the 2537 A region is given in Fig. 7-23, curve 3.

TABLE 7-4   Filter Solution for Isolation of the 2652–2655 A Region from the Medium-Pressure Hg-Arc Spectrum

Components:	(1) $NiSO_4 \cdot 6H_2O$, 27.6 grams/100 cc aqueous solution	(2) $CoSO_4 \cdot 7H_2O$, 8.4 grams/100 cc aqueous solution	(3) Cl_2 gas, 1 atm at 25°	(4) KI, 0.170 gram/100 cc aqueous solution
Path length:	5 cm	5 cm	5 cm	1 cm
Testing time:	95 hr	95 hr	24 hr	22 hr

Light stability: (T represents per cent transmission; $+\Delta T/T$ represents an increase in transparency.)

(a) First 4 hr

$\Delta T/T = +4\%$/hr at 2650 A	$\Delta T/T = +1.5\%$/hr at 2650 A	T constant	$\Delta T/T = -5.9$ %/hr at 2650 A

(b) Subsequent hours

$\Delta T/T = +0.016\%$/hr at 2650 A	$\Delta T/T = +0.05\%$/hr at 2650 A	T constant	$\Delta T/T = -1.0\%$/hr at 2650 A (average); -1.8%/hr at 2700 A (average)

Impurity light: approximate relative intensity of the medium-pressure Hg-arc lines after transmission through the 2652-2655 A filter: 2537 A (3); 2571 A (4); *2652–2655 A (100)*; 2700 A (24); 2753 A (9); 2804 A (5).

Remarks:

1. For $NiSO_4$ and $CoSO_4$ stability, see remark 1, Table 7-3, p. 729.

2. The KI solution should be made with highly purified water, made free of air, and handled in the dark. The rate of decrease of transparency is very high at the beginning of the

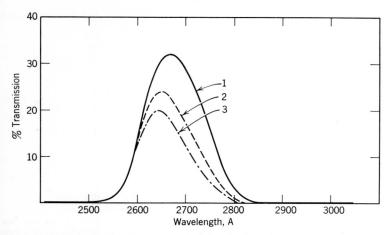

Fig. 7-24   Transmission of filter combination for isolation of the 2652–2655 A region from the medium-pressure mercury-arc spectrum. Curve 1, filter as described in Table 7-4 (preirradiated $NiSO_4$ and $CoSO_4$ solutions); curve 2, same filter after 4 hr irradiation of entire filter; curve 3, same filter after 22 hr irradiation.

irradiation and becomes smaller and smaller as irradiation is continued; no plateau was reached in 24 hr.

3. $KMnO_4$ (0.042 gram/100 cc H_2O, 1 cm) transmits between 2400 and 2930 A, with a maximum transmission of 11.6% at 2700 A. This solution, carefully treated to remove MnO_2, was tested in combination with $NiSO_4$ and $CoSO_4$ and found to become opaque very rapidly when irradiated. The transmittance at 2700 A dropped from 11.6% before irradiation to 4.3% after 15 min, 2.0% after 30 min, and 0.4% after 1 hr irradiation.

4. The transmission of the combined recommended filter for the 2652–2655 A region is given in Fig. 7-24, curve 1.

filters which appear to us to be the best suited for the isolation of mercury arc lines among those which have been reported for use in the visible and ultraviolet regions. Our criteria for selection of these filters were purity of transmitted light, transparency of the filter at the desired line, and photochemical stability of the filter components. Transmission and stability information on each filter is summarized in the tables. All solutions tested for use in the chemical filters were placed in individual, cylindrical quartz cells (internal diameter, 20 mm) with glass stoppers and irradiated by the full light of a medium-pressure, 500 w, Hanovia type 673 A mercury arc. The transmission of each component was followed during irradiation by recording periodically its absorption spectrum versus a reference cell on a Bausch and Lomb Spectronic 505 recording spectrometer. The distance between the front window of the first cell and the arc was 15 cm, and no space was left between cells. Solutions were arranged in the order shown with solution (1) nearest the light, (2) next, etc., to ensure the longest useful life of the filter solutions. The solutions were made with reagent

TABLE 7-5   Filter Solution for Isolation of the 3126–3132 A Region from the Medium-Pressure Hg-Arc Spectrum

Components:	(1)	(2)	(3)	(4)
	$NiSO_4$, 0.178 M, aqueous solution	K_2CrO_4, 5.0×10^{-4}, aqueous solution	Potassium biphthalate, 0.0245 M, aqueous solution	Corning glass filter 7-54 (9863)
Path length:	5 cm	5 cm	1 cm	0.3 cm
Testing time:	115 hr			

Light stability: (T represents per cent transmission; $+\Delta T/T$ represents an increase in transparency.)

$\Delta T/T = +5\%$ during first 2 hr; T constant subsequent hours	T constant	$\Delta T/T = -0.04\%/hr$ at 3130 A; $-1.06\%/hr$ at 3200 A; however, see note 2 below	T constant

Impurity light: approximate relative intensity of the medium-pressure Hg-arc lines after transmission through the "3126–3132 A" filter: 3341 A (~0.3); *3126–3132 A (100)*; 3022–3028 A (~0.2).

Remarks:

1. $NiSO_4$ is to be preferred to $NiCl_2$. The transmittance by $NiCl_2$ was found less constant than that of $NiSO_4$ upon irradiation. The stability of the $NiSO_4$ solution is discussed in remark 1, Table 7-3, p. 729.

2. The light stability of the potassium biphthalate solution can be considerably less than that found for the solution described above; $\Delta T/T$ values may be as high as $-0.3\%/hr$ with some preparations; the transmission of the solution should be checked regularly, since the stability is apparently a function of certain undefined variables. The solution should be prepared by dissolving the salt in hot, freshly boiled water to prevent bacterial mold formation. This solution kept in darkness in a well-stoppered bottle showed no spectral change over a period of 3 months.

3. The transmission of the combined recommended filter for the 3126–3132 A region is given in Fig. 7-25.

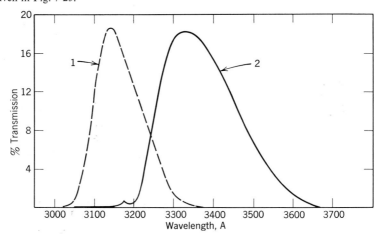

Fig. 7-25 Transmission of the filter combinations for isolation of the 3126–3132 A region (dotted curve 1) and 3341 A region (solid curve 2) from the medium-pressure mercury-arc spectrum; filters described in Tables 7-5 and 7-6, respectively.

TABLE 7-6 Filter Solution for Isolation of the 3341 A Region from the Medium-Pressure Hg-Arc Spectrum

Components:	(1)	(2)	(3)
	$NiSO_4 \cdot 6H_2O$, 10.0 grams/100 cc aqueous solution	Corning glass filter 7-51 (5970)	Naphthalene in isooctane, 1.28 grams/100 cc
Path length:	5 cm	0.5 cm	1 cm

Testing time: 48 hr

Light stability: (T represents per cent transmission; $+\Delta T/T$ represents an increase in transparency.)

$\Delta T/T = +2.5\%/hr$ T constant T constant
at 3340 A during
the first hr;
subsequently T
constant

Impurity light: Approximate relative intensity of the medium-pressure Hg-arc lines after transmission through the "3341 A" filter: 3126–3132 A ($\sim$0); 3341 A (100); 3650–3663 A ($\sim$0); however, see remark 3 below.

Remarks:

1. $NiSO_4$ stability discussed in remark 1, Table 7-3, p. 729.
2. Solution of naphthalene should be kept in a well-stoppered cell. Loss of solvent can be prevented by using a mercury seal in addition to the ground-glass stopper; this is conveniently achieved by slipping a piece of rubber tubing over the cell joint and filling it with mercury.
3. Small impurity from fluorescence of naphthalene (3200–3900 A) may be a problem in some applications of this filter.
4. The transmission of the combined recommended filter for the 3341 region is given in Fig. 7-25.

grade substances when available, and salts were recrystallized when necessary. Demineralized double-distilled water was used for aqueous solution preparation.

The spectral distributions of the resultant filter combinations, shown in Figs. 7-23 to 7-30, were calculated from the measured transmittance of the individual components. Since the transmittance of each component was measured versus a reference cell, the spectral distribution curves give the transmittance of the solutions alone, without taking into account the loss of light intensity due to reflections on the windows. In actual use the filter solutions will transmit from 91% to 78% of the values shown, depending on the number of windows and the nature of the cells used.

TABLE 7-7 Filter Solution for Isolation of the 3650–3663 A Region from the Medium-Pressure Hg-Arc Spectrum

Components:	(1)	(2)	(3)
	$CuSO_4 \cdot 5H_2O$, 5.0 grams/100 cc, aqueous solution	Corning glass filter, 7-37 (5860)	2,7-Dimethyl-3,6-diazocyclohepta-1,6-diene perchlorate, 0.010 gram/100 cc H_2O
Path length:	10 cm	0.5 cm	1 cm

Testing time: 113 hr

Light stability: (T represents per cent transmission; $+\Delta T/T$ represents an increase in transparency.)

$\Delta T/T = +1\%/hr$ first 4 hr; $+0.25\%/hr$ during next 8 hr; T constant after 12 hr T constant T constant

Impurity light: approximate relative intensity of the medium-pressure Hg-arc lines after transmission through the "3650–3663 A" filter: 3341 A ($\sim$0); *3650–3663 A* (*100*); 4045–4078 A ($<$0.2).

Remarks:

1. A 12 hr preirradiation of the $CuSO_4$ vessel will bring the transmittance of the solution to a higher value, which remains constant on continued irradiation. This high value is retained after the light is cut off and the vessel kept in the dark for as long as 1 month.
2. The compound in solution (3) was obtained from the K and K Laboratories, Inc., Jamica, New York.
3. The transmission of the combined recommended filter for the 3650–3663 A region is given in Fig. 7-26.

From an inspection of the filter data it is apparent that with present filters the regions at 2537, 2652–2655, 2804, and 2967–3022 A cannot be isolated well from the spectrum of a medium-pressure arc. It is possible that further improvement of the properties of the nickel-salt-containing filters could be effected by using the nickel sulfate-sorbital complex described by Strait and co-workers.[56]

The chemical filters for isolation of the 1849 A resonance line from 2537 A line of the low-pressure mercury arc have been evaluated by Pertel.[57a]

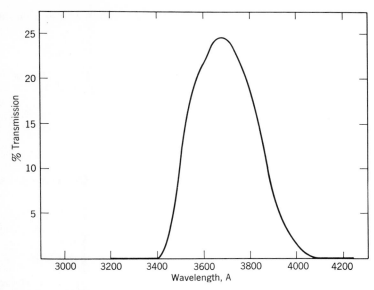

Fig. 7-26   Transmission of filter combination for isolation of the 3650–3663 A region from the medium-pressure mercury-arc spectrum; filter as described in Table 7-7.

He has suggested the use of a 1 mm path of a solution of 9,10-dimethyl-anthracene (3.5×10^{-4} M) in deoxygenated cyclohexane; it transmits 20% at 1849 A and 0.16% at 2537 A. After 13 hours of exposure to the low-pressure arc there was very little change in transmission at these two wavelengths, provided that the solution was degassed and sealed off from oxygen.

Another filter that absorbs the 2537 A resonance line selectively and transmits useful intensities of the 1849 line is a 3 mm plate of lithium fluoride that has been irradiated with ^{60}Co gamma rays.[57b] This filter bleaches with time, but both Martin and Willard[57c] and Holroyd and Pierce[57d] have used it successfully to obtain quantitative data on photolyses at 1849 A. In each case the filter transmission was carefully monitored; it ranged from 10% to 30% at 1849 A transmitting less than 0.04% at 2537 A. The lithium fluoride was reirradiated with gamma rays (a 0.2 Mrad dose) before each photolysis to bring back the absorbancy at 2537 A to an appropriate value (see Refs. 57c and 57d for details).

Many of the filters require the use of a series of Pyrex (for the visible and near-ultraviolet regions) or quartz (for the ultraviolet region) cells of specified path length. Thus one should note that each additional air-fused quartz-aqueous solution interface added between the photolysis cell and

TABLE 7-8   Filter Solution for Isolation of the 4045–4078 A Region from the Medium-Pressure Hg-Arc Spectrum

Components:	(1)	(2)	(3)
	$CuSO_4 \cdot 5H_2O$, 0.44 grams/100 cc 2.7 M NH_4OH	I_2, 0.75 gram/100 cc CCl_4	Quinone hydrochloride, 2.00 grams/100 cc H_2O
Path length:	10 cm	1 cm	1 cm

Testing time: 41 hr

Light stability: (*T* represents per cent transmission; $+\Delta T/T$ represents an increase in transparency.)

$\Delta T/T =$ +0.05%/hr, fairly linear with time	$\Delta T/T =$ +0.05%/hr, fairly linear with time	$\Delta T/T = -3.9$%/hr during first 2 hr; -1.2%/hr subsequent time

Impurity light: approximate relative intensity of the medium-pressure Hg-arc lines after transmission through the "4045-4078 A" filter: 3650–3663 A ($\sim$0); *4045–4078 A (100)*; 4358 A (5).

Remarks:

1. Both components (1) and (2) become slightly more transparent on standing after preparation in the dark and in the light, and at approximately the same rate in dark and in light. Both cells were equipped with a mercury seal (see remark 2 of Table 7-6) to reduce loss of volatile substances. It did not prevent entirely loss of NH_3 from (1) or I_2 from (2); in the latter case reaction with mercury occurs. The rate of increase in transparency of those solutions might be slightly different in different sized cells with glass stoppers. No attempt was made to close the cells hermetically with a glass seal, although this would be recommended.

2. All three components transmit about 7000 A. If transmission in the red and infrared presents a problem, a 5–61 (5562, 5 mm) Corning glass filter may be added to improve the monochromaticity at the expense of the transmittance at 4045–4078 A.

3. The transmission of the combined recommended filter for the 4045–4078 A region is given in Fig. 7-27, curve 1; combined with 5–6l glass filter, curve 2.

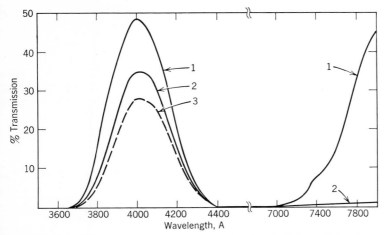

Fig. 7-27   Transmission of the filter combination for isolation of the 4045–4078 A region from the medium-pressure mercury-arc spectrum. Curve 1, filter as described in Table 7-8; curve 2, same as 1 plus Corning glass 5-61 (5562), 5 mm; curve 3 same as 1 after 41 hr irradiation.

TABLE 7-9   Filter Solutions for Isolation of the 4358 A Region from the Medium-Pressure Hg-Arc Spectrum

Components for filter A:	(1)	(2)
	CuSO$_4$·5H$_2$O, 0.44 gram/100 cc 2.7 M NH$_4$OH	NaNO$_2$, 7.50 grams/100 cc aqueous solution
Path length:	10 cm	10 cm

Testing time: 74 hr

Light stability: (T represents per cent transmission; $+\Delta T/T$ represents an increase in transparency.)

$$\Delta T/T = +0.05\%/hr \qquad \Delta T/T = +0.02\%/hr$$

Impurity light: Approximate relative intensity of the medium-pressure Hg-arc lines after transmission through the "4358 A" filter: 4045-4078 A (<1); *4358 A (100)*; 5461 A ($\sim$0).

Remarks:

1. About CuSO$_4$–NH$_4$OH solution see Table 7-8, remark 1.
2. The NaNO$_2$ solution ages slowly in the dark; it becomes more transparent, $\Delta T/T = +0.06\%/hr$, and reaches a constant transmittance 3-5 days after it is prepared. It is recommended that the solution age in the dark for a few days before use.

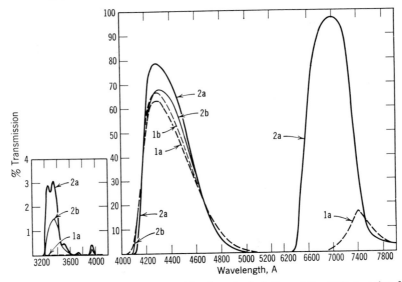

Fig. 7-28   Transmission of filter combinations for isolation of the 4358 A region from the medium-pressure mercury-arc spectrum. Curve 1a, filter A of Table 7-9; curve 1b, filter A after 74 hr irradiation; curve 2a, filter B of Table 7-9 without plate glass; curve 2b, filter B after 90 hr irradiation.

Components for filter B [A. Buraway and A. G. Reach, *Nature*, **181**, 762 (1958)]:

(1)	(2)	(3)
Plate glass (transmission appreciable for only $\lambda > 3150$ A)	9,10-Dibromoanthracene, 20 mg/100 cc toluene	Crystal violet, 2.5 mg/100 cc 95% ethanol
Path length: 0.5 cm	1 cm	5 cm
Testing time: 110 hr		
Light stability:		
	$\Delta T/T \cong -0.1\%/hr$; smaller during first hours, higher during last hours	T constant

Remarks:

1. The plate glass may be omitted if the 9,10-dibromoanthracene is placed in a Pyrex cell instead of a quartz cell. The short ultraviolet radiations transmitted by quartz were found to cause a very fast decrease of transmittance of solution (2). The change of the solution placed in a quartz vessel, without plate glass protection, after 3 hr irradiation is the same as after 90 hr irradiation with plate glass protection.

2. A 3% transmittance of 3340 A as well as 97% transmittance at 7000 A may be a problem in some applications.

3. The vessels should be well stoppered to prevent evaporation of solvent; a mercury seal is efficient (see remark 2 of Table 7-6).

4. The transmissions of filter combinations A and B are shown in Fig. 7-28. Both combinations have excellent light stability and filtering properties; solution A may be favored since it has much lower impurity transmission in the red.

TABLE 7-10   Filter Solutions for Isolation of the 5461 A Region from the Medium-Pressure Hg-Arc Spectrum

Components:	(1)	(2)
	$CuCl_2 \cdot 2H_2O$, 20.0 grams plus $CaCl_2$ (anhyd.), 27.0 grams/100 cc aqueous solution, slightly acidified with HCl	Neodymium nitrate, 60 grams/100 cc aqueous solution
Path length:	1 cm	5 cm
Testing time:	96 hr	
Light stability:	Transmission constant with time	

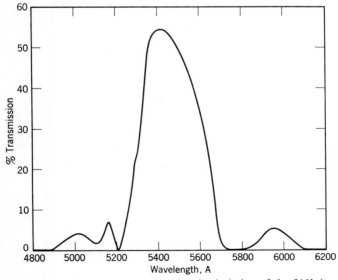

Fig. 7-29   Transmission of filter combination for isolation of the 5461 A region from the medium-pressure mercury-arc spectrum; filter as described in Table 7-10.

Impurity light: approximate relative intensity of the medium-pressure Hg-arc lines after transmission through the "5461 A" filter: 4358 A (~0); *5461 A (100)*; 5770–5790 A (~0).

Remarks:

1. Solutions (1) and (2) should be filtered to clarify or remove any trace of precipitate.

2. The transmission of the combined recommended filter for the 5461 A region is given in Fig. 7-29.

TABLE 7-11   Filter Solutions for Isolation of the 5770–5790 A Region from the Medium-Pressure Hg-Arc Spectrum

Components for filter A:	(1)	(2)
	$CuCl_2 \cdot 2H_2O$, 10.0 grams plus $CaCl_2$ (anhyd.), 30.0/grams/100 cc aqueous solution, slightly acidified with HCl	$K_2Cr_2O_7$, 3.00 grams/100 cc aqueous solution
Path length:	1 cm	10 cm

Testing time: 76 hr

Light stability: transmission of both solutions constant with time.

Impurity light: approximate relative intensity of the medium-pressure Hg-arc lines after transmission through the "5770–5790 A" filter: 5461 A (~0); *5770–5790 A (100)*.

Remarks:

1. Solution (1) should be filtered to clarify.

2. The similar filter suggested by E. J. Bowen (*Chemical Aspects of Light,* Second Edition, Clarendon Press, Oxford, 1946, p. 278) used 15 grams of $K_2Cr_2O_7/200$ cc H_2O, 2 cm path. Combined with component (1), this filter would transmit 36.5% at 5770–5790 A and 1.3% at 5460 A; the filter proposed here transmits only 30.7% as 5770 A and 31.5% at 5790 A and 0% at 5460 A.

Components for filter B:		
	$CuSO_4 \cdot 5H_2O$, 11.1 grams/100 cc aqueous solution	$K_2Cr_2O_7$, 3.00 grams/100 cc aqueous solution
Path length:	1 cm	10 cm

Testing time: 68 hr

Light stability: transmission of both solutions constant with time.

Remarks:

1. The B filter solution combination transmits more highly at 5770–5790 A than the A filter, but the cut-off of B is not as sharp on the long-wavelength sides, and B transmits highly at 7400 A.

2. The transmission of filter combinations A and B are shown in Fig. 7-30.

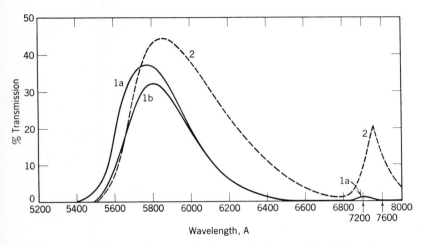

Fig. 7-30   Transmission of filter combinations for isolation of the 5770–5790 A region of the medium-pressure mercury-arc spectrum. Curve 1a, filter A as described in Table 7-11 except that 5 cm path of $K_2Cr_2O_7$ solution used; curve 1b, filter A as recommended in Table 7-11; curve 2, filter B as described in Table 7-11.

the light source decreases the transmitted light energy by approximately 4%; each air-fused quartz-low pressure gas interface decreases it by about 7%. The reflection losses can be minimized by using a multicompartment filter cell with shared windows; see Fig. 7-31. In principle such a three-compartment quartz cell containing water will transmit about 91% of the incident visible or ultraviolet light, while three separate water-containing quartz cells in series will transmit only about 78% of the incident light. For use in the ultraviolet the cells may be made entirely of fused quartz (a tricky glassblowing job), or quartz windows can be sealed to Pyrex-tubing spacers with a suitable unreactive, insoluble cement (e.g., Aryldite, Ceba Pharmaceutical Co.). A multicomponent cell should be placed in the light beam so that the most light stable of the solutions (copper, cobalt, or nickel salt solutions) is toward the light source, and the least stable component furthest from the source. Certain of the least stable components noted in Tables 7-3 and 7-11 need periodic renewal. Salts which are particularly free of iron impurity must be used in the preparation of the

Fig. 7-31   A three-compartment quartz solution filter cell with optical paths of 5, 5, and 1 cm; suitable for use with the 3125–3132 A filter of Table 7-5 or others; the two windows in the body of the cell are common to two solutions and minimize reflection losses.

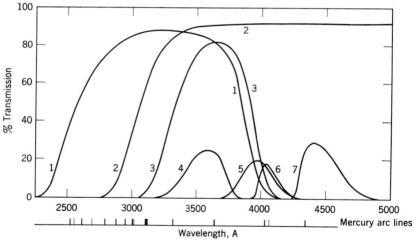

Fig. 7-32   Transmissions of some common glass filters useful for the 2500–4700 A region; filter designations of the Corning Glass Works, Optical Sales Dept., Corning, N.Y. The number of the curve in the figure, the Corning color specification number, and the glass code number (in parentheses) are given: *1*, 7–54 (9863); *2*, 0–53 (7740, Pyrex plate, 2 mm thick, transmission not controlled); *3*, 7–51 (5970); *4*, 7–37 (5860); *5*, 7–51½ (5970½) plus 3–75 (3060); *6*, 7–51½ (5970½) plus 3–74 (3391); *7*, 3–73′ (3389²) plus 7–59 (5850); data of Sill.[59]

filters, or poor ultraviolet transmission will result. It may be necessary to jacket the side walls of the filter cell and cool them with circulating water to protect the solutions and cell seals (in the case of cemented windows) when placement near the hot arc or a photolysis cell thermostat is required.

A number of useful commercial glass filters are available for isolation of mercury-arc lines in the visible range; in Figs. 7-32 and 7-33 are shown the transmission properties of Corning commercial glass filters suitable for this purpose.[59] Some similar filters are supplied by other companies in the United States and overseas (Bausch and Lomb Optical Co., Baird Atomic Inc., Farrand Optical Co., Jena Optical Works, Eastman Kodak Co., Ilford Ltd., Chance). Filters available in England have been reviewed by Nicholas and Pollak.[58] It is seen from the spectra of Figs. 7-32 and 7-33 that any desired visible line from a medium-pressure mercury arc can be separated cleanly through the use of glass filters. No such series of filters have been developed for the ultraviolet range. However, certain glass filters are valuable additions to chemical filter systems for the ultraviolet,

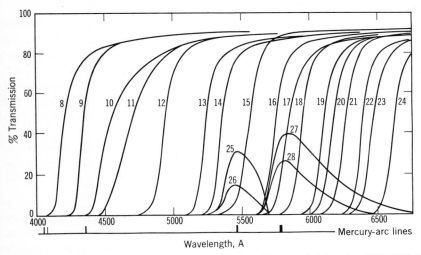

Fig. 7-33   Transmission of some commercial glass filters useful for the 4200–6900 A region; filter designations of the Corning Glass Works, Optical Sales Dept., Corning, N.Y. The number of the curve in the figure, the Corning color specification number, and the glass code number (in parentheses) are given: 8, 3–73 (3389); 9, 3–73′ (3389²); 10, 3–72′ (3387²); 11, 3–72″ (3387³); 12, 3–70′ (3384²); 13, 3–69 (3486); 14, 3–70 (3484); 15, 3–67 (3482); 16, 3–66 (3480); 17, 2–73 (2434); 18, 2–63 (2424); 19, 2–62 (2418); 20, 2–61 (2412); 21, 2–60 (2408); 22, 2–59 (2404); 23, 2–58 (2403); 24, 2–64 (2030); 25, 4–96 (9782) plus 1–60 (5120) plus 3–68 (3484); 26, 5–56 (5031) plus 1–60 (5120) plus 3–68 (3484); 27, 3–66 (3480) plus 4–97 (9788); 28, 3–66 (3480) plus 4–76 (9780); data of Sill.[59]

as noted in the components in Tables 7-3 to 7-11. In Figs. 7-32 and 7-33 are summarized the absorption spectra of the Corning 7-37, 7-51, and 7-54 ultraviolet transmitting filters commonly employed in ultraviolet filter combinations, several useful sharp cut-off filters, and Pyrex glass. A useful set of more complete spectral curves for the Corning glass filters has been published by Sill.[59]

Certain precautions should be observed in the use of glass filters:

1. If the filter glasses are to be used in very intense light and/or they are placed so that they may be heated by the lamp or photolysis cell housing, they should be mounted in a Pyrex water-cooled trough (visible region) or a quartz-windowed water-cooled trough (ultraviolet region). Most of the commercial glass filters are not heat resistant (they are designated HR by Corning if they are heat resistant), and they will crack if there is a significant temperature gradient across them. The trough with its windows and the cooling water (distilled H_2O for ultraviolet use) not only will control the temperature of the filters but also will absorb an appreciable fraction of the unwanted ultraviolet and infrared frequencies emitted by the lamp and will extend the life of the filters.

2. The homogeneity and the transmission characteristics of commercial glass filters may not be all that the purchaser expects from the typical transmission data provided by the company. Some commercial ultraviolet-transmitting filters may contain areas opaque to the ultraviolet.[60] Therefore the actual transmission properties of a filter should be determined experimentally for the particular area of the filter which will intercept the light beam in the optical train of the photochemical system in which it is to be employed.

3. The transmission of the glass filter should be checked occasionally, say after every 100 hours of use, to detect any undesirable changes in the transmission curve. Certain filters age rapidly; others remain efficient for many hundreds of hours of use in intense light.

The Wratten (Eastman Kodak Co.) filters and other commercial gelatin-containing filters are most useful for isolation of light of relatively low intensity, for example, in fluorescence measurements, etc.; they are more susceptible to change in transmission properties than the glass filters when used in very high-intensity beams.

Interference filters for frequencies of light in the visible range are available from several companies (Baird Atomic, Inc., Cambridge, Mass.; Bausch and Lomb Optical Co., Rochester, N.Y.; Photovolt Corporation, New York, N.Y.; Axler Associates, Inc., Corona, N.Y.; Barr and Stroud, Inc., Glasgow, Scotland; etc.). Conventional types consist of two semitransparent evaporated metal films on glass plates which are separated by a transparent layer of a thickness comparable to the wavelength of light. The filter reflects all incident light except for some characteristic band.

A much narrower band filter with very high peak transmission is offered by some companies; it is constructed of 5–25 non-metallic layers of alternating high and low refractive indices. Manufacturers claim that peak

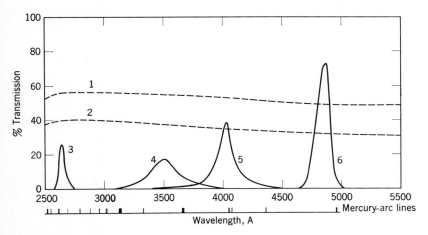

Fig. 7-34 Transmission of some uniform density and interference filters. Curve 1, "50%" uniform-density filter; curve 2, "35%" uniform-density filter; curve 3, Christiansen-type filter for isolation of 2654 A (after Sinsheimer and Loofbourow[61g]); curve 4, commercial interference filter for ultraviolet work; note the broad band passed; curve 5, commercial interference filter for visible work; poor quality, broad band; curve 6, "square wave" commercial filter for visible work (Baird Atomic's blue filter, B-3 series).

transmissions up to 90% can be attained, and the half-peak width can be as small as 40 A. Many commercial interference filters are sold today which have transmission bands as broad as or broader than those of comparable glass filters. Tracings of the transmission curves of two types available in commercial interference filters are shown in Fig. 7-34. Filter 5, provided presumably for isolation of the 4045 line of the mercury arc, is poorer than commercial glass or chemical filter solutions in its properties. The so-called "squared-wave filter" 6, shown in Fig. 7-34 (Baird Atomic's blue filter, B-3 series), has a much narrower band pass and greater peak transmission, and filters of this quality are quite useful for most photochemical work.

For the visible range it is possible to obtain today excellent interference filters, but all filters prepared to isolate a given wavelength range do not have the same transmission properties; hence caution must be exercised by the buyer. To the authors' knowledge there are no completely satisfactory interference filters for the ultraviolet range at present; note the band of frequencies passed by the ultraviolet interference filter 4 shown in Fig. 7-34. Interference filters offer in principle several advantages over other types of visible filters: they do not become excessively warm in use, since practically all the radiation which is not transmitted is reflected; they are stable to heat up to about 80°C; most of them cannot fade or change their transmission properties seriously since the nature of the filtering action does not depend on light absorption.

Attention should be called to the interesting Christiansen filter, which has received relatively little attention in recent years.[61] It is based on the principle that a finely divided solid suspended in a liquid will have a minimum reflection and scatter (maximum transmission) for that wavelength of the incident light for which the refractive indices of the solid and liquid phases are equal. Usually the densities and hence the refractive indices of the solid and liquid phases will vary at unequal rates as the temperature is changed, so that for each new temperature at which the filter is fixed the refractive indices of the solid and liquid will become equal at some different wavelength, and the maximum in the transmission curve will shift. Thus by control of the temperature the same filter can be used to isolate bands over a wide range of wavelengths. A suspension of crown glass in methyl benzoate has been used to obtain maxima in the range 6800–4600 A (temperature 18–50°),[61c,d] and fused quartz particles suspended in a solution of benzene and ethanol gave maxima in the 3800–2800 A range (temperature 15–50°).[61e] Decahydronaphthalene and cyclohexane together with quartz chips can be used effectively for isolation of wavelengths down to about 2400 A.[61g] If these systems are employed, following the geometrical arrangement described by the workers, the filters have excellent transmission properties at the maxima, and the band width is comparable to or narrower than that of other more conventional filter types. With the proper choice of liquid and solid a very light stable filter is possible. Very close temperature control is necessary, since the maximum transmission may shift as much as 100 A/degree. Curve 3 of Fig. 7-34 shows the transmission of a typical Christiansen-type filter for isolation of 2654 A.[61g]

Uniform-density filters are an invaluable addition to any photochemical laboratory. The most reliable means of intensity variation in photolyses with continuous illumination can be effected by interposition of such filters in the light path. They can provide a quick check on the linearity of the response of phototube detectors, and they are useful for many other purposes. A uniform-density filter may be prepared by the vacuum deposition of thin metal films on quartz plates; they can be made in the laboratory or purchased from commercial sources for any desired lowered transmissions. The transmission of such a quartz base filter is rather independent of wavelength over the entire visible and ultraviolet range. See curves 1 and 2 for "50%" and "35%" transmission uniform-density filters shown in Fig. 7-34. A relatively few filters can cover an enormous range of light intensities. For example, the use of a stable light source operated at a given set of conditions together with 50, 25, 5, and 1% transmission filters allows variation of the incident light intensity (using individual filters and combinations of filters) in a series of controlled increments: 100, 50, 25, 12.5, 5, 1.25, 1, 0.625, 0.05, and 0.00625% of the incident light.

7-3   THE DESIGN OF PHOTOCHEMICAL REACTION SYSTEMS

A reaction vessel for ordinary synthetic work may be as simple as a Pyrex flask. Place the flask in a thermostat, and it is a suitable reactor for some kinetic studies. However, such simple equipment is rarely satisfactory for even qualitative photochemical studies. In the design of reaction systems for photochemical studies there are peculiar complications which must be faced; provision must be made for the introduction of an important additional reactant, namely, the light. The proper choice of construction materials must be made so that the desired wavelengths of light will be transmitted to the reactant. The proper positioning of the light source, lenses, stops, and detectors, the thermostating of the reaction vessel with continued access to the light source and light detector system, and many other problems are peculiar to photochemical research. In this section we will consider some of the common solutions to these design problems.

7-3A   The Choice of Construction Materials for the Reaction Cell and Optical Parts

In Table 7-12 the approximate wavelengths (A) for transmissions for 50, 30, and 10% of the incident light are shown for various thicknesses of optical materials. The ultraviolet transmission of many materials is quite dependent on the method of synthesis, the amount of iron impurity present, and other factors often difficult to control, so the figures of Table 7-12 represent only the order of magnitude of the cut-off wavelengths. For example, Taft[62] found that 31 different $\frac{1}{16}$ in. samples of fused quartz from two manufacturers varied in their transmission at 2000 A from 84 to 73%.

TABLE 7-12 Approximate Wavelength Limits for Transmission of Various Optical Materials and Water near Room Temperature

Material	Thickness, mm	Approximate λ (A) for % Transmission Indicated		
		50%	30%	10%
Window glass (standard)	1	3160	3120	3070
	3	3300	3230	3140
	10	3520	3420	3300
Optical (white crown) glass	1.8	3270	3200	3090
Pyrex (Corning 774)	1	3060	2970	2800
	2	3170	3090	2970
	4	3300	3190	3100
Corex D [Pyrex, Corning 9-53 (9700)]	1	2780	2670	2500
	2	2880	2800	2670
	4	3040	2920	2810
Corex A	2.9	2480	2430	2400
Vycor 790	2			>2540
Vycor 791	1	2150	2130	2120
	2	2230	2170	2130
	4	2360	2250	2170
Quartz, crystal	5	1850		
	10	1930	1920	1860
Quartz, clear fused (General Electric Co.)	10	1940	1810	1720
Suprasil (Englehard Industries, Inc.)	10	1700	1680	1660
Sapphire (synthetic, Linde Air Products)	0.5			1425
Fluorite (CaF_2), natural	5	1350		
	10	1570	1450	1380
CaF_2, synthetic (Linde Air Products)	3			1220
Lithium fluoride (synthetic)	5	1070		
	10	1420	1270	1150
Plexiglas (polymethylmethacrylate)	2.5	3220	3100	2970
	5.0	3380	3250	3110
	10.0	3500	3420	3260
Water (distilled)	20	1880	1860	1850
	40	1920	1880	1860
	80	2020	1940	1880

The variations in transmission are most serious at the shorter wavelengths.

An inspection of the data of Table 7-12 provides a basis for the selection of construction materials for photochemical reaction cells, lamp cooling jackets, windows, lenses, and any other optical pieces through which the light must travel to reach the reactant.

1. For photochemical experiments in the visible or long-wavelength ultraviolet (3660 A) ordinary Pyrex or soft-glass materials are suitable. Of course, if an immersion mounting of the lamp is placed within the reaction vessel, as is the case in many preparative set-ups, a Pyrex reaction vessel is suitable (in fact, desirable because of the protection given the operator by its filtering action) for experiments with any wavelengths. The cooling jacket on the lamp must be constructed of materials transparent to the desired wavelengths.

2. For experiments at wavelengths greater than 3000 A, Corvex D or Vycor 790 may be used.

3. When wavelengths as short as 2500 A are desired, Vycor 791 and possibly Corex A are suitable.

4. For equipment to be useful in experiments to wavelengths as short as 2000 A, fused quartz is the most satisfactory construction material. Fused quartz of transmission equal to or better than that of the best crystal quartz is now available commercially. The choice of quartz (or Vycor 791 and Corex A) is desirable even in many cases when the high ultraviolet transmission is not necessary. Quartz has a very small thermal coefficient of expansion and is ideal for use in systems which must withstand the sudden and extreme temperature changes often necessary in experimental operations of degassing, distillation of the reactant in low-temperature photolysis in solvent glasses, etc. Furthermore, only one apparatus need be built if it is made of quartz, and the investigator is not restricted to any one range; glass or other filters can be introduced for the experiments in which the short wavelengths are not desired.

5. Synthetic CaF_2 crystals are the most satisfactory for experiments at wavelengths to 1200 A. CaF_2 is a little harder, is scratched less easily, and can be ground more readily than LiF. The transparency of LiF extends to slightly shorter wavelengths and is useful to about 1100 A. The transmission of synthetic LiF shows gross variations in the short-wavelength range which seem dependent on the procedures employed in the synthesis. The transparency of each individual piece of LiF which is intended for use should be measured.[63]

6. For photochemical work in the extreme ultraviolet ($\lambda < 1100$ A) very thin windows of LiF or windowless reaction cells are necessary.

7. One must be aware of the fact that the absorption of short-wavelength radiation by most optical materials increases markedly with increase in temperature.[126]

Note that there are many different types of soft glass, Pyrex, Corex, Vycor, and quartz. For example, windows of Corex D and Vycor 790 are opaque and useless for experiments at wavelengths over most of the ultraviolet range, while Corex A and Vycor 791 are transparent and most useful. It is evident that in ordering materials the number of the glass as well as the trademark of the class of material must be given.

7-3B The Design of Reaction Vessels
for Synthetic Photochemistry

The most important considerations in the design of vessels for synthetic work are the following: (1) the location of the arc with respect to the reactant so as to irradiate the reactant with the maximum possible intensity of the useful light, and (2) the proper choice of construction materials for the arc cooling jacket or other parts between the lamp and the reactant. Obviously the best geometrical arrangement of parts to satisfy condition (1) is to have the arc placed in the center of the reaction vessel and surrounded on all sides by the reactant. This is very nearly accomplished in the simple systems shown in Figs. 7-35a,b,c (available commercially from Hanovia). Water is passed through the cooling jacket to maintain temperature control. The medium-pressure mercury arcs (Fig. 7-35a) or the low-pressure resonance lamps (Fig. 7-35b) may be used to obtain the desired wavelength region. Large units available for industrial-scale photochemical synthesis are also available; see Fig. 7-35c.

If one plans to use short-wavelength ultraviolet, the absorption of the tap water at 2537 A should be checked for a path length equivalent to that in the condenser; this may be a serious problem in some areas, and it may be necessary to use purified water for cooling. The cooling jacket should be constructed of fused quartz or other ultraviolet-transmitting material if the middle- and short-wavelength ultraviolet is desired. The immersion lamp system can be made with a standard taper glass joint to fit the conventional three-neck flasks as shown in Fig. 7-35a.

Several useful types of photochemical systems for synthetic work have been described by Berg and Beyer.[64] In Fig. 7-36 is shown one of their reaction vessels designed for use in either a flow or static system for which gas introduction is necessary (chlorinations, etc.). The reader who is planning to do photochemical synthetic work will find considerable help in arriving at a suitable cell design from the numerous examples which have appeared in the literature.[65-67]

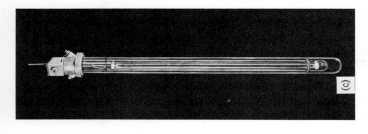

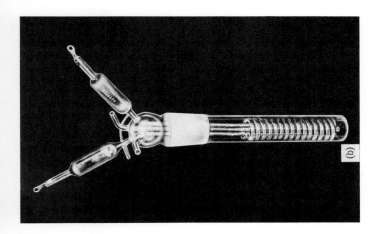

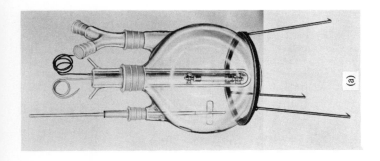

Fig. 7-35 (a) Laboratory photochemical reactor for immersion operation of medium-pressure mercury lamp in standard 12-liter flask; quartz, Vycor, or Corex construction (Hanovia Chemical and Manufacturing Co.). (b) Low-pressure mercury lamp (2537 A) laboratory photochemical source in quartz condenser for immersion in standard 12-liter flask (Hanovia Chemical and Manufacturing Co.). (c) Large-scale, commercial-type photochemical reactor, with 4500 w medium-pressure lamp (Hanovia light-well assembly 19460).

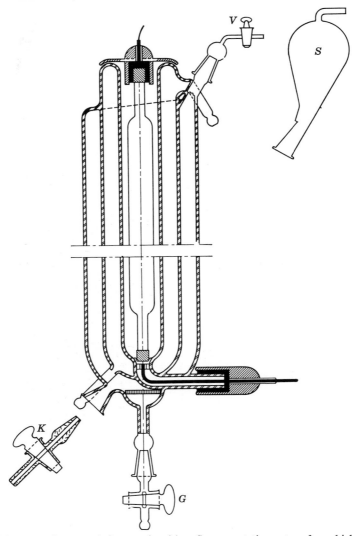

Fig. 7-36 Reaction vessel for use in either flow or static system for which a gas introduction is necessary (chlorinations, oxidations, etc.); the gas enters the water-cooled reactor through the fritted disc by way of the regulating stopcock G; the vessel S can be attached to replace the closure V in order to control reactant and solvent liquids which tend to froth with gas introduction; when used as a flow system, reactant enters through the capillary valve at K and leaves through V. From Berg and Beyer.[64]

7-3C   The Design of Photolysis Cells
for Quantitative Studies

The most common and functional design for reaction cells for quantitative gaseous and liquid-phase studies is the cylindrical cell with optically flat circular windows fused to the cell body at right angles to its axis; see Fig. 7-37. The size of the tubing and windows should be consistent with the dimensions of the light beam to be used in the experiment. There

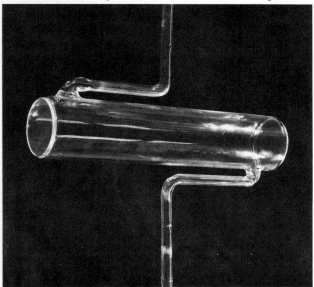

Fig. 7-37   A cylindrical fused-quartz cell with optically flat windows designed for quantitative gas studies; see text.

should be as little unirradiated cell volume as possible so that there can be no question about the actual effective volume of the cell, which must be known to evaluate rate constants from photochemical experiments.

In quantitative photochemical work it is desirable to use flat windows on cells and to have nearly perpendicular incidence of the light beam on the window. For these conditions the fraction of light reflected at the window interface is a minimum and is calculable from Fresnel's law (Eq. 1-5). The wavelength of the incident light, its polarization, the angle of incidence, the surface and bulk imperfections of the window, and the nature of the interface involved determine, in an often unpredictable fashion, the fraction of non-perpendicularly incident light which is reflected at a window. This fraction rises markedly with increased deviation from perpendicular incidence; see Fig. 7-38. It is apparent that, if a curved surface such as the wall of a test tube or a flask is placed in a homogeneous light beam, the fraction of the incident light transmitted by the flask wall furthest from perpendicular will be nearly zero, and the distribution of light within the vessel will be very non-homogeneous. For cells which are about 5 cm or more in length the connections of the two side arms which

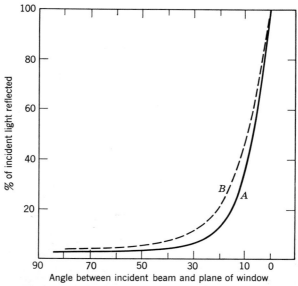

Fig. 7-38   Reflection of 3082 A light from the surface of (*A*) glass and (*B*) water as a function of the angle between the incident beam and the plane of the surface. Adopted from Koller,[11] p. 217.

lead the fluid reactant through the cell are best made near opposite ends of the cell and above and below the cell, respectively; this avoids a "dead" space in which the circulation of the reactant is poor and mixing of reactants is difficult. About 5 mm distance between the side arms and the windows should be left to avoid distortion of the planar windows.

In gas-phase photochemical work the photolysis cell is commonly housed within a quartz-windowed oven, the two halves of which can be separated at the middle. In this case the side arms may be parallel to the cell body and emerge in opposite directions at the center of the cell and perpendicular to the cell axis; the construction of the cell shown in Fig. 7-37 is of this type. If a quartz cell is used and the entire glass system is not to be quartz, as is the usual case, it is necessary to attach quartz-to-Pyrex graded seals to the entrance and exit tubes at some points which lie outside the oven proper.

It is not easy for an inexperienced glass blower to work quartz with the precision demanded for a good photolysis cell. For example, if the entire surface of the windows is not kept very warm during the construction of the cell, a white solid deposit of vaporized oxides of silicon will condense on the windows, etc.; this destroys the high transmission of the cell and cannot be tolerated.

The choice of a cylindrically shaped cell is based largely on the shape of commercial tubing which has been available. Pyrex and quartz square tubing (unpolished) can now be obtained (e.g., General Electric Co., Willoughby Quartz Division, Willoughby, Ohio; Thermal American Fused Quartz Co., Montville, N.J.) and is ideal for liquid cell construction, particularly for the study of photochemical systems which are easily analyzed by visible and near-ultraviolet spectrophotometry; the sealed reaction vessel can be transferred to the spectrophotometer for analysis after photolysis, or, better, the photochemical exposure can be made at right angles to the spectrophotometric beam and analysis carried on continuously during the irradiation. This type of cell and others for liquid-phase studies are shown in Fig. 7-39.

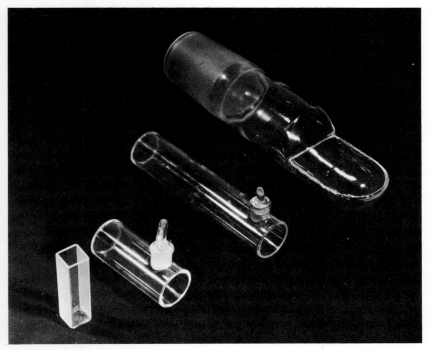

Fig. 7-39 Some typical solution-phase quartz cells for photochemical work.

In the study of photosensitized reactions or in other experiments in which the 2537 A low-pressure mercury lamp is used, the low brilliancy of the source demands some different types of cells and arrangements of the arc. The cell may be an ordinary quartz tube (no windows), and the

Fig. 7-40   A quartz reaction cell designed for the photochemical study of heterogeneous systems which require introduction of a gas.

source coiled around it (as pictured in Fig. 7-4) or parallel to it. Of course the non-homogeneity of the light intensity in the reaction cell may be serious in this case, especially for the parallel-tube arrangement. The electrode chambers of the low-pressure lamp must be cooled and kept outside the oven used to control the cell temperature as described in Sec. 7-1A.

In the quantitative study of the photochemical reactions of solids only one flat window is necessary usually, since the light absorption even in thin layers of solids is almost complete in their photochemically active regions. A cell of this type is shown in Fig. 7-39. In Fig. 7-40 is pictured a cell for use in the photochemical study of heterogeneous systems involving a solid suspended in a liquid which can be continually saturated with a gas. The gas is introduced beneath the suspension through a very fine sintered glass plug located at the bottom of the inner chamber containing dark liquid in Fig. 7-40; not only does the gas saturate the solution but also its continued bubbling helps to maintain the suspension.

The photolysis of compounds in rigid media at low temperatures demands the use of reaction cells with insulated Dewar-flask construction to avoid serious heat transfer, evaporation of refrigerant, and condensation on cell windows. The photolysis and spectral analysis of compounds in EPA (ether, isopentane, ethyl alcohol, 5:5:2, 3:3:5, or other combinations) or other solvents which form glasses at liquid-nitrogen temperature (77.3°K) can be accomplished in the cell shown in Fig. 7-41, which is based on the design of Linschitz and Rennert.[68] The cell can be used with a Beckman DU and other spectrophotometers at liquid-nitrogen temperature. Four planar quartz windows in the Dewar walls allow parallel light to pass through the sample, which is contained in a quartz 1 cm spectrophotometric cell. The upper and lower portions of the Dewar extend above and below a modified 10 cm cell compartment housing of commercial spectrophotometers. The cells containing the sample and the blank solutions rest on a metal block within the Dewar. The blank cell or reactant cell transmission can be monitored in the spectrophotometer as desired by rotating the metal block (not shown in Fig. 7-41) which is attached to an insulated control handle extending above the Dewar. The glass solutions are formed by placing liquid nitrogen in the Dewar to a level near the top of the cells. After irradiation the liquid nitrogen level is allowed to drop below that of the cell windows so that bubbles of nitrogen formed by evaporation of the liquid do not interfere with the spectrophotometric measurements. The temperature of the sample may be maintained near that of the liquid nitrogen by intermittent periods of complete sample immersion and through the use of a thermal barrier placed over the sample. The barrier may be made from an inverted brass can which is divided into two halves and provided with holes to allow light passage through the windows and access to the insulated control handle. The sides of the can extend into the liquid nitrogen, and through effective heat conduction it surrounds the sample cell with walls at near liquid-nitrogen temperature. The cell may be silvered on surfaces other than the windows or the sides left transparent for access to the beam of the light used for photolysis. With the latter arrangement observations of reactant and product changes can be monitored during the photolysis. A dry

Fig. 7-41   Windowed quartz Dewar for mounting photochemical reaction cell for photolyses and spectrophotometric analysis of compounds at liquid-nitrogen temperature.   After Linschitz and Rennert;[68]   see text.

atmosphere must be maintained to avoid condensation of moisture on cell windows.

Photochemical cells for optical studies of frozen intermediates from photochemical experiments in matrices at liquid-helium (4.2°K) or hydrogen (20.3°K) temperatures require much more intricate design to avoid serious loss of the refrigerant.   Schoen, Kuentzel, and Broida[69] have described several glass cells designed for use at liquid-helium temperature;   the construction of one such vessel is shown in Fig. 7-42.   Liquid helium is placed in the large Pyrex glass chamber H to which is attached through a graded seal g the quartz photolysis cell q.   Liquid nitrogen is placed in the

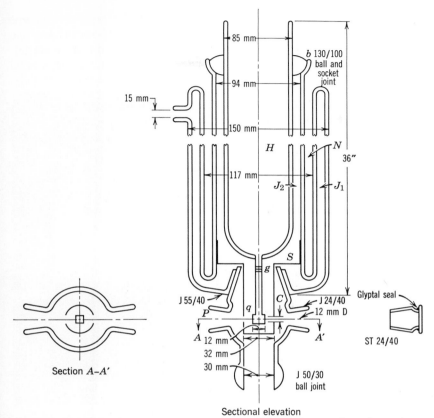

Fig. 7-42   Photochemical cell for optical studies of frozen intermediates from photochemical experiments in matrices at liquid-helium temperature. From Schoen, Kuentzel, and Broida;[69] see text.

outer well, labeled N. The vacuum jackets J_1 and J_2 between the Dewar walls containing refrigerants are evacuated, and the radiation shield S, made of gold-plated copper, is in thermal contact with the liquid-nitrogen-cooled wall; the thermal connection may be made by means of a metal conductive lacquer (e.g., Dag Dispersion 235, Michigan Colloids Co., Port Huron, Mich.). With a total of 2.5 cm² open area in the thermal shield and no silvering of the walls the average rate of evaporation of the helium was only 3.5 cm³/min. A deposit of the matrix containing the reactant is formed on the outside of the quartz cell q. Photolysis and subsequent ultraviolet spectroscopic analysis of the trapped species are effected through the quartz windows attached to male portions of the standard taper ground-glass joint ports P. If infrared analysis of products is to be used, the matrix must be deposited on an infrared-transparent surface (such as NaCl or CsI), cooled to the desired temperature, and the windows in the access ports must be constructed of similar material. Reference to the original papers of Pimentel and his co-workers should be made for the details of inert-gas matrix preparation and properties.[70] Even

Fig. 7-43   The multipurpose EPR cavity of the Varian Associates, Palo Alto, Calif., V-4531. Slits visible in cavity allow irradiation of sample held in a quartz tube at any selected temperature from −186°; the spin spectrum of the photolysis products may be examined during or after the irradiation of the compound.

the seemingly simple operations involving very-low-temperature equipment, such as the transfer of liquid helium, require special know-how. Mauer has given an excellent review of low-temperature equipment and techniques, to which the potential worker in this area is referred.[71]

Special cell designs have been described for low-temperature photochemical experiments in the cavity of an electron spin resonance spectrometer.[72] The multipurpose ESR cavity of the Varian Associates (V-4531) is constructed with slots to permit ultraviolet or visible irradiation of a sample during ESR examination; see Fig. 7-43.

For fluorescence studies cells are designed to permit the observation of fluorescence at some large angle, usually 90°, from the direction of the beam of exciting radiation. The cell may be as simple as a rectangular four-faced quartz spectrophotometric cell, but for solutions which must be degassed and given special treatment some more elaborate design is needed; a useful cell for such experiments has been described by Bäckström and Sandros[73] and is pictured in Fig. 7-44. The presence of oxygen

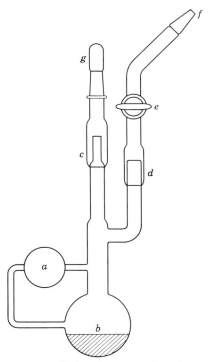

Fig. 7-44   Fluorescence cell of Bäckström and Sandros;[73] see text.

in a solution can alter the efficiency of fluorescence markedly. The apparatus of Fig. 7-44 is designed to remove oxygen from solutions conveniently. The cylindrical cell a of 40 ml volume, viewed end on in Fig. 7-44, is constructed of non-fluorescing glass. The solution to be studied is placed in the spherical bulb b of 110 ml volume through the access joint and cap g. It is degassed by cooling the bulb to $-78°$, evacuating through stopcock e by means of a high-vacuum system, closing e, warming the solution to $20°$, and then repeating these operations four or five times until the solution in b is degassed thoroughly. The solution is warmed to room temperature, and the apparatus is removed from the vacuum system and tipped so that the cell a is filled. Pockets c and d are for trapping stopcock grease.

Photochemical cells for use in the far ultraviolet require special care in fabrication of a seal between window material and cell body which can withstand temperature variation. In Fig. 7-45 a seal between LiF and Pyrex is shown. The details of its preparation have been given by McNesby and Okabe.[23b] The Pyrex and LiF edges which will contact the AgCl

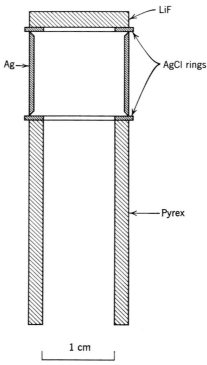

Fig. 7-45   A high-temperature LiF-AgCl-Ag-AgCl-Pyrex seal useful in the design of photochemical cells for the far ultraviolet. From McNesby and Okabe;[23b] see text.

gaskets are painted with "liquid Bright Platinum" (Hanovia Chemical and Manufacturing Co.) and baked at 500° for 5 min. A silver tube is reamed to the shape shown in Fig. 7-45 and then cleaned in nitric acid. The parts are assembled as shown in the figure and placed in a furnace at 300°. The temperature is raised to 450° over a period of 1 hr. When the AgCl melts, the furnace is allowed to cool to 250° and the assembly can be removed. This type of seal has been used successfully by McNesby and co-workers in studies up to 400°.[23b]

For each quantitative photochemical study there will be some special design or modification of the cell designs shown which will work best for the purposes intended. These few illustrations of cell types can only serve to illustrate some of the problems of cell design.

7-3D   The Optical Train

In quantitative photochemical studies the arrangement of the components comprising the optical train (the light source, lenses, monochromator or filter system, light stops, photolysis cell, and light detector) is usually a compromise between that required for maximum intensity and that producing maximum homogeneity of the monochromatic light beam within the reaction cell. The relatively large illuminated area of the arc

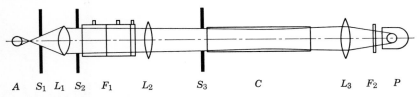

A S_1 L_1 S_2 F_1 L_2 S_3 C L_3 F_2 P

Fig. 7-46   Optical train for use with a chemical or glass filter system; see text.

source in most studies is far from a true point source, and it is impossible to produce a completely parallel light beam. However, there is some optimum arrangement of the components which can be found.

A suitable arrangement for the two basic systems involving the mono-chromator and the filter system may be considered here. A simple mono-chromator set-up is shown in Fig. 7-20, to which reference should be made. The settings of the slits S_1 and S_2 and the other adjustments of the mono-chromator have been described in Sec. 7-2A. Light of the desired wave-length is focused on the slit S_2 and then passed into the lens L_3, where it is converged to form a nearly parallel beam; this beam is passed to the light stop S_3, where it is limited to keep it within the reaction cell (C) volume and of dimensions not to exceed the length of window of the thermopile T, on which it falls after traversing the cell length.

In Fig. 7-46 is a train for use with a chemical or glass filter system. Light from the arc A is limited by the circular opening S_1 on the arc housing. With a Hanovia 673 A lamp source S_1 may be about $3\!/\!4''$ in diameter. A lens L_1 of short focal length (about $3''$) is placed at a distance along the optical bench, about $3''$ from S_1; its position is adjusted finally to give a nearly parallel beam of light through the filter cell F_1. An additional stop S_2, with a circular hole slightly smaller than the I.D. of the filter cell, ensures that all the light reaching the cell passes through the filter. As few lenses and windows should be used as are consistent with the creation of the desired beam in order to minimize reflection losses. However, it is often advantageous to use a second long-focal-length lens L_2 (about 16″) following the filter cell F_1; this serves to converge the beam slightly so that it reaches its smallest diameter at about the center of the photolysis cell C, and at this point its diameter should be only slightly smaller than that of the cell. The light then passes either directly to the photocell P or first through an additional lens L_3 which condenses the beam to the dimensions of the

Fig. 7-47   Photochemical system for utilizing simultaneous cross beam infrared analysis to follow reactions; see text.

receiver element of the tube. F_2 is a suitable uniform-density filter which lowers the intensity of the beam so that the phototube is not overloaded. This is discussed more fully in the consideration of phototubes in Sec. 7-4C.

To follow the progress of the invisible ultraviolet light during the alignment of the pieces in the optical train, it is convenient to use as a detector a piece of filter paper impregnated with a highly fluorescent compound such as commercial anthracene or copper-doped ZnS. As this is placed at the front and the rear of the cell and then moved along the cell sides, evidence of misalignment is readily obtained.

A much more intense and nearly perfectly aligned beam can be obtained with point-source lamps, but because of the continuous background in their emission there is some sacrifice in the monochromatic character of the light beam. Even the best filter systems pass a rather broad band which extends almost to the mercury lines on either side of the one for which the filter was designed; see Figs. 7-23 to 7-30.

The special geometrical arrangements used for low-pressure lamps have been reviewed briefly in Secs. 7-1A and 7-3C and pictured in Fig. 7-4.

There are many unusual photochemical systems designed for special purposes. One example is shown in Fig. 7-47; this system was designed to study the photolysis of near-ultraviolet-absorbing compounds in the low concentration range; it is essentially a modified Perkin-Elmer long-path infrared spectrometer. The reaction cell consists of a large, heavy-walled Pyrex tank which also serves as the housing for the long-path infrared optical system. Three Hanovia 637 A lamps are placed within a Pyrex, water-cooled condenser; this is normally backed by an aluminum reflector of parabolic cross section (removed in Fig. 7-47) which concentrates the light into the cell volume. The metal optical bench of the long-path infrared system, located at the bottom of the cell, is painted with a highly reflecting baked-enamel finish so that several passes of the ultraviolet light through the cell can occur by reflection. When an azo-alkyl compound is irradiated in this system, the emission of the medium-pressure arcs, the absorption character of the condenser, the cell walls, and the reactant, all restrict the absorbed energy to nearly monochromatic 3660 A radiation. The rates of formation of products (or metastable intermediates) are followed during the photolysis by the crossed-beam long-path (40 meter) infrared system. A quartz windowed cell of similar design is used for ultraviolet irradiation.

7-3E Auxiliary Equipment for the Photolysis System

In most photochemical studies the reactant must be freed from air and either maintained in pure form or placed in controlled mixtures. The nature of the products and the mechanism of the photolysis are usually markedly affected by oxygen. Hence a prerequisite to most studies is a high-vacuum system consisting of a suitable mechanical fore-pump, a high-vacuum diffusion pump (mercury or oil), pressure-indicating devices (McLeod gauge, ionization gauge, manometer, etc.), and other equipment needed to carry out product separation, purification, and analysis (Leroy-Ward stills, vapor-liquid partition chromatography, Toepler pumps, stopcocks, metal valves, mercury valves, etc.). A diagram of a typical vacuum system associated with photolysis equipment is shown in Fig. 7-48. The details of the design and the use of high-vacuum apparatus are given in several excellent treatises on the subject to which the reader is referred.[74]

In the design of his photolysis system the experimentalist must decide between flow and static systems. For quantitative studies in either type of system, the lower the extent of photolysis (within the limit of accurate analysis) the easier is the job of correct interpretation of the product quantum yield or rate data. Often the products formed are so inert that they may be allowed to build up to relatively large concentrations without altering the reaction mechanism seriously [e.g., $(C_3F_7)_2CO$ photolysis].

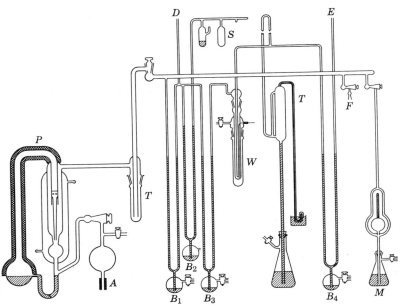

Fig. 7-48   Typical vacuum system associated with photolysis equipment: P, mercury diffusion pump; A, attachment to mechanical forepump; T, removable trap, usually maintained at $N_2(l)$ temperature; B_1, B_2, B_3, B_4, mercury valves to control access to photolysis system attached at D, reactant storage bulbs S, LeRoy-Ward still W, and chromatographic system connected at E; T, Toepler pump; M, McLoed gauge.

Even in these systems it is desirable to restrict the reactant conversion to less than a few per cent; otherwise changes in the absorbed light intensity and rates of formation of products will be significant during the run, and the estimation of quantum yields becomes less accurate.

In the flow system, the reactant moves through the irradiated region and then into a trap. This arrangement offers a real advantage over the static system in that many highly reactive or unstable products may be retained for analysis; in the static system, for which contact times are much longer, such unstable primary products may not last and may be missed. If the flow system is to retain its stated virtue, a fast flow is necessary. This complicates analysis, since the condensable products will be collected together with a relatively huge amount of unchanged reactant. Of course, impurities in the original reactant must be kept to an absolute minimum, since the actual products can be lost among them.

If a static system is used, a series of runs should be carried out in which all the experimental variables are nearly identical but in which the extent of conversion is altered from the shortest exposure run for which analysis can be made to a run of longer exposure in which several per cent conversion results. From these data it should be apparent to what extent the conversion can be carried and still provide "initial" rate data. If the static system is used correctly, it can yield data which are in most cases as reliable as those of the flow system.

The flow rate in a flow system may be controlled in a number of ways. One system involves maintaining a selected fixed pressure head of reactant on one side of a capillary tube which leads to the photolysis cell; in the exit tube of the photolysis cell another capillary tube may be placed, behind which is connected an evacuated volume and low-temperature trap into which products and reactants flow and are condensed. The pressure and the flow rate of the reactant in the cell can be regulated by choice of capillary sizes and the pressure head of reactant.

Even in the "static" system it is wise to have available some means of forcing reactant circulation in the main loop of the reaction system. An in-line, all-glass pump, operated by a solenoid mechanism, can be an invaluable aid in the preparation of homogeneous mixtures and in the avoidance of overirradiation of reactant in the front of the cell.

The control of temperature and pressure of the reactant in the cell can be accomplished in a variety of ways. To control the temperature the cell can be housed in a suitably designed thermostat or oven. Good liquid-bath thermostats are available in most laboratories and need not be discussed here. However, the ovens available for thermal studies are not suited for photochemical use, and a brief description of a photolysis cell oven of useful design is in order. In Fig. 7-49 an oven can be seen surrounding the photolysis cell; it is constructed in two halves (shown open in the figure) so that convenient access to the cell is possible. The overall length of the oven should be about twice that of the cell to ensure uniformity of temperature along the cell. The main core of the oven is made from two cast-aluminum cylindrical shells, about 1–2″ thick and with about 2.5″ diameter hole; it is machined so that the two halves key together to form a draft-tight but non-binding joint. A hole slightly larger than the cell side arms is drilled through the center of the two halves, and the two halves of the machined joint are slotted. Circular Transite ends (about $\frac{1}{2}$″ thick, 10″ in diameter, 2.5″ hole) are bolted to the aluminum block.

First each half of the oven is wrapped with an electrically insulating layer of thin sheet mica (about 0.005″ thick) and then with approximately 30 ft of resistance tape or wire (about 1 Ω/ft); the ends of the tape are secured in terminals in the Transite ends. The winding is covered with about a 2″ thickness of asbestos or heat pipe insulation and a layer of aluminum foil. The oven is held by a large split-cylinder made of thin metal ($\sim$1/8″) which can be clamped to the oven firmly. Wheels are joined to each half of the oven assembly and run on a matching track mounted under the

Fig. 7-49   Aluminum block furnace for temperature control of a photolysis cell; see text.

photolysis cell. Quartz windows cover the open ends of the oven. The rear window of the oven and any other optical surfaces which lie between the oven and the detector should be mounted at some suitable angle other than 90° with respect to the light beam so that light which is transmitted through the cell and reflected from the window will not re-enter the photolysis cell. The calculation of the fraction of light absorbed by a system is simplified if this procedure is followed (see Sec. 7-4C-2).

When a regulated source of voltage is applied to the oven (two half-oven windings connected in parallel), it heats slowly and after several hours reaches an equilibrium temperature which is quite uniform ($\pm$0.3°) over its middle two-thirds, in which the cell is located. When 120 v is applied the temperature will reach about 350–400°, the usual practical limit for most photochemical studies.

The temperature of the cell is best measured with a series of thermo-couples (Cu-Constantan, Fe-Constantan, or other). The temperature should be noted at several positions along the cell; for example, thermo-couples may be placed near the front cell window at the bottom of the cell, at the rear window near the top of the cell, and at the center of the cell half-way up its side. There should be no great difference between the temperature readings from different points along the cell if the oven is functioning correctly. If the resistance wire windings for the two halves are of unequal length, the oven halves are not the same in length or con-struction, or the atmosphere surrounding the two halves is of different temperature, it may be necessary to operate each half of the oven on a separate voltage source at a voltage picked to match the temperature of that half. In a fast-flow system the reactant should be preheated to a temperature only a few degrees below that desired for the experiment before it is introduced into the cell.

There are many good methods of controlling the oven and the cell temperatures.[75] An instructive review of modern procedures involving calibration of thermocouples and temperature measurements using thermocouples has been given by Roeser and Lomberger.[76]

Pressure control and measurement are usually no problem. Manometers of mercury or other less dense materials (dibutylphthalate, etc.) are often satisfactory. In the study of compounds of low vapor pressure it is often desirable to use a reactant pressure above that of the reactant at room temperature so that reasonable intensities of absorbed light can be realized. In this case the photolysis cell and its associated glass tubing, circulating system, pressure-measuring device, and valves which isolate this system, must all be heated to some temperature above that at which the vapor pressure of the reactant is equal to the pressure of reactant to be used. The entire system may be suspended in suitable air or liquid thermo-stat to accomplish this purpose. (See Fig. 7-50.) However, liquid manom-eters are then quite difficult to use with precision, and a Bodenstein quartz-spiral manometer, a spoon gauge, or other indirect-reading instrument is most useful.

7-4 THE MEASUREMENT OF LIGHT INTENSITIES IN PHOTOCHEMICAL WORK

Today photochemists use primarily three methods of light-intensity determination; these involve the use of the thermopile-galvanometer system, the chemical actinometer, and the phototube. Only one of these systems, the thermopile-galvanometer, is sufficiently versatile to be useful for absolute light-intensity measurements over the entire spectral range

Fig. 7-50 A typical photochemical system housed in an air thermostat for gas-phase studies of low-vapor pressure compounds; see text.

from visible to far ultraviolet; this system can be calibrated directly by using standard radiation sources. Although measurements with the thermopile are tedious and very time consuming, recourse to its use is almost mandatory for quantitative work in the visible range, where chemical actinometry is not well established today. The chemical actinometers are the most useful absolute light intensity-measuring device for the ultraviolet region, while the phototube offers the simplest determination of the fraction of light absorbed and other relative light-intensity measurements. Since each of these systems has some unique value in photochemistry, a brief description of each will be given here.

7-4A   The Use of the Thermopile-Galvanometer System in Photochemistry

Many different types of thermopiles have been found useful for photochemical work. The geometrical distribution of intensities within the light beam dictates the nature of the thermopile to be chosen. If a near-point-source lamp is used with a point-focusing monochromator or chemical filter system, then the light beam may be condensed to a small spot (less than 5 mm in diameter) after passage through the photolysis cell, and a single receiver thermopile of the Beckman and Dickinson type may be employed in this case.[77] The "line" thermopile is best suited for measurement of light separated by the monochromators which employ the rectangular slit image most common to photochemistry. A brief description of the construction of this instrument and its use should be instructive and also serve to impress one with the fragility and temperamental character of the thermopile.

7-4A-1   The Principles of Operation and the Construction of the Line Thermopile

The thermopile measures the energy of the light beam by converting to heat all the light energy incident on its blackened receivers; in turn the heat released raises the temperature of the receiver and an attached thermocouple. This creates a thermal emf relative to a similar "cold" junction, which is kept in the dark; the deflection produced in a sensitive galvanometer or modern high-impedance microvoltmeter is then used as a measure of the incident light energy. The design of the "line" thermopile is such as to maximize the effects.

A typical commercial "line" thermopile and its internal construction are shown in Fig. 7-51. The light-receiving surface is made of several small rectangular receivers; each is constructed from very thin metal foil with a very fine-wire thermocouple junction soldered or welded to its back side. This construction keeps the heat capacity of the receivers to a minimum so that the temperature rise and the voltage generated will be a maximum. The total length of the receivers must exceed the length of the light beam to be measured. The width may be about 3.5 mm, but the area exposed to the beam should be limited in width to something less, say about 3.0 mm, either by a fixed light shield or by adjustable slits on the face of the thermopile. To accommodate the slightly non-parallel nature of the photochemist's light beam, it is important to have a small reserve of thermopile surface which is in the dark for the parallel rays but is available to intercept the non-parallel light. In photochemical use, the thermopile is

(a)

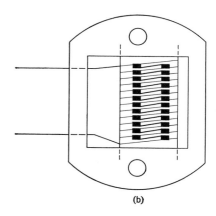

(b)

Fig. 7-51   (a) Commercial linear, 12-element, surface type thermopile (Eppley Laboratory, Inc., Newport, R.I.) (b) Internal construction of receivers and wiring in the Eppley 12-element thermopile.

usually located behind the photolysis cell on a track which is perpendicular to the path of the light beam. A micrometer screw adjustment moves the thermopile across the beam by accurately known increments. The slit width is chosen to match closely this increment of distance which the thermopile is moved between readings. A suitable thermopile tracking system is pictured in Fig. 7-52.

The surface of each receiver is coated with platinum black, lamp black, gold black, "Parson's black," or other optically black, thermally conducting material, so that light of any frequency can be absorbed effectively and detected.* Each receiver which is exposed to the light is joined by one of

---

* Since radiation from a standard lamp is commonly employed to calibrate a thermopile detector, and since much of the radiation from this lamp falls in the 1–3 μ region, the black coating must not show any spectral selectivity over the infrared as well as the visible and ultraviolet regions, or an incorrect measure of the light energy will result. Lee and Seliger[78g] have studied the problem of obtaining such non-selective surfaces for thermopile receivers and found that some gold black surfaces of thermopiles were selective; they had a measurable reflection in the infrared. "Parson's black" and lamp black appear to be the most uniformly black surfaces found.

the thermocouple wires to a nearly identical receiver (same size, black finish, etc.) to which a cold junction is attached. In some cases two cold-junction receivers each of one-half the area of the "hot" receiver have been employed;[78e] see Fig. 7-53. The receivers attached to the cold and hot junctions are cooled or heated by the natural background emission, absorption, and conductive processes when temperature differences exist

Fig. 7-52 Thermopile tracking system used to move the line thermopile measured increments across the light beam; 1 mm of lateral motion is achieved with 3 revolutions of the control wheel with the system shown.

between the components and their surroundings. The nearly identical construction of the light and dark receivers tends to equalize these processes in the two receivers and minimize the background "drift" of the voltage supplied by the unexposed thermocouple. The thermocouple leads of the hot- and cold-junction pairs are connected in a series-parallel arrangement (such as that diagrammed in Fig. 7-53) to the output terminals of the thermopile unit. The thermocouple wires form a delicate grid which mechanically supports the receivers. The light-receiving elements are covered commonly by a crystal-quartz window. Thermal conduction processes of diffusion and convection may dissipate a good share of the heat liberated by light absorption at the receiver in a thermopile filled with gas at 1 atm pressure. These losses can be greatly reduced and the sensitivity of the thermopile increased markedly (by as much as 10 times) by evacuating the instrument; this also lowers appreciably the thermal drift characteristic of these instruments.

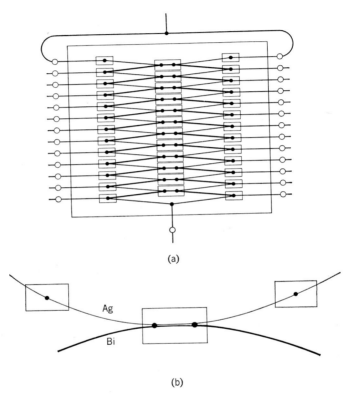

(a)

(b)

Fig. 7-53 (a) The arrangement of the receivers and bismuth (heavy lines) and silver (light lines) thermocouple wires in a line thermopile from Leighton and Leighton;[78e] the central receivers are the hot junctions which see the light; two outside columns of receivers are the cold junctions which remain in the dark. (b) Close-up of receivers.

From this brief description the reader should recognize that the thermopile is an extremely fragile instrument which must be handled with great care. An experimentalist with both the patience of Job and the manual dexterity of a brain surgeon may choose to construct his own thermopile, following detailed published directions.[78] Commercial models of various designs are available from several companies (e.g., Eppley Laboratory,

Inc., Newport, R.I.; Hilger and Watts, Ltd., London, England; Kipp and Zonen, Delft, Holland).

The line thermopile has been used most often in conjunction with a high-sensitivity, mirror galvanometer with a short period (e.g., the Leeds and Northrop 2284 series). A suitable critical damping resistance may be needed to match the thermopile and galvanometer; the optimum size of this is stated in the manufacturer's instructions or can be found by trial and error. The galvanometer should be mounted so that it is free from vibration (e.g., use a Julius suspension[74a]) and perfectly level so that the galvanometer coil swings freely and symmetrically between the magnetic

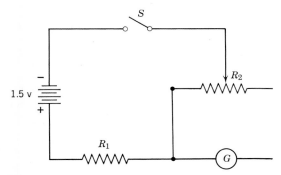

Fig. 7-54 Simple circuit for adjustment of zero position and compensation for thermal drift of a galvanometer. Best choice of R_1 and R_2 will depend on sensitivity of the galvanometer employed; for a high-sensitivity instrument, $R_1 = 1$ MΩ, and $R_2 = 1$ kΩ Helipot.

pole pieces. Non-linear response of the thermopile-galvanometer system is often traceable to improper galvanometer positioning. The deflection of the galvanometer mirror is magnified by some simple optical system. For example, the operator may focus a fixed telescope on the reflection of a numbered scale (backwards and upside-down numbers) which is located some 3–5 meters from the mirror; of course, this distance determines the radius of curvature used in the construction of the scale. Since the galvanometer is so sensitive to disturbances of any kind, it is convenient to adjust the zero position and also compensate for thermal drifts by imposing a small continuously variable external voltage on the thermopile-galvanometer circuit. A simple circuit which can be used for this purpose is shown in Fig. 7-54.

Through the use of a reflector multiplier the sensitivity of a galvanometer can be extended close to the theoretical limit set by Brownian movement ($\sim$0.001 μv).[79]

7-4A-2 The Calibration of the
Thermopile-Galvanometer System

Standard lamps with detailed instructions for their use are available from the U.S. National Bureau of Standards. The Bureau calibrates the total radiant-energy output from these lamps by reference to the radiation from a "black-body" radiator (see Sec. 1-4A). The total energy emitted from a small hole in a black-body radiator at temperature T is well established both theoretically and experimentally to be given by relation 7-1, derivable from relation 1-18 by integration:

$$\mathscr{E}_{\text{total}} = \frac{2\pi^5 \mathbf{k}^4}{15 c^2 h^3} T^4 = 5.670 \times 10^{-5} T^4 \text{ erg/cm}^2\text{-deg}^4\text{-sec} \qquad (7\text{-}1)$$

Here $\mathbf{k}$ is Boltzmann's constant, h Planck's constant, and c the velocity of light. The standard lamp is mounted vertically in a specified direction such that etched markings on the bulb sight toward the thermopile receivers; its distance is adjusted so that there are exactly 2.00 meters between another designated mark on the bulk and the light-limiting slit of the thermopile. A large shield with manually operated shutter separates the lamp from the thermopile as desired. The shield and lamp must be mounted independently so that opening and closing the shutter does not jar the lamp. The background behind the lamp, its base, the clamps, shields, shutter, and supports are all painted with a flat-black paint to reduce reflected light from the lamp. Lamp energy calibrations at specified currents (both a-c and d-c operation) are provided. The lamp, connected in series with a variable resistance and an accurate ammeter (0–400 ma), is best operated from a regulated voltage source. The current through the lamp is adjusted to certain values (250, 300, 350, or 400 ma or other values) for which calibration data are available. The lamp must be thermally equilibrated at a given current setting before use in calibration.

The so-called "swinging equilibrium" method is employed commonly with thermopile-galvanometer systems. The shutter is opened, the galvanometer mirror is rotated, and in a few seconds the operator notes a maximum scale reading through his telescope. The shutter is then closed for a few seconds until the motion of the mirror ceases and a minimum reading is observed. It is then opened again, etc. The procedure is continued until about five minima and four maxima have been recorded. If the system is operating correctly, for a fixed intensity of light the difference between a given maximum reading and the average of the minimum values before and after the maximum should be independent of any small background drift in the circuit. An average of the four differences represents a good estimate of the galvanometer deflection for a given lamp setting. In order to test the system for the desired linearity of the response to intensity the process should be repeated for each of the lamp current settings for which intensity data are available.

Pairs of lamps may be used to extend the range of intensity. For this procedure the two standard lamps are mounted about 50 cm apart behind a common light shield, but each lamp may be exposed to the thermopile by means of a separate shutter; a black cloth between the lamps avoids having light from one lamp reflecting from the glass envelope of the other and into the thermopile. In this case the thermopile face is placed parallel to the line between the two lamps so that the perpendicular area intercepted by the exposed thermopile slit is slightly smaller than that of the actual slit area (0.99 times slit area). Reflection at the window will be only slightly greater than that for perpendicular incidence; see Fig. 7-38.

Some data obtained during the calibration of a thermopile-galvanometer system are summarized in Table 7-13. Four standard lamps and two observers were used to test the reliability and reproducibility of the system. The ergs/second-centimeter² at a distance of 2 meters from the lamps (as determined by the N.B.S.) are listed in column 3 for several lamp currents. The ergs/second impinging on the area of the slit opening of the thermopile (0.9557 cm²) are given in column 4. The average deflections of the galvanometer as determined independently by two observers for each condition are compared in column 5. It is seen that there is good agreement between the results of different observers using the swinging equilibrium technique described. The galvanometer constant (*GC*) of column 6 is defined by

$$GC = \frac{\text{ergs/sec-slit area}}{\text{galvanometer deflection, cm}} \qquad (7\text{-}2)$$

The relative constancy of *GC* for experiments at different intensities shows that the response of the system is nearly linear over the range tested; this should be the case for a properly adjusted system.

It is important to check the linearity of the system over the complete range of intensities of the light to be measured in the photochemical work. If a range of standard intensities higher than that obtained by the above procedures is required, two secondary standards may be used as described by Leighton and Leighton.[78e] Note in Table 7-13 that lamps C-185 and 186, obtained some ten years before the receipt of C-467 and 468, gave results equal within the experimental error to those for the new lamps. If the standard lamps are treated with care, used sparingly and according to the operating instructions, they deteriorate only slowly. However, it is wise to use more than one standard so that evidence of lamp aging will be

TABLE 7-13 Example of Actual Data from the Calibration of a Thermopile-Galvanometer System

(1) Lamp Used	(2) Current (d-c), ma	(3) Ergs/sec-cm² at 2 meters (N.B.S. data)	(4) Ergs/sec-Slit Area	(5) Deflections on Galvanometer Scale, cm Observer: A	B	(6) Galvanometer Constant (GC)
C-467	300	449	429	18.2	18.5	23.4
	350	628	600	26.3	26.0	22.9
	400	834	797	35.1	35.3	22.6
C-468	300	437	418	18.2	18.5	22.8
	350	614	587	26.0	26.3	22.5
	400	811	775	35.3	35.4	21.9
C-467	300	886	847	37.4	37.5	22.6
plus	350	1242	1187	52.2	53.4	22.5
C-468	400	1645	1572	70.8	70.8	22.2
C-185	300	452	432	18.9	…	22.9
	400	830	793	34.7	…	22.9
C-186	300	455	435	19.3	…	22.5
	400	835	798	35.6	…	22.4
C-185	300	907	867	38.1	…	22.8
plus	400	1665	1591	71.2	…	22.4
C-186						

$$\text{Thermopile slit width} = 0.298_2 \text{ cm}$$
$$\text{Thermopile slit length} = 3.20_5 \text{ cm}$$
$$\text{Area slit} = 0.955_7 \text{ cm}^2$$

immediately detected. If prolonged service of a lamp is necessary, the standard lamps should be used to calibrate another lamp which can serve as a secondary standard.

7-4A-3 The Measurement of Absolute Light Intensities Using the Calibrated Thermopile-Galvanometer System

In the measurement of the intensity of light in a beam by using a line thermopile it is convenient to move the thermopile laterally a distance nearly equal to the thermopile slit width and corresponding to a whole number of revolutions of the control shaft. It is virtually impossible to adjust the slit width of a thermopile to some distance which corresponds exactly to that moved by the thermopile for a whole number of revolutions of the control shaft, and it is equally difficult to obtain a control shaft thread with the exact pitch necessary to move the thermopile the precise distance equal to the slit width for a whole number of revolutions. This introduces a minor complication in our attempt to integrate the intensity of a light beam. Let us say, for example, that each revolution moves the thermopile 0.100 cm across the light beam. If the thermopile described in Table 7-13 with a slit width of 0.298_2 cm were used to make the measurements, the readings would be taken every three revolutions of the control shaft, or at intervals of 0.300 cm across the beam. Now if the sum of these deflections were used together with the value for GC derived from the data of Table 7-13 to determine the total light energy, a definite fraction of the light would be missed, since the slit width is less than the distance through which the thermopile was moved.

Leighton and Leighton[78e] have suggested that very little error is introduced into the measurement of a non-homogeneous beam of radiant energy if a definite slit width of the thermopile (comparable in size to the actual width) is *assumed*, both in calibration and in use; calculations are simplified if this width is assumed equal to the accurately controlled distance between positions of the thermopile at which measurements are made. In this regard they define a thermopile constant (TC) which will be useful in quantum yield determinations.

$$TC = \frac{GC \text{ (Assumed slit width)}}{\text{(Measured slit width)}} \tag{7-3}$$

Coblentz[78b] has shown in a series of experiments that a suitably constructed thermopile-galvanometer system can be used to determine the energy of light striking *directly* on the active surface of a thermopile, quite independent of the wavelength or intensity of the incident light. However, when the active surface of the thermopile is covered by a protective window, reflection and absorption of a different percentage of the light incident on the window occurs at each wavelength. For a quartz window only reflection is important in the visible and ultraviolet regions to about 2000 A. The fraction reflected can be calculated from Fresnel's law for each wavelength (Eq. 1-5).

The range of the wavelengths in the spectral distribution from the standard lamps extends from the near ultraviolet to the far infrared, and the range of light is transmitted by the thermopile window with a different efficiency from monochromatic light. Therefore to utilize a thermopile which has a protective window and which has been calibrated by using standard lamps, a correction must be made to account for these transmission differences. This correction factor, termed the transmission ratio

(TR), has been calculated for a crystal-quartz window by Leighton and Leighton[78e] from the data of Coblentz;[80] these values are given in Table 7-14. The *true* energy of the monochromatic light incident on the window

TABLE 7-14 The Transmission Ratio (TR) and the Fraction of Incident Light Reflected from an Air-Crystal Quartz-Air Interface (F) for Several Wavelengths[a]

Wavelength, A	TR	F
5770	1.003	9.2
4350	1.006	9.5
3663	1.008	9.7
3130	1.014	10.2
2654	1.017	10.5
2537	1.022	10.9

[a] From Leighton and Leighton.[78e]

of the thermopile at any one position in a beam is related to the observed galvanometer deflection, Δ cm, by

$$\mathscr{E} = (TR)(GC)(\Delta) \text{ ergs/sec} \qquad (7\text{-}4)$$

The value of TR is picked from the data of Table 7-14 for the appropriate wavelength of the monochromatic beam being measured.

When the *true* total energy in the beam is to be estimated from the sum of all the deflections $\left(\sum_{i=1}^{n} \Delta_i \right)$ measured across the entire beam at each of the n positions at selected intervals as described, relation 7-5 applies:

$$\mathscr{E}_{\text{total}} = (TR)(TC)\left(\sum_{i=1}^{n} \Delta_i \right) \qquad (7\text{-}5)$$

The determination of absorbed light intensities and quantum yields in photochemical systems through thermopile measurements requires that further corrections be made for reflection and scattering of light at cell windows. These additional formulae are discussed in Sec. 7-5A.

Through the use of a windowless thermocouple detector it has been possible to determine absolute intensities in the short-wavelength ultraviolet to 900 A.[81]

7-4B   Chemical Actinometers for the Determination of Ultraviolet Light Intensities

Through the years photochemists have determined quantum yields of products of many photochemical systems by using the thermopile-galvanometer combination. Among these systems are some which have been studied extensively by several laboratories and for which there can be little doubt about the accuracy of the quantum yield data. Several systems show a product quantum yield which is rather insensitive to changes in temperature, concentration of reactant, light intensity, and wavelength of the absorbed light over quite a wide range of the variables, and the analysis for the product is simple and precise. These systems provide ideal secondary standards which are most useful for rapid and highly accurate light-intensity determinations.

Consider the relative simplicity of this determination. We are to find the intensity of a monochromatic beam within a reaction cell. A suitable reactant A is chosen which absorbs light of the wavelength of interest and for which the quantum yield Φ_B of some product B is known accurately for specific experimental conditions. A small advantage is gained by choosing a liquid-phase actinometer for photochemical studies involving liquids and a gas-phase actinometer for studies involving gases. Not only is the introduction of the actinometer to the photolysis cell usually easier for this choice, but also corrections are eliminated for differences between the fraction of incident light reflected from the front window of the photolysis cell for experiments using the actinometer and the fraction reflected in the actual photochemical study. Reactant A can be placed within the photolysis cell and with the exact optical train, etc., which is to be used in the photochemical study. The temperature and pressure or concentration of reactant A is adjusted to the required range, and an exposure of A to the light beam is made for t sec.

The fraction of the incident light absorbed by A, $1 - (I/I_0) = 1 - 10^{-\epsilon[A]l}$, is either measured experimentally (usually by a photometric method; see Sec. 7-4C) or calculated from known values of ϵ, concentration of A, and path length l. The number of molecules of product B formed, n_B, in the time t is determined by analysis. From these data, the intensity of the light beam incident just within the photolysis cell front window, $I_0{}^i$, can be calculated from Eq. 7-6. (Complications due to reflected light may enter when the fraction of incident light which is absorbed is small; see Secs. 7-4C-2 and 7-5B.)

$$I_0{}^i = \frac{n_B}{\Phi_B t(1 - 10^{-\epsilon[A]l})} \text{ quanta/sec} \tag{7-6}$$

If one contrasts the relative simplicity of actinometer use with the rather complex and tedious procedures required in the calibration and application of the thermopile-galvanometer system, the trend among photochemists in recent years toward the use of chemical actinometers for light-intensity determination is understandable. Photochemists who have used both the thermopile-galvanometer and the chemical actinometer systems to determine ultraviolet light intensities generally agree today that results obtained with a well chosen, sensitive chemical actinometer are not only much simpler to determine but also are often more reproducible and more reliable than those obtained with the thermopile-galvanometer system.

Many possible actinometer systems have been suggested through the years. A few of the most attractive systems which have found rather general acceptance will be considered here.

7-4B-1   Gaseous Actinometer Systems for Photochemical Use

Probably the most widely used and reliable gaseous chemical actinometer for the wavelength range 3200–2500 A is acetone photolysis. At temperatures above about 125° and at pressures of about 50 mm or less, $\Phi_{CO} = 1.0$, independently of wavelength, light intensity, pressure ($p <$ 50 mm), and temperature ($t > 125°$).[82] If the acetone reactant and its photolysis products are cooled to liquid-nitrogen temperature after the exposure, the only important non-condensable products which can be removed with a Toepler pump are CO and CH_4. The amount of CO can be determined easily by standard chemical or physical methods.[83]

Diethyl ketone photolysis at moderate pressures ($p < 50$ mm) and high temperatures ($t > 125°$) is also a convenient gaseous actinometer for the 3200–2500 A region; the quantum yield of carbon monoxide is near unity for these conditions.[84] This ketone has an advantage over acetone in that CO is the only gaseous product which is non-condensable at liquid-nitrogen temperature, so that only a single volume measurement is required and no analysis is necessary provided that efficient trapping of the other products is achieved. In the use of acetone and diethyl ketone actinometry, the ketones must be highly purified. Biacetyl and possibly other impurities could lead to excited molecule quenching and erroneous results; see Sec. 6-7C.

The photolysis of gaseous hydrogen bromide ($\sim$100 mm, $\sim$25°) is a useful actinometer for mercury-free systems in the range 2500–1800 A. Φ_{H_2} is unity (for conversions of less than 1 %) over a range of conditions.[85] The H_2 product is the only compound which is not condensed by liquid nitrogen, so only a single volume measurement is needed for analysis. However, the photolysis cell windows may become coated with mercury bromides and the tramsmission seriously altered if mercury vapor is allowed to enter the cell; in the usual system it is very difficult to avoid this.

Gaseous oxygen photolysis at nearly 1 atm pressure has been employed for actinometry in the range 1900–1300 A, although it too has certain difficulties and uncertainties associated with its use. The product ozone is formed, with $\Phi_{O_3} = 2.0$ in runs of small conversion and fast flow rates.[86] In this case the use of a fast-flow system is imperative; ozone decomposes readily both photochemically and thermally.

The photolysis of nitrous oxide at moderate pressures and near room temperature may be used conveniently to estimate intensities of light in the 1470–1849 region. The quantum yield of nitrogen formation is 1.44.[87a,87b] In work with an 1849 A resonance lamp this actinometer has the particular advantage of being transparent to 2537 A light. Martin and Willard,[57c] when employing it as an actinometer in studies of HI photolysis at 1849 A, used $\Phi_{N_2} = 1.44$ to calculate Φ_{H_2} from photolysis of hydrogen bromide; the agreement was within experimental error ($\Phi_{H_2} = 1.03$ based on N_2O actinometer versus a literature value of $\Phi_{H_2} = 1.00$). They report that the molar extinction coefficient (ϵ) of nitrous oxide is 36 at 1849 A.

Carbon dioxide photolysis in a fast-flow system has been used as an actinometer for wavelengths below about 1700 A;[88a,b] presumably $\Phi_{CO} = 1.0$ provided that the products are not allowed to build up. However, there are complications which leave some uncertainty in the use of this system.[88c] The oxidation of CO by oxygen atoms and the formation of O_3 become important even with relatively small conversions. The CO/O_2 ratio at 25° $\simeq$ 5, and there is some evidence that oxygen atoms are absorbed strongly on the surface of the cell and effectively lost to the products. The rate of product formation is temperature dependent. Obviously the system is quite complex and is not recommended as an actinometer at this writing.

In the visible range there is no completely adequate gaseous actinometer system. The photolysis of nitrosyl chloride vapor, $\Phi_{NO} = 2.0$ in the range 6350–3650 A,[89] could be useful conceivably for mercury-free systems.

7-4B-2 Liquid-Phase Chemical Actinometry Using Potassium Ferrioxalate

By far the best solution-phase chemical actinometer for photochemical research today is the potassium ferrioxalate system developed by Parker and Hatchard.[90] It is very sensitive over a wide range of wavelengths, and it is simple to use. When sulfuric acid solutions of $K_3Fe(C_2O_4)_3$ are irradiated in the range from 2500 to 5770 A, simultaneous reduction of iron to the ferrous state and oxidation of oxalate ion occur. The quantum yields of Fe^{2+} formation have been accurately determined, and light absorption by the reactant is good for the range 4800–2537 A (see Table 7-15). The product ferrous ion and its oxalate complex in these solutions do not absorb the incident radiation measurably during the photolysis, but after the exposure the ferrous ion is made to be highly absorbing and easily analyzable by formation of the red-colored 1,10-phenanthroline-Fe^{2+} complex. The very high absorption coefficient of the complex makes possible useful exposures about one hundredth of the duration required for the classical uranyl oxalate actinometer procedures. The quantum

TABLE 7-15   Quantum Yields[a] of Fe^{2+} in the $K_3Fe(C_2O_4)_3$ Chemical Actinometer at 22°

Wavelength, A	[$K_3Fe(C_2O_4)_3$], M	Fraction of Light Absorbed ($l = 15$ mm)	$\Phi_{Fe^{2+}}$
5770⎫ 5790⎭	0.15	0.118	0.013
5460	0.15	0.061	0.15
5090	0.15	0.132	0.86
4800	0.15	0.578	0.94
4680	0.15	0.850	0.93
4360	0.15	0.997	1.01
	0.006	0.615	1.11
4050	0.006	0.962	1.14
3660	0.006	1.00	1.21
			1.26*
	0.15	1.00	1.15
			1.20*
3340	0.006	1.00	1.23
3130	0.006	1.00	1.24
2970⎫ 3020⎭	0.006	1.00	1.24
2537	0.006	1.00	1.25

[a] Most of the data shown are those of Hatchard and Parker;[90b] values marked with an asterisk are from Lee and Seliger.[78g]

yields increase only slowly and in a regular fashion with decrease in wavelength as seen in Table 7-15. The very small dependence of these yields on reactant and product concentrations, intensity of the incident light, and temperature over a considerable range adds to the utility of this actinometer. Since the Parker actinometer undoubtedly will continue to gain in popularity among photochemists, details concerning its experimental use are included here.

Pure solid reactant is prepared by mixing (with vigorous stirring) 3 volumes of 1.5 M $K_2C_2O_4$ solution and 1 volume of 1.5 M $FeCl_3$ solution (reagent grade chemicals). The precipitated $K_3Fe(C_2O_4)_3 \cdot 3H_2O$ should be recrystallized, preferably three times, from warm water and then dried in a current of warm air (45°). The solid can be stored *in the dark* for long periods of time without change; however, a noticeable color change of the pure green crystals to a yellowish brown occurs rapidly, accompanied by crystal decomposition, when the crystals are placed in ultraviolet light. A $0.006\ M$ solution of $K_3Fe(C_2O_4)_3$ can be used conveniently for wavelengths up to 4300 A; it absorbs, in a 1 cm path, 99% or more of the light up to 3900 A and 50% at 4300 A. To prepare the $0.006\ M$ solution of $K_3Fe(C_2O_4)_3$, 2.947 grams of the solid are dissolved in 800 ml of H_2O, 100 ml $1.0\ N\ H_2SO_4$ are added, and the solution is diluted to 1 liter and mixed. For wavelengths longer than 4300 A, a $0.15\ M$ solution is necessary. It is prepared as above except that 73.68 grams of the solid are required. For all quantitative work the preparation and the manipulation of the ferrioxalate solutions must be carried out in a dark room, using a red photographic safelight.

Hatchard and Parker recommended that a standard calibration graph for analysis of the Fe^{2+} complex be prepared for use with the particular spectrophotometer or colorimeter available in the laboratory. To do this a standard solution (a), about 0.4×10^{-6} mole of Fe^{2+}/ml and $0.1\ N$ in H_2SO_4, is freshly prepared from a standardized $0.1\ M$ $FeSO_4$ solution which is $0.1\ M$ in H_2SO_4 by dilution with $0.1\ N\ H_2SO_4$. Also necessary for the calibration and for subsequent use in the actinometry are a solution (b) containing 0.1% (by weight) 1,10-phenanthroline in water, and a buffer solution (c) prepared from 600 ml of $1\ N\ NaO_2CCH_3$ and 360 ml $1\ N$ H_2SO_4 diluted to 1 liter. Now to a series of eleven 20 (or 25) ml volumetric flasks add with analytical pipets 0, 0.5, 1.0, 1.5, . . . , 4.5, 5.0 ml of standard solution (a). Add sufficient $0.1\ N\ H_2SO_4$ to each flask to make the total volume of solution in each about 10 ml. Add approximately 2 ml of (b) and about 5 ml of (c), dilute to volume, mix well, and allow to stand for at least 60 min;[127] the solution may stand for several hours (in the dark) before measurement if desired. Then determine the transmission of each solution at 5100 A in a 1 cm cell, using the blank iron-free solution which you have prepared, in the reference beam. A linear plot of $\log I_0/I$ versus molar concentration of Fe^{2+} complex is found usually; instrumental variations may alter slightly the apparent molar extinction coefficient (slope of plot), but it would be surprising if a value greatly different from $\epsilon = 1.11 \times 10^4$ liters/mole-cm were obtained with a modern well-adjusted spectrophotometer.

To determine the light intensity in a photochemical reaction cell, the ferrioxalate solution of the appropriate concentration is added to the cell and irradiated. The total volume V_1 of the solution used to fill the cell must be known accurately, so it is best added by means of a pipet or series of pipets of the appropriate size. During the irradiation it is desirable (although not required except for long exposures at low-light intensities) to stir the solution with a current of O_2-free N_2 gas. If some qualitative notion of the intensity of the light beam is available from previous experience, regulate the time of exposure so as to produce about 5×10^{-8} mole of Fe^{2+}/ml.

After an irradiation of t sec, mix the solution well, and pipet an aliquot volume V_2 (say 10 ml) of the solution into a small volumetric flask of volume V_3 (say 25 ml). Add in succession about 2 ml of the phenanthroline solution (b) and a volume of buffer solution (c) equal to about one-half the volume of the photolyte taken. Dilute to the V_3 volume line with water, mix well, and allow to stand for 1 hr. Then prepare an identical but unirradiated solution for use as the blank in the reference beam and allow it to stand as before. Measure the transmission of the solution in the spectrophotometer at 5100 A in a 1 cm, 5 cm, or other suitable standard path-length cell, using the blank solution in the reference beam. From these data the number of ions of Fe^{2+} formed during the photolysis ($n_{Fe^{2+}}$) may be calculated by using

$$n_{Fe^{2+}} = \frac{6.023 \times 10^{20} V_1 V_3 \log_{10}(I_0/I)}{V_2 l \epsilon} \tag{7-7}$$

where V_1 = the volume of actinometer solution irradiated (ml),

V_2 = the volume of aliquot taken for analysis (ml),

V_3 = the final volume to which the aliquot V_2 is diluted (ml),

$\log_{10}(I_0/I)$ = the measured optical density of the solution at 5100 A,

l = the path length of the spectrophotometer cell used (cm),

ϵ = the experimental value of the molar extinction coefficient of the Fe^{2+} complex as determined from the slope of the calibration plot (approximately equal to 1.11×10^4 liters/mole-cm).

By using $n_{Fe^{2+}}$ calculated from 7-7, the value of $\Phi_{Fe^{2+}}$ selected from Table 7-15 for the appropriate wavelength, the time of exposure, and the fraction of the light absorbed by the length of actinometer solution employed (measured for the actual solution used, if not near unity), the light intensity incident just inside the front window of the photolysis cell can be calculated from Eq. 7-6.

7-4B-3 Other Useful Liquid-Phase Chemical Actinometers for Photochemical Use

Although the $K_3Fe(C_2O_4)_3$ system should satisfy most of the needs of the photochemist for a liquid-phase actinometer, several others are in current use and should be described briefly. The uranyl oxalate actinometer[91] continues to be a highly dependable light-measuring device, although when used with the classical procedures its sensitivity is far less than that of the $K_3Fe(C_2O_4)_3$ actinometer. This actinometer depends on the uranyl ion-photosensitized decomposition of oxalic acid, although the reaction is not of simple stoichiometry; CO, CO_2, HCO_2H, U^{4+}, and H_2O appear to be the major products. The reaction occurs in the range 4350–2080 A. For the actinometer prepared from 0.01 M UO_2SO_4 and 0.05 M $H_2C_2O_4$, the quantum yields of oxalate ion loss for temperatures near 25° are as follows: 0.58 at 4358 A; 0.56 at 4050 A; 0.49 at 3660 A; 0.53 at 3350 A; 0.56 at 3130 A; 0.57 at 3020 A; 0.58 at 2780 A; 0.58 at 2650 A; 0.61 at 2450 A; 0.48 at 2080 A. The quantum yields are relatively insensitive to variations in temperature; the 10° temperature coefficient for 5–22° is 1.033, and for 22–58°, 1.030. For the 0.001 M UO_2SO_4 and 0.005 M $H_2C_2O_4$ solutions the temperature coefficient up to 58° (using a base temperature of 25°) is 1.02 ± 0.01.[91d] The yields are also insensitive to reactant concentration and to intensity of the incident light; even at intensities obtainable in flash photolysis experiments, there is no marked variation in the quantum yield.[92]

The oxalate loss is usually determined from the difference between the equivalents of $KMnO_4$ needed to titrate equal aliquots of unirradiated and irradiated actinometer solutions. Since a difference between two nearly equal numbers is required by this method, rather long exposures are needed to obtain accurate results at the usual intensities employed. The details of the experimental procedures and calculations involved in the application of this titration method are well described in the literature.[93] A modification of the analytical procedures using differential absorption spectrophotometry increases the sensitivity of the method greatly,[94a] but the analytical procedures are more involved than those of the $K_3Fe(C_2O_4)_3$ actinometer, and the sensitivity is still not as high.

Porter and Volman[94b] have developed a very sensitive procedure for carbon monoxide analysis, using gas chromatographic analysis with flame ionization detection. They have applied this method to the determination of CO product from the uranyl oxalate photodecomposition[94c] and claim that this technique provides the most sensitive chemical actinometer presently available.

Volman and Seed[94d] report the following values for Φ_{CO}: $[UO_2C_2O_4]$, 0.01 M, and $[H_2C_2O_4]$, 0.05 M, at 30°C: 0.33 (2537 A); 0.26 (3660 A); 0.31 (4350 A); Φ_{CO} is dependent on the reactant concentration, but it is independent of I_a (0.7 − 4.6 × 10^{-6} einstein/cm^3-min).

The history of chloroacetic acid photolysis at 2537 A as an actinometer is rather notorious; it was used for many years with an incorrect value of unity for the quantum yield of chloride ion formation from its photolysis in aqueous solution. It still has a limited usefulness; the quantum yield of chloride ion is relatively independent of reactant concentration and light intensity, but it is strongly temperature dependent: at 2537 A $\Phi_{Cl^-} = 0.31$ at 25°C; 0.69 at 69°C.[95] It is much less sensitive than the $K_3Fe(C_2O_4)_3$ actinometer.

Actinometers employing the photoionization of the leucocyanides of crystal violet[96] or malachite green[97] in ethanol solution have been suggested for use in the 2480–3300 A range. The quantum yield of dye formation in light of very low intensity is unity, over the range of wavelengths and independent of reactant concentration and temperature. The sensitivity is about 10 times that of the $K_3Fe(C_2O_4)_3$ actinometer (employing 1,10-phenanthraline as the complexing agent), but on the whole it is far less satisfactory for most quantitative photochemical work. Its major limitation is a result of the absorption of ultraviolet light by the product dye molecules; this absorption is so large that at intensities usually employed in photochemical work the dye acts as an internal filter and leads to erroneously low results. Furthermore, the solvent employed is easily oxidized and is difficult to clean up for spectrophotometric work. These actinometers should be of some use for experiments at very low light intensities (10^{10}–10^{12} quanta/sec-cm^2 surface).

For those versed in the techniques of radiochemistry, the photochemical exchange between methyl iodide and iodine labeled with ^{131}I can be employed as a convenient actinometer at 2537 A, where the quantum yield of iodine exchange has been shown to be unity.[98] After the exposure of the CH_3I-I_2 mixture, a separation of the I_2 and CH_3I is accomplished by extraction with aqueous sulfite and CCl_4. The relative activities of the inorganic and organic phases are determined, from which the intensity of the light beam can be calculated.[99]

Liquid-phase actinometers for use in the visible range have been described, particularly in the biochemical literature.[100] Many depend on the measurement of oxygen uptake in solutions of highly colored porphyrins which must be shaken as the irradiation occurs. Warburg and Schocken[100a] report that the quantum yield of oxygen uptake is near unity in the photooxidation of thiourea in pyridine with ethyl chlorophyllid as sensitizer in red, yellow, or blue light. The pheophytin- and pheophorbid-containing actinometers of Schwartz[100b] have a quantum yield of oxygen uptake equal to 0.74 ± 0.04, independent of the wavelength between 6400 and 4360 A. Because of difficulties in maintaining O_2 saturation in the usual photochemical systems these actinometers are not well suited for most nonphotosynthetic reaction set-ups.

7-4C   The Use of Phototubes in the Measurement of Light Intensities in Photochemistry

The phototube is of the greatest utility to the photochemist as a means of determining the fraction of the incident beam of light which is absorbed by a system. If a phototube is frequently calibrated against a thermopile-galvanometer system, it can be used in monochromatic light to measure the absolute intensity.

There are several types of electrical light-sensitive devices: (1) photo-emissive cells, which operate as a result of the photoelectric effect or the emission of electrons from an irradiated surface; (2) photoconductive cells, which depend upon light absorption in a solid, promoting immobile electrons to the conduction band of the solid; (3) photovoltaic cells, sometimes called "barrier layer" cells, which create a potential difference between cell layers on absorption of light. In the photovoltaic cells light is absorbed in an asymmetrically illuminated sandwich of semiconductor material between metal electrodes, the top one of which is very thin and transparent. The devices in the first group, the photoemissive cells, have the properties best suited for photochemical applications; the output current of the photocells is very nearly a linear function of the intensity of a monochromatic beam of light over a large range of intensities. They show very little fatigue, are relatively insensitive to temperature change, and respond quickly to changes in light intensity. Usually photocells which are of the other two types show either non-linear response, poor sensitivity in the ultraviolet region, or fatigue on operation, and thus they are less desirable for quantitative photochemical use.

7-4C-1 The Photoemissive Cells for Photochemical Use

Two major types of photoemissive cells are available today: the single-cathode phototube and the multielement photomultiplier. For most photochemical work at high intensities the simple phototube is the best choice. Its sensitivity is adequate for intensities of light encountered in most photochemical work when it is used with a sensitive galvanometer or recorder system, and it can be employed in a very simple circuit as shown in Fig. 7-55.

The photomultiplier tube is ideal for use in the measurement of fluorescence and other light of very low intensity. Within the envelope of the photomultiplier tube an electron released from the photoactive surface is accelerated to the first of several plates at which several secondary electrons are released as the first electron strikes; these secondary electrons are in turn accelerated to another plate, where each releases several more. The process is repeated until amplifications up to 10^6 can be realized. The photomultiplier tube is too sensitive for use directly in light intensities ordinarily employed by photochemists, and its response is non-linear when overloaded in such beams. Note that most commercial photometer units are designed for use with photomultipliers, and they cannot be directly utilized in most photochemical work other than fluorescence studies without incorporation of a high-density filter system.

The spectral response of the phototube can be altered in several ways: (1) variation of the transparent envelope material within which the photosensitive element lies; (2) alteration of the nature of the light-sensitive cathode or the material deposited on it; (3) coating the envelope with fluorescent materials. The nature of the spectral response of a tube

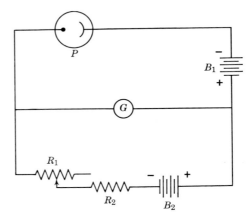

Fig. 7-55 Simple circuit for relative light-intensity measurements with a phototube; the voltage of dry cells B depends on the characteristics of the phototube employed and the intensity of the beam to be monitored (usually 100 v is adequate); B_2 can be a 1.5 v cell; magnitudes of R_1 and R_2 (used to zero galvanometer) depend on the galvanometer employed (see Fig. 7-54).

determines the key response number assigned to it by the manufacturer.

In Fig. 7-56 are shown the spectral responses (relative current/unit of energy of the given wavelength) of several photochemically useful types of phototubes. By coating the face of the phototube with a layer of fluorescent material, it is possible to extend the useful range of these tubes to wavelengths as short as 850 A.[101] It is apparent from the curves of Fig. 7-56 that the response of phototubes is very wavelength dependent. Contrast these curves with the perfectly flat response of the thermopile-galvanometer system. The wavelength dependence of the response of the phototube is a major complication in fluorescence work; here the energy of a wide band of frequencies must be measured (see Sec. 7-5C). Of course it is no complication if the phototube is used only to monitor relative intensities of truly monochromatic light. If impurity light is present, serious errors may be introduced in the attempt to measure fractions of light absorbed; see point 6 on p. 792.

Consider the operation of the phototube and the simple circuit in Fig. 7-55. The battery pack B_1 is of voltage sufficient to prevent current saturation at the intensities employed, usually about 100 v; it is connected in series with the two leads of the phototube and the galvanometer G. The galvanometer response should be about 10^{-11} amp/mm deflection at 1 meter distance. The parallel circuit involving the two resistances R_1 and R_2 and the battery B_2 (1.5 v) allows adjustment of the galvanometer zero

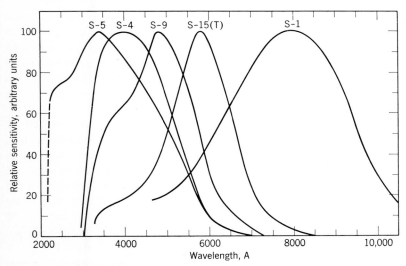

Fig. 7-56   The spectral response of several types of phototubes useful in photochemical applications; relative current per unit energy of the given wavelength is shown as a function of the wavelength; the designation by each curve is the manufacturer's key response number.

position and correction for thermal drift; this additional balancing circuit is not necessary in some applications. The use of the phototube is the utmost in simplicity, but the inexperienced operator may benefit from a few special comments about it.

1. The phototube should be mounted in a light-tight housing at the end of the optical train. The opening to the phototube should be controlled with a shutter and protected from scattered room light by fastening a light shield to the phototube housing next to the active element: for example, a light shield can be made from a 2″ length of tubing about the diameter of the phototube itself, painted inside with flat-black paint. In some set-ups it is possible to mount the phototube housing directly to the thermostat in which the cell is mounted, and then shielding problems are less difficult.

2. Since phototubes are somewhat sensitive to temperature changes,

water coils for cooling the housing may be necessary when the mounting is near a source of heat.

3. A condensing lens of suitable focal length may be placed in front of the phototube housing and at a distance such that the light in the beam is reduced to an area slightly smaller than that of the photoactive cathode. Even with near-point sources, where it is possible to focus to a small spot, do not do so; it is desirable to focus to cover the entire cathode area as uniformly as possible to avoid overloading a small area.

4. With the lamp and phototube operating, the shutter on the phototube should be opened and closed. The galvanometer should move quickly to near full-scale when the tube is exposed and then drop quickly to near zero as the shutter is closed. Some adjustment of the galvanometer sensitivity or the voltage applied to the tube, or the insertion of a filter before the phototube, may be necessary to obtain the desired magnitude of the galvanometer deflection in the light beam employed.

5. The linearity of the response of the system should be checked by inserting a spectrophotometrically calibrated plate, uniform-density filter, or screen in the beam. If a screen is used, it should be placed well back in the optical train near the light source so that suitable mixing of the dark and light regions it transmits will occur before striking the phototube. If the galvanometer reading does not drop to the reading anticipated, it is likely that the phototube is overloaded or saturated; the applied voltage on the tube can be increased (not to exceed the recommended maximum value) or a further reduction can be made in the light intensity incident on the active element. This is the common experience when a photomultiplier unit is employed for this type of measurement.

6. A further test for impurity light in the beam should be made. Let us say, for example, that the light beam is presumed to be 3130 A radiation within a narrow range. If a thick plate glass is inserted into the beam at any point in the optical train, the response of the system should drop to near zero. If this is not the case, a significant amount of impurity radiation of wavelength greater than 3130 A is reaching the detector. The filter should be checked. This result does not necessarily mean that the impurity radiation in the photolysis cell beam is too high, but it may be the result of the improper choice of either the light-lowering filter at the phototube or the spectral response of the phototube employed. If a plate of Pyrex or soft glass is chosen as the filter for the phototube to lower the intensity reaching it (this would be a poor choice), the fraction of the light reaching the photocell which is of the longer wavelengths is greatly increased, so that the phototube response will be dominated by the variation in the intensity of the longer wavelengths; of course, with this situation the measurement of the fraction of light absorbed by a reactant

in the 3130 A region is impossible. Whatever the intended wavelength of the system used, pick a selective filter and carry out a similar test to ensure that the response of the phototube is keyed to the wavelength range of interest.

7. In making readings with the phototube-galvanometer system a consistent method must be employed. When a phototube is exposed to a beam, the current often rises quickly to a maximum reading and then decreases in a few seconds to a slightly lower value. Thus it is important to make all readings at some definite time (say 5 sec) after opening the shutter.

7-4C-2   The Use of the Phototube in the Determination of the Fraction of the Incident Light Absorbed by a Reactant

Just before the reactant is introduced into the photolysis cell at the start of a run, the phototube shutter is opened and the galvanometer deflection (Δ_0) should be determined, as described in Sec. 7-4C-1, for the empty cell. The reactant is then introduced quickly, the phototube shutter opened, and the galvanometer deflection (Δ) determined as before. Photochemists often assume that the fraction of the light (incident just inside the photolysis cell front window) which is transmitted by the reactant is equal to the ratio Δ/Δ_0. This procedure gives an approximate value only, and one using it should be cognizant of the magnitude of the errors involved. An error results largely as a consequence of the reflection of a fraction of the light at the interfaces at the rear window of the photolysis cell. Light which is not absorbed in the first pass through the cell and is reflected in part at the rear window makes an additional pass through the reactant, and an additional fraction of this is also absorbed; a fraction of the reflected light is re-reflected, and so on. As a result the actual fraction of the light which is absorbed is somewhat larger than the factor $1 - (\Delta/\Delta_0)$ estimated with the phototube-galvanometer readings.

Hunt and Hill[102a] have considered this problem in some detail. They assumed an ideal system with a parallel beam of light, perpendicularly incident on the front window of the cell, no absorption or scattering of light occurs within the windows, and F is the fraction of light incident on any one of the four optical material-gas interfaces of the two identical windows which is reflected. Let I_a be the true intensity of the absorbed light, I_0 the intensity of the light incident on the outside of the cell front window, $I_0{}^i$ the true intensity of the light beam incident just *inside* the front window of the photolysis cell, and $I_t{}^0$ the intensity of the light beam transmitted from the rear of the photolysis cell when it is empty; I_t is the intensity of the light transmitted by the gaseous reactant in the cell. If F^2

is small compared to unity, which is usually the case ($\sim$0.002 for quartz-air) and there is no absorption or scattering of light by the windows, then to a first approximation the true fraction of the light (incident just inside the front cell window) which is absorbed by the reactant (I_a/I_0^i) is related to the observed galvanometer deflection ratio Δ/Δ_0 by

$$\frac{I_a}{I_0^i} = \left(1 - \frac{\Delta}{\Delta_0}\right)\mathbf{F} \tag{7-8}$$

$$\mathbf{F} = \frac{(I_t^0/I_0)^{\frac{1}{2}}(1 - F)^2}{(I_t^0/I_0) - F\left[1 + \dfrac{(I_t^0/I_0)}{(1 - F)^2}(I_t/I_0)\right]} \tag{7-9}*$$

The factor **F** is not equal to unity (as is sometimes assumed) except for the case of complete absorption by the reactant. Values of **F** are given in Table 7-16 for typical gas-phase and liquid-phase systems using a good

TABLE 7-16   Correction Factor **F** for Various Measured "Fractions of Light Absorbed"[a] (See Eq. 7-9)

Measured "Fraction of Light Absorbed"	Air-Quartz-Gas Interfaces			Air-Quartz-Water Interfaces		
	5770 A	3660 A	2537 A	5770 A	3660 A	2537A
0.05	1.077	1.085	1.095	1.038	1.041	1.043
0.10	1.074	1.080	1.089	1.036	1.039	1.040
0.20	1.065	1.070	1.079	1.032	1.034	1.036
0.30	1.057	1.061	1.068	1.028	1.030	1.031
0.40	1.048	1.052	1.058	1.024	1.025	1.027
0.50	1.040	1.043	1.048	1.020	1.021	1.022
0.60	1.032	1.034	1.038	1.016	1.017	1.018
0.70	1.023	1.025	1.028	1.012	1.012	1.013
0.80	1.015	1.017	1.019	1.008	1.008	1.009
0.90	1.007	1.008	1.009	1.004	1.004	1.004
0.95	1.004	1.004	1.005	1.002	1.002	1.002

[a] These correction factors represent approximate values which apply to an optically perfect fused quartz cell in a perfectly parallel beam of light; **F** values for the air-quartz-gas interfaces were calculated from Eq. 7-9; those for the air-quartz-water interfaces were derived from a similar modified expression.

---

* The approximate relation 7-9 given here is of slightly different form from that of Hunt and Hill.[102a] The factor $(1 - F)^2$ appears in 7-9 to convert the ratio I_a/I_0 to the more useful one for our purposes, I_a/I_0^i; I_0^i, not I_0, is measured directly by actinometry.

fused quartz cell and a parallel beam of light in the visible (5770 A), the near ultraviolet (3660 A), and the far ultraviolet (2537 A) regions. The correction factor **F** is largest for the gas-phase short-wavelength ultraviolet experiments in which the fraction of light absorbed is low; it is least for visible, liquid-phase studies at high absorption. In the actual experimental case encountered the light beam is not parallel, and not all the reflected beam traverses the cell length and has the opportunity for additional absorption by the reactant. Thus thé magnitude of **F** may be somewhat smaller than that calculated for a parallel beam. Note that all windows which follow the rear window of the photolysis cell up to the phototube detector must be mounted at such an angle that they do not reflect light from the beam back into the photolysis cell, or the corrections discussed are more serious and of course Eq. 7-9 does not apply.

The data of Table 7-16 may be of some value in correcting observed galvanometer deflection ratios Δ/Δ_0 to estimate fractions of light transmitted; however, for accurate work the characteristics of the actual optical components used in a system must be determined and a more accurate consideration given to the correction. As we shall see in Sec. 7-5-B it is possible in the determination of quantum yields to eliminate completely the possible errors due to uncertainties in the fraction of the incident light which is absorbed.

7-5 THE DETERMINATION OF QUANTUM YIELDS

Whether we determine the quantum yield of a given product of a photochemical reaction or the fluorescence quantum yield, basically the same experimental measurements must be made. Either the number of product molecules n_B of the given type B or the number of quanta n_f emitted by the reactant must be determined for a given length of exposure t. The calculation of both quantities requires as well the determination of the light intensity incident on the reactant I_0^i and the fraction of this light which is absorbed by the reactant (I_a/I_0^i). From these data the respective quantum yields of product B (Φ_B) or fluorescence quantum yields (φ_f) can be calculated from 7-10 and 7-11:

$$\Phi_B = \frac{n_B}{I_0^i(I_a/I_0^i)t} = \frac{n_B}{I_a t} \tag{7-10}$$

$$\varphi_f = \frac{n_f}{I_0^i(I_a/I_0^i)t} = \frac{n_f}{I_a t} \tag{7-11}$$

Although the quantum yield determination is always basically that outlined, there is a variety of useful methods of arriving at the end result. In this section we will review two distinct methods used for product quantum yield determinations: one employed with the thermopile-galvanometer detection system and the other for experiments using the chemical actinometer. We must also consider the unique problems and interesting methods of determining n_f, the number of quanta emitted as fluorescence by a reactant, and the fluorescence quantum yield.

7-5A   Product Quantum Yields from Thermopile-Galvanometer Data

The calibration and use of the thermopile-galvanometer system to determine light intensities have been described in Secs. 7-4A-2 and 3. For the determination of product quantum yields three specific light-intensity measurements are neccesary in addition to analytical determination of the number of molecules of product formed (n_B). Each is made using the thermopile galvanometer system in the fashion described previously; the summation of the individual average galvanometer deflections for each of the regularly spaced positions of the thermopile across the light beam is made: (1) at the front of the cell (with the cell removed), about 1 mm behind the screen S_3 in Fig. 7-20 ($\Sigma\Delta_0$); (2) at the rear of the empty cell ($\Sigma\Delta_t^0$); (3) at the rear of the cell filled with the reactant ($\Sigma\Delta_t$). If arc aging is serious during the run time (not normally the case with modern commercial arcs), steps 2 and 3 should be repeated at the end of the run and the average values $\overline{\Sigma\Delta_t}$ and $\overline{\Sigma\Delta_t^0}$ derived. By using these measured quantities, the value of the fraction of the incident light reflected at each cell material fluid interface F, and the number of molecules of product n_B, the product quantum yield can be calculated. The calculation method and most of the symbolism given here are those of Leighton and Forbes.[50a,103]

The cell constant $1 - x$, the fraction of the energy entering the empty cell which reaches the rear window, is given by

$$1 - x = \frac{\overline{\Sigma\Delta_t^0}}{\overline{\Sigma\Delta_0}(1 - F)^2} \qquad (7\text{-}12)$$

The fraction of energy entering the cell window that passes through the absorbing substance and reaches the rear window L is

$$L = \frac{(\overline{\Sigma\Delta_t})(1 - x)}{\overline{\Sigma\Delta_t^0}} \qquad (7\text{-}13)$$

Using L, $1 - x$, and F, the fraction of the energy entering the cell which is absorbed by the reactant (Q_m) can be calculated; by taking into account multiple reflections from the cell windows,

$$Q_m = (1 - L)(1 + FL)\frac{\log L - \log (1 - x)}{\log L} \qquad (7\text{-}14)$$

The total energy $\mathscr{E}_t$ which enters the photolysis cell during the exposure of t sec is

$$\mathscr{E}_t = \frac{(\Sigma \Delta_t^0)(TC)(TR)t}{(1 - F)(1 - x)} \qquad (7\text{-}15)$$

where TC and TR represent the thermopile constant and transmission ratio as defined in Secs. 7-4A-2 and 3. Since the energy per quantum of absorbed light is equal to hc/λ, the number of quanta absorbed in the photolysis run n_q is given by

$$n_q = \frac{\mathscr{E}_t Q_m \lambda}{hc} \qquad (7\text{-}16)$$

The quantum yield of product B is derived from n_B and 7-16:

$$\Phi_B = \frac{n_B}{n_q} \qquad (7\text{-}17)$$

7-5B Quantum Yields Using the Chemical Actinometer Systems

In Sec. 7-4B the use of the actinometer for the measurement of the light intensity just inside the front cell window (I_0^i) was discussed. In Sec. 7-4C the use of the phototube to derive the fraction of light incident just inside the front cell window which is transmitted by the reactant (I_t^i/I_0^i) was outlined. If the number of molecules of a product B (n_B) found in an exposure time t is known together with the above data, the quantum yield of B can be estimated from

$$\Phi_B = \frac{n_B}{(I_0^i)t(1 - I_t^i/I_0^i)} \qquad (7\text{-}18)$$

However, with this approach, there is some finite uncertainty in the accuracy of the I_t^i/I_0^i measurement (see Sec. 7-4C), and hence the same uncertainty is reflected in Φ_B.

A much more accurate approach to the determination of quantum yields by using the actinometer and phototube data follows the suggestion of Claesson.[104] This entails the equating of the fractions of light absorbed by reactant and actinometer solution. The phototube is employed as usual to measure Δ_t/Δ_t^0, as described in Sec. 7-4C, for a reactant at a certain concentration and temperature; then an actinometer of the same phase as the reactant is chosen, and its concentration in the photolysis cell is so regulated that exactly the same ratio of Δ_t/Δ_t^0 is obtained as measured by the phototube. Regardless of the true value of the fraction of the light absorbed by the reactant or the actinometer solution, it must be the same, since any reflection, absorption, or scattering of the light by the cell windows is identical in the two cases, and the number of quanta absorbed by each solution must be identical if the incident light intensity is kept constant in the two experiments. If the reactant is irradiated for t_b sec and forms n_B molecules of its decomposition product B, and the chemical actinometer solution forms n_A molecules of its product A when irradiated for t_a sec, the quantum yield of product B must be given by

$$\Phi_B = \frac{n_B t_a \Phi_A}{n_A t_b}$$ (7-19)

If a reliable actinometer is chosen, this is a very accurate and convenient method of quantum yield determination.

7-5C   The Measurement of Absolute Quantum Yields of Fluorescence

The precise determination of absolute quantum yields of fluorescence presents great difficulties because one has to compare with the number of quanta absorbed from a directed beam of monochromatic light, the number of quanta of polychromatic fluorescent light, whose distribution in space may be geometrically complicated. The first measurements were made by Vavilov,[105] who in 1924 obtained surprisingly accurate results with the limited apparatus available. Essentially his method involved the comparison of the light from an illuminating beam scattered from a pure white matt surface with the fluorescence from the surface of a cell of material similarly placed in the beam; he assumed idealized laws of surface scattering and of fluorescence radiation and took into account variations of wavelength sensitivity of the detector and the other factors.

The method was elaborated by Gilmore, Gibson, and McClure[106] in a heroic attempt to overcome the added difficulties of low-temperature measurement; elaborate corrections for polarization effects, refractive index,[107] etc., were made. The uncertainty in most of these corrections is automatically eliminated by enclosing both comparison scattering surface and fluorescence surface in an integrating sphere,[108] but it is difficult to combine this arrangement with wide temperature control of the sample.

To simplify the comparison in terms of quanta between the exciting and the emitted light the "quantum counter" method of Bowen and Sawtell[109] may be used. Here both comparison scattered light and fluorescent light are successively caught by a suitably chosen fluorescence screen (such as rhodamine B),[109c] which converts all incident light, of whatever wavelength (within limits), with uniform efficiency into a fixed band of longer wavelengths to be received by the detector. A further refinement has been applied by Weber and Teale[110] in which the comparison white matt surface is replaced by a protein solution of calculable scattering power. This permits the use of dilute solutions, with avoidance both of concentration quenching errors and of reabsorption effects due to the overlap of fluorescence and absorption bands. The method, however, depends for its validity on the degree to which the protein solution possesses the idealized scattering properties attributed to it.

An entirely different method is described by Alentsev[111] in which the fluorescent solution is illuminated within a carefully thermally insulated enclosure and its temperature rise measured; this is compared with the rise for a non-fluorescent, light-stable solution of equal light absorption. The latter, of course, becomes hotter because it reradiates no light energy. The method is limited in accuracy and in generality of application because of the small temperature differences encountered and the occurrence of photochemical reactions in many systems. The theoretical and experimental aspects of the quantitative determination of emission spectra in solution have been thoroughly treated in an excellent article by Parker.[112a] The reader is referred to this for details, literature survey, etc.

7-5C-1   Quantum Yields of Fluorescence by Relative Fluorescence Measurements

As with all types of quantum yield measurements, relative quantum yields of fluorescence can be determined with much greater accuracy than absolute ones. Absolute fluorescence quantum yields of many compounds have been determined with considerable precision by several laboratories, and these can be used as "actinometers" for fluorescence quantum yield determinations of other compounds. For example, in the absence of oxygen or concentration quenching and in solutions dilute enough to avoid errors due to overlap of fluorescence and absorption spectra, rubrene in hexane or sodium 1-naphthylamine 4-sulfonate in glycerol or ethylene glycol has a quantum yield of fluorescence very near unity and may be a good choice for a standard.

Parker and Rees[112b] and Melhuish[109b] consider several possible standards for fluorimetric measurements: fluorescein (low concentration, in aqueous carbonate-bicarbonate buffer of pH 9.6), $\varphi_f = 0.85$; rhodamine B (in ethanol at low concentration), $\varphi_f = 0.69$; quinine bisulfate (low concentration, in 0.1 N H_2SO_4, 3130 or 3660 A excitation), $\varphi_f = 0.55$; 2-naphthol (aqueous solution, $10^{-3}\,M$, $0.05\,M$ borate buffer, pH $= 10$, 3130 A excitation), $\varphi_f = 0.21$; proflavine (aqueous solution, $10^{-4}\,M$, $0.05\,M$ acetate buffer, pH $= 4$, 4360 A excitation), $\varphi_f = 0.27$ (0.34 as concentration $\to 0$).[112b,112c]

The determination of fluorescence quantum efficiencies by the relative methods is fast and accurate and is becoming widely used by workers in this area. In view of its great utility a detailed discussion of the procedures, largely as outlined by Parker and Rees,[112b] will be given here. [See the recommendation of an international group of experts, Ref. 112(c).]

The instrumentation for fluorescence measurements can be very simple such as an ordinary spectrophotometer with an added fluorescence attachment,[113] or it may be a more elaborate commercial fluorimeter designed for some specific type of fluorescence measurements. Excitation is effected usually by a monochromatic beam or band of high-intensity radiation which passes through the cell at right angles to the direction of the fluorescence observation. The design of cells for fluorescence work has been described briefly in Sec. 7-3C.

If a solution of c moles/liter of a compound with a fluorescence quantum efficiency of φ_f, and a path length of l cm is placed in a monochromatic light beam of incident intensity I_0 (quanta/sec) for which the compound has a molar extinction coefficient ϵ, the total fluorescence intensity I_f (quanta/sec) from the solution will be given by

$$I_f = I_0(1 - 10^{-\epsilon c l})\varphi_f \qquad (7\text{-}20)$$

For dilute solutions ($\epsilon c l \leqslant 0.02$), for which only a small fraction of the incident light is absorbed, 7-20 reduces to

$$I_f = 2.303 I_0 \epsilon c l \varphi_f \qquad (7\text{-}21)$$

If relative fluorescence-intensity measurements are made in the same cell and monochromatic beam of incident light, using dilute solutions of a standard compound (1) of known fluorescence quantum efficiency $(\varphi_f)_1$ and some compound (2) whose fluorescence efficiency $(\varphi_f)_2$ is to be determined, it follows from 7-21 that $(\varphi_f)_2$ can be calculated from

$$(\varphi_f)_2 = \frac{(I_f)_2 \epsilon_1 c_1}{(I_f)_1 \epsilon_2 c_2} (\varphi_f)_1 \qquad (7\text{-}22)$$

If the concentrations of the solutions are regulated so that $\epsilon_1 c_1 = \epsilon_2 c_2$, then uncertainties due to reflections at windows, etc., are eliminated, and 7-23 applies.

$$(\varphi_f)_2 = \frac{(I_f)_2 (\varphi_f)_1}{(I_f)_1} \qquad (7\text{-}23)$$

The relative numbers of quanta emitted/second as fluorescence by the standard and the compound to be studied are required to calculate $(\varphi_f)_2$. The geometry of the irradiated region of the cell, the area and positioning of the spectrograph slit, and the optics limit the quanta/second of fluorescence entering the detector system to a small fraction α of the total quanta/second fluoresced in all directions by the solutions. Provided that the solutions of the standard and the compound to be studied are sufficiently dilute to prevent inner filter effects, the fraction α is identical for the two solutions, and the ratio of the quanta fluoresced/second from the standard and other compound solutions which enter the detection system is equal to the desired ratio $(I_f)_2/(I_f)_1$. However, the fluorescence spectra of the two compounds will not be identical, and the response of the spectrograph-photomultiplier combination used to detect the fluorescence is very wavelength dependent. Thus the observed phototube response as a function of frequency, termed the *apparent* fluorescence emission spectra, is not a direct measure of the number of quanta emitted at each frequency in a fluorescence band, but a correction to the observed phototube response must be made to obtain values proportional to the number of quanta/second; this is the major problem in the determination of fluorescence quantum yields.

The observed photomultiplier response A_ν at any frequency ν is related to the quanta/frequency interval entering the detection system, $\alpha(dI_f/d\nu)$, by

$$A_\nu = \alpha\left(\frac{dI_f}{d\nu}\right)B_\nu L_\nu P_\nu = \alpha\left(\frac{dI_f}{d\nu}\right)S_\nu \qquad (7\text{-}24)$$

B_ν is the band width in frequency units at frequency ν, L_ν is the fraction of light transmitted by the spectrometer at frequency ν, and P_ν is the output of the phototube per quantum at frequency ν. The product of the three correction factors is termed the sensitivity factor (S_ν) of the monochromator-photomultiplier combination.

For fluorescence measurements in the visible range, S_ν may be determined accurately by reference to the observed response of the detector system as a function of frequency to the radiation from a standard tungsten lamp of known spectral distribution operated at a known color temperature. Such lamps and their energy distributions are available from the U.S. National Bureau of Standards, National Physical Laboratory (England), and probably other national laboratories. The data provided with the lamps are commonly in the form of energy units/unit wavelength interval $(dE/d\lambda)$. Since $E = hc/\lambda$, these factors are converted to relative number of quanta per wavelength interval $(dI/d\lambda)$ through

$$\frac{dE}{d\lambda}\lambda = \frac{dI}{d\lambda} \qquad (7\text{-}25)$$

The number of quanta per unit frequency interval is related to $dI/d\lambda$ by

$$\frac{dI}{dv} = \frac{dI}{d\lambda}\frac{d\lambda}{dv} = -\frac{dI}{d\lambda}\frac{\lambda^2}{c} \tag{7-26}$$

From 7-25 and 7-26 it follows that

$$\frac{dI}{dv} = -\frac{dE}{d\lambda}\frac{\lambda^3}{c} \tag{7-27}$$

The sensitivity factor of the detector system S_v at each frequency for which the response to the standard lamp radiation is R_v is defined by

$$S_v = \frac{R_v}{(dE/d\lambda)\lambda^3} \tag{7-28}$$

If the observed photomultiplier response at a given frequency is divided by the sensitivity factor S_v at that frequency, then the response so corrected is proportional to the quanta emitted per unit frequency interval at the given frequency.

New standards of spectral irradiance for use in the ultraviolet as well as the visible and near-infrared ranges (2500–26,000 A) are available now from the United States National Bureau of Standards. These are 1000 w quartz-iodine lamps, with coiled-coil tungsten filaments, which have been calibrated against emission from a black-body radiator.[125] Sensitivity factors of the detector system in the ultraviolet range can be determined most readily by using these lamps. Alternatively the values of S_v can be estimated through the determination of the *apparent* fluorescence emission spectrum of a compound and its comparison with the *true* fluorescence spectrum which is available.[109c,112,114] A less satisfactory alternative is the calculation of sensitivity factors directly from the relation $S_v = B_v L_v P_v$ and manufacturers' data for these quantities.

Now let us review the steps necessary to determine the fluorescence quantum yield of a compound by this relative method:

1. Dilute solutions ($\epsilon c l \leqslant 0.02$) of the standard fluorescent compound (1) of known φ_f and the compound (2) under study are prepared such that $\epsilon_1 c_1 = \epsilon_2 c_2$.

2. The *apparent* fluorescence emission spectra of both solutions are determined, using a constant slit width of the spectrograph and a constant intensity of the exciting monochromatic light. These spectra give the response of the detecting photomultiplier recorded as a function of the frequency of the emitted fluorescence.

3. The *true* fluorescence emission spectra (proportional to the quanta/ unit frequency interval) are derived from the *apparent* spectra by division

of the ordinates at each frequency of the *apparent* spectra by the sensitivity factor S_v of the detector system for that frequency. (S_v is derived from standard lamp data using 7-28, or by other measurements described previously.)

4. The areas under the *true* fluorescence emission spectra curves of the two solutions are found; these are proportional to the total quanta fluoresced, $(I_f)_1$ and $(I_f)_2$.

5. The fluorescence quantum efficiency of the compound under study $(\varphi_f)_2$ can be calculated from these data by using 7-23 with the ratio $(I_f)_2/(I_f)_1$ = (area under the *true* fluorescence emission curve of compound (2) under study)/(area under the *true* curve for the standard compound).

Several precautions should be taken in measuring fluorescence quantum efficiencies to eliminate errors due to inner filter effects, oxygen quenching, non-monochromatic exciting light, and photodecompositions.[112b]

1. Equation 7-22 applies only for small values of ϵcl. If solutions are chosen such that $\epsilon_1 c_1 \neq \epsilon_2 c_2$, an optical density of about 0.02 (at the exciting wavelength at the depth of solution from which fluorescence is viewed) should not be exceeded, or an error greater than 4% is introduced. The use of solutions of equal optical densities avoids this complication.

2. Solutions to be used for fluorescence measurements should be free from dirt, lint, or other light-scattering particles.

3. When the exciting light is weakly absorbed and the absorption and fluorescence spectra overlap, then self-absorption of the light fluoresced in the high-frequency end of the fluorescence band may occur in the low-frequency end of the absorption band. The importance of this effect can be determined by measurement at increasing dilutions and at correspondingly higher sensitivities of the detector system; the relative intensity of the high-frequency fluorescence emission band rises with increasing dilution compared to that of the low-frequency band when self-absorption is important.

4. Because of the common occurrence of oxygen quenching of fluorescence, it is always a good practice to test qualitatively for oxygen quenching in the early stages of a fluorescence study. Fluorescence intensity for a given solution should be determined by using a purge of O_2-free nitrogen gas, and with saturation by oxygen; if a detectable difference in fluorescence intensity is found, provision must be made to eliminate oxygen from the cell and the solution (see Fig. 7-44 and the discussion of Sec. 7-3C).

5. Large errors may be introduced in the determination of fluorescence efficiency if the exciting light contains several frequencies which are absorbed to different extents by the reactant. Parker and Rees[112b] illustrate this complication with data from anthracene. The absorption

of the 2537 A radiation by anthracene is about 100 times that for 3130 A. If an exciting light beam, presumed to be pure 3130 A radiation, contains only 1% of 2537 A impurity, the observed fluorescence intensity will be about 100% greater than the true fluorescence intensity expected for a pure 3130 A beam, and the estimated φ_f will be double the true value. The purity of the exciting light beam should be checked by filling the cell with a slightly turbid, non-fluorescing solution and measuring the spectrum of the scattered light with the spectrophotometer.

6. The exposure times should not be extended unnecessarily, since products of the photodecomposition of the reactant will build up and may contribute significantly to the observed fluorescence or possibly act as efficient quenchers of the reactant's fluorescence.[115]

7-5C-2   Measurement of Fluorescence and Phosphorescence Spectra and Lifetimes

The mean lifetime τ of an excited molecule from which fluorescence or phosphorescence originates is of great interest in the consideration of the mechanisms of excited molecule reactions, and it is simple to determine in principle. The molecules may be excited to the fluorescing state by a short pulse of light, and the intensity of the fluorescence measured as a function of time. For a given set of experimental conditions the intensity of fluorescence from a single excited state should follow a first-order rate law; that is, the intensity of the fluorescence $(I_f)_t$ at some time t after the initial measurement will be related to the fluorescence intensity in the initial measurement $(I_f)_0$ by

$$\frac{(I_f)_t}{(I_f)_0} = e^{-t/\tau} \tag{7-29}$$

Thus, if I_f is measured as a function of t and a plot of $\ln (I_f)_t$ versus t is prepared, the slope of the line gives $-1/\tau$. The mean fluorescence lifetime measured experimentally τ is smaller than the "natural" radiative lifetime of the state τ_0 because of non-radiative energy dissipation processes which compete with fluorescence. τ_0 is related to τ through the absolute value of the fluorescence quantum yield φ_f:

$$\tau_0 = \frac{\tau}{\varphi_f} \tag{7-30}$$

Thus, if φ_f and τ have been measured, τ_0 is readily derived. A check on the consistency of the quantum yield and lifetime measurements can be obtained by means of theory. From the measured extinction coefficients of the reactant as a function of frequency and certain other spectral data an independent estimate of τ_0 can be made[116] (see Eq. 3-47).

The first measurements of phosphorescence decay lifetimes were made more than one hundred years ago by Becquerel, using a simple apparatus involving rotating slotted discs.[117] Today several excellent methods of high accuracy are available for the photochemist (see Refs. 112a and 117c for designs and operation of spectrofluorophosphorimeters of great utility). Many systems have been designed which depend upon the excitation of the reactant in a light pulse of short duration followed by the direct measurement of the decay of fluorescence emission in a dark cycle. Relatively simple systems can be used to measure lifetimes greater than 10^{-6} sec. The light beam can be chopped into pulses by mechanical shutters on rotating wheels or by means of optical systems with rotating mirrors. The Kerr cell has been used to advantage as a shutter of very low inertia; in this system a transparent, non-conducting compound such as nitrobenzene (transmits only $\lambda > 4400$ A) or chlorobenzene ($\lambda > 3000$ A) is placed in a cylindrical cell containing two metal electrodes which run parallel to the cell axis. Crossed Nicol prisms are located at each end of the cell. Now, when a pulse of several thousand volts is applied to the electrodes the high electric field causes polarization and orientation of the molecules such that the liquid becomes doubly refracting and rotates the plane of plane-polarized light. If the Nicol prisms are originally crossed so that no light passes through the cell-prism combination, with the proper choice of path length and applied voltage it is possible to rotate the plane of the polarized light by 90° on passage through the cell so that the system becomes transparent to the light when the voltage is applied. Rawcliff[118] describes an apparatus for fluorescence lifetimes studies for $\tau > 10^{-6}$ sec employing this system of light chopping and a photomultiplier-cathode ray oscilloscope detector system. Skarsvag[119] gives details for a stroboscopic flash tube system useful for phosphorescence lifetimes greater than 2×10^{-3} sec.

Brody[34] has incorporated the millimicrosecond flash tube of Malmberg[33] with a photomultiplier-oscilloscope detection system to measure fluorescence lifetimes in the millimicrosecond range. Photographs of the oscilloscopic trace of the lamp and fluorescence intensity decay are used in the estimation of the fluorescence lifetimes. Bennett[35] used the basic Malmberg lamp as a stroboscopic flash source and monitored the fluorescence with a photomultiplier which was gated by a high-voltage pulse at accurately varied time intervals following the flashes. The record of light-intensity decay in this case appeared as a tracing on a recorder chart. The systems of both Brody and Bennett seem well suited to accurate fluorescence lifetime determinations. Bennett's system provides the data in a somewhat more useful form. With both these systems it is necessary to correct the observed instrument response for the decay of the lamp flash intensity when the lifetime to be measured is comparable to the lifetime of the decay of the exciting light from the lamp, $\tau = 1.8 \times 10^{-9}$ sec. Bennett finds that for fluorescence lifetimes greater than 4×10^{-9} sec the time constant for the decay observed with his equipment is nearly equal to the true fluorescence lifetime, but for shorter lifetimes the correction is significant: the directly observed values are greater than the true values by 7% for lifetimes of 3×10^{-9} sec and by 30% for 2×10^{-9} sec.

A very different system of fluorescence lifetime measurements has been developed which is based upon a system originated by Lord and Rees.[120] Fluorescence may be excited with light of intensity modulated at a high frequency (5-12 Mc/sec). Because of the finite lifetime of the excited state of an absorbing molecule, there is a delay before the emission of fluorescence by the excited molecule; this results in a difference in the phase of the modulated fluorescence emission and the modulated exciting light. The difference in the phase angle ϕ can be measured experimentally, and the mean fluorescence lifetime can be calculated from its relation to ϕ.

$$\tan \phi = \tau 2\pi \nu \qquad (7\text{-}31)$$

ν is the frequency of modulation of the light. Bailey and Rollefson[121] have used the phase-shift method successfully to measure fluorescence lifetimes in the millimicrosecond range. In their work the light was modulated by using an ultrasonic standing wave on a liquid as an intermittent diffraction grating. Venetta[122] describes a microscope phase fluorimeter which uses an electronic method to modulate the beam from an AH-6 high-pressure mercury arc. Presumably these systems are capable of precisions as high as $\pm 4 \times 10^{-10}$ sec in fluorescence lifetime measurements.

Detailed circuit diagrams of the electronic systems necessary for the various techniques of measuring fluorescence decay are available in the original articles, to which the reader is referred.

After a system for measuring fluorescence decay lifetimes has been placed in working order, it should be tested using some pure compound under conditions for which the fluorescence lifetime is well established. Schäfer and Röllig[123] summarize fluorescence lifetime measurements of many workers for several compounds which would serve well in equipment calibration; one such compound is fluorescein at 10^{-3} M in 0.1 N NaOH, for which $\tau = 4.5 \pm 0.4 \times 10^{-9}$ sec.

The design of a relatively simple spectrophosphorimeter is shown in Fig. 7-57; it may be used for the determination of excitation spectra, phosphorescence emission spectra (triplet energy spacing), and phosphorescence lifetimes.* For results of high precision the reader is referred to the more

---

* Private communication from D. R. Kearns and E. J. Baum, University of California, Riverside.

elegant and complex apparatus of Parker[112a] and Haugen and Marcus.[117c] The excitation monochromator is the commercial Bausch and Lomb instrument (as pictured in Fig. 7-22) having an ultraviolet grating with a range of 200–400 mμ blazed at 250 mμ, and with variable slits. Xenon- or mercury-arc point-source lamps are employed for excitation and emission spectra determinations, respectively. The analyzing monochromator is a Bausch and Lomb 33-86-02 visible grating instrument with variable slits, a range of 350–800 mμ, and grating blazed at 500 mμ. The wavelength drive employed on each monochromator is a Bristol synchronous motor.

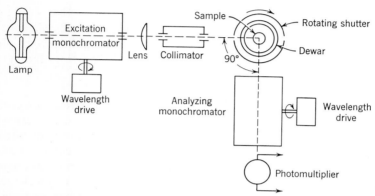

Fig. 7-57   Design of a simple spectrophosphorimeter; see text.

In phosphorescence work the elimination of possible interference from fluorescence of the sample is accomplished by providing a time delay between excitation of the phosphor and detection of the phosphorescence. In the design shown this is accomplished conveniently through the use of a rotating slotted can of the Becquerel type which surrounds the Dewar; it is driven by an Aminco-Hughes variable-speed-drive motor adjustable between 200 and 7000 rpm by controlling the voltage across it with a Variac. The quartz Dewar used to hold the sample has unsilvered strips which permit passage of excitation and phosphorescence light. It is suspended in the Dewar by means of a finger clamp attached to the Dewar housing. The detector is an RCA 1P28 phototube operated from a 900 v power supply. The output of the tube is amplified by a Leeds and Northrop model 9836 current amplifier; the resultant signal is led to a precision potentiometer, and a desired fraction then passed to a recorder. To determine excitation spectra the analyzing monochromator is adjusted to receive some desired wavelength range and the excitation monochromator is allowed to scan; of course, correction of data to constant incident intensity is necessary if the true excitation spectrum is desired. To determine the emission spectrum, the excitation monochromator is fixed at a desired region and the analyzing monochromator is allowed to scan. Phosphorescence lifetimes can be measured by feeding the output of the phototube to an oscilloscope.

The determination of triplet-state energies from phosphorescence spectra in rigid solvents is an important technique in photochemistry. Thus, we have described a simple spectrophosphorimeter with which such spectra can be obtained (see above). However, we should note that in luminescence experiments great care must be taken to have pure solvents and solutes and, for quantitative experiments, to understand the geometry of the optical system and such properties as self-absorption, stray light, etc. It is wise to run (occasionally) standard spectra (e.g., acetophenone for phosphorescence, anthracene for fluorescence) to check the entire system, chemical (e.g., check to see whether there is emission from the" pure" solvent), instrumental, and optical (e.g., spurious bands arising from stray light are common problems).

Recently Herkstroeter, Lamola, and Hammond[124] have described in some detail their experimental procedure of determining triplet excitation energies of a series of compounds used as sensitizers for triplet transfer. Their results are discussed in Chapter 4, Sec. 4-8A, and given in Table 4-13. Their work is indicative of the type of effort necessary to obtain reliable spectra. For example, in order to avoid solvent shifts of the triplet levels of the solutes, their spectra were run in hydrocarbon solvents comparable to those used in the energy-transfer studies.* Clear glasses were obtained at 77°K with 3-methylpentane; methylcyclohexane-isopentane (5:1 by volume); isopentane-methylcyclohexane,1:5; ether-isopentane-ethanol, 5:5:2; and ether-ethanol, 1:2. All samples were purified by alumina chromatography followed by recrystallization, distillation, sublimation, or a combination of these procedures. Care was taken that the solutions (about 10^{-3} M) formed clear glasses at 77°K. (Occasionally microcrystals are formed.) Sample solutions were carefully degassed on a vacuum line (see above) and sealed off in a sample tube.

The selection of the appropriate band† for assignment of the triplet level was based on the fact that at 77°K the triplet emitting molecules are in their lowest vibrational levels. Hence, the observed band of maximum energy or shortest wavelength (the 0-0 band) will correspond to the

---

* The phosphorescence from $n \rightarrow \pi^*$ transitions in carbonyl compounds shows a large hypsochromic shift in polar solvents, relative to non-polar solvents. Phosphorescence from $\pi \rightarrow \pi^*$ transitions of aromatic hydrocarbons generally shows the opposite, a small bathochromic shift in polar solvents.

† Studies on eight different systems showed that the energy of the 0-0 band is usually the most important factor in determining energy transfer from donor acceptor.

desired transition,

$$T_1^0 \rightarrow S_0^0.$$

Usually the vibronic structure of the band makes assignment of the 0-0 band straightforward (see Fig. 4-11), but this is not always the case. Finally, one should take care that the solute does not undergo photodecomposition to products that themselves emit during the time the phosphorescence spectra are run. Similarly, sensitizers for energy-transfer studies should be relatively stable and not themselves react to form competing acceptors. For a useful list of satisfactory sensitizers see Table 4-12.

REFERENCES TO CHAPTER 7

1. (a) C. C. McDonald and H. E. Gunning, *J. Chem. Phys.*, **20**, 1817 (1952); (b) H. E. Gunning and O. P. Strausz, "Isotopic Effects and the Mechanism of Energy Transfer in Mercury Photosensitization," *Advances in Photochemistry*, Vol. I, ed. by W. A. Noyes, Jr., G. S. Hammond, and J. N. Pitts, Jr., Interscience Publishers, a division of John Wiley & Sons, New York, 1963, p. 209.
2. M. Zelikoff, L. M. Aschenbrand, and P. H. Wyckoff, *J. Chem. Phys.*, **21**, 376 (1953).
3. W. A. Noyes, Jr. and P. A. Leighton, *Photochemistry of Gases*, Rheinhold Publishing Corp., New York, 1941, p. 38.
4. C. R. Masson, V. Boekelheide, and W. A. Noyes, Jr., "Photochemical Reactions," Technique of Organic Chemistry, Vol. II, 2nd Edition, *Catalytic, Photochemical, and Electrolytic Reactions*, ed. by A. Weissberger, Interscience Publishers, New York, 1956, p. 274.
5. F. P. Lossing, D. G. H. Marsden, and J. B. Farmer, *Can. J. Chem.*, **34**, 701 (1956).
6. L. J. Heidt and H. B. Boyles, *J. Am. Chem. Soc.*, **73**, 5728 (1951).
7. H. W. Melville, *Trans. Faraday Soc.*, **32**, 1525 (1936).
8. J. R. Dacey and J. W. Hodgins, *Can. J. Research*, **B28**, 90 (1950).
9. E. Sauter, *Z. Angew. Phys.*, **9**, 105 (1957).
10. (a) B. T. Barnes, *J. Appl. Phys.*, **31**, 852 (1960); (b) H. D. Beckey, W. Groth, H. Okabe, and H. J. Rommel, *Z. Naturforsch.*, **A19**, 1511 (1964).
11. L. R. Koller, *Ultraviolet Radiation*, Second Ed., John Wiley & Sons, New York, 1965, p. 50.
12. P. Schulz, *Ann. Physik* [6 Folge], **1**, 95 (1947).
13. W. A. Baum and L. Dunkelman, *J. Opt. Soc. Am.*, **40**, 782 (1950).
14. We are indebted to Mr. John H. Jacobs, Senior Physicist, Bell and Howell Research Center, Pasadena, Calif., for his private communications to us on lamp housing and special arc operation.
15. E. W. R. Steacie and R. Potvin, *Can. J. Research*, **B16**, 337 (1938).
16. H. Habeeb, D. J. LeRoy, and E. W. R. Steacie, *J. Chem. Phys.*, **10**, 261 (1942).
17. S. Robin and B. Vodar, *J. Phys. Radium*, **13**, 671 (1952).
18. F. J. Comes and E. W. Schlag, *Z. Physik. Chem. (Frankfurt)*, **21**, 212 (1959).
19. P. L. Hartman, *J. Opt. Soc. Am.*, **51**, 113 (1961).
20. P. G. Wilkinson and Y. Tanaka, *J. Opt. Soc. Am.*, **45**, 344 (1955).
21. P. G. Wilkinson, *J. Opt. Soc. Am.*, **45**, 1044 (1955).
22. E. W. Schlag and F. J. Comes, *J. Opt. Soc. Am.*, **50**, 866 (1960).

23. (a) J. Romand and V. Vodar, *Spectrochim. Acta*, **8**, 229 (1956); (b) J. R. McNesby and H. Okabe, *Advances in Photochemistry*, Vol. 3, ed. by W. A. Noyes, Jr., G. S. Hammond, and J. N. Pitts, Jr., Interscience Publishers, a division of John Wiley & Sons, New York, 1964, p. 157; (c) H. Okabe, *J. Opt. Soc. Am.*, **54**, 478 (1964).

24. (a) H. E. Edgerton and K. J. Germeshausen, *Rev. Sci. Instr.*, **3**, 535 (1932); (b) P. M. Murphy and H. E. Edgerton, *J. Appl. Phys.*. **12**, 848 (1941); (c) J. N. Aldington and A. J. Meadowcroft, *J. Inst. Elec. Engr.* (*London*), **95**, Pt. 2, 671 (1948).

25. R. G. W. Norrish and G. Porter, *Nature*, **164**, 658 (1949).

26. (a) G. Porter, *Proc. Roy. Soc.* (*London*), **A200**, 284 (1950); (b) G. Porter, "Flash Photolysis," *Technique of Organic Chemistry*, Vol. VIII, Part II, 2nd Edition, *Investigations of Rates and Mechanisms of Reactions*, ed. by S. L. Friess, E. S. Lewis, and A. Weissberger, Interscience Publishers, a division of John Wiley & Sons, New York, 1963, p. 1055.

27. N. Davidson, R. Marshall, A. E. Larsh, Jr., and T. Carrington, *J. Chem. Phys.*, **19**, 1311 (1951).

28. D. A. Ramsay, *J. Chem. Phys.*, **20**, 1920 (1952).

29. For example of types of studies see (a) M. A. Khan, R. G. W. Norrish, and G. Porter, *Proc. Roy. Soc.* (*London*), **A219**, 312 (1953); (b) W. C. Sleppy and J. G. Calvert, *J. Am. Chem. Soc.*, **81**, 769 (1959).

30. M. I. Christie and G. Porter, *Proc. Roy. Soc.* (*London*), **A212**, 398 (1952).

31. (a) S. Claesson and L. Lindqvist, *Arkiv Kemi*, **11**, 535 (1957); (b) *ibid.*, **12**, 1 (1958).

32. R. J. Charlson, H. Harrison, and R. Hardwick, *Rev. Sci. Instr.*, **31**, 46 (1960).

33. J. H. Malmberg, *Rev. Sci. Instr.*, **28**, 1027 (1957).

34. S. S. Brody, *Rev. Sci. Instr.*, **28**, 1021 (1957).

35. R. G. Bennett, *Rev. Sci. Instr.*, **31**, 1275 (1960).

36. K. Breitschwerdt and A. Weller, *Z. Physik. Chem.* (*Frankfurt*), **20**, 353 (1959).

37. (a) J. A. Golden and A. L. Myerson, *J. Opt. Soc. Am.*, **48**, 548 (1958); (b) G. Black and G. Porter, *Proc. Roy. Soc.* (*London*), **A266**, 185 (1962).

38. G. J. Mains, J. L. Roebber, and G. K. Rollefson, *J. Phys. Chem.*, **59**, 733 (1955).

39. (a) S. Claesson, B. Nyman, and G. Wettermark, to be published; (b) equipment described briefly by G. Wettermark, *Arkiv Kemi*, **18**, 1 (1961).

40. G. J. Singer and A. Crosse, *Phil. Mag.*, **46**, 161 (1815).

41. W. M. Conn, *J. Opt. Soc. Am.*, **41**, 445 (1951).

42. G. K. Oster and R. A. Marcus, *J. Chem. Phys.*, **27**, 189, 472 (1957).

43. M. Cloupeau, *Compt. Rend.*, **244**, 744 (1957).

44. R. A. Marcus, *Can. J. Chem.*, **36**, 102 (1958).

45. H. Kwart, H. S. Broadbent, and P. D. Bartlett, *J. Am. Chem. Soc.*, **72**, 1060 (1950).

46. G. M. Burnett and H. W. Melville, *Technique of Organic Chemistry*, Vol. VIII, Part II, 2nd Edition, *Investigation of Rates and Mechanisms of Reactions*, ed. by S. L. Friess, E. S. Lewis, and A. Weissberger, Interscience Publishers, a division of John Wiley & Sons, New York, 1963, p. 1107.

47. (a) W. E. Forsythe and F. Christison, *J. Opt. Soc. Am.*, **20**, 396 (1930); (b) P. A. Leighton, *Photochemistry of Air Pollution*, Academic Press, New York, 1961.

48. (a) C. A. Papp, *Ind. Eng. Chem.*, **55**, 48 (1963); (b) I. Wideer, *Rev. Sci. Instr.*, **30**, 995 (1959); (c) S. Vogel and L. Dulberger, *Electronics*, p. 39, Oct. 27, 1961, and subsequent articles; *ibid.*, p. 40, Nov. 3, 1961, Nov. 10, p. 81, 1961, and Nov. 24, p. 54, 1961.

49. For excellent discussions on the design and construction of monochromators for photochemical use see (a) D. S. Villars, *J. Am. Chem. Soc.*, **49**, 326 (1927); (b)

G. S. Forbes, *J. Phys. Chem.*, **32**, 482 (1928); (c) L. J. Heidt and F. Daniels, *J. Am. Chem. Soc.*, **54**, 2384 (1932); (d) F. Benford, *J. Opt. Soc. Am.*, **26**, 99 (1936); (e) Ref. 3, p. 63; (f) G. R. Harrison, *Rev. Sci. Instr.*, **5**, 149 (1934).

50. (a) P. A. Leighton and G. S. Forbes, *J. Am. Chem. Soc.*, **51**, 3549 (1929); (b) P. A. Leighton and F. E. Blacet, *J. Am. Chem. Soc.*, **54**, 3165 (1932).

51. For examples of designs in grating monochromators for photochemical work see (a) C. S. French, G. S. Rabideau, and A. S. Holt, *Rev. Sci. Instr.*, **18**, 11 (1947); (b) P. Douzou and S. Gerstenkorn, *Compt. Rend.*, **239**, 49 (1954).

52. S. Mitchell and I. M. Dawson, *J. Chem. Soc.*, **1944**, 452; references to the earlier literature given here and in Ref. 53.

53. T. L. Davis and J. Ackerman, Jr., *J. Am. Chem. Soc.*, **67**, 486 (1945).

54. R. E. Hunt and W. Davis, Jr., *J. Am. Chem. Soc.*, **69**, 1415 (1947).

55. For a partial review of the literature and discussion of chemical filters for the ultraviolet see (a) E. J. Bowen, *Chemical Aspects of Light*, 2nd Edition, Clarendon Press, Oxford, 1946; (b) M. Kasha, *J. Opt. Soc. Am.*, **38**, 929 (1948); (c) H. Melville and B. G. Gowenlock, *Experimental Methods in Gas Reactions*, 2nd Edition, Macmillan & Co. Ltd., London, 1964; and Refs. 3 and 4.

56. L. A. Strait, F. M. Goyan, and W. D. Kumler, *J. Opt. Soc. Am.*, **46**, 1038 (1956).

57. (a) R. Pertel, *Abstracts Sixth Informal Photochemistry Conference*, University of California, Davis, Calif., June, 1964; (b) J. L. Weeks, S. Gordon, and G. M. A. C. Meaburn, *Nature*, **191**, 1186 (1961); (c) R. M. Martin and J. E. Willard, *J. Chem. Phys.*, **40**, 2999 (1964); (d) R. A. Holroyd and T. E. Pierce, *J. Phys. Chem.*, **68**, 1392 (1964).

58. J. W. Nicholas and F. F. Pollak, *Analyst*, **75**, 662 (1950).

59. C. W. Sill, *Anal. Chem.*, **33**, 1584 (1961).

60. J. W. Nicholas and F. F. Pollak, *Analyst*, **77**, 49 (1952).

61. (a) C. Christiansen, *Ann. Physik Chem.*, **23**, 298 (1884); (b) *ibid.*, **24**, 439 (1885); (c) F. Weigert and H. Staude, *Z. Physik. Chem.*, **130**, 607 (1927); (d) F. Weigert and J. Shidei, *Z. Physik. Chem.*, **B9**, 329 (1930); (e) H. Kohn and K. von Fragstein, *Physik. Z.*, **33**, 929 (1932); (f) B. M. Duggar, Ed., *Biological Effects of Radiation*, McGraw-Hill Book Co., New York, 1936; (g) R. L. Sinsheimer and J. R. Loofbourow, *Nature*, **160**, 674 (1947).

62. Data of E. A. Taft, quoted by L. R. Koller, Ref. 11, 1st Edition, p. 150.

63. S. S. Ballard, L. S. Combes, and K. A. McCarthy, *J. Opt. Soc. Am.*, **41**, 772 (1951).

64. H. Berg and W. Beyer, *Chem. Tech.* (*Berlin*), **8**, 235 (1956).

65. For examples of the industrial chemist's approach to problems of cell design for photochemical use see (a) C. M. Doede and C. A. Walker, *Chem. Eng.*, **62**, February, 1955, p. 159; (b) W. T. Anderson, Jr., *Ind. Eng. Chem.*, **39**, 844 (1947).

66. For examples of the physical chemist's approach to synthetic cell design see (a) L. J. Heidt, *Science*, **90**, 473 (1939); J. Stauff and H. -J. Schumacher, *Z. Elektrochem.*, **48**, 271 (1942); S. W. Benson and G. B. Kistiakowsky, *J. Am. Chem. Soc.*, **64**, 80 (1942).

67. For examples of the synthetic photochemist's approach to the problems of cell design see (a) M. S. Kharasch and H. N. Friedlander, *J. Org. Chem.*, **14**, 239 (1949); (b) E. Krautz, *Abhandl. Braunschweig. Wiss. Ges.*, **4**, 5 (1952).

68. (a) H. Linschitz and J. Rennert, *Nature*, **169**, 193 (1952); (b) J. Rennert, Ph.D. Thesis, Syracuse University, February, 1953.

69. L. J. Schoen, L. E. Kuentzel, and H. P. Broida, *Rev. Sci. Instr.*, **29**, 633 (1958).

70. (a) E. Whittle, D. A. Dows, and G. C. Pimentel, *J. Chem. Phys.*, **22**, 1943 (1954); (b) E. D. Becker and G. C. Pimentel, *J. Chem. Phys.*, **25**, 224 (1956); (c) H. W. Brown and G. C. Pimentel, *J. Chem. Phys.*, **29**, 883 (1958); (d) G. C. Pimentel,

Chapter 4, *Formation and Trapping of Free Radicals*, ed. by A. M. Bass and H. P. Broida, Academic Press, New York, 1960, pp. 69–116.

71. F. A. Mauer, Chapter 5, Ref. 70d, p. 117–167.

72. For example, see D. J. E. Ingram, *Free Radicals as Studied by Electron Spin Resonance*, Butterworths Scientific Publications, London, 1958, p. 173.

73. H. L. J. Bäckström and K. Sandros, *Acta Chem. Scand.*, **12**, 823 (1958).

74. (a) J. Strong, *Procedures in Experimental Physics*, Prentice-Hall, Englewood Cliffs, N.J., 1946; (b) S. Jnanananda, *High Vacua, Principles, Production, and Measurement*, D. Van Nostrand Co., Princeton, N.J., 1947; (c) S. Dushman, *Scientific Foundations of Vacuum Technique*, 2nd Edition, John Wiley & Sons, New York, 1962; (d) R. E. Dodd and P. L. Robinson, *Experimental Inorganic Chemistry*, Elsevier Publishing Co., New York, 1954; (e) W. E. Barr and V. J. Anhorn, *Scientific and Industrial Glass Blowing and Laboratory Techniques*, Instruments Publishing Co., Pittsburgh, Pa., 1959; (f) E. L. Wheeler, *Scientific Glass Blowing*, Interscience Publishers, New York, 1958; (g) H. Melville and B. G. Gowenlock, *Experimental Methods in Gas Reactions*, Macmillan and Co., London, 1964.

75. For example, see American Institute of Physics, *Temperature, Its Measurement and Control in Science and Industry*, Rheinhold, Publishing Corp., New York, 1962–3.

76. W. F. Roeser and S. T. Lomberger, *Natl. Bur. Standards (U.S.), Circ.* No. 590 (1959).

77. A. O. Beckman and R. G. Dickinson, *J. Am. Chem. Soc.*, **52**, 124 (1930).

78. For example, see (a) W. W. Coblentz, *J. Opt. Sci. Am.*, **5**, 356 (1921); (b) W. W. Coblentz, *Natl. Bur. Standards (U.S.), Bull.*, **9**, 7 (1913); *ibid.*, **14**, 507 (1918); (c) J. Strong, *Rev. Sci. Instr.*, **3**, 65 (1932); (d) C. H. Cartwright, *Rev. Sci. Instr.*, **3**, 73 (1932); (e) P. A. Leighton and W. G. Leighton, *J. Phys. Chem.*, **36**, 1882 (1932); (f) R. A. Crane and F. E. Blacet, *Rev. Sci. Instr.*, **21**, 259 (1950); (g) J. Lee and H. H. Seliger, *J. Chem. Phys.*, **40**, 519 (1964).

79. T. M. Dauphinee, *Rev. Sci. Instr.*, **26**, 873 (1955).

80. W. W. Coblentz, *Natl. Bur. Standards (U.S.), Bull.*, **9**, 81 (1913).

81. D. M. Packer and C. Lock, *J. Opt. Soc. Am.*, **41**, 699 (1951).

82. (a) D. S. Herr and W. A. Noyes, Jr., *J. Am. Chem. Soc.*, **62**, 2052 (1940); (b) E. I. Akeroyd and R. G. W. Norrish, *J. Chem. Soc.*, **1936**, 890; (c) H. S. Taylor and C. Rosenblum, *J. Chem. Phys.*, **6**, 119 (1932); (d) J. A. Leermakers, *J. Am. Chem. Soc.*, **56**, 1899 (1934); (e) C. A. Winkler, *Trans. Faraday Soc.*, **31**, 761 (1935).

83. For example the CO can be removed selectively by reaction with $Ag_2O(s)$ [F. E. Blacet, G. D. MacDonald and P. A. Leighton, *Ind. Eng. Chem. (Anal. Ed.)*, **5**, 272 (1933)]; or a molecular sieve (Linde) column packing can be used to separate the CO and CH_4 chromatographically.

84. (a) V. R. Ells and W. A. Noyes, Jr., *J. Am. Chem. Soc.*, **61**, 2492 (1939); (b) W. Davis, Jr., *J. Am. Chem. Soc.*, **70**, 1868 (1948); (c) L. M. Dorfman and Z. D. Sheldon, *J. Chem. Phys.*, **17**, 511 (1949); (d) K. O. Kutschke, M. H. J. Wijnen, and E. W. R. Steacie, *J. Am. Chem. Soc.*, **74**, 714 (1952).

85. (a) E. Warburg, *Sitzber. Preuss. Akad. Wiss., Physik-Math. Kl.*, **1916**, 314; (b) G. S. Forbes, J. E. Cline, and B. C. Bradshaw, *J. Am. Chem. Soc.*, **60**, 1413 (1938).

86. For an example of the extensive work see (a) W. E. Vaughan and W. A. Noyes, Jr., *J. Am. Chem. Soc.*, **52**, 559 (1930); (b) J. C. Boyce, *Revs. Modern Phys.*, **13**, 1 (1941).

87. (a) M. Zelikoff and L. M. Aschenbrand, *J. Chem. Phys.*, **22**, 1680, 1685 (1954); (b) G. A. Castellion and W. A. Noyes, Jr., *J. Am. Chem. Soc.*, **79**, 290 (1957).

88. (a) W. Groth, *Z. Physik. Chem.* (*Leipzig*), **B37**, 307 (1937); (b) B. H. Mahan, *J. Chem. Phys.*, **33**, 959 (1960); (c) A. Ung and H. I. Schiff, *Abstracts Sixth Informal Photochemistry Conference*, University of California, Davis, Calif., June, 1964.

89. G. B. Kistiakowsky, *J. Am. Chem. Soc.*, **52**, 102 (1930).

90. (a) C. A. Parker, *Proc. Roy. Soc.* (*London*), **A220**, 104 (1953); (b) C. G. Hatchard and C. A. Parker, *Proc. Roy. Soc.* (*London*), **A235**, 518 (1956).

91. (a) W. G. Leighton and G. S. Forbes, *J. Am. Chem. Soc.*, **52**, 3139 (1930); (b) G. S. Forbes, G. B. Kistiakowsky, and L. J. Heidt, *J. Am. Chem. Soc.*, **54**, 3246 (1932); (c) F. P. Brackett, Jr., and G. S. Forbes, *J. Am. Chem. Soc.*, **55**, 4459 (1933); (d) B. M. Norton, *J. Am. Chem. Soc.*, **56**, 2294 (1934); B. M. Norton, *J. Ohio Acad. Sci.*, in press; (e) C. A. Discher, P. F. Smith, I. Lippman, and R. Turse, *J. Phys. Chem.*, **67**, 2501 (1963).

92. M. I. Christie and G. Porter, *Proc. Roy. Soc.* (*London*), **A212**, 390 (1952).

93. See Ref. 4, p. 295.

94. (a) J. N. Pitts, Jr., J. D. Margerum, R. P. Taylor, and W. Brim, *J. Am. Chem. Soc.*, **77**, 5499 (1955); (b) K. Porter and D. H. Volman, *Anal. Chem.*, **34**, 748 (1962); (c) K. Porter and D. H. Volman, *J. Am. Chem. Soc.*, **84**, 2011 (1962); (d) D. H. Volman and J. R. Seed, *J. Am. Chem. Soc.*, **86**, 5095 (1964).

95. (a) R. N. Smith, P. A. Leighton, and W. G. Leighton, *J. Am. Chem. Soc.*, **61**, 2299 (1939); (b) L. B. Thomas, *J. Am. Chem. Soc.*, **62**, 1879 (1940).

96. E. Weyde and W. Frankenburger, *Trans. Faraday Soc.*, **27**, 561 (1931).

97. (a) L. Harris, J. Kaminsky, and R. G. Simard, *J. Am. Chem. Soc.*, **57**, 1151 (1935); (b) L. Harris and J. Kaminsky, *J. Am. Chem. Soc.*, **57**, 1154 (1935); (c) J. G. Calvert and H. J. L. Rechen, *J. Am. Chem. Soc.*, **74**, 2101 (1952).

98. G. M. Harris and J. E. Willard, *J. Am. Chem. Soc.*, **76**, 4678 (1954).

99. Private communication from S. V. Filseth, Harvey Mudd College, Claremont, Calif.

100. For examples, see (a) O. Warburg and V. Schocken, *Arch. Biochem.*, **21**, 363 (1949); (b) M. Schwartz, *Biochim. et Biophys. Acta*, **22**, 175 (1956).

101. F. S. Johnson, K. Watanabe, and R. Tousey, *J. Opt. Soc. Am.*, **41**, 702 (1951).

102. (a) R. E. Hunt and T. L. Hill, *J. Chem. Phys.*, **15**, 111 (1947); see also (b) M. J. Dignam and D. J. LeRoy, *J. Chem. Phys.*, **26**, 964 (1957); (c) J. A. Davies and P. P. Manning, *J. Am. Chem. Soc.*, **79**, 5148 (1957).

103. See also R. Luther and F. Weigert, *Z. Physik. Chem.*, **53**, 385 (1905).

104. I. M. Claesson, *Arkiv Kemi*, **10**, 1 (1956); see also D. H. Volman and J. C. Chen, *J. Am. Chem. Soc.*, **81**, 4141 (1959).

105. S. I. Vavilov, *Z. Physik*, **22**, 266 (1924).

106. E. H. Gilmore, G. E. Gibson, and D. S. McClure, *J. Chem. Phys.*, **20**, 829 (1952).

107. J. J. Hermans and S. Levinson, *J. Opt. Soc. Am.*, **41**, 460 (1951).

108. L. S. Forster and R. Livingston, *J. Chem. Phys.*, **20**, 1315 (1952).

109. (a) E. J. Bowen and J. W. Sawtell, *Trans. Faraday Soc.*, **33**, 1425 (1937); (b) W. H. Melhuish, *New Zealand J. Sci. Technol.*, **B37**, 142 (1955); (c) W. H. Melhuish, *J. Opt. Soc. Am.*, **52**, 1256 (1962).

110. G. Weber and F. W. J. Teale, *Trans. Faraday Soc.*, **53**, 646 (1957); *ibid.*, **54**, 640 (1958).

111. M. N. Alentsev, *Zhur. Eksp. Teoret. Fiz.*, **21**, 133 (1951).

112. (a) C. A. Parker, "Phosphorescence and Delayed Fluorescence," *Advances in Photochemistry*, ed. by W. A. Noyes, Jr., G. S. Hammond, and J. N. Pitts, Jr., Interscience Publishers, a division of John Wiley & Sons, New York, 1964, p. 305. (b) C. A. Parker and W. T. Rees, *Analyst*, **85**, 587 (1960); (c) J. H. Chapman,

T. Förster, G. Kortüm, C. A. Parker, E. Lippert, W. H. Melhuish, and G. Nebbia, *Appl. Spectroscopy*, **17**, 171 (1963).

113. For examples see (a) M. H. Fletcher, C. E. White, and M. S. Sheftel, *Ind. Eng. Chem. (Anal. Ed.)*, **18**, 204 (1946); (b) R. A. Burdett and L. C. Jones, Jr., *J. Opt. Soc. Am.*, **37**, 554 (1947); (c) R. V. Swann, *Analyst*, **79**, 176 (1954); (d) G. W. Luckey and W. A. Noyes, Jr., *J. Chem. Phys.*, **19**, 227 (1951); (e) J. S. McAnally, *Anal. Chem.*, **26**, 1526 (1954); (f) C. W. Sill, *Anal. Chem.*, **33**, 1579 (1961).

114. An increasing number of such standards are becoming available; for example, see (a) E. Lippert, W. Nägele, I. Seibold-Blankenstein, U. Staiger, and W. Voss, *Z. Anal. Chem.*, **170**, 1 (1959).

115. C. A. Parker and W. J. Barnes, *Analyst*, **82**, 606 (1957).

116. T. Förster, *Fluoreszenz Organischer Verbindungen*, Vandenhoeck u. Ruprecht, Göttingen, 1951.

117. (a) E. Becquerel, *Ann. Chem. Phys.*, **55**, 5 (1859); **57**, 40 (1859), **62**, 5 (1861); (b) a brief review of the early methods of fluorescence and phosphorescence measurements is given by P. Pringsheim, *Fluorescence and Phosphorescence*, Interscience Publishers, New York, 1949, pp. 10–24; (c) G. R. Haugen and R. J. Marcus, *Appl. Optics*, **3**, 1049 (1964).

118. R. D. Rawcliffe, *Rev. Sci. Instr.*, **13**, 413 (1942).

119. K. Skarsvag, *Rev. Sci. Instr.*, **26**, 397 (1955).

120. M. P. Lord and A. L. G. Rees, *Proc. Phys. Soc. (London)*, **58**, 280 (1946).

121. E. A. Bailey, Jr., and G. K. Rollefson, *J. Chem. Phys.*, **21**, 1315 (1953).

122. B. D. Venetta, *Rev. Sci. Instr.*, **30**, 450 (1959).

123. F. P. Schäfer and K. Röllig, *Z. Physik. Chem. (Frankfurt)*, **40**, 198 (1964).

124. W. G. Herkstroeter, A. A. Lamola, and G. S. Hammond, *J. Am. Chem. Soc.*, **86**, 4537 (1964).

125. R. Stair, W. E. Schneider, and J. K. Jackson, *Appl. Optics*, **2**, 1151 (1963).

126. A. H. Laufer, J. A. Pirog, and J. R. McNesby, *J. Opt. Soc. Am.*, **55**, 64 (1965).

127. A more rapid development of the full color of the complex is possible through the addition of 1 cc of 2 M NH_4F solution as recommended by J. H. Baxendale and N. K. Bridge, *J. Phys. Chem.*, **59**, 783 (1955); under these conditions a 30-min waiting period is sufficient. These authors also suggest that the ferrioxalate actinometer solution can be prepared directly by mixing ferric alum and potassium oxalate solutions with results equivalent to those obtained from solutions prepared from the recrystallized $K_3Fe(C_2O_4)_3 \cdot 3H_2O$ salt.

Appendix

TABLE A-1 Enthalpies of Formation and Entropies of Hydrocarbon Gases at 1 Atm (Ideal Gas)[a]

Compound	$S°$, cal/mole-deg			$\Delta H_f°$, kcal/mole		
	298.2°K	500°K	700°K	298.2°K	500°K	700°K
C(graphite)	1.36	2.79	4.13	0.0	0.0	0.0
H_2	31.21	34.81	37.17	0.0	0.0	0.0
CH_4	44.50	49.48	53.68	−17.89	−19.30	−20.40
C_2H_6	54.85	62.79	69.93	−20.24	−22.44	−23.98
C_3H_8	64.51	75.89	86.17	−24.82	−27.62	−29.49
n-C_4H_{10}	74.12	89.10	102.51	−30.15	−33.51	−35.70
Iso-C_4H_{10}	70.42	85.45	98.96	−32.15	−35.48	−37.61
n-C_5H_{12}	83.40	101.88	118.38	−35.00	−38.94	−41.48
$(CH_3)_2CHCH_2CH_3$	82.12	100.52	117.16	−36.92	−40.88	−43.34
$(CH_3)_4C$	73.23	92.17	109.23	−39.67	−43.42	−45.63
n-C_6H_{14}	92.83	114.83	134.44	−39.96	−44.48	−47.36
$(CH_3)_2CHCH_2CH_2CH_3$	90.95	113.2	133.0	−41.66	−46.06	−48.82
$C_2H_5CH(CH_3)C_2H_5$	90.77	112.8	132.4	−41.02	−45.54	−48.43
$(CH_3)_2CHCH(CH_3)_2$	87.42	109.27	129.0	−42.49	−47.05	−49.87
$(CH_3)_3CCH_2CH_3$	85.62	107.8	127.6	−44.35	−48.83	−51.60
n-C_7H_{16}	102.24	127.74	150.45	−44.89	−49.99	−53.21
n-C_8H_{18}	111.55	140.56	166.37	−49.82	−55.49	−59.07
$[CH_3CH_2CH(CH_3)\text{-}]_2$	107.15	136.6	162.8	−50.91	−56.42	−59.74
$[(CH_3)_2CHCH_2\text{-}]_2$	104.93	134.9	161.3	−53.21	−58.58	−61.66
$(CH_3)_3CC(CH_3)_3$	93.06	123.2	150.4	−53.99	−59.20	−61.97
C_2H_4	52.45	58.98	64.68	12.50	11.14	10.14
C_3H_6	63.80	73.47	82.04	4.88	2.79	1.30
$CH_2{=}C{=}CH_2$	58.30	67.02	74.36	45.92	44.85	44.03
1-C_4H_8	73.04	86.20	97.91	−0.03	−2.70	−4.51
2-$C_4H_8(cis)$	71.90	84.19	95.46	−1.67	−4.68	−6.75
2-$C_4H_8(trans)$	70.86	84.04	95.64	−2.67	−5.34	−7.22
Iso-C_4H_8	70.17	83.60	95.38	−4.04	−6.61	−8.39
$CH_2{=}C{=}CHCH_3$	70.03	81.95	92.20	38.77	37.00	35.72
$CH_2{=}CHCH{=}CH_2$	66.62	78.86	89.48	26.33	24.70	23.63
1-C_5H_{10}	82.65	99.41	114.25	−5.00	−8.22	−10.37
2-$C_5H_{10}(cis)$	82.76	98.68	113.21	−6.71	−10.24	−12.56
2-$C_5H_{10}(trans)$	81.36	97.87	112.55	−7.59	−10.90	−13.15
C_2H_2	48.00	54.09	58.69	54.19	54.09	53.79

815

TABLE A-1 *continued*

Compound	$S°$, cal/mole-deg			$\Delta H_f°$, kcal/mole		
	298.2°K	500°K	700°K	298.2K	500°K	700°K
CH_3CCH	59.30	68.09	75.38	44.32	43.28	42.42
CH_3CCCH_3	67.71	79.21	89.10	34.97	33.03	31.55
C_2H_5CCH	69.51	81.60	91.90	39.48	37.78	36.52
Cyclo-C_3H_6	56.84	66.03	74.73	12.74		
Cyclo-C_4H_8	63.43	75.42	86.99	6.38		
Cyclo-C_5H_{10}	70.00	84.14	98.24	−18.46	−22.67	−25.25
Cyclo-C_5H_8	69.23	81.80	94.17	7.87	4.43	2.22
Methylcyclo-C_5H_{10}	81.24	99.36	116.81	−25.50	−30.11	−32.88
Cyclo-C_6H_{12}	71.28	89.24	107.14	−29.43	−34.08	−36.59
Cyclo-C_6H_{10}	74.27	91.63	108.09	−1.70	−5.21	−7.18
C_6H_6	64.34	77.74	90.30	19.82	17.54	16.04
$CH_3C_6H_5$	76.42	93.13	108.64	11.95	9.01	7.07

[a] Most of the data are from F. D. Rossini, K. S. Pitzer, R. L. Arnett, R. M. Braun, and G. C. Pimentel, "Selected Values of Physical and Thermodynamic Properties of Hydrocarbons and Related Compounds," Carnegie Press, Pittsburgh, Pa., 1953; data for cyclo-C_3H_6 from G. B. Kistiakowsky and W. W. Rice, *J. Chem. Phys.*, **8**, 610 (1940); R. A. Ruehrwein and T. M. Powell, *J. Am. Chem. Soc.*, **68**, 1063 (1946); J. W. Knowlton and F. D. Rossini, *J. Research Natl. Bur. Standards*, **43**, 113 (1949); data for cyclo-C_4H_8 from G. W. Rathjens, Jr., N. K. Freeman, W. D. Gwinn, and K. S. Pitzer, *J. Am. Chem. Soc.*, **75**, 5634 (1953); G. W. Rathjens, Jr., and W. D. Gwinn, *ibid.*, 5629; S. Kaarsemaker and J. C. Coops, *Rec. Trav. Chim.*, **71**, 261 (1952).

TABLE A-2   Approximate Enthalpies of Formation and Entropies of Various Gaseous Organic Compounds (Ideal Gas, 298.2°K, 1 atm)

Compound	$S°$, cal/mole-deg	$\Delta H_f°$, kcal/mole	Reference
CH_3Br	58.74	-8.5	2
CH_2Br_2	70.16	-1	2
$CHBr_3$	79.18	6	2
CBr_4	85.6	12	2
CH_3Cl	55.81	-20.6	1
CH_2Cl_2	68.6	-22.4	1
$CHCl_3$	70.6	-25	1
CCl_4	74.29	-25.5	1
CH_3F	53.24	-59	1
CH_2F_2	58.9	-105.5	1
CHF_3	62.04	-163	1
CF_4	62.47	-218	1
CH_3I	60.85	4.9	2
C_2F_4	71.7	-151.9	12
C_2H_5Br	68.7	-13.0	3,2
C_2H_5Cl	66.2	-25.7	3
CH_3CF_3	68.7	-166	3,4
C_2F_6	79.1	-295.6	9,12
C_3F_8	94.6	-411	12
$n\text{-}C_4F_{10}$	110.7	-505.5	12
$Iso\text{-}C_4F_{10}$	107	-515.6	12
CH_3OH	57.3	-48.1	11
C_2H_5OH	67.6	-56.2	11
$n\text{-}C_3H_7OH$	76.2	-61.9	11
$Iso\text{-}C_3H_7OH$	73.9	-65.4	11
$n\text{-}C_4H_9OH$	89.4	-66.9	11
$sec\text{-}C_4H_9OH$	82.4	-70.1	3,11
$Iso\text{-}C_4H_9OH$	83.5	-67.9	3,11
$tert\text{-}C_4H_9OH$	76.8	-74.9	11,3
$n\text{-}C_5H_{11}OH$	95	-71.9	5,11
$n\text{-}C_6H_{13}OH$	105	-76.8	5,11
$n\text{-}C_7H_{15}OH$	114.4	-81.7	3,11
$n\text{-}C_8H_{17}OH$	123	-86.6	5,11
$(\text{-}CH_2OH)_2$	77.3	-95.1	11
$Cyclo\text{-}C_5H_9OH$	83	-60.1	5,6
$Cyclo\text{-}C_6H_{11}OH$	84	-71.8	5,6
$C_6H_5CH_2OH$	85.9	-22.4	3,6
CH_2O	52.3	-27.7	11
CH_3CHO	63.2	-39.7	11
$CH_2{=}CO$	58	-14.5	5,2
C_2H_5CHO	73.0	-46.1	3
$n\text{-}C_3H_7CHO$	82.4	-51.1	3
CH_3COCH_3	70.5	-51.7	3
$C_2H_5COCH_3$	80.8	-57.0	13
$CH_3COCOCH_3$	78.2	-78.1	3,7
$HCO_2H(\text{monomer})$	59.5	-90.5	11

TABLE A-2 *continued*

Compound	$S°$, cal/mole-deg	$\Delta H_f°$, kcal/mole	Reference
CH_3CO_2H(monomer)	67.5	−103.8	11
$CH_3CH_2CO_2H$	80.0	−111.6	3
$(CH_3)_2O$	63.7	−44.3	11
$\overline{CH_2CH_2O}$	58.1	−12.2	11
$CH_3OC_2H_5$	75.0	−53.4	3
$(C_2H_5)_2O$	83.7	−61.5	3
HCO_2CH_3	70.1	−81.0	3,11
$CH_3CO_2CH_3$	80.1	−99.2	3
$CH_3CO_2C_2H_5$	90.1	−103.4	11
$C_2H_5CO_2CH_3$	90.0	−105.0	3
tert-$C_4H_9O_2H$		−52	3
$(CH_3CO_2-)_2$		−119	8
$(C_2H_5CO_2-)_2$		−138	8
$(n-C_3H_7CO_2-)_2$		−150	8
(*tert*-$C_4H_9O-)_2$	116	−84.7	3,6
CH_3NH_2	57.7	−6.7	3
$(CH_3)_2NH$	65.3	−6.6	3
$C_2H_5NH_2$	68.5	−11.6	3
CH_3ONO	68.0	−14.9	3
C_2H_5ONO	78	−24.8	5,2
$n-C_3H_7ONO$	87	−31.2	5,6
CH_3ONO_2	76.0	−29.0	3
$C_2H_5ONO_2$	85.1	−36.6	3
$n-C_3H_7ONO_2$	111	−41.6	5.6
CH_3SH	60.9	−5.5	3,10
$(CH_3)_2S$	68.3	−9.0	3,10

1. *JANAF Interim Thermochemical Tables*, Thermal Laboratory, The Dow Chemical Company, Midland, Mich., 1960.
2. "Selected Values of Chemical Thermodynamic Properties," *Circ. Natl. Bur. Standards (U.S.)* 500, 1952.
3. Compilations and estimations of S. W. Benson and J. H. Buss, *J. Chem. Phys.*, **29**, 546 (1958).
4. W. D. Good, D. R. Douslin, D. W. Scott, A. George, J. L. Lacina, J. P. Dawson, and G. Waddington, *J. Phys. Chem.*, **63**, 1133 (1959).
5. Authors' estimates, using Benson and Buss additivity rules of Ref. 3, or the hydrocarbon analog method.
6. P. Gray and A. Williams, *Chem. Revs.*, **59**, 239 (1959).
7. G. R. Nicholson, M. Szwarc, and J. W. Taylor, *J. Chem. Soc.*, **1954**, 2767.
8. L. Jaffe, E. J. Prosen, and M. Szwarc, *J. Chem. Phys.*, **27**, 416 (1957).
9. R. A. Carney, E. A. Piotrowski, A. G. Meister, J. H. Braun, and F. F. Cleveland, *J. Mol. Spectroscopy*, **7**, 209 (1961).
10. J. P. McCullough and W. D. Good, *J. Phys. Chem.*, **65**, 1430 (1961).
11. Compilation of J. H. S. Green, *Quart. Revs. (London)*, **15**, 125 (1961).
12. W. M. D. Bryant, *J. Polymer Sci.*, **56**, 277 (1962).
13. G. C. Sinke and F. L. Oetting, *J. Phys. Chem.*, **68**, 1354 (1964).

TABLE A-3 Approximate Enthalpies of Formation and Entropies of Gaseous Organic Free Radicals (Ideal Gas, 298.2°K, 1 atm)

Radical	$S°$, cal/mole-deg	$\Delta H_f°$, kcal/mole	Reference
C(graphite)	1.36	0.0	1
H	27.39	52.1	1
C	37.76	170.9	1
CH	43.72	141.1	1
CH_2	43.2	66	1
CH_3	46.0	32.0	1,2
CCl	53.88	121.6	1
CCl_3	70.6	13	3,4
CF	50.89	76.1	1
CF_2	57.49	−23	1
CF_3	62.35	−112.7	21
C_2	47.63	197	1
C_3	50.69	190	1
C_2H_5	59.11	26.2	5,7
C_2F_5	77.0	−212	21
$n\text{-}C_3H_7$	66.38	20.9	18
$n\text{-}C_3F_7$	93.1	−306.5	21
Iso-C_3H_7	65.85	17.3	5,19
Iso-C_3F_7	91.7	−319.9	21
$n\text{-}C_4H_9$	76.85	15.9	5,18
$sec\text{-}C_4H_9$	76.9	11.9	3,9
Iso-C_4H_9	74.0	13.5	3,9
$tert\text{-}C_4H_9$	70.82	6.7	5,24
$n\text{-}C_5H_{11}$	86.02	11.2	5,18
$(CH_3)_3CCH_2$	76.0	6.7	3,9
$n\text{-}C_6H_{13}$	95.20	6.3	5,18
$n\text{-}C_7H_{15}$	104.39	1.3	5,18
$n\text{-}C_8H_{17}$	113.57	−3.6	5,18
$CH_2{=}CH$	54.27	65	5,6
$CF_2{=}CF$	70.2	−45.8	21
CH_2CHCH_2	62.5	35	3,8,25
$CH_2C(CH_3)CH_2$	72.1	21	3,8
$CH_3CHCHCH_2$	74.5	26	3,8
Cyclo-C_3H_5	59.8	64	3,9
Cyclo-C_4H_7	68.9	53	3,9
Cyclo-C_5H_9	71.4	24	3,9
Cyclo-C_6H_{11}	74.1	13	3,9
C_6H_5	69.34	71	5,22
$C_6H_5CH_2$	76.4	43	3,10
O	38.47	59.56	1
OH	43.92	9.3	1
O_2H	54.5	4.9	3,11

TABLE A-3 *continued*

Radical	$S°$, cal/mole-deg	$\Delta H_f°$, kcal/mole	Reference
CH_3O	56.7	−0.5	3,13
C_2H_5O	68.7	−8.5	3,13
$n\text{-}C_3H_7O$	78.1	−13.0	3,13
Iso-C_3H_7O	75.3	−15	3,13
$n\text{-}C_4H_9O$	90.7	−17	3,13
Iso-C_4H_9O	84.9	−18	3,13
$sec\text{-}C_4H_9O$	83.8	−20	3,13
$tert\text{-}C_4H_9O$	78	−24.5	23
$n\text{-}C_5H_{11}O$	96	−22	3
$n\text{-}C_6H_{13}O$	106	−27	3
$n\text{-}C_7H_{15}O$	116	−32	3
$n\text{-}C_8H_{17}O$	124	−37	3
Cyclo-C_5H_9O	84	−10	3,13
Cyclo-$C_6H_{11}O$	85	−21	3,13
$C_6H_5CH_2O$	87	25	13
HO_2	54.5	4.9	3,11
CH_3O_2	64.6	6	25
$C_2H_5O_2$	74.1	−2	25
Iso-$C_3H_7O_2$	82.5	−11	25
$tert\text{-}C_4H_9O_2$	85.9	−21	25
$CH_2{=}CHCH_2O_2$	83.7	23	25
$C_6H_5CH_2O_2$	96.0	31	25
HCO	53.7	2	1,12
CH_3CO	63.4	−4.3	3,14
CH_3CO_2	70.1	−45	3,15
$CH_3CH_2CO_2$	81.4	−54	3,15
$n\text{-}C_3H_7CO_2$		−60	15
CH_3NH	58.7	37	3,16
$(CH_3)_2N$	66.0	34	3,16
C_2H_5NH	69.3	33	3,16
$(C_2H_5)_2N$		22	20
C_6H_5NH		54	20
$(C_6H_5)_2N$		83	20
CH_3S	61.9	30	3,17

1. *JANAF Interim Thermochemical Tables*, Thermal Laboratory, The Dow Chemical Company, Midland, Mich., 1960.
2. F. P. Lossing, K. U. Ingold, and I. H. S. Henderson, *J. Chem. Phys.*, **22**, 1489 (1954); average of values summarized.
3. Authors' estimate, using rules of S. W. Benson and J. H. Buss, *J. Chem. Phys.*, **29**, 546 (1958), or hydrogen analog method.
4. J. B. Farmer, I. H. S. Henderson, F. P. Lossing, and D. G. H. Marsden, *J. Chem. Phys.*, **24**, 348 (1956).

5. W. M. D. Bryant, *J. Polymer Sci.*, **6**, 359 (1951).

6. A. G. Harrison and F. P. Lossing, *J. Am. Chem. Soc.*, **82**, 519 (1960).

7. J. B. Farmer and F. P. Lossing, *Can. J. Chem.*, **33**, 861 (1955).

8. C. A. McDowell, F. P. Lossing, I. H. S. Henderson, and J. B. Farmer, *Can. J. Chem.*, **34**, 345 (1956).

9. Authors' best guess from thermal and kinetic data for related systems.

10. S. W. Benson and J. H. Buss, *J. Phys. Chem.*, **61**, 104 (1957); J. I. Genco, F. R. Duke, M. Griffel, and L. D. Jennings, U.S. Atomic Energy Comm., ISC-746 (1956); A. H. Sehon and M. Szwarc, *Ann. Revs. Phys. Chem.*, **8**, 439 (1957).

11. P. Gray, *Trans. Faraday Soc.*, **55**, 408 (1959).

12. The value of $\Delta H_f(\text{HCO})$ is uncertain, but the best present evidence from photodissociation limit, spectral data, and electron impact experiments with CH_2O favors that given here. See (a) R. Klein and L. J. Schoen, *J. Chem. Phys.*, **29**, 953 (1958); (b) M. Venugopalan and K. O. Kutschke, *Can. J. Chem.*, **42**, 2451 (1964); (c) R. D. McQuigg and J. G. Calvert, "Symposium on Structure and Photochemistry of Excited States," American Chemical Society, 149th Meeting, Detroit, Mich., April, 1965; (d) T. W. Shannon and A. G. Harrison, *Can. J. Chem.*, **39**, 1392 (1961); (e) G. W. Robinson and V. E. DiGiorgio, *Can. J. Chem.*, **36**, 31 (1958). Kinetic data favor a somewhat higher value, $\Delta H_f(\text{CHO}) \simeq 9$ kcal/mole; see J. G. Calvert and J. T. Gruver, *J. Am. Chem. Soc.*, **80**, 1313 (1958); J. G. Calvert, *J. Phys. Chem.*, **61**, 1206 (1957).

13. P. Gray and A. Williams, *Chem. Revs.*, **59**, 239 (1959).

14. From the average values of E. O'Neal and S. W. Benson, *J. Chem. Phys.*, **36**, 2196 (1962), the data of Ref. 12, J. A. Kerr and J. G. Calvert, *J. Phys. Chem.*, **69**, 1022 (1965), and E. Murad and M. G. Inghram, *J. Chem. Phys.*, **41**, 404 (1964).

15. L. Jaffe, E. J. Prosen, and M. Szwarc, *J. Chem. Phys.*, **27**, 416 (1957).

16. B. G. Gowenlock, P. P. Jones, and J. R. Majer, *Trans. Faraday Soc.*, **57**, 23 (1961).

17. H. Mackle and R. T. B. McClean, *Trans. Faraday Soc.*, **58**, 895 (1962).

18. Authors' estimate, assuming $\Delta H_{298.2}^0 = 82$ for $CH_3(CH_2)_{n+m}CH_3 \rightarrow CH_3(CH_2)_n + CH_3(CH_2)_m$, where $n,m \neq 0$; see Ref. 3.

19. F. H. Field and J. L. Franklin, *Electron Impact Phenomena*, Academic Press, New York, 1957; D. P. Stevenson, *Trans. Faraday Soc.*, **49**, 867 (1953); P. S. Nangia and S. W. Benson, *J. Am. Chem. Soc.*, **86**, 2770 (1964).

20. B. G. Gowenlock and D. R. Snelling, *Advances in Chemistry*, No. 36, 150 (1962).

21. W. M. D. Bryant, *J. Polymer Sci.*, **56**, 277 (1962).

22. Derived from the average of $D_{C_6H_5-H}$ estimates of W. Fielding and H. O. Pritchard, *J. Phys. Chem.*, **66**, 821 (1962), and F. J. Duncan and A. F. Trotman-Dickenson, *J. Chem. Soc.*, **1962**, 4672.

23. H. Hershenson and S. W. Benson, *J. Chem. Phys.*, **37**, 1889 (1962).

24. H. Teranishi and S. W. Benson, *J. Am. Chem. Soc.*, **85**, 2887 (1963).

25. S. W. Benson, *J. Am. Chem. Soc.*, **87**, 972 (1965).

TABLE A-4 Approximate Enthalpies of Formation and Entropies of Some Inorganic Compounds and Free Radicals at 1 Atm (Ideal Gas State)

Compound or Free Radical	$S°$, cal/mole-deg			$\Delta H_f°$, kcal/mole			Reference
	298.2°K	500°K	700°K	298.2°K	500°K	700°K	
B	36.65	39.22	40.89	133	133	133	1
BH	41.05	44.68	47.12	115	115	114	1
BH_2	47	52	55	66	66	65	1
BH_3	44.88	49.67	53.31	18	17	16	1
HBO	48.57	53.43	57.05	−47	−47	−48	1
BO	48.61	52.26	54.75	4	4	3	1
B_2H_6	55.33	64.02	71.97	7.5	5.2	3.8	1
B_2O_2	57.51	64.99	70.49	−111	−111	−111	1
B_2O_3	64.42	71.87	77.94	−208	−209	−210	1
Br	41.81	44.37	46.05	26.74	23.17	23.27	1,2
Br_2	58.65	63.17	66.17	7.39	0	0	1
CN	48.41	52.04	54.51	109	109	109	1,14
$(CN)_2$	57.69	65.25	70.72	73.8	74.3	74.5	1
CO	47.22	50.85	53.29	−26.42	−26.29	−26.41	1
CO_2	51.07	56.11	59.90	−94.04	−94.08	−94.16	1
$O{=}C{=}C{=}C{=}O$	61.24	70.28	77.09	−8.3	−7.9	−7.8	1
COS	55.32	60.93	65.04	−32.8	−33.9	−34.7	1
CS	50.30	54.11	56.78	71.5	70.4	69.5	1
CS_2	56.83	62.90	67.26	27.6	25.3	23.7	1
Cl	39.46	42.22	44.05	28.95	29.18	29.40	1
Cl_2	53.30	57.63	60.57	0	0	0	1
ClF	52.06	56.21	59.07	−13	−13	−13	1
ClO	53.93	58.14	61.00	24.21	24.42	24.48	1
ClO_2	61.41	67.03	71.12	25	25	25	1
Cl_2O	63.65	69.66	73.93	18.1	18.0	18.1	1
ClOH	56.39	61.29	64.82	−21	−22	−22	1
F	37.92	40.69	42.45	18.9	19.1	19.3	1
F_2	48.45	52.51	55.33	0	0	0	1
H	27.39	29.96	31.63	52.10	52.40	52.69	1
H_2	31.21	34.81	37.17	0	0	0	1
HCN	48.21	53.00	56.51	31.2	31.1	31.0	1
HBr	47.43	51.05	53.44	−8.66	−12.53	−12.70	1
HCl	44.65	48.25	50.63	−22.06	−22.20	−22.36	1
HF	41.51	45.11	47.46	−65.1	−65.2	−65.4	1
HI	49.35	52.98	55.42	6.30	−1.35	−1.49	1
HO	43.92	47.58	49.96	9.33	9.33	9.27	1
HO_2	54.5			4.9			8,3
H_2O	45.11	45.33	52.25	−57.80	−58.28	−58.71	1
H_2O_2	55.66	61.57		−32.53	−33.07	−33.35	1
HS	46.75	50.67	53.18	35			1,13
H_2S	49.11	53.50	56.62	−4.82	−6.55	−7.75	1
I	43.18	45.75	47.42	25.54	18.18	18.28	1,2
I_2	62.28	66.88	69.90	14.92	0	0	1
N	36.61	39.18	40.86	113.0	113.1	113.6	1
NH	43.3	46.9	49.3	84			16
NH_2	45.11	49.34	52.27	40	40	39	1

822

TABLE A-4 *continued*

Compound or Free Radical	$S°$, cal/mole-deg			$\Delta H_f°$, kcal/mole			Reference
	298.2°K	500°K	700°K	298.2°K	500°K	700°K	
NH_3	46.03	50.76	54.33	−11.04	−12.00	−12.69	1
N_2	45.76	49.38	51.80	0	0	0	1
$(NH)_2$	52.3			52			4,6
N_2H_3	59			47			8,7
N_2H_4	56.97	64.50	70.62	22.75	21.51	20.92	1
NO	50.35	54.05	56.56	21.6	21.7	21.7	1
HNO	52.73			25.1			1,15
NO_2	57.32	62.27	65.97	8.1	7.8	7.8	10,1
$NO_2H(cis)$	59.57	65.83	70.62	−18.0			10,9
$NO_2H(trans)$	59.54	65.88	70.71	−18.0			10,9
NO_3	60.36			16.59			12
NO_3H	63.68	71.40		−32.0			11,9
$NOCl$	62.08	67.55	71.46	13	12	12	1
N_2O	52.56	57.77	61.64	19.5	19.4	19.5	1
N_2O_3	73.92			20.0			12
N_2O_4	72.73	83.50	91.86	2.54			12
N_2O_5	85.00	96.98	106.4	3.35			12
O	38.47	41.13	42.83	59.56	59.87	60.11	1
O_2	49.01	52.73	55.30	0	0	0	1
O_3	57.05	62.38	66.35	34.0	33.9	34.0	1
S	40.09	42.96	44.76	66	66	65	1
S_2	54.51	58.69	61.56	30.8	28.4	26.8	1
SO	53.06	56.96	59.68	0.1	−1.1	−1.9	1
SO_2	59.29	64.61	68.54	−70.96	−72.37	−73.22	1
SO_3	61.34	68.53	74.18	−94.45	−95.84	−96.43	1

1. Data from *JANAF Interim Thermochemical Tables*, Thermal Laboratory, The Dow Chemical Company, Midland, Mich., 1960.
2. W. H. Evans, T. R. Munson, and D. D. Wagman, *J. Research Natl. Bur. Standards*, **55**, 147 (1955).
3. P. Gray, *Trans. Faraday Soc.*, **55**, 408 (1959).
4. P. Smith, *J. Chem. Phys.*, **29**, 683 (1958).
5. J. W. C. Johns and D. A. Ramsay, *Can. J. Phys.*, **39**, 210 (1961).
6. S. N. Foner and R. L. Hudson, *J. Chem. Phys.*, **28**, 719 (1958).
7. S. N. Foner and R. L. Hudson, *J. Chem. Phys.*, **29**, 442 (1958).
8. Authors' estimates of $S°$ of R from $S°$ of RH with corrections for symmetry differences and degeneracy of the ground state of R.
9. Compilation of S. W. Benson and J. H. Buss, *J. Chem. Phys.*, **29**, 546 (1958).
10. A. P. Altschuller, *J. Phys. Chem.*, **61**, 251 (1957).
11. A. Palm and M. Kilpatrick, *J. Chem. Phys.*, **23**, 1562 (1955).
12. I. C. Hisatsune, *J. Phys. Chem.*, **65**, 2249 (1961).
13. H. Mackle and R. T. B. McClean, *Trans. Faraday Soc.*, **58**, 895 (1962).
14. J. Berkowitz, *J. Chem. Phys.*, **36**, 2533 (1962).
15. M. A. A. Clyne and B. A. Thrush, *Trans. Faraday Soc.*, **57**, 1305 (1961); J. L. Holmes, *Proc. Chem. Soc. (London)*, **1962**, 75; M. J. Y. Clement and D. A. Ramsay, *Can. J. Phys.*, **39**, 205 (1961).
16. M. A. A. Clyne and B. A. Thrush, *Proc. Chem. Soc. (London)*, **1962**, 227.

TABLE A-5 Some Approximate Bond Dissociation Energies;[a] $\Delta H^\circ_{298.2}$ for $R'—R(g) \rightarrow R'(g) + R(g)$

Bond Broken, R—R'	$\Delta H^\circ_{298.2}$, kcal/mole	Bond Broken, R—R'	$\Delta H^\circ_{298.2}$, kcal/mole
CH_3—H	102	$n\text{-}C_4H_9$—CH_3	83
C_2H_5—H	99	$(CH_3)_3C$—CH_3	78
$n\text{-}C_3H_7$—H	98	$n\text{-}C_3H_7$—$(CH_2)_2CH_3$	82
Iso-C_3H_7—H	94	$n\text{-}C_4H_9$—C_2H_5	82
$n\text{-}C_4H_9$—H	98	$n\text{-}C_5H_{11}$—CH_3	83
sec-C_4H_9—H	94	$n\text{-}C_4H_9$—$(CH_2)_3CH_3$	82
Iso-C_4H_9—H	98	$n\text{-}C_5H_{11}$—$(CH_2)_2CH_3$	82
tert-C_4H_9—H	91	$n\text{-}C_6H_{13}$—C_2H_5	82
$n\text{-}C_5H_{11}$—H	98	$n\text{-}C_7H_{15}$—CH_3	83
$(CH_3)_3CCH_2$—H	99		
$n\text{-}C_6H_{13}$—H	98		
$n\text{-}C_7H_{15}$—H	98	CH_2—CH_2	120
$n\text{-}C_8H_{17}$—H	98	CH—CH	228
Cyclo-C_3H_5—H	103		
Cyclo-C_4H_7—H	99	C_2H_4—CH_3	24
Cyclo-C_5H_9—H	95	C_2H_4—C_2H_5	23
Cyclo-C_6H_{11}—H	94	CH_3CHCH_2—CH_3	25
		$CH_2CH(CH_3)$—CH_3	23
CH_2=CH—H	105	$n\text{-}C_3H_7$—C_2H_4	22
CH_2=CHCH$_2$—H	82	$n\text{-}C_5H_{11}$—C_2H_4	22
CH_2=C(CH$_3$)CH$_2$—H	77		
CH_3CH=CHCH$_2$—H	81		
		CH_3—Br	67
C_6H_5—H	103	CH_3—Cl	82
$C_6H_5CH_2$—H	83	CH_3—F	110
		CH_3—I	53
C—H	82	C—Cl	78
CH—H	127	CCl_3—Cl	68
CH_2—H	86	CCl_3—H	90
CH_2CH_2—H	38	C—F	114
$CH_3CH(CH_2)$—H	36	CF—F	118
CH_3CHCH_2—H	40	CF_2—F	109
$C_2H_5CH(CH_2)$—H	36	CF_3—F	124
$C_2H_5CHCH_2$—H	40	CF_3—H	102
$CH_3CHCH(CH_3)$—H	38	CF_3—CH_3	85
$(CH_3)_2C(CH_2)$—H	35	CF_3—CF_3	70
$(CH_3)_2CCH_2$—H	46		
		CH_3O—H	100
CH_3—CH_3	84	C_2H_5O—H	100
C_2H_5—CH_3	83	$n\text{-}C_3H_7O$—H	101
C_2H_5—C_2H_5	83	Iso-C_3H_7O—H	102
$n\text{-}C_3H_7$—CH_3	83	$n\text{-}C_4H_9O$—H	102
Iso-C_3H_7—CH_3	82	tert-C_4H_9O—H	102
$n\text{-}C_3H_7$—C_2H_5	82	$n\text{-}C_5H_{11}O$—H	102

TABLE A-5 *continued*

Bond Broken, R—R'	$\Delta H^\circ_{298.2}$, kcal/mole	Bond Broken, R—R'	$\Delta H^\circ_{298.2}$, kcal/mole
n-$C_6H_{13}O$—H	102	CH_3—CO	10
n-$C_8H_{17}O$—H	102		
		HCO—OH	102
Cyclo-C_5H_9O—H	102	CH_3CO—OH	109
Cyclo-$C_6H_{11}O$—H	103		
		CH_3CO_2—H	111
CH_3—OH	89	$C_2H_5CO_2$—H	110
C_2H_5—OH	92		
n-C_3H_7—OH	92	CH_3O—CH_3	76
Iso-C_3H_7—OH	92	CH_3O—C_2H_5	79
n-C_4H_9—OH	92	C_2H_5O—CH_3	77
sec-C_4H_9—OH	91	C_2H_5O—C_2H_5	79
Iso-C_4H_9—OH	91		
tert-C_4H_9—OH	91	HCO—OCH_3	83
n-C_5H_{11}—OH	92	CH_3CO—OCH_3	94
n-C_6H_{13}—OH	92	CH_3CO—OC_2H_5	91
n-C_7H_{15}—OH	92	CH_3CO_2—CH_3	86
n-C_8H_{17}—OH	92	$C_2H_5CO_2$—CH_3	83
OCH_2—H	24	HO—OH	51
$OCH(CH_3)$—H	21	HO_2—H	90
$OCH(C_2H_5)$—H	19	RO_2—H	~90[b]
$OC(CH_3)_2$—H	15	H—O_2	47
$OC(C_2H_5)(CH_3)$—H	13	HO—O	64
		tert-C_4H_9O—OH	36
CH_3—CH_2O	13	CH_3CO_2—O_2CCH_3	29
C_2H_5—CH_2O	12	$C_2H_5CO_2$—$O_2CC_2H_5$	30
n-C_3H_7—CH_2O	11	n-$C_3H_7CO_2$—$O_2CC_3H_7$	30
$(CH_3)_2CH$—CH_2O	10	$(CH_3)_3CO$—$OC(CH_3)_3$	35
n-C_4H_9—CH_2O	12		
C_2H_5—$CHOCH_3$	6	H—O_2	47
CH_3—$CO(CH_3)_2$	5	CH_3—O_2	26
		C_2H_5—O_2	28
HCO—H	82	Iso-C_3H_7—O_2	28
CH_3CO—H	88	tert-C_4H_9—O_2	28
		CH_2=$CHCH_2$—O_2	12
CH_3—CHO	74	$C_6H_5CH_2$—O_2	12
C_2H_5—CHO	74		
n-C_3H_7—CHO	74	CH_3—NH_2	79
		C_2H_5—NH_2	78
H—CO	24	CH_3NH—H	96
		$(CH_3)_2N$—H	93
CH_2—CO	54	C_2H_5NH—H	97
CH_3—$COCH_3$	79		
C_2H_5—$COCH_3$	79	CH_3O—NO	36
CH_3CO—$COCH_3$	70	C_2H_5O—NO	38

TABLE A-5   *continued*

Bond Broken, R—R'	$\Delta H^{\circ}_{298.2}$, kcal/mole	Bond Broken, R—R'	$\Delta H^{\circ}_{298.2}$, kcal/mole
$n\text{-}C_3H_7O\text{—NO}$	40	HC—N	223
$CH_3\text{—ONO}$	55	H—Cl	103.1
$C_2H_5\text{—ONO}$	59	H—F	136
$n\text{-}C_3H_7\text{—ONO}$	60	H—I	71.3
$CH_3O\text{—NO}_2$	37	H—OH	119
$C_2H_5O\text{—NO}_2$	36	H—O	102
$n\text{-}C_3H_7O\text{—NO}_2$	37	HO—OH	51
$CH_3\text{—ONO}_2$	78	$HO_2\text{—H}$	90
$C_2H_5\text{—ONO}_2$	79	$H\text{—O}_2$	47
$n\text{-}C_3H_7\text{—ONO}_2$	79	HS—H	93
$CH_3S\text{—H}$	88	H—S	83
$CH_3\text{—SH}$	73	I—I	36.1
$CH_3S\text{—CH}_3$	72	N—H	81
		NH—H	96
B—H	70	$NH_2\text{—H}$	103
BH—H	101	N—N	226
$BH_2\text{—H}$	100	NH—NH	116
$BH_3 \cdots\cdots H_3B$	29	$NH_2NH\text{—H}$	76
		$NH_2\text{—NH}_2$	57
Br—Br	46.1	N—O	151
NC—CN	144	H—NO	49
C—O	257	ON—O	73
OC—O	127	ONO—H	78
OC—S	72	ON—OH	49
SC—O	164	$O_2NO\text{—H}$	101
SC—S	110	$O_2N\text{—OH}$	49
Cl—Cl	57.9	ON—Cl	38
Cl—F	61	$N_2\text{—O}$	40
Cl—O	64	N—NO	115
OCl—O	59	$O_2N\text{—NO}_2$	13.7
ClO—Cl	35	$O_2N\text{—ONO}_2$	21
ClO—H	97	O—O	119.1
Cl—OH	59	$O_2\text{—O}$	26
F—F	38	S—S	101
H—H	104.2	S—O	126
H—Br	87.5	OS—O	131
H—CN	130	$O_2S\text{—O}$	83

[a] Data are derived from the $\Delta H^{\circ}_{298.2}$ data of Tables A-1, A-2, A-3, and A-4. To obtain the $\Delta E^{\circ}_{298.2}$ values subtract 0.6 kcal/mole from the above numbers.
[b] R is an alkyl radical.

TABLE A-6   Refractive Indices of Various Optical Materials as a Function of Wavelength (18°C)

| | Quartz, crystalline | | | | | | | |
Wave-length, A	Ordinary Ray[a]	Extra-ordinary Ray[a]	Quartz, Fused[a]	Pyrex #7740 Glass[b]	Fluorite[a] (CaF$_2$)	LiF (20°)[c]	NaCl[a]	H$_2$O (20°)[a]
1855	1.6758	1.6900	1.5744	...	1.5099	...	1.8932	...
1862	...	...	...	...	...	...	...	1.4534
1936	1.6600	1.6734	1.5600	...	1.5012	1.4450	1.8280	...
2082	...	...	...	...	1.4889	...	1.7540	...
2100	...	...	...	...	...	1.4346	...	...
2195	1.6250	1.6370	1.5291	...	1.4815	1.4300	1.7170	1.3988
2313	...	...	...	...	1.4752	1.4244	1.6883	1.3888
2573	1.5962	1.6071	1.5038	...	1.4648	1.4162	1.6461	1.3735
2749	1.5875	1.5981	1.4962	...	1.4597	1.4128	1.6269	1.3664
3034	1.5770	1.5872	1.4859	...	...	...	...	...
3082	...	...	...	...	1.4526	...	1.6019	1.3567
3123	1.5743	1.5845	...	...	...	...	...	...
3130	...	...	...	...	...	1.4070	...	...
3404	1.5675	1.5774	1.4787	...	...	...	...	1.3504
3612	...	...	...	...	1.4454	...	1.5784	1.3474
3650	...	...	...	...	...	1.4013	...	...
4102	1.5565	1.5660	...	...	1.4411	...	1.5655	...
4358	1.5538	1.5632	1.4668	...	...	1.3967	...	1.3403
4416	...	...	...	...	1.4392	...	1.5596	1.3398
4861	1.5497	1.5590	1.4632	1.4776	...	...	...	1.3371
5086	1.5482	1.5575	1.4619	...	1.4362	...	1.5509	...
5770	...	...	...	...	...	1.3929	...	1.3334
5893	1.5442	1.5534	1.4585	1.4727	1.4339	1.3921	1.5443	1.3330
6563	1.5419	1.5509	1.4564	1.4705	...	...	...	1.3312

[a] Data from *International Critical Tables*, edited by E. W. Washburn, McGraw-Hill Book Co., New York, 1926.
[b] Data from the Corning Glass Works, Corning, N.Y., private communication from C. J. Parker.
[c] Data from Z. Gyulai, *Z. Physik*, **46**, 80 (1927); for a graph of indices in the far ultraviolet (1200–2000 A) see E. G. Schneider, *Phys. Rev.*, **49**, 341 (1936).

TABLE A-7 Electronic Configurations of the Ground States of Atoms and Their Term Symbols[a]

Element	Number of Electrons	Inner Electrons	Outermost Electrons	Ground Term Symbol
H	1	...	$1s$	$^2S_{1/2}$
He	2	...	$(1s)^2$	$^1S_0$
Li	3	↑	$2s$	$^2S_{1/2}$
Be	4	│	$(2s)^2$	$^1S_0$
B	5	Helium	$(2s)^2 2p$	$^2P_{1/2}$
C	6	shells	$(2s)^2(2p)^2$	$^3P_0$
N	7	│	$(2s)^2(2p)^3$	$^4S_{3/2}$
O	8	│	$(2s)^2(2p)^4$	$^3P_2$
F	9	│	$(2s)^2(2p)^5$	$^2P_{3/2}$
Ne	10	↓	$(2s)^2(2p)^6$	$^1S_0$
Na	11	↑	$3s$	$^2S_{1/2}$
Mg	12	│	$(3s)^2$	$^1S_0$
Al	13	│	$(3s)^2 3p$	$^2P_{1/2}$
Si	14	Neon	$(3s)^2(3p)^2$	$^3P_0$
P	15	shells	$(3s)^2(3p)^3$	$^4S_{3/2}$
S	16	│	$(3s)^2(3p)^4$	$^3P_2$
Cl	17	│	$(3s)^2(3p)^5$	$^2P_{3/2}$
Ar	18	↓	$(3s)^2(3p)^6$	$^1S_0$
K	19	↑	$4s$	$^2S_{1/2}$
Ca	20	│	$(4s)^2$	$^1S_0$
Sc	21	│	$3d(4s)^2$	$^2D_{3/2}$
Ti	22	│	$(3d)^2(4s)^2$	$^3F_2$
V	23	│	$(3d)^3(4s)^2$	$^4F_{3/2}$
Cr	24	│	$(3d)^5 4s$	$^7S_3$
Mn	25	│	$(3d)^5(4s)^2$	$^6S_{5/2}$
Fe	26	│	$(3d)^6(4s)^2$	$^5D_4$
Co	27	│	$(3d)^7(4s)^2$	$^4F_{9/2}$
Ni	28	│	$(3d)^8(4s)^2$	$^3F_4$
Cu	29	│	$(3d)^{10} 4s$	$^2S_{1/2}$
Zn	30	Argon	$(3d)^{10}(4s)^2$	$^1S_0$
Ga	31	shells	$(3d)^{10}(4s)^2 4p$	$^2P_{1/2}$
Ge	32	│	$(3d)^{10}(4s)^2(4p)^2$	$^3P_0$
As	33	│	$(3d)^{10}(4s)^2(4p)^3$	$^4S_{3/2}$
Se	34	│	$(3d)^{10}(4s)^2(4p)^4$	$^3P_2$
Br	35	│	$(3d)^{10}(4s)^2(4p)^5$	$^2P_{3/2}$
Kr	36	↓	$(3d)^{10}(4s)^2(4p)^6$	$^1S_0$
Rb	37	↑	$5s$	$^2S_{1/2}$
Sr	38	│	$(5s)^2$	$^1S_0$
Y	39	│	$4d(5s)^2$	$^2D_{3/2}$
Zr	40	│	$(4d)^2(5s)^2$	$^3F_2$
Nb	41	│	$(4d)^4 5s$	$^6D_{1/2}$
Mo	42	│	$(4d)^5 5s$	$^7S_3$
Tc	43	│	$(4d)^5(5s)^2$	$^6S_{5/2}$
Ru	44	Krypton	$(4d)^7 5s$	$^5F_5$
Rh	45	shells	$(4d)^8 5s$	$^4F_{9/2}$
Pd	46	│	$(4d)^{10}$	$^1S_0$
Ag	47	│	$(4d)^{10} 5s$	$^2S_{1/2}$
Cd	48	↓	$(4d)^{10}(5s)^2$	$^1S_0$

TABLE A-7   *continued*

In	49	↑	$(4d)^{10}(5s)^2 5p$	$^2P_{1/2}$
Sn	50		$(4d)^{10}(5s)^2(5p)^2$	$^3P_0$
Sb	51	Krypton	$(4d)^{10}(5s)^2(5p)^3$	$^4S_{3/2}$
Te	52	shells	$(4d)^{10}(5s)^2(5p)^4$	$^3P_2$
I	53		$(4d)^{10}(5s)^2(5p)^5$	$^2P_{3/2}$
Xe	54	↓	$(4d)^{10}(5s)^2(5p)^6$	$^1S_0$
Cs	55	↑	$6s$	$^2S_{1/2}$
Ba	56		$(6s)^2$	$^1S_0$
La	57		$5d(6s)^2$	$^2D_{3/2}$
Ce	58		$4f5d(6s)^2$ or $(4f)^2(5d)^0(6s)^2$	$^3H_4$
Pr	59		$(4f)^3(6s)^2$	$^4I_{9/2}$
Nd	60		$(4f)^4(6s)^2$	$^5I_4$
Pm	61		$(4f)^5(6s)^2$	$^6H_{5/2}$
Sm	62		$(4f)^6(6s)^2$	$^7F_0$
Eu	63		$(4f)^7(6s)^2$	$^8S_{7/2}$
Gd	64		$(4f)^7 5d(6s)^2$	$^9D_2$
Tb	65		$(4f)^9(6s)^2$	$^6H_{15/2}$
Dy	66		$(4f)^{10}(6s)^2$	$^5I_8$
Ho	67		$(4f)^{11}(6s)^2$	$^4I_{15/2}$
Er	68		$(4f)^{12}(6s)^2$	$^3H_6$
Tm	69		$(4f)^{13}(6s)^2$	$^2F_{7/2}$
Yb	70	Xenon	$(4f)^{14}(6s)^2$	$^1S_0$
Lu	71	shells	$(4f)^{14}5d(6s)^2$	$^2D_{3/2}$
Hf	72		$(4f)^{14}(5d)^2(6s)^2$	$^3F_2$
Ta	73		$(4f)^{14}(5d)^3(6s)^2$	$^4F_{3/2}$
W	74		$(4f)^{14}(5d)^4(6s)^2$	$^5D_0$
Re	75		$(4f)^{14}(5d)^5(6s)^2$	$^6S_{5/2}$
Os	76		$(4f)^{14}(5d)^6(6s)^2$	$^5D_4$
Ir	77		$(4f)^{14}(5d)^7(6s)^2$	$^4F_{9/2}$
Pt	78		$(4f)^{14}(5d)^9 6s$	$^3D_3$
Au	79		$(4f)^{14}(5d)^{10}6s$	$^2S_{1/2}$
Hg	80		$(4f)^{14}(5d)^{10}(6s)^2$	$^1S_0$
Tl	81		$(4f)^{14}(5d)^{10}(6s)^2 6p$	$^2P_{1/2}$
Pb	82		$(4f)^{14}(5d)^{10}(6s)^2(6p)^2$	$^3P_0$
Bi	83		$(4f)^{14}(5d)^{10}(6s)^2(6p)^3$	$^4S_{3/2}$
Po	84		$(4f)^{14}(5d)^{10}(6s)^2(6p)^4$	$^3P_2$
At	85		$(4f)^{14}(5d)^{10}(6s)^2(6p)^5$	$^2P_{3/2}$
Rn	86	↓	$(4f)^{14}(5d)^{10}(6s)^2(6p)^6$	$^1S_0$
Fr	87	↑	$7s$	$^2S_{1/2}$
Ra	88		$(7s)^2$	$^1S_0$
Ac	89		$6d(7s)^2$	$^2D_{3/2}$
Th	90	Radon	$(6d)^2(7s)^2$	$^3F_2$
Pa	91	shells	$(5f)^2 6d(7s)^2$ or $5f(6d)^2(7s)^2$	$^4K_{11/2}$ or $^4I_{9/2}$
U	92		$(5f)^3 6d(7s)^2$	$^5L_6$
Np	93		$(5f)^4 6d(7s)^2$ or $(5f)^5(7s)^2$	$^6L_{11/2}$ or $^6H_{5/2}$
Pu	94		$(5f)^6(6d)^0(7s)^2$	$^7F_0$
Am	95		$(5f)^7(6d)^0(7s)^2$	$^8S_{7/2}$
Cm	96	↓	$(5f)^7 6d(7s)^2$	$^9D_2$

[a] Adapted from G. R. Harrison, R. C. Lord, and J. R. Loofbourow, *Practical Spectroscopy*, Prentice-Hall, Englewood Cliffs, N.J., 1948, pp. 256–8; W. F. Meggers, C. H. Corliss, and B. F. Scribner, "Tables of Spectral-Line Intensities," Part I, *Natl. Bur. Standards (U.S.) Monogr.* 32, U.S. Government Printing Office, Washington, D.C., issued December, 1961.

TABLE A-8   Values of Some Fundamental Physical Constants[a]

Constant	Symbol	Value	Error[b]
Speed of light in vacuum	c	2.997925×10^{10} cm/sec	3
Elementary charge	e	4.80298×10^{-10} cm$^{3/2}$ gram$^{1/2}$/sec	20
Avogadro constant	N	6.02252×10^{23} molecule/mole	28
Electron rest mass	m_e	9.1091×10^{-28} gram	4
Proton rest mass	m_p	1.67252×10^{-24} gram	8
Neutron rest mass	m_n	1.67482×10^{-24} gram	8
Planck constant	h	6.6256×10^{-27} erg-sec	5
Gas constant	R	8.3143×10^{7} ergs/°K-mole	12
Normal volume of perfect gas (S.T.P).	V_0	2.24136×10^{4} cm^3/mole	30
Boltzmann constant	**k**	1.38054×10^{-16} erg/°K	18
Charge to mass ratio for electron	e/m_e	5.27274×10^{17} cm$^{3/2}$/gram$^{1/2}$-sec	6
Rydberg constant	R_∞	1.0973731×10^{5} cm^{-1}	3
Bohr radius	a_0	5.29167×10^{-9} cm	7

[a] From *Natl. Bur. Standards* (*U.S.*) *Tech. News Bull.*, October, 1963.
[b] Estimated error limit based on three standard deviations applied to last digits in the significant figures given.

Author Index*

Ackerman, J., Jr., 728, 811
Adams, G. E., 430, 563
Adamson, A., 268, 358
Adrian, F. J., 371, 577
Airey, P. L., 271(2), 360
Akeroyd, E. I., 16, 26, 782, 812
Akhtar, M., 482, 483, 484, 526, 530, 531, 566
Akimoto, H., 499, 565
Akimov, I., 342, 363
Albrecht, A. C., 458, 556, 564, 576
Alder, K., 351, 363
Aldington, J. N., 710, 810
Alentsev, M. N., 799, 813
Alire, R. M., 354(2), 364
Allen, E. R., 374, 375, 576
Allen, W. F., 102, 123, 125(3), 595(2), 601(2), 680(2)
Allsop, C. B., 283, 359
Almasy, F., 231, 239
Almy, G. M., 328, 365
Alpert, D., 64, 78, 83, 121, 122
Altschuller, A. P., 823
Altwicker, E. R., 416, 572
Alumbaugh, R. L., 390, 409, 410, 578
Amako, Y., 278, 365(2)
Amrich, M. J., 467, 579
Anacker, F., 12, 25
Anderson, D. G., 460, 578
Anderson, K. D., 477(2), 565
Anderson, L. C., 198, 234
Anderson, R. A., 85, 122

Anderson, R. S., 505, 514, 515, 567
Anderson, W. T., Jr., 750, 811
Anderton, E. J., 515, 517, 568
Anet, F. A. L., 467, 565, 573
Anet, R., 536
Angus, H. J. F., 517, 568
Anhorn, V. J., 765, 812
Appleyard, M. E. S., 596, 680
Arai, S., 101, 102(3), 123(2)
Arends, B., 433, 452, 563
Arigoni, D., 426(3), 568, 574(2)
Armbruster, C. W., 419, 574
Arnett, R. L., 816
Arnold, D. R., 539(2), 573
Arnold, G., 510, 512, 568
Arnot, C., 193, 194, 195, 234
Arrhenius, S., 605, 682
Asada, T., 80, 122
Aschenbrand, L. M., 65, 66, 121, 213(2), 216, 237(2), 514, 568, 690, 783, 809, 812
Ashmore, P. G., 230, 238
Aslakson, C. A., 2, 25
Atkinson, B., 103, 123
Atwood, K., 434, 563
Auerbach, J., 414, 572
Ausloos, P., 370, 372(5), 373, 384, 385, 393(3), 396(3), 397, 400, 430, 431, 433, 434, 435(3), 436(3), 437(5), 438(3), 439, 463(3), 498(3), 526, 557, 558(5), 559(2), 560, 561(4), 562(2), 563(4), 564(2),

---

* Numbers in parentheses following a page number signify the frequency of reference to the given author on that page.

Subject Index and Glossary of Symbols*

---

* Greek letters used as symbols are alphabetized according to their English names and are placed at the beginning of the section for the appropriate letter.

NOTE. A page number in italics indicates the most significant reference among the group of multiple references given.

excited states of molecules (*cont.*):
reactivity of $^3(n, \pi^*)$, $^3(\pi, \pi^*)$ states, 528
experimental methods in photo-chemistry, 686

f, electronic subshell designation, 44
f, oscillator strength, f-number, 170
f_{mn}, oscillator strength of electronic transition from state m to state n, 171
F, rotational energy term (cm^{-1}), 129
F, electronic state designation of atoms, 48
F, fraction of incident light reflected, 780
F, quantum number, 65
F, correction factor in estimation of fraction of light absorbed, 794
$\Delta F\ddagger$, free energy of activation, 612
ferric ion, aqueous photo-reduction of, 270
in complexes, 271, 783
ferrocyanide ion, aqueous, electron detachment in, 270
quantum yield of, 271
ferrous ion, aqueous:
absorption in, 269
quantum yield of electron release in, 271
filters:
chemical, for isolation of regions of light from the mercury arc spectrum:
2537 A region, 729
2652–2655 A region, 730
3126–3132 A region, 732
3341 A region, 733
3650–3663 A region, 734
4045–4078 A region, 736
4358 A region, 737
5461 A region, 739
5770–5790 A region, 740
design of cell for solutions of, 742
Christiansen, 746
glass, 742, 743
interference, 744
uniform density, 746
flash photolysis, 20

flash photolysis (*cont.*):
identification of primary processes with, 590
study of triplets with, 291
systems, design of, exploding wires, 719
gas discharge at low pressures, 710
problems associated with, 720
spark discharge, 718
flavone, triplet (T_1) state, energy of, 298
fluoranthene, delayed emission from, 316
fluorene:
primary photophysical processes in, 309, 310
triplet (T_1) state, energy of, 298
triplet-triplet absorption spectrum in, 292
fluorenone:
quantum yield of intersystem crossing in, 309
triplet (T_1) state, energy of, 298
fluorescein:
fluorescence emission as a standard for lifetime measurements, 806
triplet state in, 285
effect of halogen substitution on lifetime of, 307
magnetism of, 289
fluorescence:
definition of, 72
delayed, 313, 316
of diatomic gases, 189, 191
of dyes, quenching of, by ions, 272
of excited dimers, 314
intensity of bands in, and evidence for predissociation, 584
of iodine, 190, 193
lifetimes of, measurement of, 804
by decay of intensity of emission, 805
by phase shift method, 806
mirror-image symmetry in, 275
of polyatomic molecules, 273, 274
quantum yields of, in aromatic hydrocarbons (table), 310
effect of physical state on, 281
effect of wavelength on, 277

γ_A, activity coefficient of species A, 625

g, gerade (even) state, 150

g, Landé g-factor, 39

g_m, statistical weight of mth state, 54

G, vibrational energy term (cm^{-1}), 131

galvanometer constant in calibration of a thermopile system, 778

galvinoxyl as a free radical "trap," 603

gamma-ray radiolysis of molecules, relation to other types of excitation, 557, 558

GC, galvanometer constant, 777

gerade state, 150, 154

glycidaldehyde, primary photochemical processes in, 376

glyoxal:
    primary photochemical processes in, 376
    role of vibrationally excited ground-state molecules in 4358 A photolysis of, 623

Grotrian energy-level diagram, 31
    for H, 32
    for Hg, 52, 70

h, Planck's constant, 13, 830

H, the Hamiltonian, 154

H, magnetic field strength vector, 3

H$_z$, magnetic field strength vector along z-axis, 4

$\Delta H\ddagger$, enthalpy of activation, 612

$\Delta H^\circ_{298.2}$, enthalpy change with reactants and products in their standard states at 298.2°K, 824

ΔH°_f, enthalpy of formation, product and reactants in standard states, 815

halides (organic):
    nature of absorption processes in, 522
    primary photochemical processes in, 523

halogens:
    absorption spectra of, 184
    origin of continuum in, 183
    photochemistry of, 226

Hamiltonian operator, 154

harmonic oscillator, 131
    probability density distribution of, 138

He$_2$, bonding in, 165

He$_2{}^+$, bonding in, 163

Heisenberg uncertainty principle, 36

hemin, 303

heptafluoro-n-butyraldehyde, primary photochemical processes in, 373

heptafluoronitropropane, photolysis of, 479

heptafluoropropyl ethyl ketone, primary photochemical processes in, 399

2-heptene, radical formation in photolysis of, 505

3-heptene, radical formation in photolysis of, 505

n-heptylazide, photolysis of, 474

hexachloracetone, primary photochemical processes in, 394

1,5-hexadiene, absorption spectrum of, 497

hexafluoroacetone, primary photochemical processes in, 393

hexafluoroazomethane, primary photochemical processes in, 463

hexafluorocyclobutanone, photoreaction with hexafluoropropylene, 542

hexane, Hg($^3P_1$) reaction with, 117

2,5-hexanedione, Hg($^3P_1$) reaction with, 107

3,4-hexanedione, primary photochemical processes in, 423

n-hexanoamide, primary photochemical processes in, 462

1,3,5-hexatriene, primary photochemical processes in, 512

1-hexene:
    absorption spectrum of, 494
    radicals formed in photolysis of, 505

cis-2-hexene:
    absorption spectrum of, 495
    radicals formed in photolysis of, 505

$trans$-2-hexene, absorption spectrum of, 495

cis-3-hexene, absorption spectrum of, 495

hex-5-ene-2-one, primary photochemical processes in, 399